HORSES
AND
HORSEMANSHIP

(Animal Agriculture Series)

8/29/81

1532

HORSES
AND
HORSEMANSHIP

(Animal Agriculture Series)

by

M. E. ENSMINGER, B.S., M.A., PH.D.

Formerly: Assistant Professor in Animal Science
University of Massachusetts

Chairman, Department of Animal Science
Washington State University

Consultant, General Electric Company
Nucleonics Department (Atomic Energy Commission)

Currently: President
Consultants-Agriservices
Clovis, California

President
Agriservices Foundation

Collaborator
U.S. Department of Agriculture

Adjunct Professor
California State University

Distinguished Professor
University of Wisconsin

Fifth Edition

THE INTERSTATE
PRINTERS & PUBLISHERS, INC.
Danville, Illinois

Editions:

First 1951
Second 1956
Third 1963
Fourth 1969
Fifth 1977

Translation: Fourth Edition translated into Spanish under the direc-
tion of Dr. Mauricio B. Helman, Professor, Veterinary Sciences,
Catholic University of Argentina; and published by El Ateneo,
Florida 34-344, Buenos Aires, Argentina.

Library of Congress Catalog Card No. 76-45238

Reorder No. 1888

DEDICATION

To

King Ranch

World-Famed

FOR QUARTER HORSES:

Major founder of the breed.
Charter member of the American Quarter Horse Association.
Breeder-owner of Wimpy P-1, a double grandson of Old Sorrel, chosen
by the Association to receive registration Number One.

FOR THOROUGHBREDS:

Breeder of Assault, winner of the Triple Crown.
Breeder of Middleground, winner of the Kentucky Derby.
Breeder-owner of Bold Venture, Stymie, Rejected, High Gun, To Market,
Better Self, But Why Not, Curandero, Bridal Flower, Scattered,
Dawn Play, Too Timely, and Buffel.

FOR SANTA GERTRUDIS CATTLE:

Founder of first American-created breed of beef cattle, which was
molded to perfection on the Santa Gertrudis Land Grant, from which
it takes its name, now the headquarters division of the Ranch.

FOR THE GREAT PEOPLE BACK OF IT:

Captain Richard King, the founder, and the Klebergs---and their
descendants, whose famous running W brand is a symbol of service,
a pledge of integrity, a mark of courage, character, and wisdom,
and indicative of the quality of the horses and cattle raised and
the condition of the range.

Preface to the Fifth Edition

More than any other factor, suburbia—the new link between the city and the country—has been responsible for the expansion in light horses numbers. There are now 74.9 million people in the United States classified as suburbanites, a 25 percent increase over 1960. They're craftsmen, foremen, and operators; white-collar workers; manufacturers; and other commuters. Some are part-time farmers. Others moved to the country to recapture a romantic ideal, to escape the hustle and bustle of city life, to cut the cost of living, to get away from crime and mugging, and/or to find a better place for their children. Still others moved to the country to acquire a status symbol, for prestige reasons, or for gracious living. Among this new breed of country squires are many ardent horsemen.

Suburbia also made for increased confinement and stabling of horses, accompanied by many abnormal behaviors to plague those who raise them, including finicky appetites, degenerate sexual behavior, cribbing, and a host of other disorders. This has prompted great interest in horse behavior, especially as a factor in their vices, training, performance, and efficiency. Those who grew up around horses and dealt with them in practical ways have already accumulated substantial workaday knowledge about the reaction of horses to certain stimuli or to their environment. But those who are less familiar with them may need to familiarize themselves with their behavior, better to feed, care for, and train them, and in order to recognize the early signs of illness.

Hand in hand with the coming of suburbia and greater confinement of horses, a new era of horse breeding and care was ushered in. In the past, the horse business was an art, the foundations of which were animal instinct and a blend of the caretaker's fads, foibles, and trade secrets. To the art, we recently added science—founded on chemistry, physics, physiology, and bacteriology.

The application of scientific principles to the art of animal production proceeded rather rapidly in cattle, sheep, swine, and poultry. But, for many years, no such progress was made in the application of science to the art of horses and horsemanship. Today, this situation is being righted. This revision of *Horses and Horsemanship* was prepared to bridge the gap between the art and the science of horse production, care, and use.

Many people contributed richly to this major revision. The author is especially grateful to the following, without whose dedicated assistance and encouragement he would never have made it: Audrey Ensminger, who doubled as office manager and understanding wife; Sonja Hansen, who ably edited and supervised the preparation of the manuscript; Joan Wright and Virginia Watkins, who ingeniously deciphered my Missouri hieroglyphics and typed the manuscript; Toby Escola, who did the artwork; the rest of my staff, who contributed directly or indirectly; and all those who responded so liberally to my call for pictures and information and who reviewed certain portions of the manuscript, due acknowledgment of which is made in the appropriate places throughout the book.

M. E. Ensminger

Clovis, California
August, 1977

References

The following books are by the same author and the same publisher as *Horses and Horsemanship:*

The Stockman's Handbook
Animal Science
Beef Cattle Science
Dairy Cattle Science
Sheep and Wool Science
Swine Science
Poultry Science

The Stockman's Handbook is a modern "how to do it" book which contains, under one cover, the pertinent things that a stockman needs to know in the daily operation of a farm or ranch. It covers the broad field of animal agriculture, concisely and completely, and, whenever possible, in tabular and outline form.

Animal Science presents a perspective or panorama of the far-flung livestock industry; whereas each of the specific class-of-livestock books presents specialized material pertaining to a class of farm animals.

Other Selected References

Title of Publication	Author(s)	Publisher
Approved Practices in Raising and Handling Horses	D. E. Ulmer E. M. Juergenson	The Interstate Printers & Publishers, Inc., Danville, Ill., 1974
Breeding and Raising Horses, Ag. Hdbk. No. 394	M. E. Ensminger	Agricultural Research Service, USDA, Washington, D.C., 1972
Complete Book of the Horse, The	Ed. by E. H. Edwards C. Geddes	Ward Lock Limited, London, England, 1974
Every Horse Owners' Cyclopedia	Ed. by R. McClure	I-Tex Publishing Company, Inc., Huntsville, Tex., 1971
Fair Exchange	H. S. Finney	Charles Scribner's Sons, New York, N.Y., 1974
First Horse	R. Hapgood	Chronicle Books, San Francisco, Calif., 1972
Harper's Encyclopedia for Horsemen: The Complete Book of the Horse	L. Taylor	Harper & Row, Publishers, New York, N.Y., 1973
Horse, The	D. J. Kays, rev. by J. M. Kays	A. S. Barnes & Co., Inc., Cranbury, N.J., 1969
Horse, The	P. D. Rossdale	The California Thoroughbred Breeders Association, Arcadia, Calif., 1972
Horse Breeding Farm, The	L. C. Willis	A. S. Barnes & Co., Inc., Cranbury, N.J., 1973
Horse Care	F. Harper	Popular Library, New York, N.Y., 1966
Horse Science Handbook, Vols. 1-3	Ed. by M. E. Ensminger	Agriservices Foundation, Clovis, Calif., 1963, 1964, and 1966
Horseman's Encyclopedia, The	M. C. Self	A. S. Barnes & Co., Inc., Cranbury, N.J., 1963
Horsemanship and Horse Care, Ag. Info. Bull. No. 353	M. E. Ensminger	Agricultural Research Service, USDA, Washington, D.C., 1972
Horsemanship & Horsemastership	G. Wright	Doubleday & Company, Inc., Garden City, N.Y., 1962
Horses and Horsemanship	L. E. Walraven	A. S. Barnes & Co., Inc., New York, N.Y., 1970
Horses, Horses, Horses	M. E. Ensminger	M. E. Ensminger, Clovis, Calif., 1965
Horses, Horses, Horses	Ed. by S. Wilding	Van Nostrand Reinhold Company, New York, N.Y., 1970
Horses: Their Selection, Care and Handling	M. C. Self	A. S. Barnes & Co., Inc., New York, N.Y., 1943
Horses of Today	H. H. Reese	Wood & Jones, Pasadena, Calif., 1956
Light Horse Management, An Introduction to	R. C. Barbalace	Caballus Publishers, Fort Collins, Colo., 1974

(continued)

Title of Publication	Author(s)	Publisher
Light Horses, Farmers' Bull. No. 2127	M. E. Ensminger	Agricultural Research Service, USDA, Washington, D.C.
Saddle Up!	C. E. Ball	J. B. Lippincott Co., Philadelphia, Penn., 1970
Shetland Pony, The	L. F. Bedell	Iowa State University Press, Ames, Iowa, 1959
Shetland Pony, The	M. C. Cox	Adam & Charles Black, Ltd., London, England, 1965
Stud Managers Course Lectures		Stud Managers Course, University of Kentucky, Lexington, Ky., intermittent years since 1951
Stud Managers' Handbook, The	Ed. by M. E. Ensminger	Agriservices Foundation, Clovis, Calif., annually since 1965
Summerhays' Encyclopedia for Horsemen	R. S. Summerhays	Frederick Warne and Co., Inc., New York, N.Y., 1966
Western Horse Behavior and Training	R. W. Miller	Doubleday & Company, Inc., Garden City, N.Y., 1975
Western Horse, The	J. A. Gorman	The Interstate Printers & Publishers, Inc., Danville, Ill., 1967

Contents

Appendix

CHAPTER 1

HISTORY AND DEVELOPMENT OF
THE HORSE INDUSTRY[1]

The evolution and transformation of the horse from the early-day wild forms, its subsequent domestication, and the overlapping uses made of it in both war and peace is a fascinating story.

EVOLUTION OF THE HORSE

Fossil remains prove that members of the horse family roamed the plains of America (especially what is now the Great Plains area of the United States) during most of Tertiary time, beginning about 58 million years ago. Yet no horses were present on this continent when Columbus discovered America in 1492. Why they perished, only a few thousand years before, is still one of the unexplained mysteries of evolution. As the disappearance was so complete and so sudden, many scientists believe that it must have been caused by some contagious disease or some fatal parasite. Others feel that perhaps it was due to multiple causes, including (1) climatic changes, (2) competi-

tion, and/or (3) failure to adapt. Regardless of why horses disappeared, it is known that conditions in America were favorable for them at the time of their reestablishment by the Spanish conquistadores, less than 500 years ago.

Through fossil remains, it is possible to reconstruct the evolution of the horse (see Table 1-1), beginning with the ancient 4-toed ancestor, the *Eohippus* (meaning "dawn horse"). This was a small animal, scarcely more than a foot high, with 4 toes on the front feet and 3 toes on the hind feet, and with slender legs, a short neck, and even teeth. It was well adapted to traveling in and feeding on the herbage of swamplands. Gradually, the descendants of *Eophippus* grew in size and changed in form, evolving into a 3-toed animal known as *Mesohippus*, which was about 24 inches in height or about the size of a Collie dog. Further changes continued, transforming the animal from a denizen of the swamp to a creature capable of surviving in the forest and finally to one

---

[1]In the preparation of Chapter 1, the author was especially fortunate in having the valued counsel and suggestions of Mr. Karl P. Schmidt, formerly Chief Curator of the Department of Zoology, Chicago Natural History Museum, Chicago, Illinois, who so patiently and thoroughly reviewed this historical material.

TABLE
EVOLUTION OF THE HORSE AS

Eras	Periods	Epochs	Approximate Duration in Years	Approximate Number of Years Since Beginning	General Characteristics
Cenozoic (recent life) Age of Mammals and Angiosperms	Quaternary	Recent	12,000±	12,000±	Post-Glacial Age. Rise of Modern Man, *Homo sapiens*. Development of complex cultures and civilizations. Domestication of animals.
		Pleistocene (Gr. *pleistos*, most+*kainos*, recent)	1,000,000	1,000,000	Ice Age: 4 major advances. Evolution of primitive man, Neanderthal, Heidelberg, Peking, Java, etc. Mammoth, mastodon, great slot, saber-tooth tiger, etc. 90-100% modern species. Rise of Alps and Himalayas.
	Tertiary	Pliocene (Gr. *pleion*, more+*kainos*)	11,000,000	12,000,000	Mammals increase in size. 50-90% modern species.
		Miocene (Gr. *meion*, less *kainos*)	16,000,000	28,000,000	The "Golden Age" of mammals. Luxuriant grasses; culmination of plains-dwelling mammals. 20-40% modern species.
		Oligocene (Gr. *oligos*, little+*kainos*)	10,000,000	38,000,000	Modern mammals predominate over primitive ones. 10-15% modern species.
		Eocene (Gr. *eos*, dawn+*kainos*)	20,000,000	58,000,000	Archaic mammals, the advent of the horse. 1-5% modern species.
		Paleocene	17,000,000	75,000,000	The beginning of the age of mammals. Great development of the angiosperms. 1% modern species.

[1]Grateful acknowledgement is made to the following eminent authorities for their help in the preparation of this table: Dr. Frank Scott, Department of Geology, Washington State University, and Mr. Karl P. Schmidt, formerly Chief Curator, Department of Zoology, Chicago Natural History Museum, Chicago, Illinois. (Drawings by Prof. R. F. Johnson)

1-1

DECIPHERED FROM THE FOSSIL RECORD[1]

The Horse[2]

Equus (Modern Horse; *Equus* is Latin for horse). Beginning about 25,000 years ago, during the Paleolithic (Old Stone Age), man hunted horses and used them as a source of food. They were probably the last of the common domestic animals to be domesticated. This domestication is thought to have occurred toward the end of the Neolithic (New Stone Age) about 5,000 years ago. The horse was returned to the "New World" by the Spanish conquistadores less than 500 years ago.

Equus (Modern Horse). One large functional toe on each foot with the 2 side toes reduced to mere splint bones and entirely nonfunctional. The horse reached the climax of his evolutionary development with *Equus*. Several known species in North America. Most of these were the size of small ponies but one fully equaled the greatest of modern draft horses. However, in the Americas he died out toward the end of the Pleistocene Epoch, perhaps due to multiple causes, including (1) climatic changes, (2) competition, (3) epidemic, and/or (4) failure to adapt. Fortunately, however, horses had found a land bridge (probably via Alaska and Siberia) into the Old World, where they survived to become a servant and friend to man. They had entered the Old World by this same route at other times in the Tertiary past.

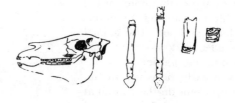

Pliohippus (Gr. *pleion*, more+*hippos*, horse). First one-toed horse, the side toes being reduced to splints. High-crowned grazing type teeth. Pony size. This was the immediate and virtually full-grown forerunner of *Equus*. Also *Hipparion* (Gr. dim. of *hippos*; a pony), a 3-toed grazer, and several other genera.

Merychippus (Rudimentary horse; Gr. *Meryx*, ruminant+*hippos*, horse). Three toes on each foot with the middle much heavier than the others which failed to touch the ground. A slim, graceful animal about the size of a Shetland Pony. His teeth were high crowned and hard surfaced, suitable for eating grass. Thus *Merychippus* was thoroughly adapted to life on the prairie. Also *Protohippus* (Gr. *Protos*, first, primordial+*hippos*) generally similar to *Merychippus*, *Miohippus* (Gr. *Meion*, less+*hippos*) with foot structure like *Merychippus* but with short-crowned, browsing teeth; *Parahippus* (Almost, nearly *hippos*) and others.

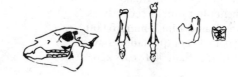

Mesohippus (Gr. *meso*, in the middle, intermediate-*hippos*). Three toes on each foot with the middle toe distinctly larger and a fourth toe on the front foot reduced to a splint, all touched the ground and shared in carrying the animal's weight. Teeth low crowned, probably for browsing. *Mesohippus* was about the size of a Collie dog with longer legs and a straighter back than his tiny Eocene forerunner. Also his intelligence and agility increased.

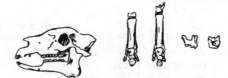

Eohippus (Gr. *eos*, dawn—*hippos*). Four functional toes on the front foot, one larger than the others, with a fifth reduced to a splint; the hind foot had 3 functional toes and a splint. *Eohippus* was a small graceful animal, scarcely more than a foot high with a slender face, an arched back, short neck, slender legs and a long tail. He was adapted for living in swamps. Also *Orohippus* (Gr. *oros*, mountain—*hippos*), having foot structure like *Eohippus* but without vestigial splints, and *Epihippus* (Gr. *epi*, upon, among—*hippos*).

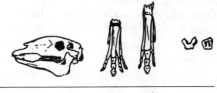

Prehorse. The 5 toes (one a splint) on the forefeet of *Eohippus* indicate that its ancestor probably had 5 toes all around, but no 5-toed horse has yet been found. The ancestors of the horse were probably primitive 5-toed ungulates, perhaps similar to some primitive Condylarth.

---

[2]In some cases, other genera might well be listed, but the leading ones of the respective epochs are here given.

adapted to the prairie. In terms of conformation, the animal grew taller. The teeth grew longer, stronger, and more roughened to suit the gradual changes to grazing on the prairie. The cannon bones—metacarpals and metatarsals—lengthened; the middle toe (or third toe) grew longer and stronger, forming a hoof; and the other toes (second and fourth toes) gradually disappeared except for vestiges, the slender bones known as splints, under the skin. The transformation in length and structure of foot made for greater speed over prairie type of terrain, thereby enabling the animal to feed farther and farther from water, and providing for greater safety in its struggle to survive. The horse is an excellent example, therefore, of the slow adaptation of animal life to changing conditions in environment, climate, food, and soil. The animal was transformed from one adapted to a swamp type environment to one adapted to the prairie.

Though all horses eventually perished in the New World and none were present on the continent when America was discovered, fortunately some of these animals had long before emigrated to Asia and Europe at a time when there was a land bridge connecting Alaska and Siberia (now the Bering Strait). These emigrants formed the sturdy wild European stock from which the horse family of today descended, and this stock also populated Africa with its asses and zebras.

From Table 1-1, it can be seen that the evolution of the horse covered a period of approximately 58 million years, but that man hunted him as recently as 25,000 years ago and domesticated him a mere 5,000 years ago, and that the Spanish conquistadores returned him to the New World less than 500 years ago.

ORIGIN AND DOMESTICATION OF THE HORSE

The horse was probably the last of present-day farm animals to be domesticated by man. According to early records, after subduing the ox, the sheep, and the goat, man domesticated the ass and then the camel; and, finally, the horse became his servant.

Horses appear to have been domesticated first in Central Asia or Persia more than 3,000 years B.C., for they spread westward through southern Europe in the time of the Lake Dwellers. They were reported in Babylonia as early as 2000 B.C., perhaps coming into the country via neighboring Persia.

Although the Egyptians—the most advanced civilization of the day—had·domesticated and used the ass from the earliest times, horses were wholly unknown to them until the dynasty of the Shepherd Kings, who entered Egypt from Asia in 1680 B.C. It is reported that, thereafter, the horse was much favored in Egypt.

Presence of the horse seems to have prompted

the invention of the chariot, a type of vehicle drawn by horses that the Egyptians used in war and other pursuits. The Bible also relates that when Joseph took his father's remains from Egypt back to Canaan "there went up with him both chariots and horsemen."[2] It is probable that the Egyptians were largely responsible for the spread of domesticated horses to other countries.

Fig. 1-1. Joseph using horses in his move to Egypt (about 1500 B.C.), from a miniature painting in the Bible of the Counts of Toggenburg, 16th Century. (Courtesy, The Bettmann Archive)

Certainly, Greece was not even peopled, and there were no horses in Arabia during the early period when they were flourishing in Egypt. But horses and chariots were used in Greece at least a thousand years before Christ, to judge from the account of their use in the siege of Troy. It is also interesting to note that the first and most expert horsemen of Greece, the Thessalonians, were colonists from Egypt. As evidence that the Greeks were accomplished horsemen, it might be pointed out that they developed the snaffle bit at an early period. Also, one of their number is said to have originated the axiom "No foot, no horse." Yet the use of the saddle and stirrups appears to have been unknown at this time.

----

[2]Genesis 50:9.

Fig. 1-2. Distinguished young Greek in fashionable riding habit. Bowl painting, 500 B.C. Though the Greeks were accomplished horsemen, at this time the use of the saddle and stirrups appears to have been unknown. (Courtesy, The Bettmann Archive)

Fig. 1-3. Horses vary in size and use. The Shetland Pony foal (left) is thought to have descended from the small, shaggy, wild stock of northern Europe; whereas the draft horse (right) is thought to have descended primarily from the ponderous, wild black horse of Flanders. (Courtesy, Iowa State University)

From Greece, the horse was later taken to Rome and from there to other parts of Europe. The Romans proved to be master horsemen. They invented the curb bit. According to historians, when Caesar invaded Britain, about 55 B.C., he took horses with him. Although there were other horses in Britain at the time of the Roman occupation, Eastern breeding was probably greatly infused at this time—thus laying the foundation for the Blood Horse of today.

The Arabs, strangely enough, did not use horses to any extent until after the time of Mohammed (570 to 632 A.D.), depending on camels before that time. As evidence of this fact, it is noted that in the 7th Century after Christ, when Mohammed attacked the Koreish near Mecca, he had but 2 horses in his whole army; and at the close of his murderous campaign, although he drove off 24,000 camels and 40,000 sheep and carried away 24,000 ounces of silver, not one horse appeared in his list of plunder. This would seem to indicate rather conclusively that Arabia, the country whose horses have done so much to improve the horses of the world, was not the native home of the horse and that the Arabs did not use horses until after the time of Christ.

Of course, it seems incredible that all the various breeds, colors, and types of draft, light, and pony horses should have descended from a common, wild ancestor. Rather, there were probably many different wild stocks giving descent to domestic horses.

The Wild Horse of Asia

The wild horses of Asia, which are sometimes referred to as the Oriental light-legged horses, were of Asiatic origin, tracing to a wild horse (now extinct) of the Asiatic deserts. Historic evidence indicates that this group of horses gave rise to most of the swift and slenderly built breeds of modern times. The Arabian, the Barb, and the Turk are all descendants of these animals; and, in turn, the Thoroughbred originated from these stocks.

The Wild Horse of Europe

The European wild horse, sometimes referred to as the European forest type, continued to live in the forests of Germany and Scandinavia until historic times; and wild horses are believed to have lived in the Vosges Mountains on the western border of Alsace until the year 1600. One of the pagan practices of the ancient German tribes was the sacrifice of horses and the eating of their meat at religious feasts. To this day one may find a relic of horse worship in the horse skulls set on the gables of houses and barns in southern Germany.

The European wild horse was the wild black horse of Flanders. This was a stocky animal that possessed considerably more size and scale than the Oriental type. This draft type was native to Western

Europe at the time of the Roman invasion. It was the forerunner of the Great War Horse of the Middle Ages. The latter, in turn, fathered the modern draft breeds.

Not all wild horses of Europe were large, however, for small, shaggy animals were native to northern Europe. They were strong and hardy and required less feed than other types of horses. These animals are thought to be the progenitors of the Shetland Pony.

The Tarpan

Though now extinct, the Tarpan—a small duncolored, genuine wild species of horse—was formerly abundant everywhere in southern Russia and Central Asia. These animals were hated by the farmers because they devoured their crops and especially because the Tarpan stallions constantly recruited domestic mares for their wild bands. For these reasons, they were killed off by the Russians, finally being completely exterminated by the year 1870.[3]

Przewalsky's Horse

The only surviving species of original wild horses—not feral or escaped from domestication—known to exist at the present time is Przewalsky's horse (or the Asiatic wild horse). This is the wild horse discovered by the Russian explorer, Przewalsky, in 1879, in the northwestern corner of Mongolia. It is a small, stockily built, and distinctly yellowish horse, with an erect mane and no forelock. There is

usually a dark stripe on the shoulders and down the middle of the back. Like the wild mustang or feral horses of the frontier days, Przewalsky's horses separate into bands, seldom more than 40 in number, with a stallion leader in each group. At the present time, it is reported that only three wild bands remain. Fortunately, however, live specimens have been brought to Europe and America where they are being preserved and propagated successfully in captivity. When crossed on domestic horses, the hybrids are fertile, which proves that Przewalsky's horse is very closely related to the domestic horse.

It is not intended to imply that Przewalsky's horse was the foundation stock of any or all of the present-day improved breeds throughout the world. Rather, this wild horse of Asia is extremely interesting because it is the only one known to have survived the vicissitudes of time.

ORIGIN AND DOMESTICATION OF THE DONKEY

The two species of the horse family that have been tamed by man are *Equus caballus*, the horse, and *Equus asinus*, the ass or donkey. The history of the domestic donkey is as clear as that of the horse is obscure. Donkeys were first domesticated in Egypt, where they served man from earliest times. Good figures of them appear on slates of the 1st Dynasty, about 3400 B.C. Domestic donkeys are descended from the wild donkey (the Nubian wild ass) of North Africa, a species which is now almost extinct. Because of the frequent tendency to stripes on the legs, however, some zoologists also think that the domestic donkey is related to the Somali wild ass of Africa.

From Egypt, the use of the domestic donkey spread into southwestern Asia sometime prior to the year 1000 B.C. The Bible first refers to the ass in relating how Abraham, the patriarch of the Old Testament, rode one of these animals from Beersheba to

Fig. 1-4. Przewalsky's horse. This is the only surviving species of original wild horses—not feral or escaped from domestication—known to exist at the present time. Note that the animal is small and stockily built, with an erect mane and no forelock. (Courtesy, New York Zoological Society, New York, N.Y.)

---

[3]Some authors believe the Tarpan to have been a feral type; i.e., a horse escaped from domestication, and not a distinct wild form. Certainty as to this point can now scarcely be determined.

Fig. 1-5. A Mongolian wild ass in the Gobi desert in Asia. (Courtesy, American Museum of Natural History, New York, N.Y.)

Mount Mordah. Every child is familiar with the fact that Jesus rode into Jerusalem on an ass. This mode of transporation was not unusual at the time of Christ, for donkeys were then the common saddle animals throughout the Near East.

As is generally known, the donkey is commonly used in this country in the production of mules.[4] Mules have been known from very ancient times, as we learn from the accounts of the Trojan War.

POSITION OF THE HORSE IN THE ZOOLOGICAL SCHEME

The following outline shows the basic position of the domesticated horse in the zoological scheme:

Kingdom *Animalia*. Animals collectively; the Animal Kingdom.

Phylum *Chordata*: One of approximately 21 phyla of the animal kingdom, in which there is either a backbone (in the vertebrates) or the rudiment of a backbone, the chorda.

Class *Mammalia*: Mammals, or warm-blooded, hairy animals that produce their young alive and suckle them for a variable period on a secretion from the mammary glands.

Order *Perissodactyla*: Nonruminant hoofed mammals, usually with an odd number of toes, the third digit the largest and in line with the axis of the limb. This suborder includes the horse, tapir, and rhinoceros.

Family *Equidae*: The members of the horse family may be distinguished from the other existing perissodactyla (rhinoceros and tapir) by their comparatively more slender and agile build.

Genus *Equus*: Includes horses, asses, and zebras.

Species *Equus caballus*: The horse is distinguished from asses and zebras by the longer hair of the mane and tail, the presence of the "chestnut" on the inside of the hind leg, and by other less constant characters such as larger size, larger hoofs, more arched neck, smaller head, and shorter ears.

MAN'S USE OF THE HORSE

The name "horse" is derived from the Anglo-Saxon, *hors*, meaning swiftness; and the word horse-man comes from the Hebrew root "to prick or spur."[5] These early characterizations of the horse, within themselves, tell somewhat of a story. Perhaps the very survival of the wild species was somewhat dependent upon its swiftness, which provided escape from both beast and man. The Hebrew description of a horseman was obviously assigned after the horse had been domesticated and ridden by man.

The various uses that man has made of the horse down through the ages, in order of period of time, are (1) as a source of food, (2) for military purposes, (3) in the pastimes and sports of the nations, (4) in agricultural and commercial pursuits, and (5) for recreation and sport.

The Horse as a Source of Food

Man's first use of the horse was as a source of food, these animals being hunted by Paleolithic (Old Stone Age) man. This was prior to their domestication. These earliest records date back to some 25,000 years ago. Perhaps the best-preserved record of this type consists of the cracked and dismembered bones of horses, mostly young animals, found around old campsites. One bone heap of this sort is at Solutre, in the Rhone Valley in southern France. It is estimated that this one campsite contains the remains of 100,000 horses.

Following domestication, which is thought to have occurred sometime toward the end of the New Stone Age, it is reasonable to surmise that mares were milked for human food—a practice still followed in certain parts of the world. Mares may give up to 4½ gallons of milk per day.[6] Also, the use of horses for meat still persists in many parts of the world, including France, Belgium, and Switzerland.

The Horse for Military Purposes

Unfortunately, not long after domestication of the horse, man used him for waging war. About 1500 B.C., Pharaoh pursued the Israelites to the Red Sea, using chariots and horses.[7] This would seem to imply that the Egyptian army used horses, both as cavalry and to draw vehicles.

During the glamorous days of the knight in armor, horses of size, strength, and endurance were essential. The Great Horse of medieval times was the knight's steed. Usually stallions were used. Often the knight and his armor weighed 350 to 425 pounds. During the Crusades and for several centuries after, the clad-in-armor type of warrior relied upon sheer weight to beat down the enemy.

---

[4]In recent years, some miniature donkeys are being used as children's pets in the U.S.

[5]The Jews were forbidden by divine authority to use horses. In fact, they were required to hamstring horses captured in war.
[6]Mares of mature weights of 600, 800, 1,000, and 1,200 lb may produce 36, 42, 44, and 49 lb of milk daily, respectively.
[7]Exodus 14:7.

The deeds of great warriors, mounted on their favorite chargers, were long perpetuated in marble or bronze. Every schoolboy vividly associates Alexander the Great with his charger, Bucephalus; Napoleon with his famous horse, Marengo; the Duke of Wellington with his favorite mount, Copenhagen; George Washington, receiving the surrender of Cornwallis' army at Yorktown, with his handsome mount, Nelson; and General Grant with his horse, Jack.

Many people are under the erroneous impression that no horses were used in World War II. Nothing could be further from the truth. But this is another story, to be related at the end of the present chapter.

The Horse in the Pastimes and Sports of Nations

As early as 1450 B.C., the sports-loving Greeks introduced the horse in the Olympic games, in both chariot and horse races. The most celebrated of these events was held at Olympia every fourth year in honor of Jupiter. However, because of the scarcity of horses, very few were used in early contests. Classes were divided according to age—and sometimes sex—and the distance of the course was approximately 4 miles.

Fig. 1-6. Chariot driven through Pompeii. The horse-drawn chariot was used by the sports-loving Greeks in chariot races, as well as in war and other pursuits (Courtesy, The Bettman Archive)

For these important events, the Greeks trained both themselves and their horses. The chariot races were even provided with settings to tempt the charioteers to daring deeds. The chariots in use were a low, two-wheeled, narrow track type of vehicle.

The Horse in Agricultural and Commercial Pursuits

For many years following domestication, horses were used for purposes of war and sport. Their use in pulling loads and tilling the soil is a comparatively recent development.

There is no evidence to indicate that the horse was used in Europe to draw the plow prior to the 10th Century, and oxen remained the common plow animal in England until the end of the 18th Century. Remains of ancient art show conclusively that, long after domestication of the horse, the ox and the camel continued as the main source of agricultural power and transporation, respectively.

It is interesting to note that heavier draft-type animals had their development primarily in those countries in which Caesar campaigned in western Europe, including England. Without doubt, the improved roads that the Romans constructed during their long occupation were largely instrumental in encouraging the breeding of heavier horses capable of drawing heavier loads. The Great Horse served as the progenitor of the draft horse of agriculture.

The Horse for Recreation and Sport

In 1974, leisure time spending consumed an average of 5 percent of personal income, or an amount equal to 60 billion dollars. The combination of available money, leisure time, and emphasis on the out-of-doors has created great interest in light horses for recreation and sport. As a result, the race crowds are bigger than ever, the bridle paths in the city parks are being lengthened each year, the game of polo is expanding, riding to hounds is sharing its glamour with greater numbers, people of all walks of life enjoy the great horse shows throughout the land, and saddle clubs are springing up everywhere. This trend will continue.

INTRODUCTION OF HORSES AND MULES TO, AND EARLY HISTORY IN, THE UNITED STATES

It has been established that most of the evolution of the horse took place in the Americas, but this animal was extinct in the Western World at the time of Columbus' discovery, and apparently extinct even before the arrival of the Red Man some thousands of years earlier.

Columbus first brought horses to the West Indies on his second voyage in 1493. Cortez brought Spanish horses with him to the New World in 1519 when he landed in Mexico (16 animals were in the initial contingent, but approximately 1,000 head more were subsequently imported during the 2-year conquest of Mexico). Horses were first brought directly to what is now the United States by de Soto in the year 1539. Upon his vessels, he had 237 horses. These animals traveled with the army of the explorer in the hazardous journey from the Everglades of Florida to the Ozarks of Missouri. Following de Soto's death and burial in the upper Mississippi 3 years later, his followers returned by boats down the Mississippi, abandoning many of their horses.

One year following de Soto's landing in what is now Florida, in 1540, another Spanish explorer, Coronado, started an expedition with an armed band of horsemen from Mexico, penetrating to a point near the boundary of Kansas and Nebraska.

Beginning about 1600, the Spaniards established a chain of Christian missions among the Indians in the New World. The chain of missions extended from the eastern coast of Mexico up the Rio Grande, thence across the mountains to the Pacific Coast. Each mission brought animals, including horses, from the mother country.

There are two schools of thought relative to the source of the foundation stock of the first horses of the American Indians, and the hardy bands of Mustangs—the feral horses of the Great Plains. Most historians agree that both groups were descended from animals of Spanish (Arabian) extraction. However, some contend that their foundation stock came from the abandoned and stray horses of the expeditions of de Soto and Coronado, whereas others claim that they were obtained chiefly from Santa Fe, an ancient Spanish mission founded in 1606. It is noteworthy that Santa Fe and other early Spanish missions were the source of Spanish Longhorn cattle, thus lending credence to the theory that the missions were the source of foundation horses for the Indian and the wild bands of Mustangs.

Much romance and adventure is connected with the Mustang, and each band of wild horses was credited with leadership by the most wonderful stallion ever beheld by man. Many were captured, but the real leaders were always alleged to have escaped by reason of speed, such as not possessed by a domesticated horse. The Mustang multiplied at a prodigious rate. In one high luxuriant bunchgrass region in the state of Washington, wild horses thrived so well that the region became known as "Horse Heaven," a name it bears even today.

The coming of the horse among the Indians increased the strife and wars between tribes. Following the buffalo on horseback led to greater infringement upon each other's hunting grounds, which had ever been a cause for war. From the time the Indians came into possession of horses until the country was taken over by the white man, there was no peace among the tribes.

Later, animals of both light- and draft-horse breeding were introduced from Europe by the colonists. For many years, however, sturdy oxen continued to draw the plows for turning the sod on many a rugged New England hillside. Horses were largely used as pack animals, for riding, and later for pulling wagons and stagecoaches. It was not until about 1840 that the buggy first made its appearance.

Six mares and two stallions were brought to Jamestown in 1609, these being the first European importations. Some of these animals may have been eaten during the period of near starvation at Jamestown, but importations continued; and it was reported in 1611 that a total of 17 horses had been brought to this colony.

The horse seems to have been much neglected in early New England, as compared with cattle and sheep. This is not surprising, inasmuch as oxen were universally used for draft purposes. Roads were few in number; speed was not essential; and the horse had no meat value like that of cattle. Because of the great difficulty in herding horses on the commons, they were usually hobbled. Despite the limited early-day use of the horse, the colonists must have loved them, because, very early, the indiscriminate running of stallions among the mares upon the commons was recognized as undesirable. Massachusetts, before 1700, excluded from town commons all stallions "under 14 hands high and not of comely proportion."[8]

Fig. 1-7. A covered wagon, drawn by horses. This was a common method of transportation in this country prior to the advent of the railroad and the motor vehicle. (Photo by Ewing Galloway, New York, N.Y.)

Even before horses found much use in New England, they became valuable for export purposes to the West Indies for work in the sugar mills. In fact, this business became so lucrative that horse stealing became a common offense in New England in the 18th Century. Confiscation of property, public whippings, and banishment from the colony constituted the common punishments for a horse thief.

As plantations materialized in Virginia, the need for easy-riding saddle horses developed, so that the owners might survey their broad estates. Racing also became a popular sport among the Cavaliers in Virginia, Maryland, and the Carolinas—with the heat races up to 4 miles being common events. The plantation owners took considerable pride in having animals worthy of wearing their colors. So great was the

[8]Thompson, J. W., *History of Livestock Raising in the United States, 1607-1860*, Agricultural History Series No. 5, USDA, Nov. 1942.

desire to win that by 1730 the importation of English racehorses began.

George Washington maintained an extensive horse- and mule-breeding establishment at Mount Vernon. The President was also an ardent race fan, and riding to hounds was a favorite sport with him. As soon as Washington's views on the subject of mules became known abroad, he received some valuable breeding stock through gifts. In 1787, the Marquis de Lafayette presented him with a jack and some jennets of the Maltese breed. The jack, named Knight of Malta, was described as a superb animal, of a black color, with the form of a stag and the ferocity of a tiger. In 1795, the King of Spain gave Washington a jack and 2 jennets that were selected from the royal stud at Madrid. The Spanish jack, known as Royal Gift, was 16 hands high, of a gray color, heavily made, and of a sluggish disposition. It was said that Washington was able to combine the best qualities of the 2 gift jacks, especially through one of the descendants named Compound. General Washington was the first to produce mules of quality in this country, and soon the fame of these hardy hybrids spread throughout the South.

The Dutch, Puritan, and Quaker colonists to the north adhered strictly to agricultural pursuits, frowning upon horse races. They imported heavier types of horses. In Pennsylvania, under the guidance of William Penn, the farmers prospered. Soon their horses began to improve, even as the appearance and fertility of their farms had done. Eventually, their large horses were hitched to enormous wagons and used to transport freight overland to and from river flatboats and barges along the Ohio, Cumberland, Tennessee, and Mississippi rivers. Both horses and wagons were given the name Conestoga, after the Conestoga Val-

ley, a German settlement in Pennsylvania. The Conestoga wagon[9] was the forerunner of the prairie schooner, and before the advent of the railroad it was the freight vehicle of the time. It was usually drawn by a team of six magnificent Conestoga horses, which were well groomed and expensively harnessed. At one time, the Conestoga horses bid to become a new breed—a truly American creation. However, the railroads replaced them, eventually driving them into permanent oblivion. Other breeds were developed later, but this is another story.

PONY EXPRESS

The Pony Express was a mail service, operated as a private venture under contract, which carried U.S. mail on horseback from St. Joseph, Missouri, to

Fig. 1-9. The statue of the Pony Express which stands in the St. Joseph, Missouri, Civic Center. It was erected in 1940, when the Postal Department honored the riders of the Pony Express with a commemorative postage stamp. (Courtesy, St. Joseph Museum, St. Joseph, Mo.)

Fig. 1-8. Conestoga freight wagon drawn by six Conestoga horses, in front of a country inn. These improved horses and large wagons were both given the name Conestoga, after the Conestoga Valley, a German settlement in Pennsylvania. The advent of the railroads drove the Conestoga horses into oblivion, and the Conestoga wagon was succeeded by the prairie schooner. (Courtesy, The Bettmann Archive)

[9]It is noteworthy that the American custom of driving to the right on the road, instead of to the left as is the practice in most of the world, is said to have originated among the Conestoga wagon drivers of the 1750s. The drivers of these 4- and 6-horse teams either sat on the left wheel horse or on the left side of the seat, the better to wield their whip hand (the right hand) over the other horses in the team. Also, when 2 Conestoga drivers met, they pulled over to the right so that, sitting on the left wheel horse or on the left side of the seat, they could see that the left wheels of their wagons cleared each other. Lighter vehicles naturally followed the tracks of the big Conestoga wagons.

Placerville, California, in the days before railways or telegraph. It was started in 1861, and it had a brief existence of but 18 months before it was supplanted by a telegraph line. The riders' steeds were, of course, not ponies but fleet horses. The horses were stationed at points 10 to 15 miles apart, and each rider rode 3 to 7 animals successively, covering about 75 miles before passing the pouch to his successor. There were 80 riders, some 420 horses, and 190 relay stations. Riders were paid $25 per week.

The fastest trip ever made was in 7 days and 17 hours, when Lincoln's first inaugural address was carried to the West Coast. But the normal schedule was 8 days, which was about 24 days faster than the schedule of Butterfield's Overland Stage line on the southern route. The maintenance of this schedule through the wilderness, often in blinding snows and howling storms and in the face of Indian dangers, won for the service a fame that has not diminished with the passing of time.

The Pony Express lost money. The average charge for sending a letter during the period was $3, but it cost about $16 per letter to operate the service; thus, the private venture lost $13 per letter, and it is estimated that the Pony Express cost its backers $390,000.

Despite its short life, the Pony Express was credited with many important contributions, not the least of which was its help in keeping East and West joined together during the early crucial days of the Civil War. A 7,200-pound life-size bronze statue of a Pony Express rider and his mount stands in St. Joseph's Civic Center, in Missouri. It was unveiled on April 20, 1940, when the Postal Department honored the riders of the Pony Express with a commemorative postage stamp.

THE STORY OF HORSES AND MULES IN WORLD WAR II; THE REMOUNT SERVICE

Though declining in numbers and considered "old fashioned" by those persons who are enthralled by the speed of the machine age, the horse—man's good friend and stout companion through the ages—dramatically proved his worth again and again on the field of battle and on our farms during World War II.

Once the bulwark of armies—its numbers often deciding the issue of conflict—the horse in World War II was practically jeeped, tanked, and trucked out of his long-held place of importance in military history. Despite the unparalleled mechanization, however, horses played an indispensable role on many fronts during the great struggle for freedom. It is an old cavalry axiom that a horse can go wherever a man can travel, a feat which even the Army's famous little jeep could not accomplish.

The use of horses in World War II reached its greatest proportions in the Russian Army. Long famous for its Cossacks and centuries of cavalry tradition, Russia had, in 1940, about 200,000 horses in cavalry and 800,000 more in artillery, draft, and pack. It is also estimated that the U.S.S.R. had 2 mounted armies available for combat. The Russian cavalry is credited with playing a decisive role in the defense of both Moscow and Stalingrad—striking swift, devasting blows, then quickly withdrawing and melting into the forests and countryside. The full story of the role played by the Russian Cossacks may never be known.

Germany and Japan also recognized the place of the horse in modern warfare. According to the most reliable sources available, the Germans at one time had 50,000 horses for cavalry use and approximately 910,000 draft and pack animals. The Japanese—constantly building up their horse units in China, where large areas were prohibitive to motor vehicles—probably had a cavalry force of 50,000 horses with an additional 300,000 in use for draft and pack purposes.

The U.S. Army had relatively few horses during World War II—only about 25,000 for cavalry use and 12,000 for draft and pack—but these units performed magnificently in combat. The 26th Cavalry fought a brilliant delaying action on Luzon; and both horses and mules were used in the Burma and Italian campaigns, which were conducted through jungles and over mountains where no vehicle of any sort could go.

On the civilian front, the contribution of horses and mules, though less spectacular than on the field of battle, were nonetheless substantial. Though statistics show a continued gradual but steady decline in horse and mule numbers throughout the war years,

Fig. 1-10. Pack mules and "mule skinners" in service during World War II. Horses and mules dramatically proved their worth again and again on the field of battle and on our farms during World War II. (U.S. Army Photo)

perhaps figures alone do not tell the true story. With the rationing of critical rubber and gasoline, the diverting of iron and steel to war production, and the consequent shortage of equipment—all resulting in a scarcity of mechanized power—there is little doubt that the horses and mules on farms in the United States were utilized to the maximum to help carry the major load of farm production.

During the five war years, 1941 to 1945, the total number of horses on farms declined 13.5 percent below the average of 1936 to 1940.

The Remount Service, which was established by Act of Congress in 1921, was transferred to the U.S. Department of Agriculture on July 1, 1948, following which the program was liquidated. At the time of the transfer, approximately 700 remount stallions were in service throughout the country.

In summary, it may be said that the relentless wheels of progress lifted from the horse—that faithful beast of burden—his role in both agriculture and war. But the horse is rising to a more happy position in contributing to the fields of recreation and sport.

SELECTED REFERENCES

Title of Publication	Author(s)	Publisher
Appaloosa: The Spotted Horse in Art and History	F. Haines	University of Texas Press, Austin, Tex., 1963
Asiatic Wild Horse, The	E. Mohr, trans. by D. M. Goodall	J. A. Allen & Co. Ltd., London, England, 1971
"Changes in Horse Numbers as Related to Farm Mechanization, Recreation, and Sport"	B. G. Stark	Thesis, Washington State University, Pullman, Wash., 1960
Encyclopaedia Britannica		Encyclopaedia Britannica, Inc., Chicago, Ill.
Evolution of the Horse	W. D. Matthew S. H. Chubb	American Museum of Natural History, New York, N.Y., 1921
First Horsemen, The	F. Trippett	Time-Life Books, New York, N.Y., 1974
History of Domesticated Animals, A	F. E. Zuener	Harper & Row, Publishers, Inc., Great Britain
History of Thoroughbred Racing in America	W. H. Robertson	Prentice-Hall, Inc., Englewood Cliffs, N.J., 1965
Horse, The	J. M. Kays	A. S. Barnes & Co., Inc., Cranbury, N.J., 1969
Horses	G. G. Simpson	Oxford University Press, New York, N.Y., 1951
Horses in America	F. Haines	Thomas Y. Crowell Company, New York, N.Y., 1971
Horses and Americans	P. D. Strong	Frederick A. Stokes Company, New York, N.Y., 1939
Horses and Horsemanship Through the Ages	L. Gianoli	Crown Publishers, Inc., New York, N.Y., 1969
Horses of Today	H. H. Reese	Wood & Jones, Pasadena, Calif., 1956
Our Friendly Animals and Whence They Came	K. P. Schmidt	M. A. Donohue & Co., Chicago, Ill., 1938
Principles of Classification and a Classification of Mammals, The, Vol. 85	G. G. Simpson	American Museum of Natural History, New York, N.Y., 1945
Wild Horse of the West, The	W. D. Wyman	University of Nebraska Press, Lincoln, Neb., 1945

CHAPTER 2

DISTRIBUTION, ADAPTATION, AND THE FUTURE OF THE HORSE INDUSTRY

Since prehistoric times, there has been nearly worldwide distribution of the horse. Moreover, man's effective use of the horse has constantly progressed, especially from the standpoint of improvement in the equipment to which he was attached for the purpose of drawing loads.

After the horse was domesticated and no longer hunted down and killed for meat, he was used to carry riders and support goods upon his strong back. In an effort to provide transportation for a longer load than could be fastened directly to the back of the horse, ingenious man devised a basketlike arrangement which was fitted between 2 long poles. One end of these poles rested on the back of the horse and the other end dragged on the ground to the rear. In an effort to reduce the resistance of this vehicle and permit the carrying of still heavier loads, man supported the poles on a wooden axle and 2 wheels made of wood, thus inventing a 2-wheeled cart. Next, the leather harness was developed, transferring the pull from the back of the horse to the better-adapted shoulders. Finally, man developed the 4-wheeled, self-supporting vehicle with improved axles made of iron instead of wood; and eventually he replaced steel wheels with pneumatic tires mounted on ball bearings.

But horsemen recognize the passing of the horse as a source of power. A century ago, muscles provided 94% of the world's energy needs; coal, oil, and waterpower provided the other 6%. Today, the situation is reversed in the developed nations. They now obtain 94% of their energy needs from coal, oil, natural gas,

Fig. 2-1. The way it used to be done.

and waterpower, and only 6% from the muscle power of men and animals.

For the most part, the future of the horse is in the fields of recreations and sport and as the cow pony of the West.

WORLD DISTRIBUTION OF HORSES AND MULES

At a very early date and throughout the world, the versatility and adaption of the horse were recognized.

He was unexcelled in carrying a rider comfortably and swiftly on a long journey; he possessed a long life of usefulness; and, above all, he was intelligent. Despite all these virtues, in some areas the horse has been unable to replace patient "roughage-burning" oxen and water buffalo. To this day, oxen are still the main source of power on farms in such densely populated countries as India, Pakistan, and the People's Republic of China, in many Near Eastern and African countries, and in some countries of Latin America; and water buffalo are the main source of power in rice-producing areas, because of their ability to work in muddy paddy fields. In the more isolated portions of the New England states, oxen are occasionally used, and stoneboat-pulling contests are a great attraction at the New England fairs.

Members of the ass family (mules and donkeys) are distributed in the warmer regions of the world, where they still occupy a rather important place among the animals used for both pack and draft purposes.

Table 2-1 shows the size and density of the horse population of the important horse countries of the world. As noted, world horse numbers totaled 64,006,000 in 1974. This was far below the 1934-38 prewar average of 96.4 million head. The decline in horse numbers since 1938 can be attributed chiefly to the mechanization of agriculture. For example, the number of tractors in use in agriculture in the world in 1973 totaled 16,423,746,[1] compared with fewer than 2 million in 1939.

Fig. 2-2 shows the 10 leading horse countries of the world in 1974. As noted, by rank they are: Brazil, United States, People's Republic of China, U.S.S.R., Mexico, Argentina, Poland, Mongolia, Ethiopia, and Yugoslavia.

---

[1]*Production Yearbook 1974*, Vol. 28-1, FAO of the United Nations, p. 130.

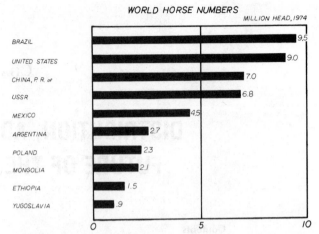

Fig. 2-2. Ten leading horse countries of the world, 1974. (Based on data from FAO *Production Yearbook 1974*, Vol. 28-1, pp. 193-195)

GROWTH AND DECLINE OF U.S. HORSE AND MULE PRODUCTION

The golden age of the horse extended from the Gay Nineties to the mechanization of agriculture—to the advent of the automobile, truck, and tractor. During this era, everybody loved the horse. The town livery stable, watering trough, and hitching post were trademarks of each town and village. People wept when the horse fell on the icy street, and they jailed men who beat or mistreated horses. The oat bag, carriage, wagon, buggy whip, axle grease, horseshoe, and horseshoe-nail industries were thriving and essential parts of the national economy. Every schoolboy knew and respected the village blacksmith.

Bobtailed Hackneys attached to high-seated rigs made a dashing picture as they pranced down the avenue; they were a mark of social prestige. A few memorable dinner parties of the era were even staged on horseback, with the guests lining up in exclusive restaurants astride their favorite mounts. One of the

TABLE 2-1

LEADING HORSE-PRODUCING COUNTRIES OF THE WORLD, 1974

Country	Horses[1]	Human Population[2]	Size of Country[2]		Horses per Capita[3]	Horses per	
	(thousands)	(thousands)	(sq. mi.)	(sq. km.)		(sq. mi.)	(sq. km.)
Brazil	9,500	105,137	3,286,470	8,511,957	.09	2.8	1.1
United States	8,984	213,900	3,628,066	9,396,691	.04	2.5	1.0
China, P.R. of	7,000	800,000	3,691,502	9,560,990	.009	1.9	.7
U.S.S.R.	6,848	250,900	8,647,250	22,396,378	.02	.8	.3
Mexico	4,459	52,640	758,259	1,963,891	.08	5.9	2.3
Argentina	2,700	23,920	1,072,067	2,776,653	.12	2.6	1.0
Poland	2,312	33,360	120,359	311,730	.06	19.2	7.4
Mongolia	2,100	1,360	604,247	1,564,999	1.54	3.5	1.3
Ethiopia	1,453	26,080	457,142	1,183,997	.05	3.2	1.2
Yugoslavia	945	21,126	98,766	255,803	.05	9.6	3.7
World Total.	64,006	3,967,000	52,403,746	135,725,702	.02	1.2	.5

[1]*Production Yearbook 1974*, Vol. 28-1, FAO of the United Nations, p. 193.
[2]*The World Almanac and Book of Facts 1975*, pub. by Newspaper Enterprise Assn., Inc.
[3]Horses per capita computed from most recent census figures available.

Fig. 2-3. Horse-drawn covered wagons. This photograph was taken when making the film for the "Covered Wagon," founded on Emerson Hough's novel of the same name. When the news was spread that gold had been discovered in California, the Oregon Trail split in half, one part branching off to the south while the other part turned north toward Oregon. Improved roads and the advent of the motor vehicle have practically eliminated horses from the highways and city streets. (From Ewing Galloway)

opened $200,000 stable at 196th Street and Fort Washington Road (now Fort Tryon Park), Mr. Billings converted the grand ballroom of Sherry's into a woodland paradise by means of $10,000 worth of full-scale scenic props, artificial foliage, potted palms, and a tanbark floor covering—borrowed, at Mr. Sherry's insistence, from the Barnum and Bailey Circus. Thirty-six mystified horses were conveyed up to the ballroom by freight elevators, and the guests—members of the New York Riding Club—attired in white ties and tails, and gingerly astride their favorite mounts, drank and ate to the merriment of music, while their steeds munched oats, and costumed lackeys cleaned up behind them. Miniature tables were attached to the saddle pommels (drive-in style), and apprehensive waiters dressed in riding attire served drink after drink, and course after course, topped off by Jack Horner pies—huge, ornamental concoctions which, when cut open, revealed a covey of nymphs in their birthday suits. Only one guest fell off his horse.

most notable of these horseback bashes was staged in Louis Sherry's restaurant, corner of Fifth Avenue and 44th Street, New York City, on March 28, 1903, with Cornelius K. G. Billings—racing enthusiast, Chicago utilities heir, and self-styled "American Horse King"—as host (see Fig. 2-4). To publicize his newly

In 1900, the automobile was still the plutocrat's plaything, and the truck and tractor were unknown. Most of the expensive 8,000 cars in the country at the time were either imported or custom-built. Tires cost about $40 each, and lasted only 2,000 miles. Few really loved the auto. Complaints were made of the noise they made; laws were enacted against their going through the city parks; and people split their sides with laughter when autos had to be pushed uphill or got stuck in the mud.

Fig. 2-4. Horseback dinner in Louis Sherry's restaurant in New York City, hosted by Cornelius K. G. Billings, 1903. (Photo by Byron, The Byron Collection, Museum of the City of New York)

Then, in 1908, Henry Ford produced a car to sell at $825. The truck, the tractor, and improved highways followed closely in period of time. Old dobbin did not know it at the time, but his days were numbered. As shown in Table 2-2 and Fig. 2-5, the passing of the horse age and the coming of the machine

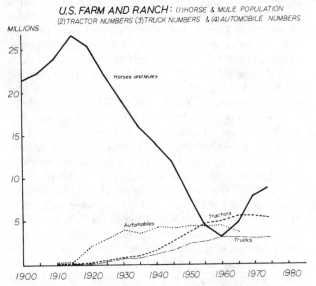

Fig. 2-5. Growth and decline of U.S. horse and mule production. The period of decline in horse and mule numbers coincided closely with the advent of mechanized power, especially the tractor, truck, and automobile. (Source: See Table 2-2)

age went hand in hand; as automobile, truck, and tractor numbers increased, horse and mule numbers declined.

The number of horses in the United States increased up to 1915, at which time there was a record number of 21,431,000 head (horses only; not including mules). Horse production expanded with the growth and development of farms.

Mules on farms slowly but steadily increased in numbers for 10 years after horses began their decline, reaching a peak in 1925 at 5,680,897 head. Mule numbers decreased proportionally less rapidly than horses because of their great use in the deep South where labor was cheaper and more abundant and the farms smaller in size.

In 1915—the peak year, there were 26,493,000 horses and mules, combined, on farms and ranches in the United States and an additional 2,000,000 head in cities. By January 1, 1960, the census showed that there were only 3,089,000 head of horses and mules on the nation's farms and ranches (not counting suburban owned horses and those kept on parcels under 10 acres in size)—the lowest number ever recorded.

Ironical as it may seem, the development of manufacturing and commerce was responsible for both the rise and the fall of the horse and mule industry of the United States. The early growth of American industry created a large need for horses to transport the raw and manufactured goods and to produce needed agricultural products for those people who lived in

TABLE 2-2

U.S. FARM AND RANCH (1) HORSE AND MULE POPULATION,
(2) TRACTOR NUMBERS, (3) TRUCK NUMBERS, AND
(4) AUTOMOBILE NUMBERS, FROM 1900 to 1974

Year	Horses and Mules	Tractors Nos. (including garden)	Truck Nos.	Automobiles Nos.
1900	21,531,635[1]	—	—	—
1905	22,077,000[2]	—	—	—
1910	24,042,882[1]	1,000[3]	0[3]	50,000[3]
1915	26,493,000[2]	25,000[3]	25,000[3]	472,000[3]
1920	25,199,552[1]	246,083[4]	139,169[4]	2,146,362[4]
1925	22,081,520[1]	505,933[4]	459,000[3]	3,283,000[3]
1930	18,885,856[1]	920,021[4]	900,385[4]	4,134,675[4]
1935	16,676,000[1]	1,048,000[3]	890,000[3]	3,642,000[3]
1940	13,931,531[1]	1,567,430[4]	1,047,084[4]	4,144,136[4]
1945	11,629,000[5]	2,422,000[6]	1,490,000[6]	4,148,000[6]
1950	7,604,000[5]	3,610,000[6]	2,207,000[6]	4,199,000[6]
1955	4,309,000[5]	4,692,000[6]	2,701,000[6]	4,258,000[6]
1960	3,089,000[5]	5,138,000[6]	3,110,000[6]	4,260,000[6]
1965	4,580,000[7]	5,486,000[8]	3,030,000[8]	3,593,000[8]
1970	7,701,000[9]	5,424,000[8]	2,984,000[8]	N/A[10]
1974	8,985,000[7]	5,236,000[8]	2,906,000[8]	N/A[10]

[1]1950 Census of Agriculture, pp. 385, 387.
[2]Agricultural Statistics 1952, p. 455.
[3]Agricultural Statistics 1952, p. 631.
[4]1950 Census of Agriculture, p. 204.
[5]Agricultural Statistics 1960, p. 370.
[6]Agricultural Statistics 1960, p. 449.
[7]Production Yearbook 1974, Vol. 28-1, FAO of the United Nations, p. 193.
[8]Agricultural Statistics 1974, p. 430.
[9]Production Yearbook 1972, Vol. 26, FAO of the United Nations, p. 183.
[10]NA = Not available.

the cities and villages. With further scientific developments—especially the invention of the tractor, truck, and automobile—the horse was replaced, first ever so slowly but then rapidly and drastically.

Today, very few horses are found on city streets. The old-time livery stable has long since passed out of existence; draft horses are seldom hitched to large dray wagons; and horses hitched to a delivery wagon or to a plow are almost a novelty.

But, the horse is coming up fast in the fields of recreation and sport. In 1974, there were 8,984,000 horses in the United States, most of which were light horses; and there were only 1,000 mules.[2] Draft horses and mules were the victims of mechanization—farming changed. From 1915 to 1974, farm tractors increased from 25,000 to 5,236,000—more than a 200-fold increase; and, during this same period of time, truck numbers increased from 25,000 to 2,906,000 (Table 2-2).

Based on the 1971 VEE vaccination program conducted by the U.S. Department of Agriculture, the 10 leading states in horse numbers at that time, by rank, were: Texas, California, Tennessee, Oklahoma, Ohio, Mississippi, Michigan, Missouri, Kentucky, and Kansas.

PRESENT STATUS OF THE U.S. HORSE INDUSTRY

The unique thing about the horse business, not found in any other industry, is the human values back of it. It's a people's business, and a way of life for many.

---

[2]*Production Yearbook 1974*, Vol. 28-1, FAO of the United Nations, p. 193.

Also, the U.S. horse industry is big and important business, and it will get bigger. The following facts and figures attest to the magnitude and importance of the industry:

● There are approximately 9 million horses in the United States.

● Horses represent an estimated $13 billion investment.

● Annual expenditures for horse feed, drugs, tack, and equipment average about $1,000 per horse.

● U.S. horses make for a gross business—from vitamins to saddlery—of $9 billion per year.

● Annual wages paid in the horse industry exceed $1 billion.

● There are more 4-H Club horse projects than beef cattle projects. In 1966, for the first time in history, 4-H Club horse and pony projects took the lead over 4-H beef cattle projects. Subsequently, this lead has been widened further and further. These figures are presented in Table 2-3.

● Horse shows are increasing in size and numbers. They have more than doubled during the past 20 years. In 1975, 1,434 horse shows were sanctioned by the American Horse Shows Association, with prize money totaling $5,015,426. The horse show story is given in Table 2-4.

● Horse racing continues to be America's leading spectator sport. In 1975, 82,339,060 people went to horse races (Thoroughbred and harness racing); 32,939,060 more than witnessed automobile racing—the second-ranking spectator sport. That same year, the rankings in attendance of the other leading sports were: football, third; baseball, fourth; basketball, fifth; hockey, sixth; and Greyhound racing, seventh. The rankings and figures of the 7 leading spectator sports are given in Table 2-5.

Fig. 2-6. An attractive horse farm. (Courtesy, Kentucky Department of Public Information, Frankfort, Ky.)

TABLE 2-3

4-H CLUB BEEF CATTLE AND HORSE PROJECTS[1]

	1965	1966	1970	1974	1975
Beef cattle	160,914	157,949	150,056	160,846	164,208
Horses	146,541	165,510	231,206	320,767	320,050

[1]USDA.

TABLE 2-4

HORSE SHOWS

Year	AHSA Sanctioned Shows	Major Shows (over 50% of divisions with "A" rating)	Prize Money
	(no.)	(no.)	($)
1959	425	142	1,453,322
1968	825	275	2,879,280
1971	958	325	3,615,550
1973	1,178	375	4,458,659
1974	1,258	405	4,987,649
1975	1,434	435	5,015,426

TABLE 2-5

U.S. SPORTS ATTENDANCE 1975[1]

Leading Sports	Fan Attendance
1. Horse racing (Thoroughbred and harness)	82,339,060
2. Auto racing	49,400,000
3. Football	43,374,483
4. Baseball	41,981,629
5. Basketball	33,538,226
6. Hockey	23,134,242
7. Greyhound racing	16,921,990

[1]1975 Survey of Sports Attendance, Triangle Publications, Inc., Hightstown, N.J.

● Saddle clubs are springing up everywhere, and more people are riding horses for pleasure than ever before.

● On the western range, cow ponies are still used in the traditional manner; mechanical replacement for them has not yet been devised.

● Horses are benefactors of mankind in numerous other ways. Limited numbers of them are used by the Forest Service; others are used as pack animals into remote areas not otherwise accessible by surface travel. They are still the show in many motion pictures and in parades. Those responsible for law enforcement have found that mounted patrols are one of the most effective ways in which to handle crowds and riots.

In the laboratory, horses serve as a factory for the manufacture of antitoxins that are used for rendering animals and people immune to certain diseases, such as tetanus. Also, medical doctors use equine produced estrogens (female sex hormones), obtained from the urine of pregnant mares, to relieve the menopause (change of life) of women.

Despite the magnitude of the industry, U.S. horse owners suffer appalling losses. They are—

1. Spending millions of dollars on needless concoctions and using unbalanced and deficient rations.

2. Producing only a 50 percent foal crop, which means that they are keeping two mares a whole year to produce one foal.

3. Keeping a stallion for each 7.3 foals produced.

4. Maintaining horse breeding establishments that return little or nothing on investment.

5. Retiring an appalling number of horses from tracks, shows, and other uses due to unsoundnesses.

6. Losing through inefficiency and deaths millions of dollars due to diseases and parasites.

Such wanton losses prompt the question: If the horse industry is so good, why not better?

FUTURE OF THE HORSE INDUSTRY

This generation has more money to spend and more leisure time in which to spend it than any population in history. A shorter workweek, increased automation, more suburban and rural living, and the continued recreation and sports surge, with emphasis on physical fitness and the out-of-doors, will require more horses and support more racetracks, shows, and other horse events. So, horse numbers will continue to increase.

It is expected that the estimated 500,000 horses in the 17 western range states will continue to hold their own. Even the Jeep is not sufficiently versatile for use in roping a steer on the range. It is reasonable to assume, therefore, that the cow pony will continue to furnish needed assistance to man in the West.

Horse racing will continue to be America's lead-

Fig. 2-7. The cow pony of the West will continue to furnish needed assistance in handling the range herds. (Courtesy, *The Quarter Horse Journal*, Amarillo, Tex.)

Fig. 2-8. White Lipizzan stallion literally flying through the air with perfectly seated stirrupless rider. The horse is decorated with gold trappings and the rider is smartly dressed in an old-time Napoleonic military uniform. The stallion is pictured doing the Capriole, one of several intricate movements resembling the leaping, twisting, fighting, and frolicking of high-spirited horses in pasture.

The Lipizzan breed—named after the town of Lipizza, one-time site of the old Hapsburg stud farm—was founded back in 1565 by Emperor Maximilian of Austria. The emperor assembled white animals of Arabian and Spanish breeding, and established the Spanish Riding School in Vienna, Austria. Foals of the Lipizzan breed are brown or gray at birth, but turn completely white at four to six years of age.

Toward the close of World War II, the Spanish Riding School and the Lipizzan breed were threatened with extinction by both the German and Russian armies. In desperation, the school heads appealed to excavalryman George S. Patton whose tanks were dashing across Austria in the spring of 1945. After observing a special exhibition of the historic white horses, the horse fancier General agreed to preserve and protect the entire herd as a part of European culture. To this end, the Spanish Riding School and its horses were moved to Wels, Austria, near Salzburg. (Courtesy, Spanish Riding School, Wels, Austria)

ing spectator sport, although there will be increased competition for the recreation and sports dollar in the years ahead.

In the final analysis, the dominant factors that will determine the future of the horse situation are (1) the need for the cow pony, and (2) the use of horses for recreation and sport.

Horse production will, in common with most businesses, encounter increasing competition in the years ahead. Competition will be keen for land, labor, and capital, as well as from other sports.

Skilled management and production programs geared to produce horses that meet more exacting market demands will be the two essential ingredients for success. Also, it will require greater skill and understanding of fundamental relationships to take care of highly bred, sensitive animals in forced production.

Never has there been so much reason to have confidence in, and to be optimistic about, the future. The years ahead will be the most rewarding in the history of the horse industry.

Horse Research

The Age of Research was ushered in with World War II, the most notable accomplishment of which was the developing and unleashing of the atom bomb. Now we are in a space age, and all industry, big and little—including the horse business—must be geared to it. Other animal industries have long been cognizant of new frontiers possible through research. But horse research has lagged, with the result that we have just begun to apply science, automation, and technology to light horses. In 1974, the scientific man

years (a man year is defined as one person devoting full time to research for one year) devoted to research on each class of livestock by USDA and college personnel was a follows:

Class of Animal	Scientific Years Devoted to Research, in 1975
Beef Cattle	348.4
Dairy Cattle	308.0
Poultry	253.5
Swine	150.7
Sheep and Wool	79.2
Laboratory Animals	44.2
Horses, Ponies, and Mules	24.8
Pets	9.6
Goats and Mohair	2.3
Other Animals	4.8

There is every reason to believe that today's research will be reflected in a host of tomorrow's advances—that many of today's horse problems will be solved through research. Indeed, horse research should be expanded. More specifically, and among other things, we need to know the following in the horse business:

1. We need to know how to modernize rations and effect savings in costs; we need to eliminate

needless concoctions and unbalanced and deficient rations.

2. We need to know how to rectify appalling and costly sterility and reproductive failures; we need to produce more than a 50 percent foal crop.

3. We need to know how to bring mares in heat at will.

4. We need to improve artificial insemination of horses.

5. We need to be able to transplant fertilized horse eggs.

6. We need to know more about the relationship between soil fertility, plant nutrients, and horses.

7. We need to know how to provide laborsaving buildings and equipment—how to automate the horse business. Seventy-five percent of horse work is still hand labor, one-third of which could be eliminated by mechanization and modernization.

8. We need to know how to improve upon the control of diseases and parasites.

9. We need to know how to increase the durability and useful life of a horse—in racing, in showing, and in breeding; we need to lessen the appalling number of horses that we are retiring from tracks, shows, and other uses due to unsoundnesses.

10. We need to know how to make a fair return on capital invested in horse breeding establishments.

We must remember, however, (1) that horse research is both slow and costly, and (2) that other industries have long liberally supported research costs with no assistance from the taxpayer, simply including them as a normal part of their operating costs. In addition to individual owners contributing to the support of research programs, the time has arrived when horsemen should review where racing dollars go. Perhaps a liberal proportion of racing revenue which now goes into the treasuries of the 30 states having pari-mutuel betting should be earmarked for horse research, teaching, and extension. Otherwise, there is grave danger of starving "the goose that laid the golden egg."

Finally, it should be emphasized that research can make the information available, but it is still up to each individual—each horseman—to secure and apply the results. "You can lead a horse to water but you can't make him drink." Nevertheless, in the years ahead horsemen will not be able to cling to horse-and-buggy methods while the rest of industry forges ahead. For sheer survival, they must use science and technology.

SELECTED REFERENCES

Title of Publication	Author(s)	Publisher
Breeding and Raising Horses, Ag. Hdbk. No. 394	M. E. Ensminger	U.S. Department of Agriculture, Washington, D.C., 1972
"Changes in Horse Numbers as Related to Farm Mechanization, Recreation, and Sport"	B. G. Stark	Thesis, Washington State University, Pullman, Wash., 1960
Horse, The	D. J. Kays, rev. by J. M. Kays	A. S. Barnes & Co., Inc., Cranbury, N.J., 1969
Horsemanship and Horse Care, Ag. Info. Bull. No. 353	M. E. Ensminger	U.S. Department of Agriculture, Washington, D.C., 1972
Horses in America	F. Haines	Thomas Y. Crowell Company, New York, N.Y., 1971
Light Horses, Farmers' Bull. No. 2127	M. E. Ensminger	U.S. Department of Agriculture, Washington, D.C., 1965
Power to Produce: Yearbook of Agriculture, 1960		U.S. Department of Agriculture, Washington, D.C., 1960
Use of Horses and Mules on Farms, The	J. J. Csorba	U.S. Department of Agriculture, Washington, D.C., 1959

CHAPTER 3

FUNCTIONAL ANATOMY
OF THE HORSE

Contents

This chapter is not designed to cover the structure of the horse purely from an anatomical standpoint. Rather, its purpose is to relate the structure to desired function and usefulness. Broadly speaking, one type of animal is required for slow, heavy, draft purposes, and quite another for recreation and sport. This is really the distinction between draft and light horse breeds. However, further and very fundamental differences in structure fit the respective types and breeds for more specific purposes. Thus, the Thoroughbred running horse possesses certain hereditary structural characteristics which better fit him for speed and endurance than for usage as a five-gaited saddle horse. For the same reason, hunters are seldom obtained from among American Saddle Horses. In general, these structural differences between different types of horses are as marked as the fundamental differences between beef-type and dairy-type cattle. Yet, it must be pointed out that, regardless of the usage to which the animal is put, horsemen universally emphasize the importance of good heads and necks, short couplings, strong loins, and good feet and legs.

SKELETON OF THE HORSE

The skeleton of the horse consists of 205 bones, as follows:

Vertebral column 54
Ribs 36
Sternum 1
Skull (including auditory ossicles) 34
Thoracic limbs 40
Pelvic limbs 40

Total 205

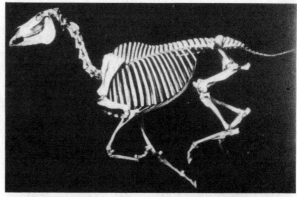

Fig. 3-1. Skeleton of the famous American racehorse Sysonby, showing action at the run. This illustration shows how the bones act as levers as (1) the hind legs are drawn up beneath the body, then moved forward preparatory to straightening out and propelling the horse forward with a long stride typical of great running horses, and (2) the front legs sustain a tremendous jar as the horse lands. The run is a four-beat gait where the feet strike the ground separately; first one hind foot, then the other hind foot, then the front foot on the same side as the first hind foot, then the other front foot which decides the lead. (Courtesy, The American Museum of Natural History, New York, N.Y.)

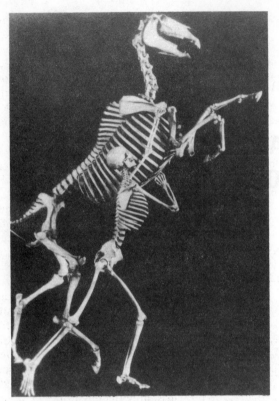

Fig. 3-2. Skeleton of horse and man. It can be seen that (1) the knee joint in the horse is the counterpart of the wrist joint in man; (2) the stifle joint in the horse is the counterpart of the knee joint in man; and (3) the hock joint in the horse is the counterpart of the ankle joint in man. (Courtesy, The American Museum of Natural History, New York, N.Y.)

Vertebral Column

In the preceding summary, it is considered that there is an average of 18 coccygeal (tail) vertebrae. In addition, the vertebral column consists of 7 cervical (neck) vertebrae, 18 dorsal (back), 6 lumbar (loin), and 5 sacral (croup) vertebrae.

In horses of the correct conformation, the lower line of the dorsal vertebrae (commonly referred to as the backbone) is arched slightly upward. The degree to which the backbone is arched in different horses varies greatly. If the arch is extreme, the animal is referred to as "roach backed"; whereas if the backbone sags very markedly, the animal is known as "swaybacked." Either of these conditions represents a weakness in conformation and is objectionable.

Desired height at the withers and proper topline are obtained through variation in the length of the spinous processes which project upward from the vertebrae. Thus, the structure at this point is of especial importance in the saddle horse, determining the desirableness of the seat.

There is a close correlation between the length of the individual vertebrae and the length of the component parts of the entire animal. Thus, an animal with long vertebrae has a long neck, back, loin, croup, and tail. Within limits, length is desired. For example, the longer neck on a saddle horse gives the desired effect of "much horse in front of the rider." On the other hand, a very long back and loin are objectionable, denoting lack of strength. Apparent length of back may

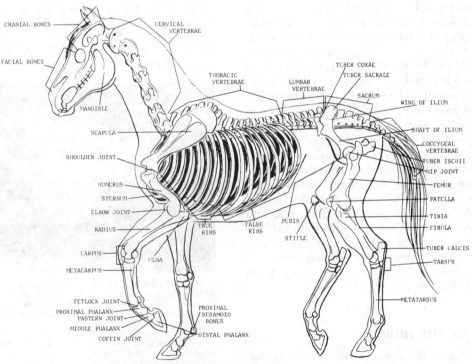

Fig. 3-3. Skeleton of horse.

be alleviated by having a sloping shoulder, with the upper end joining the back at the rear part of the withers.

Ribs

There are usually 18 pairs of ribs in the horse, but a nineteenth rib on one side or both is not at all rare. Eight pairs are known as true ribs, joining the segments of the sternum or breastbone; whereas the remaining 10 pairs are floating, merely overlapping and being attached to each other. The seventh and eighth ribs are longest, with the back ribs much shorter.

A capacious chest and middle, which is desirable in all horses, is obtained through long, well-sprung ribs. Such a structural condition allows for more room for the vital internal organs, and experienced horsemen know that such horses eat better and stand up under more hard work.

Sternum

The sternum or breastbone of the horse is composed of eight segments, the whole of which is shaped somewhat like a canoe. There are indentures in the sides for the reception of the cartilages extending from the ribs.

Skull

The skull encloses the brain and the most important organs of sense. It consists of 34 bones, mostly flat, which yield and overlap at points of union at the time of birth, thus making for greater ease of parturition.

The size of the head should be proportionate to the size of the horse, and the shape true to the characteristics of the breed or type represented. Thus, the Thoroughbred possesses a broad forehead, with the face gradually tapering from the forehead to the muzzle, giving the animal an intelligent and alert expression.

The lower jaw should always be strong and well defined, with good width between the branches so as not to compress the larynx when the neck is flexed.

The mature male horse has 40 teeth, and the female 36. Animals of each sex possess 24 molars or grinders and 12 incisors or front teeth. In addition, the male has 4 tushes or pointed teeth, and sometimes these occur in females.

The young animal, whether male or female, has 24 temporary or milk teeth. These include 12 incisors and 12 molars.

Thoracic Limbs

This includes all the bones of the foreleg; namely, the scapula, humerus, radius and ulna, 7 or 8 carpal bones, cannon bone and 2 splint bones, 2 sesamoid bones, large pastern bone, small pastern bone, navicular bone, and coffin bone. The correctness of these bones determines the action and consequent usefulness and value of the animal. Since the front feet maintain about 60 percent of the horse's weight and are subject to great concussion, they should receive careful attention.

The scapula, humerus, radius, and ulna are enclosed in heavy muscles which move them; whereas the parts of the leg below the knee are motivated by long tendons.

The carpal bones collectively comprise the knee of the horse, which corresponds to the wrist in man. The knee should be broad, deep, straight, clean-cut, strongly supported, and free from soft fluctuating swellings. The cannons should be wide, flat, and clean with large, sharply defined, cordlike tendons.

The degree of slope of the pasterns is closely associated with that of the shoulders, and moderate slope (about 45°) to these parts of the anatomy—the scapula and large and small pastern bones—is desirable. Oblique shoulders and pasterns aid in producing elastic springy action and absorb concussions or jars much better than short, straight pasterns and straight shoulders—thereby lessening the possibility of an unsoundness.

The set to the front legs should also be true. When viewed from the front, a vertical line dropped from the point of the shoulder should fall upon the center of the knee, cannon, pastern, and foot. When viewed from the side, a vertical line dropped from the center of the elbow joint should fall upon the center of the knee and fetlock and strike the ground just back of the hoof.

Pelvic Limbs

The pelvic limbs, embracing 40 bones, are the horse's chief means of propulsion forward. The stifle and hock joints will be discussed separately under this heading.

The stifle joint of the horse corresponds to the knee in the human. Excepting for an occasional dislocation of the patella (a condition known as stifled), this joint is not subject to much trouble.

The hock is the most important single joint of the horse, probably being the seat of more serious unsoundnesses than any other part of the body—among them bone spavins, bog spavins, curbs, and thoroughpins. The hock should be wide, deep, flat, clean, hard, strong, well supported, and correctly set with prominent points.

The rear pasterns should be similar to the front ones, although they may be slightly less sloping (a 50° angle being satisfactory for the hind foot).

TABLE 3-1
PARTS OF THE HOOF

The Parts	Description	Functions	Comments
The four major parts: Bones	They are: Long pastern bone Short pastern bone Coffin bone Navicular bone	Provide framework of the foot and facilitate locomotion.	Long pastern bone lies entirely above the hoof. Only lower end of short pastern bone is within hoof.
Elastic structure	Consists of: Lateral cartilages Plantar cushion	Overcomes concussion or jar when the foot strikes the ground.	Normally, heel expands about 1/16 in. on each side of foot.
Sensitive structure, called the corium or pododerm	Consists of: Coronary band Perioplic ring Sensitive laminae Sensitive sole Sensitive frog	Furnishes nutrition to corresponding part of hoof.	All 5 parts are highly sensitive and vascular.
Horny wall	The outer horny covering.	Encloses and protects the sensitive parts beneath.	
The exterior of the hoof: Horny wall	The basic shell and wearing surface of the foot.	Protects; there is no feeling in the wall of the foot until the area of the coronary band is reached.	The horny wall extends vertically from the edge of the hair around the front and sides of the foot, then turns in upon itself at the heel, forming the bar which extends forward toward the center.
Perioplic ring	The seat where periople is produced.	Produces periople, the varnishlike substance that covers the outer surface of the wall and seals it from excess drying.	The wall of a normal foot consists of about ¼ water, by weight.
White line	The juncture of the wall and horny sole. It is about ⅛ in. wide.	Serves as the horseman's "red light," beyond (toward the inside of the foot) which nails should not go.	A nail past the white line may either enter the sensitive structure or produce pressure, with resulting lameness.
Horny frog	The V-shaped pad in the middle of the sole.	Compresses under weight, and transmits pressure to the elastic structures. Aids blood circulation, absorbs concussion, and prevents slippage.	Without this normal pressure, the hoof has a tendency to shrink and become dormant, with contracted feet and unsoundness resulting.
Commissures	The deep grooves on both sides of the frog.	Give elasticity.	Thrush is often found in the commissures.
Horny sole	The bottom of the foot. It is a thick (about ⅜ in.) plate or horn which grows out from the fleshy sole.	Protects the foot from the bottom. Nature didn't intend that the horny sole should carry weight, for it is convex in shape so that most of the weight rests on the wall and frog area.	The sensitive sole is directly under the horny sole. Pressure on the horny sole area will usually produce lameness.
Bars	The horny protrusions that lie along the frog between the commissures and the sole.	Help support the foot and keep it open at the heels.	
The perimeter sections: Inside and outside toe Quarters Heel		*(See above)*	

The set to the hind legs should be such that, when viewed from the rear, a vertical line dropped from the point of the buttock will fall upon the center of the hock, cannon, and foot. When viewed from the side, this vertical line should touch the point of the hock and run parallel with the back of the cannon.

ANATOMY OF THE FOOT

When it is realized that the horse has been transplanted from his natural roving environment and soft, mother-earth footing to be used in carrying and drawing loads over hard, dry-surfaced topography by day and then stabled on hard, dry floors at night, it is not surprising that foot troubles are commonplace. Nor are these troubles new. The Greeks alluded to them in the age-old axiom, "No foot, no horse."

In order to lessen foot troubles, and to permit intelligent shoeing, knowledge of the anatomy of a horse's foot, pasterns, and legs is necessary.

Parts of the Foot

Fig. 3-4 shows the parts of the foot, and Table 3-1 gives the pertinent facts about each part.

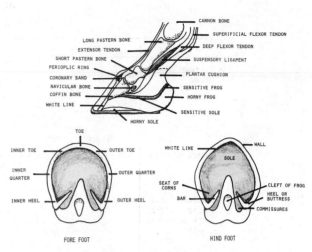

Fig. 3-4. Parts of the foot.

How the Hoof Grows

The hoof grows downward and forward. A complex system of arteries, veins, and nerves inside the outer structure provides for its growth. The average rate of growth of the horny portions of the hoof (wall, sole, and frog) is ⅛ to ¼ inch per month.

SELECTED REFERENCES

Title of Publication	Author(s)	Publisher
Anatomy and Conformation of the Horse	G. B. Edwards	Dreenan Press Ltd., Croton-on-Hudson, N.Y., 1973
Anatomy of the Domestic Animals	S. Sisson	W. B. Saunders Company, Philadelphia, Penn., 1953
Anatomy of the Horse, The	R. F. Way D. G. Lee	J. B. Lippincott Co., Philadelphia, Penn., 1965
Anatomy and Physiology of Farm Animals	R. D. Frandson	Lea & Febiger, Philadelphia, Penn., 1965
Dukes' Physiology of Domestic Animals	Ed. by M. J. Swenson	Comstock Publishing Associates, a Division of Cornell University Press, Ithaca, N.Y., 1970
Horseshoeing Theory and Hoof Care	L. Emery J. Miller N. Van Hoosen	Lea & Febiger, Philadelphia, Penn., 1977
Horse Structure and Movement, The	R. H. Smythe, rev. by P. C. Goody	J. A. Allen & Co., London, England, 1972
Lameness in Horses	O. R. Adams	Lea & Febiger, Philadelphia, Penn., 1966
Leg at Each Corner, A	N. Thelwell	E. P. Dutton & Co., Inc., New York, N.Y., 1963
Points of the Horse	M. H. Hayes	Arco Publishing Co., Inc., New York, N.Y., 1969

CHAPTER 4

SELECTING AND JUDGING HORSES

Contents

The great horse shows throughout the land have exerted a powerful influence in molding the types of certain breeds of horses. Other breeds have been affected primarily through selections based on performance, such as the racetrack. It is realized, however, that only a comparatively few animals are subjected annually to the scrutiny of experienced judges or to trial on the racetrack. Rather, the vast majority of them are evaluated—bought and sold—by persons who lack experience in judging, but who have a practical need for an animal and take pride in selecting and owning a good horse. Before buying a horse, the amateur should enlist the help of a competent horseman.

Fig. 4-1. Horse auction in process—the Select Saratoga Yearling Sales. Pictured in the ring is Catoctin Stud's chestnut filly (Hip.No. 108) by Buckpasser out of Exclusive Dancer by Native Dancer, which sold for $170,000 to Cynthia Phipps. (Courtesy, Fasig-Tipton Company, Elmont, N.Y.)

PARTS OF A HORSE

In selecting and judging horses, parts are usually referred to, rather than to the individual as a whole. It is important, therefore, to master the language that describes and locates the different parts of a horse. In addition, it is necessary to know which of these parts are of major importance; that is, what comparative evaluation to give the different parts. Nothing so quickly sets a real horseman apart from a novice as a thorough knowledge of the parts and the language commonly used in describing them. Fig. 4-2 shows the parts of a horse.

HOW TO SELECT A HORSE

As with other classes of farm animals, any one or a combination of all four of the following methods may serve as bases for selecting horses: (1) individuality, (2) pedigree, (3) show-ring winnings, and/or (4) performance testing. One must also be aware of the fact that environment, including feeding and training, plays a tremendously important part in the individuality and performance of a horse.

Selection Based on Individuality

In addition to obtaining a sound horse of desira-

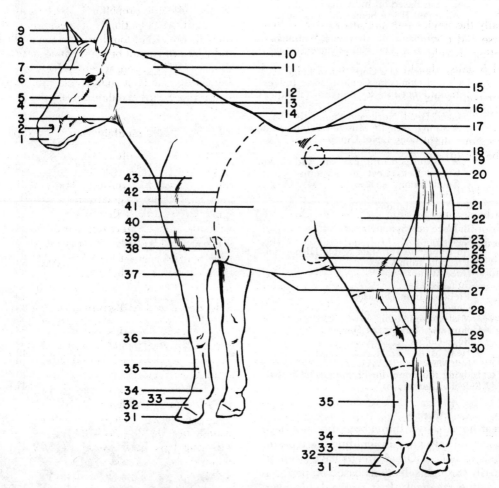

Fig. 4-2. Parts of a horse. The first step in preparation for judging horses consists in mastering the language that describes and locates the different parts of the animal.

1. Muzzle	12. Neck	23. Quarter	34. Fetlock
2. Nostril	13. Throatlatch	24. Stifle	35. Cannon
3. Jaw	14. Wither	25. Rear flank	36. Knee
4. Cheek	15. Back	26. Sheath	37. Forearm
5. Face	16. Loin	27. Underline	38. Point of elbow
6. Eye	17. Croup	28. Gaskin	39. Arm
7. Forehead	18. Hip	29. Point of hock	40. Point of shoulder
8. Poll	19. Coupling	30. Hock	41. Ribs
9. Ear	20. Tail	31. Foot	42. Heart girth
10. Mane	21. Point of buttocks	32. Coronet	43. Shoulder
11. Crest	22. Thigh	33. Pastern	

ble conformation, consideration should be given to the following points:

1. The mount should be purchased within a price range that the rider can afford.

2. The amateur or child should have a quiet, gentle, well-broken horse that is neither headstrong nor unmanageable. The horse should never be too spirited for the rider's skill.

3. The size of the horse should be in keeping with the size and weight of the rider. A very small child should have a small horse or pony, whereas a heavy man should have a horse of the weight-carrying type. An exceedingly tall man or woman also looks out of place if not mounted on a horse with considerable height.

4. Usually the novice will do best to start with a 3-gaited horse and first master the 3 natural gaits before attempting to ride a horse executing the more complicated 5 gaits, should a 5-gaited horse be desired.

5. Other conditions being equal, the breed and color of horse may be decided on the basis of preference.

6. The mount should be well suited to the type of work to be performed.

ALL-BREED HORSE SCORECARD

First, a horse must conform to the specific type which fits him for the function he is to perform. Second, he should be true to the characteristics of the breed that he represents. The use of a scorecard is a good way in which to make sure that (1) no part is overlooked, and (2) proper weight or value is assigned to each part.

A scorecard is a listing of the different parts of an animal, with a numerical value assigned to each according to its relative importance. Fig. 4-3 shows an All-breed Horse Scorecard, developed by the author. Breed characteristics may be, and are, considered in this scorecard. (See page 30.)

Selection on the basis of individuality and performance alone is still the best single method for obtaining suitable using horses, whether they be used for heavy harness, light harness, saddle, or pony purposes. In other words, the individuality of the horse, its phenotype, is closely correlated with its performance. However, if the animals are selected for breeding purposes, additional criteria—pedigree, record of both the individual and near relatives, progeny if the animal is old enough and has produced, family name, etc.—should be taken into consideration. Also, show-ring winnings may be helpful.

Selection Based on Pedigree

The Arabians were the first livestock breeders to trace the lineage of their animals, often memorizing many generations of the pedigree. Moreover, they accorded particular importance to the dam's side of the heritage, a practice that still persists in certain breeds of livestock today as evidenced by the family names tracing to certain great females many generations removed.

If the pedigree is relatively complete in terms of records of performance (speed, show winnings, etc.) of the ancestors, particularly those close up, it can be of very great usefulness in providing a safer basis for selection. A pedigree of this type is of value in predicting (1) the usefulness of the individual (whether it be for racing under the saddle or jumping, etc.), and (2) the probable prepotency as a breeding animal.

Pedigree selection is of special importance where animals are either too thin or so young that their individual merit cannot be ascertained with any degree of certainty. Then, too, where selection is being made between animals of comparable individual merit, the pedigree may be the determining factor.

Selection Based on Show-ring Winnings

Breeders of pleasure horses have long used show-ring records as a basis of selection. Because training plays such an important part in the performance and show-ring winnings of pleasure horses, however, it is likely that this basis of selection is less valuable from a breeding standpoint than with any other class of animals. At the same time, the show record may be a most valuable criterion in indicating the utility value of the horse.

Selection Based on Performance Testing

Although selection on the basis of progeny testing is the most infallible tool available to the horse breeder, it must be pointed out that the following limitations exist:

1. Because of relatively few offspring, it is difficult to apply it to females.

2. Even with males, a progeny testing rating cannot be obtained until late in life, after sufficient offspring have been born and have reached an age when they can be tested.

3. There is the hazard that the stallion being tested will be bred to only a few select mares and that only the top offspring will be tested.

4. Training and feeding play such a major part in the development of horses that it is always difficult to separate out environmental from hereditary influences.

Performance testing is easier to apply because it is an individual matter. In fact, most racehorses used for breeding purposes are first performance tested on the track.

	POINTS OR %	(name and/or no. of horse)	(name and/or no. of horse)	(name and/or no. of horse)	(name and/or no. of horse)
BREED TYPE	15				
The breed is distinguished by its unique combination of style and beauty, with ruggedness.					
COLOR: In keeping with the breed.					
HEIGHT AT MATURITY: Proper height; extremes undesirable.					
WEIGHT AT MATURITY: Proper weight; extremes undesirable.					
FORM	35				
STYLE AND BEAUTY: Attractive, good carriage, alert, refined, symmetrical, and all parts nicely blended together.					
BODY: Nicely turned; long, well-sprung ribs; heavily muscled.					
BACK AND LOIN: Short and strong, wide, well muscled, and short coupled.					
CROUP: Long, level, wide, muscular, with a high-set tail.					
REAR QUARTERS: Deep and muscular.					
GASKIN: Heavily muscled.					
WITHERS: Prominent, and of the same height as the high point of the croup.					
SHOULDERS: Deep, well laid in, and sloping (about a 45° angle).					
CHEST: Fairly wide, deep, and full.					
ARM AND FOREARM: Well muscled.					
FEET AND LEGS	15				
LEGS: Correct position and set (when viewed from front, side, and rear).					
PASTERNS: Long, and sloping (about a 45° angle).					
FEET: In proportion to size of horse, good shape, wide and deep at heels, dense texture of hoof.					
HOCKS: Deep, clean-cut, and well supported.					
KNEES: Broad, tapering gradually into cannon.					
CANNONS: Clean, flat, with tendons well defined.					
HEAD AND NECK	10				
Alertly carried, showing style and character.					
HEAD: Well proportioned to rest of body, refined, clean-cut, with chiseled appearance; broad, full forehead with great width between eyes; ears medium sized, well carried and attractive; eyes large and prominent.					
NECK: Long, nicely arched, clean-cut about the throatlatch; with head well set on, gracefully carried.					
QUALITY	10				
Clean, flat bone; well defined and clean joints and tendons, and fine skin and hair.					
ACTION	15				
WALK: Easy, springy, prompt, balanced, a long step, with each foot carried forward in a straight line; feet lifted clear of the ground.					
TROT: Prompt, straight, elastic, balanced, with hocks carried closely, and high flexion of knees and hocks.					
DISCRIMINATION: Any abnormality that affects the serviceability of the horse.					
DISQUALIFICATION: Blindness (except by injury), bone spavin, stifled, stringhalt, cryptorchid.					
TOTAL SCORE	100				

Fig. 4-3. All-breed horse scorecard.

Perhaps it might be added that the progressive breeder will continue to use all four methods of selection—individuality, pedigree, show-ring winnings, and production testing—but with increasing emphasis upon the latter method.

JUDGING HORSES

The discussion that follows represents a further elucidation of the first point discussed under selection—individuality. But, in addition to individual merit, the word judging implies the comparative appraisal or placing of several animals.

Judging horses, like all livestock judging, is an art, the rudiments of which must be obtained through patient study and long practice. Successful horsemen are usually competent judges. Likewise, shrewd traders are usually masters of the art, even to the point of deception.

Accomplished stockmen generally agree that horses are the most difficult to judge of all classes of farm animals. In addition to considering conformation—which is the main criterion in judging other farm animals—action and numerous unsoundnesses are of paramount importance.

Qualifications of a Good Horse Judge

The essential qualifications that a good horse judge must possess, and the recommended procedure to follow in the judging assignment, are as follows:

1. *Knowledge of the parts of a horse*—This consists in mastering the language that describes and locates the different parts of a horse (see Fig. 4-2). In addition, it is necessary to know which of these parts are of major importance; that is, what comparative evaluation to give to the different parts.

2. *A clearly defined ideal or standard of perfection*—The successful horse judge must know for what he is looking. That is, he must have in mind an ideal or standard of perfection.

3. *Keen observation and sound judgment*—The good horse judge possesses the ability to observe good conformation and performance, as well as defects, and to weigh and evaluate the relative importance of the various good and bad features.

4. *Honesty and courage*—The good horse judge must possess honesty and courage, whether it be in making a show-ring placing or in conducting a breeding and selling program. For example, it often requires considerable courage to place a class of animals without regard to (a) winnings in previous shows, (b) ownership, and (c) public applause. It may take even greater courage and honesty within oneself to discard a costly stallion or mare whose progeny have failed to measure up.

5. *Logical procedure in examining*—There is always great danger of the beginner making too close an inspection; he often gets "so close to the trees that he fails to see the forest."

Good judging procedure consists in the following three steps: (a) observing at a distance and securing a panoramic view where several horses are involved, (b) seeing the animals in action, and (c) inspecting close up. Also, it is important that a logical method be used in viewing an animal from all directions (front view, rear view, and side view), and in judging its action and soundness—thus avoiding overlooking anything and making it easier to retain the observations that are made.

6. *Tact*—In discussing either (a) a show-ring class, or (b) horses on a farm or ranch, it is important that the judge be tactful. The owner is likely to resent any remarks which indicate that his animal is inferior.

Do's and Don'ts for Contest Horse Judges

College judging classes, F.F.A. students, 4-H Club members, and other prospective horse judges should first become thoroughly familiar with the six qualifications of a good judge as outlined in the previous section. Next, they should observe the following do's and don'ts:

1. *Do's:*

a. Make certain how the class is numbered, and keep the numbers straight.

b. Get a clear picture of the class and of each individual animal in mind, so that they will be remembered.

c. Keep in a position of vantage, where the class can be seen at all times; usually this means some distance away rather than too close.

d. Make placings on the basis of the big things.

e. Make certain that the card is filled out completely and correctly, and that the correct numbers are kept in mind.

f. If permissible, make concise notes that will assist in recalling each individual in the class; record such things as distinctive color markings, outstanding faults, etc.

g. When giving reasons, use good poise and look the judge in the eye.

h. State reasons clearly, and with conviction and confidence.

i. Give reasons in a logical sequence; give the major reasons first.

j. Use terms appropriate to the class of animals; for example, use breeding terms in a breeding class.

k. Use comparative and descriptive terms in giving reasons. Avoid such vague terms as "good," "better," and "best."

l. Concede or grant good points and faults, regardless of the placing of the animal.

2. *Don'ts:*

a. Don't act on hunches; if the first placing is arrived at after due consideration and in a logical manner, stick to it.

b. Don't place animals on the basis of small, relatively unimportant characters.

c. Don't destroy self-confidence and self-respect by discussing the class with others before giving reasons.

d. Don't pay attention to what you overhear others say about a class; be an independent judge.

e. Don't give wordy and meaningless reasons.

f. Don't bluff; if you don't know the answer to a question, say so.

**Judging Procedure for Breeding
or Halter Classes**

It is suggested that the beginner proceed as follows:

1. Master the nomenclature of the animal—the parts (see Fig. 4-2).

2. Have an ideal in mind, and be able to recognize both desirable characteristics and common faults (see Fig. 4-4, page 33).

3. Follow a procedure in examining, such as is indicated in Table 4-1; namely (a) front view, (b) rear view, (c) side view, (d) action, and (e) soundness. This applies to breeding or halter classes in particular.

4. Rank or place animals of each class on each of the points listed under "what to look for," keeping in mind the "ideal type" and "common faults" (see Table 4-1).

5. Rank or place the animals according to their consistent rating on all points, especially the most important ones (see Table 4-1, page 34).

What to Look For

A horse must first conform to the specific type which fits him for the function he is to perform. Secondly, he should be true to the characteristics of the breed that he represents. Regardless of type or breed, however, Fig. 4-4 shows certain desirable and undesirable characteristics in horses, and Table 4-1 is a handy judging guide.

GOOD HEAD, NECK, AND SHOULDERS

The head should be well proportioned to the rest of the body, refined and clean-cut, with a chiseled appearance. A broad, full forehead with great width between the eyes indicates intelligence. A straight face is usually perferable to a concave profile or a convex one (Roman nose), the former suggesting a timid disposition and the latter strong will power. The jaw should be broad and strongly muscled. There should be great width between large, clear eyes; and the ears should be of medium size, well carried and active. The neck should be fairly long. It should be carried high, slightly arched, lean and muscular, and clean-cut about the throatlatch, with the head well set on. Also, the neck should neatly join long, oblique, smooth shoulders. The head and neck of the animal should show sex character—boldness and masculinity in the stallion and refinement and femininity in the broodmare.

A STRONG, HEAVILY MUSCLED TOPLINE, WITH A SHORT BACK AND LOIN AND A LONG LEVEL CROUP

The topline should include a short, strong back and loin, with a long, nicely turned and heavily muscled croup, and a high, well-set tail. The withers should be rather clearly defined and of the same height as the hips. Good withers and oblique shoulders make for a better seat in riding horses. Moreover, a sloping shoulder is usually associated with sloping pasterns and more springy, elastic action. The back and loin muscles help sustain the weight of the rider, lift the forequarters of the horse, and strengthen the arch of the back of the horse in motion. A desirable short coupling is obtained when the last rib is close to the hip.

AMPLE CHEST AND MIDDLE

Ample chest and middle due to long, well-sprung ribs is desired. A deep, wide chest and large, full heart girth—together with a good middle—provide needed space for the vital organs and indicate a strong constitution and good feeding and staying qualities. All horses should be fairly well let down in the hind flank, though racehorses in training may show much less depth at this point than other types of horses. Even with racehorses, however, the extremely high-cut, so-called "wasp-waisted" ones will not endure heavy racing. Moreover, racehorses usually deepen materially in the rear flank with age or higher condition.

WELL-MUSCLED ARM, FOREARM, AND GASKIN

The muscles of the arm, forearm, and gaskin should be well developed. Since little or no fat can be placed upon the forearm and gaskin, these areas are a good indication of the muscular development of the

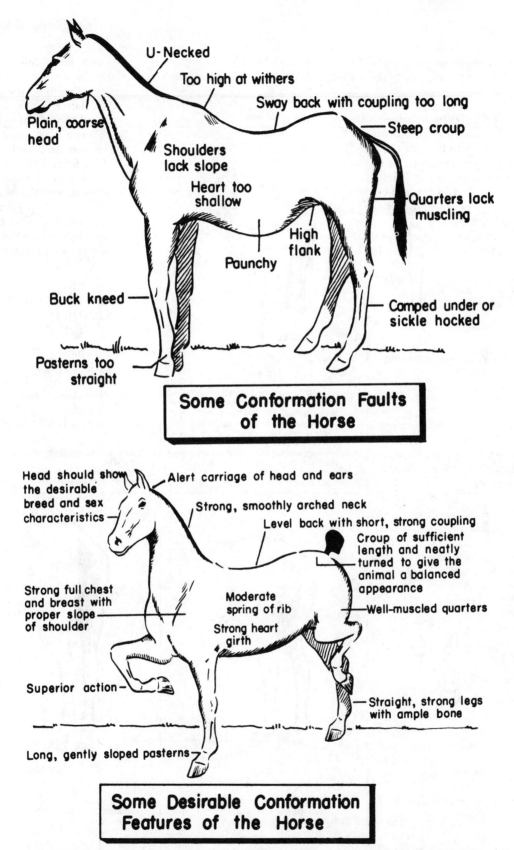

U-Necked

Too high at withers

Sway back with coupling too long

Plain, coarse head

Steep croup

Shoulders lack slope

Heart too shallow

Quarters lack muscling

High flank

Paunchy

Buck kneed

Camped under or sickle hocked

Posterns too straight

Some Conformation Faults of the Horse

Head should show the desirable breed and sex characteristics

Alert carriage of head and ears

Strong, smoothly arched neck

Level back with short, strong coupling

Croup of sufficient length and neatly turned to give the animal a balanced appearance

Strong full chest and breast with proper slope of shoulder

Moderate spring of rib

Well-muscled quarters

Strong heart girth

Superior action

Straight, strong legs with ample bone

Long, gently sloped pasterns

Some Desirable Conformation Features of the Horse

Fig. 4-4. Ideal type vs common faults. Regardless of type or breed, certain desirable characteristics should be present in all horses. The successful horse judge must be able to recognize both the desirable characteristics and the common faults, and the relative importance of each. (Drawing by Prof. R. F. Johnson)

TABLE 4-1

HANDY JUDGING GUIDE FOR LIGHT HORSES[1]

Procedure for Examining, and What to Look for	Ideal Type	Common Faults
Front View:		
 Fig. 4-5	 Fig. 4-6	 Fig. 4-7
1. Head.	1. Head well proportioned to rest of body, refined, clean-cut, with chiseled appearance; broad, full forehead with great width between the eyes; jaw broad and strongly muscled; ears medium sized, well carried and attractive.	1. Plain headed.
2. Sex character.	2. Refinement and femininity in the broodmare; boldness and masculinity in the stallion.	2. Mares lacking femininity; stallions lacking masculinity.
3. Chest capacity.	3. A deep, wide chest.	3. A narrow chest.
4. Set to the front legs.	4. Straight, true, and squarely set.	4. Crooked front legs.
Rear View:		
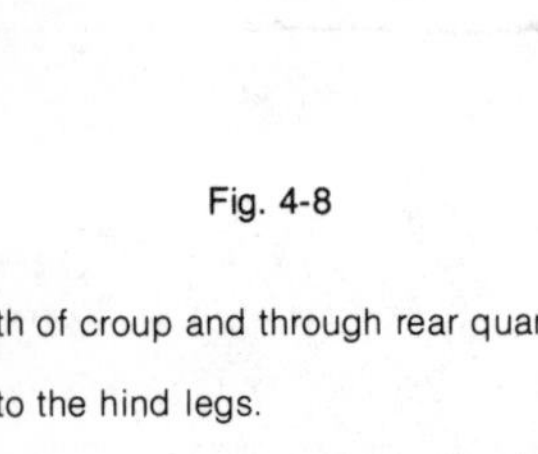 Fig. 4-8	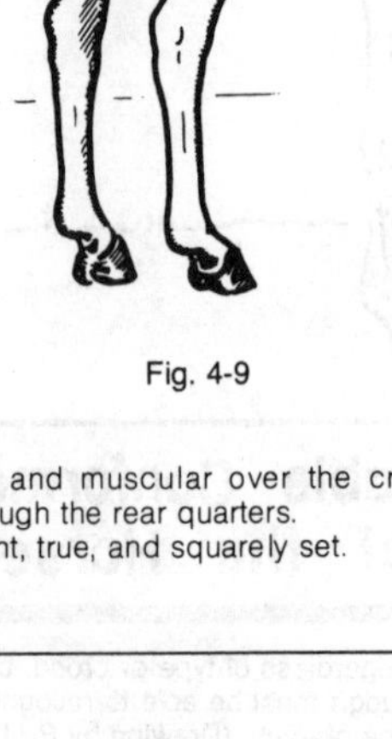 Fig. 4-9	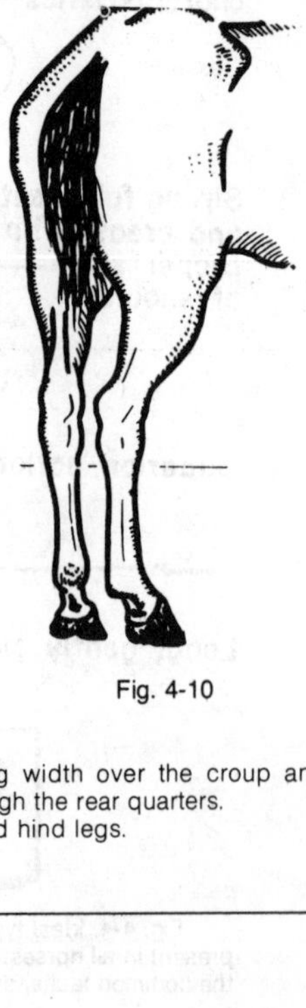 Fig. 4-10
1. Width of croup and through rear quarters.	1. Wide and muscular over the croup and through the rear quarters.	1. Lacking width over the croup and muscling through the rear quarters.
2. Set to the hind legs.	2. Straight, true, and squarely set.	2. Crooked hind legs.

Footnotes at end of table.   *(Continued)*

Table 4-1 (Continued)

Procedure for Examining, and What to Look for	Ideal Type	Common Faults
Side View:		

Fig. 4-11

Fig. 4-12

Fig. 4-13

Procedure for Examining, and What to Look for	Ideal Type	Common Faults
1. Style and beauty.	1. High carriage of head, active ears, alert disposition and beauty of comformation.	1. Lacking style and beauty.
2. Balance and symmetry.	2. All parts well developed and nicely blended together.	2. Lacking in balance and symmetry.
3. Neck.	3. Fairly long neck, carried high; clean-cut about the throatlatch; with head well set on.	3. A short, thick neck; ewe-necked.
4. Shoulders.	4. Sloping shoulders (about a 45° angle).	4. Straight in the shoulders.
5. Topline.	5. A short, strong back and loin, with a long, nicely turned and heavily muscled croup, and a high, well-set tail; withers clearly defined and of the same height as the high point of croup.	5. Swaybacked; steep croup.
6. Coupling.	6. A short coupling as denoted by the last rib being close to the hip.	6. Long in the coupling.
7. Middle.	7. Ample middle due to long, well-sprung ribs.	7. Lacking middle.
8. Rear flank.	8. Well let down in the rear flank.	8. High cut rear flank or "wasp waisted."
9. Arm, forearm, and gaskin.	9. Well-muscled arm, forearm, and gaskin.	9. Light-muscled arm, forearm, and gaskin.
10. Legs, feet, and pasterns.	10. Straight, true, and squarely set legs; pasterns sloping about 45°; hoofs large, dense, and wide at the heels.	10. Crooked legs; straight pasterns, hoofs small, contracted at the heels, and shelly.
11. Quality.	11. Plenty of quality, as denoted by clean, flat bone, well-defined joints and tendons, refined head and ears, and fine skin and hair.	11. Lacking quality.
12. Breed type (size, color, shape of body and head, and action true to the breed represented).	12. Showing plenty of breed type.	12. Lacking breed type.

(Continued)

Table 4-1 (Continued)

Procedure for Examining, and What to Look for	Ideal Type	Common Faults
Soundness: 1. Soundness, and freedom from defects in conformation that may predispose unsoundness.	1. Sound, and free from blemishes.	1. Unsound; blemished (wire cuts, capped hocks, etc.).
Action[2] 1. At the walk. . Fig. 4-14	1. Easy, prompt, balanced; a long step, with each foot carried forward in a straight line; feet lifted clear of the ground.	1. A short step, with feet not lifted clear of the ground.
2. At the trot.  Fig. 4-15	2. Rapid, straight, elastic trot, with the joints well flexed.	2. Winging, forging, and interfering.
3. At the canter.	3. Slow collected canter, which is readily executed on either lead.	3. Fast and extended canter.

[1]The illustrations for this table were prepared by Prof. R. F. Johnson.
[2]The three most common gaits are given here. Five-gaited horses must perform two additional gaits. In selecting for gait, (1) observe horse at each intended gait, and (2) examine trained horses while performing at use for which they are intended.

entire animal, even when horses are in high condition. The powerful muscles of the croup, thigh, and gaskin give the animal ability to pull, jump, or run.

CORRECT LEGS, FEET, AND PASTERNS

There has long been a saying "no foot, no horse." After all, the value of a horse lies chiefly in his ability to move, hence the necessity of good underpinning. The legs should be straight, true, and squarely set; the bone should be well placed and clearly defined. The pasterns should be sloping; the feet large and wide at the heels. (See Fig. 4-16. Also see Fig. 4-17 on page 38.)

The hock should be large, clean, wide from front to back, deep, clean-cut, and correctly set. The knee should be deep from front to rear, should be wide when viewed from the front, should be straight, and should taper gradually into the leg. Since the hock and knee joints of the horse are subject to great wear and are the seat of many unsoundnesses, they should receive every attention.

GOOD ACTION

Although the degree of action of the horse will vary somewhat with the type (speed, show, and saddle), the usefulness of all horses is dependent upon their action and their ability to move in various types of racing, driving, hunting, riding, polo, etc. In all types and breeds, the motion should be straight and true with a long, swift, and elastic stride.

SOUNDNESS

The horse should be serviceably sound, and in the young animal there should be no indication of defects in conformation that may predispose unsoundnesses. The horseman must first know and recognize the normal structure and function before attempting to determine unsoundnesses. Practically speaking, *an unsoundness is any deviation in form or function that interferes with the usefulness of the individual; whereas, a blemish is an abnormality which may detract from the appearance of the animal but*

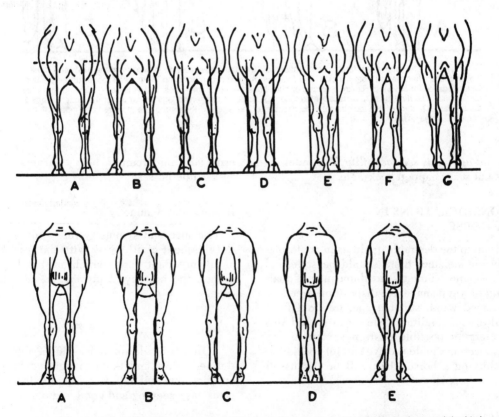

Fig. 4-16. The proper and faulty conformation of the forelegs (top) when viewed from the front, and the hind legs (bottom) when viewed from the rear. *The forelegs:* A, represents correct conformation; B, splay-footed or base narrow forefeet, toes cut out, heels in; C, bowed legs; D, knock-kneed, knees set close together with toes pointing outward; E, conformation predisposing to interfering; F, knees set close together; G, pigeon-toed or toe narrow—a conformation which will cause the animal to wing or throw out the feet as they are elevated. *The hind legs:* A, represents correct conformation; B, hind legs set too far apart; C, bandy-legged—wide at the hocks and hind feet toe in; D, hind legs set too close together; E, cow-hocked. The direction of the leg and the form of the foot are very important in the horse. (Courtesy, USDA)

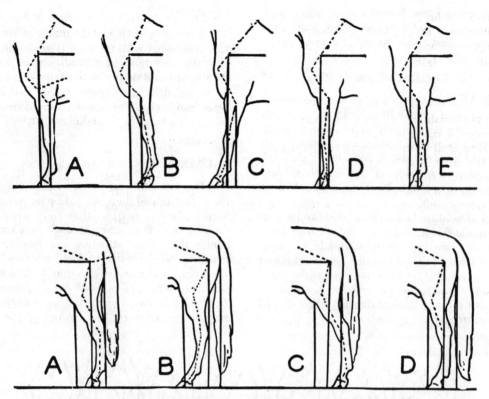

Fig. 4-17. The proper and faulty conformations of (top) the forelegs when viewed from the side, and (bottom) the hind legs when viewed from the side. *The forelegs*: A, correct conformation; B, forelegs too far under the body; C, forelegs too far advanced; D, knee-sprung or buck-kneed—over in the knees; E, calf-kneed—standing with knees too far back. *The hind legs*: A, correct conformation; B, sickle hocked—hind legs too far under the body; C, legs set too far back; D, hock joint is too straight. The direction of the legs and the form of the foot are very important in the horse. (Courtesy, USDA)

which does not affect his serviceability. The latter includes wire-cut scars, capped hocks, etc.

OTHER CONSIDERATIONS IN BUYING A HORSE

In addition to the desirable qualities in conformation already enumerated, there should be style and beauty, balance and symmetry, an abundance of quality, an energetic yet manageable disposition, freedom from vices, good wind, suitable age, freedom from disease, and proper condition. The buyer should also be on the alert for possible misrepresentations. As each of these factors should receive careful consideration when buying a horse, they will be discussed separately.

Style and Beauty

This has reference to the attractiveness with which the horse displays himself at all times. Good carriage of the head, active ears, an alert, active disposition, and beauty of conformation are factors contributing to the style of the horse. This quality is especially important in heavy harness, fine harness, and saddle horses.

Balance and Symmetry

Balance and symmetry refers to the harmonious development of all parts. With the full development of all important parts, which are nicely blended together, the horse will present an attractive appearance.

Quality

Quality is denoted by clean, flat bone, well-defined joints and tendons, refined head and ears, and fine skin and hair. Good quality in the horse indicates easy keeping and good endurance.

An Energetic Yet Manageable Disposition

Both sexes and all types of horses should at all times display energetic yet manageable dispositions. The disposition of a horse, whether good or bad, is usually considered as being a product of both inheri-

tance and environment. Regardless of the cause of a nasty disposition, one should avoid purchasing such an animal. Superb manners and disposition are especially important in all types of pleasure horses.

Freedom from Vices

Although not considered as unsoundnesses, such stable vices as cribbing, weaving, tail rubbing, kicking, stall walking, stall trotting, and halter pulling do detract from the value of a horse. But vices are not confined to actions in the stall. Some horses object to taking a bit in their mouths; others are touchy about the ears; still others jump when an attempt is made to place a saddle or harness on their backs. Any of these traits is objectionable.

Good Wind

Good wind is imperative. Defects of wind may be easily detected by first moving the animal at a rapid gait for some distance, then suddenly bringing him to a stop and listening in near proximity to the head. Unsound animals are usually noisy in breathing.

Suitable Age

The horse is usually considered as being in his prime between the ages of 3 and 8. Since younger horses are still growing and becoming hardened, many 2- and 3-year-olds do not stand up under heavy racing or other use. Although a horse's market value begins to depreciate when he reaches his eighth year, he may be useful in performing certain services until he is well over 20 years old.

Freedom from Diseases

In transporting a horse, there is always a possible exposure to the many ills to which he is subject. Sometimes these prove to be of sufficiently serious nature as to make working impossible at a time when the animal is most needed; and occasionally they even prove fatal. It must also be remembered that such diseases as contracted may very likely spread to the other horses on the farm and even in the community, thus exposing them to the same risk.

Condition

Both productive ability and endurance are lowered by either a thin, run-down condition or an overfat and highly fitted condition. A good, vigorous, thrifty condition is conducive to the best work and breeding ability, and horses so fitted attract the eye of the prospective buyer. However, extremes in feeding and lack of exercise are to be avoided in purchasing a

horse for either work or breeding. It must be remembered that fat will cover up a multitude of defects. In buying valuable mares or stallions, the purchaser should insist on having a health certificate signed by a licensed veterinarian. Such examination should also show that the reproductive organs are normal and healthy.

Misrepresentations

The inexperienced man is especially likely to encounter misrepresentations as to age, soundness, vices, and the training and working ability of the horse. Perhaps knowing the seller as well as the horse is the best preventative of this sort of thing.

COLORS AND MARKINGS OF HORSES

Izaak Walton, in *The Compleat Angler*, says, "There is no good horse of a bad color." Yet, within certain breeds, some colors are preferred, or even required, whereas others are undesirable or even constitute disqualifications for registry. Also, a good horseman needs a working knowledge of horse colors and patterns because it is the most conspicuous feature by which a horse can be described or identified.

Body Colors

The five basic horse body colors and their descriptions follow:

1. *Bay*—Bay is a mixture of red and yellow. It includes many shades, from a light yellowish tan (light bay) to a dark, rich shade which is almost brown (dark bay); a bay horse usually has a black mane and tail and black points.

2. *Black*—A black horse is completely black, including the muzzle and flanks. If there is doubt as to whether a horse is dark brown or black, one should note the color of the fine hairs on the muzzle and the hair on the flanks; tan or brown hairs at these points indicate that the horse is not a true black, but a seal brown.

3. *Brown*—A brown horse is almost black but can be distinguished by the fine tan or brown hairs on the muzzle or flanks.

4. *Chestnut (sorrel)*—A chestnut horse is basically red. The shades vary from light washy yellow (light chestnut) to a dark liver color (dark chestnut), between which come the brilliant red gold and copper shades. Normally, the mane and tail of a chestnut horse are the same shade as the body, although they may be lighter in color; these are termed a flaxen mane and tail. Chestnut color is never accompanied by a black mane and tail.

5. *White*—A true white horse is born white and remains white throughout its life. A white horse has

snow-white hair, pink skin, and brown eyes (rarely blue).

In addition to the five basic horse colors given, there are five major variations to these coat colors; namely:

1. *Dun (buckskin)*—A dun horse has a yellowish color of variable shading from pale yellow to a dirty canvas color; the horse also has a stripe down its back.

2. *Gray*—A gray horse has a mixture of white and black hairs. Sometimes gray is difficult to distinguish from black at birth, but grays get lighter with age.

3. *Palomino*—Palomino is a golden color (the color of a newly minted gold coin, or three shades lighter or darker), with a light-colored mane and tail (white, silver, or ivory).

4. *Pinto (calico or paint)*—Pinto is a Spanish word, meaning "painted." The Pinto horse is characterized by irregular colored and white areas, as (a) piebald (white and black), and (b) skewbald (white and any color other than black).

5. *Roan*—A roan horse has a mixture of white hairs intermingled with one or more base colors, as (a) white with bay (red roan), (b) white with chestnut (strawberry roan), and (c) white with black (blue roan).

Head Marks

When identifying an individual horse, it is generally necessary for one to be more explicit than to refer to body color only; for example, it may be necessary further to identify the dark sorrel as the one with the blaze face. The most common head marks are shown in Fig. 4-18.

Leg Marks

Leg marks are usually used, along with head marks, to describe a horse. The most common leg marks are shown in Fig. 4-19.

JUDGING PROCEDURE FOR PERFORMANCE CLASSES

Custom decrees somewhat different show-ring procedure in judging different classes. Halter classes are first examined while lined up side by side, or while being led in a circle and later inspected while moved one at a time; whereas performance classes are first examined with the entire class in action, and later lined up for close inspection. In judging performance

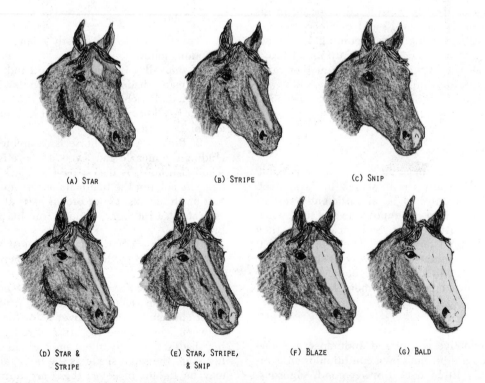

(A) STAR   (B) STRIPE   (C) SNIP

(D) STAR & STRIPE   (E) STAR, STRIPE, & SNIP   (F) BLAZE   (G) BALD

Fig. 4-18. The head marks of horses. (A) *Star* is any white mark on the forehead located above a line running from eye to eye; (B) *stripe* is a narrow white marking that extends from about the line of the eyes to the nostrils; (C) *snip* is a white mark between the nostrils or on the lips; (D) *star and stripe* includes both a star and stripe; (E) *star, stripe, and snip* includes all three of these marks—star, strip, and snip; (F) *blaze* is a broad, white marking covering almost all the forehead but not including the eyes or nostrils; (G) *bald* is a bald, or white, face including the eyes and nostrils, or a partially white face.

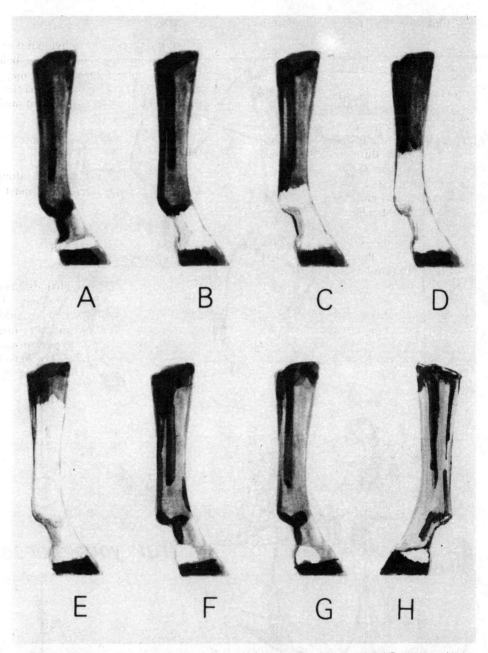

Fig. 4-19. Most common leg marks: A, *coronet*—a white strip covering the coronet band; B, *pastern*—white extends from the coronet to and including the pastern; C, *ankle*—white extends from the coronet to and including the fetlock; D, *half stocking*—white extends from the coronet to the middle of the cannon; E, *stocking*—white extends from the coronet to the knee. When the white includes the knee, it is known as a full stocking; F, *white outside heels*—both heels are white; G, *white outside heel*—outside heel only is white; H, *white inside heel*—inside heel only is white. (Courtesy, USDA)

classes, the officials should be thoroughly familiar with, and follow, the show rules—either local or the American Horse Shows Association, Inc., whichever applies. If the judge is in doubt as to what is expected of a performance class, he should seek the advice of the steward.

After a judge has inspected a light horse performance class, both in action and when lined up, it is considered entirely proper to request that certain animals be pulled out and again put through their gaits. Fig. 4-20 shows the common method of examining a three-gaited saddle Horse performance class.

Fig. 4-20. Diagram showing the customary procedure in examining a 3-gaited Saddle Horse in the show-ring. The animal herein is shown (1) walking, (2) trotting, (3) cantering, and (4) lined up. Traditionally, the judge or judges work from the center of the ring, while the ringmaster requests the riders to execute the different gaits.

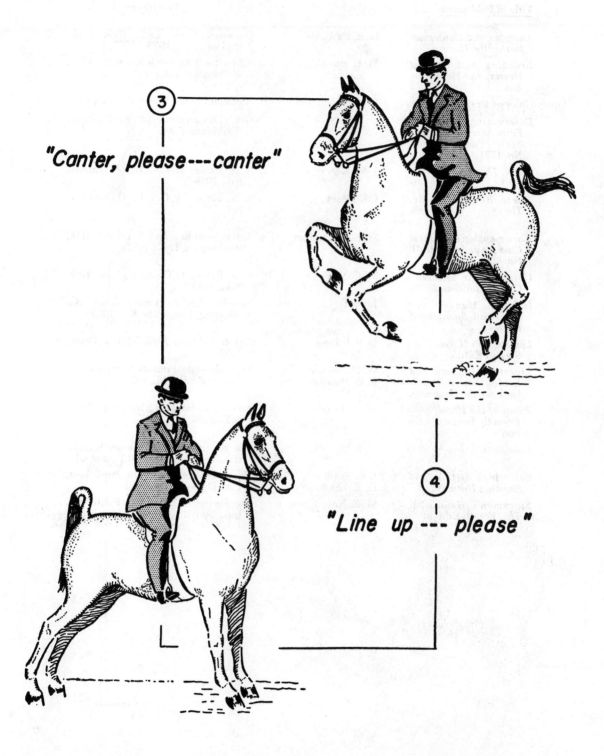

"Canter, please---canter"

"Line up --- please"

Fig. 4-20 (continued). Three-gaited horses are expected to walk, trot, and canter. Five-gaited horses must perform 2 additional gaits; namely, (a) slow gait (which is the stepping pace in the show-ring), and (b) the rack. In addition to performing the gaits with perfection, both 3- and 5-gaited horses should possess desirable conformation, perfect manners, and superior style and animation. (Drawings by Prof. R. F. Johnson)

SELECTED REFERENCES

Title of Publication	Author(s)	Publisher
Anatomy and Conformation of the Horse	G. B. Edwards	Dreenan Press Ltd., Croton-on-Hudson, N.Y., 1973
Breeding and Raising Horses, Ag. Hdbk. No. 394	M. E. Ensminger	Agricultural Research Service, USDA, Washington, D.C., 1972
Color of Horses, The	B. K. Green	Northland Press, Flagstaff, Ariz., 1974
Determining the Age of Farm Animals by Their Teeth, Farmers' Bull. No. 1721		U.S. Department of Agriculture, Washington, D.C.
Horse, The	J. M. Kays	A. S. Barnes & Co., Inc., Cranbury, N.J., 1969
Horse Buyer's Guide, The	J. K. Posey	A. S. Barnes & Co., Inc., Cranbury, N.J., 1973
Horsemanship and Horse Care, Ag. Info. Bull. No. 353	M. E. Ensminger	Agricultural Research Service, USDA, Washington, D.C., 1972
Horses: Their Selection, Care & Handling	M. C. Self	A. S. Barnes & Co., Inc., New York, N.Y., 1943
Judging Manual for American Saddlebred Horses	J. Foss	American Saddle Horse Breeders Association, Louisville, Ky., 1973
Lameness in Horses, Second Edition	O. R. Adams	Lea & Febiger, Philadelphia, Penn., 1966
Livestock Judging and Evaluation: A Handbook for the Student	W. M. Beeson R. E. Hunsley J. E. Nordby	The Interstate Printers & Publishers, Inc., Danville, Ill., 1970
Points of the Horse, Seventh Revised Edition	M. H. Hayes	Arco Publishing Co., Inc., New York, N.Y., 1969
Rule Book		The American Horse Shows Association, Inc., New York, N.Y., annual
Selecting, Fitting and Showing Horses	J. E. Nordby H. E. Lattig	The Interstate Printers & Publishers, Inc., Danville, Ill., 1963
Stockman's Handbook, The, Fourth Edition	M. E. Ensminger	The Interstate Printers & Publishers, Inc., Danville, Ill., 1970

CHAPTER 5

DETERMINING THE AGE AND HEIGHT OF HORSES

Fig. 5-1. (Courtesy, Kentucky Department of Public Information, Frankfort, Ky.)

45

Establishing the age of horses through the appearance of the teeth is not new. Apparently this technique was known in ancient days. It is not surprising, therefore, to find that the old saying, "Do not look a gift horse in the mouth," is attributed to Saint Jerome, a Father of the Latin Church and papal secretary in the 5th Century, who used this expression in one of his commentaries.

Physical changes within the body are constant. As they affect the general outward appearance and disposition of the horse within certain limits, it is possible by mere general appearance to estimate the age of the animal. Changes in the teeth, however, afford a much more accurate method.

There is nothing mysterious about the determination of the age by the teeth. In horses up to 5 years of age, it is simply a matter of noting the number of permanent and milk teeth present. From 6 to 12 years, the number of cups or indentations in the incisor teeth is used; whereas the age of horses beyond 12 years may be estimated by studying the cross section and slant of the incisor teeth. It must be realized, however, that theoretical knowledge is not sufficient and that anyone who would become proficient must also have practical experience. The best way to learn how to recognize age is to examine the teeth in horses of known ages.

THE IMPORTANCE OF AGE

As the productive life of the horse is comparatively brief and the height of his usefulness is even more limited, the market value of the animal increases rather sharply with maturity and then decreases beyond eight years of age. On the other hand, for many purposes horses are quite useful up to 12 years of age or longer.

January 1 Birth Date

Regardless of when a foal is born, its birth date is always considered as January 1. Thus, a foal born May 1, 1980, will be 10 years old on January 1, 1990. This is done from the standpoint of racing and showing. As a result, horsemen who race or show make every effort to have foals arrive as near January 1 as possible, thereby getting the advantage of more growth than animals born later in the year. This is especially important in the younger age groups; for example, when racing or showing a two-year-old.

Oldest Horse

Authentic records of very old horses are hard to come by. Old Bill, a horse owned throughout his lifetime by a Mr. Petrie, of Edinburgh, Scotland, lived

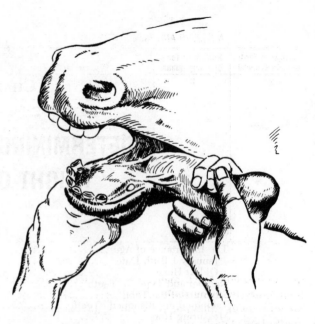

Fig. 5-2. How to look a horse in the mouth. With the tongue held in one hand and the lower jaw grasped with the other hand, you can look at the teeth for as long as you like. (Drawing by Prof. R. F. Johnson)

to age 62, according to B. S. Dystra, hippologist, of Holland.[1]

An ex-Italian Army horse, Topolino, was foaled on February 24, 1909, and died in February, 1960, at the age of 51.

Old Nellie, a black mare of draft breeding, raised by a Missouri farmer, was 53 years and 8 months old when she died in 1969.

Since the average life-span of a horse is about one-third the life expectancy of a person in the United States, in terms of human life a 50-year-old horse would be equivalent to a 150-year-old man.

NUMBER AND TYPES OF TEETH

The mature male horse has a total of 40[2] teeth; whereas the young animal, whether male or female, has 24. These are listed in Table 5-1.

As the tushes are usually not present in the mare, the mature female may be considered as having a total of 36 teeth rather than 40 as in the male.

The good horseman is also aware of the difference between permanent and temporary teeth. The temporary or milk teeth are smaller, much whiter, and have a distinct neck at the junction of the crown and fang, which is at the gum line. After their eruption,

[1]*American Shetland Pony Journal*, Nov. 1969, p. 25.
[2]Quite commonly, a small pointed tooth, known as a "wolf tooth," may appear in front of each first molar tooth in the upper jaw, thus increasing the total number of teeth to 42 in the male and 38 in the female. Less frequently, 2 more wolf teeth in the lower jaw increase the total number of teeth in the male and female to 44 and 40, respectively.

TABLE 5-1
NUMBERS AND TYPES OF TEETH

TABLE 5-1

NUMBERS AND TYPES OF TEETH

Number of Teeth of Mature Animal	Number of Teeth of Young Animal	Types of Teeth
24	12	Molars or grinders.
12	12	Incisors or front teeth (the 2 central incisors are known as middle incisors, centrals, pinchers, or nippers; the next 2—one on each side of the nippers—are called intermediates; and the last—or outer pair—the corners).
4	None	Tushes or pointed teeth. These are located between the incisors and the molars in the male.

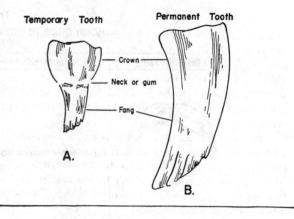

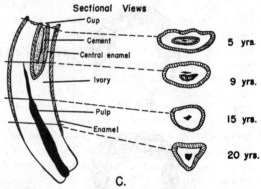

Fig. 5-3. The horse's tooth. A, temporary lower pincher tooth; B, permanent lower pincher tooth. Temporary or milk teeth are smaller and much whiter than permanent teeth, and constricted at the gum line (neck). C, longitudinal section of a permanent lower middle pincher tooth; and cross section of permanent lower middle pincher teeth at different age levels. These drawings show why, with advancing age, the teeth of a horse (1) slant out toward the front, (2) change in wearing surface as noted in the cross-sectional shape, (3) change in shape of cups and in the time of disappearance of the cups, and (4) change in appearance and shape of the dental star. (Drawing by Prof. R. F. Johnson)

the permanent teeth may be distinguished from the temporary teeth by their greater size, darker color, a broader neck showing no constriction, and greater width from side to side.

The permanent incisor teeth of young horses five to seven years of age are elliptical or long from side to side; whereas when the animal becomes older, these teeth become triangular, with the apex of the triangle pointed upward. As the animal advances still more in age, the teeth become more slanting. Instead of curving to approach a right angle with the jaws, they slant outward.

From 5 to 12 years of age the wearing surface of the cups is the most reliable indication of age. At fairly regular intervals, according to age, the cups disappear with wear.

STRUCTURE OF THE TOOTH

The tooth consists of an outside cement and a second layer of a very hard enamel followed by the dentine and a dark center known as the pulp. The enamel passes up over the surface of the teeth and extends inward, forming a pit. The inside and bottom of the pit, which is blackened by feed, constitutes the "mark" or "cup." As the rims of these cups disappear through wear, two distinct rings of enamel remain, one around the margin of the tooth and the other around the cup. With wear, the cups become smaller—first more oval or rounding in shape, then triangular and more shallow, and they finally disappear completely. Further wear on the table or grinding surface of the tooth exposes the tip of the pulp canal or cavity in the center of the tooth. The exposed tip of this canal, which appears between what is left of the cup and the front of the tooth, is known as the "dental star." The gradual wearing and disappearance of the cups according to a rather definite pattern in period of time enables the experienced horseman to

judge the age of an animal with a fair degree of accuracy up to 12 years.

A summary showing the changes in teeth according to usual age intervals is given in Table 5-2. (See page 48.)

After 12 years of age, even the most experienced horseman cannot determine accurately the age of an animal. It is known, however, that with more advanced age the teeth change from oval to triangular and that they project or slant forward more and more each year (see Fig. 5-22, page 51).

It must also be realized that the environment of the animal can very materially affect the wear on the teeth, often making it impossible to determine accurately the age of animals. For example, the teeth of horses raised in a dry, sandy area will show more than normal wear. Thus, the 5-year-old western horse may have a 6- or even 8-year-old mouth. The unnatural wear resulting in the teeth of cribbers, or animals with parrot mouth or undershot jaw, also makes it difficult to estimate age.

TABLE 5-2

HANDY GUIDE TO DETERMINING THE AGE OF HORSES
BY THE TEETH[1]

Drawing of Teeth	Age of Animal	Description of Teeth	
 Fig. 5-4	At birth or before 10 days of age	First or central upper and lower incisors appear.	Appearance of temporary teeth
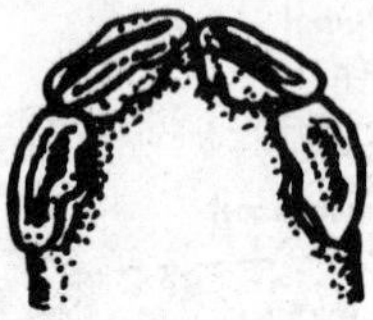 Fig. 5-5	4 to 6 weeks of age	Second or intermediate upper and lower incisors appear.	
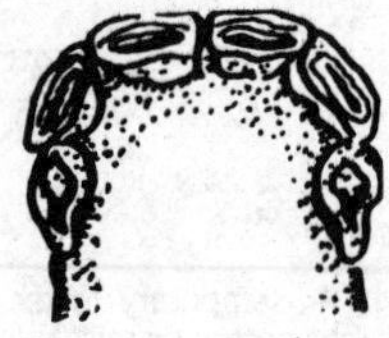 Fig. 5-6	6 to 10 months	Third or corner upper and lower incisors appear.	
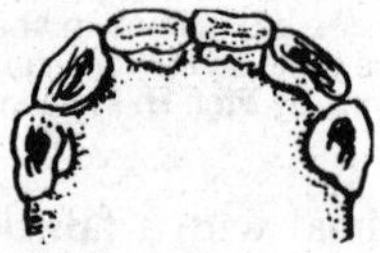 Fig. 5-7	1 year of age	Crowns of central incisors show wear.	Wear of temporary teeth
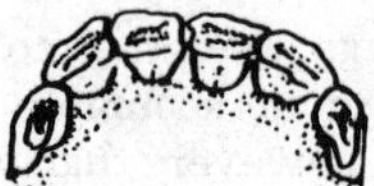 Fig. 5-8	1½ years of age	Intermediate incisors show wear.	
 Fig. 5-9	2 years of age	All temporary incisors show wear.	

(Continued)

TABLE 5-2 (Continued)

Drawing of Teeth	Age of Animal	Description of Teeth	
Fig. 5-10	2½ years of age	First or central incisors appear.	Appearance of permanent teeth
Fig. 5-11	3½ years of age	Second or intermediate incisors appear.	
Fig. 5-12	4½ years of age	Third or corner incisors appear.	
Fig. 5-13	4 to 5 years of age (in male)	Canines appear.	
Fig. 5-14	5 years of age	Cups in all incisors.	Wear of permanent teeth
Fig. 5-15	6 years of age	Cups worn out of lower central incisors.	

(Continued)

TABLE 5-2 (Continued)

Drawing of Teeth	Age of Animal	Description of Teeth
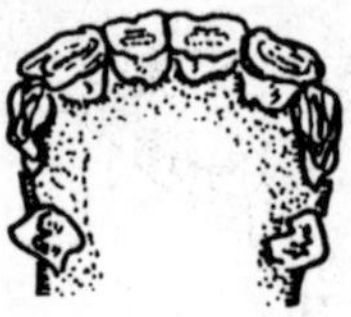 Fig. 5-16	7 years of age	Cups also worn out of lower intermediate incisors.
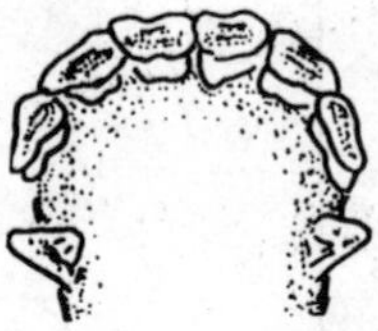 Fig. 5-17	8 years of age	Cups worn out of all lower incisors, and dental "star" appears on lower central and intermediate pairs.
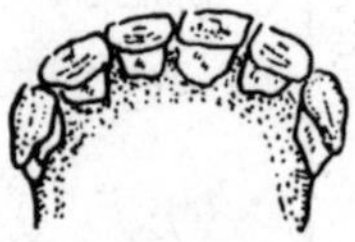 Fig. 5-18	9 years of age	Cups also worn out of upper central incisors, and dental "star" appears on upper central and intermediate pairs.
 Fig. 5-19	10 years of age	Cups also worn out of upper intermediate incisors, and dental "star" is present on all incisors both upper and lower.
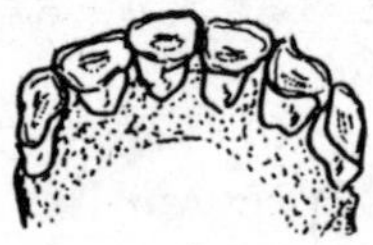 Fig. 5-20	11 years of age	Cups worn out of all upper and lower incisors, and dental "star" approaches center of cups.
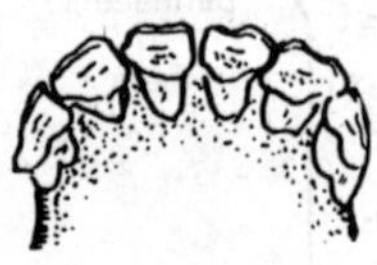 Fig. 5-21	12 years of age	No cups. "Smooth mouthed."

Wear of permanent teeth

¹The illustrations for this table were prepared by Prof. R. F. Johnson.

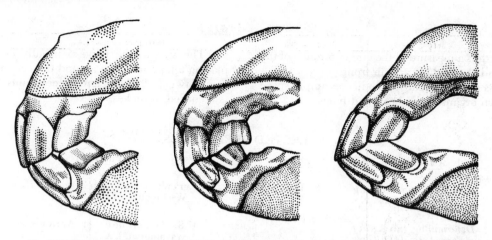

Fig. 5-22. Side view of horse's mouth at 5, 7, and 20 years. Note that as the horse advances in age, the teeth change from nearly perpendicular to slanting sharply toward the front. (Drawing by Prof. R. F. Johnson)

TAMPERED OR "BISHOPED" TEETH

Occasionally, unscrupulous horsemen endeavor to make the amateur a victim of their trade tricks, especially through tampering with the teeth. As very young horses increase in value to a certain stage, the milk teeth are sometimes pulled a few months before they would normally fall out. This hastens the appearance of the permanent teeth and makes the animal appear older.

"Bishoping" is the practice of artificially drilling, burning, or staining cups in the teeth of older horses in an attempt to make them sell as young horses. The experienced horseman can detect such deception because the ring of enamel that is always present around the natural cup cannot be reproduced. This makes the practice more difficult than counterfeiting money. Moreover, the slanting position and triangular shape of the teeth of an older animal cannot be changed. An experienced horseman should always be called upon to make an examination if there is any suspicion that the teeth have been tampered with.

MEASURING HORSES

The normal measurements pertinent to a horse are his (1) height, (2) weight, (3) girth, and (4) bone.

Height

The height of a horse is determined by standing him squarely on a level area and measuring the vertical distance from the highest point of his withers to the ground. The unit of measurement used in expressing height is the "hand," each hand being 4 inches. Thus, a horse measuring 62 inches is said to be 15-2 hands (15 hands and 2 inches) high. Animals standing less than 14-2 (meaning 14 hands and 2 inches) are classed as ponies.

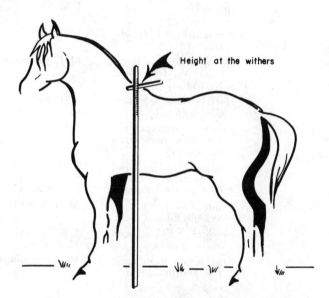

Fig. 5-23. The height of a horse is measured from the highest point of the withers to the ground. The experienced horseman deftly estimates the height of a horse in relation to his own stature, and does not use any measuring device. (Drawing by Prof. R. F. Johnson)

Instead of actually measuring by calipers or tape, the experienced horseman deftly estimates the height of a horse in relation to his own stature. Thus, by knowing the exact height from the ground to the level of his eyes, the horseman can stand opposite the front limbs of the horse, look to the highest point of the withers, and estimate the height very quickly and accurately.

Weight

The weight of a horse is best determined by placing the animal on a properly balanced scale. The weight is recorded in pounds.

Girth

The girth is a measure of the circumference of the chest behind the withers and in front of the back. A large girth is desired because it indicates ample space for such vital organs as the heart and lungs.

Bone

The size of the bone is usually determined by placing a tape measure around the cannon bone halfway between the knee and fetlock joints. The reading is recorded in inches.

SELECTED REFERENCES

Title of Publication	Author(s)	Publisher
Breeding and Raising Horses, Ag. Hdbk. No. 394	M. E. Ensminger	Agricultural Research Service, USDA, Washington, D.C., 1972
Determining the Age of Farm Animals by Their Teeth, Farmers' Bull. No. 1721		U.S. Department of Agriculture, Washington, D.C.
Horse, The	J. M. Kays	A. S. Barnes & Co., Inc., Cranbury, N.J., 1969
Horse Buyer's Guide, The	J. K. Posey	A. S. Barnes & Co., Inc., Cranbury, N.J., 1973
Horsemanship and Horse Care, Ag. Info. Bull. No. 353	M. E. Ensminger	Agricultural Research Service, USDA, Washington, D.C., 1972
Horses: Their Selection, Care & Handling	M. C. Self	A. S. Barnes & Co., Inc., New York, N.Y., 1943
Judging Manual for American Saddlebred Horses	J. Foss	American Saddle Horse Breeders Association, Louisville, Ky., 1973
Livestock Judging and Evaluation: A Handbook for the Student	W. M. Beeson R. E. Hunsley J. E. Nordby	The Interstate Printers & Publishers, Inc., Danville, Ill., 1970
Points of the Horse, Seventh Edition	M. H. Hayes	Arco Publishing Co., Inc., New York, N.Y., 1969
Selecting, Fitting and Showing Horses	J. E. Nordby H. E. Lattig	The Interstate Printers & Publishers, Inc., Danville, Ill., 1963
Stockman's Handbook, The, Fourth Edition	M. E. Ensminger	The Interstate Printers & Publishers, Inc., Danville, Ill., 1970

CHAPTER 6

UNSOUNDNESSES AND STABLE VICES

Contents   **Page**

An integral part of selecting and judging horses is the ability to recognize the common blemishes and unsoundnesses and to rate the importance of each.

DISTINCTION BETWEEN BLEMISHES AND UNSOUNDNESSES

Technically speaking, *any abnormal deviation in structure or function constitutes an unsoundness.* From a practical standpoint, however, a differentiation is made between those abnormalities that do and those that do not affect the serviceability of a horse. Thus, the following definitions usually apply:

1. *Blemishes include those abnormalities that do not affect the serviceability of the horse.* Such unsightly things as wire cuts, rope burns, nail punctures, shoe boils, capped hocks, etc., are generally placed under this category.

2. *Unsoundnesses include those more serious abnormalities that affect the serviceability of the horse.*

CAUSES OF UNSOUNDNESSES

Unsoundnesses may be caused by any one or various combinations of the following:

1. An inherent or predisposing weakness.

2. Subjection of the horse to strain and stress far beyond the capability of even the best structure and tissue.

3. Accident and injury.

4. Nutritional deficiencies, particularly minerals. Unsoundnesses that can be definitely traced to the latter three causes should not be considered as hereditary. Unless one is very positive, however, serious unsoundnesses should always be regarded with suspicion in the breeding animal. Probably no unsoundness is actually inherited, but the fact that individuals may inherit a predisposition to an unsoundness through faulty conformation cannot be questioned.

LOCATION OF COMMON BLEMISHES AND UNSOUNDNESSES

Fig. 6-1 and the accompanying outline give the body location of the common blemishes and unsoundnesses. As would be suspected, the great preponderance of troubles affect the limbs.

DESCRIPTION AND TREATMENT OF COMMON BLEMISHES AND UNSOUNDNESSES

The following brief description and treatment pertain to the common blemishes and unsoundnesses of different body areas.

Unsoundnesses of the Head

The most serious unsoundnesses of the head are those that affect the sight of the animal; namely, blindness and moon blindness. In addition, poll evil is very serious, and the parrot mouthed and undershot jaw conditions are most undesirable.

I. Head:
   1. Blindness
   2. Moon blindness
     (periodic ophthalmia)
   3. Parrot mouth and under-
     shot jaw
   4. Poll evil

II. Withers and shoulders:
   1. Fistulous withers
   2. Sweeney

III. Front limbs:
   1. Bowed tendons
   2. Calf-kneed
   3. Cocked ankles
   4. Knee-sprung
   5. Ringbone
   6. Shoe boil
   7. Splints
   8. Wind-puffs

   9. Contracted feet
  10. Corns
  11. Navicular disease
  12. Founder or laminitis
  13. Quarter crack or
     sand crack
  14. Quittor
  15. Scratches or grease
     heel
  16. Sidebones
  17. Thrush
} Front Feet

IV. Rear limbs:
   1. Cocked ankles
   2. Ringbone
   3. Stifled
   4. Stringhalt
   5. Wind-puffs

   6. Blood spavin
   7. Bog spavin
   8. Bone spavin or jack
   9. Capped hock
  10. Curb
  11. Thoroughpin
} Hocks

  12. Contracted feet
  13. Corn
  14. Founder or laminitis
  15. Quarter crack or
     sand crack
  16. Quittor
  17. Scratches or
     grease heel
  18. Thrush
} Hind Feet

V. General:
   1. Heaves
   2. Hernia or rupture
   3. Roaring
   4. Thick wind

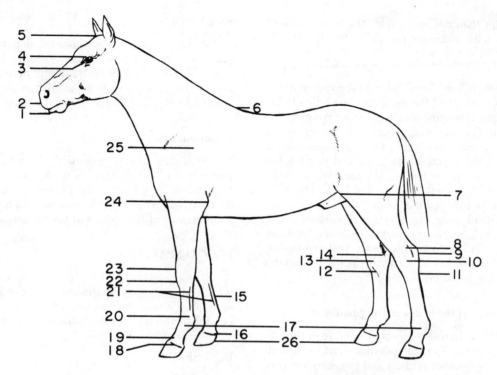

Fig. 6-1. Location of points of common unsoundness in horses.

1. Undershot jaw	10. Stringhalt	19. Ringbone
2. Parrot mouth	11. Curb	20. Wind-puffs
3. Blindness	12. Bone spavin or jack	21. Splints
4. Moon blindness	13. Bog spavin	22. Knee-sprung
5. Poll evil	14. Blood spavin	23. Calf-kneed
6. Fistulous withers	15. Bowed tendons	24. Capped elbow
7. Stifled	16. Sidebones	25. Sweeney
8. Thoroughpin	17. Cocked ankles	26. Contracted feet, corns, founder,
9. Capped hock	18. Quittor	thrush, quarter crack or sand
		crack, scratches or grease heel

General: heaves, hernia, roaring, thick wind

BLINDNESS

Partial or complete loss of vision is known as blindness. Either or both eyes may be affected. A blind horse usually has very erect ears and a hesitant gait. Frequently, blindness also can be detected by the discoloration of the eye. Further and more certain verification can be obtained by moving the hand gently in close proximity to the eye.

MOON BLINDNESS (OR PERIODIC OPHTHALMIA)

Moon blindness (or periodic ophthalmia) is a cloudy or inflamed condition of the eye which disappears and returns in cycles that are often completed in about a month. Because many people formerly believed the cycle to be related to changes of the moon, it was given the name of "moon blindness."

It appears that moon blindness may result from several conditions. Experiments initiated at the Front Royal Remount Depot, beginning in 1943, showed that, in some cases, it is a nutritional deficiency disease, caused by a lack of riboflavin.[1] Today, much evidence exists that leptospirosis may cause periodic ophthalmia. Also, some cases appear to be caused by the presence of the parasite *Filaria equina* within the eye, or from a reaction to systemic parasitism elsewhere in the body. Other investigations have suggested that periodic ophthalmia is a reaction of the eye to antigens from repeated streptococcal infections.

PARROT MOUTH AND UNDERSHOT JAW

Both parrot mouth and undershot jaw are hereditary imperfections in the way in which the teeth come together. In parrot mouth or overshot jaw, the lower

[1]In the Front Royal experiments, when crystalline riboflavin was added to the ration at the rate of 40 mg per horse per day, no new cases of periodic ophthalmia developed.

jaw is shorter than the upper jaw. The reverse condition is known as undershot jaw.

POLL EVIL

This is an inflamed condition in the region of the poll (the area on top of the neck and immediately behind the ears). It is usually caused by bruising the top of the head. The swelling, which may be on one or both sides, usually contains pus or a straw-colored fluid. At first the affected area is hot and painful, but later the acute symptoms of inflammation subside. Treatment, which should be handled by a veterinarian, consists in establishing proper drainage and removing all dead tissue. In addition to surgery, some veterinarians claim that recovery is hastened by injections of a specially prepared bacterin. Poll evil is slow to yield to treatment, and it may break out again after it is thought to be cured.

Unsoundnesses of the Withers and Shoulders

Though less frequent in occurrence than the unsoundnesses of the feet, the conditions of the shoulders known as fistulous withers and sweeney are very injurious to animals which are affected.

FISTULOUS WITHERS

Fistulous withers is an inflamed condition in the region of the withers, commonly thought to be caused by bruising. Fistula and poll evil are very similar except for location. As in poll evil, therefore, treatment for fistulous withers, which should be handled by a veterinarian, consists in establishing proper drainage and removing all dead tissue. Caustic applications to destroy the diseased tissues should be used only on the advice of a veterinarian.

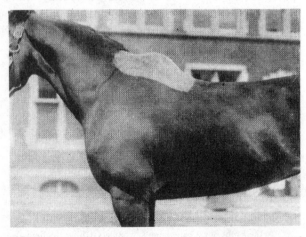

Fig. 6-2. Horse with fistulous withers. (Courtesy, University of Pennsylvania)

SWEENEY

A depression in the shoulder due to atrophied muscles is known as sweeney. Sweeney is caused by nerve injury. No known treatment will restore the nerve, but it is possible to fill in the depression by injecting irritants into the affected area.

Unsoundnesses of the Limbs

Although they are confined to a relatively small proportion of the anatomy of the horse, there appears to be hardly any limit to the number of unsoundnesses that may affect the front limbs. The major unsoundnesses of this type will be discussed briefly.

BLOOD SPAVIN

Blood spavin is a varicose vein enlargement which appears on the inside of the hock but immediately above the location of bog spavin. No successful treatment for blood spavin is known.

BOG SPAVIN

Bog spavin is a filling of the natural depression on the inside and front of the hock. A bog spavin is much larger than a blood spavin. Treatments usually include some combination of cold packs, antiphlogistic applications (clay, mud, cooling lotions, etc.),

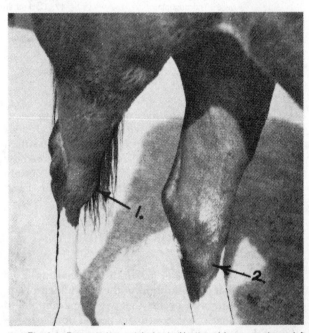

Fig. 6-3. Bog spavin on right hock (No.1) and bone spavin on left hock (No.2). Bog spavin is a filling of the natural depression on the inside and front of the hock. Bone spavin is a bony enlargement that appears on the inside and the front of the hock at the point where the base of the hock tapers into the cannon part of the leg.

stimulating liniments, mild to severe blisters, the aspiration or withdrawal of the fluid from the joint, and injections of hydrocortisone. Some equine veterinarians prefer patient daily massage with an absorbent type liniment for two to three weeks. Treatment consists in applying a special bog spavin truss or in applying tincture of iodine. Blistering or firing is seldom successful.

BONE SPAVIN (OR JACK SPAVIN)

Bone spavin (or jack spavin) is a bony enlargement that appears on the inside and front of the hock at the point where the base of the hock tapers into the cannon part of the leg. It is one of the most destructive conditions affecting the usefulness of a horse.

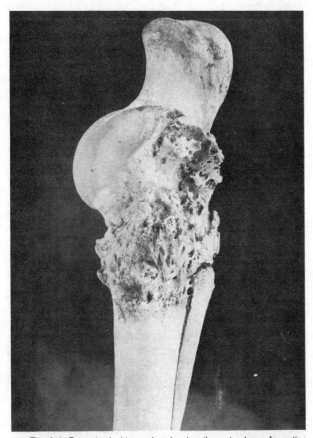

Fig. 6-4. Bone (or jack) spavin, showing the extra bone formation (exostosis) of the metatarsal and tarsal bones. This is a medial, or inside, view of the hock area. (Photo by J. C. Allen & Son, West Lafayette, Ind.)

The lameness is most evident when the animal is used following rest. A hereditary weakness—together with such things as bruises, strains, and sprains—appears to cause bone spavin. Rest seems to be the most important treatment. Counterirritants, iodine, liniments, and blistering agents have all been used with varying degrees of success. Surgery or firing by a qualified veterinarian may be in order.

BOWED TENDONS

Enlarged tendons behind the cannon bones, in both the front and hind legs, are called bowed tendons. Descriptive terms of "high" and "low" bow are used by horsemen to denote the location of the injury; the high bow appears just under the knee and the low bow just above the fetlock. This condition is often brought about by severe strains, such as heavy training or racing. When bowed tendons are pronounced, more or less swelling, soreness, and lameness are present. Treatment consists in blistering or firing. The object of blistering and firing is to convert a chronic into an acute inflammation. This hastens nature's processes by bringing more blood to the part, thus inducing a reparative process which renders the animal suitable for work sooner than would otherwise be the case.

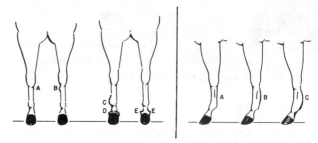

Fig. 6-5. Unsoundness of the front limbs. *Left*—Front legs of the horse, as viewed from the front: A, sound legs; B, splint; C, wind-puffs; D, ringbone; and E, sidebones. *Right*—Front legs of the horse, as viewed from the side: A, sound leg; B, bowed tendon; and C, filled tendon.

Blisters consist of such irritating substances as Spanish fly and iodide of mercury (one common preparation consists of 15 parts Spanish fly, 8 parts iodide of mercury, and 120 parts of lard). Before applying a blister, the hair should be closely clipped from the affected area, the scurf brushed from the skin, and the animal tied so that it cannot rub, lick, or bite the treated area. The blistering agent is then applied by rubbing it into the pores of the skin with the palm of the hand. Three days later the blistered area should be bathed with warm water and soap, dried, and treated with sweet oil or Vaseline to prevent cracking of the skin. Firing, which is used for about the same purposes as blistering, consists of the application of a hot iron or the use of thermocautery to the affected area. Surgical treatment of bowed tendons has been tried on a limited scale with varying degrees of success.

BUCKED SHINS

Bucked shins refers to a temporary racing unsoundness. For the most part, it is peculiar to 2-year-olds, although occasionally a 3-year-old that did little

campaigning at 2 will fall victim to the condition. It usually strikes early in the final stages of preparation to race or early in the racing career. It is a very painful inflammation of the periosteum (bone covering) along the greater part of the front surface of the cannon bone, caused by constant pressure from concussion during fast works or races. Afflicted horses become very lame and are very sensitive when the slightest pressure is applied about the shins; many horses will almost lie down to keep a person from touching the sore area.

When a horse starts to "buck," most experienced trainers feel that it is wise to continue rather vigorous exercise until the acute form is produced, following which the routine treatment consists in cooling the shins out with antiphlogistic treatment (and time) and applying a good blister. When a pronounced case of shin-buck is treated in this manner, the condition will not likely return. However, if exercise is discontinued at the first indication that the horse is about to "buck" and treatment is given, he will often develop the condition again about the time he is ready to start racing. It is not uncommon for a 2-year-old to buck 2 or 3 times before he can race successfully.

CALF-KNEED

Standing with knees too far back, directly opposite to buck-kneed or knee-sprung, is called calf-kneed.

CAPPED HOCK

Capped hock is an enlargement at the point of the hock; it is usually caused by bruising. Daily painting of the enlargement with tincture of iodine may help to diminish it. Though it may be unsightly, capped hock need not be considered serious unless it inter-

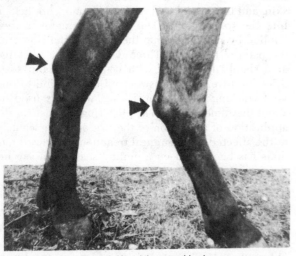

Fig. 6-6. Unsightly capped hocks.

feres with the work of the horse. Successful reduction of the swelling depends on prompt and persistent treatment, with antiphlogistic applications, before the fluid has a chance to form the fibrinous tissue in the sheath or bursa. Once the "cap" has set or become fibrinous, all that can be done is to remove any inflammation present, and then, by a series of blisters, attempt to cause resorption (reduction in size).

COCKED ANKLES

Cocked ankles refers to horses that stand bent forward on the fetlocks in a cocked position. This condition can be corrected by proper trimming, allowing the toes to grow out while keeping the heels trimmed. However, where cocked ankles are of nutritional origin (as a result of the rickets syndrome), they should be treated by correcting the causative nutritional deficiency or imbalance.

CONTRACTED FEET

This condition, known as contracted, most often occurs in the forefeet and is characterized by a drawing in or contracting at the heels (see Fig. 6-7). A tendency toward contracted feet may be inherited, but improper shoeing usually aggravates the condition. Paring, removal of shoes, or use of special shoes constitutes the best treatment.

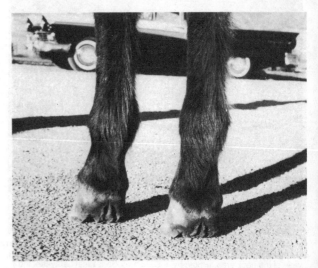

Fig. 6-7. Contracted heels on forefeet. (Courtesy, *Western Horseman*, Colorado Springs, Colo.)

CORNS

A bruise to the soft tissue underlying the horny sole of the foot—which manifests itself in a reddish discoloration of the sole immediately below the affected area—is known as a corn. Fast work on hard

and rough roads, flat soles, weakened bars, and poor shoeing may cause corns. Paring, special shoeing, poulticing, sanitation, and rest constitute the best treatment.

CURB

Curb is the name given to the condition in which there is a fullness at the rear of the leg and below the point of the hock. This fullness is due to enlargement of the ligament or tendon. The condition is caused by anything that brings about a thickening in the ligament, tendon, or skin of this region so as to cause a deviation in the straight line that normally extends from the point of the hock to the fetlock. Firing and blistering are the usual treatment.

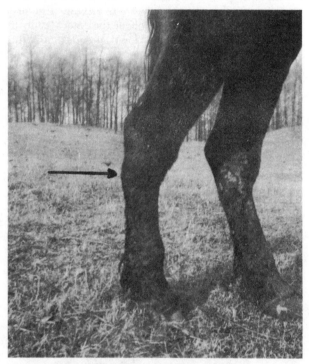

Fig. 6-8. Curb. (Courtesy, Michigan State University)

FOUNDER (OR LAMINITIS)

Founder (or laminitis) is a serious ailment of the fleshy laminae. It may be caused by (1) overeating (grain, or lush legume or grass—known as "grass founder"), (2) overwork, (3) giving animals too much cold water when they are hot, or (4) inflammation of the uterus following foaling. All feet may be affected, but the front feet are more susceptible. Prompt treatment by a competent veterinarian will usually prevent permanent injury. Until the veterinarian arrives, the horse may be given great relief by applying cold

Fig. 6-9. Hoof of a foundered horse. In founder, the foot undergoes structural changes. As it grows down, successive rings appear and it becomes deformed through a bulging or "dropped" sole, and the horse walks on the heels with a shortened stride. (Drawing by Prof. R. F. Johnson)

applications to the feet. This may be accomplished by wrapping the feet with burlap bags saturated with cold water or by standing the horse in a foot bath. If the condition is neglected, chronic laminitis will develop and will cause dropping of the hoof soles and a turning up of the toe walls.

FRACTURED FIBULA

Most cases of acute or chronic lameness due to fibula fractures are found on the racetrack.

The fibula is a small, long bone extending along the back side of the tibia from the stifle downward. The upper end articulates with the end of the tibia and the lower end eventually becomes fused with this same bone. In young horses, only the upper third is visible on X-ray plates, because the long, thin shaft has not changed from cartilage to bone. In older horses, the entire length is easily seen on X-ray plates.

The fracture of the fibula causes lameness of the stifle, hip, and back. Horses in training are able to negotiate turns well, but they tend to turn sideways (away from the injured leg) on the straight. An X-ray examination is the only conclusive way to arrive at a diagnosis.

Fibular fracture is caused by undue stress, a strain, or a blow—from (1) sudden starts from off-balanced positions at the starting gate, (2) sudden stops or propping, (3) bad racetracks, (4) sudden shifting of weight in rearing or shying, (5) being cast in the stall, or (6) kicks or collisions. Also, faulty nutrition may be a causative factor in some cases.

Rest is the only effective treatment at the present time. Counterirritant injections and blisters, antiinflammatory drugs (corticosteroids) and drugs which tend to relieve muscle spasms, and improved nutrition may be used along with rest.

GRAVEL

Gravel is usually caused by penetration of the protective covering of the hoof by small bits of gravel or dirt. Access to the sensitive tissue is usually gained at the "white line" or junction of the sole and wall, where the horn is somewhat softer. Once in the soft tissue inside the wall or sole, bacterial infection carried by the foreign material develops rapidly, producing pus and gas that create pressure and intense pain in the foot. In untreated cases, it breaks out at the top of the coronary band and the pus and gas are forced out through this opening.

Treatment consists in (1) opening the pathway used by the gravel or dirt going into the foot, thus draining the pus at the bottom and relieving the pressure, (2) administering antitoxin, and (3) protecting the opening from further infection.

KNEE-SPRUNG

A condition of over in the knees, or with the knees protruding too far forward, is known as knee-sprung or buck-kneed.

NAVICULAR DISEASE

Navicular disease is an inflammation of the small navicular bone and bursa of the front foot. It is often impossible to determine the exact cause of the disease. Affected animals go lame; have a short stubby stride; and usually point the affected foot when standing. Few animals completely recover from the disease. Treatment consists in special shoeing. In cases of persistent and severe lameness, unnerving may be performed by a veterinarian, who can destroy sensation in the foot.

OSSELETS

Osselets, like bucked shins, are primarily an affliction of younger horses and the result of more strain or pressure from training or racing than the immature bone structure can stand. However, osselets are not so common among two-year-olds as bucked shins.

Osselets is a rather inclusive term used to refer to a number of inflammatory conditions around the ankle joints. Generally it denotes a swelling that is fairly well defined and located slightly above or below the actual center of the joint, and, ordinarily, a little to the inside or outside of the exact front of the leg. When touched, it imparts the feeling of putty or mush, and it may be warm to hot. The pain will be in keeping with the degree of inflammation as evidenced by swelling and fever. Afflicted horses travel with a short, choppy stride and show evidence of pain when the ankle is flexed.

Standard treatment consists in (1) stopping training at the first sign that the condition is developing, (2) "cooling out," and (3) resting. Firing, or firing followed by blistering, gives very satisfactory results.

POPPED KNEE

Popped knee (so named because of the sudden swelling that accompanies it) is a general term describing inflammatory conditions affecting the knees. It is due either to (1) sprain or strain of one or more of the extensive group of small but important ligaments that hold the bones of the knee in position, or (2) damage to a joint capsule, followed by an increase in the amount of fluid within the capsule and a distention or bulging out between the overlying structure. Of course, faulty conformation of the knees contributes largely to the breaking down of some individuals.

Horses suffering severe popped knees rarely are able to regain a degree of soundness that will allow them to return to the racing form shown before the injury. Thus, the usual cooling applications followed by counterirritant (blistering and firing) treatment are used with varying degrees of effectiveness in the treatment of knee troubles.

QUARTER CRACK (OR SAND CRACK)

A vertical split in the horny wall of the inside of the hoof (in the region of the quarter), which extends from the coronet or hoof head downward, is known as quarter crack or sand crack. It is seldom found in the hind legs. When the crack is on the forepart of the toe, it is termed toe crack. This condition usually results from the hoof being allowed to become too dry and

Fig. 6-10. Hoof showing sand crack and the method of treatment. (Courtesy, Michigan State University)

brittle or from improper shoeing. Special shoeing or clamping together of the cracks is the usual treatment. Also, the coronet may be blistered; or a crescent may be burned through the hoof wall over the crack with a hot iron.

QUITTOR

Quittor is a deep-seated running sore at the coronet or hoof head caused by necrosis of the cartilage of the third phalanx. It results in severe lameness. The infection may arise from a puncture wound, corns, and sand cracks; or it may be carried in the bloodstream. Quittor is usually confined to the forefeet, but it sometimes occurs in the hind feet. Drainage and antiseptics may relieve the condition, although surgery by a veterinarian may be necessary.

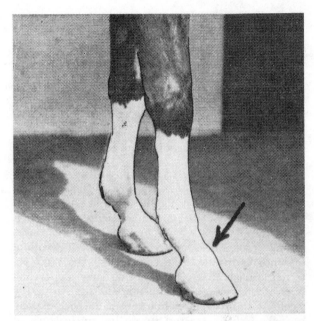

Fig. 6-12. Ringbone on the right foot. This is a bony growth on the pastern bone, generally of the forefoot, although occasionally the hind foot is affected.

Fig. 6-11. Quittor on right hind foot. This is a deep-seated running sore at the coronet or hoof head. It causes severe lameness.

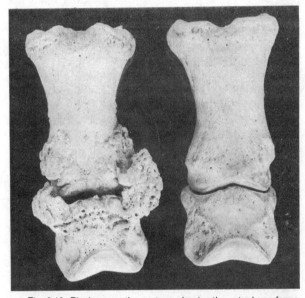

Fig. 6-13. Ringbone on the pastern, showing the extra bone formation, in corallike masses, on the surface of the first and second phalanges. (Photo by J. C. Allen & Son, West Lafayette, Ind.)

RINGBONE

Ringbone is a bony growth on the pastern bone generally of the forefoot, although occasionally the hind foot is affected. The condition usually causes a lameness, accompanied by a stiff ankle. This condition generally follows severe straining, blows, sprains, or improper shoeing. Treatment consists in the application of cold-water bandages for temporary relief. For more permanent relief, veterinarians sometimes resort to blistering, firing, or severing of the nerve leading to the area. The condition is thought to be hereditary.

SCRATCHES (OR GREASE HEEL)

Scratches or grease heel is a mangelike inflammation of the posterior surfaces of the fetlocks, most frequently confined to the hind legs. Treatment consists in placing the affected animal in clean quarters, clipping closely all hair on the affected areas, cleaning with mild soap and water, and applying astringent, antiseptic substances at regular intervals.

SESAMOID FRACTURES

The sesamoids are two pyramidlike bones that form a part of the fetlock or ankle joints (on both front and rear legs) and articulate with the posterior part of the lower end of the cannon bone. They lie imbedded in ligaments and cartilage which form a bearing surface over which the flexor tendons glide.

The fracture of these fragile little bones is more frequent than has been supposed.

SHOE BOIL (OR CAPPED ELBOW)

Shoe boil is a soft, flabby swelling caused by an irritation at the point of the elbow, hence the common name "capped elbow." The two most common causes of this unsoundness are injury from the heel calk of the shoe and injury from contact with the floor. Affected animals may or may not go lame, depending upon the degree of inflammation and the size of the swelling. If discovered while yet small, shoe boil may be successfully treated by daily applications of tincture of iodine and the use of the shoe boil boot or roll. The latter is strapped about the pastern in such manner as to keep the heel from pressing upon the elbow while the horse is in a recumbent position. For treatment of large shoe boils, surgery by a veterinarian may be necessary, but such treatment is not always successful. Some horsemen report good results from the use of ligature which is passed around the neck of the swelling and tightened each day until circulation is stopped and the whole mass sloughs off.

SIDEBONES

Sidebones are ossified lateral cartilages immediately above and toward the rear quarter of the hoof head. They occur most commonly in the forefeet. Lameness may or may not be present. The condition may occur on one or both sides of the foot, or on one or both front feet. This is perhaps the most common unsoundness of the feet of horses.

Sidebones may be partially or entirely of genetic origin; or the condition may result from running or working horses on pavement or other hard surface. Sidebones may also develop following sprains, cracks, quittor, or other injuries. Treatments vary and are not always successful. Temporary relief from fever and soreness can usually be obtained through the application of cold-water bandages. Veterinarians sometimes apply blistering agents, fire, or sever the nerve leading to the area; but the "nerving" operation has fallen into disfavor among most horsemen and racing officials.

SPLINTS

Splints are abnormal bony growths found on the

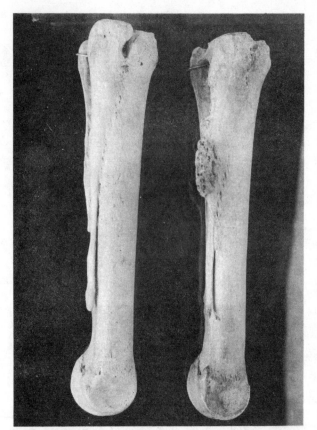

Fig. 6-14. Two cannon (forelimb) bones. The left one is normal. The right one shows a splint on the median, or inside, involving the second and third metacarpal bones. (Photo by J. C. Allen & Son, West Lafayette, Ind.)

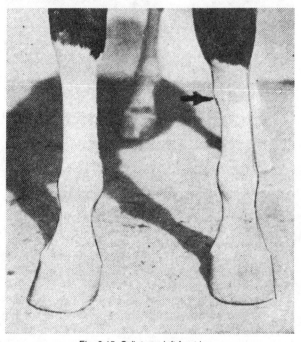

Fig. 6-15. Splints on left front leg.

cannon bone, usually on the inside surface, but occasionally on the outside. They are most common on the front legs. When found on the hind cannon, they are generally on the outside. Splints may enlarge and interfere with a ligament and cause irritation and lameness. Their presence detracts from the appearance of the animal, even when there is no lameness. When found on young horses, they often disappear. Point firing, blistering agents, and tincture of iodine have been employed with variable success in treating splints.

STIFLED

The stifle corresponds to the knee in man. A horse is said to be stifled when the patella (or kneecap) slips out of place and temporarily locks in a location above and to the inside of its normal location. Technically, this condition is known as dorsal patellar fixation. Sometimes it is possible to place the patella back in normal position manually. However, the most effective treatment is surgery, known as medical patellar desmotomy, which consists in the removal of one of the ligaments which attach to the patella.

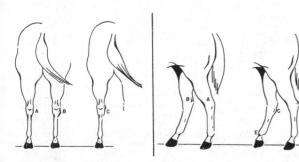

Fig. 6-16. Unsoundnesses of the rear limbs. *Left*—Hind legs of the horse, as viewed from the rear: A, sound leg; B, bog spavin; C, bone spavin. *Right*—Hind legs of the horse, as viewed from the side: A, sound legs; B, thoroughpin; C, curb; D, capped hock; and E, cocked ankle.

STRINGHALT

Stringhalt is characterized by excessive flexing of the hind legs. It is most easily detected when backing a horse. The condition may be cured or greatly relieved by a surgical operation on the lateral extensor tendon. An incision is made over the tendon on the outside of the leg just below the hock, and about 2 inches of the tendon is removed.

SUSPENSORY LIGAMENT SPRAIN

The suspensory ligament is situated over the back of the leg and passes over the fetlock or ankle joint, both in the fore and hind legs. Its principal function is to support the fetlock. This ligament is frequently the object of severe strain; the swelling begins just above the ankle and extends obliquely downward and forward over the sides of the ankle. Should the injury be further up on the leg, the exact location at first may appear obscure as the ligament is covered by the flexor tendons.

When the suspensory ligament is affected, the swelling will be found right up against the bone. If it is the flexor tendons that are involved, the swelling will be farther back near the surface on the back of the leg.

The front legs are more frequently affected than the hind leg, except in the Standardbred breed, where suspensory ligament injury most commonly occurs in the hind legs.

THOROUGHPIN

Thoroughpin is a puffy condition in the web of the hock. It can be determined by movement of the puff, when pressed, to the opposite side of the leg. Treatment consists in applying pressure and massaging, but these may not always be successful.

THRUSH

Thrush is a disease of the frog. It is most commonly found in the hind feet and is caused by unsanitary conditions in the animal's stall. Most cases will respond to trimming away of the affected frog, sanitation, and the use of an antiseptic. Every horseman has his favorite thrush remedy; among them are calomel, creolin, iodine, bichloride of mercury, formalin, and carbolic acid.

WIND-PUFFS (OR WINDGALLS)

Windgalls or "puffs" are an enlargement of the fluid sac (bursa) located immediately above the pastern joints on the fore and rear legs. They are usually the result of too fast or hard road work, especially on hard surfaces. Treatment consists in applying cold packs followed by liniments or sharp blistering agents. Firing or draining by a veterinarian may be in order, but experienced horsemen report that in many cases no permanent benefit results from such treatment.

General Unsoundnesses of the Horse

Hernia and certain abnormal respiratory conditions are classed as general unsoundnesses. These unsoundnesses greatly lower the usefulness and value of affected animals.

64

HEAVES

Heaves is a difficulty in forcing air out of the lungs. It is characterized by a jerking of the flanks (double-flank action) and coughing after drinking cold water. There is no satisfactory treatment, although affected animals are less bothered if turned to pasture, if used only at light work, if the hay is sprinkled lightly with water at the time of feeding, or if the entire ration is pelleted.

HERNIA (OR RUPTURE)

Hernia (or rupture) refers to the protrusion of any internal organ through the wall of its containing cavity, but it usually means the passage of a portion of the intestine through an opening in the abdominal muscle. Umbilical, scrotal, and inguinal hernias are fairly common in young foals.

An umbilical hernia may be present at birth or may develop soon thereafter. In the majority of cases, the condition corrects itself. If surgery becomes necessary, it is usually postponed until after weaning.

A scrotal hernia, which may be noticed at birth or shortly thereafter, will usually correct itself also, although such natural correction may require several weeks' time. Nevertheless, it is well to advise the veterinarian of the trouble.

ROARING

An animal that whistles or wheezes when respiration is speeded up with exercise is said to be a "roarer." Within recent years a surgical operation has been perfected which when properly performed is successful in about 70 percent of the cases so treated.

THICK WIND

Difficulty in breathing is known as thick wind.

Racing Unsoundnesses

The author surveyed a select group of Thoroughbred, Standardbred, and Quarter Horse breeders. This study revealed the following reasons, by rank and percentages, for retiring horses from racing: (See unnumbered table bottom of page.)

Experienced trainers estimate that one-third of the horses in training require treatment in one form or another.

UNSOUNDNESS, INJURY OR DISEASE FOR ALL THREE BREEDS (RANKED ORDER)

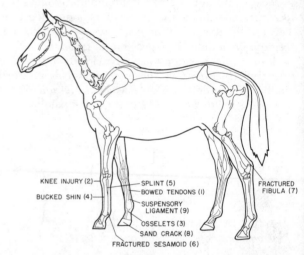

Fig. 6-17. Most common causes, by rank, for retiring horses (composite of Thoroughbred, Standardbred, and Quarter Horse breeds) from racing.

Rank	Thoroughbred	Standardbred	Quarter Horse	Three Breeds Combined
1	Bowed tendons (23%)	Bowed tendons (34%)	Bowed tendons (27%)	Bowed tendons (25%)
2	Osselets (21%)	Splint (14%)	Bucked shin (18%)	Knee injury (16%)
3	Knee injury (20%)	Fractured fibula (12%)	Knee injury (12%)	Osselets (16%)
4	Splint (6%)	Curb (5%)	Fractured sesamoid (9%)	Bucked shin (7%)
5	Bucked shin (5%)	Knee injury (5%)	Osselets (8%)	Splint (7%)
6	Fractured sesamoid (4%)	Suspensory ligament (4%)	Splint (5%)	Fractured sesamoid (5%)
7	Sand crack (3%)	Osselets (3%)	Suspensory ligament (2%)	Fractured fibula (3%)
8	Fractured fibula (2%)	Ringbone (2%) Parasites (2%)	Sand crack (2%)	Sand crack (2%)
9	Suspensory ligament (1%)	Sidebones (2%)	Shoulder injury (2%)	
			Arthritis (2%)	Suspensory ligament (2%)
10	Other (15%)	Other (11%)	Other (13%)	Other (17%)

VICES

Vices are difficult to suspect for they are often present in the most handsome and lovable creature. Some vices are vicious and dangerous to man and other animals; others inflict punishment upon the offender himself; and still others merely use energy wastefully. Regardless of the type of vice, it is undesirable and to be avoided. In general, vices may be divided into two classifications: stable vices, and other vices.

Common Stable Vices

As the name would indicate, stable vices are those which are observed in confinement. Perhaps many of these have arisen because of the unnaturalness of stable conditions.

BOLTING

Bolting is the name given to the habit that ravenous horses have of eating too fast. This condition may be controlled by adding chopped hay to the grain ration or by placing some large, round stones, as big or bigger than baseballs, in the feed box.

CRIBBER

A horse that has the vice of biting or setting the teeth against some object, such as the manger, while sucking air is known as a cribber. This causes a bloated appearance and hard keeping; and such horses are more subject to colic. The common remedy for a cribber is a strap buckled around the neck in a way that will compress the larynx when the head is flexed, but that will not cause any discomfort when the horse is not indulging in the vice. A surgical operation to relieve cribbing has been developed and used with some success.

HALTER PULLING

Halter pulling refers to pulling back on the halter rope when tied in the stable.

KICKING

Occasionally, unusual excitement or injury will cause the so-called gentle horse to kick. However, a true stable kicker appears to have no other excuse than the satisfaction of striking something or somebody with his hind feet.

TAIL RUBBING

Persistent rubbing of the tail against the side of the stall or other objects is objectionable. The presence of parasites may cause animals to acquire this vice. Installation of a tail board or electric wire may be necessary in breaking animals of this habit. A tail board is a board projecting from the wall of the stall high enough to strike just below the point of the buttock, instead of the tail, of the rubbing horse.

WEAVING

A rhythmical swaying back and forth while standing in the stall is called weaving.

Other Vices

Other vices that are often difficult to cope with and which detract from the value of the animal are: balking, backing, rearing, shying, striking with the front feet, a tendency to run away, and objection to harnessing, saddling, and grooming. Many of these vices originate with incompetent handling; nevertheless, they may be difficult to cope with or to correct. This is especially true in older animals, thus lending credence to the statement, "You can't teach an old horse new tricks."

SELECTED REFERENCES

Title of Publication	Author(s)	Publisher
Anatomy and Conformation of the Horse	G. B. Edwards	Dreenan Press Ltd., Croton-on-Hudson, N.Y., 1973
Anatomy of the Horse, The	R. P. Way D. G. Lee	J. B. Lippincott Co., Philadelphia, Penn., 1965
Anatomy and Physiology of Farm Animals	R. D. Frandsen	Lea & Febiger, Philadelphia, Penn., 1965
Disorders of the Horse	E. Hanauer	A. S. Barnes & Co., Inc., Cranbury, N.J., 1973
Equine Medicine and Surgery	Ed. by J. F. Bone, et al.	American Veterinary Publications, Inc., Wheaton, Ill., 1963

(continued)

Title of Publication	Author(s)	Publisher
First Aid Hints for the Horse Owner	W. E. Lyon	Collins, London, England, 1950
Horse, The	J. M. Kays	A. S. Barnes & Co., Inc., Cranbury, N.J., 1969
Horse Owner's Vet Book, The	E. C. Straiton	J. B. Lippincott Co., Philadelphia, Penn., 1973
Horsemanship and Horse Care, Ag. Info. Bull. No. 353	M. E. Ensminger	U.S. Department of Agriculture, Washington, D.C., 1972
Horseshoeing Theory and Hoof Care	L. Emery J. Miller N. Van Hoosen	Lea & Febiger, Philadelphia, Penn., 1977
Horses' Injuries	C. L. Strong	Arco Publishing Co., Inc., New York, N.Y., 1973
Horses: Their Selection, Care and Handling	M. C. Self	A. S. Barnes & Co., Inc., Cranbury, N.J., 1943
How to Select a Sound Horse, Farmer's Bull. No. 779	H. H. Reese	U.S. Department of Agriculture, Washington, D.C., 1949
Lame Horse, The	J. R. Rooney	A. S. Barnes & Co., Inc., Cranbury, N.J., 1974
Lameness in Horses	O. R. Adams	Lea & Febiger, Philadelphia, Penn., 1967
Progress in Equine Practice	Ed. by E. J. Catcott, J. M. Smithcors	American Veterinary Publications, Inc., Wheaton, Ill., 1966
TV Vet Horse Book	TV Vet	Farming Press Ltd., Ipswich, Suffolk, England, 1971
Veterinary Notebook	W. R. McGee	The Blood Horse, Lexington, Ky., 1958
Veterinary Notes for Horse Owners	M. H. Hays	Arco Publishing Co., Inc., New York, N.Y., 1972
Veterinary Notes for the Standardbred Breeder	W. R. McGee	United States Trotting Assn., Columbus, Ohio

THE HORSE IN ACTION

In the wild state, the horse executed four natural gaits—the walk, trot, pace, and gallop or run. Under domestication, these gaits have been variously modified, and additions have been made through (1) type, (2) breeding and selection, and (3) schooling.

RELATION OF TYPE TO ACTION

Regardless of the use to which horses are put, certain points in conformation are stressed—for example, a shapely, clean-cut head with a large, clear eye; a strong, heavily muscled topline; heavy muscling in the forearm and gaskin; and correct set to the feet and legs. Yet, certain differences in conformation better adapt the animal for use in specific types of work—as draft animals, gaited saddle horses, running horses, heavy harness horses, or hunters, etc. These differences are often as marked as those in the build of the 10-second track man and the champion wrestler. The thickness, massiveness, and low station of the draft horse are points of conformation that adapt him to power at the walk; whereas the angular form, relatively long legs, well-muscled hindquarters, and close-to-the-ground action of the Thoroughbred constitute form conducive to great speed at the run. But many less exaggerated differences exist. Thus, a horse with straight shoulders and short, straight pasterns is almost certain to be short and choppy in his action, and a very widefronted conformation often predisposes paddling.

RELATION OF BREEDING AND SELECTION TO ACTION

The relation of breeding and selection to action becomes especially obvious in a group of weanlings of mixed breeding. Upon starting across a field, some amble off in a rhythmic running walk, nodding their heads as they go; others travel high enough to clear the tops of the daisies; still others break away in an easy gallop. Each of these three types of action is executed with equal ease and naturalness. The first weanlings described are Tennessee Walking Horses, the second are Hackneys, and the third are Thoroughbreds. In each of these breeds, the distinctive way of going has been accomplished through years of breeding and selection.

RELATION OF SCHOOLING TO ACTION

If the offspring of Man o' War and six of the fastest mares ever to grace the tracks had merely worked on laundry trucks until six years old, and if at that time they had suddenly been placed upon a racetrack—without prior training or other preparation—the immediate results would have been disappointing. Their natural aptitude in conformation and breeding would not have been enough. Schooling and training would still have been necessary in order to bring out their inherent ability. No horse—whether he be used for saddle, race, or other purposes—reaches a high degree of proficiency without an education.

On the other hand, it must be emphasized that it is equally disappointing to spend time and money in educating a colt for purposes to which he is not adapted. It is difficult, for example, to train a Hackney as a five-gaited park hack; and it is equally unsatisfactory to school a born Standardbred to the high action of the heavy harness horse.

It should also be pointed out that horses, like people, are likely to revert to an untrained status if placed in an improper environment—despite type, breeding, and early schooling. Thus, an inexperienced rider may, through ignorance, allow the most beautifully trained 5-gaited park hack to revert to a very ordinary mount. Proper and frequent handling is necessary if a horse of this training is to retain the 5 distinct gaits which are executed in a proud and collected manner. For this reason, the less experienced rider often rightfully prefers and will pay more for a 3-gaited saddle horse than for a 5-gaited one.

GAITS

A gait is a particular way of going, either natural or acquired, which is characterized by a distinctive rhythmic movement of the feet and legs. In proper show-ring procedure, horses are brought back to a walk each time before being called upon to execute a different gait. An exception is made in five-gaited classes, where the rack may be executed from the slow gait.

Walk

The walk is a natural, slow, flat-footed, four-beat gait, the latter meaning that each foot takes off from and strikes the ground at a separate interval. It should be springy, regular, and true.

On the draft horse, in which class of animals it constitutes the most important gait, the walk should be executed as a powerful stride; whereas the American Saddle Horse displays what is known as a proud walk, which calls for high action and attractiveness in contrast to power.

Trot

The trot is a natural, rapid, two-beat, diagonal gait in which the front foot and the opposite hind foot take off at the same split second and strike the ground simultaneously. There is a brief moment when all four feet are off the ground and the horse seemingly floats through the air.

This gait varies considerably according to breed and training. The trot of the Standardbred is characterized by the length and rapidity of the individual strides; whereas the trot of the Hackney shows extreme flexion of the knees and hocks that produces a very high-stepping show gait.

Canter; Lope

The canter is a slow, restrained, three-beat gait in which the two diagonal legs are paired, thereby

Fig. 7-1. The right lead at the lope, which should be toward the inside of the ring when going clockwise.

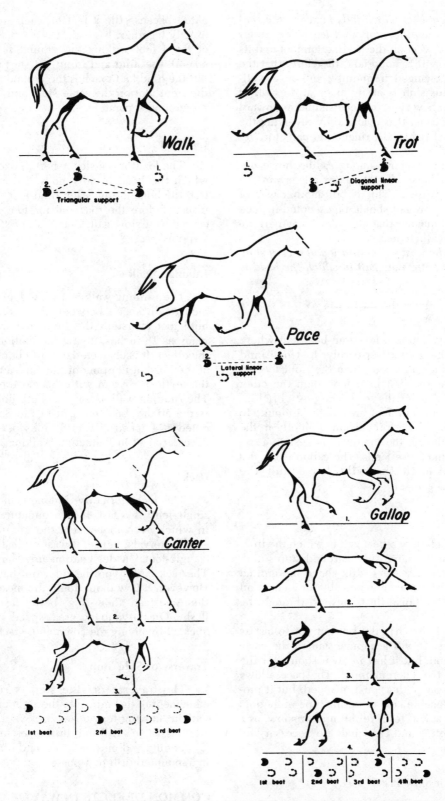

Fig. 7-2. Diagrams showing the features of 5 gaits: walk, trot, pace, canter (3 stages), and gallop (4 stages). Note the movement of the feet and legs of each gait (above), and the support base and beat of the feet (below). (Drawing by Prof. R. F. Johnson)

producing a single beat which falls between the successive beats of the other unpaired legs. The canter imposes a special wear on the leading forefoot and its diagonal hindfoot. It is important, therefore, that the lead should be changed frequently; and in a well-trained horse, this shift is easily made at the will of the rider. In the show-ring, the lead should be toward the inside of the ring. It is changed by reversing the direction of travel (when the ringmaster calls for "reverse and canter").

It is a common saying among saddle horse enthusiasts that "a horse should canter all day in the shade of an apple tree." This is but another way of emphasizing that this gait should be executed in such a slow, collected manner that the animal may perform in a relatively small circle.

The lope is the western adaptation of a very slow canter. It is a smooth, slow gait in which the head is carried low.

Run or Gallop

The run or gallop is a fast, four-beat gait where the feet strike the ground separately; first one hind foot, then the other hind foot, then the front foot on the same side as the first hind foot, then the other front foot which decides the lead. There is a brief interval in which all four feet are off the ground. In executing the gallop, the propulsion is chiefly in the hindquarters, although the forequarters sustain a tremendous jar as the horse lands. The gallop is the fast natural gait of both the wild horse and the Thoroughbred racehorse.

Pace

The pace is a fast, two-beat gait in which the front and hind feet on the same side start and stop simultaneously. The feet rise very little above the ground level. There is a split second when all four feet are off the ground and the horse floats forward through the air.

The pace is faster than the trot but not so fast as the run or gallop. It was a popular gait in the early history of England, but it lost in favor soon after the development of the Thoroughbred. The pace allows for a quick getaway with a burst of speed, but it produces an objectionable side or rolling type of motion. The pace is not suited to travel in mud or snow, as a smooth, hard footing and easy draft are necessary for its best execution.

Stepping Pace (or Slow Pace)

This is the preferred slow gait for 5-gaited show horses. It is a modified pace in which the objectionable side or rolling motion of the true pace is eliminated because the 2 feet on each side do not move exactly together. Instead, it is a 4-beat gait with each of the 4 feet striking the ground separately. In the takeoff, the hind and front feet start almost together, but the hind foot touches the ground slightly ahead of the front foot on the same side, and each foot strikes the ground separately.

Fox Trot

The fox trot is a slow, short, broken type of trot in which the head usually nods. In executing the fox trot, the horse brings each hind foot to the ground an instant before the diagonal forefoot. This gait is accepted as a slow gait, but it is not so popular as the stepping pace.

Running Walk

The running walk is a slow, four-beat gait, intermediate in speed between the walk and rack. The hind foot oversteps the front foot from a few to as many as 18 inches, giving the motion a smooth gliding effect. It is characterized by a bobbing or nodding of the head, a flopping of the ears, and a snapping of the teeth in rhythm with the movement of the legs. The running walk is easy on both horse and rider. It is the all-day business gait of the South and is executed at a speed of 6 to 8 miles per hour. This is a necessary gait in Plantation Walking Horses.

Rack

The rack (formerly, but now incorrectly, called single-foot) is a fast, flashy, unnatural, four-beat gait in which each foot meets the ground separately at equal intervals; hence, it was originally known as the "single-foot," a designation now largely discarded. The rack is easy on the rider but hard on the horse. However, it is without doubt the most popular gait in the American show-ring, being fast, brilliant, and flashy. On the tanbark, great speed at the rack is requested by giving the command, "rack on."

Traverse or Side Step

The traverse or side step is simply a lateral movement of the animal to the right or left as desired, without moving forward or backward. This trick will often assist in (1) lining up horses in the show-ring, (2) opening and closing gates, and (3) taking position in a mounted drill or a posse.

COMMON DEFECTS IN WAY OF GOING

The feet of an animal should move straight ahead and parallel to a center line drawn in the direction of

travel. Any deviations from this way of going constitute defects.

Cross-firing

Cross-firing, a defect in the way of going, is generally confined to pacers and consists of a scuffing on the inside of the diagonal fore and hind feet.

Dwelling

Dwelling, most noticeable in trick-trained horses, consists of a distinct pause in the flight of the foot, as though the stride were completed before the foot reaches the ground.

Forging

The striking of the forefoot by the toe of the hind foot is known as forging.

Interfering

The striking of the fetlock or cannon by the opposite foot that is in motion is known as interfering. This condition is predisposed in horses with base-narrow, toe-wide, or splayfooted standing positions.

Lameness

Lameness is a defect that can be detected when the affected foot is favored when standing. In action, the load on the ailing foot is eased, and there is characteristic bobbing of the head of the horse as the affected foot strikes the ground.

Paddling

Throwing the front feet outward as they are picked up is known as paddling. This condition is predisposed in horses with toe-narrow or pigeon-toed standing positions.

Pointing

Perceptible extension of the stride with little flexion is called pointing. This condition is likely to occur in the Thoroughbred and Standardbred breeds— animals bred and trained for great speed with a long stride.

Pounding

Pounding is a condition in which there is heavy contact with the ground in contrast to the desired light, springy movement.

Rolling

Excessive lateral shoulder motion, characteristic of horses with protruding shoulders, is known as rolling.

Scalping

Scalping is that condition in which the hairline at the top of the hind foot hits the toe of the forefoot as it breaks over.

Speedy Cutting

Speedy cutting is a condition of a horse at speed in which a hind leg above the scalping mark hits against the shoe of a breaking-over forefoot. In trotters, legs on the same side are involved. In pacers, diagonal legs are involved.

Stringhalt

Stringhalt is characterized by excessive flexing of the hind legs. It is most easily detected when backing a horse.

Trappy

A short, quick, choppy stride is known as trappy. This condition is predisposed in horses with short, straight pasterns and straight shoulders.

Winding or Rope-Walking

A twisting of the striding leg around in front of the supporting leg so as to make contact in the manner of a "rope-walking" artist is known as winding or rope-walking. This condition most often occurs in horses with very wide fronts.

Winging

Winging is an exaggerated paddling, particularly noticeable in high-going horses.

SELECTED REFERENCES

Title of Publication	Author(s)	Publisher
Anatomy and Conformation of the Horse	G. B. Edwards	Dreenan Press Ltd., Croton-on-Hudson, N.Y., 1973

(continued)

Title of Publication	Author(s)	Publisher
Approved Practices in Raising and Handling Horses	D. E. Ulmer E. M. Juergenson	The Interstate Printers & Publishers, Inc., Danville, Ill., 1974
Breeding and Raising Horses, Ag. Hdbk. No. 394	M. E. Ensminger	Agriculture Research Service, USDA, Washington, D.C., 1972
Horse, The	D. J. Kays, rev. by J. M. Kays	A. S. Barnes & Co., Inc., Cranbury, N.J., 1969
Horse Buyer's Guide, The	J. K. Posey	A. S. Barnes & Co., Inc., Cranbury, N.J., 1973
Horse Structure and Movement, The	R. H. Smythe, rev. by P. C. Goody	J. A. Allen & Co., London, England, 1972
Horsemanship	Mrs. A. W. Jasper	Boy Scouts of America, New Brunswick, N.J., 1963
Horsemanship and Horse Care, Ag. Info. Bull. No. 353	M. E. Ensminger	Agriculture Research Service, USDA, Washington, D.C., 1972
Horsemanship and Horsemastership	Ed. by G. Wright	Doubleday & Company, Inc., Garden City, N.Y., 1962
Horseshoeing Theory and Hoof Care	L. Emery J. Miller N. Van Hoosen	Lea & Febiger, Phildelphia, Penn., 1977
Horses: Their Selection, Care and Handling	M. C. Self	A. S. Barnes & Co., Inc., Cranbury, N.J., 1943
Judging Manual for American Saddlebred Horses	J. Foss	American Saddle Horse Breeders Association, Louisville, Ky., 1973
Lameness in Horses, Second Edition	O. R. Adams	Lea & Febiger, Philadelphia, Penn., 1966
Leg at Each Corner, A	N. Thelwell	E. P. Dutton & Co., Inc., New York, N.Y., 1963
Livestock Judging and Evaluation: A Handbook for the Student	W. M. Beeson R. E. Hunsley J. E. Nordby	The Interstate Printers & Publishers, Inc., Danville, Ill., 1970
Practical Dressage for Amateur Trainers	J. M. Ladendorf	A. S. Barnes & Co., Inc., Cranbury, N.J.
Rule Book		The American Horse Shows Association, Inc., New York, N.Y., annual
Saddle Up!	C. E. Ball	J. B. Lippincott Co., Philadelphia, Penn., 1970
Spanish Riding School, The	H. Handler	McGraw-Hill Book Co., Ltd., Maidenhead, England, 1972

CHAPTER 8

TYPES AND CLASSES OF LIGHT HORSES ACCORDING TO USE

Contents   **Page**

Fig. 8-1. Historic bronze horse of China. This was among the artifacts found in a tomb of the late Eastern Han Dynasty (25 A.D. to 220 A.D.) in China. Note that the horse has one foot on a swallow to indicate swiftness as he literally floats through the air, with head up, tail high, and three feet off the ground. Note, too, that he is doing the rack—a fast, flashy, four-beat gait in which each foot meets the ground separately at equal intervals. Contrary to many reports, he is not galloping. (Photo by A. H. Ensminger)

The improvement of horses dates back to the time when man first domesticated them and sought to improve them more nearly to fulfill his needs. Through selection, different types and breeds evolved, better adapted to different uses and better meeting different human desires.

Today, horses are classified according to weight, size, build, and use as light horses, draft horses, or ponies.

Light horses stand 14-2 to 17 hands high, weigh 900 to 1,400 pounds, and are used primarily for riding, driving, or racing, or for utility purposes on the farm. Light horses generally are more rangy and are capable of more action and greater speed than draft horses.

Draft horses stand 14-2 to 17-2 hands high, weigh 1,400 pounds or more, and are used primarily for drawing loads and other heavy work.

Ponies stand under 14-2 hands high and weigh 500 to 900 pounds. Not every small horse is a pony, however. Some small horses are merely small animals of established light horse breeds; others are nondescript runts. In ponies, there is a distinct conformation; in miniature, they are either of draft horse, heavy harness horse, or saddle or harness horse type. The breeding, feeding, care, and management are essentially the same for ponies as for larger light horses; the only differences result from their diminutive size. The discussion which follows in this chapter will be limited to light horses and ponies.

In no class of animals have so many diverse and distinct types been developed as in the horse. The descendants of the Oriental light-legged horse have, for generations, been bred and used for riding and driving purposes—first as the chariot and riding horses of Egypt, Greece, and Arabia; later as the running horse of England; and finally for purposes of recreation and sport in the United States and throughout the world. In due time, further refinements in breeding light horses were made, and these animals were adapted for more specific purposes. In this manner, light horses specifically adapted to the purposes enumerated in Table 8-1 have evolved.

In attempting to produce animals to meet these specific purposes, new breeds of light horses have been developed. In certain cases, however, the particular use or performance is so exacting that only one breed appears to be sufficiently specialized; for example, in running races the Thoroughbred is used almost exclusively,[1] and harness races are now synonymous with the Standardbred breed.

RIDING HORSES

Riding horses have many and varied uses, but, as

the name indicates, they are all ridden. They may have a very definite utility value, as is true of stock horses, or they may be used chiefly for purposes of recreation and sport. For the latter use, training, manners, and style are of paramount importance, although durability and efficiency are not to be overlooked in any horse.

Three- and Five-Gaited Saddle Horses

Long after the development of the New England town, the opening up of roads along the Eastern Seaboard, and the development of the buggy and the popularity of the roadster type of horse, the states of Virginia, West Virginia, Kentucky, Tennessee, and Missouri still consisted of large plantations under the ownership of southern gentlemen. Roads were few and far between, and travel was largely on horseback over the most natural paths that could be found. Thus, there was need for a horse that would carry the plantation owners with dignity befitting their station in life and with the least distress possible to both rider and horse. As the plantation owners rode over their broad estates, easy gaits were a necessity. Such was the need, and out of this need arose the beautiful American Saddle Horse.

Animals qualifying as either 3- or 5-gaited saddle horses in the leading American horse shows are generally of American Saddle Horse breeding, a truly American creation.[2] Occasionally, however, animals of the other light horse breeds are trained to execute the 5 gaits. It must also be remembered that the vast majority of American horses of all breeds are of the 3-gaited variety and that only a relatively small proportion of these animals are ever exhibited. Instead, most of the 3-gaited horses are used for pleasure riding.

The gaits of 3-gaited horses are: the walk, the trot, and the canter. In addition to performing these same gaits, the 5-gaited horse must possess a slow gait and the rack. The slow gait may be either the running walk, fox trot, or stepping pace (slow pace); but for show purposes only the stepping pace is accepted. In the show-ring, generally the judge requests that 5-gaited horses execute the gaits in the following order: the walk, the trot, the slow gait, the rack, and the canter.

Whether an animal is 3-gaited or 5-gaited is primarily a matter of training. Custom decrees that 3-gaited horses be shown with their manes roached or clipped short and their tails clipped or sheared for a short distance from the base; whereas 5-gaited horses are shown with flowing manes and full-length tails.

---

[1]Except for Quarter Horse races, and races limited to certain other breeds.

[2]Herein reference is made to the Saddle Horse Division as described by The American Horse Shows Association, and not to the several performance classes in which three-gaited horses of various breeds compete.

TABLE 8-1
LIGHT HORSE SUMMARY

Type	Primary Use	Breeds
Riding Horses	Three-gaited saddle horses	American Bashkir Curly American Saddle Horse American White; American Creme Andalusian Appaloosa Arabian Cleveland Bay Galiceno Hanoverian Hungarian Horse Lipizzan Morab Morgan Morocco Spotted Horse Paint Horse Palomino Pinto Quarter Horse Rangerbred Spanish-Barb Thoroughbred Trakehner Ysabella
	Gaited horses	American Saddle Horse Missouri Fox Trotting Horse Paso Fino Peruvian Paso Tennessee Walking Horse
	Stock horses	Grades, crossbreds, or following purebreds: American Mustang Appaloosa Arabian Bucksin Chickasaw Hungarian Horse Morgan Paint Horse Pinto Horse Quarter Horse Spanish-Barb Spanish Mustang Thoroughbred
	Polo mounts	Grades, crossbreds, and purebreds of all breeds, but predominantly of Thoroughbred breeding.
	Hunters and Jumpers	Grades, crossbreds, and purebreds of all breeds, but predominantly of Thoroughbred breeding.
	Ponies for riding	American Gotland Horse American Walking Pony Connemara Pony National Appaloosa Pony Shetland Pony Welsh Pony
Racehorses[1]	Running racehorses	Thoroughbred
	Quarter racehorses	Quarter Horse
	Harness racehorses (trotters and pacers)	Standardbred
Driving Horses	Heavy harness horses	Hackney
	Fine harness horses	American Saddle Horses (predominantly, although other breeds are so used)
	Roadsters	Standardbred
	Ponies for driving: 1. Harness show ponies 2. Heavy harness ponies	Hackney Shetland Pony Welsh Pony

[1]In a few states, Appaloosa and Arabian horses are also being raced under saddle.

Fig. 8-2. Technistar, a three-gaited American Saddle Horse. Note that the mane is roached, or clipped short, and that the tail is clipped, or sheared, for a short distance from the base—as custom decrees. (Courtesy, American Saddle Horse Breeders Assn., Louisville, Ky.)

Also, because of the speed at which 5-gaited horses are expected to perform at the trot and the rack, they are permitted to wear quarter boots to protect the heels of the front feet, a practice which is forbidden in 3-gaited classes.

Both 3- and 5-gaited horses are shown under saddle; and each may be shown in combination classes, in which they must perform both in harness and

Fig. 8-3. Beau Fortune, a five-gaited American Saddle Horse. Note the flowing mane and full-length tail—as custom decrees. (Courtesy, American Saddle Horse Breeders Assn., Louisville, Ky.)

under saddle. Also, 5-gaited horses (but not 3-gaited horses) may be shown in a third division; namely, in fine harness classes.

In combination classes, the entries enter the ring hitched to an appropriate four-wheeled vehicle, with the saddle and bridle hidden in the back of the rig. The judge works the class both ways of the ring, then lines them up in the center for inspection and backs each horse in order to test his manners. Next the judge orders that the entries be unhitched, unharnessed, saddled, bridled and worked under saddle both ways of the ring. Finally, the horses are again lined up in the center of the ring, and each animal is backed under saddle.

A fine harness horse is exactly what the name implies—a fine horse presented in fine harness. The entire ensemble is elegant, and represents the ultimate in grace and charm.

Fine harness horses are penalized if driven at excessive speed. Combination horses, especially five-gaited ones, should be driven at a more speedy trot than fine harness horses.

In addition to executing the gaits with perfection, both three- and five-gaited animals should possess the following characteristics:

1. *Superior conformation*, in which the principal requirements are:

   (a) Graceful lines obtained through a fairly long, arched neck; short, strong back and loin with a good seat; a nicely turned croup; a smartly carried, flowing tail; and a relatively long underline.

   (b) A shapely and smart head.

   (c) Nicely sloping shoulders and pasterns.

   (d) Symmetry and blending of all parts.

   (e) Quality, as evidenced by a clean-cut, chiseled appearance throughout, and soundness.

   (f) Style, alertness, and animation, sometimes said to be comparable to that of a "peacock."

2. *Perfect manners*, which include form, training, and obedience—those qualities that make for a most finished performance.

3. *Superior action*, including an elastic step, high action, and evidence of spirit and dash.

Walking Horses

This particular class of horses is largely comprised of one breed—the Tennessee Walking Horse.[3]

Horses of this type were first introduced into Tennessee by the early settlers from Virginia and the Carolinas. For many years, the plantation owners of middle Tennessee—men who spent long hours daily

---

[3]A more detailed description of this and other breeds may be found in Chapter 10.

in supervising labor from the saddle—selected and bred animals for their easy, springy gaits, good dispositions, and intelligence. Particular stress was placed upon the natural gait known as the running walk and upon the elimination of the trot. Thus, the three gaits that evolved in the walking horse (also called Plantation Walking Horse) were: the walk, the running walk, and the canter.

Fig. 8-4. The Tennessee Walking Horse, Son's Shadow, in action and well ridden by Sam Paschal. Owned by Mr. and Mrs. Carl Hengen, Lawn Vale Farm, Gainsville, Virginia. (Courtesy, *The National Horseman* and Mr. Paschal)

In animals of this type, the head is somewhat low in carriage, and at the running walk there is a characteristic nodding of the head. Sometimes there is also a flopping of the ears and a snapping of the teeth while the animal is in this rhythmic movement. Walking horses are also noted for their wonderful dispositions. Their easy gaits and a superb disposition make them an ideal type of horse for the amateur rider or the professional or society person who rides infrequently.

Stock Horses

Stock horses constitute the largest single class of light horses of this country; there are approximately 500,000 of them in use in the 17 range states. They are the cow ponies of the West.

Usually, stock horses are of mixed breeding. Most generally they are descended from the Mustang—the feral horse of the United States. Subsequently, Mustang mares were mated to sires of practically every known light horse breed—especially Thoroughbreds and Quarter Horses. Stallions of the Palomino, Morgan, Arabian, and other breeds have also been used. Such grading-up has improved the size, speed, and perhaps the appearance of the cow pony, but most horsemen will concede that no amount of improved

Fig. 8-5. A cutting horse in action, separating a cow from the herd and preventing its return. This event is one of the most popular tests of the inherent "cow sense" of a horse. (Courtesy, American Quarter Horse Assn., Amarillo, Tex.)

breeding will ever produce a gamier, hardier, and more durable animal than the Mustang. In addition to being game and hardy, the stock horse must be agile, surefooted, fast, short coupled, deep, powerfully muscled, durable, and must possess good feet and legs. Above all, the cowboy insists that his pony be a good companion and that he possess "cow sense."

Polo Mounts

As the name would indicate, polo mounts include that type and class of horses particularly adapted for use in playing the game of polo. This game, which was first introduced into this country in 1876, is played by 4 mounted men on each team. The object is to drive a wooden ball between goalposts at either

Fig. 8-6. Belle of All, one of the most famous polo mounts that ever played at Meadowbrook, Long Island. Note the pronounced Thoroughbred type. Polo ponies must be quick and clever in turning, and they must be able to dodge, swerve, or wheel while on a dead run.

end of a playing field 300 yards long and 120 to 150 yards wide. Long-handled regulation mallets are used to drive the ball.

At the time the game was first introduced into the United States, there was a decided preference for ponies under 13-2 hands in height. Later, horses up to 14-2 hands were accepted, and more recently horses up to 15-2 and over have been used.

Although very similar to the hunter in type, the polo mount is smaller in size. He must be quick and clever in turning, and he must be able to dodge, swerve, or wheel while on a dead run. He must like the game and be able to follow the ball.

The polo mount is trained to respond to the pressure of the reins on the neck, so that the rider may be free to guide him with only one hand. Up to 5 or 6 years is required to complete the schooling of a polo horse, and as many as 4 to 6 mounts may be used by each player in a single game—all of which contributes to the expensiveness of the sport.

Polo ponies are usually of mixed breeding, but most of them are predominantly Thoroughbred. Type and training, together with native ability and intelligence, are the primary requisites.

The American Horse Shows Association has developed show classifications for polo ponies. For information relative to same, the reader is referred to the A.H.S.A. Rule Book.

Hunters and Jumpers

The hunter is that type of horse used in following the hounds in fox hunting. The sport is traditional in England, and each year it is sharing its glamour with greater numbers in the United States.

The hunter is not necessarily of any particular breeding, but Thoroughbred blood predominates. The infusion of some coldblood (draft breeding) is often relied upon in order to secure greater size and a more tractable disposition.

The American Horse Shows Association Rule Book classifies hunters as follows: *lightweight* (those expected to carry a rider weighing under 165 lb); *middleweight* (those expected to carry weights ranging from 165 to 185 lb); and *heavyweight* (those expected to carry over 185 lb but under 205 lb). As many folks who ride to hounds do so in order to keep down their weight, their need for a sizable mount can be fully appreciated. It must also be realized that a 5-foot object is 4 inches lower for a 16-hand horse than for one only 15 hands in height. Hunters are further classified as a Green Hunter or a Regular Hunter. A Green Hunter is a horse of any age that is in his first or second year of showing. A Regular Hunter is a horse of any age that is not restricted by previous showing in any division.

In addition to being of ample size and height, the hunter must possess the necessary stamina and conformation to keep up with the pack. He must be able to hurdle with safety such common field obstacles as fences and ditches. The good hunter, therefore, is rugged, short coupled, and heavily muscled throughout.

All hunters are jumpers to some degree, but a high jumper is not necessarily a good hunter. To qualify as a hunter, the horse must do more. He must execute many and varied jumps over a long period of time.

Jumpers are a nondescript group, consisting of all breeds and types. The only requisite is that they can jump. In the show-ring, an unsoundness does not penalize a jumper unless it is sufficiently severe to be considered an act of cruelty.

There is also a hunter and jumper pony division, for ponies not exceeding 14-2 hands, and for children that have not reached their eighteenth birthday.

Fig. 8-8. A jumper in action. (Courtesy, McLaughlin Photography, Morrison, Colo.)

Fig. 8-7. A hunter in action, and well ridden. (Courtesy, Polaris Farm, Charlottesville, Va.)

Ponies for Riding

These are children's mounts. In addition to their miniature size, they should possess the following characteristics: (1) gentleness, (2) sound feet and legs, (3) symmetry, (4) good eyes, (5) endurance, (6) intelligence, (7) patience, (8) faithfulness, and (9) hardiness. Above all, they must be kind and gentle in disposition.

Fig. 8-9. Pony ridden by Olivia and Anastasia Musgrave of Co. Dublin, Ireland. (Courtesy, Sir Richard Musgrave)

RACEHORSES

The term "racehorse" refers to a horse that is bred and trained for racing.

According to some historians, the Greeks introduced horse racing in the Olympic games in 1450 B.C. Also, it is reported that a planned horse race of consequence was run in England in 1377 A.D., between animals owned by Richard II and the Earl of Arundel. The sporting instinct of man being what it is, it is reasonable to surmise, however, that a bit of a contest was staged the first time that two proud mounted horsemen chanced to meet.

The development of horse racing in Britain dates from the 17th Century, although it is known to have taken place much earlier. Records exist of racing during the Roman occupation; and during the reign of Henry II races took place at Smithfield, which was the great London horse market at the time. But it was in the reign of James I that racing first began to be an organized sport. He took a great liking to Newmarket, where he had a royal palace and a racecourse built. Also, he established public races in various parts of the country.

The famous Rowley Mile Course at Newmarket, the home of English flat racing, is named after Charles II. "Old Riley" was his nickname, after his

Fig. 8-10. Kentucky's historic Churchill Downs, familiar to millions of people all over the world. The Kentucky Derby—first run in 1875, now run the first Saturday of each May—is one of the most beautiful and exciting contests in all the world of sport. (Courtesy, Kentucky Department of Public Information, Frankfort, Ky.)

favorite riding horse by that name. Charles II loved racing; he rode in matches, founded races called the Royal Plates, and sometimes adjudicated in the disputes.

The Jockey Club came into existence at Newmarket in 1752, with many rich and influential men among its members. It gradually became the governing body of English racing.

Today, three types of horse races are run: (1) running races (including steeplechase races), (2) quarter races, and (3) harness races. For the most part, each type of race is dominated by one breed. Thus, in running races, it's Thoroughbreds; in quarter races, it's Quarter Horses; and in harness races, it's Standardbreds. However, on a limited basis, and in a few states, Appaloosa and Arabian horses are now being raced under saddle.

Racing Colors

The Jockey Club assigns colors to racing stables. They may be assigned for one year, or they may be assigned for a lifetime. Sometimes colors are reassigned when no longer in use, but this is not the case with the colors of very famous stables. Jockeys must wear the colors assigned to the stable.

Racing Attendance

In 1974, 78.8 million fans went to Thoroughbred and harness racing. Auto racing ranked second, with 47.5 million fans; football (pro and college) ranked third, with 42.9 million fans; baseball (major and minor leagues) was in a close fourth place, with an attendance of 41.7 million; and basketball (pro and college) stood fifth, with an attendance of 33.8 million.[4]

Racing Records

In running races (Thoroughbreds), the records at some of the popular American distances are: *For 1 mile*—Dr. Fager set the world's record at 1:32 1/5 minutes, as a 4-year-old and carrying 134 lb, at Arlington Park, Chicago, in 1968; *for 1⅜ miles on the dirt*—Man o' War set the American record at 2:14 1/5 minutes, as a 3-year-old and carrying 126 lb, at Belmont Park, New York, in 1920; and *for 1⅜ miles on the turf*—Cougar 2nd set the world's record at 2:11 minutes, as a 6-year-old and carrying 126 lb, at Hollywood Park, California, in 1972. It is noteworthy that the fastest mile (run by Dr. Fager) at 1:32 1/5 was equal to a speed of 45.4 miles per hour.

In quarter races (Quarter Horses), Truckle Feature set the U.S. record for a quarter mile (440 yards) at :21.02 in 1969.

[4]Statistics courtesy of Triangle Publications, Inc.

Fig. 8-11. Secretariat shown winning the $250,000 Marlboro Cup at Belmont Park in 1:45.2, setting a new world record for 1⅛ mile. (Courtesy, The Jockey Club, New York, N.Y.)

In harness racing (Standardbreds), Nevele Pride holds the world's trotting record for a mile at 1:54 4/5 minutes, which was established in 1969; and Steady Star set the world's pacing record for a mile at 1:52 minutes in 1971.

Running Racehorses

Racehorses used for running (an extended gallop) under the saddle are now confined almost exclusively to one breed, the Thoroughbred. On the other hand, the Thoroughbred breed (including both purebreds and crossbreds) has been used widely for other purposes, especially as polo mounts, hunters, and cavalry horses.

Although trials of speed had taken place between horses from the earliest recorded history, the true and unmistakable foundation of the Thoroughbred breed as such traces back only to the reign of Charles II, known as the "father of the British turf."

Although the length of race, weight carried, and type of track have undergone considerable variation in recent years, the running horse always has been selected for speed and more speed at the run. The distinguishing characteristics of the running horse, as represented by the Thoroughbred, are the extreme refinement, oblique shoulders, well-made withers, heavily muscled rear quarters, straight hind legs, and close travel to the ground.

Quarter Racehorses

Quarter racing has become an increasingly popular sport. For the most part, races of this type are confined to animals of the Quarter Horse breed, which animals derived their name and initial fame for their extraordinary speed at distances up to a quarter of a mile. Although the great majority of Quarter Horses

are used to work cattle and never appear on the race-track, the proponents of quarter racing advocate the racetrack as a means of proving animals. Performance, so they argue, is the proof of whether or not a horse can do the job for which he is bred. Thus, quarter racing is used as a breed proving ground for the Quarter Horse, for in this racing the fundamental quality of speed can be accurately measured and recorded in such a way that the performance of horses in all parts of the country can be compared.

Fig. 8-12. As a racehorse, the American Quarter Horse continues his early colonial heritage by sprinting with blinding speed down 440-yard straightaways for some of the richest purses in racing history. (Courtesy, American Quarter Horse Assn., Amarillo, Tex.)

Harness Racehorses (Trotters and Pacers)

Prior to the advent of improved roads and the automobile, but following the invention of the buggy, there was need for a fast, light-harness type of horse. This horse was used to draw vehicles varying in type from the light roadster of the young gallant to the dignified family carriage. In the process of meeting this need, two truly American breeds of horses evolved—the Morgan and the Standardbred. The first breed traces to the foundation sire, Justin Morgan; and the latter to Hambletonian 10, an animal which was line bred to imported Messenger.

As horse-and-buggy travel passed into permanent oblivion, except for recreation and sport, the Standardbred breeders wisely placed greater emphasis upon the sport of racing; whereas the Morgan enthusiasts directed their breeding programs toward transforming their animals into a saddle breed.

The early descendants of Messenger were sent over the track, trotting (not galloping) under the saddle; but eventually the jockey races in this country came to be restricted to a running type of race in which the Thoroughbred was used. With this shift, qualifying standards—a mile in 2:30 at the trot and 2:25 at the pace when hitched to the sulky—were set up for light harness races; and those animals so qual-

ifying were registered.[5] The pneumatic-tire racing vehicles, known as sulkies, were first introduced in 1892. With their use that year, the time was reduced nearly 4 seconds below the record of the previous year. Thus, were developed harness racing and the Standardbred breed of horses, which today is the exclusive breed used for this purpose.

Trotters and pacers are of similar breeding and type, the particular gaits being largely a matter of training. In fact, many individuals show speed at both the trot and the pace. It is generally recognized, however, that pacers are handicapped in the mud, in the sand, or over a rough surface.

The Standardbred breed—like the Thoroughbred—also finds other uses, as driving horses in roadster classes, delivery horses, and general utility horses. By way of comparison with the Thoroughbred, the Standardbred possess a more tractable disposition, is smaller, longer bodied, closer to the ground, heavier-limbed, and sturdier in build. The latter characteristic is very necessary because harness races are usually "heat races"—for example, the best two out of three races.

In the beginning, horses of this type found their principal use in harness races at county and state fairs. However, in recent years parimutuel harness racing has been established at a number of tracks. Today, harness racehorses are almost exclusively of the Standardbred breed.

DRIVING HORSES

At the present time, driving horses are used chiefly for purposes of recreation. According to the specific use made of them, driving horses are classified as heavy harness horses, fine harness horses, roadsters, or ponies.

Heavy Harness Horses

These are also known as carriage horses. At the present time, this type of horse has very little place in the utility field, its use being largely confined to the show-ring. As the name implies, the heavy harness horse of the show-ring wears heavier leather than the fine harness horse or the roadster, though it in no way approaches draft harness. The heavy leather used on these animals was first decreed by fashion in England, the idea being that to drive handsomely one must drive heavily. The vehicles drawn were of heavy construction and elegant design and logically and artistically the harness had to be in proportion thereto.

---

[5]On January 1, 1933, registration on performance alone was no longer granted, and registration of both sire and dam was required. The qualifying standards were initiated in 1879.

Heavy harness horses were especially popular during the Victorian era, and the ownership of a handsome pair was an indication of social prestige. In this country during the Gay Nineties, bobtailed Hackneys attached to high-seated rigs made a dashing picture as they pranced down the avenue.

Fig. 8-13. Heavy harness pony—a Hackney—in action. Note the high action and the smooth, gracefully curved form. (Courtesy, *The Hackney Journal*, Peekskill, N.Y.)

At one time, there were several heavy harness breeds, but at present all except the Hackney have practically ceased to exist in America. In this country, therefore, the Hackney is now the heavy harness breed; and the American Horse Shows Association officially refers to show classifications as Hackneys rather than as Heavy Harness Horses.

The heavy harness horse should possess the following distinguishing characteristics:

1. *Beauty*—Beauty is obtained through graceful, curved lines; full-made form; and high carriage. Show-ring style decrees that heavy harness horses be docked and have their manes pulled.

2. *High action*—Animals of this type are bred for high hock and knee action, but skilled training, bitting, and shoeing are necessary for their development. In the show-ring, heavy harness horses must be able to fold their knees, flex their hocks, and set their chins. "Woodenlegged" horses cannot take competition.

3. *Manners and temperament*—Perfection in the manners and disposition of pleasure horses of this type is a requisite of first rank.

4. *Color*—Seal brown, brown, bay, and black colors are preferred in heavy harness horses. White stockings are desired for the purpose of accentuating high action.

5. *Height*—For horse show purposes, the maximum height of Hackney ponies shall be 14-2 hands.

Fine Harness Horses

A fine harness horse is exactly what the name implies—a fine horse presented in fine harness. The entire ensemble is elegant and represents the ultimate in grace and charm.

Fig. 8-14. Fine harness horse. (Courtesy, *The Horse World*, Lexington, Ky.)

In the show-ring, fine harness horses are, according to the rules of the American Horse Shows Association, limited to the American Saddle Horse breed. In some shows, however, other breeds are exhibited in fine harness classes. Fashion decrees that fine harness horses shall be shown wearing long mane and tail and drawing a four-wheeled road show wagon without top, or with top drawn. Light harness with a snaffle bit is required. Fine harness horses are shown at an animated park trot and at an animated walk.

Roadsters

The sport of showing a roadster originated in the horse and buggy era. It was founded upon the desire to own an attractive horse that possessed the necessary speed to pass any of its rivals encountered upon the city or country thoroughfares.

In the show-ring, roadsters are generally shown in either or both (1) roadster to bike, or (2) roadster to road wagon or buggy classes. The latter are hitched singly or in pairs. Some shows also provide a class or classes[6] for roadsters under saddle. In all divisions—whether shown to bike or buggy, or under saddle—entries must trot; pacing is barred.

Originally, roadster classes included animals of both Standardbred and Morgan extraction. In recent years, however, the Morgan has developed in the di-

[6]In many of the larger shows, a roadster appointment class is provided. Appointments are listed in the A.H.S.A. Rule Book.

Fig. 8-15. Roadster to bike—a Shetland. (Courtesy, American Shetland Pony Club, Fowler, Ind.)

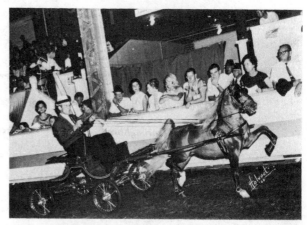

Fig. 8-16. Harness show pony—a Shetland. (Courtesy, American Shetland Pony Club, Fowler, Ind.)

rection of a saddler. Today, the *Rule Book* of the American Horse Shows Association lists two divisions for roadsters: (1) Roadster Division, for Standardbred and non-Standardbred horses; and (2) Roadster Ponies, for ponies under 12-2 hands (50).

Particular stress is placed in roadster show classes upon the manners, style, and beauty of conformation, combined with speed. In striking contrast to heavy harness classes, the roadster is shown hitched to very light vehicles permitting fast travel.

Custom decrees that roadsters shall enter the ring at a jog, and work the wrong way (clockwise) of the track first. After jogging for a brief time, usually the judge asks that they perform at the road gait, then jog again (all clockwise of the ring). Then, in succession, the judge asks them to reverse, jog, road gait, and turn on or trot at speed. Lastly, they are called to the center of the ring for inspection in a standing position, at which time the judge usually tests their manners by asking each driver to back his horse.

Ponies for Driving

Ponies for driving are of two kinds; namely, (1) harness show ponies, and (2) heavy harness ponies.

The best harness show ponies are vest-pocket editions of fine harness horses; that is, they possess the same desirable characteristics, except that they are in miniature. According to the rules of the American Horse Shows Association, harness show ponies may be of any breed or combination of breeds; the only requisite is that they must be under 14-2 hands in height. Three breeds produce animals that qualify under this category; namely, the Shetland, Welsh, and Hackney breeds.

Heavy harness ponies are, as the name indicates, miniature heavy harness horses—they're under 14-2 hands. Generally they are either purebred Hackneys, or predominantly of Hackney breeding.

Three breeds produce animals that qualify as ponies; namely, the Hackney, Welsh, and Shetland breeds. The Hackney is generally exclusively of the harness type, but the Welsh and Shetland breeds are used either under saddle or in harness. In the major horse shows of the land, the latter two breeds may be exhibited in harness, but in practical use they are children's mounts.

SELECTED REFERENCES

Title of Publication	Author(s)	Publisher
America's Quarter Horses	P. Laune	Doubleday & Company, Inc., Garden City, N.Y., 1973
Breeding and Raising Horses, Ag. Hdbk. No. 394	M. E. Ensminger	U.S. Department of Agriculture, Washington, D.C., 1972
Encyclopedia of the Horse, The	Ed. by C. E. Hope, G. N. Jackson	The Viking Press, New York, N.Y., 1973
From Dawn to Destiny	F. Jennings	The Thoroughbred Press, Inc., Lexington, Ky., 1962

(continued)

Title of Publication	Author(s)	Publisher
Harper's Encyclopedia for Horsemen: The Complete Book of the Horse	L. Taylor	Harper & Row, Publishers, New York, N.Y., 1973
History of Horse Racing, The	R. Longrigg	Stein and Day Publishers, New York, N.Y., 1972
History of Thoroughbred Racing in America, The	W. H. Robertson	Prentice-Hall, Inc., Englewood Cliffs, N.J., 1964
Horse, The	D. J. Kays, rev. by J. M. Kays	A. S. Barnes & Co., Inc., Cranbury, N.J., 1969
Horse America Made, The	L. Taylor	American Saddle Horse Breeders Association, Louisville, Ky., 1961
Horse Shows	A. N. Phillips	The Interstate Printers & Publishers, Inc., Danville, Ill., 1956
Horseman's Encyclopedia, The	M. C. Self	A. S. Barnes & Co., Inc., Cranbury, N.J. 1963
Horsemanship and Horse Care, Ag. Info. Bull. No. 353	M. E. Ensminger	Agriculture Research Service, USDA, Washington, D.C., 1972
Horsemanship and Horsemastership	Ed. by G. Wright	Doubleday & Company, Inc., Garden City, N.Y., 1962
Horses	M. C. Self	A. S. Barnes & Co., Inc., Cranbury, N.J. 1953
Horses and Horsemanship	L. E. Walraven	A. S. Barnes & Co., Inc., New York, N.Y., 1970
Light Horses, Farmers' Bull. No. 2127	M. E. Ensminger	Agricultural Research Service, USDA, Washington, D.C., 1965
Rule Book		The American Horse Shows Association, Inc., New York, N.Y., annual
Shetland Pony, The	L. F. Bedell	Iowa State University Press, Ames, Iowa, 1959
Shetland Pony, The	M. C. Cox	Adam and Charles Black Ltd., London, England, 1965
Steeplechasing	J. Hislop	J. A. Allen & Co., Ltd., London, England, 1970
Summerhays' Encyclopaedia for Horsemen	R. S. Summerhays	Frederick Warne & Co., Inc., New York, N.Y., 1966
Trotting Horse of America, The	H. Woodruff	University Press; Welch, Bigelow, & Co., Cambridge, Mass., 1871
Using the American Quarter Horse	L. N. Sikes	The Saddlerock Corporation, Houston, Tex., 1958
Western Horse, The	J. A. Gorman	The Interstate Printers & Publishers, Inc., Danville, Ill., 1967

CHAPTER 9

TYPES AND CLASSES OF WORK
HORSES AND MULES

Contents   Page

Fig. 9-1. The magnificent eight-horse hitch of champion Clydesdale horses, exhibited by Anheuser-Busch, Inc. (Courtesy, Anheuser-Busch, Inc., St. Louis, Mo.)

85

As with light horses, similar distinct types—though smaller in number—evolved in the draft horse. From the ponderous beast of Flanders, used as foundation stock, the Great War Horse of the Middle Ages was developed; the Great War Horse, in turn, served as the forerunner of the draft horse of commerce and agriculture. Further and eventual refinement through breeding and selection adapted the draft animals to many and diverse uses, most of which have subsequently passed into oblivion with mechanization. For example, expressers—fast-stepping, delivery-type horses in great demand during the early part of the present century—are seldom seen in the United States at the present time.

During their heyday, certain distinct types of mules were also bred. The type of mule desired was largely controlled through the selection of certain types of mares for breeding purposes.

Today, draft horses and mules are of negligible importance, and types, classes, and market terms are primarily of historic interest.[1] They're reminiscent of an era of horse power in agriculture and commerce, of the village blacksmith, of few improved roads, and of little automation.

WORK HORSES

Work horses are classified according to use as (1) draft horses, (2) wagon horses, (3) farm chunks, and (4) southerners. Originally, classes for loggers and artillery horses were included, but except for a few loggers, these have been the victims of mechanization.

Although marked differences in size and weight exist between these various classes, all possess a deep, broad, compact, muscular form suited to the pulling of a heavy load at the walk. A detailed description of a draft type of animal is as follows: He should have plenty of size, draftiness, and substance. The head should be shapely and clean-cut, the eyes large and clear, and the ears active. The chest should be especially deep and of ample width. The topline should include a short, strong back and loin, with a long, nicely turned, and well-muscled croup, and a well-set tail. The middle should be wide and deep, and there should be good depth in both fore and rear flanks. Muscling should be heavy throughout, especially in the forearm and gaskin; the shoulder should be sloping; the legs should be straight, true, and squarely set; the bone should be strong and flat and show plenty of quality. The pasterns should be sloping and the feet should be large and have adequate width at the heels and toughness in conformation. With this splendid draft type, there should be style, balance, and symmetry; an abundance of quality; an

---

[1]After 1957, the USDA discontinued publishing horse and mule receipts and dispositions at public markets.

energetic yet manageable disposition; soundness; and freedom from disease. The action should be straight and true, with a long, swift, and elastic stride, both at the walk and the trot.

The market classification of work horses according to the use to which they are put and their range in height and weight is shown in Table 9-1.

TABLE 9-1
MARKET CLASSIFICATION OF WORK HORSES

Class	Range in Height	Range in Weight	
	(hands)	(lb)	(kg)
Draft horses	16 to 17-2	1,600 upward	726 upward
Wagon horses	15-2 to 16-2	1,300 to 1,600	590-726
Farm chunks	15 to 16	1,300 to 1,400	590-635
Southerners	14-2 to 15-2	600 to 1,100	272-499

Draft Horses

Draft horses stand from 16 to 17-2 hands in height and weigh from 1,600 pounds upward. They represent the ultimate in power type. Formerly, draft-type horses of quality and style were used on city streets, but these have long since been replaced by trucks. Industry's most glamorous use of draft horses today consists of the 6- and 8-horse hitches used for exhibition—a type of advertising.

Fig. 9-2. High-quality draft horses drawing a plow.

Wagon Horses

Wagon horses are intermediate in weight and height between the drafter and chunk but have more action than either. They weigh from 1,300 to 1,600 pounds and stand from 15-2 to 16-2 hands in height. They usually have less depth of body and longer legs than draft horses and thus are better able to jog along at the trot. Occasionally, animals of this type still find limited use for delivery purposes, mostly on milk and laundry wagons. In addition to possessing suitable conformation, wagon horses should have an attractive appearance to provide advertising value for the service in which they are used.

Farm Chunks

The term "chunk" is descriptive of the farm chunk type of animals. They are "small-sized" drafters standing 15 to 16 hands in height and weighing from 1,300 to 1,400 pounds.

Southerners

Southerners are a smaller, plainer type of animal formerly used in the South. Many of them were formerly obtained from the western range states. A few of them are still used by southern planters as a utility type of animal for tilling the land and for riding and driving. They usually stand from 14-2 to 15-2 hands and weigh from 600 to 1,100 pounds.

MULES

It has been correctly said that the mule is without pride of ancestry or hope of posterity. He is a hybrid, being a cross between two species of the family *Equidae*—the *caballus* or horse and the *asinus* or ass.[2] Like most hybrids, the mule is seldom fertile.

Fig. 9-3. A Classy span of draft mules (Courtesy, University of Missouri)

The use of the mule in the United States was first popularized by two early American statesmen, George Washington and Henry Clay. The first jack to enter this country, of which there is authentic record, was presented by the King of Spain to General Washington in 1787, shortly after the close of the Revolutionary War. Other importations followed; and from that day until mechanization, the hardy mule furnished the main source of animal power for the South. In comparison with the horse, the mule can (1)

---

[2]The cross between a jennet and a stallion is known as a hinny. The mule and the hinny are indistinguishable.

withstand higher temperatures; (2) endure less experienced labor; (3) better adapt his eating habits to either irregularity or self-feeding with little danger of founder or digestive disturbances; (4) work or stable in lower areas without head injury (the mule lowers his head when the ears touch an object, whereas a horse will throw his head upward under similar conditions); (5) encounter less foot trouble, wire cuts, etc.; and (6) generally maneuver about without harm to himself.

Fig. 9-4. A near-perfect model of a young jack. Note his heavy bone, well-set legs, and good head and ears.

Although the mule resembles his sire, the jack, more than the mare, the desired conformation is identical to that described for the horse; perhaps the one exception is that more stress is placed upon the size, set, and quality of the ear. The most desirable mules must be of good size and draftiness, compact and heavily muscled; must show evidence of plenty of quality; must stand on correct feet and legs; and must be sound. As the natural tendency of the mule is to be lazy and obstinate, an active, energetic disposition is sought.

The market classification of mules according to the use to which they are put, including range in height and weight, is shown in Table 9-2.

Naturally, there is considerable spread in value between the animals within each class—depending

TABLE 9-2
MARKET CLASSIFICATION OF MULES

Class	Range in Height	Range in Weight	
	(hands)	(lb)	(kg)
Draft	16 to 17-2	1,200 to 1,600	545-726
Sugar	16 to 17	1,150 to 1,300	522-590
Farm	15-2 to 16	900 to 1,250	409-568
Cotton	13-2 to 15-2	750 to 1,100	341-499
Pack and mining ..	12 to 16	600 to 1,350	272-613

upon weight, conformation, quality, temperament, condition, action, age, and soundness. Mare mules usually outsell horse mules. The most desirable age is between four and eight years, and well-matched spans of sorrel mules are most popular.

Draft Mules

Draft mules are the finest mules in type and quality, weighing from 1,200 to 1,600 pounds and standing 16 to 17-2 hands in height. Limited numbers are still exhibited in livestock shows.

Fig. 9-6. A farm mule. These mules are often more plain looking, thinner in flesh, and show less evidence of quality than draft mules.

Fig. 9-5. A draft mule—a mare mule named Jane, Grand Champion at the Missouri State Fair, in Sedalia. Exhibited by E. D. Frazier & Son, Drexel, Missouri. (Courtesy, E. D. Frazier)

Sugar Mules

Sugar mules derive their name from their most common usage prior to mechanization; they were the sugar plantation mules of the South. Sugar mules are intermediate in size and have a weight somewhere between that of draft and farm mules. Sugar mules weigh 1,150 to 1,300 pounds and are 16 to 17 hands tall. Mules of this class must show considerable quality and finish.

Farm Mules

Farm mules are those purchased for use on farms. These mules are often plainer looking, thinner in flesh, and show less evidence of quality than draft

mules. The most desirable farm mules stand 15-2 to 16 hands in height and weigh from 900 to 1,250 pounds.

Cotton Mules

As the name would indicate, mules of this type were once used primarily by cotton growers in the South to plant, cultivate, and harvest the cotton crop. They weigh from 750 to 1,100 pounds and stand from 13-2 to 15-2 hands high. Cotton mules are somewhat lighter and more angular than sugar mules. They also possess less quality.

Fig. 9-7. A cotton mule. This is a smooth, well-finished type of excellent quality and with an unusually good set of legs and pasterns.

Pack and Mine Mules

Pack mules are used for transport work—carrying heavy loads on their backs—in very rough or wooded

country not accessibly to vehicles. The Forest Service still uses some animals of this type. A limited number of mining mules are still used to haul cars of ore or coal to the hoisting shafts.

Both pack and mining mules are of similar size and type. They must be close to the ground, thick and blocky, and possess a strong back and loin. They range in weight from 600 to 1,350 pounds and in height from 12 to 16 hands. Horse mules are often preferred to mare mules for this class.

Fig. 9-8. A pack mule. This mule is a very deep-chested, thick-made animal, with powerful back and loin, and with excellent slope of pasterns. However, he is crooked on the hind legs, being sickle hocked.

Fig. 9-9. Pack mules in use in rough country not accessible to motor vehicles.

SELECTED REFERENCES

Title of Publication	Author(s)	Publisher
Breeding and Rearing of Jacks, Jennets and Mules, The	L. W. Knight	The Cumberland Press, Nashville, Tenn., 1902
History of American Jacks and Mules	F. C. Mills, ed. by H. L. Hall	Hutch-Line, Inc., Hutchinson, Kan., 1971
History of the Percheron Horse, A	A. H. Sanders W. Dinsmore	Breeder's Gazette Print, Chicago, Ill., 1917
Horse, The	D. J. Kays, rev. by J. M. Kays	A. S. Barnes & Co., Inc., Cranbury, N.J., 1969
People with Long Ears	R. Borwick	Cassell & Company Ltd., London, England, 1970
Percheron Horse, The	M. C. Weld	O. Judd Co., New York, N.Y., 1886

BREEDS OF LIGHT HORSES[1]

Contents — Page

A breed of horses *may be defined as a group of horses having a common origin and possessing certain well-fixed, distinctive, uniformly transmitted characteristics that are not common to other horses.*

There is scarcely a breed of horses that does not possess one or more distinctive breed characteristics in which it excels all others. Moreover, any one of several breeds is often well adapted to the same use.

[1]Sometimes people construe the write-up of a breed of livestock in a book or in a USDA bulletin as an official recognition of the breed. Nothing could be further from the truth, for no person or office has authority to approve a breed. The only legal basis for recognizing a breed is contained in the Tariff Act of 1930, which provides for the duty-free admission of purebred breeding stock provided they are registered in the country of origin. But the latter stipulation applies to imported animals only.

In this book, no *official* recognition of any breed is intended or implied. Rather, the author has tried earnestly, and without favoritism, to present the factual story of the breeds in narrative and picture. In particular, such information relative to the new and/or less widely distributed breeds is needed, and often difficult to come by.

To the amateur, this is most confusing, and he is prone to inquire as to the best breed. Certainly, if any strong preference exists, it should be an important factor, though it is recognized that certain breeds are better adapted to specific purposes.

It is noteworthy that most of the breeds of light horses are American creations. There are two primary reasons for this; namely, (1) the diverse needs and uses for which light horses have been produced, and (2) the fact that many men of wealth have bred light horses.

RELATIVE POPULARITY OF BREEDS OF LIGHT HORSES

Table 10-1 shows the 1975 and total registrations to date of the various breeds of light horses.

The recent annual figures reflect the current popularity and numbers of the respective breeds, although it is recognized that one year's data fails to show trends, and that new breeds have few numbers in the formative period.

TABLE 10-1
1975 AND TOTAL REGISTRATIONS OF LIGHT HORSES IN U.S. BREED ASSOCIATIONS

Breed	1975 Registration	Total Registrations (since breed registry started)
Quarter Horse[1]	98,329	1,142,610
Thoroughbred		
Purebred	27,937	667,839
Half-Bred[2]	106	41,894
Appaloosa	20,175	234,175
Standardbred[3]	16,666	406,612
Arabian		
Purebred[2]	13,500	110,000
Half-Arabian	11,295	152,679
Anglo-Arabian	245	3,718
Tennessee Walking Horse	6,633	159,343
Paint Horse	5,896	37,646
American Saddle Horse	4,042	157,635
Morgan[2]	3,700	56,000
Pinto	2,177	25,288
Palomino[4]	1,673	42,854
Pony of the Americas	1,477	19,477
Buckskin[5]	1,199	5,845
Missouri Fox Trotting Horse	1,041	10,832
Hackney	1,002	20,910
Shetland Pony[2]	645	130,592
Paso Fino[6]	631	3,887
Welsh Pony	483	25,425
Peruvian Paso[7]	312	1,587
Connemara Pony	204	1,893
Trakehner	183	228
National Appaloosa Pony	150	—
Rangerbred	94	1,612
American White[8]	72	710
Spanish Mustang	70	620
Galiceno	69	2,067
Morab	28	96
American Creme[8]	25	189
American Mustang	25	737
American Bashkir Curly	23	55
American Gotland	23	301
American Walking Pony	22	136
Andalusian[2]	19	187
Lipizzan	16	23
Spanish-Barb	9	50
Chickasaw	—	631

[1]American Quarter Horse Assn.: 1975 registrations, 97,679; total registrations, 1,136,019. Standard Quarter Horse Assn.: 1975 registrations, 650; total registrations, 6,591.

[2]1974 figures.

[3]United States Trotting Assn.: 1975 registrations, 14,592; total registrations, 406,612. National Trotting & Pacing Assn.: 1974 registrations, 2,074.

[4]Palomino Horse Breeders of America: 1975 registrations, 1,514; total registrations, 34,213. The Palomino Horse Assn., Inc.: 1974 registrations, 159; total registrations, 8,641.

[5]American Buckskin Registry Assn.: 1975 registrations, 299; total registrations, 3,095. International Buckskin Horse Assn., Inc.: 1975 registrations, 900; total registrations, 2,750.

[6]Paso Fino Owners and Breeders Assn.: 1975 registrations, 367; total registrations, 1,423. American Paso Fino Horse Assn., Inc.: 1975 registrations, 264; total registrations, 2,464.

[7]American Assn. of Owners & Breeders of Peruvian Paso Horses: 1975 registrations, 115; total registrations, 1,186. Peruvian Paso Horse Registry of North America: 1974 registrations, 197; total registrations, 401.

[8]The American Creme and the American White are registered as separate divisions by the American Albino Assn., Inc. The American Albino Assn. and its predecessor, American Albino Horse Club, have registered the following numbers in all divisions: In 1975, 97; total in period 1936-1975, 3,334.

AMERICAN BASHKIR CURLY

The long, curly coat of hair, for which the American Bashkir Curly is noted, makes them especially well adapted to extremely cold weather, such as exists in their native home—the eastern slopes of the Ural Mountains of the U.S.S.R.

Origin and Native Home

Horses with curly hair are known to have been raised for centuries by the people of Bashkiria on the eastern slopes of the Ural Mountains; hence, the name Bashkir. In this rugged climate, the Bashkiri people depended upon their curly horses for transportation, clothing, meat, and milk. In their native land, mares give 3 to 6 gallons of milk per day, which is highly prized. In addition to being consumed as fresh milk, cream, and butter, it makes a delicious cheese. Also, the milk is fermented to make a drink called "koumiss," which the natives drink both as an intoxicating liquor and for medicinal purposes. History also records that the nomadic Mongols rode curly horses.

The modern history of curly horses in America began in 1898, when Peter Damele of Ely, Nevada, cut three curly animals from a herd of wild horses in the Peter Hanson Mountain Range. Most of today's curly horses trace to Damele ranch breeding.

Thus, the Bashkir Curly originated in the U.S.S.R. How and when these curly animals came to the United States is clouded in obscurity. Although they were known to have existed on a Nevada ranch as early as 1898, the American Bashkir Curly Registry was not formed until August 14, 1971.

American Bashkir Curly Characteristics

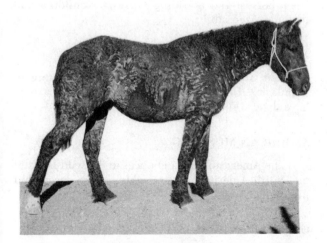

Fig. 10-1. American Bashkir Curly, at two years of age. Owned by Peter Damele & Son, Dry Creek Ranch, Austin, Nevada. (Courtesy, American Bashkir Curly Registry, Ely, Nev.)

The curly coat, with corkscrew mane and wavy tail, is the most unique characteristic of the breed. The mane hair, and often the tail hair, falls out completely each summer and grows back during the winter. In build, Curlies are medium size and chunky, somewhat resembling the early-day Morgan in conformation. The breed is noted for small nostrils, a gentle disposition, and heavy milking. Many of the animals have a natural fox-trot gait. All colors are accepted. Horses weighing in excess of 1,350 pounds or having faulty conformation are disqualified for registry.

Adaptation and Use

The American Bashkir Curly is used as a pleasure horse and for utility purposes—including light draft work. Because of their ruggedness, endurance, and gentle dispositions, they make ideal family trail horses and children's mounts.

Present Status of the Breed

The American Bashkir Curly has two primary things going for it: (1) the nostalgia imparted by its ancient origin in the Soviet Union, and (2) a curly coat of hair, not possessed by any other breed. But its registry association is new and numbers are limited.

AMERICAN CREME HORSE

This is a color breed, rather than a distinctive type.

Origin and Native Home

Pale cream horses have been around for a very long time, primarily in Oregon and Washington. However, they were not given breed status until 1970, at which time the American Albino Association, Inc., established a separate American Creme Horse Division for their registration.

American Creme Horse Characteristics

The following color classifications of American Creme Horses are registered:

A—Body ivory white, mane white (lighter than body), eyes blue, skin pink.

B—Body cream, mane darker than body, cinnamon buff to ridgeway, eyes dark.

C—Body and mane of the same color, pale cream, eyes blue, skin pink.

D—Body and mane of same color, sooty cream, eyes blue, skin pink.

Combinations of the above classifications are also acceptable.

Fig. 10-2. American Creme stallion, Polar Bar, owned by Edward Bales, Princeville, Oregon. He is light cream in color. Polar Bar is used in all types of ranch work, including cutting, roping, and Western-type riding. (Courtesy, American Albino Assn., Inc., Crabtree, Ore.)

The American Creme Horse may possess the characteristics of any breed.

Pink eyes or any color other than ivory white or cream are disqualifications.

Adaptation and Use

American Creme horses are used as pleasure horses, for exhibition purposes, as parade and flag bearer horses, and as stock horses.

Present Status of the Breed

Both the American Creme Horse and the American White Horse are registered and well promoted by the American Albino Association, Inc., Crabtree, Oregon, with separate divisions provided for each. It's an attractive breed, but numbers are limited.

AMERICAN GOTLAND HORSE

The Gotland, a small horse dating from prehistoric times in Sweden, is gradually gaining popularity in the United States.

Origin and Native Home

The breed originated on the Baltic Island of Gotland, a part of Sweden.

Early American Importations

Gotland Horses were first imported to the United States in 1957.

American Gotland Horse Characteristics

Fig. 10-3. American Gotland mare, Leeward Erika, American Gotland Horse Association high-point halter mare—as a yearling in 1973, and as a two-year-old in 1974. Bred and owned by Leeward Farm, Elkland, Missouri. (Courtesy, American Gotland Horse Assn., Elkland, Mo.)

Coat colors are bay, brown, black, dun, chestnut, roan, or palomino, and some leopard and blanket markings. They average about 51 inches high, with a range of 11 to 14 hands.

Pintos and animals with large white markings are disqualified for registration.

Adaptation and Use

American Gotland Horses are used for harness racing (trotting), as pleasure horses and jumpers, as stock horses, and as riding horses for children and medium-sized adults.

Present Status of the Breed

The American Gotland Horse is increasing in popularity. In competition with other breeds, they have done well.

AMERICAN MUSTANG

The American Mustang traces to the wild horse of the North American plains, which were descended from Spanish stock.

Origin and Native Home

American Mustang horses originated along the Barbary Coast of North Africa; from here they were

taken to Spain by the conquering Moors, propagated in Andalusia, and brought to America by the conquistadores. The American Mustang Association was formed in 1962.

American Mustang Characteristics

Fig. 10-4. American Mustang stallion, Cholla Jubilee. Owned by Deborah J. Maline, El Cajon, California. (Courtesy, American Mustang Assn., Yucaipa, Calif.)

They may be any color, but they must be between 13-2 and 15 hands high. Animals under 13-2 hands or over 15 hands are disqualified for registry.

Adaptation and Use

American Mustangs are used for show, pleasure riding, trail riding, endurance trials, stock horses, and jumping.

Present Status of the Breed

Although the American Mustang is of ancient origin, the breed registry is relatively new and numbers are limited. The breed enthusiasts are wisely promoting its historic origin, along with its hardiness and versatility.

AMERICAN SADDLE HORSE

The American Saddle Horse is distinctly an American creation. With at least passable roads in the East, the breeding of harness horses was centered in this area, particularly in the vicinity of New York and Philadelphia. Farther inland, however, roads were few and far between, and horses' backs afforded the chief means of transportation. The early residents of Kentucky, Tennessee, Virginia, and West Virginia selected animals with easy, lateral, ambling gaits,

finding these to be most desirable to ride over plantations and hilly and rolling grazing areas, especially on long journeys.

Origin and Native Home

The creation of the American Saddle Horse had its unplanned beginning with the settlement of the plantations of the states mentioned above. Later, Missouri took up the breeding of easy-gaited saddle horses. These southern pioneers, who never rode with short stirrups and who regarded posting as a heathenish invention of the English, very early selected and imported ambling types of horses from Canada and the New England states. Canada at that time had a sturdy little horse which paced, known as the Canadian pacer. Animals of the Thoroughbred breed and what later proved to be the forerunners of the Morgan and Standardbred breeds were also infused. The type of horse demanded was one that could travel long distances without distress to either the horse or the rider and which possessed beauty, speed, tractability, intelligence, courage, durability, longevity, and versatility (adapted to harness use if desired). Conditions calling for horses of this type prevailed throughout the states mentioned, beginning with the earliest settlement. It is not surprising, therefore, that the men, women, and children of this area became equestrians.

The amalgamation of diverse blood continued and with it constant selection for the desired qualities, particularly adaptability to easy riding gaits. Eventually, the plantation owners fixed a definite and beautiful type, even though it was not to be known as a breed until many years later, since no breed registry association was formed until 1891.

The modern American Saddle Horse now traces most of its origin to a Thoroughbred 4-mile race stallion, Denmark (foaled in 1839). Although this horse did not achieve great fame on the track, his races were said to be characterized by unusual stamina and gameness. Denmark left numerous progeny, but his most notable offspring was Gaine's Denmark, out of a natural ambler of native stock, known as the Stevenson mare. Many have credited this mare with being of greater foundation importance than Denmark himself. Certainly the Stevenson mare supplied the genetic basis for the gaits so easily attained by her descendants. To Denmark, however, credit must be given for the courage, breediness, shoulders, fineness of head and neck, clean dense bone, and quality of the sons and daughters of many subsequent generations. In considering the diverse breeding of the native stock from which the breed sprung, including the Stevenson mare—and without in any way minimizing the influence of the Thoroughbred—one might even conclude that the American Saddle Horse is indebted to

the Canadian Pacer for his easy riding gaits; to the Morgan for his docility, beauty, and animation; and to the Standardbred for a good trot.

In 1901, the American Saddle Horse Breeders Association approved a list of 10 stallions entitled to rank as the great foundation sires of the breed. There can be little question, however, that Denmark, largely through his illustrious son, Gaine's Denmark, was the greatest of all.

American Saddle Horse Characteristics

Fig. 10-5. American Saddle Horse filly, Merry Commander. (Courtesy, American Saddle Horse Breeders Assn., Louisville, Ky.)

The chief distinguishing characteristic of horses of this breed is their ability to furnish an easy ride with great style and animation. Park hacks may be either 3- or 5-gaited, the choice being largely a matter of preference and training. Walk-trot-canter horses are known as 3-gaited; whereas animals possessing the rack, and a show-gait in addition (running walk, fox trot, or slow pace), are known as 5-gaited.

Members of the breed are usually bay, brown, chestnut, gray, black, or golden in color. Most of them stand from 15 to 16 hands in height and weigh from 1,000 to 1,200 pounds.

The American Saddle Horse is noted for a beautiful head carried on a long, graceful neck; for a short, rounded back, a level croup, and a high-set tail; and for proud action. The entire ensemble is without a peer when it comes to style, spirit, and animation. At the same time, members of the breed are docile, intelligent, and tractable.

Adaptation and Use

The American Saddle Horse is now used almost exclusively as 3- or 5-gaited saddle horses, primarily as pleasure horses—either on the bridle paths or in the show-ring.

Fine harness show horses come from the American Saddle Horse, and it has been said that horses of this breed meet the demand for combination horses better than any other group. Animals of American Saddle Horse extraction are occasionally used as stock horses, jumpers, and for other light horse purposes; but their versatility does not approach that of the Thoroughbred. They are primarily a park hack, for which use they are preeminent.

Present Status of the Breed

Well-trained American Saddle Horses of good type have enjoyed a broad demand at good prices for many years. This demand has come mostly from city people who use the saddle horse for purposes of pleasure, recreation, and exercise. Although representatives of the breed are found in every state, Kentucky and Missouri continue as the great breeding centers.

AMERICAN WALKING PONY

The American Walking Pony is a pony (under 14-2 hands) with the running walk gait.

Origin and Native Home

The breed originated near Macon, Georgia, in 1968.

American Walking Pony Characteristics

Fig. 10-6. American Walking Pony stallion, BT Golden Splendor, winner of the first performance class for the American Walking Pony breed and undefeated in open halter classes; owned by Browntree Stables, Macon, Georgia. (Courtesy, American Walking Pony Assn., Macon, Ga.)

American Walking Ponies must perform the running walk gait.

There is no coat color stipulation. Since it is a cross between the Welsh Pony and the Tennessee Walking Horse, the colors of both parent breeds occur—bay, chestnut, gray, black, brown, white, palomino, and paint. They range in height from 13 to 14-2 hands.

Appaloosa color is not accepted for registry.

Adaptation and Use

They are used for pleasure riding, and as mounts for children or small adults.

Present Status of the Breed

The American Walking Pony is a relatively new breed with limited numbers.

AMERICAN WHITE HORSE

The American White Horse is a color breed with snow-white hair.

Origin and Native Home

The breed originated on White Horse Ranch, Naper, Nebraska. It traces to the white stallion, Old King, of unknown pedigree, foaled in 1906, which the White Horse Ranch purchased in Illinois.

In 1936, the White Horse Ranch owners—Caleb R. Thompson and his wife, Ruth E. White Thompson—organized the American Albino Horse Club, which later became the American Albino Association.

Both the American White Horse and the American Creme Horse are registered by the American Albino Association, Crabtree, Oregon, with separate divisions provided for each.

American White Horse Characteristics

American White Horses have snow-white hair, as white as clean snow, with pink skin. The eyes are light blue, dark blue (near black), brown, or hazel, but never pink. Both horses and ponies are accepted for registry; animals above 14-2 hands are classed as horses, those below 14-2 are classed as ponies.

Adaptation and Use

American White Horses are used as pleasure horses. Their snow-white color makes them very attractive as trained horses for exhibition purposes and as parade and flag bearer horses.

Fig. 10-7. American White stallion, M. M. Snow Colonel, owned by Rex Seitzinger, Sioux City, Iowa. (Courtesy, American Albino Assn., Crabtree, Ore.)

Present Status of the Breed

Numbers are limited, but the breed is attractive and well promoted.

ANDALUSIAN

Although the Andalusian traces its origin to the cave dwellers of the Mesolithic Age, in the mountains of the Iberian Penninsula, about 8,000 years ago, it is little known in America. This obscurity is attributed to the embargo, which was placed on the breed by the government of Spain and continued for over a century.

Origin and Native Home

Andalusian horses originated in Spain. The Spanish call the breed Español; the Portugese call it Lusitano. The American Andalusian Horse Association, with headquarters at Silver City, New Mexico, was founded in the 1960s. All purebred Andalusians must trace to the Registration Books of the Spanish Army.

Early American Importations

Since the lifting of the Spanish embargo in the 1960s, more than 200 purebred Andalusians have been imported into the United States.

Andalusian Characteristics

In type, the Andalusian resembles the Arabian, except that they are not dish-faced. Whites, grays, and

Fig. 10-8. Andalusian stallion, Caballero De Nevasco, shown as a seven-year-old. (Courtesy, Glenn O. Smith, American Andalusian Assn., Silver City, N.M.)

bays are the most common colors, but there are a few blacks, roans, and chestnuts.

Adaptation and Use

Andalusian horses are used for bullfighting, parade, dressage, jumping, and pleasure riding.

Present Status of the Breed

In 1975, the American Andalusian Horse Association estimated that there were approximately 400 purebred Andalusians in the United States.

Animals not tracing to the Spanish Registry, which is supervised by the Army in Spain, are not eligible for registry.

APPALOOSA

The Appaloosa played a major role in the Indian wars and in the development of the early-day livestock industry of northwestern United States.

Origin and Native Home

Appaloosa horses originated in the United States—in Oregon, Washington, and Idaho—from animals that first came from Fergana, Central Asia.

Ancient art attests to the fact that spotted horses are as old as recorded history. Without doubt, the ancestors of the Appaloosa were introduced into Mexico by the early Spanish explorers. Eventually (about 1730), through trading, wars, and capturing strays, the Nez Perce tribe of American Indians came into possession of some of these spotted horses. The Indians were pleased with these colorful mounts and greatly increased their numbers on their fertile ranges in northeastern Oregon, southeastern Washington, and

Fig. 10-9. Appaloosa stallion, Pete McCue, owned by Dr. W. R. Jacobs, M.D., Lewiston, Idaho; and ridden by Jesse Redheart, a full-blooded Nez Perce Indian. Note (1) that the horse is wearing a war bridle (Himpaiein), a type of "chin rein"; (2) that the Indian rider is wearing a bonnet of Golden Eagle feathers, of a type denoting the rank of warrior; and (3) that the rider is seated on a blanket, for the Nez Perces did not use saddles. Other standard equipment of the Nez Perce included a buffalo hide shield, a bow and arrows. This entry won first in the Appaloosa Mounted Costume Class (a horse show class originated by the author of this book) in the Washington State University Horse Show. (Courtesy, Washington State University)

the bordering area in Idaho. Eventually, these horses came to be known as the Appaloosa, which name is said to be derived from the word Palouse, which in turn came from the French word "peluse," meaning grassy sward. The rolling Palouse country was formerly covered by virgin prairie, but it is now a world-famous wheat and pea country.

For many years, most of the Appaloosa horses were owned by the Nez Perce tribe, but the War of 1877 resulted in their being scattered throughout the West. Finally, on December 30, 1938, the Appaloosa Horse Club was organized for the purpose of preserving and promoting the breed.

Appaloosa Characteristics

Appaloosas show many variations and combinations of unusual coat patterns. They may be black, bay, brown, chestnut, white with dark spots over the loin and hips, white with dark spots over the entire body, or mottled dark and white or with white spots over a dark body. The eye is encircled by a white sclera, the same as the human eye; and the hoofs are striped vertically black and white.

Fig. 10-10. Appaloosa stallion, Romanno. He stands 16 hands high and is one of the popular sires of the breed. Owned by James and Linda McKay, Purcell, Oklahoma. (Courtesy, Appaloosa Horse Club, Inc., Moscow, Ida.)

Any one of the following constitute a disqualification and make the animal ineligible for registry: Under 14 hands high after five years of age; parrot mouth; cryptorchid or monorchid, or sired by a cryptorchid or a monorchid; paint or pinto markings; gray or non-Appaloosa roan, or the progeny of a gray or non-Appaloosa roan; or draft or albino breeding.

Adaptation and Use

Though once used for war, racing, and buffalo hunting, Appaloosas are now used for stock horses, pleasure horses, parade mounts, and racehorses.

Present Status of the Breed

In recent years, the Appaloosa has made great strides—increasing in both quality and numbers.

Much credit for the present status of the Appaloosa breed is due to the dedicated efforts of George B. Hatley, longtime executive secretary of the Appaloosa Horse Club, Inc., who served the club without compensation for many years.

The Appaloosa Horse Club maintains two types of registrations: (1) *Tentative Registration*, with the registration number prefixed by a "T"; and (2) *Permanent Registration*, with no prefix. When a tentative horse passes to permanent, the "T" prefix is dropped and the same number is issued. Formerly, there was a third type of registration—an "F" prefix to indicate *Foundation Registration*. But the latter was dropped when Appaloosas obtained racing under pari-mutuel, at which time it was necessary that a horse carry the same number all of its life in order to comply with tattooing and racing rules.

ARABIAN

Many writers have credited the Arabs with having first domesticated the horse, but this is not the case. The preponderance of evidence favors the belief that the foundation stock of the Arabian horse was obtained many centuries following their domestication from either the Egyptians or the Libyan tribes of northern Africa.

In addition to purebred Arabians, there are *Half-Arabians* and *Anglo-Arabs*, both of which are registered by the International Arabian Horse Association, Burbank, California, with eligibility as shown in Table VIII-1 of the Appendix of this book.

Origin and Native Home

The Arabian, oldest breed of horses and the fountainhead of all the other light horse breeds, was developed in the desert country of Arabia, from which it derives its name. Regardless of the clouded obscurity that surrounds the early origin of the breed, it is generally recognized that, through long and careful mating, the Arabs produced a superior type of horse which would carry them swiftly and safely over long stretches of sandy soil and at the same time withstand deprivations in feed and water to a remarkable degree. As the Bedouins of the desert were a warring, pilfering tribe, the very safety of their lives often depended upon a swift escape. Such was the need, and out of this need was developed the Arabian horse. Legend has it that at night the Arabs would often steal semen from a highly prized stallion owned by an enemy tribe and inseminate their mares therefrom. This was the first artificial insemination of farm animals.

Fig. 10-11. Rhita McNair on Faleh in Arabian Mounted Costume Class. (Courtesy, Tom McNair, Gleannloch Farms, Spring, Tex.)

It is easy to understand how the environmental conditions surrounding the development of the Arabian breed could and did give rise to myth and exaggerated statements as to the speed, endurance, docility, and beauty of the breed. At one moment, the Arab was cruel to his mount; then again he would shower him with kindness. During the latter moments, he was inclined to remark, "Go and wash the feet of your mare and drink the water thereof."

Early American Importations

The Arabian stallion, Ranger, was imported into Connecticut in 1765. Ranger was the sire of the gray charger ridden by General Washington in the Revolutionary War. Throughout the 19th Century many other notable importations followed, all of which gave a good account of the breed and encouraged other purchases.

The Arabian Horse Registry of America was established in 1908.

Arabian Characteristics

Fig. 10-12. Arabian stallion, Khemosabi, U.S. National Champion Arabian Stallion of 1973; owned by Dr. and Mrs. B. P. Husband, Haifa Arabians, Whittier, California. (Courtesy, International Arabian Horse Assn., Burbank, Calif.)

The distinctive characteristics of the Arabian breed are: medium to small in size, a beautiful head, short coupling, docility, great endurance, and a gay way of going. The usual height is from 14 to 15-1 hands and the weight from 850 to 1,100 pounds. A typical Arabian has a beautiful head, broad at the forehead and tapering toward the nose; a dished face; short alert ears; large clear eyes that are set wide apart; large nostrils; and deep, wide jaws. The Arabian also possesses an anatomical difference in comparison with other breeds, having one less lumbar (back) vertebra and one or two fewer vertebrae in the tail. In conformation, the Arabian breed is further noted for proud carriage of the head on a long and graceful neck; well-sloped shoulders and pasterns; a short back and loin; well-sprung ribs, a high, well-set tail; deep quarters; and superior quality of underpinning without any tendency to appear leggy.

The predominating colors are bay, gray, and chestnut, with an occasional white or black. According to an old Arab proverb, "The fleetest of horses is the chestnut, the most enduring the bay, the most spirited the black, and most blessed the white." White marks on the head and legs are common, but purebred Arabians are never piebald, skewbald, or spotted—circus and movie information to the contrary. The skin is always black, no matter what the coat color.

The better horses in Arabia, consisting of a relatively small number of animals owned by the tribes in the interior desert, have always been bred and raised in close contact with the families of their masters and are renowned for affection, gentleness, and tractability.

Adaptation and Use

The Arabian was primarily developed as a saddle horse, a use which still predominates. They are also used as stock, show, race, and pleasure horses.

Generally animals of this breed are trained and used at the three gaits—the walk, trot, and canter. Occasionally, however, purebred Arabians are trained to execute five gaits to perfection. Animals of this breed are easily broken to make a safe, although not a fast, driver in light harness.

The Arabian has made an invaluable contribution in the development of most all breeds, adding to their courage, endurance, quality, intelligence, docility, and beauty. It is no exaggeration to say that the prepotent blood of the Arabian has refined and improved all those breeds with which it has been infused.

Present Status of the Breed

At the present time, no great number of high-class Arabians remain in the country of their origin. In addition, World Wars I and II devastated many of the better breeding establishments of Europe. Thus, the future preservation of the breed would appear to rest primarily with American breeders.

BUCKSKIN

There are two different breeds of Buckskin horses. Officially, one is known as the American Buckskin and is registered by the American Buckskin

Registry Association, Inc., and the other is known as the International Buckskin and is registered by the International Buckskin Horse Association. Although the breed standards and registry rules of the two associations differ somewhat, to most horsemen they are one and the same breed—they're all Buckskins.

Origin and Native Home

Buckskin horses originated in the United States, largely from horses of Spanish extraction.

Buckskin Characteristics

Fig. 10-13. Buckskin stallion, Leo Reno; a golden buckskin, with dorsal stripe and dark ear tips and ear outline. Owned by Holiday Farm, Dyer, Indiana. (Courtesy, International Buckskin Horse Assn., Inc., St. John, Ind.)

Coat colors are buckskin, dun, red dun, or grulla (mouse-dun). The International Buckskin Horse Association lists the following added color characteristics: dorsal stripe, leg barring, shoulder stripe or shadowing, black ear tips, cobwebbing on face, and/or frosted mane and tail.

The Buckskin is primarily a color breed, with no particular type favored. It is important, however, that each animal be a good specimen of the type represented.

Disqualifications for registration are:

1. *American Buckskin Registry Association*: Palominos, chestnuts, sorrels, or bays with dorsal stripe; draft type; blue or glass eyes; white spots on body (indicating Pinto or Appaloosa blood) or white markings above knees or hocks.

2. *International Buckskin Horse Association*: Excessive white; showing Paint, Pinto, or Appaloosa characteristics.

Adaptation and Use

Buckskins are used as stock horses, pleasure horses, and show horses.

Present Status of the Breed

Horses of buckskin color have always been popular in the West, especially as stock horses.

CHICKASAW

The Chickasaw horse is one of two breeds of horses developed by American Indians (American Indians also developed the Appaloosa).

Origin and Native Home

Chickasaw horses were developed by the Chickasaw Indians of Tennessee, North Carolina, and Oklahoma, from horses of Spanish extraction.

Chickasaw Characteristics

The breed is characterized by a short head and ears; a short back; a short neck; square, stocky hips; a low-set tail; a wide chest; and great width between the eyes. The preferred height is from 53 to 59 inches. Coat colors are bay, black, chestnut, gray, roan, sorrel, and palomino.

Adaptation and Use

Chickasaw horses are used primarily as cow ponies.

Present Status of the Breed

The Chickasaw horse is one of the less populous breeds.

CLEVELAND BAY

The Cleveland Bay takes its name from the Cleveland district of Yorkshire, England, where it originated, and from its color, which is invariably solid bay with black legs, mane, and tail.

Early American Importations

Cleveland Bays were imported into the United States as Early as 1820. The Cleveland Bay Society of America was organized in 1885. Around 1900, Cleveland Bays were used as general purpose horses—for driving and farm work. Subsequently, they were imported for two purposes: (1) to cross on Thoroughbreds to obtain heavyweight hunters; and (2) to cross

on heavy draft mares to produce an active type of farm horse. The need for farm horses has passed. Although heavyweight hunters are still in demand, sources other than Thoroughbred X Cleveland Bay crosses seem to suffice.

Cleveland Bay Characteristics

Fig. 10-14. Cleveland Bay stallion, Cleveland Farnley. (Courtesy, Cleveland Bay Assn. of America, Middleburg, Va.)

The coat color is always solid bay on the body and black on the legs. These horses are larger than most light horse breeds; they weigh from 1,150 to 1,400 pounds.

Animals are disqualified for registration if they are any color but bay, although a few white hairs on the forehead are permissible.

Adaptation and Use

Cleveland Bays are used for riding, driving, and utility work. They also are used in crossbreeding to produce heavyweight hunters.

Present Status of the Breed

Cleveland Bays are limited in numbers in the United States.

CONNEMARA PONY

The Connemara Pony is Ireland's gift to the equine world.

Origin and Native Home

Connemara Ponies originated on the west coast of

Ireland where, for generations, subsistence under the most difficult conditions produced a hardy breed. Although the exact origin of the Connemara is unknown, legend has it that Andalusian, Spanish Barb, and Arabian horses were crossed on hardy, native ponies to produce the ancestors of the Connemara.

Early American Importations

The first Connemara Ponies for breeding purposes were imported to the United States in 1951.

The American Connemara Society was formed in 1956.

Connemara Pony Characteristics

Fig. 10-15. Connemara Pony mare, Oak Hills Miss Independence, as a four-year-old. Owned by Joseph Bates, Brandywine, Pennsylvania. (Courtesy, Mavis Connemara Farm, Rochester, Ill.)

These ponies are heavy boned, hardy, and docile. They range rather widely in height; hence, the American Connemara Society registers in two sections: Section 1, "pony" 13 to 14-2 hands; section 2, "small horse," over 14-2 hands.

Coat colors usually are gray, black, bay, dun, brown, or cream, and occasionally roan or chestnut.

Animals are disqualified for registration if they are piebald, skewbald, or cream with blue eyes.

Adaptation and Use

Connemara Ponies are unexcelled as jumpers. Additionally, they are used for most other riding purposes. They are unexcelled as advanced children's mounts and for riding by small adults.

Present Status of the Breed

The Connemara is a new and less populous breed

in the United States. However, it is increasing in popularity and numbers.

GALICENO

The Galiceno lays claim to being the ancestor of the Mustang—the feral horse of western United States.

Origin and Native Home

Galiceno horses originated in Galicia, a province in northwestern Spain. Horses of this lineage were first brought to America by the conquistadores.

Early American Importations

Galiceno horses were officially introduced as a breed into the United States in 1958. Two Texans, in search of a new breed that could double (1) as a small pleasure horse, and (2) as a good stock horse, met their need by importing Galicenos from Mexico.

The Galiceno Horse Breeders Association was organized in 1959.

Galiceno Characteristics

Fig. 10-16. Galiceno mare, Hunky Dory, many times Grand Champion. Owned by Roy L. Pepper, Pepper Galiceno Horse Ranch, Granbury, Texas. (Courtesy, Roy L. Pepper)

The most common coat colors are bay, black, chestnut (sorrel), dun (buckskin), gray, brown, or palomino. Solid colors prevail. Animals of pinto or albino color are disqualified for registry.

At maturity, Galiceno horses must be between 12 and 13-2 hands high.

Cryptorchids and monorchids are not eligible for registration unless gelded.

Adaptation and Use

The Galiceno is adapted to and used for pleasure riding, barrel racing, cutting, jumping, and Spanish Fiesta.

Present Status of the Breed

The Galiceno is one of the less populous breeds.

HACKNEY

The Hackney is the most prominent of the five breeds of heavy harness or carriage horses. In fact, except for the Hackney, the other breeds of this type are now practically extinct in the United States and are of historic interest primarily.

Origin and Native Home

The very name Hackney, and its abbreviated derivative "Hack," is suggestive of the type and adaptation of this breed, denoting both a general-purpose horse and the vehicle which it draws.

The breed originated in Norfolk and adjoining counties on the eastern coast of England. Here, in the first half of the 18th Century, was developed a trotting type of horse that was fast and that would go a distance, known as the Norfolk Trotter. It was this native stock with Thoroughbred infusion from which the Hackney was later derived. In this period, roads and vehicles were few and primitive, so that these Norfolk Trotters were used chiefly under saddle. Well-authenticated records exist of travel at the rate of 17 miles per hour over ordinary roads.

The real beginning of the Hackney breed is traced to a stallion known as Blaze,[2] a Thoroughbred foaled in 1733 and a grandson of the immortal Darley Arabian, the latter being the most noted of the foundation sires of the Thoroughbred breed. Blaze and his noted son, Old Shales (foaled in 1755), produced a remarkably valuable riding and driving horse when crossed on the native stock of Norfolk.

The early formative period of the Hackney was before the advent of either the carriage or the railroad. Thus, these sturdy foundation animals were first used under saddle and were even employed for some light agricultural purposes. It was not uncommon in that era to see a farmer riding to market with his spouse behind him on a pillion.[3] Such use called for attractive animals with adequate size and substance and the ability to trot long distances at a fair speed.

---

[2]The same Blaze from whom imported Messenger, the foundation sire of the Standardbred, was descended. Thus, on the sire's side the Hackney and Standardbred were of similar origin, but the native mares which served as foundation stock for the respective breeds and the objectives sought were very different.

[3]A seat or cushion which was put behind the gentleman's saddle.

With the development and use of the British hackney coaches of the 18th Century, the Hackney became specialized for driving purposes. It soon became the leading heavy harness horse of the world, which position it still retains. With this specialized use and its increased popularity with the aristocracy of England, the Hackney's naturally high, trappy action was cultivated. As many of the vehicles were heavy, animals with size and a robust conformation were demanded. With it all, graceful, curved form, beauty, and style were emphasized. In brief, the quality and performance of the heavy harness horse became an indication of social prestige.

Early American Importations

One of the earliest, if not the first, Hackneys to be brought to America was a stallion named Pretender, a great grandson of Old Shales, imported to Virginia in 1801. Subsequent importations followed, but it was not until the era of the Gay Nineties that any great numbers were brought over. At this time, a boom in Hackneys developed in this country as prancing carriage horses became characteristic of the avenues traversed by the wealthy in the eastern cities.

The American Hackney Horse Society was organized in 1891.

Hackney Characteristics

Fig. 10-17. Hackney stallion, May Day Creation, champion stallion and sire of champions. (Courtesy, USDA)

In size, the Hackney varies more than any other breed, ranging from 12 to 16 hands. The small Hackney pony, under 14-2 hands in height, and the larger animals are registered in the same stud book.

When used in a pair for a lady's phaeton, smaller animals are preferred. Because of the weight of the vehicle, however, a larger animal is necessary when driven single. As would be expected with the wide range in height of the breed, Hackneys vary considerably in weight, from 800 to 1,200 pounds.

Typical Hackneys are relatively short-legged horses, rather robust in conformation; heavy in proportion to their height; smooth and gracefully curved in form, with symmetry and balance; and upheaded, clean-cut, alert, and stylish to a high degree. High natural action—which is accentuated by skilled training, bitting and shoeing—is perhaps their most distinguishing feature. In the show-ring, custom decrees that heavy harness horses and ponies be docked and have their manes pulled.

Chestnut, bay, and brown are the most common colors found in the Hackney breed, although roans and blacks are seen. Regular white marks are rather common and are even desired for purposes of accentuating high action.

Animals of piebald or skewbald color are not eligible for registry.

Adaptation and Use

The Hackney is the heavy harness horse par excellence for both the show-ring and park driving. Many hunters and jumpers are half-bred Hackneys, a cross which gives animals of the desired size.

Today, the Hackney is essentially a show animal, noted for superb quality, beautiful condition, and spirited high action. When drawing a proper vehicle devoid of shiny parts (which serve to blind the spectators), the well-trained Hackney is a wonderful spectacle to behold.

Present Status of the Breed

The nearer the street surfaces approach perfection for automobile traffic, the less satisfactory they are for use by horses. Thus, at the present time, the use of the Hackney is almost exclusively confined to the show-ring. On the tanbark, these high-stepping horses are still the show, and, to many, their appearance is reminiscent of the Gay Nineties.

HANOVERIAN

Approximately 70 percent of the horses of Germany are Hanoverians, and it is the most numerous light horse breed in Europe.

Origin and Native Home

The Hanoverian breed originated in the Hanover section of Germany, beginning in 1732. An English-

man went to Hanover and became its Prince. Later, he returned to England and became King George II. But, during his stay in Germany, he assembled outstanding individuals of certain breeds for the purpose of developing a superior horse for military use, with emphasis on size, intelligence, and temperament. Out of this effort evolved the Hanoverian breed of horses.

In Germany, the breeding, selection, and registration of Hanoverian horses are under government supervision. The State Stud, at Celle, was founded in 1735. Today, 160 stallions are maintained at Celle. Each spring, these stallions are sent out to 60 stallion stations, where they breed more than 12,000 registered Hanoverian mares. Without doubt, the breeding and selection program followed with Hanoverian horses in Germany is the finest equine production testing program in the world. It involves a rigid inspection of all stallions at 2½ years of age, with only 60 selected, and the 15 top ones of these sent to the State Stud, at Celle. Next, the stallions are put in intensive training and performance tested for one year in pulling, jumping, and dressage. During this time, temperament is also noted. If an animal does not measure up in any category, he is gelded.

The American Hanoverian Society was formed in 1973, with headquarters at Carmel, Indiana.

Early American Importations

The date of the first Hanoverian importation is clouded in obscurity. In the 1960s and early 1970s, sufficient animals were imported to prompt the formation of a breed registry.

Hanoverian Characteristics

Fig. 10-18. Hanoverian stallion, Denar, imported foundation sire. (Courtesy, The American Hanoverian Society, Carmel, Ind.)

Hanoverian horses are big and powerful. Many of them stand 16½ hands or better and weigh 1,200 pounds or more. They combine nobility, size, and strength in a unique way.

Adaptation and Use

In Europe, Hanoverian horses are used for riding, driving (carriage horses), hunting, jumping, dressage, and utility purposes. In the United States, the breed is used for all light horse purposes, especially for hunting, jumping, and dressage.

Present Status of the Breed

In the United States, the Hanoverian is in the position of being a new breed trying to get established where many breeds are already firmly entrenched.

HUNGARIAN HORSE

The Hungarian Horse is a very old breed in Hungary, where it is without a peer as a cavalry mount, and where it is involved in every conceivable equine use—including horse racing.

Origin and Native Home

Fig. 10-19. Mrs. Margit Sigray Bessenyey, Hungarian breeder, of Hamilton, Montana, in native Hungarian csikos (cowboy) costume, holding a Hungarian Horse. The csikos rides on a girthless saddle and carries a long whip. (Photo by Ernst Peterson, Hamilton, Mont.; courtesy, Mrs. Bessenyey)

Hungarian Horses originated in Hungary, the product of generations of selective breeding extending back to the conquering Magyars (Hungarians) at the end of the 9th Century, who brought with them swift and sturdy horses of Asiatic origin.

Early American Importations

Hungarian Horses were brought to the United States at the close of World War II (in 1945), as spoils of war. They were auctioned off at the U.S. Remount Station, Ft. Reno, Oklahoma.

The Hungarian Horse Association of the United States was formed in September 1966, with headquarters at Bitterroot Stock Farm, Hamilton, Montana.

Hungarian Horse Characteristics

Fig. 10-20. Hungarian mare, Hungarian Barna. (Courtesy, USDA)

These horses possess a unique combination of style and beauty, with ruggedness.

The coat may be any color, either broken or solid.

Animals are disqualified for registration if they are cryptorchids or have glass eyes.

Adaptation and Use

The primary uses of Hungarian Horses in the United States are: stock horses, cutting horses, pleasure horses, trail riding, hunters, and jumpers.

Present Status of the Breed

A few purebred Hungarian Horse breeders, each with limited numbers, control the destiny of the Hungarian Horse in the United States. The breed has given a good account of itself, as stock horses and pleasure horses, and in competitive events.

LIPIZZAN

Most horse lovers rightfully associate the Lipizzan breed with the Spanish Riding School, near Vienna, Austria, where representatives of the breed are superbly trained and exhibited.

Origin and Native Home

The Lipizzan traces to 1504, at which time Andalusian stallions were crossed on Spanish-Barb mares. It was recognized as a breed by Prince Maximillian in 1564. In 1580, 6 stallions and 27 mares were shipped to the village of Lipizza, in what is now Yugoslavia, from which the breed got its name.

The Spanish Riding School was established in 1735 by the Hapsburg King of Spain, Charles VI, who had lost his Spanish Kingdom to Phillip V. During the closing days of World War II, in 1945, horse-loving General Patton of the United States interceded to save the Lipizzan horses for posterity. They were moved to another location, where they remained for the next 10 years. Thence, they were returned to Vienna in 1955.

Early American Importations

Lipizzan horses were first imported from Austria by Evelyn L. Dreitzler, Raflyn Farms, in 1960.

The American Lipizzan Horse Registry was formed in 1974, with headquarters at Platteville, Wisconsin.

Fig. 10-21. Lipizzan mare, Mora; owned by Mrs. Evelyn L. Dreitzler, Snohomish, Washington. (Courtesy, Mrs. Dreitzler)

Lipizzan Characteristics

Lipizzan horses are noted for graceful movements, placid nature, high knee action, and a remarkable memory. As high school and dressage horses, they are without a peer.

Most mature animals of the breed are white. But Lipizzan foals are born dark (brown or gray), then turn white at 4 to 6 years of age. About one in 600 remains black or brown throughout life. When the latter happens, it is considered good luck.

Animals having glass eyes, extreme Roman nose, or deformed or crooked limbs are disqualified for registration.

Adaptation and Use

The suitability of the Lipizzan for dressage and high school horses is well known. However, the same qualities that make them stellar performers—placid nature, tractability, stamina, action, and a remarkable memory—also make them ideal pleasure horses (either English or Western), jumpers, stock horses, and horses for trail riding.

Present Status of the Breed

At the prsent time, there are Lipizzans in Austria, Yugoslavia, Hungary, Czechoslavakia, and the United States.

The promising start of the breed in the United States received a severe blow when Raflyn Farms, Snohomish, Washington, the fountainhead of the breed in this country, was destroyed by a flash flood (due to a broken dam) in December 1975. Only one Lipizzan, a stallion, survived. Without doubt, the breed will survive; nevertheless, progress will be slowed.

MISSOURI FOX TROTTING HORSE

The Missouri Fox Trotting Horse is noted for the fox-trot, a slow gait in which the head usually nods and in which the horse brings each hind foot to the ground an instant before the diagonal forefoot.

Origin and Native Home

This breed originated in the Ozarks of Missouri.

Missouri Fox Trotting Horse Characteristics

The Missouri Fox Trotting Horse is distinguished by the fox-trot gait. Sorrel is the most common color, but any color is accepted.

Animals are disqualified for registration if they cannot fox-trot.

Fig. 10-22. Missouri Fox Trotting mare, winner in the Show and Celebration. (Courtesy, Missouri Fox Trotting Horse Breed Assn., Ava, Mo.)

Adaptation and Use

The Missouri Fox Trotting Horse is used primarily as pleasure horses, stock horses, and for trail riding.

Present Status of the Breed

The breed is relatively new and numbers are limited. Moreover, it must compete with such old and well-established breeds as the American Saddle Horse and the Tennessee Walking Horse for a place in the horse world.

MORAB

The Morab resulted from fusing the Arabian and the Morgan, breeds whose characteristics genetically complemented each other, to give a unique and versatile new breed.

Origin and Native Home

The Morab Horse Registry of America was formed in Fresno County, California, on July 19, 1973, based on the foundation stock of Martha Doyle Fuller. On her ranch at Clovis, California, she bred Morgan mares to Arabian stallions, to produce stock horses. In 1955, she began selecting and perpetuating animals based on this cross. However, crosses of this kind occurred in the 1800s; and many people crossed Morgans and Arabians following World War I. William Randolph Hearst, Sr., bred Morabs for his California ranch operations in the 1930s and 1940s.

The Morab is predominantly Morgan and Arabian, although it may be part Thoroughbred.

Morab Characteristics

Fig. 10-23. Morab mare, Tezya. (Courtesy, Morab Horse Registry of America, Clovis, Calif.)

The breed possesses the muscular strength and ruggedness of the Morgan and the refinement and beauty of the Arabian. Morabs average about 15 hands in height.

Animals are disqualified if they have breed characteristics other than Morgan, Arabian, and Thoroughbred; if they have albino, appaloosa, paint, or pinto color; or if they are under 14 hands at maturity.

Adaptation and Use

Morabs are used for show, pleasure riding, endurance rides, and ranch work.

Present Status of the Breed

The breed is new, and there are few registered animals. However, the Morab Horse Registry of America estimates that there are approximately 50,000 horses in the United States of similar breeding—animals produced by, or descended from, Arabian X Morgan crosses.

MORGAN

The Morgan has been known as the first family of American horses. The early development of the breed took place in the New England states, thus giving the eastern section of the country primary credit for founding three light horse breeds.

Fig. 10-24. Memorial to Justin Morgan, foundation sire of the Morgan breed, located on the former U.S. Morgan Horse Farm (now operated by the University of Vermont), Middlebury, Vermont. The inscription reads as follows: "1921. Given by the Morgan Horse Club to the U.S. Department of Agriculture in memory of Justin Morgan who died in 1821." (Photo by M. E. Ensminger)

Origin and Native Home

The origin of the Morgan breed was a mere happenstance, and not the result of planned effort on the part of breeders to produce a particular breed of horse which would be adapted to local conditions. Whatever may be said of the greatness of Justin Morgan, he was the result of a chance mating—one of nature's secrets for which there is no breeding formula. In fact, it may be said that had a British general downed his liquor in his own parlor and had a Springfield, Massachusetts, farmer been able to pay his debts, the first family of American horses might never have existed. Legend has it that, one evening during the Revolutionary War, Colonel De Lancey, commander of a Tory mounted regiment, rode up to an inn at King's Bridge and after hitching his famous stallion, True Briton, to the rail, went into the inn for some liquid refreshments, as was his custom. While the Colonel was celebrating with liquor and song, the Yankees stole his horse, later selling the animal to a farmer near Hartford, Connecticut. The whimsical story goes on to say that True Briton later sired the fuzzy-haired colt that was to be christened after his second owner, Justin Morgan.

According to the best authorities, Mr. Morgan, who first lived for many years near Springfield, Massachusetts, moved his family to Randolph, Vermont, in 1788. A few years later, he returned to Springfield to collect a debt. But instead of getting the money, he bartered for a three-year-old gelding and a two-year-old colt of Thoroughbred and Arabian extraction. The stud colt, later named after the new owner as was often the custom of the day, became the noted horse, Justin Morgan, the progenitor of the first famous breed of horses developed in America.

Justin Morgan was a dark bay with black legs, mane, and tail. His high head was shapely; his dark eyes were prominent, lively, and pleasant; his wide-set ears were small, pointed, and erect; his round body was short backed, close ribbed, and deep; his thin legs were set wide and straight, and the pasterns and shoulders were sloping; his action was straight, bold, and vigorous; and his style was proud, nervous, and imposing. Justin Morgan was a beautifully symmetrical, stylish, vibrant animal—renowned for looks, manners, and substance. It was claimed of him that he could outrun for short distances any horse against which he was matched. He was a fast trotter, a great horse on parade under saddle, and he could outpull most horses weighing several hundred pounds more.

Justin Morgan lived his 32 years (1789-1821) in an era of horses rather than in an era of power machinery. The westward expansion had been limited; roads and trails were in the raw, as nature had left them, and were often impassible even with a horse and buggy. Virgin forest had to be cleared, and the tough sod of the prairie had to be broken. These conditions called for an extremely versatile type of horse—one that could pull a good load on the farm, could be driven as a roadster, could be raced under saddle, and could be ridden in a parade. Justin Morgan and his progeny filled this utility need in a most remarkable manner. In due time, in 1893 to be exact, many years following the death of the foundation sire and after a decade of exhaustive research, Colonel Joseph Battell published Volume I of the American Morgan Horse Register. Such was the beginning of preservation of the lineage of the breed—a registry assignment now handled under the same name by the American Morgan Horse Association.

Morgan Characteristics

Fig. 10-25. Morgan stallion, Bennefield's Ace, Grand Champion Stallion at the 1973 Grand National Morgan Horse Show. (Courtesy, American Morgan Horse Assn., Hamilton, N.Y.)

With shifts in use, it is but natural to find considerable variation in the size of present-day Morgans. Yet throughout the vicissitudes of time and shifts in emphasis that have occurred during the past hundred years, Morgan horses to an amazing degree have continued to have certain unique characteristics which distinguish them as a breed.

The height of representative animals ranges from 14-2 to 16 hands, with the larger animals now given preference by most horsemen. The average Morgan weighs from 800 to 1,200 pounds. Standard colors are bay, brown, black, and chestnut; and white markings are not uncommon.

In conformation, the breed has retained most of the characteristics attributed to the foundation sire. With greater emphasis on use under saddle, however, modern Morgans are inclined to be more upstanding, to have longer necks, and to possess more slope to their shoulders and pasterns. Regardless of type changes, the breed continues to be noted for easy keeping qualities, stamina, docility, beauty, courage, and longevity. The presence of only five lumbar vertebrae in many Morgans is attributed to the use of Arabian breeding.

Animals with walleye (lack of pigmentation of the iris), or with natural white markings above the knee or hock except on the face, are disqualified for registry.

Adaptation and Use

In the early formative period of the breed, the Morgan was thought of as a general purpose type of animal—for use in harness racing, as roadsters, on the farm, on the avenue, in the park, on the range, and on the trail. With the development of mechanization, many of these needs passed into oblivion. The more progressive breeders, fully cognizant of the change in needs, took stock of the breed's inherent possibilities and shifted their efforts in breeding and selection to the production of a superior riding horse. At the present time, therefore, it is not surprising to find that there is considerable variation in emphasis in different sections of the United States. In the West, the Morgan is primarily a stock horse; whereas in the East the emphasis is upon the Morgan as a saddle horse, particularly for general country use and for recreational purposes over the hundreds of miles of trails.

The comparatively small number of purebred Morgans today is no criterion of the true importance of the breed. Their influence has literally extended to the entire horse population of the continent. Morgan blood was used in laying the foundation for many breeds. The leading Standardbred families of today are a fusion of Hambletonian lines with the Morgan—Axworthy, Mako, and Peter the Great all carried Morgan blood in their veins. Likewise, the

American Saddle Horse is indebted to the Morgan, for the Peavine and Chief families both contained Morgan ancestry. Allen, the foundation sire of the Tennessee Walking Horse, was a great grandson of a Morgan, Vermont Black Hawk.

Present Status of the Breed

During the period of transition and shift in emphasis from a utility and harness type of horse to use under the saddle, the registration of Morgan horses declined, and the identity of many registered animals was lost. This greatly reduced the number of available breeding animals to use as a base for the rapid expansion of breeding interest that occurred beginning in the late 1930s.

In 1907, Colonel Battell—an admirer, breeder, and founder of the Register of Morgan Horses—presented to the U. S. Department of Agriculture what became known as the United States Morgan Horse Farm, near Middlebury, Vermont. Colonel Battell's primary objective in presenting the farm to the federal government was that of providing a place upon which the breed could be perpetuated and improved. Though it would appear ironical today, it was also rumored that the old gentleman was disturbed with the high taxes of the period and had decided that the only way to beat the government was to give his holdings to the United States. Regardless of the possible latter objective, it must be agreed that the U. S. Morgan Horse Farm was a powerful influence in perpetuating and improving the Morgan breed. Effective July 1, 1951, by authorization of the U. S. Congress, the United States Morgan Horse Farm was transferred without cost to the Vermont Agricultural College.

MOROCCO SPOTTED HORSE

Morocco Spotted Horses are a color breed—they're spotted.

Origin and Native Home

The breed originated in the United States, from spotted descendants of the horses of the Spanish conquerors.

Morocco Spotted Horse Characteristics

Morocco Spotted Horses must be spotted. Moreover, the secondary color, white, must comprise not less than 10 percent, not including white on the legs or face.

Animals that are under 14-2 hands, or that are of draft or pony breeding, or that show such characteristics, are not elegible for registration.

Fig. 10-26. Morocco Spotted Horse, a chestnut and white stallion. (Courtesy, USDA)

Adaptation and Use

Morocco Spotted Horses are used as parade horses, saddle horses, stock horses, pleasure horses, and harness horses.

Present Status of the Breed

Although the breed registry—the Morocco Spotted Horse Cooperative Association of America—was formed a number of years ago, the Morocco Spotted Horse is among the less populous breeds.

NATIONAL APPALOOSA PONY

The National Appaloosa Pony is similar to the Appaloosa, except they are smaller.

Origin and Native Home

The breed originated in the United States, near Rochester, Indiana.

National Appaloosa Pony Characteristics

The National Appaloosa Pony is a pony breed; hence, they must be under 14-2 hands in height. They are varicolored, but leopard, blanket-type, snowflake, or roan are most popular. The skin, nose, and area around the eyes are mottled. White scleras encircle the eyes.

Albino-, pinto-, or paint-colored animals are not eligible for registration.

Fig. 10-27. National Appaloosa Pony gelding, Frisco's Fancy Pants, owned by Eugene Hayden, Gaston, Indiana. (Courtesy, National Appaloosa Pony, Inc., Gaston, Ind.)

Adaptation and Use

National Appaloosa Ponies are used as working ponies, show ponies, and for trail riding, jumping, and racing.

Present Status of the Breed

Except for being smaller, the breed is very similar to Appaloosas. Yet, they have never achieved anywhere near the numbers or popularity of their larger counterparts.

PAINT HORSE

The words "paint" and "pinto" are synonymous—both refer to spotted or two-tone horses with body markings of white and another color. However, when used to refer to the two registry associations—The American Paint Horse Association and the Pinto Horse Association of America—the words take on different meaning. The American Paint Horse Association is devoted strictly to the stock type horse and bases its registry on the blood of registered Paints, Quarter Horses, and Thoroughbreds; whereas the Pinto Association registers horses of all types and breeds, including ponies, saddlebreds, parade, and fine harness horses. Thus, the Paint Horse represents a combination of breeding, conformation, and color, whereas the Pinto is primarily a color breed.

Origin and Native Home

Paint Horses originated in the United States. The American Paint Stock Association was formed in 1962.

In 1965, this association combined with the American Paint Quarter Horse Association to establish the American Paint Horse Association.

Paint Horse Characteristics

Paint Horses are distinguished by 2 color patterns—they may be either overo or tobiano. Tobiano are most numerous (there are about 4 tobianos to 1 overo).

Fig. 10-28 illustrates the two patterns.

Fig. 10-28. Coat patterns. Overo (left) and tobiano (right).

Coat colors are white plus any other color, but the coloring must be a recognizable paint. No discrimination is made against glass, blue, or light-colored eyes.

Animals are disqualified for registration unless they have natural white markings above the knees or hocks, except on the face; if they have Appaloosa coloring or breeding; if they are adult horses under 14 hands high; or if they are five-gaited horses.

Fig. 10-29. Paint Horse stallion, Versary Bars, a sorrel overo. He was the National Champion American Paint Horse halter horse in both 1973 and 1974. Owned by Barbara Thomas, Council Bluffs, Iowa. (Courtesy, American Paint Horse Assn., Ft. Worth, Tex.)

Adaptation and Use

Paint Horses are used as stock horses, pleasure horses, and for showing and racing.

Present Status of the Breed

The breed is gaining in popularity and numbers.

PALOMINO

The word palomino correctly implies a horse of a golden color with white, silver, or ivory mane and tail. Originally, Palominos were not considered either a breed or a type, but simply a color. Today, animals of palomino color and meeting certain other stipulations may be recorded in either of two registry associations.

Origin and Native Home

Palomino horses originated in the United States, from animals of Spanish extraction.

When, in the course of the Mexican War—which ended in 1848, over 100 years ago—the United States acquired what is now the state of California, many attractive golden-colored horses of good type were found in the new territory.

According to the best records available, these animals were first introduced from Spain to the New World beginning with Cortez, in 1519, and their introduction was continued by other Spanish explorers. Evidently these horses had long been bred for color in Spain, being used exclusively as the distinctive mounts of the royal family, the nobility, and high military officials. In Spain these golden-colored animals were known as "The Horse of the Queen," and their use by commoners was forbidden. It is also known that the Spaniards obtained the golden horse from Arabia and Morocco, but further than this its origin is clouded in obscurity.

In the early days of California, Palominos were extremely popular. Spanish gentlemen took pride in ownership of these beautiful mounts, which were also used as the racehorses in early California. However, with the importation of the Thoroughbred and other horses of light horse extraction from the Eastern Seaboard and Europe, the golden horse was threatened with extinction. Only in recent years has its popularity again come to the fore, finally resulting in the formation of two breed registry associations—the Palomino Horse Association, which was incorporated in 1936, and the Palomino Horse Breeders of America, which was organized in 1941.

Palomino Characteristics

The Palomino must be golden in color (the color

Fig. 10-30. Buzzie Bars, leading Palomino sire of the nation for six consecutive years and winner of 50 Grand Championships. (Courtesy, Palomino Horse Breeders of America, Mineral Wells, Tex.)

of a newly minted gold coin or three shades lighter or darker), with a light-colored mane and tail (white, silver, or ivory, with not more than 15 percent dark or chestnut hair in either). White markings on the face or below the knees or hocks are acceptable. The skin and eyes shall be dark or hazel. The usual height range is from 14-2 to 16 hands and the weight from 1,000 to 1,200 pounds. As might be expected, in an attempt to form a new breed with a color requirement as first and foremost, considerable variation in type exists.

Some authorities feel that the palomino color may be unfixable—that it cannot be made true breeding, no matter how long or how persistent the effort. (See discussion relative to Incomplete Dominance, in Chapter 12.) Further, there appears to be ample theory—substantiated by practical observation—to indicate that palomino colored foals may be produced by any one of the following four types of matings:

1. Palomino X palomino resulting in the production of foals in the ratio of 1 chestnut:2 palomino:1 albino.[4]

2. Palomino X chestnut producing foals in the ratio of 1 chestnut: 1 palomino.

3. Palomino X albino, producing foals in the ration of 1 palomino: 1 albino.

4. Chestnut X albino, producing only palomino foals.

As indicated, when palomino mares are bred to a palomino stallion, the foals are, on the average, of the following colors: ½ of them palominos, ¼ of them chestnut, and ¼ of them albinos. Also, it is notewor-

[4]The term albino as herein used is familiar to horsemen, but it does not refer to a true albino as exists in white mice, rats, and rabbits.

thy that chestnut X albino matings produce only palomino foals.

The Palomino Horse Breeders of America lists the following disqualifications: Patches of stained or blackened discoloration; dorsal stripe along the spine; zebra stripes or lighter or darker color running around the legs or across the shoulders or withers; or patches of white hair except as caused by an injury or saddle.

The Palomino Horse Association lists the following disqualifications: Blue, moon, or pink eyes; white or dark spots on the body (known as pinto markings); or an animal whose sire or dam was an Albino, Pinto, or Appaloosa.

Adaptation and Use

Palominos are used as stock, parade, pleasure, saddle, and fine harness horses.

Present Status of the Breed

It is to the credit of the breed associations and the breed enthusiasts that they have done a wonderful job in selling the public on the beauty of the Palomino. They have accepted palomino colors from among the light horse breeds and have wisely admonished the breeders themselves to improve the type.

The following types of registries are maintained by the Palomino Horse Breeders of America (PHBA):

● *Junior Registry (Before one year of age)*—A Junior Certificate of Registration may be issued on any Palomino stallion, mare or gelding *under one year of age*, without inspection, providing such Palomino stallion, mare or gelding qualifies for registration upon bloodlines, pedigree and color as specified under the registration rules of this Association.

● *Regular Registry (After one year of age)*—For the Regular Registry, the following rules apply:

1. No Palomino, except a gelding, is eligible for registration in the Regular Registry unless its sire or dam is registered in PHBA, or unless the animal itself, or its sire or dam is registered in one of the following recognized breed associations:

American Remount Association (ARA)
Arabian Horse Club (AHC)
American Quarter Horse Association (AQHA)
American Saddle Horse Breeders Association (ASHBA)
Jockey Club (JC)
Morgan Horse Club (MHC)
National Quarter Horse Breeders Association (NQHBA, absorbed by AQHA by consolidation)
Tennessee Walking Horse Breeders Association (TWHBA)
United States Trotting Association (USTA)

2. A gelding is acceptable for registration strictly on color and conformation, regardless of whether or not it has a registered sire or dam.

3. No Palomino is eligible for registration in this Association if its sire or its dam is a draft horse or pony, or if its sire or dam is a piebald (having a body coat made up of patches of different color) or an albino (lacking pigment in skin, hair and iris).

● *Palomino Breed Registry (After one year of age)*—For the Palomino Breed Registry, the following rules apply:

1. No Palomino is eligible for registration in the Palomino Breed Registry unless the animal qualifies either by pedigree or by its progeny.

2. To qualify by pedigree, both the sire and the dam must be registered, one of which must be registered in the records of Palomino Horse Breeders of America. The other parent, either the sire or the dam, not registered in PHBA shall then qualify as to bloodline, such bloodline to be registered American Quarter Horse, Arabian, Thoroughbred, or American Saddlebred.

3. To qualify by its progeny, a Palomino stallion must be registered in Palomino Horse Breeders of America and must also have five of his get registered in PHBA. For a mare to qualify, she must be registered in Palomino Horse Breeders of America and must also have three of her produce registered in PHBA.

● *PHBA Hardship Clause*—PHBA Hardship Clause has been set up for the registration of outstanding horses which do not meet the registration requirements of PHBA. The fee is $100 plus the registration fee and inspection fee of $5. The $100 hardship clause fee shall not be refundable, but the registration fee will be refunded should animal not be approved by the PHBA Board of Directors. Four pictures must be submitted, showing the front, back, and both sides of the animal.

PASO FINO

In the United States, there are two offshoots of Paso horses, the Paso Fino and the Peruvian Paso, with registration and promotion by four different breed registries.[5]

Origin and Native Home

Paso Fino horses originated in the Caribbean area, where they have existed for over 400 years. They have been registered in stud books in Peru, Puerto Rico, Cuba, and Colombia.

[5]In the U.S., four different breed associations have evolved for the registration and promotion of horses which come under the general heading of "Paso" horses. But each of the registries has slightly different standards. The American Paso Fino Horse Association, Inc., and the Paso Fino Owners and Breeders Association, Inc., call their breed "Paso Fino"; the American Association of Owners and Breeders of Peruvian Paso Horses and the Peruvian Paso Horse Registry of North America call their breed "Peruvian Paso."

Paso Fino Characteristics

Fig. 10-31. Paso Fino stallion, Monolito LaCE, 1973 Horse of the Year; owned, trained, and exhibited by George J. La Hood, Jr., Casa LaCE, Valdosta, Georgia. (Courtesy, Paso Fino Owners and Breeders Assn., Inc., Columbus, N.C.)

First and foremost, the Paso Fino is characterized by the paso gait, essentially a broken pace—a lateral (not a diagonal) gait. The sequence of the movement of the hooves is: right rear, right fore, left rear, and left fore; with the hind foot touching the ground a fraction of a second before the front foot. When performed on a hard surface, a definite 1, 2, 3, 4 beat can be heard. The paso gait is performed at three speeds: (1) paso fino, which is the classic show-ring gait, performed with the horse fully balanced and collected; (2) paso corto, which is a more relaxed form of the gait and is commonly referred to as the natural paso gait; and (3) paso largo, which is the speed form of the gait. Additionally, Paso Finos walk and canter; hence, they are three-gaited horses.

The coat may be any color, although solid colors are preferred. Bay, chestnut, or black with white markings are most common. Occasionally, palominos and pintos appear.

Adaptation and Use

Paso Finos are used as pleasure, cutting, and parade horses and for endurance riding and drill team work.

Present Status of the Breed

Numbers are limited, but the breed is gaining in popularity.

PERUVIAN PASO[6]

The Peruvian Paso is original only to Peru. In this respect, it should not be confused with the Paso Fino breeds, whose ancestors were scattered throughout the Caribbean area.

Origin and Native Home

The Peruvian Paso is descended from three breeds brought to Peru by the Spanish conquistadores—the Andalusian, the Barb, and the Friesian. No other blood, other than these three original breeds, was ever introduced into the Peruvian Paso breed.

Early Importations

The first importation to the United States of Peruvian horses of any consequence was made in the 1960s. Prior to that time, the breed was practically unheard of in North America.

Peruvian Paso Characteristics

Fig. 10-32. Peruvian Paso filly, Alhaja, 1974 North American Champion Filly. Owned by Hacienda De La Solana, Guerneville, California. (Courtesy, Peruvian Paso Horse Registry of North America, Guerneville, Calif.)

The trademark of the breed is the piso, or gait, a natural (inborn), smooth, four-beat, lateral gait—in essence, a broken pace. In executing his gait, the Peruvian Paso moves with a "termino"—a graceful, flowing movement in which the forelegs are rolled toward the outside as the horse strides forward, much like the arm motions of a swimmer. Termino is a spectacular

———————
[6]Ibid.

and beautiful natural action. Breed enthusiasts insist that the Peruvian Paso does only two acceptable gaits, the "paso llano" and the "sobreandando"; and they do not admit to a canter. At the annual National Show in Lima, Peru, the Peruvian Paso is asked to do only the "paso llano" and "sobreandando" gaits.

Mature Peruvian Pasos average about 14 to 15-1 hands high and weigh 900 to 1,200 pounds.

Peruvian horses come in all basic, solid colors, as well as grays, roans, and palominos, with some rather striking variations of these colors.

The Peruvian Paso Horse Registry of North America disqualifies for registry animals with light forequarters, coarseness, or extreme height.

The American Association of Owners and Breeders of Peruvian Paso Horses disqualifies paint, pinto, or albino coloration.

Adaptation and Use

The primary uses of Peruvian horses are: pleasure horses, parade horses, and endurance horses.

Present Status of the Breed

In 1975, the American Association of Owners and Breeders of Peruvian Paso Horses estimated that there were approximately 1,400 Peruvian horses in North America and no more than 5,000 in the world. The demand for these horses exceeds the supply.

PINTO HORSE[7]

The word pinto refers to a spotted horse, a description first applied to the spotted descendants of the horses of the Spanish conquerors.

Pinto Horses are also referred to as piebalds, (English term for black-and-white pinto), skewbalds (English term for all pintos other than black-and-white in color), and paints (a term of old American West translating "pinto"—a derivation of the Spanish word "pintado," meaning painted).

Origin and Native Home

The Pinto breed originated in the United States, from horses of Spanish ancestry. Spotted or Pinto horses first arrived in the New World with the Spanish conquistadores. From that day forward, animals of this color played a leading role in the de-

velopment of the West. Many of them were captured and used as the highly prized riding horses of the American Indians. Later, they were found among the feral horses of the West; and, most important, through the years many of them have been used as stock horses.

Pinto Characteristics

Fig. 10-33. Pinto mare, Miss Super Chick, Champion Halter Mare, a bay overo. Owned by Mr. and Mrs. George A. Jacobs, Flintridge, California. (Courtesy, Pinto Horse Assn. of America, San Diego, Calif.)

The most distinctive characteristic of the Pinto horse is its color. The ideal Pinto possesses a 50-50 color pattern distribution. However, the patterns and markings are extremely varied and are found in many colors ranging from the predominantly white to the predominantly dark-colored horse. Horses with less than 50-50 percentage of markings will be accepted. But a Pinto must have noticeable markings on the body, not including the face and legs. Glass eyes are a part of Pinto lineage and are not to be discounted.

There are two basic patterns or markings, called *tobiano* and *overo* (see Fig. 10-28 under "Paint Horse").

Most tobianos have color on the head, chest, flanks, and some in the tail. The legs are nearly always white, and the white markings extend over the back. The edges of the markings are usually fairly smooth and rounded.

The overo often has jagged or lacy-edged white markings, mostly on the midsection of the body and neck area. The white rarely crosses the backline; legs are usually a color rather than white. There is more variation of pattern with overos than with tobianos.

The following three types of Pinto horses are raised:

1. *Stock type*—This is a Western-type horse, with Quarter Horse breeding and conformation, suitable

[7]The words "pinto" and "paint" are synonymous—both refer to spotted or two-tone horses with body markings of white and another color. However, the Pinto Horse, which is registered by the Pinto Horse Association of America, embraces all types and breeds, whereas the Paint Horse, which is registered by The American Paint Horse Association, is limited to stock type and to registered animals of the Paint, Quarter Horse, and Thoroughbred breeds.

for use on the range or for competing in Western show events.

2. *Saddle type*—This is a saddle or parade type, with American Saddler breeding and conformation, suitable for parades, gaited events, fine harness competition, or for park riding.

3. *Pleasure type*—Most pleasure-type Pintos carry Arabian or Morgan breeding. This is the versatile Pinto, suitable for all events, either English or Western.

Animals with Appaloosa ancestry or color, or of known draft horse breeding, are ineligible for registry. Animals with pony breeding of any kind are eligible for registry only in the Pony Division of the Pinto Horse Association of America.

Adaptation and Use

Colonel F. W. Koester has well summarized the adaptation and use of the Pinto horse in the following statement:[8] "There is the Pinto pony—long the pride and joy of millions of American youth. We find Pintos, too, among the cow ponies and polo ponies, jumpers, hunters, and other sporting types. Again, among the pleasure types such as trail horses, hacks, and particularly parade horses, the pinto enjoys wide and deserved popularity." In brief, the Pinto is adapted for use for any light horse purpose, but it is especially superb as a show, parade, novice, stock horse, and pleasure animal.

Present Status of the Breed

The breed enthusiasts have never attempted to dominate other breeds nor to make wild claims for their representatives. Rather, they are wisely attempting to preserve, improve, and extend the use of horses of a color whose development has gone hand in hand with the transformation of America itself.

The Pinto Horse Association of America, Inc., maintains the following types of registries:

1. *Tentative Registration*—This is for foals. They become eligible for permanent registry at two years of age if they meet the standards.

2. *Permanent Registration Division*—Horses recorded herein must be two years of age, 14 hands or over, and of acceptable conformation, quality, refinement, and color.

3. *Premium Registration*—This division is for the purpose of encouraging and recording the breeding of fine Pintos. The registration certificate is so marked.

4. *Approved Breed Division*—The Approved

Breed Division is for the purpose of establishing purebred Pinto bloodlines for future generations of Pintos.

5. *Solid Color Breeding Stock Division*—The Solid Color Stock Division provides for solid color horses with Pinto Horse Association registered ancestry.

6. *Pony Registry*—The Pony Registry provides registration for Pintos under 14 hands (56 inches).

PONY OF THE AMERICAS (POA)

The Pony of the Americas is an all-around pleasure pony that is small enough for a child but large enough for a teen-ager.

Origin and Native Home

The Pony of the Americas is, as the name indicates, a pony breed that originated in America. The registry, known as the Pony of the Americas Club, Inc. (POAC), was formed in 1954, with headquarters in Mason City, Iowa, with Mr. Leslie L. Boomhower, an able lawyer and horseman, as the first executive secretary.

Fig. 10-34. Pony of the Americas gelding, Heather Hancock. (Courtesy, Pony of the Americas Club, Inc., Mason City, Iowa)

---

[8]Koester, Colonel F. W., "The Pinto's Place Now and in the Future," *Official Stud Book and Registry*, The Pinto Horse Society, Vol. 4, December 31, 1945, pp. 13 and 14.

Pony of the Americas Characteristics

The Pony of the Americas is a happy medium of Arabian and Quarter Horse in miniature, ranging in height from 46″ to 54″, with appaloosa coloring. It's a Western-type using pony.

Ponies possessing any of the following characteristics are disqualified for registry: not having the appaloosa color; exceeding 54″, or under 46″ at maturity (6 years); pinto, albino, or roan color, or whose sires and/or dams were pinto or albino colored; white stockings above either knee and/or either hock, or a bald face that covers any part of the sides of the head; or cryptorchids or monorchids.

Adaptation and Use

The primary use of the Pony of the Americas is for juniors who have outgrown Shetlands but who are not ready for horses.

Present Status of the Breed

The breed has made remarkable progress. In the formative years, it was not easy to obtain a pony of the size and color that would meet the type standard.

The two types of registrations are as follows:

1. *Tentative (T)*—Any foal with appaloosa coloring and one registered Pony of the Americas parent is eligible for tentative (T) registration. However, if a pony matures under 46″ or over 54″, its POA pedigree will be voided and the registration fee forfeited.

2. *Permanent Registry*—Pony of the Americas are eligible to be considered for transfer to the Permanent Registry on or after January 1, following their fifth birthday. Any appaloosa-colored pony passing the inspection and within the following height range is eligible for Permanent Registration:

Age	Height
(yrs.)	(in.)
2	46-48
3	46-50
4	46-52
5	46-53
6	46-54

QUARTER HORSE

The earliest form of horse racing in America—particularly in Maryland, Virginia, and the Carolinas—was through necessity usually over a quarter-mile track. The topography and the wilderness were such as to make difficult the construction of formal racetracks. Rather, small race paths were literally hewn out of the wilderness. Many of these courses were down the main street of town, as this was the only straight and cleared stretch available. To race over these tracks, the pioneers selected sturdy stock possessed of a great burst of speed at short distances.

Origin and Native Home

Quarter Horses originated in the United States.

Although the breed registry association did not come into existence until 1940, the Quarter Horse had its beginning some 300 years earlier with the crude quarter-mile race paths of pioneer days. Those heavily muscled, sturdy animals, best adapted to rugged courses in matched races, were to serve as the foundation stock of a now popular western breed. With the advent of the Thoroughbred and the construction of formal racetracks of greater length in the East, Quarter Horse racing stock was pushed to the West and Southwest. In the range states these rugged animals continued to flourish for quarter racing, and they endeared themselves as the ideal cow pony.

There are two schools of thought relative to the ancestry of the Quarter Horse: (1) that the foundation stock consisted of the native mares of Spanish extraction in Virginia, Maryland, and the Carolinas which were mated to Thoroughbred stallions; and (2) that little or no Thoroughbred blood was infused, for—so it is argued—the foundation of the Quarter Horse was laid a hundred years before the first Thoroughbred horse was imported to America in 1730.

It is known that the early improvement of the Quarter Horse and that of the Thoroughbred were closely associated. Perhaps the truth of the matter is that certain animals contributed notably to each breed.

Most authorities recognize as the Quarter Horse patriarch, the imported Thoroughbred stallion Janus (1756-1780), a tested 4-mile racer in England. It is reported that Janus' progeny were unexcelled for a great burst of speed over short distances, and, like their sire, they were sturdy in build and possessed powerful muscling in the hindquarters.

Since there was no Quarter Horse registry prior to 1940, it is incredible that the purity of the breed could have been maintained through more than 300 years of an unplanned beginning. Suffice it to say that the distinctive breed that evolved at the end of this period is ample evidence of the potency of the foundation stock and of the superior quality of the blood infused through the years—regardless of its source.

Steel Dust, the most famous of all Quarter Horses, made his debut in Texas around the middle of the 19th Century. Until his fame became known, it was said that he nearly bankrupted a certain Texas community in which he first appeared in a matched race with a notorious racer of the day. In commenting on the influence of Steel Dust in molding the breed,

Robert Denhart[9] states that, "Every horse trader who has not recently joined a church will modestly admit that his horses are direct descendants of Steel Dust." There are some 11 prominent families listed in the Stud Book and Registry, most of which either originated in or were introduced in Texas.

Quarter Horse Characteristics

Fig. 10-35. Quarter Horse stallion, Jose Uno, World Champion Cutting Horse, owned by Lloyd Brinkman, Brink's Quarter Horses, Kerrville, Texas. (Courtesy, Lloyd Brinkman).

Quarter Horses are powerfully built, but modern animals no longer have the once-sought "bulldog build." Although a well-muscled horse is desired, the moderate type is more useful than the muscle-bound type. Also, certain families are being selected for racing—for great speed at short distances. The latter approach the build of the Thoroughbred, but they possess more substance.

The head is somewhat short and is distinct because of the small alert ear. The neck is well developed, the back and loin short and heavily muscled, the forearms and rear quarters are well muscled, and the legs relatively short. The entire ensemble is such as to make him an ideal stock horse—an animal that is agile and speedy, capable of outrunning any "critter." He possesses sufficient weight and power to hold a heavy steer when roped and has a calm disposition even in the roundup.

The most predominating colors of the breed are chestnut, sorrel, bay and dun. Palominos, blacks,

browns, roans, and copper-colored animals, however, are not uncommon.

Animals are disqualified for registration if they have pinto, appaloosa, or albino coloring. Also, no animal having white markings or underlying light skin beyond the following locations is eligible for registration: (1) white above a knee or hock, (2) white back of a line from the ear to the corner of the mouth, or (3) white on the lower lip above a line connecting the two corners of the mouth.

Adaptation and Use

Quarter Horses are adapted and used chiefly for 2 purposes: (1) for quarter-mile racing, and (2) for cow ponies. Thus, it follows that there are 2 schools of thought as to the best method of testing the performance of Quarter Horses: (1) to race them up to distances of a quarter-mile; and (2) to work cattle with them. Advocates of the first method are interested primarily in speed and racing, whereas advocates of the second method are interested chiefly in a superior cow pony. Perhaps some combination of the 2 criteria is desirable in most Quarter Horses.

Present Status of the Breed

Despite the decline in the horse and mule population during the past three decades, the stock horse will always remain on the western range. Even the versatile Jeep does not threaten to take over the job of roping a steer. Also, Quarter Horse racing is increasing in importance. Thus, the future of the Quarter Horse breed seems assured.

Since 1962, the American Quarter Horse Association has maintained (1) *a Numbered (permanent and closed) registry*, for which inspection is no longer required—following 22 years of such inspection, and (2) *an Appendix registry* for horses under 2 years of age with one parent in the *Numbered registry* and the other parent a Thoroughbred registered in The Jockey Club (one cross and one breed only). The latter may advance to *Numbered registry* only after reaching 2 years of age, qualifying in performance (known as Register of Merit, of which there are 2—one for working events, and the other for racing), and passing a conformation inspection. Additionally, there is a *Hardship Clause* through which an owner of an outstanding horse can pursue *Numbered registration* for his horse if it has permanent disabilities which would prevent him from obtaining a Register of Merit.

RANGERBRED

Had two men of different races and countries—Sultan Abdul Hamid II of Turkey and General Ulysses S. Grant of the United States—not met and sealed

---

[9]*The Quarter Horse—A History*, The American Quarter Horse Association, Stud Book and Registry, Vol. I, 1941, p. 18.

their friendship with the gift of two stallions, the Rangerbred breed of horses might never have been born.

Origin and Native Home

The Rangerbred (or Colorado Rangers) originated in the United States, in Colorado, in 1937. However, the two prized foundation stallions of the breed—Leopard, an Arabian, and Linden Tree, a pure Barb—were imported from Turkey by Ulysses S. Grant, retired general and ex-president of the United States, in 1878.

The breed registry, known as the Colorado Ranger Horse Association, was formed in 1937. The name Colorado Rangers was selected for the breed, to signify that they were Colorado-bred, and that they were bred under range conditions. The breed traces to the two Turkish-bred stallions, primarily through their influence on Mustang mares in the Colby Ranch, near Beatrice, Nebraska, and Mike Ruby's Lazy J Bar Ranch, of Thurman, Colorado.

Rangerbred Characteristics

Fig. 10-36. Rangerbred mare, Miss Sugar Charge, National Champion Halter Mare of 1975. (Courtesy, Colorado Ranger Horse Assn., Inc., Woodbine, Md.)

Color is neither an objective of the breed nor a prerequisite for eligibility to registry. Nevertheless, it is noteworthy that many Rangerbreds are spotted. The breed registry eloquently states its position on color as follows:

> "Color is a fickle jade. It is merely pigment in the skin. It cannot be ridden. Fads fade. Bloodlines endure."

In type, Rangerbreds are similar to Appaloosas.

Animals of draft or pony breeding are not eligible for registration.

Adaptation and Use

Rangerbreds are used primarily as stock horses.

Present Status of the Breed

During World War II, the Colorado Ranger Horse Association was inactive, and few horses were registered. In 1967, the Association was reactivated, and both memberships and horse registrations increased. Simultaneously, the breed moved from the range to the show-ring. Numbers are still small, but in history, the Rangerbred stands tall among the breeds.

SHETLAND PONY

The Shetland Pony is the smallest of all horses. In addition to its diminutive size, it is noted for its hardiness and good disposition.

Origin and Native Home

The Shetland Pony is native to the Shetland Isles, which lie 100 miles north of Scotland, parallel with central Norway, and not more than 400 miles from the Arctic Circle. Historic records give evidence that the breed was located in this rugged area as early as the 6th Century A.D. This qualifies the breed as one of the oldest in existence. Centuries of survival in the rigors of the northland climate and on sparse vegetation have endowed the breed with that hardiness for which it is justly famed.

Early American Importations

The first importations of Shetlands to the United States took place about the middle of the 19th Cen-

Fig. 10-37. Shetland Pony mare. (Courtesy, American Shetland Pony Club, Fowler, Ind.)

tury. Large numbers of subsequent importations followed.

The American Shetland Pony Club was organized in 1888.

Shetland Pony Characteristics

There are two distinct types of Shetlands, one of which is a pocket-sized draft horse and the other a small edition of a road-type horse. The latter, which evolved in this country through selective breeding, is often referred to as the American type.

The true Shetland is less than 11-2 hands in height (ponies over 46″ in height are not eligible for registry), and most individuals are less than 10-2 hands. Colors run almost the whole gamut of horse colors, with both broken and solid colors existing. Spotted ponies are more likely to have "glass" eyes, which are not desired.

By heritage, the Shetland Pony is gentle and faithful, as it was developed about the house and with children and dogs in its native Shetland Islands.

Adaptation and Use

Modern Shetland Ponies are used in many ways; as show ponies, for racing, and as children's mounts.

A harness-show type for use in the American show-ring has been developed by crossing Welsh or Hackneys on Shetlands. These crossbreds, which may be registered as such, are active, stylish, and showy—beautiful to behold on the tanbark.

Present Status of the Breed

Wherever there are children, Shetland Ponies will continue to be in demand. It is likely that more and more Shetlands will come to provide healthful outdoor recreation for the boys and girls of America.

In addition to registering purebred Shetlands, the American Shetland Pony Club also records *Harness Show Ponies*. The latter may be the result of crossing a registered Hackney or a registered Welsh on a registered Shetland, providing said animal carries no less than 50 percent Shetland blood. Also, recognized as acceptable parents of Harness Show Ponies are registered Harness Show Ponies and registered Americana Ponies, provided matings of these animals produce offspring that carry no less than 50 percent Shetland blood.

SPANISH-BARB

The unique thing about the Spanish-Barb is the genetic phenomenon of 5 lumbar vertebrae and 17 thoracic vertebrae found in the breed.

Origin and Native Home

The Barb horse was taken from Africa to Spain with the conquest of Spain by the Moors in 711 A.D. From Spain, they were taken to Cuba in 1511, to Mexico in 1519, to southwestern United States in 1540, and to Florida in 1565. The Spanish-Barb Breeders Association was organized in 1972.

Spanish-Barb Characteristics

Fig. 10-38. Spanish-Barb mare, Coche, an excellent representative of the breed. (Courtesy, Spanish-Barb Breeders Assn., Colorado Springs, Colo.)

Spanish-Barbs are small horses (the standard height is 13-3 to 14-1 hands), with short coupling, deep bodies, good action, and without extreme muscling. All colors are represented in the breed, but dun, grulla. sorrel, and roan are most common. Most animals are solid colored. A dorsal stripe and zebra markings occur in all duns and grullas and in some sorrels.

Adaptation and Use

Spanish-Barbs are used for cow ponies, Western riding, English riding, and packhorses.

Present Status of the Breed

The Spanish-Barb horse is in the hands of people who believe in both (1) the historical importance of the breed, and (2) the exceptional capabilities of the breed. Because of the past efforts of a handful of dedicated people, the Spanish-Barb has survived into the 20th Century. These ardent supporters will continue to perpetuate the breed.

SPANISH MUSTANG

The Spanish Mustang descends from the feral

horse that once roamed the plains of North America.

Origin and Native Home

The Spanish Mustang originated in the United States. They trace to the feral and the semiferal (Indian-owned) horses of Barb and Andalusian ancestry that were brought to America by the Spanish conquistadores in the early 1500s and 1600s. Beginning about 1925, Robert E. Brislawn, Sr., and his brother, Ferdinand L. Brislawn, began gathering pure Spanish Mustangs. To retain the purity of the strain, The Spanish Mustang Registry, Inc., was founded in 1957, at Sundance, Wyoming.

Spanish Mustang Characteristics

Fig. 10-39. Spanish Mustang mare, Supai SMR, caught wild in Arizona. (Courtesy, The Spanish Mustang Registry, Inc., Marshall, Tex.)

Spanish Mustangs run the whole gamut of equine colors, including all the solid colors and all the broken colors. They stand 13 to 14½ hands; and some have 5 to 5½ lumbar vertebrae.

Adaptation and Use

Spanish Mustangs are used for cow ponies, Western riding, English riding, packhorses, and trail horses.

Present Status of the Breed

Spanish Mustang breeders are dedicated to perpetuating the breed. They appear to be making progress.

STANDARDBRED

Both the Standardbred and the American Saddle Horse are the result of a Thoroughbred top cross on native mares; both are truly American creations—the former developing as a road horse in the East and the latter as a saddle horse of the southern plantations. In each case, the descendants of one Thoroughbred individual dominated the breed. Messenger, imported in 1788, largely shaped the Standardbred through his great grandson, Hambletonian 10; whereas Denmark, foaled in 1839, largely determined the destiny of the American Saddle Horse through his illustrious son, Gaine's Denmark. Despite these similarities in background, two very different breeds evolved because of (1) the differences in the native mares used, and (2) selection as influenced by the respective ends in view. In the case of the Standardbred, the native foundation mares were trotters or pacers adapted to fast driving in harness; whereas the native mares used in molding the American Saddle Horse were amblers, easy to ride.

Origin and Native Home

Fig. 10-40. The immortal Hambletonian 10 (also known as Rysdyk's Hambletonian), the descendant of Messenger who solidified the Standardbred breed. William Rysdyk, a poor farmhand, purchased him as a suckling colt, along with his dam, for $125. Hambletonian 10 never raced. He began his stud career at 2 and lived to the age of 27, during which time he earned approximately $500,000 for his owner. Today, it is estimated that 99 percent of the trotters and pacers in America trace to this great sire. (Courtesy, The United States Trotting Assn., Columbus, Ohio)

The Standardbred horse originated in the United States. Originally developed for road driving and racing, it descended from five sources: (1) the Thoroughbred, (2) the Norfolk Trotter or Hackney, (3) the Arabian and Barb, (4) the Morgan, and (5) certain pacers of mixed breeding. In the beginning, this breed was often referred to as the American Trotter, but this designation is now discarded because the breed embraces both trotters and pacers, all of which

are registered in the same association. The name "Standardbred" is derived from the fact that, beginning in 1879, eligibility for registration was based on the ability of the animal to trot the mile at 2:30 or pace the same distance at 2:25. Today, a record of performance is no longer a prerequisite to registration—it is merely necessary that animals be the offspring of recorded sires and dams.[10]

The great pillar of the Standardbred was Rysdyk's Hambletonian, or Hambletonian 10 (the latter designating his Standard number in Vol. IV of the Register). This great stallion, foaled in 1849, carried the blood of Messenger, a gray Thoroughbred stallion imported from England to Philadelphia in 1788 at the age of 8, and Bellfounder, a Norfolk Trotter or Hackney, foaled in England in 1815 and imported to Boston in 1822. No breed can boast of a greater sire than Hambletonian 10. During his 21 years in the stud, he sired 1,321 foals, and so famous did he become by virtue of the speed of his get that his service fee was placed at $500.

Fig. 10-41. Standardbred stallion, Adios, leading sire of money winners of the breed. (Courtesy, USDA)

Standardbred Characteristics

In general, animals of this breed are smaller, longer bodied, less leggy and possess less quality than the Thoroughbred, but they show more substance and ruggedness and they possess a more tractable disposition. The head, ears, and bone show less refinement, and the hind legs are not quite so straight as in the Thoroughbred. Standardbred animals attain speed through ability to extend themselves into long strides, repeated rapidly, because of the long forearm and long, narrow muscles.

In weight, the Standardbred ranges from 900 to 1,300 pounds, and in height from 15 to 16 hands, with

[10]On January 1, 1933, registration on performance alone was no longer granted, and registration of both sire and dam was required.

the average being around 15-2 hands. Bay, brown, chestnut, and black are the most common colors; but grays, roans, and duns are found.

Though possessing a common ancestry, some families produce a much larger proportion of pacers than others. Many individuals show speed at both gaits. Shoeing and training are also important factors in determining whether an animal shall be a trotter or a pacer.

Adaptation and Use

As previously indicated, the Standardbred was primarily originated as a trotting horse and for the purpose of providing a superior road horse in the days of the horse and buggy. He was first put under saddle and eventually into harness hitched to a sulky. With the coming of improved highways and the automobile, the progressive breeders, ever alert to new developments, turned their attention almost exclusively to the production of a speedy harness racehorse—either at the trot or the pace. The gameness and stamina of the Standardbred is unexcelled, thus adapting him to race heats wherein it is necessary that he go mile after mile at top speed. Animals of this breed are also exhibited as light harness horses in the great horse shows of the land.

The early foundation animals of the Standardbred contributed to the development of the American Saddle Horse and the Tennessee Walking Horse. Many hunters are also of Standardbred extraction. It may be said that the Standardbred has proved to be a valuable utility horse—animals of such extraction having speed, endurance, and a tractable disposition.

Present Status of the Breed

It is quite likely that new harness racetracks will be developed; and with their development, a limited increase in numbers of Standardbreds may be expected. Further improvements in both conformation and speed may be expected, also.

The Standardbred breed has the unique distinction of being one of the few breeds of livestock that the United States has exported rather than imported. Many good specimens of the breed have been shipped to the U.S.S.R., Austria, Germany, and Italy.

In addition to registering animals both of whose parents are recorded in the United States Trotting Association, any horse sired by a registered horse may be accepted for racing purposes as follows:

Non-Standardbred: Any horse may be registered as Non-Standard if an application is filed showing satisfactory identification of the horse for racing purposes. This identification may be accomplished by furnishing the name, age, sex, sire, dam, color and

Fig. 10-43. Dan Patch. (Courtesy, United States Trotting Assn., Columbus, Ohio)

Fig. 10-42. The world's fastest Standardbred filly of all time, Handle With Care, shown leading a field of pacers around the turn on the way to another of her 47 wins in 68 starts, with earnings of $615,366 through her third season of racing in 1975. Handle With Care is the third leading distaff 2-minute star of all time, and her record of 1:54.2, 1:54.4 ranks with only 2 other horses who have managed to pace faster than 1:55 in a race. (Courtesy, United States Trotting Assn., Columbus, Ohio)

markings; also required is a history of the previous owners, if any. A mating certificate must accompany this application, showing the sire to be some type of a registered horse. For foals of 1973 and thereafter, prior approval must be obtained from the Standing Committee on Registration before breeding any horse not meeting the requirements for Standard registration, except for foals of mares registered Non-Standard prior to November 1972.

The Dan Patch Story

Dan Patch was a great Standardbred horse whose exploits took place soon after the turn of the century, from 1902 to 1910. In 1906, he paced the fastest mile ever, in 1:55, at the Minnesota State Fair. That record stood until 1938. But it was not recognized, because a windshield was pulled in front of the sulky to break the wind. But to the 93,000 rabid fans who witnessed the feat, and to his worshippers everywhere, the record stood.

The great horse's owner, Will Savage, was a fabulous and colorful character. Will and Dan belonged to each other, when winning—yes, even in

death. Mr. Savage made headlines of a sort when he paid $60,000 for the six-year-old Standardbred pacer in 1902. Even his friends referred to the deal as "Savage's folly." But subsequent events proved how wrong they were.

Dan Patch brought fame and fortune to his master, and to himself. A railroad line—The Dan Patch Line—was named after him. There were also Dan Patch sleds, coaster wagons, cigars, washing machines (a 2-minute performer like Dan), and shoes for kiddies. Mr. Savage built the great horse an empire, surroundings befitting his station in life. The stable was equipped with modern living quarters for 60 caretakers. Two racetracks were constructed—the best mile strip ever built, and a covered half-miler with 8,400 panes of glass. Even during a Minnesota blizzard, Dan and his stablemates could train in comfort—and style.

Dan Patch was the idol of his day—the Babe Ruth, the Bing Crosby, and the Beatles. People came to see him, as they do any other notable. Lili Langtry, the famous actress, arranged to have her train stopped near Dan's so that she could go to his private car for a visit. Men vied for his shoes, women fought to pluck hair from his mane and tail, small boys played Dan Patch in the backyard, and people wept when he became ill.

The town of Hamilton changed its name to Savage, in honor of the man who had put it on the map.

But there was more than a platonic relationship between horse and owner—there was something almost supernatural between Dan and Will. On July 4, 1916, Dan Patch and Will Savage both took ill on the same day. Those keeping vigil over the horse saw him snuff out his last race—the race with life itself—on July 11. He died at age 20. Thirty-two hours later, Dan's master, Will Savage, was dead at age 57. Both were buried at the same hour; Mr. Savage in

Lakewood Cemetery, and Mr. Patch under the shade of an oak tree on the bank of the Minnesota River.

TENNESSEE WALKING HORSE

Today, the Tennessee Walking Horse is synonymous with the Plantation Walking Horse, as the latter show-ring classification is constituted by this one breed. In the early formative period of the breed, animals of the walk, running walk, canter variety were referred to as the Plantation Walking Horse because the southern owners and overseers used this type of animal in riding over their estates daily. They liked these animals because of their stamina and comfortable gaits.

Origin and Native Home

The Tennessee Walking Horse was at home in the Middle Basin of Tennessee for more than a hundred years prior to the formation of a breed registry in 1935. Like other American breed creations, the Tennessee Walking Horse is of composite origin. Yet, through constant breeding and selection, distinct characteristics evolved, molding the horse into an entity of its own. The sturdy native saddle stock of Tennessee accompanied the early settlers from Virginia. According to the best authorities, the breed represents an amalgamation of the Thoroughbred, Standardbred, Morgan, and American Saddle Horse breeds, together with whatever else may have constituted the native stock. Thus, throughout a century or more of meticulous breeding, the Tennessee Walking Horse came to possess some of the endurance and upstanding qualities of the Thoroughbred, the substance and sturdiness of the Standardbred, the graceful lines and docility of the Morgan, and the style and beauty of the American Saddle Horse.

The real patriarch, or foundation sire, of the Tennessee Walking Horse was a stallion known as Allan F-1, sometimes called Black Allan because of his color. This horse, of mixed Standardbred and Morgan ancestry, foaled in 1886, proved to be a progenitor of remarkable prepotency when crossed on native mares. Moreover, his offspring carried on. Thus, in many respects, the origin of the Tennessee Walking Horse is not unlike the development of the Morgan.

The Tennessee Walking Horse Breeders' Association of America was organized in 1935.

Tennessee Walking Horse Characteristics

In comparison with the American Saddle Horse, the average member of the Tennessee Walking Horse breed is larger, stouter, and more rugged. He is plainer about the head, shorter necked, carries the head lower, and possess more massiveness about the body and quarters. Although he has less style and

Fig. 10-44. Tennessee Walking Horse stallion, Go Boy's Sundust, World Grand Champion Walking Horse. Owned by Dr. and Mrs. B. S. Henry; standing at S. W. Beech Stables, Belfast, Tennessee. (Courtesy, Tennessee Walking Horse Breeders' Assn. of America, Lewisburg, Tenn.)

elegance, the Tennessee Walking Horse excels the American Saddle Horse when it comes to temperament and disposition. He has been referred to as the "gentleman of the equines."

The Tennessee Walking Horse averages around 15-2 hands in height and weighs from 1,000 to 1,200 pounds. A great array of colors exists, including sorrel, chestnut, black, roan, white, bay, brown, gray, and golden. White markings on the feet and legs are common.

The 3 gaits characterizing the breed are all natural gaits. They are free and easy and are called the flat-footed walk, the running walk, and the canter. Particular emphasis is placed upon the running walk, an all-day gait which is executed at a speed of 6 to 8 miles per hour. It is started like the flat-footed walk and is a diagonally opposed foot movement. As the speed is increased, the hind foot usually oversteps the front track from a few to as many as 18 inches. This gives the rider a gliding sensation.

Adaptation and Use

Although the Tennessee Walking Horse arose as the business or plantation horse of Tennessee and the South, it is now largely a pleasure horse. Because of its gentle manners and easy gaits, it is an ideal horse for the amateur or the person who rides infrequently. The experienced horseman, likewise, enjoys these same traits.

Present Status of the Breed

In addition to recording progeny out of registered Tennessee Walking Horse parents, the Association will register the following:

Any gelding carrying 50 percent Walking Horse blood provided it is shown to the satisfaction of the executive committee that he performs the true walking horse gaits.

Because of the many sterling qualities of the breed, especially its fine disposition and the easy-on-the-rider running walk, the Tennessee Walking Horse has established a wide niche for itself in the horse world.

THOROUGHBRED

The term "Thoroughbred" is applied properly only to the breed of running racehorses developed originally in England. It should not be confused with nor used synonymously with the designation purebred, an adjective used to denote the pure lineage of any breed of livestock regardless of class or breed. Today, the Thoroughbred has become the equine synonym for speed and racing quality.

Part-Thoroughbreds may be registered in the American Remount Association, Inc., Thoroughbred Half-Bred Registry, Perris, California. It has seven different sections, with eligibility as given in Table VIII-1 of the Appendix of this book.

Origin and Native Home

The history of the Thoroughbred, as we think of it today, had its beginning in the 17th Century, though the Oriental lineage of the breed is as old as civilization itself. The nature of man being what it is, there was racing wherever there were horses. However, the real molding of the fleet light horse in England became a necessity with the shift from medieval warfare—in which the fighting unit consisted of a mounted knight in full armor—to the use of arrows and finally gunpowder. Speed and stamina became imperative. Simultaneously, interest in horse racing in England was greatly accelerated. As early as the reign of Henry VIII, a royal stud was established.

The real impetus to the development of a superior English running horse, however, had its beginning under Charles II, who reigned from 1660 to 1685. King Charles imported a number of outstanding Barb mares for the royal stable. Upon the descendants of this improved foundation stock were subsequently crossed 3 immortal stallions known respectively as: the Byerly Turk, imported in 1689; the Darley Arabian, imported in 1706; and the Godolphin Arabian, brought from Paris in 1724. From these 3 illustrious sires sprang 3 male lines: Matchem, tracing to the Godolphin Arabian; Eclipse, tracing to the Darley Arabian; and Herod, tracing to the Byerly Turk. Such was the development of the Thoroughbred, a breed predominantly of Arabian, Barb,[11] and Turk[12] extraction; though it may have in its veins the blood of the Galloway, Scotch Pony, and Highland Dun—animals used for cart or draft purposes, and "heaven only knows what else."

The first edition of the General (English) Stud Book was published in 1793.

Early American Importations

The first Thoroughbred imported to America was the 21-year-old stallion, Bulle Rock, by Darley Arabian and out of a dam by Byerly Turk, arriving in Virginia in 1730. Governors Ogle and Sharpe of Maryland made subsequent importations between 1747 and 1755. The Revolution interrupted the growth of Thoroughbred breeding, but at its close the stream of importations was reestablished. New racetracks were built, and the breed became firmly entrenched in America.

All U.S. Thoroughbreds are registered in The Jockey Club, established in 1894. Membership in the Club is by election. Consisting of about 75 members, it is probably the most exclusive club in the world.

Thoroughbred Characteristics

Fig. 10-45. Thoroughbred mare, Natalma, dam of champion racehorse and sire, Northern Dancer. (Courtesy, Windfields Farm, Chesapeake City, Md.)

---

[11]The Barbs were native to the Barbary States of northern Africa. They were more rugged than the Arabian but lacked the quality, refinement, and beauty of the latter.

[12]The Turk horse was found chiefly in Anatola and only to a limited extent in Turkey. These animals were noted for docility and beauty, but they lacked the vigor and endurance of the Arabian.

Thoroughbreds are bay, brown, chestnut, black, or, less frequently, gray in color. White markings on the face and legs are common. Animals of this breed range in height from 15 to 17 hands, with an average of around 16 hands. In racing trim, the Thoroughbred may weigh from 900 to 1,025 pounds, whereas stallions in breeding condition may approach 1,400 pounds.

The build of the Thoroughbred shows the speed type in the extreme. The body is long, deep chested, rather narrow, upstanding, and often a bit angular. This horse possesses a high degree of quality and refinement throughout. The head is small and well proportioned, with a straight face, small neat ear, and fine throttle. The shoulders and pastern are sloping, and the thigh and quarter are powerfully muscled. The temperament is active and energetic, being of the racy or highly nervous variety. The action of most Thoroughbreds is characterized by going low and pointed at the trot but executing the gallop or run to perfection.

Adaptation and Use

As a running racehorse, the Thoroughbred is without a peer. Yet, it is noteworthy that a considerable number of the Thoroughbreds foaled in the United States are never raced, and many that are raced never win.

Many excellent horses of straight- or part-Thoroughbred breeding have excelled as gaited saddle horses, stock horses, polo mounts, hunters, and cavalry mounts. No other breed of horses has found such diverse use and adaptation. Because of the almost incredible adaptation of the Thoroughbred and the use of his blood in producing new breeds, the breed has been referred to as the "essential oil of horse flesh."

It must be realized, however, that many of the new breeds that evolved from a Thoroughbred foundation have now reached such a high state of perfection that an outcross to the Thoroughbred might now be a step backward. Such is the status of the American Saddle Horse, the Tennessee Walking Horse, and the Standardbred—when it comes to their respective performances as three- and five-gaited park hacks, plantation walking horses, and harness racers. But until other or new breeds become better adapted and more important, the blood of the Thoroughbred will continue to predominate in the production of polo mounts and hunters.

Present Status of the Breed

Today, the race crowds are bigger than ever. New racetracks are being developed and pari-mutuels are being permitted in more and more states. These de-

velopments, together with the unquestioned value of the Thoroughbred for crossbreeding purposes, assure the breed a bright future.

About one-third of the nation's Thoroughbreds are bred in Kentucky.

The Man o' War Story

Fig. 10-46. Man o' War statue (1½ times life-size) in Lexington, Kentucky, symbolizing "the horse of the century." The plaque reads as follows:

Foaled in 1917 in this bluegrass region and purchased as a yearling by Samuel Riddle. He carried the blood of best English and American sires. He never raced in Kentucky but won 20 of his 21 starts in other areas, breaking or equaling 8-time records and also setting a record of earnings with $249,465. At stud, his get were numbered in the hundreds with winnings in the millions—more than any other. In his 30 years he answered all calls of greatness. (Courtesy, Kentucky Department of Public Information, Frankfort, Ky.)

Man o' War was a famous Thoroughbred racehorse. Ask the person on the street—one who may never have gone to a race—to name the greatest horse of all time and chances are that he'll say, Man o' War. If there is any absolute against which greatness in a horse may be measured, it is the legendary Man o' War. "Big Red," as he was known, seemed to have limitless speed. Only once in his 21 starts did his machinelike power fail to propel him first across the finish line; that was when he was beaten by the aptly named "Upset" at Saratoga on August 13, 1919, after an unfortunate start. As if to redress that wrong, Man o' War trounced Upset with authority the next 3 times they met. In 8 times of his 11 starts as a 3-year-old, he broke either a track or world's record.

Man o' War was born in 1917. Samuel D. Riddle bought him as a yearling at the Saratoga sale on August 17, 1918, for $5,000.

During his career, talented writers and eloquent speakers extolled him with such superlatives as "look of eagles" and "living flame." But it fell to his groom, Will Harbut, who had quite a way with words as well as with horses, to devise the most fitting description

Fig. 10-47. Man o' War and his groom, Will Harbut. (Courtesy, J. C. Skeets Meadors and Keeneland Library, Lexington, Ky.)

grams, carrots, and other tokens of recognition from all over the country.

The great horse, who was the first to command a $5,000 service fee, was maintained largely for private use. He sired over 300 offspring who won over 1,200 races and earned more than $3½ million.

Big Red died in 1947, at the age of 30. Ira Drymon, as the Thoroughbred Club's representative, delivered the eulogy before the 2,000 people assembled, and over a nationwide radio hookup. As taps were sounded and the mammoth coffin of polished oak containing the body of Man o' War was lowered to his final resting place, men, women and children wept unashamedly.

The Man o' War legend continues on, for he lived and died and won a lasting name and fame—a rare achievement by any beast, or man.

of all. "Man o' War," as Will never tired of telling the thousands who came to see him, "was the mostest horse that ever was." During his lifetime, more visitors went to see Man o' War than Mammoth Cave.

Physically, Man o' War was a glowing chestnut, almost red, standing 16 hands 1⅝ inches. He measured 71¾ inches at the girth and weighed 1,100 pounds in training. As a stallion, his weight reached 1,370 pounds. He was unusually long bodied and powerfully muscled in the gaskins. Estimates of his stride varied anywhere from 25 to 28 feet, although, oddly enough, it was never officially measured.

When training, Big Red's morning came early. He was given his first meal at 3:30 a.m. At 7:30 a.m., he was brushed and massaged; the bandages that he wore at all times except when in action were removed, and his legs were washed; his face, eyes, and nostrils were sponged; and he was given a rubdown with a soft cloth. After work on warm days, he was washed; then he was rubbed thoroughly, his feet were cleaned and dressed, and he was left to rest in his stall. He was fond of his caretaker; he liked to snatch his hat and carry it around as he showed off for visitors.

Most Thoroughbred horses share a universal birthday—January 1. But Big Red was different! At Faraway Farm, near Lexington, where he spent most of his life, his actual foaling date, March 29, was duly observed as a special occasion. He received tele-

TRAKEHNER

The Trakehner has gained popularity in the United States hand in hand with increased interest in combined training and dressage.

Origin and Native Home

The breed originated in Trakehnen, East Prussia, in 1732. It evolved from the blending of the indigenous Prussian horses, Thoroughbreds, and Arabians.

The American Trakehner Association was formed in September, 1974.

Trakehner Characteristics

Although the breeding goals have changed through the years to meet the needs of the time, generally speaking the emphasis has been on the development of a horse with the size of the Thoroughbred, but more rugged and possessing the elegance of the Arabian.

Adaptation and Use

The breed is superbly adapted to, and used for, dressage, combined training, and for jumper and hunter classes.

Present Status of the Breed

The Trakehner is new in the United States. However, a bright future is predicted for this big, sound athlete and good-looking horse of quiet and sensible nature, particularly on the American horse show scene, in dressage and combined training, and in hunter and jumper classes.

WELSH PONY

The Welsh breed is especially recommended for use by older children who have outgrown the use of a Shetland—children up to 15 years of age.

Origin and Native Home

The Welsh Pony is native of the rough mountainous country of Wales. Here for unknown generations, probably since Saxon times in England, these horses have ranged in bands, living a vagabond existence on the sparse vegetation. Under these conditions only the more rugged, thrifty, and agile animals survived. In more recent years, improvement has been wrought by annually rounding up the semiwild, nomadic bands and selecting the stallion leader for each.

Early American Importations

The first Welsh Ponies to be imported to America of which there is record were 20 head brought over by George Brown of Aurora, Illinois. Subsequent, but infrequent, importations followed.

The Welsh Pony and Cob Society of America was established in 1906, but in 1946 the name was changed to the Welsh Pony Society of America.

Welsh Pony Characteristics

Fig. 10-48. Welsh Pony stallion, Clan Dash (imported), owned by Robert S. Pirie. (Courtesy, Welsh Pony Society of America, White Post, Va.)

Present-day Welsh Ponies are usually gray, roan, black, bay, brown, or chestnut; though cream, dun, and white colors are found. In fact, any color except piebald and skewbald is eligible for registry. Gaudy white markings are not popular.

Representative animals range from 10 to 14 hands in height. In build, the modern Welsh Pony may be described as a miniature coach horse, being more upstanding than the Shetland. Individuals of this breed should possess good heads and necks, short coupling, plenty of muscling, and substance of bone; and with it all, there should be considerable speed and action at the trot and unusual endurance.

Adaptation and Use

Welsh Ponies are unexcelled as advanced children's mounts, for riding by small adults, and for such other general purposes as are within their size limitations. Among their uses are: as roadsters, and for harness shows, racing, trail riding, parades, stock cutting, and hunting.

Present Status of the Breed

Although it is not likely that great numbers of Welsh Ponies will ever be found in America, they will always fill a need. With the greater emphasis on physical fitness, it is quite likely that present numbers in America will be increased.

The American Welsh Stud Book maintains two divisions, according to height stipulations: Those in the A Division cannot exceed 12-2 hands; the B Division includes those over 12-2, but under 14 hands.

YSABELLA

The Ysabella is an offshoot of the American Saddle Horse.

Origin and Native Home

Ysabella horses originated in the United States, on McKinzie Rancho, Williamsport, Indiana. The foundation animals were American Saddlers.

Ysabella Characteristics

Coat colors are gold, white, or chestnut, with flaxen, silver, or white mane and tail. There may be white markings on the face and legs.

Animals having bay color, spots, or black mane and tail are not eligible for registration.

Adaptation and Use

Ysabellas are used for pleasure riding and as exhibition horses.

Present Status of the Breed

Breed numbers are small, and the breed registry association is not very active.

SELECTED REFERENCES

Title of Publication	Author(s)	Publisher
Appaloosa	F. Haines	Amon Carter Museum of Western Art, Fort Worth, Tex., 1963
Appaloosa Horse, The	F. Haines G. B. Hatley R. Peckinpah	R. G. Bailey Printing Company, Lewiston, Ida., 1957
Arabian Horse Breeding	H. H. Reese	Borden Publishing Co., Los Angeles, Calif., 1953
Breeding and Raising Horses, Ag. Hdbk. No. 394	M. E. Ensminger	Agricultural Research Service, USDA, Washington, D.C., 1972
Breeds of Livestock, The	C. W. Gay	The Macmillan Company, New York, N.Y., 1918
Breeds of Livestock in America	H. W. Vaughan	R. G. Adams and Company, Columbus, Ohio, 1937
History of Thoroughbred Racing in America	W. H. P. Robertson	Prentice-Hall, Inc., Englewood Cliffs, N. J., 1965
Horse, The	D. J. Kays, rev. by J. M. Kays	A. S. Barnes & Co., Inc., Cranbury, N.J., 1969
Horse America Made, The	L. Taylor	American Saddle Horse Breeders Association, Louisville, Ky., 1944
Horsemanship and Horse Care, Ag. Info. Bull. No. 353	M. E. Ensminger	Agricultural Research Service, USDA, Washington, D.C., 1972
Horses: Their Selection, Care, and Handling	M. C. Self	A. S. Barnes & Co., Inc., New York, N.Y., 1943
Horses of Today: Their History, Breeds, and Qualifications	H. H. Reese	Wood & Jones, Pasadena, Calif., 1956
Kellogg Arabians, The	H. H. Reese G. B. Edwards	Borden Publishing Co., Los Angeles, Calif., 1958
Light Horse Breeds, The	J. W. Patten	A. S. Barnes & Co., Inc., New York, N.Y., 1960
Light Horses, Farmers' Bull. No. 2127	M. E. Ensminger	U.S. Department of Agriculture, Washington, D.C., 1965
Modern Breeds of Livestock	H. M. Briggs	The Macmillan Company, New York, N.Y., 1969
Morgan Horse Handbook, The	J. Mellin	Stephen Green Press, Brattleboro, Vt., 1973
Pinto, The		Yearbook and Studbook of the Pinto Horse Association of America, 1958-59
Shetland Pony, The	L. F. Bedell	The Iowa State University Press, Ames, Iowa, 1959
Shetland Pony, The	M. C. Cox	Adam & Charles Black, London, England, 1965
Stockman's Handbook, The, Fourth Edition	M. E. Ensminger	The Interstate Printers & Publishers, Inc., Danville, Ill., 1970
Study of Breeds, The	T. Shaw	Orange Judd Company, New York, N.Y., 1912
Types and Breeds of Farm Animals	C. S. Plumb	Ginn and Company, Boston, Mass., 1920
World Dictionary of Breeds, Types, and Varieties of Livestock, A	I. L. Mason	Commonwealth Agricultural Bureaux, Farnham House, Farnham Royal, Slough, Bucks, England, 1951

(continued)

Title of Publication	Author(s)	Publisher
World of Pinto Horses, A	Ed. by R. D. Greene	The Pinto Horse Association of America, San Diego, Calif., 1970

Also, breed literature pertaining to each breed may be secured by writing to the respective breed registry associations (see Sec. VIII, Appendix, for the name and address of each association).

CHAPTER 11

Breeds of Draft Horses;
Jacks and Donkeys

Contents

Today, the pure breeds of draft horses are primarily of historical interest. Nevertheless, it is noteworthy that registration numbers have increased dramatically in recent years, reflecting nostaligia rather than energy shortage. Table 11-1 shows the registration numbers of draft horses by breeds—in 1975, and in total registrations since the respective breed registries were formed.

The breeds of draft horses here considered are the Belgian, Clydesdale, Percheron, Shire, and Suffolk. Regardless of the distinct breed trademarks and the virtues ascribed to each breed, all are characterized by great massiveness—their adapted field of utility being the drawing of heavy loads at a comparatively slow gait, usually at the walk.

Power rather than speed is desired. In order to possess this power, the draft horse should be blocky or compact, low set or short legged, and sufficiently heavy to enable him to throw the necessary weight into the collar to move a heavy load and at the same time maintain a secure footing. This calls for a horse around 16 to 17 hands in height and weighing not less than 1,600 pounds.

All of the modern draft breeds of horses, regardless of color or breed or later infusions of other breeding, rest upon a Flemish foundation—the large, coarse, black, hairy, and sluggish horse which, from a very early time, existed in the low-lying sections of what is now Belgium, France, Holland, and Germany. Thus, the draft breeds were of European origin, whereas the light horse breeds were of Oriental extraction.

Battle chariots, drawn by heavy horses and used to convey armored troops who fought on foot, were encountered by the Roman legions under Caesar when he invaded England in the year 55 B.C. Later, these ponderous beasts, imposing in height and bulk, were known as the Great Horses of the Middle Ages.

These animals were the cavalry mounts of the heavily armored knights when they rode forth to battle for king and country and at times to enforce their views of religion upon unbelievers in general and Mohammedans in particular. They had to be large and powerful in order to carry the immense weight of their riders, their arms, and their armor—including eventually the armor of both the horse and the rider. Often the combined weight of their load was up to 450 pounds.

Finally, in the 19th Century, when the use of armor in warfare was abandoned after invention and adoption of gunpowder by the fighting nations and when the development of agriculture and commerce received new impetus, the Great Horse served as the foundation for the draft breeds as we know them today. Lighter horses came into use for riding and the Great Horse was relegated to pulling the cart and the plow and to hauling timber, coal, and other industrial materials.

RELATIVE POPULARITY OF BREEDS
OF DRAFT HORSES

Table 11-1 shows the 1975 and total registration to date of the various breeds of draft horses. As may

be noted, the draft registry associations are doing little business.

TABLE 11-1

1975 AND TOTAL REGISTRATIONS OF DRAFT HORSES, JACKS, AND DONKEYS IN U.S. BREED ASSOCIATIONS

Breed	1975 Registrations	Total Registrations
Belgian	1,245	77,460
Percheron	759	252,743
Donkeys[1]	308	4,612
Miniature Donkeys	300	4,237
Clydesdale	100	N/A[2]
American Jacks	36	37,545
Shire	22	N/A[2]
Suffolk	17	4,292

[1]1974 figures.
[2]Not available.

BELGIAN

The Belgian breed made marked progress in this country, considering that so few animals were imported prior to the beginning of the 20th Century. Belgian stallions were especially valuable in improving the draftiness of the native stock on which they were crossed.

Origin and Native Home

The Belgian breed originated in Belgium, from which country it derives its name. The agricultural needs of this low-lying country were such as to require a horse of size and bulk. So far as is known, no Oriental blood was fused with the native stock. Thus, it may be concluded that the Belgian breed is directly and exclusively descended from the old Flemish ancestry—indigenous to the country of its origin. Even today, the great massiveness of the Belgian breed more nearly resembles the Flemish horse than does any other breed.

The Belgian Draft Horse Society was founded in 1886. In their native country, the breeding of Belgians was promoted by the government, which annually awarded prizes and subsidies to the best animals in the various provinces. Also, stallions that stood for public service had to be approved by a commission appointed by the government.

Early American Importations

The first importation of the Belgian to the United States was made in 1886 by Dr. A. G. Van Hoorebeke of Monmouth, Illinois, but the breed attracted little attention until 1900. Thus, the introduction of the breed was more recent than that of the Percheron, Clydesdale, and Shire. Despite their late entry into this country, however, Belgians gave a good account of themselves. They lead in registration numbers at the present time.

The American Association of Importers and Breeders of Belgian Draft Horses was organized in 1887. In 1937, the name of the registry was changed to the Belgian Draft Horse Corporation of America.

Belgian Characteristics

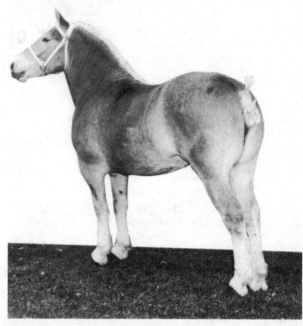

Fig. 11-1. Belgian mare, Consetta, Grand Champion at the major shows in midwestern United States and at the Canadian Royal Winter Fair. Owned by Meadow Brook Farm, Howell, Michigan. (Courtesy, Belgian Draft Horse Corporation of America, Wabash, Ind.)

Bay, chestnut, and roan are the most common colors, but browns, grays, and blacks are occasionally seen. Many Belgians have flaxen manes and tails and white-blazed faces. Mature stallions stand from 15-2 to 17 hands in height and weigh 1,900 to 2,200 pounds, or more.

The Belgian is noted for its draftiness—being the widest, deepest, most compact, most massive, and lowest set of any draft breed. Formerly, the breed was likely to be severely criticized for having small round hoofs, round bones, short thick necks, and lack of refinement. But it is to the everlasting credit of the American breeders that these defects have been very largely overcome.

The Belgian is extremely quiet, docile, and patient. The action is powerful, though less springy and high than found in the Clydesdale and Percheron. Because of their great width in front, many Belgians roll or paddle somewhat.

CLYDESDALE

Like all classes and breeds of livestock of Scotch origin—including Ayrshire, Aberdeen-Angus, Gallo-

way, and Highland cattle, and Cheviot and Black-faced Highland sheep—the Clydesdale breed of horses is distinctive for style, beauty, and action.

Origin and Native Home

This Scotch breed of draft horses derives its name from the valley of the River Clyde, an area popularly known as Clydesdale, located in the County of Lanark, Scotland.

The breed is of mixed origin, and the early history is more or less obscure. It is probable that the blood of both Flemish and English horses entered quite largely into the breed during its early formative period. Rather frequent importations of horses of Flemish extraction from England and the low countries were made, thus giving the Scotch Clydesdale and the English Shire and Suffolk similar ancestry. However, the breeders in the respective countries had very different notions as to what constituted a desirable draft animal, and their selections were governed accordingly, the Scotch placing particular emphasis upon style and action.

The British breed registry, known as the Clydesdale Horse Society of Great Britain and Ireland, was established in 1877.

Early American Importations

The first Clydesdales brought to North America were probably imported into Canada by the Scotch who settled there. Beginning in the early 1870s, Clydesdales were imported into the United States, both via Canada and direct from Scotland. The American Clydesdale Horse Association was organized in 1879.

Clydesdale Characteristics

The Clydesdale is not so heavy as the Shire, Belgian, or Percheron. Average representatives of the breed are also more rangy and lack the width and compactness of the other draft breeds. Mature stallions in average condition weigh from 1,700 to 1,900 pounds and stand from 16 to 17 hands in height.

No other breed of draft horses equals the Clydesdale in style and action. The breed is noted for a prompt walk, with a good snappy stride and a short trot, and the hocks are well flexed and carried close together. Good, clean, flat bone; well-set, fairly long and sloping pasterns; and a moderate amount of fine feather or long hair at the rear of the legs below the knees and hocks are characteristic. Sometimes, in America, the breed has been criticized for lack of width and depth of body and for having too much feather and too much white. Usually, Americans do not fancy too much white on the face and legs in any

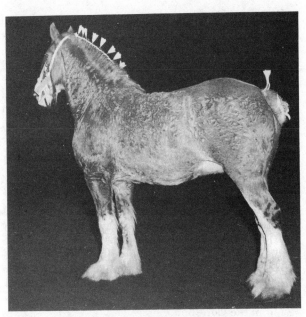

Fig. 11-2. Clydesdale mare, Nellie Dean, Champion at major Canadian shows, owned by Wreford Hewson, Beeton, Ontario, Canada. (Photo by Harold Cline, Marshalltown, Iowa; courtesy, Clydesdale Breeders Assn. of the United States, Waverly, Iowa)

breed of horses, and they object to the feather or long hair about the fetlocks because of the difficulty in keeping the legs and feet free from mud and snow. Bay and brown with white markings are the most characteristic colors, but blacks, grays, chestnuts, and roans are occasionally seen.

For show use in a six-horse hitch on the tanbark, a well-matched, carefully trained, and expertly handled hitch of Clydesdales is unexcelled. Their flowing white fetlocks and high action give them a picturesque appearance.

PERCHERON

During the draft horse era, the Percheron was the most widely distributed of all draft breeds.

Origin and Native Home

The Percheron horse originated in northwestern France, in the ancient district of La Perche, an area about one-fifteenth the size of the state of Iowa. The native stock was primarily of Flemish extraction upon which there was a subsequent and rather liberal infusion of Arab blood.

Although early records are lacking, it is known that with the defeat of the Saracens (the Moors from North Africa) at Tours and Poitiers, France, in 732 A.D. by Charles Martel, the Arab, Barb, and Turk horses upon which the Moors were mounted—mostly stallions as was the custom of the day—fell into the hands of the Franks and were eventually distributed

throughout the country. The successful Crusaders of the 12th, 13th, and 14th Centuries also brought back stallions as spoils of war from Palestine, and this again furnished a direct, though unplanned, infusion of Oriental blood. Thus, on a coldblood base, the Flemish horse, repeated top crosses of Oriental blood were made. Finally, in about 1870, a systematic effort was made to transform the mixture into a true type. Eventually, the Percheron breed evolved, and the Percheron Society of France was organized in 1883.

Early American Importations

American importations of Percherons began about 1840, but it was not until the early 1850s that any great numbers came over. Brilliant 1271, a black stallion foaled in 1877 and imported in 1881, is recognized as the most famous and prepotent animal of the breed ever imported. Other importations followed, and the center of interest in the breed came to be located in the Corn Belt.

The United States breed registry, originally known as the Percheron-Norman Horse Association, was formed in 1876, seven years earlier than its counterpart in France.

Percheron Characteristics

Fig. 11-3. Percheron stallion, Laet. He weighed 2,500 pounds and made an enviable record as a sire of offspring noted for size, width, depth, and bone. (Courtesy, Percheron Horse Assn. of America, Belmont, Ohio)

Most commonly, Percherons are black or gray (the latter being a probable Arab inheritance); but bays, browns, chestnuts, and roans are occasionally seen. Fully 90 percent, however, are black or gray.

Mature stallions stand from 16-1 to 16-3 hands in height and weight from 1,900 to 2,100 pounds. In size, the Percheron is intermediate between the larger Shire and Belgian and the smaller Clydesdale and Suffolk. In comparison with other draft breeds, the Percheron is noted for its handsome, clean-cut head; good action (being surpassed in style and action only by the Clydesdale); excellent temperament; and longevity.

SHIRE

England originated and developed two breeds of draft horses, the Shire and the Suffolk. Originally, the Shire was known by various names, such as the Great Horse, War Horse, Cart Horse, Old English Black Horse, Lincolnshire Cart Horse, etc.

Origin and Native Home

The Shire breed was originated on the low, marshy lands of east central England, particularly in Lincolnshire and Cambridgeshire; hence, comes the name "Shire."

Fig. 11-4. Robert Bakewell (1726-1795), English stockman. He contributed greatly to the improvement of the Shire. (Obtained for the author by Sir John Hammond from the Royal Agricultural Society of England)

The great size and bulk of this breed are derived directly from the Great Horse of the Middle Ages, of which Shires are held to be the nearest living reproductions. As previously indicated, the Great Horse was in turn descended from the ponderous black Flemish horse which existed in Great Britain long before the Christian era, more than 2,000 years ago.

In the year 1066, England was conquered by an army of Normans led by William the Conqueror. This marked the beginning of improvement in the native

draft stock of England. Importations of horses followed from France, Germany, and the low countries. Centuries later, Robert Bakewell (1726 to 1795), known as the first great improver of livestock, contributed to the further improvement of the Shire—as well as to that of Leicester sheep and Longhorn cattle. Bakewell imported from Holland several mares which were mated to native stallions, and selected and perpetuated the better offspring therefrom. During Bakewell's era, the Shire was being molded as a draft horse for agriculture and commerce, the use of armor in warfare having been abandoned. Thus, the development and improvement of the Shire breed antedate that of any other breed of draft horses.

The Shire Horse Society of England was organized in 1878. In addition to recording the lineage of animals, it, along with the livestock shows of England, did much to improve the Shire horse.

Early American Importations

Shire horses were first imported to London, Ontario, Canada, in 1836. A gray stallion, known as Columbus, was imported to Massachusetts prior to 1844. Small scattered importations followed, but no great numbers came over until 1880. In 1885, the American Shire Horse Breeders' Association was organized. Two years later, in 1887, more than 400 Shires were imported. Very early, horsemen became aware of the fact that Shire stallions were unsurpassed in their ability to beget draft horses from mares lacking in size and bone.

Shire Characteristics

Fig. 11-5. Little Duke, champion Shire stallion, exhibited by Horseshoe Ranch, Toppenish, Washington. The Shire is taller than any other draft breed. (Courtesy, Lou Shattuck, Toppenish, Wash.)

The Shire is a much larger horse than was his ancestor used by the mounted warriors of old. He is equaled in weight only by the Belgian. Shire stallions in fair condition weighing 2,000 pounds or over are comparatively common. In height, representatives of this breed stand from 16 to 17-2 hands. They are less compact or more rangy than the Belgian and taller than any other draft breed.

In the formative period of the breed, it was faulted for its heavy bone, feather, lack of quality and refinement, shelly- textured hoofs, sluggish temperament, and excessive white markings; but breeders made marked progress in overcoming these objections.

The common colors are bay, brown, and black with white markings; although grays, chestnuts, and roans are occasionally seen.

SUFFOLK

The Suffolk is unique among draft breeds in that (1) it was developed exclusively as a farm workhorse and not for use on city streets, and (2) all animals of the breed are chestnut in color, this color being recessive. Often the breed is referred to as the Suffolk Punch, a name descriptive of the "punched-up" conformation of the old-fashioned animals of this breed.

Origin and Native Home

The native home of the Suffolk is in the county of Suffolk, on the eastern coast of England, bordering the North Sea. The origin of the breed is unknown, but horses of similar characteristics are known to have existed in Suffolk for many centuries. Although proof is lacking, it is claimed that Norman stallions were crossed on the native mares of Suffolk County 500 years ago. Also, it has been conjectured that the chestnut color of the breed is due to a cross with Norwegian horses brought in by the early Norse invaders. It is known, however, that from a very early period these animals were produced in Suffolk by farmers and for farming purposes. It is said that every well-bred Suffolk of today is descended from a bright-colored chestnut stallion foaled in 1768 and owned by a Mr. Crisp of Ufford.

The Suffolk Horse Society of Great Britain published the first volume of the Suffolk Stud Book in 1880.

Early American Importations

Suffolks were first imported into the United States in the early 1980s, followed by limited subsequent importations. They were never available in large numbers, the area devoted to their production being rather limited and there being an active de-

mand for them at home and in the British Dominions.

The American Suffolk Horse Association was formed in 1911.

Suffolk Characteristics

Fig. 11-6. Suffolk stallion, imported from England. (Courtesy, American Suffolk Horse Assn., Des Moines, Iowa)

The Suffolk is smaller than other drafters. Average animals weigh from 1,600 to 1,800 pounds and range in height from 15-2 to 16-2 hands. Occasionally, a mature stallion may weigh 2,000 pounds or more, but such weight is not characteristic of the breed.

Suffolk horses are always chestnut in color, varying from light to dark, often with cream-colored mane and tail. When white markings occur, they are likely to be unobtrusive. Aside from color, the distinguishing characteristics of the breed include their close-to-the-ground and chunky build, smooth rotund form, and clean-boned leg devoid of the feather characteristic of the other two British draft breeds.

Although small in size, the Suffolk is celebrated for his courage and willingness to work and his excellent disposition. The story goes that in their native land the courage and strength of Suffolk horses was often tested by contests involving the hitching of individual animals or teams to an immovable object, such as a tree—with the winner being determined by the number of efforts the animal or animals made in throwing themselves into the collar and pulling with all their might at the command.

The Suffolk never gained wide popularity in this country, primarily because of lack of size and lightness of bone.

JACKS AND JENNETS; DONKEYS

Fig. 11-7. Newborn Miniature Donkey. (Courtesy, Daniel Langfeld, Miniature Donkey Registry, Omaha, Neb.)

Biologists designate the ass as *Equus asinus*; the horse as *Equus caballus*. The males of the ass family are known as jacks; the females as jennets. Compared with the horse, the ass is smaller; has shorter hairs on the mane and tail; does not possess the "chestnuts" on the inside of the hind legs; has much longer ears;

Fig. 11-8. Red Oak Chief, Grand Champion Jack of the Kansas, Missouri, and Kentucky State Fairs. Note his heavy bone, well-set legs, and good head and ears. This jack was owned by Hineman's Jack Farms, Dighton, Kansas.

has smaller, deeper hoofs; possesses a louder and more harsh voice, called a bray; is less subject to founder or injury; is more hardy and has a longer ges-

tation period—jennets carry their young about 12 months. Small asses are commonly called donkeys or burros.

SELECTED REFERENCES

Title of Publication	Author(s)	Publisher
Breeding and Rearing of Jacks, Jennets, and Mules, The	L. W. Knight	The Cumberland Press, Nashville, Tenn., 1902
History of American Jacks and Mules	F. C. Mills	Hutch-Line, Inc., Hutchinson, Kan., 1971
History of the Percheron Horse, A	A. H. Sanders W. Dinsmore	Breeder's Gazette, Sanders Publishing Co., Chicago, Ill., 1917
People with Long Ears	R. Borwick	Cassell & Company Ltd., London, England, 1970
Percheron Horse, The	M. C. Weld	O. Judd Co., New York, N.Y., 1886

CHAPTER 12

BREEDING HORSES

Contents   **Page**

Fig. 12-1. In the past, horse breeding has been an art. In the future, it is destined to be both an art and a science. (Courtesy, *The Morgan Horse*, Hamilton, N.Y.)

Horses will continue to be bred so long as they (1) provide recreation and sport, and (2) serve the livestock industry of the West. It is important, therefore, that both the student and the progressive horseman be familiar with the breeding of horses.

PART I. SOME PRINCIPLES OF HORSE GENETICS

Nature ordained that genetics be applied to horse breeding long before there were geneticists. Prior to the domestication of horses, there was natural selection for speed and stamina because one of the most important defense mechanisms of the horse was to outrun his enemies. Natural selection was probably very effective in improving speed and endurance since the slower horses were eliminated by their enemies. To the extent that faster horses were speedy because of the genes that they carried, each succeeding generation would average faster than the previous generation because many of the slower horses would not have become parents.

It is noteworthy, too, that through the years, many horse breeders have been practicing geneticists as they concerned themselves with the art of breeding, even though they may not have been cognizant of it. Their guiding concept of heredity was that "like begets like." That the application of this principle over a long period of time has been effective in modifying horse types becomes evident from a comparison of present-day horses. Thus, the speed of the modern Thoroughbred—coupled with his general lithe, angular build and nervous temperament—is in sharp contrast to the slow, easy gaits and the docility of the Tennessee Walking Horse. Yet, there is good and substantial evidence to indicate that both breeds descended from a common ancestry. Because of the di-

versity of genes carried by the original parent stock, it has been possible, through selection, to evolve with 2 distinct breeds—one highly adapted to fast running at extended distances and the other to a slow, ambling gait. Also, through selection accompanied by planned matings, this same parent stock has been altered into horses especially adept as hunters, jumpers, stock horses, polo mounts, 3- and 5-gaited park hacks, harness racehorses, etc.

Eighteenth Century breeders made a tremendous contribution in pointing the way toward horse improvement before Mendel's laws became known to the world in the early part of the 20th Century. As knowledge of genetics developed, there evolved an understanding of the science that underlies the art of horse breeding.

The application of the science of genetics to the art of breeding proceeded rather rapidly in cattle, sheep, swine, and poultry. But, for many years, no such progress was made in the application of science to the art of horse breeding. As a result, little scientific work was done on the genetics of the horse. Today, this situation is being righted. The art and the science of horse breeding are being brought together; bridges are being established between those on the scientific side and those on the art side. With the experiences of the earlier horse breeders to guide us, along with our present knowledge of genetics and physiology of reproduction, progress should now be much more certain and rapid. In the past, horse breeding has been an art. In the future, it is destined to be both an art and a science.

MENDEL'S CONTRIBUTION TO GENETICS

Modern genetics was really founded by Gregor Johann Mendel, a cigar-smoking Austrian monk, who conducted breeding experiments with garden peas from 1857 to 1865, during the time of the Civil War in the United States. In his monastery at Brünn (now Brno, in Czechoslovakia), Mendel applied a powerful curiosity and a clear mind to reveal some of the basic principles of hereditary transmission. In 1866, he published in the proceedings of a local scientific society a report covering 8 years of his studies, but for 34 years his findings went unheralded and ignored. Finally, in 1900, 16 years after Mendel's death, 3 European biologists independently duplicated his findings, and this led to the dusting off of the original paper published by the monk 34 years earlier.

The essence of Mendelism is that inheritance is by particles or units (called genes), that these genes are present in pairs—one member of each pair having come from each parent—and that each gene maintains its identity generation after generation. Thus, Mendel's work with peas laid the basis for the two basic laws of inheritance: (1) the law of segregation, and (2)

Fig. 12-2. Gregor Johann Mendel (1822-1884), a cigar-smoking Austrian monk, whose breeding experiments with garden peas founded modern genetics. (Courtesy, The Bettmann Archive)

SOME FUNDAMENTALS OF HEREDITY IN HORSES

The author has no intention of covering all of the diverse field of genetics and animal breeding. Rather, he will present a condensation of a few of the known facts in regard to the field and briefly summarize their application to horses.

Obviously, heredity in horses is identical in principle with that in other farm animals and man. Because of the difficulty in conducting breeding experiments with horses (due to their greater cost, slower reproductive rate, etc.), however, less applied knowledge of genetics is available in the equine field. Also, it is fully recognized that such systems of breeding as inbreeding and grading up are seldom deliberately planned and followed in horse breeding; yet the enlightened horse breeder will wish to be fully informed relative to them.

The Gene as the Unit of Heredity

Genes determine all the hereditary characteristics of animals, from the body type to the color of the hair. They are truly the fundamental unit of genetics.

The bodies of all animals are made up of millions or even billions of tiny cells, microscopic in size. Each cell contains a nucleus in which there are a number of pairs of bundles, called chromosomes. In turn, the chromosomes carry pairs of minute particles, called genes, which are the basic hereditary material. The nucleus of each body cell of horses contains 32 pairs of chromosomes,[1] or a total of 64, whereas there are perhaps thousands of pairs of genes. These genes determine all the hereditary characteristics of living

the independent assortment of genes. Later, other genetic principles were added; but all the phenomena of inheritance, based upon the reactions of genes, are generally known under the collective term, Mendelism.

Thus, modern genetics is really unique in that it was founded by an amateur who was not trained as a geneticist and who did his work merely as a hobby. During the years since the rediscovery of Mendel's principles (in 1900), many additional genetic principles have been added, but the fundamentals as set forth by Mendel have been proved correct in every detail. It can be said, therefore, that inheritance in both plants and animals follows the biological laws formulated by Mendel.

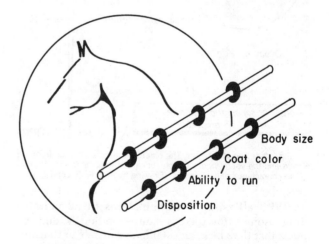

Fig. 12-3. A pair of bundles, called chromosomes, carrying minute particles, called genes. The genes determine all the hereditary characteristics of living animals, from length of leg to body size. (Drawing by Prof. R. F. Johnson)

[1]Cattle have 60 chromosomes; sheep have 54; and swine have 40.

animals. Thus, inheritance goes by units rather than by blending of 2 fluids, as our grandfathers thought.

The modern breeder knows that the job of transmitting qualities from one generation to the next is performed by the germ cells—a sperm from the male and an ovum or egg from the female. All animals, therefore, are the result of the union of two such tiny cells, one from each of its parents. These two germ cells contain the basis of all the anatomical, physiological, and psychological characters that the offspring will inherit.

In the body cells of an animal, each of the chromosomes is duplicated; whereas in the formation of the sex cells, the egg and the sperm, a reduction division occurs and only one chromosome and one gene of each pair goes into a sex cell. This means that only half the number of chromosomes and genes present in the body cells of the animal go into each egg and sperm, but each sperm or egg cell has genes for every characteristic of its species. As will be explained later, the particular half that any one germ cell gets is determined by chance. When mating and fertilization occur, the single chromosomes from the germ cell of each parent unite to form new pairs, and the genes are again present in duplicate in the body cells of the embryo.

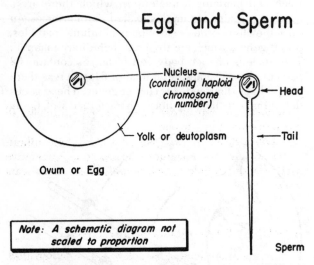

Note: A schematic diagram not scaled to proportion

Fig. 12-4. Egg and sperm. The parent germ cells, the egg from the female and the sperm from the male, unite and transmit to the offspring all the characters that it will inherit. (Drawing by Prof. R. F. Johnson)

With all possible combinations in 32 pairs of chromosomes (the species number in horses) and the genes that they bear, any stallion or mare can transmit over one billion different samples of its own inheritance; and the combination from both parents makes possible one billion times one billion genetically different offspring. It is not strange, therefore, that no two animals within a given breed (except identical twins from a single egg split after fertilization) are

exactly alike. Rather, we can marvel that the members of a given breed bear as much resemblance to each other as they do.

Even between such closely related individuals as full sisters, it is possible that there will be quite wide differences in size, growth rate, temperament, conformation, speed, and in almost every conceivable character. Admitting that many of these differences may be due to undetected differences in environment, it is still true that in such animals much of the variation is due to hereditary differences. A stallion, for example, will sometimes transmit to one offspring much better inheritance than he does to most of his get, simply as the result of chance distribution of the genes that go to different sperm at the time of the reduction division. Such differences in inheritance in offspring have been called both the hope and the despair of the livestock breeder.

If an animal gets similar determiners or genes from each parent, it will in turn produce a uniform set of offspring,[2] because any half of its inheritance is just like any other half. For example, regardless of what combination of chromosomes go into a particular germ cell, it will be just like any other egg or sperm from the same individual. Such animals are referred to as being homozygous. Unfortunately, few, if any, of our animals are in this pure hereditary state at the present time; instead of being homozygous, they are quite heterozygous. This explains why there may be such wide variation within the offspring of any given sire or dam. The wise and progressive breeder recognizes this fact, and he insists upon the production records of all get rather than those of just a few meritorious individuals.

Variation between the offspring of animals that are not pure or homozygous is not to be marveled at, but is rather to be expected. No one would expect to draw exactly 20 sound apples and 10 rotten ones every time he took a random sample of 30 from a barrel containing 40 sound ones and 20 rotten ones, although on the average—if enough samples were drawn—he would expect to get about that proportion of each. Individual drawings would of course vary rather widely. Exactly the same situation applies to the relative numbers of "good" and "bad" genes that may be present in different germ cells from the same animal. Because of this situation, the mating of a mare with a fine track record to a stallion that on the average transmits relatively good performance will not always produce a foal of a merit equal to that of its parents. The foal could be markedly poorer than the parents or, happily, it could in some cases be better than either parent.

Selection and close breeding are the tools

---

[2]Unless it is homozygous for a simple recessive and is mated to an animal that is heterozygous for that trait.

through which the horseman may obtain stallions and mares whose chromosomes and genes contain similar hereditary determiners—animals that are genetically more homozygous.

Genes Seldom Change

Gene changes are technically known as mutations. *A mutation may be defined as a sudden variation which is later passed on through inheritance and which results from changes in a gene or genes.* Not only are mutations rare, but they are prevailingly harmful. For all practical purposes, therefore, the genes can be thought of as unchanged from one generation to the next. The observed differences between animals are usually due to different combinations of genes being present rather than to mutations. Each gene probably changes only about once in each 100,000 to 1,000,000 animals produced.

Once in a great while a mutation occurs in a farm animal, and it produces a visible effect in the animal

carrying it. These animals are commonly called "sports." Such sports are occasionally of practical value. The occurrence of the polled characteristic within the horned Hereford breed of cattle is an example of a mutation or sport of economic importance. Out of this has arisen the Polled Hereford breed.

Gene changes can be accelereated by exposure to X rays, radium, ultraviolet light, and several other mutagenic agents. Such changes may eventually be observed in the offspring of both the people and animals of Japan that were exposed to the atom bombs unleashed in World War II.

Simple Gene Inheritance (Qualitative Traits)

In the simplest type of inheritance, only one pair of genes is involved. Thus, a pair of genes may be responsible for the color of body hair in horses. This situation can be illustrated by the pedigree of Whirlaway.

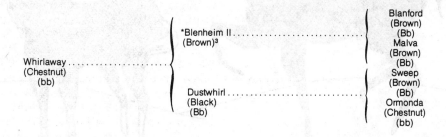

In reality, the fixation of coat color in horses may not be so simple as expected. The idea that certain basic colors may have a rather simple explanation of inheritance should not alter the fact that other genes or contributing factors may play an important role, through their influence on basic schemes. Other color patterns and shades, of more complex nature, may exhibit an almost unreal influence when crossed with the more simple genotypes. The action of certain dilution genes is, without doubt, responsible for various shades of basic colors; this is amply portrayed, for example, by the many and varied hues of chestnut (sorrel) color.

Also, it should be borne in mind that the various gene combinations and colors will appear in the offspring in the expected proportions only when relatively large numbers are concerned. The possible gene combinations, therefore, are governed by the laws of chance, operating in much the same manner as the results obtained from flipping coins. For example, if a penny is flipped often enough, the number of heads and tails will come out about even. However, with the laws of chance in operation, it is possible

that out of any four tosses one might get all heads, all tails, or even three to one.

Other possible examples of simple gene inheritance in horses (sometimes referred to as qualitative traits) might include eye color and the set of the ears on the head.

DOMINANT AND RECESSIVE FACTORS

In the example of horse colors shown in Fig. 12-5, the phenomenon of "dominance" is illustrated. In this type of expression, a factor or gene has its full effect regardless of whether it is present with another like itself or is paired with a recessive gene. Thus, black is dominant to chestnut; hence, when a pure black stallion is crossed on a chestnut mare, all of the offspring will be black. The resulting black is not genotypically pure, however; it is Bb, where B stands for the domi-

---

[3]This is not shown as (Bb) because some brown stallions mated to chestnut mares produce no chestnut offspring. Rather, it is suggested that the brown of Blenheim II was a modified black.

nant black and b for the recessive chestnut. This black animal will produce germ cells carrying black and chestnut genes in equal proportion. Then if an F₁ stallion is crossed on F₁ mares, the F₂ population will, on the average, consist of 3 blacks to one chestnut. The chestnut—being a recessive—will be pure for color; that is, the mating of 2 chestnut horses will produce chestnut offspring, which is the situation in the Suffolk breed of draft horses where all animals of the breed are chestnuts. Of the 3 blacks in the F₂, however, only one is pure for black (with the genetic constitution BB). The other 2 will be Bb in genetic constitution, and will produce germ cells carrying b and B in equal proportion.

It is clear, therefore, that a dominant character may cover up a recessive. Hence, a horse's breeding performance cannot be recognized by its phenotype (how it looks), a fact of great significance in practical breeding.

As can be readily understood, dominance often makes the task of identifying and discarding all animals carrying an undesirable recessive factor a difficult one. Recessive genes can be passed on from generation to generation, appearing only when two animals, both of which carry the recessive factor, happen to mate. Even then, only one out of four offspring produced will, on the average, be homozygous for the recessive factor and show it.

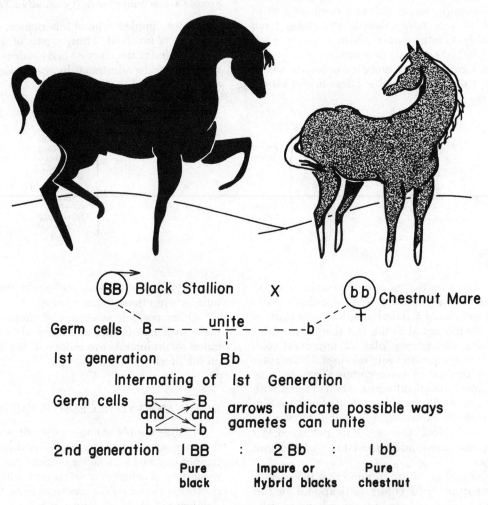

Fig. 12-5. An example of gene inheritance in horses. Note—

1. That each horse has at least a pair of genes for color, conveniently represented by symbols.
2. That each reproduction cell (egg or sperm) contains but one of each pair.
3. That the Bb genotypes, in the F₁ generation, can vary in the degree of blackness, thus tending to resemble the one black parent.
4. That the F₂ generation has the ratio of three blacks to one chestnut (phenotypically). The Bb's may be black or shading into brown.
5. That the pure blacks and certain hybrid blacks may not be distinguished on the basis of appearance, because the B gene obscures the b gene in varying degrees.
6. That the chestnut (bb) is quite likely the only pure color, in this example, that can be detected on sight.

Assuming that a hereditary defect or abnormality
has occurred in a herd and that it is recessive in nature, the breeding program to be followed to prevent
or minimize the possibility of its future occurrence
will depend somewhat on the type of herd
involved—especially on whether it is a grade or
purebred herd. In an ordinary commercial herd, the
breeder can usually guard against further reappear-
ance of the undesirable recessive by using an outcross
(unrelated) sire within the same breed or by
crossbreeding with a sire from another breed. With
this system, the breeder is fully aware of the recessive
being present, but he has taken action to keep it from
showing up.

On the other hand, if such an undesirable recessive appears in a purebred herd, the action should be
more drastic. A reputable purebred breeder has an obligation not only to himself but to his customers.
Purebred animals must be purged of undesirable
genes and lethals. This can be done by:

1. Eliminating those sires and dams that are
known to have transmitted the undesirable recessive
character.

2. Eliminating both the abnormal and phenotypically normal offspring produced by these sires and
dams (approximately half of the normal animals will
carry the undesirable character in the recessive condition).

3. In some instances, breeding a prospective
herd sire to a number of females known to carry the
gene for the undesirable recessive, thus making sure
that the new sire is free from the recessive.

Such action in a purebred herd is expensive, and
it calls for considerable courage. Yet it is the only way
in which horses can be freed from such undesirable
genes.

INCOMPLETE DOMINANCE

In some cases, dominance is neither complete nor
absent, but incomplete or partial and expressed in a
variety of ways. Perhaps the best-known case of this
type in horses is the palomino color.

Genetic studies of the Palomino indicate that the
color is probably unfixable—[4]that it cannot be made
true breeding, no matter how long or how persistent
the effort. Further, there appears to be ample
theory—substantiated by practical observation—to indicate that palomino foals may be produced by any
one of several types of matings (see discussion relative to Palomino characteristics, in Chapter 10).

Certain investigations[5] have revealed that the

palomino color is due to the interaction of three pairs
of genes; namely, bb = homozygous chestnut, Dd =
heterozygous dilution, and AA or Aa = either
homozygous or heterozygous bay coat pattern, resulting in the chestnut color bb being diluted to a cream
or golden body color by Dd (DD animals being very
pale or almost white). If it is assumed that the
Palomino's color depends on the Dd gene pair being
heterozygous, the Palomino color cannot breed true.

Multiple Gene Inheritance (Quantitative Traits)

Relatively few characters of economic importance
in farm animals are inherited in as simple a manner as
the ones just described. Rather, important characters—such as speed—are due to many genes; thus,
they are called multiple-gene characters. Because
such characters show all manner of gradation—from
high to low performance, for example—they are sometimes referred to as quantitative traits. Thus, quantitative inheritance refers to the degree to which a
characteristic is inherited; for example, all Thoroughbred horses can run and all inherit some ability
to run, but it is the degree to which they inherit the
ability which is important.

In quantitative inheritance, the extremes (either
good or bad) tend to swing back to the average. Thus,
the offspring of a world-record stallion and a world-
record mare is not apt to be so good as either parent.
Likewise, and happily so, the progeny of two very
mediocre parents will likely be superior to either
parent.

Estimates of the number of pairs of genes affecting each economically important characteristic vary
greatly, but the majority of geneticists agree that for
most such characters 10 or more pairs of genes are involved. Growth rate in a foal, therefore, is affected by
(1) the animal's appetite or feed consumption; (2) the
efficiency of assimilation—that is, the proportion of
the feed eaten that is absorbed into the bloodstream;
and (3) the use to which the nutrients are put after
assimilation—for example, whether they are used for
growth or fattening. This example indicates that such
a characteristic as growth rate is controlled by many
genes and that it is difficult to determine the mode of
inheritance of such characters.

Heredity and Environment

A beautiful horse, standing deep in straw and
with a manger full of feed before him, is undeniably
the result of two forces—heredity and environment
(with the latter including training). If turned out to
pasture, an identical twin to the beautiful horse would
present an entirely different appearance. By the same
token, optimum environment could never make a
champion out of a horse with scrub ancestry.

[4]Castle, W. E., and King, F. L., "New Evidence on Genetics of
Palomino Horses," *The Journal of Heredity*, 42:60-64, 1951.
[5]Ibid.

These are extreme examples, and they may be applied to any class of farm animals; but they do emphasize the fact that any particular animal is the product of heredity and environment. Stated differently, heredity may be thought of as the foundation, and environment as the structure. Heredity has already made its contribution at the time of fertilization, but environment works ceaselessly away until death. Generally horse trainers believe that heredity is most important, whereas horse owners believe that environment—particularly training—is most important, especially if they lose a race. Actually, qualitative traits (such as hair and eye color) are affected little by environment; whereas quantitative traits (such as ability to run) may be affected greatly by environment.

Experimental work has long shown conclusively enough that the vigor and size of animals at birth is dependent upon the environment of the embryo from the minute the ovum or egg is fertilized by the sperm, and now we have evidence to indicate that newborn animals are affected by the environment of the egg and sperm long before fertilization has been accomplished. In other words, perhaps due to storage of factors, the kind and quality of the ration fed to young, growing females may later affect the quality of their progeny. Generally speaking, then, environment may inhibit the full expression of potentialities from a time preceding fertilization until physiological maturity has been attained.

It is generally agreed, therefore, that maximum development of characters of economic importance—growth, body form, speed, etc.—cannot be achieved unless there are optimum conditions of nutrition and management.

Admittedly, after looking over an animal or studying its production record, a breeder cannot with certainty know whether it is genetically a high or low producer. There can be no denying the fact that environment—including feeding, management, and disease—plays a tremendous part in determining the extent to which hereditary differences that are present will be expressed in animals. Yet, it would appear to be more difficult to estimate the possible effect of degree of suboptimal development than it would be to make selections on the basis of optimum environment.

Within the pure breeds of livestock—managed under average or better than average conditions—it has been found that, in general, only 15 to 30 percent of the observed variation in a characteristic is actually brought about by hereditary variations. To be sure, if we contrast animals that differ very greatly in heredity—for example, a champion horse and a scrub—90 percent or more of the apparent differences in type may be due to heredity. The point is, however, that extreme cases such as the one just mentioned are not involved in the advancement within improved breeds of livestock. Here the comparisons are between animals of average or better than average quality, and the observed differences are often very minor.

The problem of the progressive breeder is that of selecting the very best animals available genetically—these to be parents of the next generation. The fact that only 15 to 30 percent of the observed variation is due to heredity, and that environmental differences can produce misleading variations, makes mistakes in the selection of breeding animals inevitable. However, if the purebred breeder has clearly in mind a well-defined ideal and adheres rigidly to it in selecting his breeding stock, some progress can be made by selection, especially if mild inbreeding is judiciously used as a tool through which to fix the hereditary material.

HERITABILITY OF PERFORMANCE

Relatively little scientific work has been done on the heritability of performance of horses—on the genetics of working ability, racing ability, cutting ability, jumping ability, etc. As a result, the horse is the last of farm animals to which the science of genetics has been added to the art of breeding. Nevertheless, horsemen have selected for performance. For example, the Thoroughbred horse has been selected and bred for speed and stamina for 300 years. Because more often than not the "best" horse wins, the breeding of the best to the best has resulted in improvement in the track performance of the Thoroughbred horse over the centuries.

The underlying genetic principle which determines the success of mating the best to the best is based upon the assumption that the phenotypes of the best for a given trait, such as speed, are due to simple additive-type genes without regard to family relationships. On the other hand, when a breeder plans his matings on the basis of a nick, family or pedigree relationships receive careful consideration.

The underlying genetic principle in making an outcross is that the members of the unrelated strains or families will bring together genes which will act in a complimentary fashion to produce hybrid vigor in the offspring for the traits desired.

Differences in the performance ability (working, racing, cutting, jumping) are due to two major forces—heredity and environment. Success in selecting superior breeding animals for each of these traits depends entirely upon how accurately we are able to partition the differences in performance capacity of horses into causes due to the environment and causes due to heredity.

The important environment factors in determining the overall performance of horses are nutrition

(both prenatal and postnatal), health care, quality of training, ability of the horseman (teamster, rider), and injuries.

An important genetic principle is that traits as such are not inherited. Rather, what is inherited is the ability to respond to a given set of environmental conditions in order to produce a trait with a measurable effect.

The key to continued genetic improvement in the performance of a horse, such as the racing capacity of the Thoroughbred, rests essentially on two factors: (1) the magnitude of the heritable component (additive genes) of performance (racing) capacity, and (2) the accuracy with which the breeder can identify those individuals which are truly genetically superior to their contemporaries.

Essentially, the breeding value of a horse is the fraction of the differences that will be transmitted to the progeny. The most straightforward measure of this is the heritability of the trait. It follows that an estimate of heritability of a trait is one of the most important considerations in formulating an effective program of improvement through breeding. Reliable estimates on the heritability of performance traits in horses are limited in comparison with other species. Nevertheless, further and important knowledge has been accumulated in recent years. Some heritability estimates follow:

● *Working ability*—In most countries, work horses, as distinct from light horses (sporting breeds), still make up the bulk of the population. In France, for example, only 15 percent of the horse population consists of the sporting breeds.

The main measure of the working ability in a horse is pulling power. This performance trait has been estimated to have a heritability of 26 percent.[6]

● *Racing ability*—Racing performance can be measured in different ways: by purses earned, time per unit distance, handicap weight, or *Timeform* ratings or other year-end handicaps. In a 1971 study, the Texas Agricultural Experiment Station[7] determined the racing ability of individual horses through a computer comparison of the number of lengths (one length = 8 ft) the horse would win or lose to other horses in a typical race. For this unique study, each horse was given a rating called the "Performance Rate." Theoretically, it was assumed that the average horse would have a Performance Rate of zero. Then, in an average race, a horse with a Performance Rate of +12 would, theoretically, finish 12 lengths in front of the average horse. Likewise, a horse whose Perform-

ance Rate was _12 would, theoretically, finish 12 lengths behind the average horse and 24 lengths behind one with a +12 Performance Rate.

The Texas Station study included all 3-year-olds which raced on North American tracks in 1971. It involved 6,458 fillies and 7,113 colts and geldings, which were sired by 3,228 different stallions. Statistical analysis of the data showed that racing ability is about 40% heritable. This means that, on the average, about 40% of the difference in racing superiority of one horse over another is due to differences in heredity. The remaining 60% is due to difference in environment—nutrition, state of health, and abilities of trainers and jockeys.

So, after nearly three centuries of selection for speed and stamina, it should still be possible to improve the racing performance of Thoroughbred horses through selection of superior stock for future parents.

● *Cutting ability*—Based on a study made by the Texas Station, the cutting ability of horses is less than 10 percent heritable.[8] Obviously, training is most important in determining cutting ability.

● *Jumping ability*—Based on a study of steeplechase results in France, involving 3,500 progeny of 326 stallions, the heritability of jumping was estimated to be 18 percent.[9]

Although the heritability estimates of performance traits in horses above reported are disturbingly low, genes are a permanent, transmissible investment, whereas environmental factors are not. When buying horses, therefore, it is important to know whether you're buying desirable genes or superior environment.

How Sex Is Determined

On the average, and when considering a large population, approximately equal numbers of males and females are born in all common species of animals. To be sure, many notable exceptions can be found in individual herds or flocks.

Sex is determined by the chromosomal makeup of the individual. One particular pair of the chromosomes is called the sex chromosomes. In farm animals, the female has a pair of similar chromosomes (usually called X chromosomes), whereas the male has a pair of unlike sex chromosomes (usually called X and Y chromosomes). In the bird, this condition is reversed, the female having the unlike pair and the male having the like pair.

The pairs of sex chromosomes separate out when

[6]Cunningham, Professor E. P., Head of Animal Breeding and Genetics, Dublin University, Ireland, "Equine Genetics," *The Blood-Horse*, Oct. 6, 1975, p. 4210.

[7]Kieffer, Dr. N. M., Geneticist, Texas A&M University, College Station, Texas, "Heritability of Racing Ability," *The Blood-Horse*, Oct. 13, 1975, p. 4292.

[8]Kieffer, Dr. N. M., Geneticist, Texas A&M University, College Station, Texas, *Research Report*, Texas A&M Experiment Station, Dec. 3, 1975.

[9]Cunningham, Professor E. P., Head of Animal Breeding and Genetics, Dublin University, Ireland, "Equine Genetics," *The Blood-Horse*, Oct. 6, 1975, p. 4210.

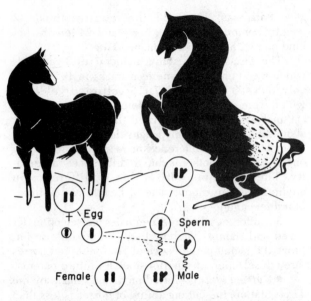

Fig. 12-6. Diagrammatic illustration of the mechanism of sex determination in horses, showing how sex is determined by the chromosomal makeup of the individual. The mare has a pair of like sex chromosomes, whereas the stallion has a pair of unlike sex chromosomes. Thus, if an egg and sperm of like sex chromosomal makeup unites, the offspring will be a filly; whereas if an egg and sperm of unlike sex chromosomal makeup unite, the offspring will be a colt. (Drawing by Prof. R. F. Johnson)

the germ cells are formed. Thus, each of the ova or eggs produced by the mare contains the X chromosome; whereas the sperm of the stallion are of two types, ½ containing the X chromosome and the other ½ the Y chromosome. Since, on the average, the eggs and sperm unite at random, it can be understood that half of the progeny will contain the chromosomal makeup XX (female) and the other ½ XY (males).[10]

Lethals in Horses

The term lethal refers to a genetic factor that causes death of the animal, either during prenatal life, at birth, or later in life. Other defects occur which are not sufficiently severe to cause death but which do impair the usefulness of affected animals.

Many abnormal foals are born each year. Unfortunately, the purebred breeder, whose chief business is that of selling breeding stock, is likely to "keep mum" about the appearance of any defective animals in his herd because of the justifiable fear that it may hurt his sales.

The embryological development—the development of the young from the time that the egg and the sperm unite until the animal is born—is very compli-

---

[10]The scientists' symbols for the male and female, respectively, are:
♂ (the sacred shield and spear of Mars, the Roman god of war), and
♀ (the looking glass of Venus, the Roman goddess of love and beauty).

cated. Thus, the oddity probably is that so many of the offspring develop normally rather than that a few develop abnormally.

Many such abnormalities (commonly known as monstrosities or freaks) are hereditary, being caused by certain "bad" genes. Moreover, the bulk of such lethals are recessive and may, therefore, remain hidden for many generations. The prevention of such genetic abnormalities requires that the germ plasm be purged of the "bad" genes. This means that, where recessive lethals are involved, the horseman must be aware of the fact that both parents carry the gene. For the total removal of the lethals, test matings and rigid selection must be practiced. The best test mating to use for a given stallion consists in mating him to some of his own daughters.

In addition to hereditary abnormalities, there are certain abnormalities that may be due to nutritional deficiencies, or to "accidents of development"—the latter including those which appear to occur sporadically and for which there is no well-defined reason. When only a few defective individuals occur within a particular herd, it is often impossible to determine whether their occurrence is due to (1) defective heredity, (2) defective nutrition, or (3) merely to accidents of development. If the same abnormality occurs to any appreciable number of animals, however, it is probably either hereditary or nutritional. In any event, the diagnosis of the condition is not always a simple matter.

The following conditions would tend to indicate a *hereditary* defect in horses:

1. If the defect had previously been reported as hereditary in the same breed.

2. If it occurred more frequently within certain families or when there had been inbreeding.

3. If it occurred in more than one season and when different rations had been fed.

The following conditions might be accepted as indications that the abnormality was due to a *nutritional* deficiency:

1. If it had previously been reliably reported to be due to a nutritional deficiency.

2. If it appeared to be restricted to a certain area.

3. If it occurred when the ration of the dam was known to be deficient.

4. If it disappeared when an improved ration was fed.

If there is suspicion that the ration is defective, it should be improved, not only from the standpoint of preventing such deformities, but from the standpoint of good and efficient management.

If there is good and sufficient evidence that the abnormal condition is hereditary, the steps to be followed in purging the herd of the undesirable gene are

identical to those for ridding the herd of any other undesirable recessive factor. An inbreeding program, of course, is the most effective way in which to expose hereditary lethals in order that purging may follow.

Some of the genetic defects that have been reported in horses are summarized in Table 12-1.

TABLE 12-1
SOME GENETIC DEFECTS OF HORSES

Trait	Description	Probable Mode of Inheritance
Abnormal sex ratio	Ratio of 55 males to 90 females reported in Oldenburger breed of horses. About ½ the males die before birth or during the early stages of prenatal development.	Recessive
Artesia coli	Closure of colon; often associated with brain defects. Affected foals stand with difficulty, soon develop colic and die. Surgery is unsuccessful.	Recessive
Barker (wanderer, dummy)	Foals completely disorientated at birth or soon thereafter. In severe cases, the animal goes down, followed by violent convulsions. In the latter stage, it emits a sound like a yelping dog; hence, the name "barker."	Unknown
Big head	Bony enlargements on both sides of face, below eyes.	Dominant
Blindness	Foals born blind.	Recessive
Cataract	Loss of transparency of the lens of the eye or its capsule.	Recessive
Chestnuts missing	Chestnuts on hind legs missing.	Dominant
Contracted heels	Drawing in or contracting at the heels.	2 pairs of recessive genes
Cryptorchidism	Both testicles small and retained in abdomen.	Dominant
Curly coat	Hair is curly.	Recessive
Fetal membrane defective	Fetal membrane fails to grow and abortion results.	Recessive
Flat feet	Flat sole, and soft keratin.	Recessive
Foal ataxia	Foal weak legged and can't walk. Dies in 8-14 days.	Recessive
Hernia, scrotal	Intestines pass through inguinal ring into stallion's scrotum.	2 pairs of recessive genes
Hernia, umbilical	Intestines protrude through umbilical opening. It usually disappears within the first few months of the foal's life. If the hernia persists, surgical repair may be necessary. The latter is usually very successful.	Recessive
Hydrocephalus	Water on the brain.	Unknown
Isoerythrolysis (Haemolytic anemia, or jaundice)	Foals born normal and remain normal until they suckle. After they suckle, they become weak and lethargic, the body temperature drops, and the yellowish discoloration of jaundice appears on the membranes of the mouth and eyes. This condition results from the destruction of the foal's red blood cells by antibodies which the foal ingests from its mother's colostrum.	Unknown
Lameness	Hind legs alternate in lameness; first one, then the other. When acute, movement is difficult.	Dominant
Lethal white	Low fertility; first reported in horses of the Frederiksborg breed, in Denmark.	Unknown
Mallenders	An eczemalike condition of the skin caused by a protozoan parasite. However, there is some evidence that susceptibility to the parasite is inherited.	Recessive
Myopia	Nearsightedness.	Recessive
Parrot mouth	Upper jaw protrudes beyond lower jaw, like the beak of a parrot.	Dominant
Roaring	Wind broken; horse makes a loud noise in drawing air into the lungs.	Recessive
Skin defect	Patches of skin on body without hair. Hoof is sometimes missing, also.	Recessive
Stiff forelegs	Foals born with stiff forelegs.	Recessive
Stringhalt	Excessive flexing of hind legs.	Recessive
Wobbles	Incoordination; weaving gait in the rear legs.	Unknown

Hybrids with the Horse as One Parent

The mule, representing a cross between the jack (male of the ass family) on the mare (female of the horse family), is the best-known hybrid in the United States. The resulting offspring of the reciprocal cross of the stallion mated to a jennet is known as a hinny.

Rarely have mules proved fertile; only five authentic cases of mare mules producing foals have been reported in the United States. This infertility of the mule is probably due to the fact that the chromosomes will not pair and divide equally in the reduction division.

Fig. 12-7. One of the rarest of nature's whims—a colt dropped by a mare mule. The colt, sired by a stallion, was born in St. Martinsville, Louisiana, Nov. 13, 1947. "Lou"—the 21-year-old mother mule—pulled a cane wagon all day on Nov. 12. She was owned by Acie Miller, a St. Martinsville mule trader. The case of this unusual birth was verified by Dr. George P. Broussard, DVM, New Iberia, Louisiana. (Photo, courtesy, Dr. Broussard)

The offspring of fertile mules are generally horse-like in appearance,[11] showing none of the characteristics of the mule's sire (or ass). For the most part, therefore, the eggs (ova) which produce them do not

[11]Not all are horselike, however. Thus, one of Old Beck's (fertile mule owned by Texas A&M College) three offspring was mulelike in appearance.

carry chromosomes from the ass; they are pure horse eggs without any inheritance from their maternal grandfathers. This indicates that in the production of eggs in mare mules the reduction division is such that all of the horse chromosomes go to the egg and none to the polar bodies.

It is interesting to project the probability of a horselike animal being produced from a fertile mare mule and a horse sire. Assuming (1) that the offspring is the result of cases where all the horse chromosomes and all the ass chromosomes go to opposite poles in the dam during oogenesis, and (2) that this "horse egg" was fertilized, the chance is 1 in 2^{32}, or 1 in 4,294,967,296. Since this is the number of ways in which the horse's chromosomes may rearrange themselves, it speaks highly for the skill of the successful horse breeder.

The zebroid—a zebra X horse hybrid—is rather popular in certain areas of the tropics because of its docility and resistance to disease and heat.

Relative Importance of the Stallion and the Mare

As a stallion can have so many more offspring during a given season or a lifetime than a mare, he is from a hereditary standpoint a more important individual than any one mare so far as the whole herd is concerned, although both the stallion and the mare are of equal importance so far as concerns any one offspring. Because of their wider use, therefore, stallions are usually culled more rigidly than mares, and the breeder can well afford to pay more for an outstanding stallion than for an equally outstanding mare.

Experienced horsemen have long felt that stallions and their fillies usually resemble each other, and that mares and their colts resemble each other. Some stallions and mares, therefore, enjoy a reputation based almost exclusively on the merit of their sons, whereas others owe their prestige to their daughters. Although this situation is likely to be exaggerated, any such phenomenon that may exist is due to sex-linked inheritance which may be explained as follows: The genes that determine sex are carried on one of the chromosomes. The other genes that are located on the same chromosome will be linked or associated with sex and will be transmitted to the next generation in combination with sex. Thus, because of sex linkage, there are more color-blind men than color-blind women. In poultry breeding, the sex-linked factor is used in a practical way for the purpose of distinguishing the pullets from the cockerels early in life, through the process known as "sexing" the chicks. Thus, when a black cock is crossed with barred hens, all the cocks come barred and all the hens come black. It should be emphasized, however,

that under most conditions it appears that the influence of the sire and dam on any one offspring is about equal. Most breeders, therefore, will do well to seek excellence in both sexes of breeding animals.

Prepotency

Prepotency refers to the ability of the animal, either male or female, to stamp its own characteristics on its offspring. The offspring of a prepotent stallion, for example, resemble both their sire and each other more closely than usual. The only conclusive and final test of prepotency consists in the inspection of the get.

From a genetic standpoint, there are two requisites that an animal must possess in order to be prepotent: (1) dominance, and (2) homozygosity. All offspring that receive dominant genes will show the effects of those genes in the particular characters which result therefrom. Moreover, perfectly homozygous animals would transmit the same kind of genes to all of their offspring. Although entirely homozygous animals probably never exist, it is realized that a system of inbreeding is the only way to produce animals that are as nearly homozygous as possible.

It should also be emphasized that it is impossible to determine just how important prepotency may be in animal breeding, although many sires of the past have enjoyed a reputation for being extremely prepotent. Perhaps these animals were prepotent, but there is also the possibility that their reputation for producing outstanding animals may have rested upon the fact that they were mated to some of the best females of the breed.

In summary, it may be said that if a given stallion or mare possesses a great number of genes that are completely dominant for desirable type and performance and if the animal is relatively homozygous, the offspring will closely resemble the parent and resemble each other, or be uniform. Fortunate, indeed, is the breeder who possesses such an animal.

Nicking

If the offspring of certain matings are especially outstanding and in general better than their parents, breeders are prone to say that the animals "nicked" well. For example, a mare may produce outstanding foals to the service of a certain stallion, but when mated to another stallion of apparent equal merit as a sire, the offspring may be disappointing. Or sometimes the mating of a rather average stallion to an equally average mare will result in the production of a most outstanding individual both from the standpoint of type and performance.

So-called successful nicking is due, genetically speaking, to the fact that the right combinations of genes for good characters are contributed by each parent, although each of the parents within itself may be lacking in certain genes necessary for excellence. In other words, the animals nicked well because their respective combinations of good genes were such as to complement each other.

The history of animal breeding includes records of several supposedly favorable nicks. Because of the very nature of successful nicks, however, outstanding animals arising therefrom must be carefully scrutinized from a breeding standpoint, because, with their heterozygous origin, it is quite unlikely that they will breed true.

Family Names

In animals, depending upon the breed, family names are traced through either the males or the females. Unfortunately, the value of family names is generally grossly exaggerated. Obviously, if the foundation stallion or mare, as the case may be, is very many generations removed, the genetic superiority of this head of a family is halved so many times by subsequent matings that there is little reason to think that one family is superior to another. The situation is often further distorted by breeders placing a premium on family names of which there are few members, little realizing that, in at least some cases, there may be unfortunate reasons for the scarcity in numbers.

Such family names have about as much significance as human family names. Who would be so foolish as to think that the Joneses as a group are alike and different from the Smiths? Perhaps, if the truth were known, there have been many individuals with each of these family names who have been of no particular credit to the clan, and the same applies to all other family names.

Family names lend themselves readily to speculation. Because of this, the history of livestock breeding has often been blighted by instances of unwise pedigree selection on the basis of not too meaningful family names.

On the other hand, certain linebred families—linebred to a foundation sire or dam so that the family is kept highly related to it—do have genetic significance. Moreover, if the programs involved have been accompanied by rigid culling, many good individuals may have evolved, and the family name may be in good repute.

SYSTEMS OF BREEDING

The many diverse types and breeds among each class of farm animals in existence today originated from only a few wild types within each species. These early domesticated animals possessed the pool of genes, which, through controlled matings and selection, proved flexible in the hands of man. In horses,

for example, through various systems of breeding, there evolved animals especially adapted to riding, racing, and driving.

Perhaps at the outset it should be stated that there is no one best system of breeding or secret of success for any and all conditions. Each breeding program is an individual case, requiring careful study. The choice of the system of breeding should be determined primarily by the size and quality of the herd, by the finances and skill of the operator, and by the ultimate goal ahead.

Purebreeding

A purebred animal may be defined as a member of a breed, the animals of which possess a common ancestry and distinctive characteristics; and it is either registered or eligible for registry in that breed.

The breed association consists of a group of breeders banded together for the purposes of (1) recording the lineage of their animals, (2) protecting the purity of the breed, and (3) promoting the interest of the breed.

The term purebred refers to animals whose entire lineage, regardless of the number of generations removed, traces back to the foundation animals accepted by the breed or to animals which have been subsequently approved for infusion. It should be emphasized that the word purebred does not necessarily guarantee superior type or high productivity. That is to say, the word purebred is not, within itself, magic, nor is it sacred. Many a person has found to his sorrow that there are such things as purebred scrubs. Yet, on the average, purebred animals are superior to nonpurebreds.

For the man with experience and adequate capital, the breeding of purebreds may offer unlimited opportunities. It has been well said that honor, fame, and fortune are all within the realm of possible realization of the purebred breeder; but it should also be added that only a few achieve this high calling.

Purebred breeding is a highly specialized type of production. Generally speaking, only the experienced breeder should undertake the production of purebreds with the intention of furnishing foundation or replacement stock to other purebred breeders. Although we have had many constructive horse breeders and great progress has been made, it must be remembered that only a few achieve sufficient success to classify as master breeders. However, this need not discourage the small operator—the owner of one mare, or of a few mares—from mating to a good purebred stallion of the same breed, in order to produce some good horses.

Inbreeding

Most scientists divide inbreeding into various categories, according to the closeness of the relationship of the animals mated and the purpose of the matings. There is considerable disagreement, however, as to both the terms used and the meanings that it is intended they should convey. For purposes of this book and the ensuing discussion, the following definitions will be used.

Inbreeding is the mating of animals more closely related than the average of the population from which they came.

Closebreeding is the mating of closely related animals—such as sire to daughter, son to dam, and brother to sister.

Linebreeding is the mating of animals more distantly related than in closebreeding, and in which the matings are usually directed toward keeping the offspring closely related to some highly admired ancestor—such as half-brother and half-sister, female and grandsire, and cousins.

CLOSEBREEDING

Closebreeding is rarely practiced among present-day horsemen, though it was common in the foundation animals of most of the breeds. There is good reason why closebreeding is seldom followed with horses, especially racehorses, because (1) experiments with other animals clearly show that closebreeding (inbreeding above a level of about 10%) results in less vigor, and (2) there is not available a desirable outlet for horses of poor type or performance, such as is afforded when discarded cattle, sheep, and swine are marketed for slaughter. Even so, the enlightened horseman will want to be familiar with the reasons for and the precautions against practicing closebreeding.

Closebreeding results in a minimum number of different ancestors. Thus, in the repeated mating of a brother with his full sister, there are only 2 grandparents instead of 4, only 2 great-grandparents instead of 8 and only 2 different ancestors in each generation farther back—instead of the theoretically possible 16, 32, 64, 128, etc. The most intensive form of inbreeding is self-fertilization. It occurs in some plants, such as wheat and garden peas, and in some of the lower animals.

The reasons for practicing closebreeding are:

1. It increases the degree of homozygosity within animals, making the resulting offspring pure or homozygous in a larger proportion of their gene pairs than in the case of linebred or outcross animals. In so doing, the less desirable recessive genes are brought to light so that they can be more readily culled. Thus, closebreeding, together with rigid culling, affords the surest and quickest method of fixing and perpetuating a desirable character or group of characters.

2. If carried on for a period of time, it tends to create lines or strains of animals that are uniform in type and other characteristics.

3. It keeps the relationship to a desirable ancestor highest.

4. Because of the greater homozygosity, it makes for greater prepotency. That is, selected inbred animals are more homozygous for desirable genes (genes which are often dominant), and they, therefore, transmit these genes with greater uniformity.

5. Through the production of inbred lines or families by closebreeding and the subsequent crossing of certain of these lines, it affords a modern approach to livestock improvement. Moreover, the best of the inbred animals are likely to give superior results in outcrosses.

6. Where a breeder is in the unique position of having his herd so far advanced that to go on the outside for seed stock would merely be a step backward, it offers the only sound alternative for maintaining existing quality or making further improvement.

The disadvantages of closebreeding may be summarized as follows:

1. As closebreeding greatly enhances the chances that recessives will appear during the early generations in obtaining homozygosity, it is almost certain to increase the proportion of worthless breeding stock produced. This may include such so-called degenerates as reduction in size, fertility, and general vigor. Lethals and other genetic abnormalities often appear with increased frequency in inbred animals.

2. Because of the rigid culling necessary in order to avoid the "fixing" of undesirable characters, especially in the first generations of a closebreeding program, it is almost imperative that this system of breeding be confined to a relatively large herd and to instances when the owner has sufficient finances to stand the rigid culling that must accompany such a program.

3. It requires skill in making planned matings and rigid selection, thus being most successful when applied by "master breeders."

4. It is not adapted for use by the man with average or below average stock because the very fact that his animals are average means that a goodly share of undesirable genes are present. Closebreeding would merely make the animals more homozygous for undesirable genes and, therefore, worse.

Judging from outward manifestations alone, it might appear that closebreeding is predominantly harmful in its effects—often leading to the production of defective animals lacking in the vitality necessary for successful and profitable production. But this is by no means the whole story. Although closebreeding often leads to the production of animals of low value, the resulting superior animals can confidently be expected to be homozygous for a greater than average number of good genes and thus more valuable for breeding purposes. Figuratively speaking, therefore, closebreeding may be referred to as "trial by fire," and the breeder who practices it can expect to obtain many animals that fail to measure up and have to be culled. On the other hand, if closebreeding is handled properly, he can also expect to secure animals of exceptional value.

Although closebreeding has been practiced less during the past century than in the formative period of the different pure breeds of livestock, it has real merit when its principles and limitations are fully understood. Perhaps closebreeding had best be confined to use by the skilled master breeder who is in a sufficiently sound financial position to endure rigid, intelligent culling and delayed returns and whose herd is both large and above average in quality.

LINEBREEDING

From a biological standpoint, closebreeding and linebreeding are the same thing, differing merely in intensity. In general, closebreeding has been frowned upon by horsemen, but linebreeding (the less intensive form) has been looked upon with favor in some quarters.

In a linebreeding program, the degree of relationship is not closer than half-brother and half-sister or matings more distantly related—cousin matings, grandparents and grand offspring, etc.

Linebreeding may be practiced in order to conserve and perpetuate the good traits of a certain outstanding stallion or mare. Because such descendants are of similar lineage, they have the same general type of germ plasm and therefore exhibit a high degree of uniformity in type and performance.

In a more limited way, a linebreeding program has the same advantages and disadvantages of a closebreeding program. Stated differently, linebreeding offers fewer possibilities both for good and harm than closebreeding. It is a more conservative and safer type of program, offering less probability of either hitting the jackpot or sinking the ship. It is a middle-of-the-road program that the vast majority of average and small breeders can safely follow to their advantage. Through it, reasonable progress can be made without taking any great risk. A greater degree of homozygosity of certain desirable genes can be secured without running too great a risk of intensifying undesirable ones.

Usually a linebreeding program is best accomplished through breeding to an outstanding sire rather than to an outstanding dam because of the greater number of offspring of the former. If a horse breeder found himself in possession of a great

stallion—proved great by the performance records of a large number of his get—a linebreeding program might be initiated in the following way: Select two of the best sons of the noted stallion and mate them to their half-sisters, balancing all possible defects in the subsequent matings. The next generation mating might well consist of breeding the daughters of one of the stallions to the son of the other, etc. If, in such a program, it seems wise to secure some outside blood (genes) to correct a common defect or defects in the herd, this may be done through selecting a few outstanding proved mares from the outside—animals whose get are strong where the herd may be deficient—and then mating these mares to one of the linebred stallions with the hope of producing a son that may be used in the herd.

The small operator—the owner of one mare, or of a few mares—can often follow a linebreeding program by breeding his mares to a stallion owned by a large breeder who follows such a program—thus, in effect, following the linebreeding program of the larger breeder.

Naturally, a linebreeding program may be achieved in other ways. Regardless of the actual matings used, the main objective in such a system of breeding is that of rendering the animals homozygous—in desired type and performance—to some great and highly regarded ancestor, while at the same time weeding out homozygous undesirable characteristics. The success of the program, therefore, is dependent upon having desirable genes with which to start and an intelligent intensification of these good genes.

It should be emphasized that there are some types of herds that should almost never closebreed or linebreed. These include herds of only average quality.

With purebred herds of only average quality, more rapid progress can usually be made by introducing superior outcross sires. Moreover, were the animals of only average quality they would have a preponderance of "bad" genes that would only be intensified through a closebreeding or linebreeding program.

Outcrossing

Outcrossing is the mating of animals that are members of the same breed but which show no relationship close up in the pedigree (for at least the first four or six generations).

Most of our purebred animals of all classes of livestock are the result of outcrossing. It is a relatively safe system of breeding, for it is unlikely that two such unrelated animals will carry the same undesirable genes and pass them on to their offspring.

Perhaps it might well be added that the majority

of purebred breeders with average or below average herds had best follow an outcrossing program, because, in such herds, the problem is that of retaining a heterozygous type of germ plasm with the hope that genes for undesirable characters will be counteracted by genes for desirable characters. With such average or below average herds, an inbreeding program would merely make the animals homozygous for the less desirable characters, the presence of which already makes for their mediocrity. In general, continued outcrossing offers neither the hope for improvement nor the hazard of retrogression of linebreeding or inbreeding programs.

Judicious and occasional outcrossing may well be an integral part of linebreeding or inbreeding programs. As closely inbred animals become increasingly homozygous with germ plasm for good characters, they may likewise become homozygous for certain undesirable characters even though their general overall type and performance remain well above the breed average. Such defects may best be remedied by introducing an outcross through an animal or animals known to be especially strong in the character or characters needing strengthening. This having been accomplished, the wise breeder will return to the original inbreeding or linebreeding program, realizing full well the limitations of an outcrossing program.

Grading Up

Grading up is that system of breeding in which a purebred sire of a given breed is mated to a native or grade female. Its purpose is to impart quality and to increase performance in the offspring. It is the common system of breeding followed on the western range, where mares of Mustang background are generally graded up by using a purebred stallion of a certain breed (usually either a Quarter Horse or a Thoroughbred), year after year, in producing cow ponies. Likewise, horse owners of the one- to two-mare variety frequently mate their grade mare(s) to a purebred stallion of the same breed, in order to produce hunters, jumpers, pleasure horses, etc.

Naturally, the greatest single step toward improved quality and performance occurs in the first cross. The first generation from such a mating results in offspring carrying 50% of the hereditary material of the purebred parent (or 50% of the "blood" of the purebred parent, as many horsemen speak of it). The next generation gives offspring carrying 75% of the "blood" of the purebred breed, and in subsequent generations the proportion of inheritance remaining from the original scrub parent is halved with each cross. Later crosses will usually continue to increase quality and performance slightly more, though in less marked degree. After the third or fourth cross, the offspring compare very favorably with purebred stock

in conformation, and only exceptionally good sires can bring about further improvement. This is especially so if the stallions used in grading up successive generations are derived from the same strain within a breed.

As evidence that horses of high merit may be produced through grading up, examples of champion performers among hunters, jumpers, polo ponies, cow ponies, etc., might be cited.

Crossbreeding

Crossbreeding is the mating of animals of different breeds. In a broad sense, crossbreeding also includes the mating of purebred sires of one breed with high-grade females of another breed.

Perhaps in the final analysis, all would agree that any merits that crossbreeding may possess are and will continue to be based on improved "seed stock." Certainly, from a genetic standpoint, it should be noted that crossbred animals generally possess greater heterozygosity than outcross animals—with the added virtue of hybrid vigor. It may also be added that, as in outcrossing, the recessive and undesirable genes remain hidden in the crossbred animal.

On purely theoretical grounds, it would appear that crossbreeding should result in some increase in vigor because the desirable genes from both breeds would be combined and the undesirable genes from each would tend to be overshadowed as recessives.

In summary, it can be said that crossbreeding has a place, particularly from the standpoint of increased vigor, growth rate, efficiency of production, and in the creation of new breeds adapted to certain conditions; but purebreeding will continue to control the destiny of further improvement in horses and furnish the desired homozygosity and uniformity which many horsemen insist is a part of the art of breeding better horses.

RECORD FORMS

An important requisite in any horse breeding program is the keeping of relatively simple but meaningful records. Figs. 12-8a, 12-8b, 12-9a, and 12-9b are record forms developed by the author. One is for the broodmare, and the other is for the stallion. These record forms may be modified somewhat to suit individual needs and desires. (See page 156-159.)

PERFORMANCE TESTING HORSES

The breeders of racehorses have always followed a program of mating animals of proved performance on the track. For example, it is interesting to note that the first breed register which appeared in 1791—known as "An Introduction to The General Stud Book,"—recorded the pedigrees of all the Thoroughbred horses winning important races. In a similar way, the Standardbred horse—which is an American creation—takes its name from the fact that, in its early history, animals were required to trot a mile in 2 minutes and 30 seconds, or to pace a mile in 2 minutes and 25 seconds, before they could be considered as eligible for registry. The chief aim, therefore, of early-day breeders of racehorses was to record the pedigree of outstanding performers rather than all members of the breed.

Thus, Thoroughbred or Standardbred animals bred for racing may be performance tested by timing on the track. The working ability of draft horses may be measured in pulling power on the dynamometer. Less satisfactory tests for saddle horses and harness horses have been devised. However, it is conceivable that actual exhibiting on the tanbark in the great horse shows of the country may be an acceptable criterion for saddle- and harness-bred animals.

PART II. SOME PHYSIOLOGICAL ASPECTS OF REPRODUCTION IN HORSES

Horse producers have many reproductive problems, a reduction of which calls for a full understanding of reproductive physiology and the application of scientific practices therein.

REPRODUCTIVE ORGANS OF THE STALLION

The stallion's functions in reproduction are (1) to produce the male reproductive cells, the sperm or spermatozoa, and (2) to introduce sperm into the female reproductive tract at the proper time. Fig. 12-10 is a schematic drawing of the reproductive organs of the stallion. (See page 160.)

The primary sex organ of the stallion is the testicle (there are two testicles). The testicles produce (1) sperm, and (2) a hormone called testosterone, which regulates and maintains the male reproductive tract in its functional state and is responsible for the masculine appearance and behavior of the stallion.

Sperm production takes place in the seminiferous tubules—a mass of minute, coiled tubules, the inner walls or surface of which produce the sperm. These tubules merge into a series of larger ducts which carry the sperm to a coiled tube called the epididymis. The epididymis is the place where the sperm are stored, and where they mature or ripen.

The testicles and epididymides are enclosed in the scrotum, the chief function of which is thermoregulatory—to maintain the testicles at temperatures several degrees cooler than the body proper.

From the epididymis, the sperm move through a tube, the vas deferens, into the urethra. The urethra

INDIVIDUAL LIFETIME BROODMARE RECORD

Name of mare _____

Number or other identity _____

Birth date _____

Show or performance record _____

Temperament _____
(gentle, nervous, cross)

Bred by _____ (name and address)

Purchased: from _____ (name and address)

Date _____ Price _____

Disposal: Sold to _____ (name and address)

Date _____ Price _____

Remarks _____

PHOTO

Production Record of Mares

Year	Sire of foal	Birth date of foal	Temperament of mare at foaling (gentle, nervous, cross)	Foaling (normal, requiring assistance ret. placenta)	Vigor foal at birth (deformities)	Sex of foal	Identity of foal	Date foal was weaned	Score of foal				Disposal of foal				
									Under 1-year	Yearling	2-year-old	3-year-old	Sold to: (name and address)	Date	Price	Reasons	Remarks

Fig. 12-8a. Individual Lifetime Broodmare Record. (See Fig. 12-8b for reverse side of record form.)

Health Record

Date	Immunization			Type of parasite treatment	Other veterinary treatment	Remarks
	Encephalomyelitis	Tetanus	Abortion			

Fig. 12-8b. Individual Lifetime Broodmare Record.   (This is the reverse side of Fig. 12-8a.)

INDIVIDUAL YEARLY STALLION BREEDING RECORD

Name of stallion _____

Number or other identity _____

Birth date _____

Show or performance record _____

_____

For breeding year of _____

For foaling year of _____

Total number of services _____

No. services/conception _____

PHOTO

Mares in Foal to Stallion

Name of mare	Date mare was bred	Date foaled	Vigor of foal at birth	Sex of foal	Disposal of foal				Remarks
					Sold to (name and address)	Date	Price	Reasons	

Fig. 12-9a. Individual Yearly Stallion Breeding Record.   (See Fig. 12-9b for reverse side of record form.)

Health Record

Date	Immunization			Type of parasite treatment	Semen test	Veterinary treatment	Remarks
	Encephalomyelitis	Tetanus	Other				

Fig. 12-9b. Individual Yearly Stallion Breeding Record. (This is the reverse side of Fig. 12-9a.)

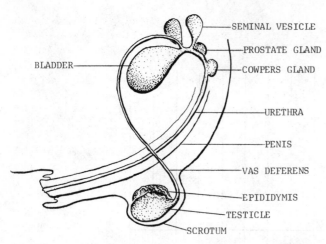

Fig. 12-10. The reproductive organs of the stallion. (Drawing by Ethel Gadberry)

has a dual role; it carries (1) urine from the bladder through the penis, and (2) sperm from the junction with the vas deferens to the end of the penis.

Among the urethra are the accessory glands—the prostate, the seminal vesicles, and Cowper's glands. Their fluids nourish and preserve the sperm, and provide a medium for its transport. The combined sperm and fluid is called semen.

REPRODUCTIVE ORGANS OF THE MARE

The mare's functions in reproduction are to (1) produce the female reproductive cells, the eggs or ova; (2) develop the new individual, the embryo, in the uterus; (3) expel the fully developed young at the time of birth or parturition; and (4) produce milk for the nourishment of the young. Actually, the part played by the mare in the generative process is much more complicated than that of the stallion. It is imperative, therefore, that the modern horseman have a full understanding of the anatomy of the reproductive organs of the mare and the functions of each part. Fig. 12-11 shows the reproductive organs of the mare.

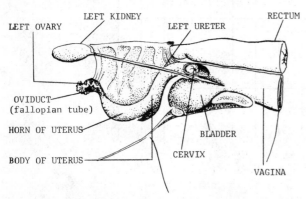

Fig. 12-11. The reproductive organs of the mare. (Drawing by Ethel Gadberry)

The primary sex organ of the mare is the ovary (there are 2 ovaries). These are somewhat bean-shaped organs 2 to 3 inches long. The ovaries produce eggs. Each egg is contained in a bubblelike sac on the ovary, called a follicle. There are hundreds of follicles on every ovary. Generally, the follicles remain in an unchanged state until the advent of puberty, at which time one of them begins to grow through an increase in the follicular liquid within, while the others remain small. The egg is suspended in the follicular fluid. When the follicle is about an inch in diameter (which coincides with the time of mating of mares that are bred), a hormone causes it to rupture and discharge the egg, which process is known as ovulation. The egg is then trapped in a funnel-shaped membrane, called the infundibulum, that surrounds the ovary. The infundibulum narrows into a tube called the oviduct. The oviduct then carries the egg to the uterus, or womb, the largest of the female reproductive organs, where the unborn young (the fetus) will develop. The lining of the uterus is soft and spongy, containing a vast network of blood vessels, which provides a "bed" for the fertilized egg to settle into and develop. At birth, the heavy layers of muscles of the uterus wall contract with great pressure to force the new animal through the cervix and vagina (birth canal) and out into the new world.

NORMAL BREEDING HABITS OF MARES

Perhaps at the outset it should be emphasized that strictly normal breeding habits of the horse do not exist under domestication. In the wild state, each band of 30 to 40 mares was headed by a stallion leader who sired all of the foals in that band. With plenty of outdoor exercise on natural footing, superior nutrition derived from plants grown on unleached soils, regular production beginning at an early age, little possibility of disease or infection, and frequent services during the heat period, 90% or higher foaling rates were commonplace. Under domestication, the average conception rate is less than 50% and only the better establishment exceeds 70%. Thus, the low fertility usually encountered under domestication must be caused to a large extent by the relatively artificial conditions under which horses are mated.

Age of Puberty

Mares generally start coming in heat when 12 to 15 months of age.

Age to Breed Mares

Only exceptionally well-grown fillies should be bred as late 2-year-olds, so as to foal at 3 years of age. Under a system of early breeding, the fillies must be

fed exceptionally well in order to provide growth for their own immature bodies as well as for the developing fetus. Furthermore, they usually should not be bred the following year. Generally speaking, it is best to breed the mare as a 3-year-old so that she will foal when 4. Not only will the 3-year-old be better grown, but there will not be the handicap of training her while she is heavy in foal.

If they are properly cared for, it is not uncommon for broodmares to produce regularly up to 14 to 16 years of age; and, of course, in the more exceptional cases they may produce up to 25 years of age.

In selecting a broodmare, it is usually advisable either to obtain a young three- or four-year-old or to make certain of the sure and regular breeding habits of any old mares.

Heat Periods

The heat periods recur approximately at 21-day intervals, with a spread of from 10 to 37 days. The duration of heat varies from 1 to 37 days and averages 4 to 6 days, although some mares (especially maiden mares) will remain in heat up to 50 to 60 days in the early spring. Maiden mares that show "in heat" signs practically every day for many weeks should not be bred, as it is a waste of time and effort. In the vast majority of such cases, patience is rewarded by the mare subsequently settling into a normal cycle.

SIGNS OF ESTRUS

The experienced horseman who is familiar with a band of mares can usually detect those that are in season by observing (1) the relaxation of the external genitals, (2) more frequent urination, (3) the teasing of other mares, (4) the apparent desire for company, and (5) a slight mucous discharge from the vagina. In shy breeders or when there is any question about the mare being in season, she should be tried as subsequently discussed. When possible, it is usually good business regularly to present mares to the teaser every day or every other day as the breeding season approaches. A systematic plan of this sort will save much time and trouble.

Above all, precaution should be taken against false heats of mares in foal, the breeding of which may result in abortion. Such precaution is obtained by properly teasing the mare under the watchful eye of an experienced horseman who is familiar with the peculiarities of the individual animal.

Fertilization

Generally, the egg is liberated during the period of one day before to one day after the end of heat. Unfortunately, there is no reliable way of predicting the length of heat nor the time of ovulation; although an expert technician can predict the time of ovulation by palpatation—by feeling the ovary (follicle) with the hand through the rectal wall.

The sperm (or male germ cells) are deposited in the uterus at the time of service and from there ascend the reproductive tract. Under favorable conditions, they meet the egg, and one of them fertilizes it in the upper part of the oviduct near the ovary.

A series of delicate time relationships must be met, however, or the egg will never be fertilized. The sperm cells live only 24 to 30 hours in the reproductive tract of the female, and it probably requires 4 to 6 hours for them to ascend the female reproductive tract. Moreover, the egg is viable for an even shorter period of time than the sperm, probably for not more than 4 to 6 hours after ovulation. For conception, therefore, breeding must take place within 20 to 24 hours before ovulation.

As mares usually stay in heat from four to six days, perhaps the highest rate of conception may be obtained by serving the mare daily or every other day during the heat period, beginning with the third day. When many mares are being bred and heavy demands are being made upon a given stallion, this condition may be obtained by reinforcing a natural service with subsequent daily artificial inseminations as long as heat lasts. In no case should the mare be bred twice the same day.

Gestation Period

The average gestation period of mares is 336 days, or a little over 11 months. This will vary, however, with individual mares and may range from 310 to 370 days. A handy "rule-of-thumb" method that may be used to figure the approximate date of foaling is to subtract 1 month and add 2 days to the date the mare was bred. Hence, a mare bred May 20 should foal April 22 the following year.

Breeding After Foaling

Mares usually come in heat 9 to 11 days after foaling (known as "foal heat"), with individual mares varying from 3 to 13 days after foaling. Provided that foaling has been entirely normal and there is no discharge or evidence of infection at this time, many good horsemen plan to rebreed the mare during this first recurrence of heat after foaling, or on about the ninth day. They believe that mares so handled are more likely to conceive than if bred at a later period. Mares suffering from an infection of the genital tract are seldom settled in service; and, even if they do conceive, there is danger of the foal being undersized and poorly developed. Also, the infection may be needlessly spread to the stallion and other mares by

allowing such a practice. Mares not bred at this time or not conceiving will come in heat between the twenty-fifth and thirtieth day from foaling.

If any of the following conditions exist, the mare should not be bred at the first heat period following foaling:

1. If the placenta was retained over three hours.
2. If all lacerations have not entirely healed.
3. If there were severe bruises, particularly of the cervix.
4. If exudate or urine is present in the vagina.
5. If vaginal and rectal examinations on the seventh day after foaling indicate that all is not well.
6. If there is lack of tone in either the uterus or vagina; if everything just seems to hang forward.
7. If the mucous membrane is discolored or congested.

The usual reasons advanced in favor of rebreeding at the first heat period following foaling are:

1. It gives an added chance to rebreed the mare in an effort to get her in foal.
2. Occasionally a mare will not again show signs of heat during the breeding season.
3. If the mare conceives, she will foal about 20 days earlier the following year. This may be important where an early foal is desired.

Some arguments against rebreeding on the ninth day following foaling are:

1. If only one service is given on the ninth day following foaling, it is estimated that not more than 25 percent of the mares conceive.
2. During the period extending up to two weeks following foaling, the broodmare is more susceptible to genital infection than during any other period of her life.
3. Older mares that have been raising foals regularly each year may require a longer period of rest between pregnancies.
4. If the chances of conception are not too great, it may be unwise deliberately to overwork the stallion.

It is noteworthy that several of the good horsemen of Kentucky do not rebreed first-foal mares (mares foaling for the first time) on the ninth day following foaling.

PERCENT OF MARES BRED PRODUCING FOALS

Without question more difficulty is experienced in breeding mares than any other kind of livestock. The percentage of mares bred that actually conceive each year will vary from 40 to a high of 85, with an average probably running less than 50; and some of this number will fail to produce living foals. This means that, on the average, 2 mares are kept a whole year in order to produce one foal. By contrast, nationally, 88% of all beef cows that are bred, calve; 95% of all ewes, lamb; and 85% of all sows bred, farrow pigs.

The lower percentage conception in mares than in other classes of livestock is due primarily to the following: (1) Research in the field has lagged, (2) an attempt is made to get mares bred in about 4 months instead of 12, (3) the breeding season has been arbitrarily limited to a period (late winter and early spring) that at its best is only about 50 percent in agreement with nature, and (4) the birth date of horses being computed on a January 1 basis, regardless of how late they may be born.

In the bluegrass country of Kentucky, where there are both good horsemen and as desirable conditions for breeding as can be secured under domestication, 66 percent foaling is considered as average for the area.

Recognition of the following facts may help to increase the percentage of foals produced:

1. Mares bred in the late spring of the year are more likely to conceive. If mares are bred out of season, spring conditions should be duplicated as nearly as possible.
2. Mares bred as three- and four-year-olds and kept in regular production thereafter are more likely to conceive and produce living foals.
3. Infections or other unhealthy conditions of either the mare or stallion are not favorable for production.
4. More conceptions will occur if the mare is bred at the proper time within the heat period. Usually mares bred just before going out of heat are more likely to conceive.
5. Returning the mare to the stallion for retrial or rebreeding is important.
6. Mares in foal should be fed and cared for properly so as to develop the young. Balance of proteins, minerals, and vitamins is important.
7. It must also be remembered that old mares, overfat mares, or mares in a thin, run-down condition are less likely to be good breeders. Unfortunately, these conditions frequently apply to mares that are bred following retirement from the racetrack or the showring.

A shift of the date of birth (the January 1 birthday, for purposes of racing and showing) to somewhere between March 1 and May 1 would improve conception rate and foaling percentage, simply because mares would be bred under more natural and ideal spring conditions. Thus, it would have considerable virtue from the standpoint of the horse producer. On the other side of the ledger, however, it would create

problems in racing and in registrations, both here and abroad. Also, such a deep-rooted tradition would be difficult to change; in fact, much consideration has been given to the matter from time to time. In the final analysis, therefore, stepping-up breeding research is the primary avenue through which the deplorably low percentage foal crop may be improved.

STERILITY OR BARRENNESS IN MARES

Sterility is a condition of infertility. Whatever the cause, there are no cure-alls for the condition. Rather, each individual case requires careful diagnosis and specific treatment for what is wrong. It should be recognized also that there are two types of sterility—temporary and permanent—although no sharp line can be drawn between them.

Regardless of the cause of sterility, it is well to give a word of caution against the so-called "opening up" of mares, which is the practice of inserting the hand and arm into the genital organs for the purpose of rearranging the organs in order to ensure conception. Few laymen, no matter how expert they may classify themselves, have either sufficient knowledge of the anatomy of the mare or appreciation of the absolutely sterile methods necessary in such procedure to be probing about. Moreover, it is only rarely that the reproductive organs are out of place. Unless the "opening up" is recommended and conducted by a veterinarian, it should not be permitted. When performed by an amateur, or even most would-be experts, it is a dangerous practice that is to be condemned.

Temporary Sterility

Some common causes of temporary sterility are:
1. Lack of exercise, irregular work, and overfeeding accompanied by extremely high condition.
2. Overwork, underfeeding, and an extremely thin and run-down condition.
3. Nutritional deficiencies.
4. Infections of various kinds.
5. Some types of physiological imbalances characterized by such things as cystic ovaries or failure to ovulate at the proper time.

Temporary sterility can be reduced by removing the cause and correcting the difficulty, whatever it may be.

Permanent Sterility

Naturally, permanent sterility is much more serious to the horse breeder. Perhaps the most common causes of permanent sterility are:
1. Old age, which is usually accompanied by irregular breeding and eventual total sterility.

2. Infections in the reproductive tract, usually in the cervix, uterus, or fallopian tubes.
3. Some types of physiological imbalances characterized by such things as cystic ovaries or failure to ovulate at the proper time.
4. Closure of the female genital organs.

Sometimes a veterinarian is able to correct the latter two conditions; and, on an extremely valuable breeding mare, it may be worthwhile to obtain such professional service in an effort to bring about conception.

Retained afterbirth or other difficulties encountered in foaling may cause inflammation and infection that will prevent conception as long as the condition exists. There is real danger of spreading the infection if the mare is bred while in such a condition.

FERTILITY OF THE STALLION

Any stallion of breeding age that is purchased should be a guaranteed breeder; this is usually understood among reputable breeders.

The most reliable and obvious indication of potency is a large number of healthy, vigorous foals from a season's service. As an added protection, or in order to follow the horse during the midst of a heavy breeding program, a microscopic examination of the semen may be made by an experienced person. As the stallion dismounts from service, some of the semen is collected in a sterilized funnel by holding the penis over the plugged funnel. A sample of the semen is then strained through sterile gauze, and a small amount is placed on a slide for examination. A great number of active sperm cells is an indication, although not definite assurance, that the stallion is fertile. Some establishments make a regular practice of making such a microscopic examination twice each week during the breeding season. If it is desired to examine a stallion's semen after the breeding season or when a mare is not in season an artificial vagina may be used. When an entire ejaculate is available for study, the four main criteria of quality are (1) semen volume, (2) spermatozoan count, (3) progressive movement, and (4) morphology.

If the stallion is a shy breeder or lacks fertility although one is certain that the feed and exercise have been up to standard, masturbation should be suspected. Some horses are very hard to catch in the act, but generally masturbation can be detected by (1) the shrinkage of the muscles of the loin, and (2) the presence of dried semen on the abdomen or on the back of the front legs. Once this practice is detected or even suspected, corrective measures should be taken. Stalling and turning the horse out where he can see other horses will help in some instances; also, giving the horse more sunshine, grass, and outdoor exercise will help. Another method consists in obtaining a

plastic stallion ring of the proper size (they may be obtained from most breeder's supply houses in sizes to fit any horse) and fitting it snugly over the penis just back of the glans. It should be of such size that it will neither come off nor slide up the penis, yet loose enough that it does not interfere with normal circulation. The ring is removed when the horse is washed for breeding, and replaced after service. Also, it should be removed and cleaned weekly when the horse is not used for breeding. Another very effective adaptation of the same idea is the "bird cage" type of stallion ring; in addition to having a ring, this type is made to encompass completely the end of the penis.

CONDITIONING THE MARE FOR BREEDING

Proper conditioning of the mare prior to breeding is just as important as in the stallion. Such conditioning depends primarily upon adequate and proper feed and the right amount of exercise.

For the highest rate of conception, mares should be neither too thin nor too fat; a happy medium in condition makes for best results. It is especially important that one avoid the natural tendency of barren or maiden mares to get too fat.

Time permitting, mares of the light-horse breeds may best be exercised and conditioned by riding under saddle or driving in harness. When these methods are not practical or feasible, permitting a band of mares to run in a large pasture will usually provide a satisfactory amount of exercise.

BREEDING OPERATIONS

No phase of horse production has become more unnatural or more complicated with domestication than the actual breeding operations.

Hand Breeding, Corral Breeding, and Pasture Breeding

Hand mating is undoubtedly the best way in which to breed mares; it is the accepted practice in the better breeding establishments throughout the world. It guards against injury to both the stallion and the mare.

Although leaving much to be desired, corral breeding is next best to hand breeding. In this system, after first ascertaining that the mare is in heat, she and the stallion are turned loose together in a small, well-fenced corral. The attendants should remain out of the corral, where they can see but not be seen by the animals, until service is completed, following which the stallion and the mare are returned to their respective quarters.

Pasture breeding simply consists in turning the stallion into a pasture with the band of mares which it is intended that he serve. Except on the ranges of the Far West, this method of breeding is seldom practiced with domestic horses. With valuable animals, both corral and pasture breeding are too likely to cause injury, and the practices should be condemned. In pasture breeding, a stallion will handle fewer mares because of the repeated services of a mare, and he may even become sterile toward the end of the breeding season. Moreover, in pasture breeding, accurate breeding records are impossible.

Examination of the Mare

Before accepting a mare for service, the stallion owner should check every possible condition with care. The stallioner should examine the mare closely and question the owner concerning her health, last foaling date, breeding record, and similar matters. He should be well acquainted with the symptoms of dourine and other venereal diseases. Even though these diseases are not common in this country, there is always danger of finding them in imported stallions and mares. It is wise to require that barren mares be accompanied by a health certificate signed by a veterinarian.

The following types of mares should be rejected:

1. Mares showing the slightest symptoms of venereal disease.

2. Mares that have an abnormal discharge (such as blood or pus) from the vagina, commonly known as the "whites."

3. Mares affected with skin diseases and parasites.

4. Mares suffering from high fevers, which accompany colds, strangles, influenza, shipping fever, and pneumonia.

5. Mares that have recently given birth to foals affected with navel ill.

6. Mares that have recently suffered from retained afterbirth.

7. Mares that have suffered lacerations in foaling.

8. Mares that do not show definite signs of heat.

9. Mares under three years of age unless mature and well developed.

10. Mares that have a very narrow or deformed pelvis.

11. Mares that stay in heat incessantly (nymphomaniacs).

12. Mares that are extremely thin or emaciated.

13. Mares that have severe unsoundnesses which may be hereditary.

When mares have been barren over an extended period or when there is the slightest suspicion of infection, it is good protection to require a veterinarian's certificate to the effect that the mare is in a healthy breeding condition.

Mating Considerations and Serving the Mare

In addition to the above considerations concerning the examination of the mare, the following suggestions may be helpful:

1. Usually the mare should be taken to the stallion as breeding facilities are generally better where a stallion is stood for service.

2. If the mare has a foal and is to be away for a period of longer than 5 or 6 hours, the foal should be taken along—care being taken to avoid injury to the foal in transit. When the mare will not be away longer than 5 to 6 hours, the foal should be left home, and the mare should be hand-milked if necessary.

3. Newly arrived mares, especially those traveling by public van or railway, may well be required to pass through a quarantine period prior to being bred.

4. The mare should be allowed to become quiet and comfortable upon reaching the destination. Usually the most desirable practice is to tie the mare in a quiet stable. In cold weather or when the mare has been difficult to get in foal, some good horsemen recommend moderate exercise just prior to mating.

5. If excited or overheated, mares should be cooled out before being bred. Never should the mare be led behind a truck or car, or raced, in going to or returning from the stallion at the time of service.

6. Make certain that the mare is in season and ready for the stallion. Mares are most likely to conceive if bred 24 to 48 hours before the end of the heat period. The chute, gateway, open door, or solid fence are the usual methods employed for teasing. Some Thoroughbred establishments, and a few Standardbred stud farms, routinely employ the "jumping" procedure before using a valuable stallion on a young mare. The mare is restrained, as for breeding, and a gentle teaser is allowed to approach and mount her, but actual breeding is prevented by directing the teaser to one side. This gives the young mare a chance to discover what is going to happen and serves as added protection to a valuable stallion.

Breeding a mare that is not absolutely ready is a wasteful practice, and, more important, it may result in damaging the future breeding efficiency.

7. After teasing the mare and making certain that she is in season, wash the reproductive organs of the stallion with castile soap and warm water, using cotton instead of a sponge. Then rinse with clean pure water. The reproductive organs should be washed in a similar manner following service.

8. Bandage the upper 6 to 8 inches of the mare's tail using 3-inch widths of cheesecloth or other inexpensive materials. This keeps the genital organs clean and avoids interference with tail hairs. The bandage is removed after service.

9. The external parts of the mare that are likely to come into contact with the reproductive organs of the stallion should be washed with castile soap and warm water and then rinsed with clean water. Use cotton instead of a sponge, and never put any cotton back in the bucket after it has touched the mare.

Fig. 12-13. Washing the mare is preparation for breeding. The external parts of the mare that are likely to come into contact with the reproductive organs of the stallion should be washed with castile soap and warm water and then rinsed with clean water.

10. Use the twitch and hobbles[12] for the mare. This assures protection of both the stallion and mare. Hobbles are used only to protect the stallion as he approaches and dismounts and not in any way to force the mare into submission to service when not ready.

Fig. 12-12. Teasing a mare, using a solid fence for separation. Breeding a mare that is not in season is a wasteful practice, and more important, it may result in damaging the future breeding efficiency. (Courtesy, Washington State University)

---

[12]Or a leg strap may be used. If hobbles are used, they should be secured to stay put, but in such manner that they can be quickly released if desired.

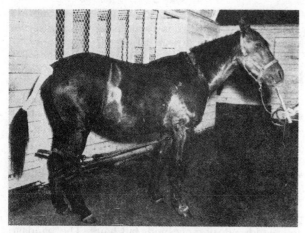

Fig. 12-14. A hobbled mare with twitch, and with tail properly bandaged, ready for service. Hobbles and twitches are used only to protect the stallion as he approaches and dismounts and not in any way to force the mare into submission to service when not ready. (Courtesy, Washington State University)

The twitch is usually removed as soon as the stallion has entered the mare.

11. Keep the stallion under control at all times. Never allow him to mount until he is ready for service. Then allow him to remain on the mare until the sexual act is completed. The same man should always handle the stallion at the time of service.

12. Allow the mare to remain quiet for a time following service. Avoid any undue excitement or exertion. If the mare has been in harness, she should not be worked for 2 or 3 days. Feed the mare as she was fed prior to breeding. Some good horsemen have the mare led quietly for 20 minutes following service; for, in moving about, she has no opportunity to strain.

13. Return the mare for retrial approximately 21 days following the first service. Such a practice will increase the percentage of in-foal mares and guard against the arrival of foals much later in the season than desired.

SIGNS AND TESTS OF PREGNANCY[13]

In order to produce as high a percentage of foals as possible and to have them arrive at the time desired, the good horseman will be familiar with the signs of and tests of pregnancy. This is doubly important when it is recognized that a great many mares may either be shy breeders or show signs of heat even when well advanced in gestation.

By identifying open mares, it is possible (1) to cull mares more intelligently and sharply reduce management costs; and (2) to separate pregnant mares from barren ones, and manage each group more effec-

[13]The author expresses his grateful appreciation for the authoritative review accorded this section by Dr. Robert G. Loy, Department of Veterinary Science, University of Kentucky, Lexington, Ky.

tively and efficiently. In some cases when a pregnancy test shows that a valuable mare is not in foal, the early diagnosis of her nonpregnant state will allow the veterinarian to initiate an early treatment program to improve her chances of conception the next year.

The signs of pregnancy follow:

1. *The cessation of the heat period*—This may be difficult to determine, as well as misleading, because some mares will continue to exhibit the characteristic heat symptoms when in foal. Sometimes they show such pronounced signs of heat that they are given the service of a stallion, which may result in abortion.

2. *The movement of the living fetus*—This movement can be seen or felt through the abdominal walls. It will not be possible, however, to use this test until about the seventh month of gestation. Movement of the fetus is most evident the first thing in the morning. This method is not so certain with young maiden mares, as the foal is carried nearer the backbone.

The absence of external signs of heat in the first weeks after breeding is only about 70 percent accurate, and the movement of the fetus is not evident in early pregnancy. Hence, the need for accurate, quick, and efficient methods of pregnancy diagnosis in the mare has engaged considerable scientific attention for many years. Out of this has evolved a number of different methods for determining whether or not mares are in foal; among them, those which follow.

At the outset, it should be noted that the Manual (Rectal) Test is by far the most used equine pregnancy test by horsemen and veterinarians, followed, to a much lesser extent, by the MIP Test. The rest of the tests given in the sections that follow are primarily of historic and scientific interest.

Manual (Rectal) Test

An experienced technician can determine pregnancy (or barrenness) of mares at 98 to 100 percent accuracy by feeling with the hand through the rectal wall. Normally, the test is made 43 to 45 days after breeding, but pregnancy in maiden mares often can be detected within 35 to 40 days following conception. When performed by an experienced person, the manual test is quite reliable.

The following procedure is employed by most experienced technicians in making the manual test:

1. The examination is made in surroundings familiar to the mare and in an unhurried manner, as this (a) makes for a minimum of restraint, and (b) avoids roughness.

2. Two helpers are used; one to twitch the mare, and the other to hold the tail to one side. If the mare objects to the twitch, it is left off.

3. The latex obstetrical sleeve with glove attached is slipped on and lubricated. The rectum is en-

tered and evacuated; the arm is inserted nearly to the shoulder, reaching forward and downward until the ovaries are located (the left ovary is most accessible for right-handed operators; the right ovary for left-handed operators); and the uterus is *gently* palpated and massaged. If the mare is 43 to 45 days pregnant, an enlargement approximately the size of a large orange can be located along the bottom of one of the uterine horns.

Biological Tests

These tests are based upon detecting either (1) the gonadotrophic hormone (PMS) in mare's blood serum, or (2) the estrogenic hormone in mare's urine, using laboratory animals for test purposes.

There are a number of biological tests; among them—

1. *The blood serum test with female rats or mice*—This test is based upon detecting the gonadotrophic hormone (pregnant mare serum, or PMS) in mare's blood serum, preferably in a blood sample taken 45 to 90 days after service. When injected into immature (21-day-old) female rats or mice (usually 2 test animals are used), PMS causes precocious (early) development of the internal reproductive organs.

In the United States, rats are normally used and the test is conducted as follows: Two ounces (one-half cup) of blood are drawn into a clean bottle, using a large bore needle in the usual manner. The blood is allowed to stand at room temperature for an hour to facilitate the separation of the serum. After the serum has separated, it is poured off and stored in the refrigerator. The blood serum is injected into female rats (21 to 24 days of age), using 0.5 cc serum on each animal. During the period extending from 40 to 120 days after conception, the pregnant mare's serum contains a gonadotrophic hormone, which, when injected into the test animals, causes activation of the ovary and consequent enlargement of the uterus. Observation of these changes may be made in the rat 96 to 120 hours after treatment. In comparison with controls, rats treated with the blood serum of pregnant mares show enlarged ovaries and uteri.

The blood serum test may also be made with immature female mice. Forty-eight hours after injection with the blood serum, the mice are destroyed and the ovaries and uteri examined. If the mare from which the blood sample came is pregnant, the reproductive organs of the mice will be noticeably enlarged as compared with normal.

This blood serum test with female rats or mice is considered very sensitive, probably approaching 100 percent accuracy.

2. *The blood serum test with male toads (Bufo)*—This test was developed by Polish workers (Bielanski et al.) and first used in the United States by

Dr. Raymond O. Berry, Texas A&M University. It is based on the fact that the toad emits sperm only (a) when stimulated by amplexus with a female toad, or (b) when stimulated by a gonadotrophic hormone, such as is found in pregnant mare's blood at certain stages. Dr. Berry's test,[14] which may be used on mares that have been bred between 45 to 120 days, is conducted as follows:

a. Draw from the jugular vein of the mare 50 to 66 cc of blood and place it in a test tube.

b. Place a cork stopper in the tube and store it in a refrigerator in a slanting position until the blood clots.

c. Pipette off the straw-colored serum for injection into the male toad.

d. Inject, at hourly intervals, into the dorsal lymph sac of the male toad (several species of toads, and the grass frog *Rana pipiens* may be used) 1 cc of the serum, until the total of 3 cc has been injected.

e. One hour after the last injection, check the toad for the presence of sperm by aspirating the cloaca with the pipette containing a few drops of water. Then mount the fluid on a slide and observe it under the microscope.

f. Consider the presence of sperm, either motile or nonmotile, as a positive test (meaning that the mare is pregnant).

g. Recheck all negatives with another toad.

In 1960, the Russian scientist, Samsonova, reported[15] upon a similar test. He used lake frogs (*Rana ridibunda*), the males of which are readily distinguishable.

In comparison with the rat or mouse test, the toad or frog test (a) is much quicker—requiring only 4 hours, (b) does not necessitate the destruction of the test animal—the same toad or frog may be used for 4 or 5 tests, and (c) is less sensitive.

3. *The urine test with female rats or mice*—This test may be used on mares from three months after breeding until termination. Four ounces of urine (and not blood) are collected in a clean bottle and are used as a sample. The urine test is used on spayed, mature female rats or mice. If the mare is pregnant, the estrogen in the urine causes symptoms of heat in the vagina and an increase in uterine weight of treated animals.

Immunological Tests

These tests are based on one of the fundamental concepts of immunology—the antigen to antibody reaction. If an antigen (usually a foreign protein) gains

---

[14]From mimeographed notes provided by Dr. Berry.

[15]Samsonova, V. M., All-Union Research Institute for Animal Husbandry, U.S.S.R., *Veterinariya* 37(10):66, 1960.

access to the body of an animal, the body responds by producing a specific immune substance, known as an antibody. If the antigen is encountered a second time, the antibody present in the animal's system mops up all the antigen by a coupling reaction. Germs and microbes are examples of antigens; and this mechanism provides one of the body's main defenses for rendering them harmless and preventing disease.

There are a number of immunological tests which utilize the antigen to antibody reaction; among them—

1. *The MIP Test*—The MIP Test (Mare Immunological Pregnancy Test) has been popularized by Dr. Ronald Chak, DVM, Ocala (Florida) Stud Farm, and Mr. Max Bruss, Dorchester Laboratory, Ocala, Florida. This test utilizes the principle whereby pregnant mare serum (gonadotrophin) inhibits the agglutination of gonadotrophin-coated erythrocytes in the presence of gonadotrophin antiserum. The result is the formation of a ring at the bottom of a test tube. The procedure is performed with 2 test tubes—a control test tube and a sample test tube. Mare serum is placed in both, along with the erythocytes and reagents. However, antiserum is placed in the sample test tube, whereas a control solution is used in the other test tube. In the control tube, the pattern of a doughnutlike ring will show at the bottom, whether or not the mare is pregnant. But the sample tube with the antiserum will show the pattern only if gonadotrophin is present in the mare's serum—signifying that the mare is pregnant. The MIP Test, which can be run in 2 hours' time, can determine with virtually 100 percent accuracy equine pregnancy from a blood sample taken 41 to 63 days after the mare is serviced. The MIP Test Kit contains all the supplies needed for running the test.[16]

2. *The Haemagglutination Inhibition (HI) Test*—This is another method of utilizing the antigen-antibody reaction for pregnancy testing. The specific haemagglutination inhibition technique, herein described to measure pregnant mare serum gonadotrophin (PMSG), was developed by Dr. W. R. Allen, of Cambridge.[17] It follows:

A blood sample (20 ml) is taken, then allowed to stand at room temperature for 12 to 24 hours following collection. The serum is then removed and stored at 20° F until assayed. All sera is extracted with acetone before assay in order to reduce the nonspecific inhibitory factors present in crude serum. The Second International Standard Preparation of PMSG or commercial PMSG, previously calibrated against the Sec-

ond International Standard, is used as a standard. No clumping (haemagglutination inhibition) means the mare is pregnant, whereas clumping (haemagglutination) indicates that she is barren.

This test is very sensitive and just as accurate as biological tests with rats or mice. Moreover, it has the following advantages over biological tests: (a) It can be set up and results obtained in 24 hours, whereas biological tests take a minimum of 48 hours; and (b) it does not require a constant supply of rats or mice of the right age.

Chemical Test

This test (known as the Cuboni test) involves chemically detecting the estrogenic hormones in mare's urine from 120 days pregnancy to term. Although several modifications exist, the original Cuboni test is herein described.

The addition of concentrated hydrochloric acid to the urine releases the estrogen. It is then taken up in benzene, in which it is very soluble. After the addition of concentrated sulfuric acid, the solution is allowed to cool thoroughly. If the mare is pregnant (if the test is positive), the solution shows a green fluorescence; if the mare is barren (if the test is negative), there is no fluorescence.

This test is fairly easy to carry out in the laboratory. However, it cannot be used for early pregnancy detection. It should not be used until 120 days after conception; and, for best results, it should be used 200 to 275 days after breeding at which stage estrogen levels are highest. Also, some experience is necessary for accurate interpretation, since a certain fluorescence is always detectable in urine from nonpregnant mares.

CARE AND MANAGEMENT OF THE STALLION

Although certain general recommendations can be made, it should be remembered that each stallion should be studied as an individual, and his care, feeding, exercise, and handling should be varied accordingly.

Quarters for the Stallion

The most convenient arrangement for the stallion is a roomy box stall which opens directly into a 2- or 3-acre pasture paddock, preferably separated from the other horses by a double fence. A paddock fence made of heavy lumber is safest. The stall door opening into such a paddock may be left open except during extremely cold weather; this will give the stallion plenty of fresh air, sunshine, and additional exercise.

[16]The MIP Test Kit may be secured from the Denver Chemical Manufacturing Co., Stamford, Conn. 06904.

[17]Allen, W. R., "The Immunological Measurement of Pregnant Mare Serum Gonadotrophin," *Journal of Endocrinology*, Vol. 43, 1969, pp. 593-598.

Fig. 12-15. Stallion barn and adjacent paddock occupied by the Thoroughbred stallion, Dewan, at Lexington, Kentucky. (Courtesy, J. Noye, Versailles, Ky.)

Feeding the Stallion

The feed and water requirements of the stallion are adequately discussed in Chapter 13. In addition to this, it may be well to reemphasize that, in season, clean lush pastures produced on fertile soils are excellent for the stallion. Grass is the horse's most natural feed, and it is a rich source of vitamins that are so necessary for vigor and reproduction. Perhaps the ideal arrangement in providing pasture for the stallion is to give him access to a well-sodded paddock.

Fig. 12-16. The Thoroughbred stallion, Secretariat, winner of the 1973 Kentucky Derby, shown in breeding condition at Claiborne Farm, Lexington, Kentucky, where he is at stud. Secretariat was syndicated for the world-record price of $6,080,000. (Courtesy, Kentucky Department of Public Information, Frankfort, Ky.)

Exercise for the Stallion

Most horsemen feel that regular, daily exercise for the stallion is important. Certainly, it is one of the best ways in which to keep a horse in a thrifty, natural condition. It has also been assumed that forced exercise is of importance in improving semen quality. However, recent studies with dairy bulls cast considerable doubt on the relationship of exercise to fertility. For example, in one study involving dairy bulls used in artificial insemination, eight bulls which were force exercised were compared with a like number which were kept in box or tie stalls, without forced exercise. The exercised group showed a nonreturn rate of 63.8 percent whereas the bulls that were not exercised showed a nonreturn rate of 65 percent; hence, the bulls without exercise were actually a little more fertile than the exercised ones.[18] This points up the need for well-controlled experiments on the importance of exercise of the stallion on semen quality.

Stallions of the light-horse breeds are most generally exercised under saddle or hitched to a cart. Thus, Standardbred stallions are usually jogged 3 to 5 miles daily while drawing a cart. Thoroughbred stallions and saddle stock stallions of all other breeds are best exercised under saddle for from 30 minutes to one hour daily, especially during the breeding season. Exercise should not be hurried or hard; the walk and the trot are the best gaits to use for this purpose. After the stallion is exercised, he should be rubbed down and cooled off before he is put up, especially if he is hot. Better yet, the ride should be so regulated at the end that the horse will be brought in cool, in which case he can be brushed off and turned into his corral.

Frequently, in light horses, bad feet exclude exercise on roads, and faulty tendons exclude exercise under the saddle. Under such conditions, one may have to depend upon (1) exercise taken voluntarily by the stallion in a large paddock, (2) longeing or exercising on a 30- to 40-foot rope, or (3) leading.

Longeing should be limited to a walk and a trot; and, if possible, the stallion should be worked on both hands; that is, made to circle both to the right and to the left. It is also best that this type of exercise be administered within an enclosure. Two precautions in longeing are (1) do not longe a horse when the footing is slippery, and (2) do not pull the animal in such manner as to make him pivot too sharply with the hazard of breaking a leg.

Leading is a satisfactory form of exercise for some stallions if it is not practical to ride them. In leading, a bridle should always be used—never a halter—and one should keep away from other horses and be careful that the horse being ridden is not a kicker.

Where several stallions are exercised, a properly

18*Physiology of Reproduction and Artificial Insemination of Cattle*, W. H. Freeman and Co. Publishers, 1961, p. 625.

installed mechanical exerciser driven by an electric motor may be used as a means of lessening labor. It is similar to the merry-go-round type of equipment used to exercise dairy bulls.

The objection to relying upon paddock exercises alone is that the exercise cannot be regulated, especially during inclement weather. Some animals may take too much exercise and others too little. Moreover, merely running in the paddock will seldom, if ever, properly condition any stallion. Nevertheless, a 2- or 3-acre grassy paddock should always be provided, even for horses that are regularly exercised. Stallions that are worked should be turned out at night and on idle days.

Grooming the Stallion

Proper grooming of the stallion is necessary, not only to make the horse more attractive in appearance, but to assist exercise in maintaining the best of health and condition. Grooming serves to keep the functions of the skin active. It should be thorough, with special care taken to keep all parts of the body clean and free from any foulness, but not so rough nor so severe as to cause irritation either of the skin or the temper.

AGE AND SERVICE OF THE STALLION

It should be remembered that the number and kind of foals that a stallion sires in a given season is more important than the total number of services. The number of services allowed during a season will vary with the age, development, temperament, health, and breeding condition of the animal and the distribution of services. Therefore, no definite best number of services can be recommended for any and all conditions, and yet the practices followed by good horsemen are not far different. All are agreed that excessive service of the stallion may reduce his fertility. Also, it must be realized that two or three services are required for each conception, and that there are breed differences, due primarily to differences in temperament.

Table 12-2 contains recommendations relative to the number of services for stallions of different ages, with consideration given to age and type of mating. Because of their more naturally nervous temperaments, stallions of the light-horse breeds are usually more restricted in services than stallions of the draft-horse breeds. Also, there is a difference between breeds.

The most satisfactory arrangement for the well-being of the stallion is to allow not more than one service each day. With proper handling, however, the mature, vigorous stallion may with certainty and apparently without harm serve two mares in a single day. During the heavy spring breeding season, this

TABLE 12-2
HANDY STALLION MATING GUIDE[1]

Age	No. of Matings/Yr.		Comments
	Hand Mating	Pasture Mating	
2-yr.-old	10-15	Preferably no pasture mating unless the stallion is prepared for same and certain precautions are taken.	1. Limit the 2-yr.-old to 2-3 services/week; the 3-yr.-old to 1 service/day; and the 4-yr.-old or over to 2 services/day.
3-yr.-old	20-40		
4-yr.-old	30-60		
Mature horse	80-100		2. A stallion should remain a vigorous and reliable breeder up to 20 to 25 yrs. of age.
Over 18 yrs. old	20-40		

[1]There are breed differences. Thus, when first entering stud duty, the average 3-year-old Thoroughbred should be limited to 20 to 25 mares per season, whereas a Standardbred of the same age may breed 25 to 30 mares; and the 4- or 5-year-old Thoroughbred should be limited to 30 to 40 mares, whereas a Standardbred of the same age may breed 40 to 50 mares. Mature stallions of the draft breeds may breed up to 100 mares in a season.

may often be necessary. It is a good plan to allow a stallion to rest at least one day a week.

In order to secure higher conception of the mares and yet avoid overwork of the stallion with an excessive number of natural services, most breeders now reinforce each natural service with one artificial insemination. Several of the breed registries stipulate that this must be done at once after natural service, with semen from the stallion performing the natural service on the mare that has just been covered.

Stallions often remain virile and valuable breeders until 20 to 25 years of age, especially if they have been properly handled. However, it is usually best to limit the number of services on a valuable old sire in order to preserve his usefulness and extend his longevity as long as possible.

Occasionally, Thoroughbred and Standardbred stallions are used to a limited extent before retirement to the stud, although many good horsemen seem to feel that it is not best to use them until it is time for them to be retired. Saddle horses may be bred to a few mares and still be used in the show-ring. However, sometimes it makes them more difficult to handle.

It frequently happens that a wonderful horse is injured in the midst of his racing career, and while awaiting the next racing season, he is bred to a few mares.

If two services a day are planned with the mature stallion, one should be rather early in the morning and the other late in the afternoon. It is also best not to permit teasing or services immediately before or soon after feeding the stallion, for this may result in a digestive disturbance, particularly in nervous, fretful individuals.

STALLION STATIONS

Recently, there has been a trend toward grouping 10 to 20 stallions on a breeding farm, commonly referred to as a Stallion Station. This development has been especially strong in the Thoroughbred, Standardbred, and Quarter Horse breeds.

These highly specialized breeding establishments have the following *advantages:*

1. It makes it convenient for an owner wishing to breed several mares to avail himself of the selection of a number of stallions.

2. It is more practical to employ expert personnel to handle the breeding operations.

3. It usually makes for superior facilities for this specialized purpose.

4. It generally results in a higher percentage of in-foal mares, earlier conception, and more efficient use of the stallion—primarily due to more expert management; examination, and medication if necessary; and improved facilities.

As with all good things, there may be, and sometimes are, *disadvantages,* such as the following:

1. The hazard of spreading contagious diseases is increased where there is a great concentration of horses, thus requiring extreme cleanliness and precautions.

2. There is considerable expense in operating a highly specialized service of this kind.

3. There is difficulty in obtaining a battery of really outstanding sires.

CARE OF THE PREGNANT MARE

Barren and foaling mares are usually kept separately because pregnant mares are sedate, whereas barren mares are more likely to run, tease, and kick. Precautions in handling the pregnant mare will be covered in the discussion that follows.

Quarters for the Mare

If mares are worked under saddle or in harness, they may be given quarters like those accorded to the rest of the horses used similarly, at least until near parturition time. Idle mares may best be turned to

pasture. Even in the wintertime, a simple shelter is adequate. In some sections of the country, an open shed is satisfactory.

Feeding the Pregnant Mare

The feed and water requirements for the pregnant mare are adequately discussed in Chapter 13, so repetition is unnecessary.

Exercise for the Pregnant Mare

The pregnant mare should have plenty of exercise. This may be obtained by allowing a band of broodmares to roam over large pastures in which shade, water, and minerals are available.

Mares of the light-horse breeds may be exercised for an hour daily under saddle or hitched to a cart. When handled carefully, the broodmare may be so exercised to within a day or two of foaling. Above all, when not receiving forced exercise or on idle days, she should not be confined to a stable or a small drylot.

CARE AT FOALING TIME

A breeding record should be kept on each mare so that it will be known when she is due to foal. As has been previously indicated, the period of gestation of a mare is about 336 days, but it may vary as much as a month in either direction. Therefore, the careful and observant horseman will be ever alert and make certain definite preparations in ample time.

The period of parturition is one of the most critical stages in the life of the mare. Through carelessness or ignorance, all of the advantages gained in selecting genetically desirable and healthy parent stock and in providing the very best of environmental and nutritional conditions through gestation can be quickly dissipated at this time. Generally speaking, less difficulty at parturition was encountered in the wild state, when the females of all species brought forth their young in the fields and glens.

Work and Exercise

Saddle or light-harness mares should be exercised moderately in the accustomed manner. If they are not used, other gentle exercise, such as leading, should be provided. This is especially important if they have not been accustomed to being on pasture and if it is desired to avoid any abrupt changes in feeding at this time.

Signs of Approaching Parturition

Usually the first sign of approaching parturition is a distended udder, which may be observed 2 to 6

weeks before foaling time. About 7 to 10 days before the arrival, there will generally be a marked shrinkage or falling away of the muscular parts of the top of the buttocks near the tailhead and a falling of the abdomen. Although the udder may have filled out previously, the teats seldom fill out to the ends more than 4 to 6 days before foaling; and the wax on the ends of the nipples generally is not present until within 2 to 4 days before parturition. About this time the vulva becomes full and loose. As foaling time draws nearer, milk will drop from the teats; and the mare will show restlessness, break into a sweat, urinate frequently, lie down and get up, etc. It should be remembered, however, that there are times when all signs fail and a foal may be dropped when least expected. Therefore, it is well to be prepared as much as 30 days in advance of the expected foaling time.

Preparation for Foaling

When signs of approaching parturition seem to indicate that the foal may be expected within a week or 10 days, arrangements for the place of foaling should be completed. Thus, the mare will become accustomed to the new surroundings before the time arrives.

During the spring, summer, and fall months when the weather is warm, the most natural and ideal place for foaling is a clean, open pasture away from other livestock. Under these conditions, there is decidedly less danger of either infection or mechanical injury to the mare and foal. Of course, in following this practice, it is important that the ground be dry and warm. Small paddocks or lots that are unclean and foul with droppings are unsatisfactory and may cause such infectious troubles as navel ill.

During inclement weather, the mare should be placed in a roomy, well-lighted, well-ventilated, comfortable, quiet box stall which should first be carefully cleaned, disinfected, and bedded for the occasion. It is best that the mare be stabled therein at nights a week or 10 days before foaling so that she may become accustomed to the new surroundings. The foaling stall should be at least 12 feet square and free from any low mangers, hay racks, or other obstructions that might cause injury to either the mare or the foal. After the foaling stall has been thoroughly cleaned, it should be disinfected to reduce possible infection. This may be done by scrubbing with boiling hot lye water, made by using 8 ounces of lye to 20 gallons of water (one-half this strength of solution should be used in scrubbing mangers and grain boxes). The floors should then be sprinkled with air-slaked lime. Plenty of clean, fresh bedding should be provided at all times.

A foaling stall somewhat away from other horses and with a smooth, well-packed clay floor is to be pre-

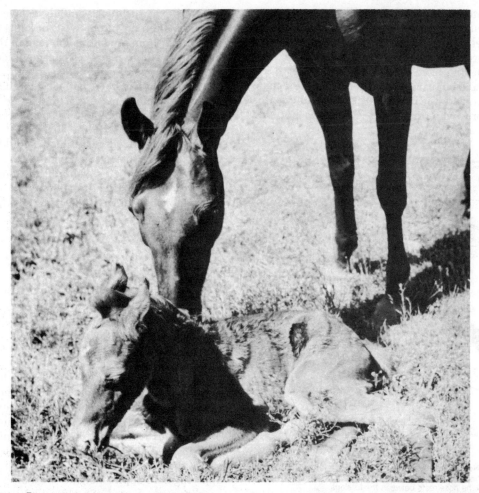

Fig. 12-17. A mare and her newborn foal on pasture. When the weather is warm, the most natural and ideal place for foaling is a clean open pasture away from other livestock. Under these conditions, there is less danger of either infection or mechanical injury to the mare and foal.

ferred. The clay floor may be slightly more difficult to keep smooth and sanitary than concrete or other such surface materials, but there is less danger to the mare and the newborn foal from slipping and falling; and it is decidedly better for the hoofs.

Feed at Foaling Time

Shortly before foaling, it is usually best to decrease the grain allowance slightly and to make more liberal use of light and laxative feeds, especially wheat bran. If there are any signs of constipation, a wet bran mash should be provided.

The Attendant

A good rule for the attendant is to *be near but not in sight*. Some mares seem to resent the presence of an attendant at this time, and they will delay foaling as long as possible under such circumstances. Mares that have foaled previously and which have been properly fed and exercised will usually not experience any difficulty. However, young mares foaling for the first time, old mares, or mares that are either over-fat or in a thin, run-down condition may experience considerable difficulty. The presence of the attendant may prevent possible injury to the mare and foal; and, when necessary, he may aid the mare or call a veterinarian.

Parturition

The immediate indications that the mare is about to foal are extreme nervousness and uneasiness, lying down and getting up, biting of the sides and flanks, switching of the tail, sweating in the flanks, and frequent urination.

The first actual indication of foaling is the rupture of the outer fetal membrane, followed by the escape of a large amount of fluid. This is commonly referred

to as the rupture of the "water bag." The inner membrane surrounding the foal appears next, and labor then becomes more marked.

With normal presentation, a mare foals rapidly, usually not taking more than 15 to 30 minutes. Usually, when the labor pains are at their height, the mare will be down; and it is in this position that the foal is generally born, while the mare is lying on her side with all legs stretched out.

Fig. 12-18. Normal presentation. The back of the fetus is toward the back of the mother, the forelegs are extended toward the vulva with the heels down, and the nose rests between the forelegs.

In normal presentation, the front feet, with heels down, come first, followed by the nose which is resting on them, then the shoulders, the middle (with the back up), the hips, and then the hind legs and feet. If the presentation is other than normal, a veterinarian should be summoned at once, for there is great danger that the foal will smother if its birth is delayed. If the feet are presented with the bottoms up, it is a good indication that they are the hind ones, and there is likely to be difficulty.

If after reasonable time and effort have been expended a mare appears to be making no progress in parturition, it is advisable that an examination be made and assistance be rendered before the animal has completely exhausted her strength in futile efforts at expulsion. In rendering any such assistance, the following cardinal features should exist:
1. Cleanliness.
2. Quietness.
3. Gentleness.
4. Perseverance.
5. Knowledge, skill, and experience.

When parturition is unduly delayed or retarded, the fetus often dies from twists or knots in the umbilical cord, or from remaining too long in the passage. In either case, there may be stoppage of fetal circulation or lack of oxygen for the fetus, or both.

If foaling has been normal, the attendant should enter the stable to make certain that the foal is breathing and that the membrane has been removed from its mouth and nostrils. If the foal fails to breathe immediately, artificial respiration should be applied. This may be done by blowing into the mouth of the foal, working the ribs, rubbing the body vigorously and permitting the foal to fall around. Then after the navel has been treated, the mare and foal should be left to lie and rest quietly as long as possible so that they may gain strength.

The Afterbirth

If the afterbirth is not expelled as soon as the mare gets up, it should either be tied up in a knot or tied to the tail of the mare. This should be done so that the foal or mare will not step on it, thereby increasing the danger of inflammation of the uterus and foal founder in the mare. Usually the afterbirth will be expelled within 1 to 6 hours after foaling. If it is retained for a longer period, or if lameness is evident, the mare should be blanketed, and an experienced veterinarian should be called. Retained afterbirth often causes laminitis, which is recognized by lameness in the mare. This is usually treated by feeding easily digested feed for a period of 36 hours and by applying cold applications to the mare's feet until the condition is relieved. (See Fig. 12-20, page 177.)

To prevent development of bacteria and foul odors, the afterbirth should be removed from the stall and burned or buried in lime as soon as possible.

Cleaning the Stall

Once the foal and mare are up, the stall should be cleaned. Wet, stained, or soiled bedding should be removed. The floor should be sprinkled with lime; and clean, fresh bedding should be provided. Such sanitary measures will be of great help in preventing the most common type of joint ill.

If the weather is extremely cold and the mare hot and sweaty, she should be rubbed down, dried, and blanketed soon after getting on her feet.

Feed and Water After Foaling

Following foaling, the mare usually is somewhat hot and feverish. She should be given small quantities of lukewarm water at intervals, but she should never be allowed to gorge. It is also well to feed lightly and with laxative feeds for the first few days. The very

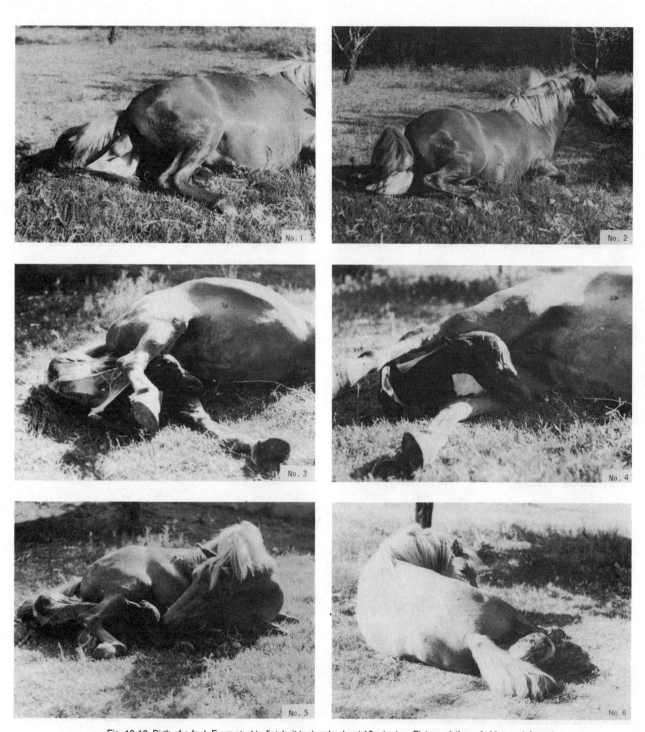

Fig. 12-19. Birth of a foal. From start to finish, it took only about 15 minutes. Pictures 1 through 11 were taken at approximately one-minute intervals. The last picture (No. 12), taken 15 minutes after birth, shows Pocohontas, the newborn Pony of the Americas foal, with a new-found friend, Debbie. (Courtesy, Dean Kenney, Blue Ribbon Ranch, Culver City, Calif.)

Fig. 12-19 (Continued)

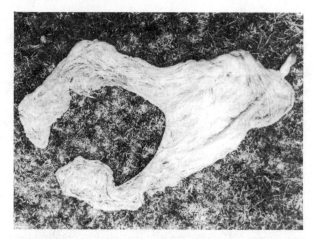

Fig. 12-20. The placenta (afterbirth), showing both horns. (Courtesy, *The Thoroughbred of California*, Arcadia, Calif.)

first feed might well be a wet bran mash with a few oats or a little oat meal soaked in warm water. About one-half the usual amount should be fed. Usually, for the first week, no better grain ration can be provided than bran and oats. The quantity of feed given should be governed by the milk flow, the demands of the foal, and the appetite and condition of the mare. Usually the mare can be back on full feed within a week or 10 days after foaling.

Observation

The good horseman will be ever alert to discover difficulties before it is too late. If the mare has much temperature (normal for the horse is about 101° F), something is wrong and the veterinarian should be called. As a precautionary measure, many good horsemen take the mare's temperature a day or two after foaling. Any discharge from the vulva should be regarded with suspicion.

Handling the Newborn Foal

Immediately after the foal has arrived and breathing has started, it should be thoroughly rubbed and dried with warm towels. Then it should be placed in one corner of the stall on clean, fresh straw. Usually the mare will be less restless if this corner is in the direction of her head. The eyes of a newborn foal should be protected from a bright light.

NAVEL CORD

At the time the umbilical cord is ruptured, there is a direct communication from without to some of the vital organs and the blood of the foal. Usually this opening is soon closed by the ensuing swelling and final drying and sloughing-off process. Under natural

conditions, the wild state, there was little danger of navel infection, but domestication and foaling under confined conditions have changed all this.

To reduce the danger of navel infection (which causes a disease known as joint ill or navel ill), the navel cord of the newborn foal should be treated at once with a solution of tincture of iodine (or Metaphen or Merthiolate may be used). This may be done by placing the end of the cord in a wide-mouthed bottle nearly full of tincture of iodine while

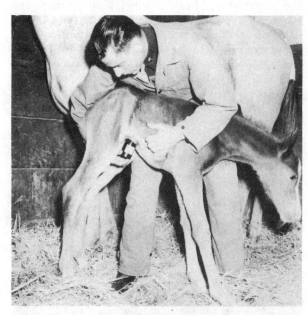

Fig. 12-21. Treating the navel cord of the newborn foal with iodine. This is done by placing the end of the cord in a wide-mouthed bottle nearly full of tincture of iodine while pressing the bottle firmly against the abdomen. (Courtesy, Thoroughbred Breeders Assn., Arcadia, Calif.)

pressing the bottle firmly against the abdomen. This is best done with the foal lying down. The cord should then be dusted with a good antiseptic powder. Dusting with the powder should be continued daily until the stump dries up and drops off and the scar heals, usually in three or four days. If an antiseptic powder is not available, air-slaked lime may be used. Any foreign matter that accumulates on the navel should be pressed out, and a disinfectant should be applied.

If left alone, the navel cord of the newborn foal usually breaks within 2 to 4 inches from the belly. Under such conditions, no cutting is necessary. However, if it does not break, it should be severed about 2 inches from the belly with clean, dull shears or it may be scraped in two with a knife. Never cut diagonally across. A torn or broken blood vessel will bleed very little, whereas one that is cut directly across may bleed excessively. If severing of the cord is resorted to, it should be immediately treated with iodine.

NAVEL INFECTION (JOINT ILL OR NAVEL ILL)

Although most newborn foal infections are referred to as navel infection—implying that the infection is postnatal, with entrance to the body gained through the umbilical cord after birth—many such troubles are of prenatal origin. In the latter type, infection of the foal takes place in the uterus (womb) of the dam before the foal is born. The infection may either be present in the dam before she is bred, or it may be introduced by the stallion, if he is infected or if he has previously bred other infected mares. If prenatal infection does not result in abortion and the mare carries the fetus to normal term, the foal is often born weak or develops navel ill within a few days and dies; or if it does not die, it becomes a hopeless cripple that must be destroyed.

Fig. 12-22. Foal with navel infection (joint ill or navel ill). The disease is fatal in about 50 percent of the cases. Also, a large proportion of the animals that survive are left with deformed joints like the foal pictured. (Courtesy, Dept. of Veterinary Pathology and Hygiene, College of Veterinary Medicine, University of Illinois)

Under unsanitary conditions, there is also great danger from infections that may enter the bloodstream through the opening of the navel cord prior to the time that it has dried up and the scar has healed over. When weather conditions permit foaling on a clean pasture in the fresh air and sunshine, danger of such infection is held to a minimum. On the other hand, foaling in a filthy paddock or stall and with no precautions taken is very likely to result in infection and navel ill. For this reason, when it is necessary to have mares foal in the stall, every precaution should be taken. The stall should be thoroughly cleaned, disinfected, and bedded; and the navel should be treated with iodine immediately after the foal arrives, followed by dusting with a good antiseptic powder several times daily.

Navel infection (joint ill or navel ill) may be recognized by a loss of appetite, soreness and stiffness in the joints, and a general listlessness of the foal. If this is recognized in the early stages and a veterinarian is called at once, the infected foal may be treated and may recover. If, however, the disease has reached the pus-forming stage, very likely it will be fatal. Blood transfusions from the dam to foal have been given in all types of foal infections, usually with good results. With certain specific types of infections, antibiotics, sulfanilamides, serums, or bacterins may be used successfully; but these should always be administered by a veterinarian. Prevention is decidedly the best protection.

In summary, it may be stated that the practice of sanitation and hygiene, starting with the stallion and broodmare at the time of mating and continuing with the broodmare and young foal at foaling time, usually prevents the most common type of joint ill. In certain areas, particularly those known to be goiterous or semigoiterous, such as the Pacific Northwest, the feeding of stabilized iodized salt to in-foal mares appears to reduce losses from joint ill.

COLOSTRUM

The colostrum is the milk that is secreted by the dam for the first few days following parturition. It differs from ordinary milk in the following aspects:

1. It is more concentrated.

2. It is higher in protein content, especially globulins.

3. It is richer in vitamin A.

4. It contains more antibodies.

5. It has a more stimulating effect on the alimentary tract.

Because of these many beneficial qualities of colostrum, the horseman should make very certain that the newborn foal secures this first milk.

The strong, healthy foal will usually be up on its feet and ready to nurse within 30 minutes to two hours after birth. Occasionally, however, a big awkward foal will need a little assistance and guidance during its first time to nurse. The stubborn foal should be coaxed to the mare's teats (forcing is useless). This may be done by backing the mare up on additional bedding in one corner of the stall and coaxing the foal

with a bottle and nipple. The attendant may hold the bottle while standing on the opposite side of the mare from the foal. The very weak foal should be given the mare's first milk even if it must be drawn in a bottle and fed by nipple for a time or two. Sometimes these weak individuals will nurse the mare if steadied by the attendant.

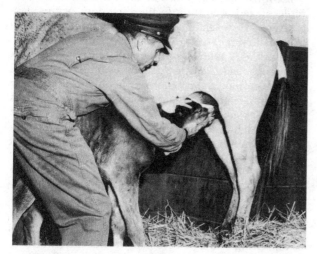

Fig. 12-23. Assisting newborn foal to nurse. (Courtesy, Thoroughbred Breeders Assn., Arcadia, Calif.)

Aside from the difference in chemical composition, the colostrum (the milk yielded by the mother for a short period following the birth of the young) seems to have the following functions:

1. It contains antibodies that temporarily protect the foal against certain infections, especially those of the digestive tract. Because newborn foals are unable to produce antibodies for some time after bith, they must acquire preformed antibodies through colostrum, which is especially high in immune lactoglobulins. To be effective in protection against disease, however, colostrum must be ingested within a few hours after birth, preferably within 15 to 30 minutes, because gut closure occurs about 24 to 30 hours after birth. Subsequently, the foal digests these large molecular weight proteins, with the loss of their immunization properties.

2. It serves as a natural purgative, removing fecal matter that has accumulated in the digestive tract.

This, therefore, explains why mares should not be milked out prior to foaling and why colostrum is important to the newborn foal.

Before allowing the foal to nurse for the first time, it is usually good practice to wash the mare's udder with a mild disinfectant and to rinse it with clean, warm water.

BOWEL MOVEMENT OF THE FOAL

The regulation of the bowel movement in the foal is very important. Two common abnormalities are constipation and diarrhea or scours.

Impaction in the bowels of the excrement accumulated during the development prior to birth—material called meconium—may prove fatal if not handled promptly. Usually a good feed of colostrum will cause elimination, but not always—especially when foals are from stall-fed mares.

Bowel movement of the foal should be observed within 4 to 12 hours after birth. If by this time there has been no discharge and the foal seems rather sluggish and fails to nurse, it should be given an enema. This may be made by using 1 to 2 quarts of water at blood heat, to which a little glycerin has been added; or warm, soapy water is quite satisfactory. The solution may be injected with a baby syringe (one having about a 3-inch nipple) or a tube and can. This treatment may be repeated as often as necessary until the normal yellow feces appear.

Fig. 12-24. Giving an enema to a foal, using a tube and can.

Diarrhea or scours in foals may be associated with infectious diseases or may be caused by unclean surroundings. Any of the following conditions may bring on diarrhea: contaminated udder or teats; nonremoval of fecal matter from the digestive tract; fretfulness or temperature above normal in the mare; an excess of feed affecting the quality of the mare's milk; cold, damp bed, or continued exposure to cold rains. As treatment is not always successful, the best practice is to avoid the undesirable conditions.

Some foals scour during the foal heat of the mare,

which occurs between the seventh and ninth day following foaling.

Diarrhea is caused by an irritant in the digestive tract that should be removed if recovery is to be expected. Only in exceptional cases should an astringent be given with the idea of checking the diarrhea; and such treatment should be prescribed by the veterinarian.

If the foal is scouring, the ration of the mare should be reduced, and a part of her milk should be taken away by milking her out at intervals.

RAISING THE ORPHAN FOAL

Occasionally a mare dies during or immediately after parturition, leaving an orphan foal to be raised. Also, there are times when mares fail to give a sufficient quantity of milk for the newborn foal. Sometimes there are twins. In such cases, it is necessary to resort to other milk supplies. The problem will be simplified if the foal has at least received the colostrum from the dam, for it does play a very important part in the well-being of the newborn young.

If at all possible, the foal should be shifted to another mare. Some breeding establishments regularly follow the plan of breeding a mare that is a good milk producer but whose foal is expected to be of little value. Her own foal is either destroyed or raised on a bottle, and the mare is used as a foster-mother or nurse mare.

Some nurseries keep a supply of colostrum on hand. They remove colostrum from mares that (1) have had dead foals, or (2) produce excess milk, then store it in a freezer for future use for foals that do not receive colostrum from their dams. When needed, it can be removed from the freezer, heated, and fed. This is an excellent practice.

If no colostrum is available, the foal should be placed on either (1) cow's milk made as nearly as possible of the same composition as mare's milk, or (2) a synthetic milk replacer.

A comparison of cow's and mare's milk is given in Table 12-3.

As can be observed, mare's milk is higher in percentage of water and sugar than cow's milk and is lower in other components.

For best results in raising the orphan foal, milk from a fresh cow, low in butterfat, should be used. To about a pint of milk, add a tablespoonful of sugar and from 3 to 5 tablespoonfuls of lime water. Warm to body temperature and for the first few days feed about one-fourth of a pint every hour. After 3 or 4 weeks the sugar can be stopped, and at 5 to 6 weeks skimmed milk can be used entirely.

Orphan foals may also be raised on synthetic milk replacer, fed according to the directions of the manufacturer. Here again the situation is simplified if the foal has first received colostrum.

For the first few days, the milk (either cow's milk or milk replacer) may be fed by using a bottle and a rubber nipple. Later, the foal should be taught to drink from a pail. It is important that all receptacles be kept absolutely clean and sanitary (cleaned and scalded each time), and that feeding be at regular intervals. Grain feeding should be started at the earliest possible time with the orphan foal.

NORMAL BREEDING SEASON AND THE TIME OF FOALING

The most natural breeding season for the mare is in the spring of the year. Usually mares are gaining in flesh at this time; the heat period is more evident; and they are more likely to conceive. Furthermore, the spring-born foal may be dropped on pasture—with less danger of infection and with an abundance of exercise, fresh air, and sunshine to aid in its development. Also, there will be good, green, succulent pasture for the mare. Such conditions are ideal.

However, when the demands for using the mares are such that spring foaling interferes and fall or perhaps late-winter foals are desired, plans may be changed accordingly. Under such circumstances, spring conditions should be duplicated at the breeding season. That is, the mare should be fed to gain in flesh, and, if necessary, should be blanketed for comfort.

Also, it must be remembered that the showman will want to give consideration to having the foals dropped at such a time that they may be exhibited to the best advantage. The same applies to the person who desires to sell well-developed yearlings or to race two-year-olds. It is noteworthy, however, that the percentage of barren mares that conceive at an early breeding is markedly lower than is obtained later in the season. Nevertheless, some mares do conceive

TABLE 12-3

COMPOSITION OF MILK FROM COWS AND MARES[1]

Source	Water	Protein	Fat	Sugar	Ash
	(%)	(%)	(%)	(%)	(%)
Cow	87.17	3.55	3.69	4.88	0.75
Mare	90.78	1.99	1.21	5.67	0.35

[1]USDA Farmers' Bull. No. 803.

Fig. 12-25. Teasing mares on pasture, with the teaser taken to the mare—a unique way to lower the cost of raising horses. (Photo by John C. Wyatt, Lexington, Ky.; courtesy, Lee Eaton, Lexington, Ky.)

early in the year, and even a small percentage is advantageous to some breeders.

HOW TO LOWER THE COST OF RAISING HORSES

Some principles that should receive consideration in lowering the cost of raising horses are:

1. Attain higher fertility in both mares and stallions; secure a higher percent foal crop. With a 50 percent foal crop, two mares are kept a whole year to raise one foal.

2. Eliminate unnecessary concoctions, including drugs, vitamins, and minerals if they are not needed.

3. Begin using the horses moderately at two years of age, at which time their use should more than compensate for the feed cost.

4. Keep all horses of usable age earning their way. Animals that are not necessary or that do not increase in value at a profitable rate are a needless expense.

5. Utilize pastures to the maximum. Such a practice will supply nutritious feeds at a low cost, save time in feeding, reduce man labor in caring for the horses, and do away with bedding the stalls and cleaning the barn.

6. Utilize the less salable roughage as much as possible, particularly during the second and third years.

7. Do not construct or maintain costly quarters for the young, growing horse.

8. Keep animals free from parasites, both internal and external. Feeding parasites is always too costly.

9. Provide least-cost balanced rations, including a balance of proteins, necessary minerals, and vitamins. Also, plenty of good, clean water should be available at all times.

BUYING HORSES OR RAISING FOALS

Where horses are needed, either they must be purchased or foals must be raised. The primary factors to consider in determining whether horses will be bought or foals raised are (1) the experience of the individual, (2) comparative cost, and (3) risks surrounding the introduction of horses.

Experience of the Horseman

Certainly it must be recognized that the man who would attempt to raise replacements must have more knowledge of horse production than the person buying mature horses. In addition to knowing the regular care and management aspects of horse production, the man who raises his replacements must be somewhat familiar with the breeding of horses and the rearing of foals.

Comparative Cost

In determining whether horses will be bought or foals raised, the comparative cost of the two methods

Fig. 12-26. Mares and foals on pasture. The cost of raising horses can be materially lessened by utilizing pastures to the maximum. (Courtesy, California Thoroughbred Breeders Assn., Arcadia, Calif.)

should be computed. In arriving at such comparative cost figures, the following factors should be remembered:

1. Such figures should be on the basis of animals of equal merit and usefulness for the purpose desired. Consideration should also be given to age and future depreciation.

2. Computing the purchase price on horses should be on the basis of price delivered to the farm. Commission, freight or trucking, and insurance charged should not be overlooked.

3. In computing the cost of raising a foal to usable age, feed price should be figured on the basis of farm values rather than on actual grain market values. Also, consideration should be given to the fact that cheap and somewhat unsalable roughages may often be used. Further, such items as service fees, manure produced, and handling charges should be considered.

Risks Surrounding the Introduction of Horses

After giving full consideration to the experience of the horseman and the comparative cost of the two methods, there are still some rather perplexing prob-

lems encountered in introducing horses. These difficulties may be summarized as follows:

1. *Misrepresentation*—The inexperienced man, especially, is likely to encounter misrepresentations as to age, soundness, vices, and the training and usefulness of the horse.

2. *Diseases*—In moving a horse, there is always a possible exposure to the many ills. Sometimes these are of sufficiently serious nature as to make the use of the animal impossible at a time when most needed; occasionally they even prove fatal. Also, it must be remembered that such diseases as are contracted very likely may spread to the other horses on the farm and even to those in the community, thus exposing them to the same risk.

3. *Acclimating*—Horses coming from a distance usually need time to become acclimated before being most useful.

4. *Condition*—In all too many instances, horses brought in for sale and speculative purposes have been made fat for the occasion. Usually such liberal feeding has been made even more harmful through accompanying lack of work and confinement to a stall. Such horses are soft and require a period of gradual fitting for work. Also, it must be remembered that fat will cover up a multitude of defects.

ARTIFICIAL INSEMINATION (A. I.)

Artificial insemination is, by definition, *the deposition of spermatozoa in the female genitalia by artificial rather than by natural means.*

Legend has it that artificial insemination had its origin in 1322, at which time an Arab chieftain used artificial methods to impregnate a prized mare with semen stealthily collected by night from the sheath of a stallion belonging to an enemy tribe. There is no substantial evidence, however, to indicate that the Arabs practiced artificial insemination to any appreciable degree.

The first scientific research in artificial insemination of domestic animals was conducted with dogs by the Italian physiologist, Lazarro Spallanzani, in 1780. A century later, American veterinarians employed artificial means to get mares in foal that persistently had failed to settle to natural service. They noticed that because of obstructions the semen was often found in the vagina and not in the uterus following natural service. By collecting the semen into a syringe from the floor of the vagina and injecting it into the uterus, they were able to impregnate mares with these anatomical difficulties.

The Russian physiologist, Ivanoff, began a study of artificial insemination of farm animals, particularly horses, in 1899; and, in 1922, he was called upon by the Russian government to apply his findings in an effort to reestablish the livestock industry following its depletion during World War I. Crude as his methods were, his work with horses must be considered the foundation upon which the success of the more recent work is based.

The shifting of the large-scale use of artificial insemination to cattle and sheep, two decades after it was first introduced for horses, was not caused by the fading importance of the horse and the increased demand for cattle and sheep. Rather, it was found that progress was quicker and more easily achieved with these animals, because the physiological mechanism of reproduction in cattle and sheep is more favorable than in horses.

Today, there is renewed interest in artificial insemination of horses, as a result of a successful method of freezing stallion semen in 1964. Stallion semen is now being collected, processed, and frozen somewhat like bull semen.

Mares are inseminated by (1) using a syringe and catheter arrangement with a speculum; (2) placing a gelatin capsule, holding 10 to 25 milliliters of extended semen, in the cervix by hand; or (3) introducing a rubber catheter by hand into the cervix and injecting the semen by means of a syringe attached to the opposite end of the tube.

The primary objective during the breeding season is to settle the maximum number of mares in the minimum amount of time. Succeeding in this objective reduces labor and other expenses, provides earlier foals, and shortens the foaling season. Artificial insemination can give a big assist in accomplishing these goals. A list of the *advantages* of A.I. follows:

1. It increases the use of outstanding stallions.
2. It alleviates the danger and bother of keeping a stallion.
3. It may lessen and control certain diseases.
4. It prevents overuse of a stallion, particularly early in the breeding season.
5. It reduces the possibility of injury to small, shy, or nervous mares or stallions.
6. It makes it possible to use stallions that have developed poor breeding habits, or that have been injured, when natural service is not possible.
7. It makes it possible to evaluate semen at each collection, with the result that minor changes in semen quality may be detected immediately.
8. It aids in the identification of reproductive problems.
9. It permits more effective use of older, more valuable stallions.
10. It makes it possible to breed mares at the most opportune time for maximum chances of conception.
11. It eliminates the problem associated with mating animals of different sizes.
12. It increases pride of ownership, when a better stallion can be used.
13. It forces an accurate record-keeping system.

But, like many other good things, the artificial insemination of horses has its *disadvantages* or limitations, too; among them, the following:

1. It must conform to physiological principles.
2. It requires skilled technicians.
3. It necessitates considerable capital to initiate and operate an A.I. breeding service for horses.
4. It is not always possible to obtain the services of a given stallion.
5. It may accentuate the damage of a poor stallion.
6. It may restrict the stallion market.
7. It may increase the spread of disease.
8. It may be subject to certain abuses. However, it appears that such abuse is more suspicioned than real. In a blood type study[19] with cattle, Rendel, of Sweden, found 4.2 percent family records in error out of 615 animals by natural service, compared to 4.0 percent family records in error out of 199 sired by artificial insemination.

Until recently, stallion semen could not be stored for any length of time. It is viable for only one to two

---

[19]Rendel, J., "Studies of Cattle Blood Groups; II. Parentage Tests," *Acta. Agric. Scand.*, 8:131, 1958, p. 140.

days in the liquid state. However, stallion semen has now been frozen successfully, and its use will grow. This development may write a new chapter in horse breeding, especially in breeding grade mares.

But before wide-scale use can be made of artificial insemination of horses, solutions to additional problems must be found. These include the following needs:

1. The ability to breed more mares per stallion.[20]
2. The ability to detect when mares are ready for breeding.
3. The ability to bring mares in heat at will.

Registration of Foals Produced Through Artificial Insemination

Although artificial insemination was first practiced with horses, many American registry associations now frown upon or forbid the practice. Moreover, there is little unanimity of opinion among them so far as their rules and regulations apply to the practice. Table 12-4 summarizes the horse association rules relative to registering young produced artificially.

Summary of Artificial Insemination

Today, artificial insemination is taking on a new look. Stallion semen is being frozen and stored, with the result that these "King Tuts" may be in production long after death.

Without doubt, from a technical standpoint, the wide-scale use of artificial insemination in horses only awaits the time when a few of the remaining problems are overcome. To be sure, there is and will continue to be resistance on the part of some horse registry associations and some breeders, with the result that research in the area of artificial insemination of horses will continue to lag. But progress cannot be stopped! Artificial insemination will expand in horses, especially with grade mares, just as it has in the dairy industry as soon as the remaining barriers are removed.

Who would not like to use a valuable stallion as widely as possible, and long after death? Imagine being able substantially to increase the number of offspring per year from a syndicated stallion whose stud fee is in the range of $5,000 to $20,000! Also, through the wide-scale use of artificial insemination in horses, many stallions could be eliminated (one stallion is now kept for each 7.3 foals produced[21]),

thereby effecting a considerable saving in keep.

The knowledge of the reproductive processes gained from artificial insemination can contribute materially to the increased efficiency of horse breeding. Perhaps, among its virtues, therefore, artificial insemination does offer some promise of assuring a higher conception rate in horses.

ARTIFICIAL LIGHTING FOR MARES

Artificial lighting will result in earlier than normal initiation of the estrous cycle in barren and maiden mares. In comparison with hormone treatments, it is relatively inexpensive, and it alleviates the risk of causing hormonal imbalances.

Mares are seasonal breeders. Normally, their natural breeding season begins in March and extends to late July or August. During this period, they usually experience regular heat cycles and ovulation every 21 days.

Seasonal influences on the estrous cycle of the mare are related to length of daylight, nutrition, and climatic factors (i.e., temperature). Length of daylight and nutrition can be controlled. It is noteworthy, too, that the reproductive function in sheep, poultry, and migratory fowl is regulated by the length of daylight.

The ratio of hours of daylight to darkness throughout the year acts on nerves in the region of the pituitary gland, and stimulates or inhibits the release of follicle-stimulating hormone (FSH). Lengthening the daylight hours activates the pituitary, and causes it to release increasing amounts of the FSH which stimulates ovarian function. Thus, sometime after the daylight period begins to increase, the estrous cycle begins in mares.

Artificial lighting of broodmares enables breeders to bring mares in season about six weeks earlier than normal. By the use of the artificial light technique, a mare that would normally conceive on March 15 may get in foal sometime in January. By avoiding the necessity of skipping a year due to late breeding, this technique may actually result in obtaining two additional foals during the lifetime of a mare.

The procedure consists in using a 200-watt light bulb in a box stall so as to extend the hours of light to 16 hours daily. By beginning the light treatment of mares about December 1, they may be bred the latter part of January.

Table 12-5 may be used as an artificial lighting guide in northern United States. (See page 187.)

Slight adjustments in the schedule given in Table 12-5 will need to be made in different locations, depending upon the sunrise and sunset times of the particular area.

The following additional points are pertinent to the artificial lighting of mares:

---

[20]Professor Cheng Pi-liu, Research Institute of Animal Production, Academy of Agricultural Sciences of China, at Peking, reported the following results in using one stallion artificially: 2,798 mares bred in one year; 15 mares per collection; 73.9% conception. (Reported in *The Blood-Horse*, Nov. 18, 1961, pp. 1302 and 1304.)

[21]Based on a survey made by the author.

TABLE 12-4

HORSE ASSOCIATION RULES RELATIVE TO REGISTERING
YOUNG PRODUCED ARTIFICIALLY

Breed	Present Rules or Attitude of Registry Association Relative to Artificial Insemination
Light Horses and Ponies:	
American Bashkir Curly	No rules relative to A.I. to date.
American Creme Horse	A.I. discouraged, but accepted.
American Gotland Horse	No rules.
American Mustang	Accepted provided certified authentication is provided by the attending veterinarian of both the mare and the stallion.
American Part-Blooded Horse Registry .	Accepted provided customary proof of breeding is provided.
American Saddle Horse	Accepted provided A.I. takes place (1) on premises where stallion is standing, and (2) in presence of owner or party authorized to sign certificate of breeding.
American Walking Pony	Accepted only if (1) stallion and mare are on same premises and insemination is done by licensed veterinarian, or (2) same veterinarian collects, transports, and inseminates if sire and dam are on different premises.
American White Horse	A.I. discouraged, but accepted.
Andalusian	The breed registry reports: "Not practiced."
Anglo-Arabian and Half-Arabian	Accepted provided (1) stallion licensed by Arabian Horse Registry for A.I., and (2) registration certificate is stamped to show animal was A.I. produced.
Appaloosa	Accepted provided (1) accompanied by natural service in same heat period, and (2) semen used only where stallion is standing.
Arabian	Accepted provided (1) stallion licensed by Arabian Horse Registry of America for A.I., (2) both collection and insemination take place on same premises, and (3) semen not stored longer than 48 hours.
Buckskin	International Buckskin Horse Association, Inc.: Accepted provided (1) registry is notified in advance of intent to use A.I., (2) collecting, storing, and inseminating performed by approved practitioner, and (3) letters A.I. incorporated in Stud Book and on certificate.
	American Buckskin Registry Association, Inc.: Accepted provided (1) prior notice of intent to use the stallion A.I. is given the Association, and (2) semen is used on premises of collection immediately following collection.
Chickasaw	No rules.
Connemara	Accepted provided (1) fresh semen is used, and (2) signed letters are on file from stallion owner, mare owner, the veterinarian who collected the semen, and the veterinarian who did the inseminating.
Galiceno	Accepted, without rules or restrictions.
Hackney	Accepted provided insemination takes place on premises where stallion is standing and in presence of owner or party authorized to sign certificate of breeding for stallion.
Lipizzan	No rules.
Missouri Fox Trotting Horse	No rules. No horses registered by A.I. to date.
Morab	Accepted provided (1) stallion owner notifies the registry, annually, of intent to use A.I., and (2) insemination is done immediately following collection.
Morgan	Accepted only if (1) collection and insemination by licensed veterinarian, (2) insemination immediately following collection, and (3) both collection and insemination are on same premises, or (4) need for medical or safety reasons.
National Appaloosa Pony	No rules.
Paint Horse	Accepted only if A.I. used (1) within 24 hours of collection, and (2) on premises of collection.
Palomino	Palomino Horse Breeders of America: Accepted provided there is a properly signed breeder's certificate, but they do not advocate.

(Continued)

TABLE 12-4 (Continued)

Breed	Present Rules or Attitude of Registry Association Relative to Artificial Insemination
	Palomino Horse Association, Inc.: Accepted only if semen used at time and place of collection.
Paso Fino	Paso Fino Owners and Breeders Association, Inc.: Each request handled on individual basis. But a veterinarian must be in attendance at time of both collection and insemination.
Peruvian Paso	Peruvian Paso Horse Registry of N.A.: Accepted only if (1) deemed necessary (in writing) by veterinarian, (2) stallion and mare are at same location, and (3) stallion serves mare naturally once each heat period.
	American Association of Owners & Breeders of Peruvian Paso Horses: A.I. accepted only (1) in case of injury to stallion, and (2) if stallion and mare are on same premises.
Pinto	Accepted provided (1) intent of each A.I. breeding requested in letter to registrar; (2) a veterinarian (not necessarily the same one for each step) certifies to collection of semen, insemination of mare, and birth of foal; and (3) blood type evidence of parentage, along with foaling date, is furnished.
Pony of the Americas	A.I. on the farm where the stallion is located is approved. But mailing of semen is not allowed.
Quarter Horse	A.I. not permitted, unless insemination (1) immediately follows collection, and (2) is at the place or premises of collection.
Rangerbred	No rules. No request to use A.I.
Shetland Pony	Accepted only if (1) sire and/or dam incapable of natural service, (2) sire and dam owned by same person, and (3) owner retains dam until she foals.
Spanish-Barb	No rules. Do not advocate A.I.
Spanish Mustang	No official ruling at this time.
Standardbred	Accepted provided (1) fresh semen is used (frozen or dessicated not permitted), and (2) insemination takes place on same day and same premises where semen was produced.
Tennessee Walking Horse	Accepted provided insemination (1) is done on premises where stallion is standing, and (2) takes place in presence of owner or party authorized to sign certificate of breeding for the stallion used.
Thoroughbred	Natural service only. But the immediate A.I. reinforcement of the stallion's service with a portion of the ejaculate produced by the stallion during such cover is permitted.
Trakehner	Accepted provided (1) there is prior approval by the Association, (2) semen is used immediately following collection and at the place or premises of collection, and (3) insemination is under supervision of licensed veterinarian.
Welsh Pony	Foals produced by A.I. not accepted for registry.
Draft Horses:	
Belgian	Accepted provided stallion and mare were on the same farm at the time mare was bred.
Clydesdale	No rules.
Percheron	Accepted provided (1) semen is obtained from member of Percheron Horse Association of America, or from reputable A.I. establishment; (2) blood type of stallion is on file with the Association; (3) authentication is furnished by owner of stallion, owner of mare, and veterinarian who implanted; and (4) application for registry of A.I. produced foal is filed before June 1 of the year following date of foaling.
Shire	Will accept. No rules.
Suffolk	No rules, but favorable toward A.I.
Jacks and Donkeys:	
Donkeys	American Donkey and Mule Society, Inc.: No rules.
	Miniature Donkey Registry of the U.S.: No rules.
Jacks and Jennets	Eligible for registration. No stipulations.

TABLE 12-5
ARTIFICIAL LIGHTING SCHEDULE

Date	A.M.		P.M.	
	Lights On	Lights Off	Lights On	Lights Off
November 1	7:00	8:30	3:30	6:00
November 8	6:45	8:30	3:30	6:00
November 15	6:45	8:30	3:30	6:15
November 22	6:30	8:30	3:30	6:15
November 29	6:30	8:30	3:30	6:30
December 6	6:15	8:30	3:30	6:30
December 13	6:15	8:30	3:30	6:45
December 20	6:00	8:30	3:30	6:45
December 27	6:00	8:30	3:30	7:00
January 3	5:45	8:30	3:30	7:00
January 10	5:45	8:30	3:30	7:15
January 17	5:30	8:30	3:30	7:15
January 24	5:30	8:30	3:00	7:30
January 31	5:30	8:30	3:00	7:45
February 7	5:30	8:30	3:00	8:00
February 14	5:30	8:30	3:30	8:15
February 20	5:30	8:30	3:30	8:30

1. Generally the light treatment is limited to barren and maiden mares.

2. For maximum effect, mares should be housed in box stalls rather than sheds. This ensures that each mare is given a similar concentration of light and is kept within about 8 feet of the source. Mares should be turned out during natural daylight hours, but they should be put into their stalls before dusk.

3. Mares should not be expected to cycle immediately after being placed under lights. Although the time lapse between the initiation of lighting and estrus will vary between individual mares, it will usually be within the range of 45 to 60 days.

4. Once estrous cycles are initiated by light treatment in mares, their cycles continue in a normal manner.

5. When once put under lights, mares should be kept under lights until spring. They should not be taken out partway through the season. A change in the lighting exposure program can bring about a severe upset to the established estrous cycle.

6. A regular teasing program accompanied by rectal examination of mares showing estrus is necessary to obtain desired results.

7. One good heat period and ovulation should occur before breeding. The mare can then be bred during the next heat period.

8. Artificial lighting will not increase fertility—it only extends the breeding season. Mares will shed their winter coats earlier, but they exhibit no other physiological changes. They will exhibit heat cycles about six weeks earlier than normal.

HORMONAL CONTROL OF HEAT IN MARES

Planned parenthood is not new. It has long been practiced among females of all species, women included. Stockmen have long "tampered with" the breeding and parturition season that was common in the wild state. Prior to domestication, animals brought forth their young in the fields and glens, inhibited only by age and feed, and influenced somewhat by seasons. But man changed all this—even without the use of hormones. Sly controls have been exercised over breeding for a very long time. For example, farm flock owners controlled reproduction in chickens by the simple act of putting eggs under an old setting hen—unless she hid out. Today, modern poultry producers regulate chick hatchings by controlling when, and how many, eggs go into the incubator. It is more difficult to accomplish the same thing in four-footed animals.

Horsemen have altered nature's way in horses (1) by hand mating or confining the stallion at certain times; (2) by emulating spring conditions—through providing better feed, shelter, and/or blankets when breeding at other times of the year; (3) by flushing—through feeding mares more liberally two to three weeks ahead of the breeding season; and (4) by artificially controlling the hours of light per day—through use of ordinary electric lights, which activate hormone production. Each of these methods has been used with varying degrees of success. All have fallen short of achieving the hoped-for goal—that of bringing females in heat at will, followed by a high conception rate. Hormonal control appears to be the answer.

Horsemen are interested in regulating estrus for the following reasons:

1. It would make for more births early in January. This is important to those who race or show, because a horse's age is computed on a January 1 basis, regardless of how late in the year he may have been born.

2. It would result in getting more clinically anestrus mares—mares with functional ovaries that are not

detected in estrus during the normal breeding season—bred. Because mares are seasonal breeders, clinically anestrus mares often are not bred.

3. It would facilitate artificial insemination. Research has shown that failure to detect estrus is the main problem associated with the use of A.I.

Many different drugs have been administered (either orally, by injection, or by implantation) in attempts to control the estrous cycle of females, with progestogens and prostaglandins heading the list. Unfortunately, low conception rates have been a problem with most drugs; prostaglandin appears to be an exception.

● *Progestogens*—These are compounds that mimic the hormone progesterone, which is produced naturally by the corpus luteum on the female's ovary.

Feeding, injecting, or implanting nonpregnant females with progestogen for a sustained period of 10 to 20 days, followed by withdrawal of the dose, will result in animals exhibiting heat 2 to 7 days after withdrawal. Essentially, this method of control places animals in a type of false pregnancy; they are fooled by the high levels of the progesterone-mimicking progestogen.

Upon withdrawal of the compound, progesterone levels in the blood drop and new follicles mature, bringing animals similarly treated into heat synchronously.

Three problems have been encountered with progestogens: (1) Heats and ovulations in animals so treated are not sufficiently synchronized to breed them successfully at a prescribed time; (2) conception at the first synchronized heat is subnormal; and (3) the progestogen must be administered over several days, which involves much labor.

● *Prostaglandins*—A completely new era of research is under way with prostaglandins. These are hormonelike substances, found in almost every cell and tissue, that are believed to play a key role in regulating cellular metabolism. The name "prostaglandin," which is a misnomer, was given to these substances because they were once believed to have originated in the male's prostate gland. Later research revealed that they actually come from the seminal vesicles (another accessory sex gland of the male).

Several natural compounds have been identified as prostaglandins. For example, the marine animal—the sea whip—which is found off the Florida coast, is a rich source. Also, all prostaglandins are now being synthesized from commercially available materials.

These highly potent substances have been called local hormones or tissue hormones because they do their work in the immediate area in which they are produced, as distinguished from circulating hormones which aim at distant targets. In females, prostaglandins are being used to regress the corpus luteum (the

growth on the ovary that prevents ovulation). This allows the natural estrous cycle to begin again.

The major criteria for measuring the success of hormone induced estrus are (1) the percentage of the females that come in heat, and (2) the percentage of conception.

In one study,[22] prostaglandin F2 Alpha was administered to 73 clinically anestrus mares that had not been detected in estrus for an average of at least 73 days, even though their herdmates had been detected in estrus over the same time interval. The average interval between prostaglandin injection and (1) first detection of estrus was 4.4 days, (2) disappearance of the follicle that had grown to maturation (ovulation) was 9 days, and (3) first breeding was 7 days. Of the 73 treated mares, 73 percent were detected in estrus as defined by standing or showing signs to the stallion. Pregnancy data were available on only 54 of the 73 treated mares, since some mares were moved prior to evaluation of pregnancy and other mares were not inseminated or bred for various reasons. Of the 54 mares, 56 percent of them became pregnant from the breeding at the estrus which occurred following administration of the prostaglandin. Mares were bred an average of 1.7 times during the estrus.

Because prostaglandin is a luteolytic, an animal must have a corpus luteum in order to respond. Since a high percentage of clinically anestrus mares do have a corpus luteum, prostaglandin is effective in regressing the corpus luteum. This allows the clinically anestrus mare either to return to estrus or to be bred, as determined by ovarian follicular development and ovulation. Treatment of clinically anestrus mares with prostaglandin has resulted in acceptable pregnancy rates.

Studies to date indicate that females treated with a single dose of prostaglandin may be bred at a predetermined time, over a short period, and still have satisfactory fertility. Although more research needs to be done on this promising new drug, it appears to be the answer to future controlled breeding.

Summary: Researchers in both colleges and industries are in general agreement that hormone controlled estrus synchronization will work, and that it offers promise of good returns when properly used in a well-managed herd. Scientists also realize that we don't know all the answers—that further research work is necessary. Nevertheless, it appears that planned parenthood is here to stay—that its wide use only awaits getting the technique perfected and the cost lowered, both of which will come. In the meantime, horsemen are admonished to keep abreast of developments and to rely on well-informed advisors.

[22]Lauderdale, J. W., "Prostaglandin F2 Alpha: Effective Tool for Control of Estrus of Cows and Mares," *Stud Managers' Handbook*, Vol. 12, Agriservices Foundation, Clovis, Calif., 1976, p. 102.

BLOOD TYPING[23]

Horse blood typing was developed at the University of California at Davis during the period 1958-64. It involves a study of the components of the blood which are inherited according to strict genetic rules that have been established in the research laboratory. By determining the genetic "markers" in each blood sample and then applying the rules of inheritance, parentage can be affirmed or denied. To qualify as the offspring of a given mare and stallion, a foal must not possess any genetic markers not present in his alleged parents. If it does, it constitutes grounds for illegitimacy.

Horse blood typing is used for the following purposes:

• *To verify parentage*—The test is used in instances where the offspring may bear some unusual color or markings or carry some undesirable recessive characteristic. It may also be used to verify a registration certificate. Through blood typing, parentage can be verified with 90 percent accuracy.[24] Although this means that 10 percent of the cases cannot be settled, it is not possible to do any better than this in human blood typing.

• *To determine which of two sires*—When a mare has been served by two or more stallions during one breeding season, blood typing can exclude the incorrect stallion and include the correct stallion in over 90 percent of the cases.

• *To provide a permanent blood type record for identification purposes*—Two samples of blood are required from each animal to be studied; and the samples must be taken in tubes and in keeping with detailed instructions provided by the laboratory. In parentage cases, this calls for blood samples from the offspring and both parents; in paternity cases, samples must be taken from the offspring, the dam, and all the sires.

• *To substitute for fingerprinting*—Much attention is now being given to the idea of utilizing blood typing as a positive means of identification of stolen animals, through proving their parentage.

• *Blood typing laboratory*—The following laboratory is capable of determining equine parentage:

Serology Laboratory
Department of Reproduction
School of Veterinary Medicine
University of California
Davis, California 95612

STALLION ENROLLMENT LAWS

At one time, 22 states had stallion enrollment laws, enacted to bring about the improvement of horses and mules through the control of the public service stallions and jacks. With the decline in horse and mule numbers, some states repealed these laws; others have been lax in enforcing them. Also, the National Stallion Board was legally liquidated several years ago.

The first stallion law was passed by the legislature of Wisconsin in 1906. In 1907, Minnesota and Iowa enacted similar laws. Other states soon followed suit. Although the laws varied considerably between states, all had similar objectives. They were designed to accomplish one or more of the following things:

1. To prevent false representation as to breeding.
2. To bar heritably unsound and diseased horses.
3. To label unsound horses and jacks.
4. To eliminate the inferior sire, whether he be scrub, grade, or purebred.

At the time these stallion laws were enacted, there was much controversy among horse breeders concerning the heritability of certain unsoundnesses and diseases; consequently, many were listed that now are not considered transmissible from parent to offspring. Even now, there is no unanimity of opinion relative to the inheritance of certain unsoundnesses, and new information is constantly revising past thinking.

The majority of stallion enrollment laws barred from public service stallions that were affected with any of the following unsoundnesses or diseases: bone spavin, ringbone, sidebones, heaves, stringhalt, roaring, blindness, glanders (farcy), dourine, and urethral gleet.

Most horsemen agree that much improvement in the horse population came about through stallion legislation. But existing laws should be either modified or repealed. If the laws are amended, consideration should be given to incorporating the following provisions:

1. Include privately used stallions as well as those stood for public service.
2. License only purebred registered stallions of approved types.
3. Revise the list of hereditary unsoundnesses

[23]The author expresses his grateful appreciation for the authoritative review accorded this section by Dr. Clyde Stormont, Director of the Serology Laboratory and Professor of Immunogenetics, University of California, Davis, Calif.

[24]In a personal communication to the author, Dr. Clyde Stormont, Professor of Immunogenetics, Department of Reproduction, School of Veterinary Medicine, University of California, Davis, reported that in the California Laboratory they have been able to solve approximately 91% of all horse parentage cases.

and transmissible diseases, and license only stallions that are free from these afflictions.

4. Scrutinize the qualifications of the veterinarians who inspect the stallions.

5. Classify stallions relative to (a) conformation, (b) performance (track record, show record, etc.), (c) breeding, and (d) progeny performance (the record of the get).

6. "Put teeth into the law" by providing for enforceable penalties for violations.

7. Provide simple lien laws for protection of the stallion owner.

SELECTED REFERENCES

Title of Publication	Author(s)	Publisher
Animal Breeding	A. L. Hagedoorn	Crosby Lockwood & Son., Ltd., London, England, 1950
Animal Breeding	L. M. Winters	John Wiley & Sons, Inc., New York, N.Y., 1948
Animal Breeding Plans	J. L. Lush	Collegiate Press, Inc., Ames, Iowa, 1963
Animal Genetics	F. B. Hutt	The Ronald Press Company, New York, N.Y., 1964
Arab Breeding in Poland	E. Skorkowski	*Your Pony*, Columbus, Wisc., 1969
Arabian Horse Breeding	H. H. Reese	Bordon Publishing Company, Los Angeles, Calif., 1953
Behavior of Domestic Animals, The	E. S. Hafez	The Williams & Wilkins Co., Baltimore, Md., 1969
Breeding Better Livestock	V. A. Rice F. N. Andrews E. J. Warwick	McGraw-Hill Book Company, New York, N.Y., 1953
Breeding and Improvement of Farm Animals	V. A. Rice et al.	McGraw-Hill Book Company, New York, N.Y., 1967
Breeding the Racehorse	F. Tesio	J. A. Allen & Co., Ltd., London, England, 1958
Breeding and Raising Horses, Ag. Hdbk. No. 394	M. E. Ensminger	U.S. Department of Agriculture, Washington, D.C., 1972
Elements of Genetics, The	C. D. Darlington K. Mather	The Macmillan Company, New York, N.Y., 1950
Farm Animals	J. Hammond	Edward Arnold & Company, London, England, 1952
Genetic Basis of Selection, The	I. M. Lerner	John Wiley & Sons, Inc., New York, N.Y., 1958
Genetic Principles in Horse Breeding	J. F. Lasley	John F. Lasley, Columbia, Mo., 1970
Genetics	M. W. Strickberger	The Macmillan Company, New York, N.Y., 1968
Genetics and Animal Breeding	I. Johansson J. Rendel	W. H. Freeman and Co. Publishers, San Francisco, Calif., 1968
Genetics Is Easy	P. Goldstein	Lantern Press, New York, N.Y., 1967
Genetics of the Horse	W. E. Jones R. Bogart	Edwards Brothers, Inc., Ann Arbor, Mich., 1971
Genetics of Livestock Improvement	J. F. Lasley	Prentice-Hall, Inc., Englewood Cliffs, N.J., 1972
Glossary of Genetics and Cytogenetics, A	R. Rieger A. Michaelis M. M. Green	Springer-Verlag, Berlin, Germany, 1968
Hammond's Farm Animals	J. Hammond, Jr. I. L. Mason T. J. Robinson	Butler & Tanner, Ltd., Frome and London, England, 1971

(continued)

Title of Publication	Author(s)	Publisher
Horse Breeding Farm, The	L. C. Willis	A. S. Barnes & Co., Inc., Cranbury, N.J., 1973
Horse Breeding and Stud Management	H. Wynmalen	J. A. Allen & Co., Ltd., London, England, 1950
Horse Science Handbook, Vols. 1-3	Ed. by M. E. Ensminger	Agriservices Foundation, Clovis, Calif., 1963, 1964, 1966
Horsemanship and Horse Care, Ag. Info. Bull. No. 353	M. E. Ensminger	U.S. Department of Agriculture, Washington, D.C., 1972
How Life Begins	J. Power	Simon and Schuster, Inc., New York, N.Y., 1965
Improvement of Live-stock	R. Bogart	The Macmillan Company, New York, N.Y., 1959
Lectures, Stud Managers Course		Stud Managers Course, Lexington, Ky., intermittant since 1951
Light Horses, Farmers' Bull. No. 2127	M. E. Ensminger	U.S. Department of Agriculture, Washington, D.C., 1965
Livestock Improvement	J. E. Nichols	Oliver and Boyd, London, England, 1957
Mare Owner's Handbook, Vol. 1	Ed. by T. Rogers	Cordovan Corporation, Houston, Tex., 1971
Mares, Foals and Foaling	F. Andrist	J. A. Allen & Co., London, England, 1959
Modern Developments in Animal Breeding	J. M. Lerner H. P. Donald	Academic Press, Inc., New York, N.Y., 1966
Principles of Genetics	I. H. Herskowitz	The Macmillan Company, New York, N.Y., 1973
Reproduction in Farm Animals	E. S. Hafez	Lea & Febiger, Philadelphia, Penn., 1974
Reproductive Physiology	A. V. Nalbandov	W. H. Freeman and Co., Publishers, San Francisco, Calif., 1958
Science of Genetics, The	G. W. Burns	The Macmillan Company, New York, N.Y., 1972
Stud Farm Diary, A	H. S. Finney	J. A. Allen & Co., Ltd., London, England, 1973
Stud Managers' Handbooks	Ed. by M. E. Ensminger	Agriservices Foundation, Clovis, Calif., annually since 1965
Studies on Reproduction in Horses	Y. Nishakawa	Japan Racing Association, Tokyo, Japan, 1959
Study on the Breeding and Racing of Thoroughbred Horses Given Large Doses of Alpha Tocopherol, A	F. G. Darlington J. B. Chassels	Reprint from *The Summary*, Vol. 8, No. 1, London, Canada, 1956

CHAPTER 13

FEEDING HORSES[1]

Feed is the most important influence in the environment of the horse. Unless the horse is fed properly, its maximum potential in reproduction, growth, body form, speed, endurance, style, and attractiveness cannot be achieved.

The following conditions make it imperative that the nutrition of horses be the best that science and technology can devise:

1. *Confinement*—Many horses are kept in stables or corrals most of the time.

2. *Fitting yearlings*—When forcing young equines, it is important to their development and soundness that the ration be nutritionally balanced.

3. *Racing two-year-olds*—In the United States, we race more two-year-olds than any other nation in the world; our richest races are for them. If the nutri-

---

[1]The author is very grateful to the following scientists who reviewed the material in this chapter: Dr. Donald J. Balch, The University of Vermont, Burlington, Vt.; Dr. Wilton W. Heinemann, Washington State University, Prosser, Wash.; Dr. Robert M. Jordon, University of Minnesota, St. Paul, Minn.; Dr. William J. Tyznik, Ohio State University, Columbus, Ohio; and Professor George W. Vander Noot, Rutgers University, New Brunswick, N.J.

ent content of the ration is not adequate, there is bound to be more breakdown on the track than with older horses—this is costly.

4. *Stress*—Stress is affected by excitement, temperament, fatigue, number of horses together, previous nutrition, breed, age, and management. Race and show horses are always under stress; and the more tired they are and the greater the speed, the greater the stress. Thus, the ration for race and show horses should be scientifically formulated, rather than based on fads, foibles, and trade secrets. The greater the stress, the more exacting the nutritive requirements.

5. *Horses are unique*—They differ from other farm animals: They have greater value; are kept for recreation, sport, and work; are fed for a longer life of usefulness; have a smaller digestive tract; should not carry surplus weight; and are fed for nerve, mettle, animation, and character of muscle.

Also, feed constitutes the greatest single cost item in the horse business.

EVOLUTION OF HORSE PARALLELED HIS FEED

Through fossil remains, it is evident that the horse's evolution has always paralleled his soil and vegetation. In the beginning, little *Eohippus*, which was about the size of a Fox Terrier dog, had four toes on the front foot and three on the hind, had soft teeth, and was adapted to feeding on the herbage of the swamp. Gradually, it grew taller, its teeth grew stronger and harder, its legs grew longer, and all but one toe disappeared, thereby enabling it to feed farther from water and adapting it to the prairies.

It is only natural, in a world so big, that some equines should fare better than others. Thus, the ponderous horse of Flanders, progenitor of the modern draft horse, was the product of fertile soils, a mild climate, and abundant vegetation; whereas the diminutive, hardy Shetland Pony evolved on the scanty vegetation native to the long, cold winters of the Shetland Isles.

The effect of feed and nutrition as a creative force on the horse did not end with his domestication, about 5,000 years ago. At that time, man replaced nature as the horse's keeper, for, from that remote day forward, he assumed primary responsibility for the breeding, feeding, caring, and managing of his charges. When one considers that among wild bands 95 percent foal crops were common and unsoundnesses were relatively unknown, it's apparent that the horse hasn't fared so well with man serving as his provider.

FEEDS, FOIBLES, AND TRADE SECRETS

Hand in hand with the horse boom, the fabulous days of the "hoss doctor"—along with fads, foibles,

and trade secrets—returned. At least this has been true in altogether too many cases.

Like Topsy, the light horse industry just grew. There was precious little organized planning. With the passing of the draft horse, the Horse and Mule Association of America was inactivated, the Army Remount Service was stilled, and those great horse specialists of the U.S. Department of Agriculture and our land grant colleges retired and were not replaced.

Conditions were ripe for "fast operators" to make a "quick buck." Many folks with more money than animal knowledge owned horses, and the breeding and using of horses shifted from farms and ranches to suburban areas. As a result, "horse practitioners," whose products and sales pitches were reminiscent of the "medicine men" of old, developed a flourishing business, pawning off on unsuspecting horsemen a myriad of potions, cure-alls, tonics, reconditioners, worm expellers, mineral mixes, vitamin mixes, and feeds of a kind.

Generally speaking, claims were made for increased growth, improved breeding, better development, more speed, and increased stamina; and the feeding directions called for a cup or for 3 or 4 tablespoonsful per horse daily.

But such "horse practitioners" were not entirely to blame. Many owners insist on some kind of treatment. Like the ulcer patient who had to go to six different doctors before he could find one who would tell him that he could have a drink, they'll keep going until they get it. Especially when a horse "starts down," they'll grasp for straws. In such frantic moments, they'll buy and try almost any formula for which claims are made, completely oblivious to the facts (1) that distilled water might do just as much good—and far less harm, and (2) that they are buying losing tickets with their eyes wide open.

Horsemen are also great imitators. They'll single out some great horse, and, in one way or another, find out what it's getting. Then, they'll get some of the "same stuff" and use it from then 'til doomsday. The author has known horsemen to pay $50 for a gallon of a mysterious concoction, in a green jug, made in some little hamlet in Kentucky. Of course, the fallacy of such imitation—of feeding what the "great horse" got—is that the "name" horse might have been even greater had it been fed properly, and that there must be a reason why there are so few truly great horses. Also, the following searching question might well be asked: Why do many horses start training in great physical shape, only to slow down and lose appetite, and be taken out of training for some rest?

PERTINENT HORSE AND FEED FACTS

There is no panacea in the horse business. Success cannot be achieved through witchcraft or old

wives' tales; some merely achieve despite such handicaps. Instead, it calls for the combined best wit, wisdom, and judgment of science, technology, and practical experience.

The horse of today cannot be fed as it was yesterday and be expected to perform as the horse of tomorrow!

The following facts are pertinent to horse feeding, either directly or indirectly, and of importance to horsemen and those who counsel with them:

1. Horse owners are[2]—

a. Spending millions for concoctions, and unbalanced and deficient rations.

b. Producing a 50% foal crop. How many cattlemen could afford to keep 2 cows a whole year to produce one calf?

c. Keeping a stallion for each 7.3 foals produced.

d. Getting a 1.2% return on breeding establishments. How many persons would buy stock on the New York Exchange if they thought that they would get a return of only 1.2% on the investment? Yet, in a nationwide survey, the author found that that was the amount of horsemen's return on investments. The survey included horse breeding establishments, and not just those people who keep horses merely as a hobby; the latter don't expect to make money, any more than hunters or fishermen expect to reap a profit.

e. Retiring an appalling number of horses from tracks, shows, and other uses, due to unsoundness.

f. Losing millions of dollars through inefficiency and from deaths due to diseases and parasites.

2. Artifical conditions have been created which have caused unsoundnesses. In the wild state, horses roamed the plains in bands, with plenty of outdoor exercise on natural footing and fed on feeds derived from unleached soils, and, they were in unforced production. Today, many horses spend 95 percent of their time in a stall or corral, are exercised before daylight, forced for early growth and use (being ridden and raced as 2-year-olds), and put under terrific stress when shown, ridden, or raced (when running, horses expend up to 100 times the energy utilized at rest).

3. Remarkable progress has been made in feeding meat animals, as a result of which (a) feed required per pound of grain has been reduced, and (b) rate of gain has been increased. But no such progress has been made in horses; altogether too many of them are being fed the same old oats and the same old timothy hay. In fact, many horses of today are being fed about

the same as they were a century ago. How many meat animal producers could survive were they to turn back the pages of time and feed as their great, great grandfathers did 100 years ago?

4. Soils have been leached and depleted. This condition has come with the passing of time. Since soil nutrients affect plant nutrients, many horses are being shortchanged nutritionally.

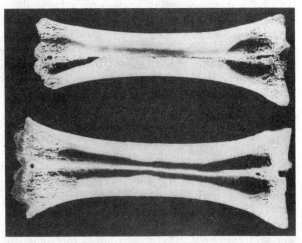

Fig. 13-1. Soil nutrients made the difference! Split bones from two animals of similar breeding and age. Small, fragile, pitted bone (top) obtained from animal pastured on belly-deep grass grown on weathered soil low in mineral content. Big, rugged, strong bone (bottom) from animal grown on moderately weathered, but highly mineralized soil. (Courtesy, University of Missouri)

5. Much can, and will, continue to be done through improved horse breeding, but this takes time. By contrast improved nutrition makes for immediate results.

6. At one time, nearly all lamenesses in horses were attributed to faulty shoeing. Later, this thought gave way to the traumatism (injury) theory—bone ailments were blamed upon bruising, pounding, and violent exertion. Still others maintain that skeletal troubles are primarily genetic in origin, that they're inherited from the parents.

7. Today, we know that a big head, bulging forehead, weak and crooked legs, enlarged joints, certain faulty conformation, and "ouchiness" are, in a vast majority of cases, deficiency symptoms resulting from improper nutrition. Many of the bone ailments that plague breeders and trainers—the sprains, spavins, splints, and ringbones—are the tragic result of improper skeletal development during the fetal and early growth stages.

8. Grass hays and farm grains are inadequate in quantity and quality of proteins, in certain minerals and vitamins, and in unidentified factors.

9. Horses are the most poorly nourished of all domestic animals from a scientific point of view.

10. Feeding horses for show or racing is more complicated and difficult than feeding any other farm

[2]Based on a survey of "Practices and Problems of Horsemen" conducted by the author of this book.

animal. This is primarily because of the stress and strain under which they are put and the absolute necessity for soundness.

11. Equine feed formulations are becoming more complex.

12. The average horse eats 11,000 pounds, or 5½ tons, of feed (hay and grain, or equivalent in pasture), each year.

13. Feed storage and labor costs have spiraled.

14. Horses reach maturity at four to five years of age. This means that many are expected to work hard, especially the racing breeds, as mere juveniles. No other animal is subjected to such stress and expected to perform so well at such an early age. This calls for the best in nutrition, so as to assure maximum growth and soundness of muscle and bone.

15. A major problem of breeders of racehorses today is to produce enough sound horses to supply the demands of racetracks.

16. If we are to improve nutrition, it must start with the fertility of the soil; it must be "from the ground up."

17. The grass on the other side of the fence is usually greener. What's more, if it's on a highway shoulder or right-of-way, it's usually more nutritious because of growing on more fertile soil.

18. Much more research has been done on diseases and parasites of horses per se than on their nutrition. Yet, it is recognized that nutrition plays a major role in disease and parasite resistance. This is true of bacterial infections, azoturia, "tying-up," some cases of periodic ophthalmia, and digestive disturbances.

19. The following parallel to the altogether too common breakdown of young horses in training or on the track is noteworthy: When young lambs or young pigs are pushed for daily gains that are twice as rapid as they were 50 years ago without simultaneously meeting their increased and more critical nutrient needs, they usually become crooked legged and crippled, much as happens to young equines that are forced. But, through proper nutrition, we generally alleviate this condition in young lambs and pigs.

20. Horsemen, and others, sometimes ask, "If so little nutrition research has been done on horses, how can one formulation or ration be superior to others?" In the judgment of the author, the answer is simple: We have made rapid strides in the fields of animal and human nutrition during the past two decades. These can be used as guides. It's a matter of fitting all these parts together, and, scientifically and practically, adapting them to the horse. It's not unlike the making of the atom bomb, which necessitated the scientific and practical fitting together of research for a specific purpose.

DIGESTIVE SYSTEM

The alimentary canal proper includes the entire tube extending from the mouth to the anus.

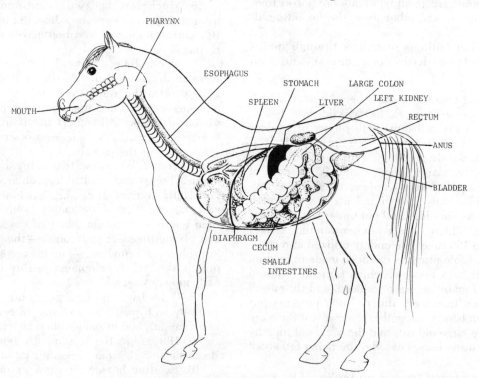

Fig. 13-2. The digestive system of the horse.

TABLE 13-1

PARTS AND CAPACITIES OF DIGESTIVE TRACTS
OF HORSE, COW, AND PIG

	Horse[1]	Cow	Pig
	←-------- (qt capacity) --------→		
Stomach	8-16	(200)	6-8
Rumen (paunch)		160	
Reticulum (honeycomb)		10	
Omasum (manyplies)		15	
Abomasum (true stomach)		15	
Small intestine	48	62	9
Cecum	28-32		
Large intestine	80	40	10

[1]Values for an average horse of 1,000 to 1,200 lb.

An understanding of the principal parts and functions of the digestive system of the horse is requisite to intelligent feeding.

Fig. 13-2 shows the anatomical position of the digestive system of the horse, whereas Table 13-1 and Fig. 13-3 show the comparative structures and sizes of the digestive tracts of farm animals. As noted, the digestive tract of the horse is anatomically and physiologically quite different from that of the ruminant.

Mouth

The mouth is the first part of the alimentary canal. In the horse, it is long and cylindrical. It includes the teeth (both uppers and lowers—24 molars and 12 incisors in the mature horse), the tongue, and 3 pairs of large salivary glands.

Digestion starts in the mouth. The feed is masticated by the teeth and moistened with saliva. In the mature horse, approximately 85 pounds (10 gallons) of saliva are secreted daily. It wets feedstuffs, thereby making for easier passage down the esophagus. In addition, the saliva contains the enzyme ptyalin, which transforms starch into maltose.

The mouth of the horse differs anatomically and physiologically from the ruminant as follows: Horses

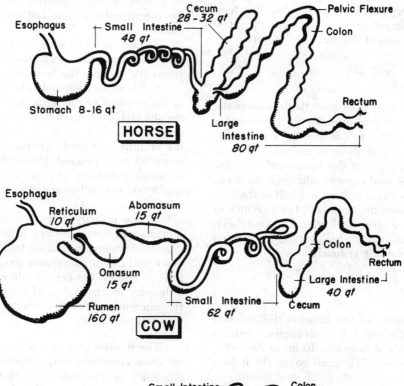

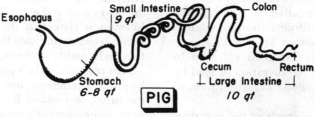

Fig. 13-3. Schematic diagram of digestive tracts of horse, cow, and pig.

have upper incisor teeth, ruminants do not; horses masticate feed with the teeth, ruminants are cud chewing; horses secrete a larger volume of saliva, and the saliva of the horse contains ptyalin, whereas the saliva of ruminants is enzyme-free.

Esophagus

This 50- to 60-inch tube provides passage of feed from the pharynx to the stomach.

Stomach

The stomach is the enlarged part of the alimentary canal which lies between the esophagus and the small intestine. It holds 8 to 16 quarts, but it functions best at two-thirds capacity. The stomach secretes gastric juices by which proteins and fats are broken down.

At the time of eating, feed passes through the horse's stomach very rapidly—so much so that feed eaten at the beginning of the meal passes to the intestine before the last part of the meal is completed.

Small Intestine

The small intestine is the tube that connects the stomach with the large intestine. On the average, it is about 70 feet long, and 3 to 4 inches thick when distended, with a capacity of about 12 gallons.

The small intestines of the horse and the cow have about the same total capacity, although the organ of the cow is nearly twice as long and half as thick.

In the horse, as in the ruminant, the enzymes of the pancreas and liver assist in further breaking down the protein, fats, and sugars which escape breakdown by the gastric juices of the stomach.

Large Intestine

The large intestine of the horse is divided into the cecum (4 ft long and 1 ft in diameter; contents fluid), great colon (12 ft long and 10 in. in diameter; contents fluid to semifluid), small colon (10 ft long and 4 in. in diameter; contents solid), and rectum.

In the cecum, sometimes called the water gut, digestion (fermentation) continues, limited vitamin synthesis occurs, and nutrients are absorbed.

The great colon is usually distended with food. In it, there is a continuation of the digestion of feed by digestive juices, bacterial action, and absorption of nutrients.

In the small colon, the contents of the digestive tract become solid and balls of dung are formed.

Anatomical and Physiological Differences

The anatomical and physiological peculiarities of the digestive system of the horse are of great significance, nutritionally. In comparison with the cow (a ruminant), the digestive tract of the horse differs as follows:

1. It is smaller (see Table 13-1), with the result that the horse cannot eat as much roughage as cattle. Not only that, it functions best at two-thirds capacity. Because of its small size, if a horse is fed too much roughage, labored breathing and quick tiring may result. Actually, the horse's stomach is designed for almost constant intake of small quantities of feed (such as happens when a horse is grazing on pasture), rather than large amounts at one time.

2. Without feed, the horse's stomach will empty completely in 24 hours, whereas it takes about 72 hours (3 times as long) for the cow's stomach to empty. At the time of eating, feed passes through the horse's stomach very rapidly—so much so that the feed eaten at the beginning of the meal passes into the intestine before the last part of the meal is completed.

3. The cow has four compartments (rumen, reticulum, omasum, and the abomasum or true stomach), whereas the horse has one.

4. There is comparatively little microbial action in the stomach of the horse, but much such action in the stomach (rumen) of the cow. As a result, the horse does not break down more than about 30 percent of the cellulose of feed, whereas the ruminant breaks down 60 to 70 percent. Hence, horses cannot handle so much roughage as can ruminants. Also, higher quality (lower cellulose content) forages must be fed to horses.

5. The primary seats of microbial activity in ruminants and horses occupy different locations in the digestive system in relation to the small intestine. In cows (and sheep), the rumen precedes the small intestine; in horses, the cecum follows it. As a result, the efficiency of absorption of nutrients synthesized by the microorganisms is likely to be lower in a horse than in a ruminant.

The limited protein synthesis in the horse (limited when compared with ruminants), and the lack of efficiency of absorption due to the cecum being on the lower end of the gut (thereby not giving the small intestine a chance at the ingesta after it leaves the cecum), clearly indicate that horse rations should contain high-quality proteins, adequate in amino acids.

In comparison to a cow, therefore, a horse should be fed less roughage, more and higher quality protein (no urea), and added B vitamins. Actually, the nutrient requirements of a horse more nearly parallel those of a pig than a cow.

FUNCTIONS OF FEEDS

The feed consumed by horses is used for a number of different purposes, the exact usage varying somewhat with the class, age, and productivity of the animal. A certain part of the feed is used for the maintenance of bodily functions aside from any useful production. This is known as the maintenance requirement. In addition, feed is used to take care of the functions for which horses are kept. Thus, young growing equines need nutrients suitable for building muscle tissue and bone; horses being readied for show or sale need a surplus of energy feeds for formation of fat; broodmares require feed for the development of their fetuses, and, following parturition, for the production of milk; whereas work (or racing) animals use feed to supply energy for work.

Maintenance

A horse differs from an engine in that the latter has no fuel requirement when idle, whereas the horse requires fuel every second of the day, whether it is idle or active.

The maintenance requirement may be defined as a ration which is adequate to prevent any loss or gain of tissue in the body when there is no production. Although these requirements are relatively simple they are essential for life itself. A mature horse must have heat to maintain body temperature, sufficient energy to cover the internal work of the body and the minimum movement of the animal, and a small amount of proteins, vitamins, and minerals for the repair of body tissues.

No matter how quietly a horse may be standing in the stall, it still requires a certain amount of fuel, and the least amount on which it can exist is called its basal maintenance requirement. Even under the best of conditions, about one-half of all the feed consumed by horses is used in meeting the maintenance requirements.

Growth

Growth may be defined as an increase in size of bone, muscles, internal organs, and other body parts.

The period of rapid growth of the young horse is one of the most critical in its life and requires the best possible nutrition. Foals attain approximately 90 percent of their mature height and 75 percent of their mature weight at 12 months of age (Fig. 13-4), followed by more gradual growth to 5 years of age.[3] Since bones and muscles are a significant part of early growth, proper nutrition is a must for their develop-

[3]Brody, S., *Bioenergetics and Growth*, Reinhold Publishing Corporation, New York, N.Y., 1945, p. 552; and *A Study of Growth and Development in the Quarter Horses*, Bull. No. 546, Louisiana State University, 1961.

ment. A foal that is severely restricted in nutrients will never reach its genetic potential. Naturally, the growth requirements become increasingly acute when horses are forced for early use, such as the training and racing of a 2- or 3-year-old.

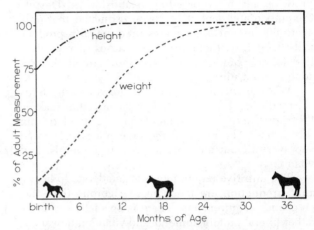

Fig. 13-4. Foals usually attain about 90% of their mature height and about 75% of their mature weight by 12 months of age. Bones and muscles are a significant part of early growth; hence, proper nutrition for young stock is very important.

Growth has been referred to as the foundation of horse production. Breeding animals may have their productive ability seriously impaired if they have been raised improperly. Nor can the most satisfactory performance be expected unless they have been well developed. For example, running horses do not possess the desired speed and endurance if their growth has been stunted or if their skeletons have been injured by inadequate rations during the growth period.

Fitting (Fattening)

This is the laying on of fat, especially in the tissues of the abdominal cavity and in the connective tissues just under the skin and between the muscles.

Usually, fitting rations contain more energy than do maintenance rations. However, the same formulation may be used for both fitting and maintenance purposes, but with larger quantities being supplied to horses that are being fitted.

In practical fitting rations, higher condition in mature animals is usually obtained through increasing the allowance of feeds high in carbohydrates and fats—a more liberal allowance of grains. Any surplus of protein may also serve for the production of fat, but usually such feeds are more expensive and are not used for economy reasons. In fitting mature horses, very little more proteins, minerals, and vitamins are required than for maintenance. In fitting young, growing animals, however, it is essential that, in addition to supplying more carbohydrates and fats, ample pro-

teins, minerals, and vitamins be provided to meet their accelerated growth.

Reproduction and Lactation

Regular and normal reproduction is the basis for profit on any horse breeding establishment. Despite this undeniable fact, it has been estimated that only 40 to 60 percent of all mares bred actually produce foals. Certainly, there are many causes of reproductive failure, but most scientists are agreed that inadequate nutrition is a major one.

With all species, most of the growth of the fetus occurs during the last third of pregnancy, thus making the reproductive requirements most critical during this period. The ration of the pregnant mare should supply sufficient amounts of protein, minerals, and vitamins.

The nutritive requirements for moderate to heavy milk production are much more rigorous than the pregnancy requirements. There is special need for a rather liberal protein, mineral, and vitamin allowance.

In the case of young, growing, pregnant females, additional protein, minerals, and vitamins, above the ordinary requirements, must be provided; otherwise, the fetus will not develop properly or milk will be produced at the expense of the tissues of the dam.

It is also known that the ration exerts a powerful effect on sperm production and semen quality. Too fat a condition can even lead to temporary or permanent sterility. Moreover, there is abundant evidence that greater fertility of stallions exists under conditions where a well-balanced ration and plenty of exercise are provided.

Work

In many respects, work requirements are similar to the needs for fitting, both functions requiring high-energy feeds.

For mature horses, not in reproduction, work is performed primarily at the expense of the carbohydrates and fats of the ration—energy that can be supplied in the form of additional grain. Theoretically, the protein is not drawn upon so long as the other nutrients are present in adequate amounts. From a practical standpoint, however, it is usually desirable to feed more proteins than the maintenance requirement, to maintain a protein-calorie ration in the diet which promotes efficiency of energy utilization. For work animals, the mineral and vitamin requirements are practically the same as for comparable idle animals—except for the greater need for salt because of increased perspiration.

NUTRIENT NEEDS

Meeting the nutrient needs of horses is a major

factor in determining their efficiency and years of service. In the discussion that follows, both requirements and allowances will be covered; and the nutritive needs of the horse will be discussed under the following headings: (1) energy (carbohydrates and fats), (2) protein, (3) minerals, (4) vitamins, and (5) water.

Nutrient Requirements Vs Allowances

In ration formulation, two words are commonly used—"requirements" and "allowances." Requirements do not provide for margins of safety. Thus, to feed a horse on the basis of meeting the bare requirements would not be unlike building a bridge without providing margins of safety for heavier than average loads or for floods. No competent engineer would be so foolish as to design such a bridge. Likewise, knowledgeable horse nutritionists provide for margins of safety—they provide for the necessary nutritive allowances. They allow for variations in feed composition; possible losses during storage and processing; day-to-day, and period-to-period, differences in needs of animals; age and size of animal; stage of gestation and lactation; the kind and degree of activity; the amount of stress; the system of management; the health, condition and temperament of the animal; and the kind, quality and amount of feed—all of which exert a powerful influence in determining nutritive needs.

Because of lack of experimental work with light horses, most nutritionists have arrived at estimated nutritive requirements of horses either (1) by proportioning down data on draft horses to a size and weight of light horses, and/or (2) by extrapolating data from cattle. The fallacy of each method is obvious. Draft horse research was conducted on ponderous, quiet beasts, that performed most of their work at the walk—animals that were subjected to few stresses in comparison with today's light horses. Extrapolating from other species (especially cattle) leaves much to be desired, simply because horses are quite different from them, anatomically and physiologically. Indeed, employing such methods may be sound arithmetic, but they do not necessarily lead to sound horse feeding.

A NUTRIENT DEFICIENCY MAY LIMIT PERFORMANCE

Nutrient deficiencies in horse rations can be, and often are, limiting factors in reproduction, growth, endurance, speed, etc. It's not unlike the "egg story" presented in Table 13-2.

In the horse, the same principle applies to speed, endurance, and every conceivable type of performance.

TABLE 13-2

HOW MANY EGGS WILL BE PRODUCED?

If the following nutrients are required for egg production, with each nutrient identified by number only (for example, No. 1 might be an essential amino acid, No. 2 might be vitamin A, etc.):	If to produce 12 (1 doz) eggs, the total units of each nutrient required are:	If the units of each nutrient present in the ration are:	Comments
No. 1	12	9	The ration lacks 3 units of having enough of this nutrient for 12 eggs.
No. 2	20	30	A surplus; ⅓ more of the nutrient than needed.
No. 3	12	13	Barely over.
No. 4	11	11	Even with the board.
etc.			
etc.			

Conclusion: *Nutrient No. 1 will be the limiting factor; only 9 eggs can be produced.*

Recommended Nutrient Allowances

Unfortunately, little experimental work has been done on the minimum nutrient requirements of horses. However, presently available information indicates that the nutrient allowances recommended in Tables 13-3 and 13-4 will meet the minimum requirements for horses and provide reasonable margins of safety.

In presenting the recommended nutrient allowances for horses in Tables 13-3 and 13-4, the author subscribes to the philosophy that it is cheap insurance to provide for reasonable margins of safety, primarily because of the paucity of experimental work. Nevertheless, the requirements and/or recommenda-

tions of the National Academy of Sciences (From: *Nutrient Requirements of Horses*, No. 6, 3rd rev. ed., 1973) are also presented in the sections devoted to minerals and vitamins, which follow.

In presenting the recommended nutritive allowances given in Tables 13-3 and 13-4, the author makes no claim either to their perfection, horse experimental derivation, or finality. Rather, they represent his best judgment based on the scientific and practical information presently available, without regard to fads, foibles, and trade secrets. Also, those using these recommended allowances as guides in horse ration formulations must give consideration to nutrients provided by the ingredients of the ration, for it's the total composition of the finished feed that counts.

TABLE 13-3

RECOMMENDED ALLOWANCES OF PROTEIN, FIBER, AND TOTAL DIGESTIBLE NUTRIENTS (TDN)

Type of Horse	Minimum Crude Protein	Maximum Crude Fiber	Minimum TDN
	(%)	(%)	(%)
Most mature horses used for race, show, or pleasure	12	25	53 to 70[1]
Broodmares	13	25	50 to 60
Stallions	14	25	50 to 68[2]
Young equines:			
Foals, 2 weeks to 10 months old	21	8	68 to 74
Weanlings to 18 months old	14	20	60
18 months to 3 years old	13	25	50 to 60

[1]The heavier the work, the more energy required.
[2]Increase the energy immediately before and during the breeding season.

TABLE 13-4

RECOMMENDED ALLOWANCES OF MINERALS AND VITAMINS

Kind of Mineral or Vitamin	Daily Allowance per 1,000-Pound Horse[1]	Allowances per Ton of Finished Feed (hay and grain combined)[2]
Minerals:		
Salt	2 oz	10 lb
Calcium	70.0 g	12.33 lb
Phosphorus	60.0 g	10.57 lb
Magnesium	6.4 g	1.3 lb
Potassium	68.1 g	12 lb
Iron	640 mg	51.2 g
Zinc	400 mg	32.0 g
Manganese	340 mg	27.2 g
Copper	90 mg	7.2 g
Iodine	2.6 mg	.21 g
Cobalt	1.5 mg	.12 g
Vitamins:		
Vitamin A (USP)	50,000	4,000,000
Vitamin D_2 (USP)	7,000	560,000
Vitamin E (IU)	200	16,000
Choline (mg)	400	32,000
Pantothenic acid (mg)	60	4,800
Niacin (mg)	50	4,000
Riboflavin (mg)	40	3,200
Thiamin (B_1) (mg)	35	2,800
Vitamin K (mg)	8	640
Folic acid (mg)	2.5	200
Vitamin B_{12} (mcg)[3]	125	10,000

[1]This is based on an allowance of 25 lb of feed per 1,000-lb horse per day, or 2.5 lb of feed per 100 lb of body weight.
[2]Where hay is fed separately, double this amount should be added to the concentrate.
[3]Micrograms.

STRESS AFFECTS NUTRITIVE NEEDS

Stress may be caused by excitement, temperament, fatigue, number of horses together, previous nutrition, breed, age, and management. Race and show horses are always under stress; and the more tired they become and the greater the speed, the greater the stress. Thus, the ration for race and show horses should be scientifically formulated. The greater the stress, the more exacting the nutritive requirements.

OTHER FACTORS AFFECT NUTRITIVE NEEDS

The feed requirements of horses do not necessarily remain the same from day to day or from period to period. The age and size of the animal; the stage of gestation or lactation of a mare; the kind and degree of activity; climatic conditions; the kind, quality, and amount of feed; the system of management; and the health, condition, and temperament of the animal are all continually exerting a powerful influence in determining its nutritive needs. How well the horseman understands, anticipates, interprets, and meets these requirements usually determines the success or failure of the ration.

No set of instructions, calculator, or book of knowledge can substitute for experience and born horse intuition. Skill and good judgment are essential.

Energy

The energy needs of horses vary with the individuality and size of the animal; the kind, amount, and severity of work performed; the condition and training of the animal; the ability of the rider or driver; the fatigue; the environmental temperature; and the diet.

In racing, horses may use up to 100 times the energy utilized at rest.

The National Academy of Sciences reports the following energy requirements for various activities of light horses:[4]

Activity	Requirement (kcal/hour/ kg of mass)
Walking	0.5
Slow trotting, some cantering	5.1
Fast trotting, cantering, some jumping	12.5
Cantering, galloping, jumping	24.0
Strenuous effort	39.0

Note that the energy requirements during "strenuous effort" are 78 times greater than in "walking."

A lack of energy may cause slow and stunted growth in foals and loss of weight, poor condition, and excessive fatigue in mature horses.

It is common knowledge that a ration must con-

---

[4]*Nutrient Requirement of Horses*, No. 6, 3rd rev. ed., National Academy of Sciences, 1973.

tain proteins, fats, and carbohydrates. Although each of these has specific functions in maintaining a normal body, they can all be used to provide energy for maintenance, for work, or for fattening. From the standpoint of supplying the normal energy needs of horses, however, the carbohydrates are by far the most important, more of them being consumed than any other compound, whereas the fats are next in importance for energy purposes. Carbohydrates are usually cheaper and more abundant; and they are very easily digested, absorbed, and transformed into body fat. Also, carbohydrate feeds may be more easily stored in warm weather and for longer periods of time. Feeds high in fat content are likely to become rancid, and rancid feed is unpalatable, if not actually injurious in some instances.

Generally, increased energy for horses is met by increasing the grain and decreasing the roughage.

CARBOHYDRATES

The carbohydrates are organic compounds composed of carbon, hydrogen, and oxygen. This group includes the sugars, starch, cellulose, gums, and related substances. They are formed in the plant by photosynthesis as follows:

$$6CO_2 + 6H_2O + \text{energy from sun} = C_6H_{12}O_6 \text{ (glucose)} + 6O_2$$

On the average, the carbohydrates comprise about three-fourths of all dry matter in plants, the chief source of horse feed. They form the woody framework of plants as well as the chief reserve food stored in seeds, roots, and tubers. When consumed by horses, carbohydrates are used as a source of heat and energy, and any excess of them is stored in the body as fat, or, in part, secreted.

No appreciable amount of carbohydrate is found in the horse's body at any one time, the blood supply of animals being held rather constant at about 0.05 to 0.1 % for most animals, but with the pig ranging from 0.05 to 0.25 %. However, this small quantity of glucose in the blood, which is constantly replenished by changing the glycogen of the liver back to glucose, serves as the chief source of fuel with which to maintain the body temperature and to furnish the energy needed for all body processes. The storage of glycogen (called "animal starch") in the liver amounts to 3 to 7 % of the weight of that organ.

From a feeding standpoint, the carbonhydrates consist of nitrogen-free extract (N.F.E.) and fiber. The nitrogen-free extract includes the more soluble, and, therefore, the more digestible, carbohydrates—such as the starches, sugars, hemicelluloses, and the more soluble part of the celluloses and pentosans. Also, N.F.E. contains some lignin. The fiber is that woody portion of plants (or feeds) which is not dissolved out by weak acids and alkalies. Fiber, therefore, is less easily digested. It includes cellulose, hemicellulose, and lignin.

The ability of horses to utilize roughages—to digest the fiber therein—depends chiefly on bacterial action. It is a true symbiotic type of relationship, carried out chiefly by anaerobic bacteria, mostly in the cecum and colon of the horse. This bacterial digestion breaks down the cellulose and pentosans of feeds into usable organic acids (chiefly acetic, propionic and butyric acids).

The fiber of growing pasture grass, fresh or dried, is more digestible than the fiber of most hay. Likewise, the fiber of early cut hay is more digestible than that of hay cut in the late bloom or seed stages. The difference is due to both chemical and physical structure, especially to the presence of certain encrusting substances (notably lignin) which are deposited in the cell wall with age. This is understandable when it is recognized that lignin is the principal constituent of wood, for no one would think of feeding wood to horses.

Young equines and working (or running) horses must have rations in which a large part of the carbohydrate content of the ration is low in fiber, and in the form of nitrogen-free extract.

To promote normal physiological activity of the gastrointestinal tract, one must feed a minimum amount of coarse roughage to horses. Finely ground roughages will not suffice.

FAT

Lipids (fat and fatlike substances), like carbohydrates, contain three elements: carbon, hydrogen, and oxygen. As horse feeds, fats function much like carbohydrates in that they serve as a source of heat and energy and for the formation of fat. Because of the larger portion of carbon and hydrogen, however, fats liberate more heat than carbohydrates when digested, furnishing approximately 2.25 times as much heat or energy per pound on oxidation as do carbohydrates. A smaller quantity of fat is required, therefore, to serve the same function.

The physical and chemical properties of fats are quite variable. From a chemical standpoint, a molecule of fat consists of a combination of three molecules of certain fatty acids with one molecule of glycerol. Fats differ in their melting points and other properties, depending on the particular fatty acids which they contain. Thus, because of the high content of unsaturated acids (such as oleic and linoleic) and acids of low molecular weight, corn fat is a liquid at ordinary temperatures; whereas, because of the high content of stearic and palmitic acids, beef fat is solid at ordinary temperatures.

Because of their unsaturation, fats often become rancid through oxidation or hydrolysis, resulting in disagreeable flavors and odors which lessen their desirability as feeds. The development of rancidity may be retarded through proper storage or by adding antioxidants. The hydrogenation of fats (adding hydrogen to the double bonds) also lessens rancidity. The latter process has long been effectively used in improving the keeping qualities of vegetable shortenings and lard.

Some fatty acids are unsaturated, which means that they have the ability to take up oxygen or certain other chemical elements. Chemically, these unsaturated acids contain one or more pairs of double bond carbon atoms.

A small amount of fat in the ration is desirable, as fat is the carrier of the fat-soluble vitamins (vitamins A, D, E, and K). There is evidence that some species (humans, swine, rats, and dogs) require certain of the fatty acids. Although the fatty acid requirements of horses have not been settled, it is thought that ordinary farm rations contain ample quantities for these nutrients.

In the past, most horsemen and scientists were of the opinion that horses could not tolerate high-fat diets. However, recent work indicates that they will readily consume 10 to 20 % added fat to the ration, without difficulty—and even with benefit.[5] In an endurance trial conducted by the Colorado Station, horses fed fat supplemented rations (9% added fat) outperformed their counterparts that were fed either (1) starch supplemented rations, or (2) protein supplemented rations.[6] This leads to speculation that added fat (2 to 6% added fat, based on experimental work with cattle) may be the answer to providing more needed energy for heavily stressed horses (racing, showing, endurance rides), which are often finicky and light eaters. Additionally, fat may give staying power, because it is digested more slowly than carbohydrates or protein. Unsaturated fats—vegetable oils, particularly corn oil or safflower oil—also have the added virtue of imparting gloss, or sheen, to the hair when as little as 2 ounces (2 tablespoons) are fed twice daily. Except for vegetable oils (unsaturated fats) producing an attractive coat, there is no difference between animal and vegetable fats; hence, the choice may be determined by economics—which is the best buy. When fat is added to the ration, it is important that it be stablized, and that there also be added protein (to maintain the protein-calorie ratio), minerals, and vitamins.

---

[5]Tyznik, W. J., "Energy for Horses," paper presented at the 1975 California Livestock Symposium.

[6]Slade, L. M., and P. L. Hambleton, "Feeding the Horse for Endurance," *Stud Managers' Handbook*, Vol. 12, ed. by M. E. Ensminger, Agriservices Foundation, Clovis, Calif., 1976, p. 140.

METHODS OF MEASURING ENERGY

One nutrient cannot be considered as more important than another, because all nutrients must be present in adequate amounts if efficient production is to be maintained. Yet, historically, feedstuffs have been compared or evaluated primarily on their ability to supply energy to animals. This is understandable because (1) energy is required in larger amounts than any other nutrient, (2) energy is most often the limiting factor in livestock production, and (3) energy is the major cost associated with feeding animals.

Our understanding of energy metabolism has increased through the years. With this added knowledge, changes have come in both the methods and terms used to express the energy value of feeds.

The methods of measuring the energy value of feedstuffs currently employed in the United States are:

1. Total digestible nutrient (TDN)
2. Calorie System, including—
   a. Gross energy (GE)
   b. Digestible energy (DE)
   c. Metabolizable energy (ME)
   d. Net energy (NE)

Each system has its advantages and advocates. Also, both the difficulty in determining energy values of feeds according to the different systems of measurement and the accuracy of the results increase in the order that they are listed above. Nevertheless, more and more feedstuffs are being evaluated in calories, with net energy being the method of choice.

TOTAL DIGESTIBLE NUTRIENTS (TDN)

Total Digestible Nutrients (TDN) is the sum of the digestible protein, fiber, nitrogen-free extract, and fat × 2.25. It has been the most extensively used measure for energy in the United States.

Back of TDN values are the following steps:

1. *Digestibility*—The digestibility of a particular feed for a specific species is determined by a digestion trial.

2. *Computation of digestible nutrients*—Digestible nutrients are computed by multiplying the percentage of each nutrient in the feed (protein, fiber, nitrogen-free extract (NFE), and fat) by its digestion coefficient. The result is expressed as digestible protein, digestible fiber, digestible NFE, and digestible fat. For example, if dent corn contains 8.9 percent protein of which 77 percent is digestible, the percent of digestible protein is 6.9.

3. *Computation of total digestible nutrients (TDN)*—The TDN is computed by use of the following formula:

$$\% \text{ TDN} = \frac{\text{DCP} + \text{DCF} + \text{DNFE} + (\text{DEE} \times 2.25)}{\text{feed consumed}} \times 100$$

where DCP = digestible crude protein; DCF = digestible crude fiber; DNFE = digestible nitrogen free extract; and DEE = digestible ether extract.

TDN is ordinarily expressed as a percent of the ration or in units of weight (lb or kg), not as a caloric figure.

The main *advantage* of the TDN system is that it has been used for a very long time and many people are acquainted with it.

The main *disadvantages* of the TDN system are :

1. It is really a misnomer, because TDN is not an actual total of the digestible nutrients in a feed. It does not include the digestible mineral matter (such as salt, limestone, and defluorinated phosphate—all of which are digestible); and the digestible fat is multiplied by the factor 2.25 before being included in the TDN figure, because its energy value is higher than carbohydrates and protein. As a result of multiplying fat by the factor 2.25, feeds high in fat will sometimes exceed 100 in percentage TDN (a pure fat with a coefficient of digestibility of 100% would have a theoretical TDN value of 225%—100% × 2.25).

2. It is an empirical formula based upon chemical determinations that are not related to actual metabolism of the animal.

3. It is expressed as a percent or in weight (lb or kg), whereas energy is expressed in calories.

4. It takes into consideration only digestive losses; it does not take into account other important losses, such as losses in the urine, gasses, and increased heat production (heat increment).

5. It overevaluates roughages in relation to concentrates when fed for high rates of production, due to the higher heat loss per pound of TDN in high-fiber feeds.

Because of these several limitations, in the United States the TDN system is gradually being replaced by other energy evaluation systems, particularly net energy. However, due to the voluminous TDN data on many feeds and long-standing tradition, it will continue to be used by many people for a long time to come.

CALORIE SYSTEM

Energy is used in many forms—as light, electricity, atomic force, work, or heat—and it is measured by several units such as candlepower, kilowatts, foot-pounds, British thermal units (Btu), joules, and calories.

Scientists generally agree that the units used to measure the nutritive requirements of animals and to evaluate feeds should be one and the same. But there is considerable disagreement, throughout the world, as to what units, or system, to use. In the United States, animal nutritionists are increasingly using the calorie system, and more specifically net energy.

Gross Energy (GE)

This is the total heat of combustion of a material as determined with an instrument known as the bomb calorimeter, in which the substance tested is placed and burned with the aid of oxygen. The procedure is as follows: An electric wire is attached to the material being tested, so that it can be ignited by remote control; 2,000 grams of water are poured around the bomb; 25 to 30 atmospheres of oxygen are added to the bomb; the material is ignited; the heat given off from the burned material warms the water; and a thermometer registers the change in temperature of the water. For example, if 1 gram of material is

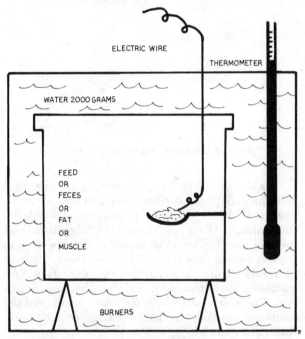

Fig. 13-5. Diagrammatic sketch of a bomb calorimeter used for the determination of the gross energy value (caloric content) of various materials.

burned and the temperature of the water is raised 1 degree Centigrade, 2,000 calories are given off. Hence, the material contains 2,000 calories per gram. This value is known as the gross energy (GE) content of the material.

Net Energy (NE)

Net energy (NE) is computed according to the following formula:

NE = Gross energy – fecal energy – gaseous
     energy – urinary energy – heat increment

Net energy may be likened to net income in a business. As every businessman knows, net income is gross income minus all expenses and losses. So, net energy is gross energy intake minus all energy expenses of metabolism and all losses during digestion.

A graphic breakdown of what happens to the energy in a feed is shown in Fig. 13-6.

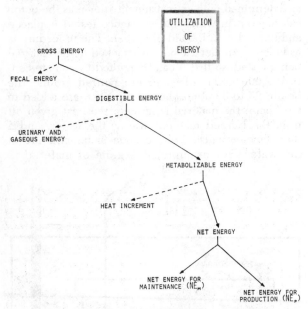

Fig. 13-6. Utilization of feed energy by an animal.

As shown in Fig. 13-6, the feed which an animal consumes contains a specific amount of total, or gross, energy. However, not all of this energy is usable by the animal; there are losses in digestion and metabolism. It follows that measures that are used to express animal requirements and the energy content of feeds differ primarily in the digestive and metabolic losses that are included in their determination. Fig. 13-6 shows where the losses occur; and the following summary details the energy retention and losses along the way.

● *Digestible energy (DE)*—Digestible energy is that portion of the GE in a feed that is not excreted in the feces. It is roughly comparable to TDN. Digestible energy has two of the same major disadvantages as the TDN system: (1) Only digestive losses are considered, and (2) roughages are overvalued compared with concentrates. Consequently, it offers little improvement over the TDN system.

Digestible energy can be calculated from TDN by using the factor 2,000 kilocalories per pound of TDN.

● *Metabolizable energy (ME)*—Metabolizable energy represents that portion of the GE that is not lost in the feces, urine, and gas (mainly methane). Although ME more accurately describes the useful

energy in the feed than does GE or DE, it does not take into account the energy lost as heat, commonly called heat increment (HI). As a result, it overevaluates roughages compared with concentrates, as does TDN and DE.

● *Net energy (NE)*—Net energy represents the energy fraction in a feed that is left after the fecal, urinary, gas, and heat increment (HI) losses are deducted from the GE.

The heat increment (HI) is the difference between ME and NE. It represents the heat unavoidably produced by an animal in digestion and metabolism. This heat is useful only for keeping an animal warm during cold weather. During very warm weather, the energy represented by this heat is a complete loss; worse yet, it may actually lower production by causing the animal to be too warm. Dr. Samuel Brody, world renowned scientist in bioenergetics and growth, formerly of the University of Missouri, referred to heat increment as the "food utilization tax."

The net energy values of feeds are different for maintenance and production. Roughages compare more favorably with grain for maintenance than for production.

1. *Net energy for maintenance (NEm)*—This is the fraction of the net energy that keeps the animal in energy equilibrium. In this state, there is no net gain or loss of energy in the body tissue.

2. *Net energy for production (NEp)*—This is the fraction of the net energy available for production (gain, work, lactation, etc.).

Because of its greater accuracy, net energy is being used increasingly in ration formulation.

Protein

For more than a century, proteins and their structural units, the amino acids, have been studied and recognized as important dietary constituents. Proteins are complex organic compounds made up chiefly of amino acids, which are present in characteristic proportions for each specific protein. This nutrient always contains carbon, hydrogen, oxygen, and nitrogen, and, in addition, it usually contains sulfur and frequently phosphorus. Proteins are essential in all plant and animal life as components of the active protoplasm of each living cell.

In plants, the protein is largely concentrated in the actively growing portions, especially the leaves and seeds. Legumes also have the ability to synthesize their own proteins from such relatively simple soil and air compounds as carbon dioxide, water, nitrates, and sulfates. Thus, plants, together with some bacteria which are able to synthesize these products, are the original sources of all proteins.

In animals, proteins are much more widely dis-

tributed than in plants. Thus, the proteins of the animal body are primary constituents of many structural and protective tissues—such as bones, ligaments, hair, hoofs, skin and the soft tissues which include the organs and muscles. The total protein content of a horse's body ranges from about 10 percent in very fat mature horses to 20 percent in thin young foals. By way of further contrast, it is also interesting to note that, except for the bacterial action in the cecum, horses lack the ability of the plant to synthesize proteins from simple materials. They must depend upon plants as a source of dietary protein. In brief, except for the proteins built by the bacterial action in the cecum, they must have amino acids or more complete protein compounds in the ration.

Horses of all ages and kinds require adequate amounts of protein of suitable quality—for maintenance, growth, fattening, reproduction, and work. Of course, the protein requirements for growth, reproduction and lactation are the greatest and most critical.

A deficiency of protein in the ration of the horse may result in the following deficiency symptoms: depressed appetite, poor growth, loss of weight, reduced milk production, irregular estrus, lowered foal crops, loss of condition, and lack of stamina.

Since the vast majority of protein requirements given in feeding standards meet minimum needs only, the allowances for race, show, breeding, and young animals should be higher.

QUALITY OF PROTEINS

In addition to an adequate quantity of proteins being supplied, it is essential that the character of proteins be thoroughly understood. Proteins are very complex compounds with each molecule made up of hundreds of thousands of amino acids combined with each other. The amino acids, of which some 23 are known, are sometimes referred to as the building stones of proteins. Certain of these amino acids can be made by the animal's body to satisfy its needs. Others cannot be formed fast enough to supply the body's needs, and, therefore are known as indispensable (or essential) amino acids. These must be supplied in the feed. Thus, rations that furnish an insufficient amount of any of the essential amino acids are said to have proteins of poor quality, whereas those which provide the proper proportions of the various necessary amino acids are said to supply proteins of good quality. In general, animal proteins are superior to plant proteins for monogastric animals (including man) because they are better balanced in the essential amino acids. For example, zein (a corn protein) is an incomplete plant protein. It is deficient in the essential amino acids lysine and tryptophane. On the other hand, animal proteins are excellent sources of lysine, and many of

them (especially milk and eggs) are abundant in tryptophane.

The necessity of each amino acid in the diet of the experimental rat has been thoroughly tested, but less is known about the requirements of large animals or even the human. According to our present knowledge, based largely on work with the rat, the following division of amino acids as indispensable and dispensable seems proper:

Indispensable	Dispensable
Arginine	Alanine
Histidine	Aspartic acid
Isoleucine	Citrulline
Leucine	Cysteine
Lysine	Cystine
Methionine (may be replaced	Glutamic acid
in part by cystine)	Glycine
Phenylalanine	Hydroxyglutamic acid
Threonine	Hydroxyproline
Tryptophane	Norleucine
Valine	Proline
	Serine
	Tyrosine

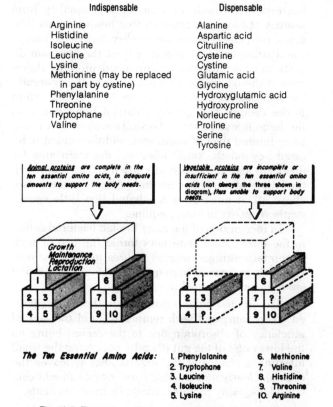

Animal proteins are complete in the ten essential amino acids, in adequate amounts to support the body needs.

Vegetable proteins are incomplete or insufficient in the ten essential amino acids (not always the three shown in diagram), thus unable to support body needs.

Growth
Maintenance
Reproduction
Lactation

The Ten Essential Amino Acids:

1. Phenylalanine	6. Methionine
2. Tryptophane	7. Valine
3. Leucine	8. Histidine
4. Isoleucine	9. Threonine
5. Lysine	10. Arginine

Fig. 13-7. The amino acids are sometimes referred to as the building stones of proteins. Rations that furnish an insufficient amount of the essential building stones (amino acids) are said to have proteins of poor quality.

Because of more limited amino acid synthesis in the horse than in ruminants, plus the fact that the cecum is located beyond the small intestine—the main area for digestion and absorption of nutrients—it is recommended that high-quality protein rations, adequate in amino acids, be fed to horses. This is especially important for young equines, because cecal synthesis is very limited early in life.

Fortunately, the amino acid content of proteins from different sources varies. Thus, the deficiencies of one protein may be improved by combining it with another, and the mixture of the two proteins often will have a higher feeding value than either one alone. It is for this reason, along with added palatability, that a considerable variety of feeds in the horse ration is desirable.

The feed proteins are broken down into amino acids by digestion. They are then absorbed and distributed by the bloodstream to the body cells, which rebuild these amino acids into body proteins.

CECUM SYNTHESIS

In the case of ruminants (cattle and sheep), there is tremendous bacterial action in the paunch. These bacteria build body proteins of high quality from sources of inorganic nitrogen that nonruminants (humans, rats, chickens, swine, poultry, and dogs) cannot use. Farther on in the digestive tract, the ruminant digests the bacteria and obtains good proteins therefrom. Although the horse is not a ruminant, apparently the same bacterial process occurs to a limited extent in the cecum—that greatly enlarged blind pouch of the large intestine of the horse. However, it is much more limited than in ruminants, and the cecum is located beyond the small intestine, the main area for digestion and absorption of nutrients. This points up the fallacy of relying on cecum synthesis in the horse; above all, it must be remembered that little cecum synthesis exists in young equines.

In recognition of the more limited bacterial action in the horse, most state laws forbid the use of such nonprotein nitrogen sources as urea in horse rations. For such an animal, high-quality proteins in the diet are requisite to normal development.

The limited protein synthesis in the horse (limited when compared with ruminants), and the lack of efficiency of absorption due to the cecum being on the lower end of the gut (thereby not giving the small intestine a chance at the ingesta after it leaves the cecum), clearly indicate that horse rations should contain high-quality proteins, adequate in amino acids.

PROTEIN POISONING

Some opinions to the contrary, protein poisoning as such has never been documented. There is no proof that heavy feeding of high-protein feeds to horses is harmful, provided (1) the ration is balanced in all other respects, (2) the animal's kidneys are normal and healthy (a large excess of protein in terms of body needs increases the work of the kidneys for the excretion of the urea), (3) any ration change to high-protein feed is made gradually, as is recommended in any change in feed, and (4) there is adequate exercise and normal metabolism.

Some horses do appear to be allergic to certain proteins or to excesses of specific amino acids, as a result of which they may develop "protein bumps."

It is recognized that protein in excess of what the body can use tends to be wasted insofar as its specific functions are concerned, since it cannot be stored in any but very limited amounts and must be catabolized. Nevertheless, some wastage of protein in terms of its known functions may be both physiologically and economically desirable in order to (1) maintain the protein reserves, (2) provide an adequate protein-calorie ratio for efficient energy utilization, and (3) assure that protein quality needs are met, despite the marked difference of quality among commonly fed rations.

Minerals[7]

When we think of minerals for the horse, we instinctively think of bones and unsoundnesses. This is so because (1) a horse's skeleton is very large, weighing 100 pounds or more in a full-grown horse, of which more than half consists of organic matter and minerals, and (2) experienced trainers estimate that one-third of the horses in training require treatments for unsoundnesses, in one form or another. But in addition to furnishing structural material for the growth of bones, teeth, and tissues, minerals regulate many of the life processes.

In an amazingly short time after birth, a healthy foal can run almost as fast as its mother—and on legs almost as long. In fact, the cannon bones (the lower leg bones extending from the knees and hocks to the fetlocks) are as long at the time of birth as they will ever be. This indicates that important development of the skeleton takes place in the fetus, before the foal is born. It is evident, therefore, that adequate minerals must be provided the broodmare if the bones of her offspring are to be sound.

The mineral requirements of mares in lactation are even more rigorous than those during gestation. Mares weighing about 1,000 lb will produce an average of 2 gallons, or more, of milk per day throughout the 7-month suckling period. That's a total of 3,360 lb of milk. Here's how this phenomenon works: The mare's skeleton is like a bank—people deposit money in a bank, then draw out or write checks on their reserves as needed. So, when properly fed before breeding, in early pregnancy, and when barren, mineral deposits are made in the mare's skeleton. Then at those times when the mineral demands are greater than can be obtained from the feed—the last of pregnancy, and during lactation—the mare draws from the stored reserves in her skeleton. Of course, if there hasn't been proper storage in the mare's skeleton, something must "give"—and that something is the mother. Nature has ordained that growth of the fetus, and the lactation that follows, shall take priority over

---

[7]In this section, when reference is made to a National Academy of Sciences recommendation, this implies the following source: *Nutrient Requirements of Horses*, No. 6, 3rd rev. ed., National Academy of Sciences, 1973.

the maternal requirements. Hence, when there is a mineral deficiency, the mare's body will be deprived, or even stunted if she is young, before the developing fetus or milk production will be materially affected.

Eighteen mineral elements are known to be required by at least some animal species. They can be divided into the following two groups based on the relative amounts needed in the ration:

Major or Macro Minerals	Trace or Micro Minerals
Calcium (Ca)	Iodine (I)
Phosphorus (P)	Manganese (Mn)
Sodium (Na)	Iron (Fe)
Chlorine (Cl)	Zinc (Zn)
Potassium (K)	Copper (Cu)
Magnesium (Mg)	Molybdenum (Mo)
Sulfur (S)	Fluorine (F)
	Chromium (Cr)
	Selenium (Se)
	Silicon (Si)
	Cobalt (Co)

Approximately 70% of the mineral content of the horse's body consists of calcium and phosphorus. About 99% of the calcium and over 80% of the phosphorus are found in the bones and teeth.

Although acute mineral deficiency diseases and actual death losses are relatively rare, inadequate supplies of any one of the essential mineral elements may result in lack of thrift, poor gains, inefficient feed utilization, lowered reproduction, and decreased performance in racing, showing, riding, or whatnot.

Thus, like a thief in the night, subacute mineral deficiencies in horses each year steal away millions of dollars from the horsemen of America, and, for the most part, go unnoticed. Only when the mineral deficiency reaches such proportions that it results in excess emaciation, reproductive failure, or death is it likely to be detected. This does not mean that all 18 mineral elements known to be required by at least one animal species must always be included in horse mineral supplements. Rather, only the specific minerals that are deficient in the ration—and in the quantities necessary—should be supplied. *Excesses and mineral imbalances are to be avoided.*

At Washington State University, in a study with rabbits, the effect of soil phosphorus—*just one mineral*—on plants, and, in turn, the effects of these plants on animals, was established.[8] Generation after generation, rabbits were fed on alfalfa, with one group receiving hay produced on low-phosphorus soils and the other group eating alfalfa grown on high-phosphorus soils. The rabbits in the low-phosphorus soil-alfalfa group (1) were retarded in growth—with 9.8% lower weaning weights, (2) required 12% more matings per conception, and (3) had a 47% lower breaking strength of bones than the rabbits on the

[8]Heinemann, W. W., et al., Wash. Ag. Exp. Sta. Tech. Bull. 24, June, 1957.

high-phosphorus soil-alfalfa group. There is reason to believe that soil nutrients can affect horses similarly—in growth, conception, and soundness of bone; but more experimental work on this subject is needed.

Fig. 13-8. Rabbit with bowed legs and enlarged joints resulting from eating alfalfa produced on low-phosphorus soils. There is reason to believe that the same thing happens to horses. (Courtesy, Washington State University)

The typical horse ration of grass hay and farm grains is usually deficient in calcium, but adequate in phosphorus. Also, salt is almost always deficient; and many horse rations do not contain sufficient iodine and certain other trace elements. Thus, horses usually need special mineral supplements. But they should not be fed either more or less minerals than needed. Also, it is recognized that mineral allowances given with the ration or in a mineral mix should vary according to the mineral content of the soil on which feeds are grown.

The proper development of the bone is particularly important in the horse, as evidenced by the stress and strain on the skeletal structure of the racehorse, especially when racing the two-year-old. Since the greatest development of the skeleton takes place in the young, growing animal, it is evident that adequate minerals must be provided at an early age if the bone is to remain sound.

A summary of individual mineral functions, defi-

ciency symptoms, recommended allowances, and sources is given in Table 13-5, Horse Mineral Chart.

In this table, the minerals are listed according to recommended daily allowances, without regard to impor-

TABLE
HORSE

Minerals Which May Be Deficient Under Normal Conditions	Conditions Usually Prevailing Where Deficiencies Are Reported	Function of Mineral	Some Deficiency Symptoms
Salt (Sodium and chlorine, NaCl)	Negligence, for salt is cheap. Horses sweating excessively, as with vigorous exercise and during warm weather.	Sodium and chlorine help maintain osmotic pressure in body cells, upon which depends the transfer of nutrients to the cells and the removal of waste materials. Sodium is associated with muscle contraction and is important in making bile, which aids in the digestion of fats and carbohydrates. Chlorine is required for the formation of hydrochloric acid in the gastric juice so vital to protein digestion.	In warm or hot weather, workhorses show heat stress. Long-term symptoms of sodium deficiency are: depraved appetite, rough hair coat, reduced growth of young animals, and decreased milk production.
Calcium (Ca)	The typical horse ration of grass hay and farm grains—usually deficient in calcium.	Builds strong bones and sound teeth. Very important during lactation. Affects availability of phosphorus.	Rickets in young horses; osteomalacia in mature horses.
Phosphorus (P)	Horses pastured on phosphorus-deficient areas or fed for a long period on mature, weathered forage.	Important in the development of bones and teeth. Essential to metabolism of carbohydrates and fats, and enzyme activation.	Rickets in young horses; osteomalacia in mature horses.
Magnesium (Mg)	Horses on high grain-low forage ration.	Reduces stress and irritability.	Horses under stress are keyed up, high-strung, and jumpy.
Iron (Fe)	Suckling foals kept away from soil and feed other than milk.	Necessary for formation of hemoglobin, an iron-containing compound which enables the blood to carry oxygen. Also, important to certain enzyme systems.	Iron-deficiency anemia, characterized by fewer than normal red cells and less than normal amount of hemoglobin.
Zinc (Zn)	Feeds low in zinc. Excess calcium may reduce the absorption and utilization of zinc.	Required for normal protein synthesis and metabolism Imparts gloss or "bloom" to the hair coat.	Rough, dull hair coat. Loss of appetite.
Manganese (Mn)	Excess calcium and phosphorus which decreases absorption of manganese.	Essential for normal bone formation (as a component of the organic matrix). Thought to be an activator of enzyme systems. Growth and reproduction.	Poor growth. Lameness, shortening and bowing of legs, and enlarged joints. Impaired reproduction (testicular degeneration of males; defective ovulation of females).

tance. Minerals may be incorporated in the ration in keeping with the recommended allowances given in this table. Additionally, horses should have free access to salt and a suitable mineral supplement.

13-5
MINERAL CHART[1]

Recommended Allowances[2]		Practical Sources of the Mineral	Comments
Daily Per 1,000 Lb Horse	Per Ton or Percent of Total Rations[3]		
2.0 oz (56 g)	10 lb/ton. 0.5 to 1.0% of ration.	Salt provided free choice, preferably in loose form, or 0.5 to 1.0% salt added to the ration.	Horses require both sodium and chlorine, but the requirement for chlorine is approximately half that of sodium. Generally, the chlorine requirements will be met if the sodium needs are adequate. Sodium and chlorine are low in feeds of plant origin. There is little danger of overfeeding salt unless a salt starved animal is suddenly exposed to too much salt, or if liberal amounts of water are not available.
70 g	12.3 lb/ton. 0.6 to 0.7% of ration.	Ground limestone or oystershell flour. Where both calcium and phosphorus are needed, use bone meal or dicalcium phosphate (see Table 13-6).	The calcium to phosphorus ratio should be maintained close to 1.1:1 although 2:1 is acceptable when the higher calcium content is due to the presence of legume. Narrower ratios may cause osteomalacia in mature horses. Where there is a shortage of calcium in the ration, it is withdrawn from the bones.
60 g	10.6 lb/ton. 0.5% of ration.	Monosodium phosphate, disodium phosphate, or sodium tripolyphosphate. Where both calcium and phosphorus are needed, use bone meal or dicalcium phosphate. (see Table 13-6).	Same as stated for calcium under "Comments" above. If plenty of vitamin D is present, the ratio of calcium to phosphorus becomes less important. Apparently phosphorus cannot be withdrawn from the bones.
3,200 mg	256 g/ton	Magnesium sulfate. Magnesium oxide.	Excess of magnesium upsets calcium and phosphorus metabolism.
640 mg	51.2 g/ton	Ferrous sulfate administered orally. Trace mineralized salt. Cane molasses.	The horse's body contains about 0.004% iron. Milk is deficient in iron, and the iron content of the mother cannot be increased through feeding iron. Thus, foals should be individually or creep fed as soon as they are old enough. A variable store of both iron and copper is located in liver and spleen, and some iron is found in the kidneys. Too much iron may be harmful.
400 mg	32 g/ton	Zinc carbonate. Zinc sulfate.	If zinc in the feed is on the low side, the addition of zinc should improve the hair coat.
340 mg	27.2 g/ton	Trace mineralized salt containing 0.25% manganese (or more).	Most natural feedstuffs are rich in manganese.

(Continued)

Minerals Which May Be Deficient Under Normal Conditions	Conditions Usually Prevailing Where Deficiencies Are Reported	Function of Mineral	Some Deficiency Symptoms
Copper (Cu)	Suckling foals. Mare's milk, along with milk from other species, is low in copper. Horses grazing pastures low in copper, as in Australia and in Florida and the Coastal Plain regions of the U.S.	Copper, along with iron and vitamin B_{12} is necessary for hemoglobin formation, although it forms no part of the hemoglobin molecule (or red blood cells). Closely associated with normal bone development in young, growing animals.	Anemia, characterized by fewer than normal red cells and less than normal amount of hemoglobin. Abnormal bone development in foals.
Iodine (I)	Iodine-deficient areas or soils (in northwestern U.S. and in the Great Lakes Region) when iodized salt is not fed. Use of feeds that come from iodine-deficient areas.	Iodine is needed by the thyroid gland in making thyroxin, an iodine-containing compound which controls the rate of body metabolism or heat production.	Foals born dead, or very weak and unable to stand or nurse. Higher than normal incidence of navel ill.
Cobalt (Co)	Animals pastured in cobalt-deficient areas, such as Australia, western Canada, and in following states of U.S.: Florida, Michigan, Wisconsin, New Hampshire, Pennsylvania, and New York.	Cobalt is required for the synthesis of vitamin B_{12} in the intestinal tract of the horse.	Anemia.
Potassium (K)	Ration that does not contain roughage, molasses, or oil meals.	Major cation of intracellular fluid where it is involved in osmotic pressure and acid-base balance. Muscle activity. Required in enzyme reaction involving phosphorylation of creatine. Influences carbohydrate metabolism.	Reduced appetite. Retarded growth, unsteady gait, general muscle weakness, distended abdomen, emaciation, followed by death.

[1]With all rations and for all classes and ages of horses, provide free access to a mineral box as follows: (1) *Where the pasture or hay is primarily grass*, use a mixture containing 2 parts of calcium to 1 part of phosphorus; and (2) *where the pasture or hay is primarily a legume*, use a mixture containing 1 part of calcium to 1 part of phosphorus. To each of these mixes, add ⅓ salt (trace mineralized) to improve acceptability. If preferred, a good commercial mineral may be used. Self-feed salt separately.

If desired, the mineral supplement may be incorporated in the ration in keeping with the recommended allowances given in this table.

SALT (SODIUM CHLORIDE)

Salt, which serves as both a condiment and a nutrient, is needed by all classes of animals, but more especially by herbivora (grass-eating animals, like the horse). It may be provided in the form of granulated, rock, or block salt. In general, the form selected is determined by price and availability. It is to be pointed out, however, that it is difficult for horses to eat very hard block and rock salt. This often results in inadequate consumption. Also, if there is much competition for the salt block, the more timid animals may not get their requirements.

The horse requires both sodium and chlorine. They are necessary in maintaining the osmotic pressure of body cells (thereby assisting in the transfer of nutrients to the cells and the removal of waste materials). Also, sodium is associated in muscle contraction and is important as one of the main body buffers and in making bile, which aids in the digestion of fats and carbohydrates. Chlorine is required for the formation

of the hydrochloric acid in the gastric juice so vital to protein digestion. Generally, the chlorine requirement will be met if the sodium needs are met.

A deficiency of sodium over a long period of time results in depraved appetite, rough coat, reduced growth, and lowered milk production.

Salt should always be available in the stall, paddock, or pasture. Horses will seldom overeat salt when they are allowed free access to it at all times and are given water at frequent intervals. Rather, they will consume only enough to meet their requirements. On the average, a horse needs about 2 ounces of salt daily or less than 1 pound per week, although salt requirements vary with work and temperature. When at hard work during warm weather—conditions accompanied by profuse perspiration and consequent loss of salt in the sweat—even greater quantities may be required. The white, encrusted sides of a horse after work are evidence of the large amount of salt drawn from the body through sweat (2 gm of salt/lb of

(Continued)

Recommended Allowances[2]		Practical Sources of the Mineral	Comments
Daily Per 1,000 Lb Horse	Per Ton or Percent of Total Rations[3]		
90 mg	7.2 g/ton	Trace mineralized salt containing copper sulfate or copper carbonate.	A copper deficiency in horses has been reported in Australia. High molybdenum in forages does not appear to affect horses so much as ruminants. However, in high-molybdenum areas, more copper may be added to horse rations; but excesses and toxicity should be avoided.
2.6 mg	0.21 g/ton	Stabilized iodized salt containing 0.01% potassium iodide (0.0076% iodine). Calcium iodate. Ethylenediamine dihydriodide (EDDI).	Enlargement of the thyroid gland (goiter) is nature's way of trying to make enough thyroxin (an iodine - containing hormone) when there is insufficient iodine in the feed. Feeding excess iodine continuously will also produce goiter in foals.
1.5 mg	0.12 g/ton	Cobaltized mineral mix made by adding cobalt at the rate of 0.2 oz/100 lb of salt as cobalt chloride, cobalt sulfate, cobalt oxide, or cobalt carbonate. Also, several good commercial cobalt-containing minerals are on the market.	The disease called "salt sick" in Florida is due to a cobalt deficiency associated with a copper deficiency.
68 g	0.6% of ration	Potassium chloride.	A ration that contains at least 50% forage will meet potassium requirements.

[2]These are recommended allowances, and not requirements. The author's position on recommended allowances vs requirements for horses is clearly stated in the narrative of this book under the heading entitled "Nutrient Requirements Vs Allowances."
[3]Where hay is fed separately, double these amounts should be added to the concentrate.

sweat). Horses at moderate work may lose 50 to 60 grams of salt in the sweat and 35 grams in the urine daily. Unless this salt is replaced, the animal will soon exhibit signs of excessive fatigue.

When incorporated in the concentrate ration, salt should be added at a level of 0.5 to 1.0 percent.

If horses have been salt starved—if they have not previously been fed salt for a considerable length of time—they may overeat, resulting in digestive disturbances and even death from salt cramps. Salt starved animals should first be hand fed salt, and the daily allowance should be increased gradually until they start leaving a little in the mineral box. When this point is reached, self-feeding may be followed.

CALCIUM AND PHOSPHORUS

Horses are more apt to suffer from a lack of calcium and phosphorus than from any of the other minerals except salt. These 2 minerals comprise about ¾

the ash of the skeleton and from ⅓ to ½ of the minerals of milk.

A deficiency of either calcium or phosphorus will cause rickets in foals.

The following general characteristics of feeds in regard to calcium and phosphorus are imporatant in rationing horses:

1. The cereal grains and their by-products and straws, dried mature grasses, and protein supplements of plant origin are low in calcium.

2. The protein supplements of animal origin and legume forage are rich in calcium.

3. The cereal grains and their by-products are fairly high or even rich in phosphorus, but a large portion of the phosphorus is not readily available.

4. Almost all protein-rich supplements are high in phosphorus. But, here again, plant sources of phosphorus contain much of this element in a bound form.

5. Beet by-products and dried, mature non-

leguminous forages (such as grass hays and fodders) are likely to be low in phosphorus.

6. The calcium and phosphorus content of plants can be increased through fertilizing the soil upon which they are grown.

The National Academy of Sciences gives the estimated daily calcium requirement of mature horses at 20 mg per pound body weight; and the daily phosphorus requirement of mature horses is estimated at 14 mg per pound body weight. Due to poor utilization, the calcium and phosphorus requirements of aged horses (animals over 20 years of age) are higher; the phosphorus requirement of older horses may be 30 to 50 percent higher than the figure given above for mature horses.

The availability to the horse of calcium and phosphorus in common feedstuffs is unknown. But the availability of calcium is assumed to be 40 to 50%, and the availability of phosphorus is assumed to be 50% in mature animals and 60% in growing animals.

In considering the calcium and phosphorus requirements of horses, it is important to realize that the proper utilization of these minerals by the body is dependent upon three factors: (1) an adequate supply of calcium and phosphorus in an available form; (2) a suitable ratio between them; and (3) sufficient vitamin D to make possible the assimilation and utilization of the calcium and phosphorus. If plenty of vitamin D is present (as provided either by sunlight or through the ration), the ratio of calcium to phosphorus becomes less important. Also, less vitamin D is needed when there is a desirable calcium-phosphorus ratio.

Normally, the calcium to phosphorus ratio should be about 1.1:1. However, the ratio varies according to age. For example, older horses can have a calcium-phosphorus ratio of 2.0:1.0. Provided adequate phosphorus is fed, weanling foals will *tolerate* a 3:1 ratio and mature horses a 5:1 ratio. It is important, however, to have more calcium than phosphorus—but not too much calcium. Feeding excessive calcium interferes with the utilization of magnesium, manganese, and iron—and perhaps with the utilization of zinc.

Bone disturbances (called osteodystrophia fibrosa, nutritional secondary hyperparathyroidism, osteomalacia, osteoporosis, and Miller's disease) develop in adult horses fed rations containing limited calcium and cereal phosphorus. The disease develops when rations with a calcium-phosphorus ratio of 0.8:1 are fed for 6 to 12 months, and it progresses rapidly when the ratio is 0.6:1.

It is to be emphasized that the National Academy of Sciences recommendations given above are requirements, without any safety factor. Further, the availability of calcium and phosphorus in feedstuffs is assumed, rather than known; and the requirements

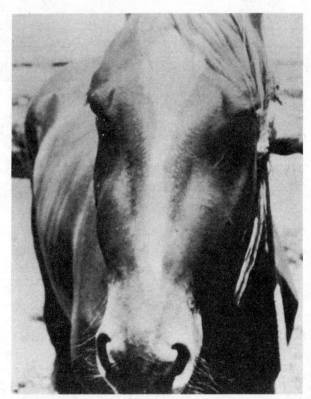

Fig. 13-9. Calcium-phosphorus imbalance. Horse with "big head disease" (nutritional secondary hyperparathyroidism) resulting from feeding a ration low in calcium and high in phosphorus. Note that the upper jaw is enlarged because calcium is replaced by fibrous connective tissue. (Courtesy, National Academy of Sciences, and College of Veterinary Medicine, Texas A&M University)

are affected by age, ratios between the two minerals, and the presence of vitamin D. After giving consideration to all these factors, and after evaluating both experiments and experiences, the author recommends that calcium be provided at a level of 0.6% to 0.7% of the ration and phosphorus at a level of 0.5%. In addition to adding reasonable amounts of minerals to the ration, the author recommends that a suitable mineral mix be self-fed in keeping with the instructions contained in the section headed "Self-Feed Minerals."

Table 13-6 gives several sources of calcium and phosphorus and the approximate percentages of the two elements in various mineral supplements.

Where both calcium and phosphorus are needed, the author favors the use of high-quality steamed bone meal for horses, because bone meal contains many ingredients in addition to calcium and phosphorus. It is a good source of iron, manganese, and zinc, and it contains such trace minerals as copper and cobalt. However, it is increasingly difficult to get good bone meal. Some of the imported products are high in fat, rancid, and/or odorous and unpalatable. Where good bone meal is not available, dicalcium phosphate is generally recommended.

When calcium alone is needed, ground limestone

TABLE 13-6
TYPICAL ANALYSIS OF CALCIUM AND PHOSPHORUS SUPPLEMENTS[1]

Compound	Phosphorus Content	Calcium Content	Sodium Content	Nitrogen Content	Fluoride Content
	(%)	(%)	(%)	(%)	(%)
Calcium compounds:					
Oystershells, ground	—	38.0			
Limestone, ground	—	34.0			
Defluorinated phosphates manufactured from defluorinated phosphoric acid:					
Monocalcium phosphate	21.0	16.0	—	—	0.16
Dicalcium phosphate	18.5	21.0	—	—	0.14
Defluorinated phosphate	18.0	32.0	—	—	0.16
Monoammonium phosphate	24.0	0.5	—	11.0	0.18
Diammonium phosphate	20.0	0.5	—	18.0	0.16
Ammonium polyphosphate solution	14.5	0.1	—	10.0	0.12
Defluorinated wet-process phosphoric acid	23.7	0.2	—	—	0.18
Defluorinated phosphates manufactured from furnace phosphoric acid:					
Monocalcium phosphate	23.0	22.0	—	—	0.03
Dicalcium phosphate	18.5	26.0	—	—	0.05
Tricalcium phosphate	19.5	38.0	—	—	0.05
Monosodium phosphate, anhy.	25.5	—	19.0	—	0.03
Disodium phosphate	21.5	—	32.0	—	0.03
Sodium tripolyphosphate	25.0	—	30.0	—	0.03
Ammonium polyphosphate solution	16.0	—	—	11.0	0.02
Feed-grade phosphoric acid	23.7	—	—	—	0.03
High-fluoride phosphates:					
Soft rock phosphate	9.0	17.0	—	—	1.2
Ground rock phosphate	13.0	35.0	—	—	3.7
Ground low-fluorine rock phosphate	14.0	36.0	—	—	0.45

[1]Except for calcium compounds, figures from *Effects of Fluorides in Animals*, National Academy of Sciences, Washington, D.C., 1974, pp. 8-9, Table 1.

or oystershell flour are commonly used, either free choice or added to the ration in keeping with nutrient requirements.

Where phosphorus alone is needed, monosodium phosphate, disodium phosphate, and sodium tripolyphosphate are the minerals of choice.

MAGNESIUM

The magnesium requirements of the horse are not known. But they have been estimated to be within the range of 6.4 to 15.5 mg per pound of body weight per day (14 to 34 mg/kg). That's 7,250 to 15,500 mg for a 1,000-pound horse per day.

Rations containing 50 percent forage will likely contain sufficient magnesium for unstressed horses. But horses at hard work (as in racing and showing) consume more grain (which is low in magnesium) and less forage. Also, horses being raced or shown, or otherwise stressed, are frequently keyed up, high-strung, and jumpy, similar to the nervousness that characterizes animals and humans known to be suffering from a magnesium deficiency.

In view of the above, it would appear prudent that ½ to ⅔ of the recommended daily magnesium allowance of the horse be added to the ration. The National Academy of Sciences estimates the magnesium requirements to be somewhere between 5,000 and 7,500 mg daily per 1,000-pound horse.

IRON

If horses are fed diets that are too low in iron, or in iron and copper, nutritional anemia results.

The National Academy of Sciences estimates the maintenance requirements of the horse for iron at 40 ppm, and the requirements of foals at 50 ppm. However, it has been reported that horses which are subjected to pressure from racing, showing, or other heavy use, require 80 to 100 ppm of iron in their daily ration, which calls for 907 to 1,134 mg of iron in the ration of a 1,000-pound horse consuming 25 pounds of feed per day. To be on the safe side, approximately one-half of the iron requirement of the horse should be added to the ration; and it should be in a biologically available form (iron oxide should not be used as a source of iron for horses because it is poorly absorbed).

Other facts pertinent to iron for horses follow.

1. *Body store of iron and copper at birth*—Nature has planned wisely. Young equines are born with a store of iron and copper in their bodies, which usually suffices until they normally begin to eat feeds which supply these constituents. This is most fortunate, as milk is very low in iron and copper. When young animals are continued on a milk diet for a long period of time, particularly under confined conditions and with little or no supplemental feeds, nutritional anemia will likely develop.

2. *Natural sources of iron*—In obtaining sources of iron, it is well to remember that simple inorganic iron salts, such as ferric chloride, are readily utilized, whereas the iron in the complex organic compounds in the hemoglobin of the blood is much less readily available, if at all. Also, though certain small amounts of iron are very essential, too much of this element in the diet may actually be deleterious—interfering with phosphorus absorption by forming an insoluble phosphate—and rickets may thus result from a diet otherwise adequate.

ZINC

Swine require 50 ppm zinc on diets properly balanced with calcium. But if excessive levels of calcium are fed (1.0% or more), then the requirement is increased to about 100 ppm. Research with cattle has shown that supplementing the ration with 50 to 100 ppm of zinc will improve the hair coat. Obviously, zinc is necessary for the maintenance and development of skin and hair.

Since beautiful hair coats are important in horses, fortifying the daily ration with 400 mg of zinc per day will prevent any possibility of a zinc deficiency; and if the zinc in the feed is on the low side, it should improve the hair coat.

MANGANESE

Based on research with other species, it is reasonable to assume that horses should meet their daily requirements on feeds containing 20 ppm, and no more than 40 ppm, of manganese.

Since most natural feedstuffs are rich in manganese, it can be assumed that part of the requirement for this element will be met by the normal ration.

Thirty ppm calls for 340 mg of manganese in the ration of a 1,000-pound horse consuming 25 pounds of feed per day.

COPPER

A copper deficiency has been reported in Australia in horses grazing on pastures low in copper. Also, mare's milk (along with milk from all species) is low in copper. The presence of 5 to 25 ppm of molybdenum in forages causes disturbances in copper utilization in horses.

Copper is of special interest to horsemen because, in addition to its effect on iron metabolism, it is closely associated with normal bone development in young growing animals. Abnormal bone development has been reported in foals on low-copper diets.

The recommended copper allowance for a 1,000-pound horse is 90 mg per day, about half of which should be added to the ration.

In any mineral mixtures containing copper, thorough mixing must be obtained in order to prevent copper toxicity or poisoning. Only limited quantities of copper can be put into the mineral mixture for this reason.

In high-molybdenum areas, it is recommended that the copper level for horses be about five times higher than the normal level.

IODINE

Pregnant mares are very susceptible to iodine deficiency. Where such a deficiency exists, the foals are usually stillborn or so weak that they cannot stand and suck. There is also some evidence to indicate that the incidence of navel ill in foals may be lessened by feeding iodine to broodmares.

Fig. 13-10. Newborn weak colt affected with simple goiter due to deficiency of iodine during prenatal period. (Courtesy, Western Washington Agricultural Experiment Station)

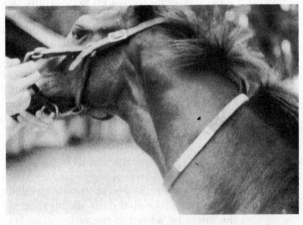

Fig. 13-11. Goiter in a foal; usually caused by an iodine deficiency, but it may result from feeding excess iodine over a long period of time. (Courtesy, Dr. D. E. Cooperrider, Chief, Diagnostic Laboratories, Division of Animal Industry, Kissimmee, Fla.)

Other facts pertinent to iodine for horses follow:

1. *Amount in body and function*—It is estimated that the mature animal body contains less than 0.00004 percent iodine, but if this minute amount is not maintained in the diet, disaster results. More than half of the total iodine content of the body is located in the thyroid gland of the neck. Iodine, which is secreted by the thyroid gland in the form of thyroxine (an iodine-containing hormone), controls the rate of metabolism of the body.

2. *Iodine deficiencies*—If the soil—and the water and feed crops coming therefrom—is low in iodine, the body is likely to show deficiency symptoms in the form of simple goiter, unless an adequate source of iodine is provided artifically. A goiter is simply an enlargement of the thyroid gland, which is nature's way of trying to make enough thyroxine when there is insufficient iodine in the feed. However, iodine-deficiency symptoms are not always evidenced by the appearance of goiter, although this is the most common characteristic of such deficiency in humans, calves, lambs, and kids. In pigs, the outstanding symptom of the deficiency is hairlessness, whereas in foals the only symptom may be extreme weakness at birth, resulting in an inability to stand and suck.

In general, it may be said that goiter is an advanced symptom of iodine deficiency but that the chief loss is from interference with reproductive processes and the birth of weak, deformed offspring that fail to survive.

Iodine deficiencies are worldwide. In the United States, the northwestern states, the Pacific Coast, and the Great Lakes region are classed as goiter areas.

3. *Recommended iodine supplements*—The addition to the daily ration of 2.6 mg of iodine will be ample. The simplest method of supplying iodine in deficient areas is through use of salt containing (a) 0.01 percent potassium iodide (0.0076 percent iodine), or (b) calcium iodate. Most of the salt companies now manufacture stabilized iodized salt.

4. *Precautions in feeding iodized salt*—Although iodized salt is an effective preventive measure, no satisfactory treatment has been developed for animals which have developed pronounced deficiency symptoms. In fact, studies with goiter in humans have clearly established that, although iodine is an effective preventative, it may be harmful rather than beneficial as a treatment after the goiter has developed.

Iodized salt should always be kept in a dry place and it should be kept fresh. It should also be provided in such form and quantities as to ensure an adequate intake of iodine.

In no instance should iodine be fed in excess. Such excesses have proved toxic to lambs, and very probably the same hazard applies to other classes of livestock. For this reason, thorough mixing of iodized salt is important, whether it be a commercial or a home prepared product.

COBALT

Cobalt is required for the synthesis of vitamin B_{12} in the intestinal tract of the horse. A lack of cobalt and/or B_{12} will result in anemia. However, the cobalt requirement of the horse is very low, for horses have remained in good health while grazing pastures so low in cobalt that ruminants confined to them have died. This means that the cobalt requirement, if any, of the horse is lower than that of ruminants. However, it is noteworthy that an anemia in horses has responded to vitamin B_{12} treatment; and, of course, B_{12} contains cobalt in the molecular structure. Thus, inclusion of cobalt in the ration of horses is in the nature of good insurance.

In different sections of the world, a cobalt deficiency is known as Denmark disease, coast disease, enzootic marasmus, bush sickness, salt sickness, nakuritis, and pining disease.

POTASSIUM

Forage-consuming animals generally require about 0.6 percent of potassium in their rations. A ration that contains at least 50 percent forage can be expected to meet potassium requirements. However, a horse ration that does not contain roughage, molasses, or oil meals may be deficient in potassium.

A reduced appetite is an early sign of a potassium deficiency.

SULFUR

Inorganic sulfur is not known to be an essential dietary constituent of the horse. If the protein requirement of the ration is met, the sulfur intake will usually be at least 0.15 percent, which appears to be adequate.

SELENIUM

Selenium is an essential mineral for horses, although the requirement does not appear to exceed 0.5 ppm, according to the National Academy of Sciences. Deficient animals have muscle disorders and lowered serum selenium. Currently, federal approval for feeding supplemental selenium is limited to swine, chickens, and turkeys. Horsemen who are faced with the problem of inadequate selenium must either buy feed with adequate levels of the trace element or inject a selenium-vitamin E preparation.

Excess selenium results in selenium poisoning, or alkali disease.

CHELATED TRACE MINERALS

The word chelate is derived from the Greek *chelae*, meaning a claw or pincerlike organ. Those selling chelated minerals generally recommend a smaller quantity of them (but at a higher price per pound) and extoll their "fenced-in" properties.

When it comes to synthetic chelating agents, much needs to be learned about their selectivity toward minerals, the kind and quantity most effective, their mode of action, and their behavior with different species of animals and with varying rations.

It is possible that their use may actually create a mineral imbalance. These answers, and more, must be forthcoming through carefully controlled experiments before they can be recommended for valuable horses.

MINERAL IMBALANCES

It has become increasingly evident that there is a delicate relationship between certain mineral elements. Thus, the requirements of any mineral may be modified by another mineral which enhances or interferes with its utilization. For this reason, playing the "minerals numbers game" can be hazardous when it comes to buying horse feeds. By the "minerals numbers game," reference is made to the gimmick of comparing products on the basis of which has the most "numbers," or units, of certain minerals, some of which may not be needed at all. So, beware of the person who extolls brand "X" on the basis that it has more units of a certain mineral(s) than brand "Y."

Indeed, excess fortification of the horse's diet with trace elements may prove more detrimental than helpful. Thus, the horseman who knows and cares will avoid harmful imbalances; he will provide minerals on the basis of *recommended allowances*. Also, when fortifying rations with minerals, consideration should be given to the minerals provided by the ingredients of the normal ration, for it is the total composition of the feed that counts.

SELF-FEED MINERALS

The ration should contain a reasonable level of minerals. Then, animal and feed differences (due to stage of maturity at harvest, weathering, length of storage, etc.) should be met by free-choice mineral feeding. Allow free access to a double-compartment mineral box, with ground trace mineralized salt in one side, and in the other a suitable mineral mix, either home mixed or commercial.

A suitable home mixed mineral may be prepared as follows:

1. *Where the pasture or hay is primarily grass*, use a mixture containing two parts of calcium to one part of phosphorus.

2. *Where the pasture or hay is primarily a legume*, use a mixture containing one part of calcium to one part of phosphorus.

To each of the above mixes, add one-third salt (trace mineralized) to improve acceptability.

Vitamins[9]

Until early in the 20th Century, if a ration contained proteins, fats, carbohydrates, and minerals, together with certain amount of fiber, it was considered to be a complete diet. True enough, the disease known as beriberi made its appearance in the rice-eating districts of the Orient when milling machinery was introduced from the West, having been known to the Chinese as early as 2600 B.C.; and scurvy was long known to occur among sailors fed on salt meat and biscuits. However, for centuries these diseases were thought to be due to toxic substances in the digestive tract caused by pathogenic organisms rather than food deficiencies, and more time elapsed before the discovery of vitamins. Of course, there was no medical profession until 1835, the earlier treatments having been based on superstition rather than science.

Funk, a Polish scientist working in London, first referred to these nutrients as "vitamines," in 1912. Presumably, the name vitamines alluded to the fact that they were essential to life, and they were assumed to be chemically of the nature of amines (the chemical assumption was later proved incorrect, with the result that the "e" was dropped—hence, the word vitamin).

The actual existence of vitamins, therefore, has been known only since 1912, and only within the last few years has it been possible to see or touch any of them in a pure form. Previously, they were merely mysterious invisible "little things," known only by their effects. In fact, most of the present fundamental knowledge relative to the vitamin content of both human foods and animal feeds was obtained through measuring their potency in promoting growth or in curing certain disease conditions in animals—a most difficult and tedious method. For the most part, small laboratory animals were used, especially the rat, guinea pig, pigeon, and chick.

The lack of vitamins in a horse ration may, under certain conditions, be more serious than a short supply of feed. Deficiencies may lead to failure in growth or reproduction, poor health, and even characteristic disorders known as deficiency diseases.

Unfortunately, there are no warning signals to tell

---

[9]In this section, when reference is made to a National Academy of Sciences recommendation, this implies the following source: *Nutrient Requirements of Horses*, No. 6, 3rd rev. ed., National Academy of Sciences, 1973.

a caretaker when a horse is not getting enough of certain vitamins. But a continuing inadequate supply of any one of several vitamins can produce illness which is very hard to diagnose until it becomes severe, at which time it is difficult and expensive—if not too late—to treat. The important thing, therefore, is to insure against such deficiencies occurring. But horsemen should not shower a horse with mistaken kindness through using shotgun-type vitamin preparations. Instead, the quantity of each vitamin should be based on available scientific knowledge.

It has long been known that the vitamin content of feeds varies considerably according to soil, climatic conditions, and curing and storing.

Deficiencies may occur during periods (1) of extended drought or in other conditions of restriction in diet, (2) when production is being forced, or during stress, (3) when large quantities of highly refined feeds are being fed, or (4) when low-quality forages are utilized.

Although the occasional deficiency symptoms are the most striking result of vitamin deficiencies, it

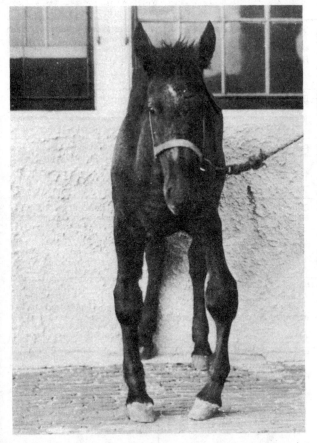

Fig. 13-12. Foal with severe rickets. Note the enlarged joints and crooked legs. Rickets may be caused by a lack of vitamin D, calcium, or phosphorus, or by an incorrect ratio of the two minerals. (Courtesy, Dept. of Veterinary Pathology and Hygiene, College of Veterinary Medicine, University of Illinois)

must be emphasized that in practice mild deficiencies probably cause higher total economic losses than do severe deficiencies. It is relatively uncommon for a ration, or diet, to contain so little of a vitamin that obvious symptoms of a deficiency occur. When one such case does appear, it is reasonable to suppose that there must be several cases that are too mild to produce characteristic symptoms but that are sufficiently severe to lower the state of health and the efficiency of production.

Certain vitamins are necessary for the growth, development, health, and reproduction of horses. Deficiencies of vitamins A and D are sometimes encountered. Also, indications are that vitamin E and some of the B vitamins are required by horses. Further, it is recognized that single, uncomplicated vitamin deficiencies are the exception rather than the rule.

High-quality, leafy, green forages plus plenty of sunshine generally give horses most of the vitamins they need. Horses get carotene (which they can convert to vitamin A) and riboflavin from green pasture and green hay not over a year old, and they get vitamin D from sunlight and sun-cured hay. If plenty of green forage and sunlight are not available, the horseman should get the advice of a nutritionist or veterinarian on the use of vitamin additives to the feed.

Table 13-7 contains a list of vitamins of practical importance in horse nutrition, together with the pertinent information relative to each. In this table, the vitamins are listed according to recommended daily allowances, without regard to importance.

The author subscribes to the view that most light horses are under stress, and that the more exacting the performance, the greater the stress; hence, that the vitamin requirements of most light horses are higher than those for draft horses. This fact is taken into consideration in the "recommended allowances" given in Table 13-7. (See page 220 for Table 13-7.)

VITAMIN A

Vitamin A is strictly a product of animal metabolism, no vitamin A being found in plants. The counterpart in plants is known as carotene, which is the precursor of vitamin A. Because the animal body can transform carotene into vitamin A, this compound is often spoken of as "provitamin A."

Carotene is the yellow-colored, fat-soluble substance that gives the characteristic color to carrots and to butterfat (vitamin A is nearly a colorless substance). Carotene derives its name from the carrot, from which it was first isolated over 100 years ago. Although its empirical formula was established in 1906, it was not until 1919 that Steenbock, of the University of Wisconsin. discovered its vitamin A activity. Though the yellow color is masked by the green chlorophyll, the

Vitamins Which May Be Deficient Under Normal Conditions	Conditions Usually Prevailing Where Deficiencies Are Reported	Functions of Vitamins	Some Deficiency Symptoms
Vitamin A	Extended drought. Bleached hays. Stall feeding where there is little or no green forage or yellow corn. Following great stress, as when race or show horses are put in training.	Promotes growth and stimulates appetite. Assists in reproduction and lactation. Keeps the mucous membranes of respiratory and other tracts in healthy condition. Makes for normal vision. Prevents night blindness.	Reproductive failure, nerve degeneration, night blindness, uneven and poor hoof development, a predisposition to respiratory infection, lacrimation (tears), incoordination, keratenization of the cornea, progressive weakness, certain bone disorders, and finicky appetite.
Vitamin D	Limited sunlight, and or limited sun-cured hay, especially when horse is kept inside most of the time.	Assimilation and utilization of calcium and phosphorus, necessary in normal bone development—including the bones of the fetus.	Rickets in foals, osteomalacia in mature horses. Both conditions result in large joints and weak bones.
Vitamin E (tocopherols)	It is possible that more vitamin E is destroyed or used up by horses during times of stress or strain than can be obtained through normal feeds.	Serves as insurance against destruction of vitamin A. Makes for improved reproduction. Prevents anhidrosis.	Lowered breeding performance in both mares and stallions. Anhidrosis—a dry, dull hair coat.
Choline	Ration low in methionine, an amino acid.	Essential in building and maintaining cell structure and in the transmission of nerve impulses.	Slow growth.
Pantothenic acid		Part of coenzyme A, a necessary factor for life processes.	Poor growth, skin rashes, poor appetite, nervous disorders.
Niacin (nicotinic acid)		Constituent of coenzymes. Hydrogen transport.	Reduced growth and appetite. Skin rashes, diarrhea, nerve disorders.
Vitamin B$_2$ (riboflavin)	When green feeds (pasture, hay, or silage) are not available.	Probably for synthesis of ocular vitamin C or its protecting substance. Important in protein metabolism.	Periodic ophthalmia (or moon blindness). Decreased rate of growth and feed efficiency. Porous and weak bones; ligaments and joints impaired.
Vitamin B$_1$ *(thiamin)*	Poor quality hay and grain. When sulfa drugs or antibiotics are given to the horse, the synthesis of B vitamins is impaired.	Required for normal carbohydrate metabolism. Promotes appetite and growth.	Decreased feed consumption (loss of weight), incoordination (especially in the hindquarters), lowered blood thiamin, elevated blood pyruvic acid, enlarged heart, and nervous symptoms.

Footnotes on last page of table.

VITAMIN CHART

Recommended Allowances[1]		Practical Sources of the Vitamin	Comments
Daily Per 1,000 Lb Horse	Per Ton of Total Feed[2]		
50,000 USP	4,000,000 USP	Stabilized vitamin A. Green grass. Green hay not over 1 year old. Grass or legume silage.	A considerable margin of safety in vitamin A and carotene is provided in the recommended allowances due to the oxidative destruction of these materials in feeds during storage. Hay over 1 year old, regardless of green color, is usually not an adequate source of carotene or vitamin A activity. The younger the animal, the quicker vitamin A deficiencies will show up. Mature animals may store sufficient vitamin A to last 6 months. When deficiency symptoms appear, add stabilized vitamin A to the ration.
7,000 USP	560,000 USP	Either vitamin D_2 (the plant form) or D_3 (the animal form) is equally effective for the horse. Exposure to sunlight. Sun-cured hays.	The vitamin D requirement is less when a proper balance of calcium and phosphorus exists in the ration. When animals are exposed to direct sunlight the ultraviolet light produces vitamin D from traces of cholesterol in the skin. Stabled horses, exercised in the early morning, will not get sufficient vitamin D in this manner.
200 IU	16,000 IU	Alpha tocopherol, a stable form of vitamin E. Germ or germ oil of plants. Green plants. Green hays.	Most rations contain ample vitamin E. Before adding it, the horseman should seek the advice of a competent authority. Utilization of vitamin E is dependent on adequate selenium.
400 mg	32,000 mg	Choline chloride. Choline dihydrogen.	Choline content of normal feeds is sufficient. All naturally occurring fats contain some choline.
60 mg	4,800 mg	Calcium pantothenate. Fish solubles.	Grain is very deficient in pantothenic acid. Intestinal synthesis of pantothenic acid likely meets the body needs of the horse.
50 mg	4,000 mg	Synthetic niacin. Animal by-products. Green alfalfa.	The horse can convert the essential amino acid tryptophan into niacin. Hence, it is important to make certain that the ration is adequate in niacin; otherwise, the horse will use tryptophane to supply niacin needs.
40 mg	3,200 mg	Synthetic riboflavin. Green pasture. Green hay. Silages. Milk and milk products.	Lack of vitamin B_2 is not the only cause of moon blindness. Sometimes, moon blindness follows leptospirosis, and it may be caused by an allergic reaction.
35 mg	2,800 mg	Thiamin hydrochloride. Green pastures. Well-cured, green, leafy hays. Cereal grains. Brewers' yeast.	Thiamin is synthesized in the lower gut of the horse by bacterial action, but there is some doubt as to its sufficiency. When neither green pasture nor high-quality roughage is available, thiamin hydrochloride should be added to the ration. Since carbohydrate metabolism is increased during physical exertion, it is important that B_1 be available in quantity at such times.

(Continued)

TABLE 13-7

Vitamins Which May Be Deficient Under Normal Conditions	Conditions Usually Prevailing Where Deficiencies Are Reported	Functions of Vitamins	Some Deficiency Symptoms
Vitamin K	Following intestinal disorders.	Concerned with blood coagulation.	Increased clotting time of the blood.
Folic acid (folacin)		Related to B_{12} metabolism. Metabolic reactions involving incorporation of single-carbon units into larger molecules.	Poor growth. Anemia.
B_{12}	When few, or no feeds of animal origin are fed.	Coenzyme in several enzyme systems. Closely linked with folic acid.	Loss of appetite and poor growth.
Unidentified factors	Since the U.S. foal crop is only around 50%, it is obvious that there is room for improvement somewhere along the line; and perhaps unidentified factors are involved. Also, optimal results with horses during the critical periods (growth, gestation-lactation and when under stress as in racing or showing) appear to be dependent upon providing unidentified factors through such ingredients as distillers' dried solubles, dehydrated alfalfa meal, condensed fish solubles, brewers' dried yeast, antibiotic fermentation residues, dried whey, and corn fermentation solubles.		

[1]These are recommended allowances, and not requirements. The author's position on recommended allowances vs requirements for horses is clearly stated in the narrative of this book under the heading entitled "Nutrient Requirements Vs Allowances."

green parts of plants are rich in carotene and have a high vitamin A value. Also, the degree of greenness in a roughage is a good index of its carotene content, provided it has not been stored too long. Early cut, leafy green hays are very high in carotene.

Vitamin A is not synthesized in the cecum. Thus, it must be provided in the feed, either (1) as vitamin A, of (2) as carotene, the precursor of vitamin A.

Aside from yellow corn, practically all of the cereal grains used in horse feeding have little carotene or vitamin A value. Even yellow corn has only about one-tenth as much carotene as well-cured hay. Dried peas of the green and yellow varieties and carrots are also valuable sources of carotene.

Studies by the New Jersey station indicate that the carotene content of alfalfa hay may be more available to the horse and more efficiently converted into vitamin A than the carotene in timothy hay.

Severe deficiency of vitamin A may cause night blindness, lacrimation (tears), keratinization of the cornea and skin, reproductive difficulties, poor or uneven hoof development, difficulty in breathing, incoordination, convulsive seizures, progressive weakness, and poor appetite. There is also some evidence that deficiency of this vitamin may cause or contribute to certain leg bone weaknesses. When vitamin A deficiency symptoms appear, the horseman should add a stabilized vitamin A product to the ration.

It is wasteful to feed more vitamin A than is needed. Also, feeding exceedingly high levels of vitamin A over an extended period of time may cause bone fragility, hyperostosis, and exfoliated

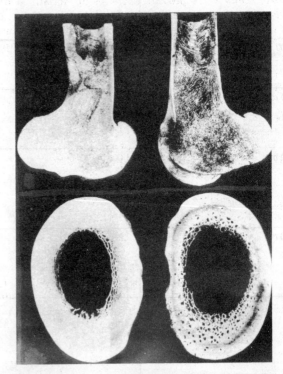

Fig. 13-13. Vitamin A made the difference! *Upper:* On the right is shown the sagittal section of the distal end of the femur of a vitamin A-deficient horse compared to normal bone (left). *Lower:* On the right is shown the cross section of the cannon bone from a vitamin A-deficient horse compared to normal bone (left). (Courtesy, G. E. Howell, California Agricultural Experiment Station)

(Continued)

	Recommended Allowances[1]		Practical Sources of the Vitamin	Comments
Daily Per 1,000 Lb Horse	Per Ton of Total Feed[2]			
8 mg	640 mg		Menadione (vitamin K₃). Green pasture. Well-cured hays. Fish meal.	High levels of vitamin K will overcome bleeding due to dicumarol. Vitamin K is generally (1) widely distributed in normal feeds, and/or (2) synthesized in adequate amounts by the intestinal microflora of the horse.
2.5 mg	200 mg		Synthetic folacin. Green, leafy plants.	Folic acid is widely distributed in horse feeds. Also, folic acid is synthesized in the lower gut.
125 mcg	10,000 mcg		Synthetic B₁₂ Protein supplements of animal origin. Fermentation products.	

[2]Where hay is fed separately—that is, where an all-in-one pellet is not fed, for example—double these amounts should be added to the concentrate.

epithelium. When fed as directed, the vast majority of horse feeds won't provide excesses of vitamin A. But where higher product levels than needed are used as a sales gimmick, there is hazard that the horseman will administer the "stuff" like the Irishman's medicine—"If a little will do some good, a larger dose will do more good." Then, too, there may be a doubling up if both the mixed feed and the "conditioner" contain vitamin A. Finally, it must be remembered that, unlike meat animals that are produced for slaughter, horses are fed for a long life of usefulness.

The National Academy of Sciences recommends the following levels of vitamin A for horses:

Function	IU/Lb Body Wt.	IU/Kg Body Wt.	IU/1000 Lb Body Wt.
Maintenance	12	25	11,350
Growth	18	40	18,160
Pregnancy and lactation	23	50	22,700

The author proposes that 50,000 IU of vitamin A per day be considered as the upper limit for a 1,000-pound horse, except for unusual circumstances.

Other facts pertinent to vitamin A for horses follow:

1. *Circumstances conducive to vitamin A deficiencies*—The circumstances most conducive to vitamin A deficiencies are (a) extended periods of drought, resulting in the pastures becoming dry and bleached; (b) a long winter feeding period on bleached hays or straws, especially overripe cereal hays and straws; and (c) using feeds which have lost their vitamin A potency as a result of either heat or extended storage (for example, it has been found that alfalfa may lose nine-tenths of its vitamin A value in a year's storage). There is reason to believe that mild deficiencies of vitamin A, especially in the winter and early spring, are fairly common.

Fortunately, horses are able to store vitamin A, primarily in the liver, during periods of abundance to tide them through periods of scarcity. Thus, horses on green pasture store reserves to help meet their needs during the winter feeding period when their rations may be deficient. Mature horses may be able to store sufficient vitamin A in the liver to last six months; young equines store much less.

It is generally believed that stressed horses have a higher vitamin A requirement than those not under stress. Among such stress factors are: racing, showing, fatigue, hot weather, confinement, excitement, and number of animals run together.

The vitamin A requirements for gestating mares may be five times the minimum maintenance requirements. Therefore, unless properly fed, broodmares may become almost depleted of their vitamin A reserves by the end of winter—at a time when a vitamin A deficiency could be critical to the rapid development of the fetus.

2. *Measurement of vitamin A potency*—The vitamin A potency (whether due to the vitamin itself, to carotene, or to both) of feeds is usually reported in terms of IU or USP units. These two units of meas-

urement are the same. They are based on the growth response of rats, in which several different levels of the test product are fed to different groups of rats, as a supplement to a vitamin A-free diet which has caused growth to cease. A USP or IU is the vitamin A value for rats of 0.30 microgram of pure vitamin A alcohol, or of 0.60 microgram of pure beta-carotene. The carotene or vitamin A content of feeds is commonly determined by colorimetric or spectroscopic methods.

VITAMIN D

For horses, both D2 (the plant form) and D3 (the animal form) are equally effective, so there is no need to use some of each.

Foals sometimes develop rickets because of insufficient vitamin D, calcium, or phosphorus. Rickets is characterized by reduced bone calcification, stiff and swollen joints, stiffness of gait, irritability, and reduction in serum calcium and phosphorus. It can be prevented by exposing the animal to direct sunlight as much as possible, by allowing free access to a suitable mineral mixture, or by providing good quality sun-cured hay or luxuriant pasture grown on well-fertilized soil. In nothern areas that do not have adequate sunshine, many horsemen provide the foal with a vitamin D supplement.

With vitamin D, as with vitamin A, there is need for adequacy without harmful excesses. Too much vitamin D may harm a horse. Vitamin D toxicity is characterized by calcification of the blood vessels, heart, and other soft tissues, and by bone abnormalities. Also, there is general weakness and loss of body weight. Although the toxic level of vitamin D in the horse has not been established, a level 10 times the requirement is known to be toxic in other species.

The vitamin D requirement is less when a proper balance of calcium and phosphorus exists in the ration. The National Academy of Sciences recommends that the daily diet provide 3 IU of vitamin D per pound of body weight. That's 3,000 IU of vitamin D per day per 1,000-pound horse, which is about one-seventh the level of vitamin A recommended by the Academy.

Other facts pertinent to vitamin D for horses follow:

1. *Vitamin D, and cholesterol and ergosterol*—Most of the commonly used feeds contain little or no vitamin D, yet there is no widespread need for special supplements containing this factor. Fortunately, the skin of horses and many feeds contain provitamins in certain forms of cholesterol and ergosterol, respectively, which, through the action of ultraviolet light (light of such short wave length that it is invisible) from the sun, are converted into vitamin D. These certain forms of cholesterol and ergosterol themselves have no antirachitic effect.

2. *Vitamin D limited in feeds*—Of all the known vitamins, vitamin D has the most limited distribution in common feeds. Very little of this factor is contained in the cereal grains and their by-products, in roots and tubers, in feeds of animal origin, or in growing pasture grasses. The only important natural sources of vitamin D are sun-cured hay and other roughages. The chief vitamin D rich concentrates include sun-cured hay, cod-liver and other fish oils, irradiated cholesterol and ergosterol, and irradiated yeast.

As might be suspected from the preceding discussion, artificially dehydrated hay contains little vitamin D.

3. *Effectiveness of sunlight in producing vitamin D*—The effectiveness of sunlight is determined by the lengths and intensity of the ultraviolet rays which reach the body. It is more potent in the tropics than elsewhere, more potent at noon than earlier or later in the day, more potent in the summer than in the winter, and more potent at high altitudes. The ultraviolet rays are largely screened out by clothing, window glass, clouds, smoke, or dust. Also, some biochemists theorize that the color of the skin of humans is nature's way of regulating the manufacture of vitamin D—that the dark skin of races near the equator filters out excess ultraviolet light. Perhaps color of hair and skin in horses exercises a similar control, although this is not known.

VITAMIN E (TOCOPHEROLS)

There is experimental evidence that vitamin E improves the fertility of both mares and stallions, and that it prevents and corrects anhidrosis (dry, dull hair coat).

Most practical rations contain liberal quantities of vitamin E, perhaps enough except under conditions of work, stress, or reproduction, or where there is interference with its utilization. Rather than buy and use costly vitamin E concentrates indiscriminately, the horseman should add them to the ration only on the advice of a nutritionist or veterinarian.

Stowe, of the University of Kentucky, reported that daily doses per mare of 100,000 USP units of vitamin A and 100 IU of vitamin E, beginning 1 month prior to the breeding season and continuing for 3 months, improved conception rate by 64 percent. But further experimental work is needed on this subject.

Anhidrosis in horses—a condition showing dull hair coat, elevated temperature, high blood pressure, and labored breathing—has been successfully treated by the oral administration of 1,000 to 3,000 IU of vitamin E daily for 1 month.

The requirements for vitamin E are influenced by interrelationships with other essential nutrients—increased by the presence of interfering substances, and spared by the presence of other substances that

may be protective or that may assume part of its functions. The addition of approximately 200 IU of vitamin E per day to most rations should be adequate.

CHOLINE

Choline is a metabolic essential for building and maintaining cell structure and in the transmission of nerve impulses. Choline deficiency has been produced in rats, dogs, chickens, pigs, and other species. Slow growth is a nonspecific symptom.

The dietary requirement for choline depends on the level of methionine (an amino acid) in the ration. Also, it is noteworthy that all naturally occurring fats contain some choline; however, normal horse feeds are low in fat. Hence, the addition to the ration of about two-thirds of the recommended choline allowance (400 mg per day is the recommended allowance for a 1,000-lb horse) is indicated.

PANTOTHENIC ACID

Intestinal synthesis of pantothenic acid has been found to occur in all species studied. In the case of the horse, such synthesis appears to be sufficiently extensive to meet body needs, at least in part. As indicated in Table 13-7, a daily allowance of 60 mg of pantothenic acid is recommended for a 1,000-pound horse.

NIACIN (NICOTINIC ACID)

Some evidence indicates that niacin is synthesized by the horse. Also, the horse can convert the essential amino acid tryptophane into niacin. Hence, it is important to make certain that the ration is adequate in niacin; otherwise, the horse will use tryptophane to supply niacin needs. Niacin is widely distributed in feeds; fermentation solubles and certain oil meals are especially good sources. Only a modest addition of niacin to the ration is indicated.

VITAMIN B$_2$ (RIBOFLAVIN)

A deficiency of riboflavin may cause periodic ophthalmia (moon blindness), characterized by inflammation of the mucous membrane that lines the inner surface of the eyelid and the exposed surface of the eyeball in one or both eyes, accompanied by abnormal intolerance to light, and excess secretion of tears. Repeated attacks affect the retina, lens, and ocular fluids and cause impaired vision or blindness. But it is known that lack of this vitamin is not the only factor that causes periodic ophthalmia, or moon blindness. Sometimes this condition follows leptospirosis in horses, and it may be caused by a localized hypersensitivity or allergic reaction. Periodic ophthalmia caused by lack of riboflavin may be prevented by feeding green hay and green pasture, supplying feeds high in riboflavin, or by adding crystalline riboflavin to the ration at the rate of 40 mg per horse per day.

The National Academy of Sciences states that 1 mg of riboflavin per pound of feed will satisfy the maintenance requirement.

VITAMIN B$_1$ (THIAMIN)

Vitamin B$_1$ is synthesized in the lower gut of the horse by bacterial action, but there is some doubt as to its sufficiency and as to the amount absorbed always meeting the full requirements.

A thiamin deficiency has been produced experimentally and has been observed in horses fed on poor quality hay and grain. It is characterized by loss of appetite, loss of weight, incoordination (especially of the hind legs), lower blood thiamin, elevated blood pyruvic acid, and dilated and hypertrophied heart.

Vitamin B$_1$ is required for normal carbohydrate metabolism. Since carbohydrate metabolism is increased during physical exertion, it is important that B$_1$ be available in quantity at such times. The National Academy of Sciences reports that thiamin added to the ration at a level of 1.4 mg per pound (3 mg/kg) of feed will maintain feed intake.

VITAMIN K

When vitamin K is deficient, the coagulation time of the blood is increased and the prothrombin level is decreased. This is the main justification for adding this vitamin to the ration of the horse. However, it appears that vitamin K is synthesized in adequate amounts by the intestinal microflora of the horse.

FOLIC ACID (FOLACIN)

Folic acid is widely distributed in horse feeds. Also, it is synthesized in the lower digestive track of the horse. Hence, it is unlikely that a dietary source is required, although a small amount may be in the nature of cheap insurance.

VITAMIN B$_{12}$

It has been reported that horses in poor nutritional condition showing anemia respond to the administration of vitamin B$_{12}$. An allowance of 125 micrograms of B$_{12}$ per day is recommended. The addition of enough B$_{12}$ to supply half of this total will probably be adequate insurance in most horse rations.

ASCORBIC ACID (VITAMIN C)

A dietary need for ascorbic acid is limited to man, the guinea pig, and the monkey. Hence, there is no need to add this vitamin to horse rations.

VITAMIN B6 (PYRIDOXINE)

There is no evidence that deficiencies of vitamin B6 occur in horses on commonly fed rations; and it is not expected that deficiencies should occur in view of the widespread distribution of vitamin B6 in feedstuffs.

BIOTIN

There is substantial intestinal synthesis of biotin in all animal species, including man. Also, biotin is widely distributed in all feeds. Hence, there is no present evidence that it should be added to horse feeds.

PARA-AMINOBENZOIC ACID

Evidence that it performs essential functions on otherwise complete horse rations is lacking.

B COMPLEX VITAMINS

Vitamins of the B complex (particularly thiamin, riboflavin, B12, choline, niacin, pantothenic acid, and folic acid) may be essential, especially for (1) young horses before the synthesis of the B complex vitamins by the microflora begins, and (2) horses that are under stress, as in racing and showing. However, it is not clear which ones are needed, in what quantities they are needed, and their status from the standpoints of synthesis and absorption in the horse. Healthy horses usually get enough of them either in natural rations or by synthesis in the intestinal tract. However, when neither green pasture nor high-quality dry roughage is available, it may be in the nature of good insurance to provide them, especially for horses that are under stress.

Although some of the B vitamins and unidentified factors are synthesized in the cecum of the horse, it is doubtful that this microbial activitiy is sufficient to meet the needs during the critical periods—growth, reproduction, and when animals are subjected to great stress as in showing or racing. Also, there is reason to question the efficacy of absorption this far down the digestive tract; for in comparison with that of man and other animals, the cecum is on the wrong end of the digestive tract. Moreover, it is known that horses fed thiamin deficient rations lose weight, become nervous, and show incoordination in the hindquarters;

then, when thiamin is added to the ration, this condition is cured. For these reasons, in valuable horses it is not wise to rely solely on bacterial synthesis. The B vitamins, along with unidentified factors, may be provided by adding to the ration such ingredients as distillers' dried solubles, dried brewers' yeast, dried fish solubles, or animal liver meal; usually through a reputable commercial feed.

There is no evidence that deficiencies of the following B complex vitamins occur in horses on normal rations: B6 (pyridoxine), biotin, and para-aminobenzoic acid.

VITAMIN IMBALANCES

Experiments have shown that the amounts needed of certain vitamins may be affected by the supply of another vitamin or of some other nutritive essential. Also, it is known that excess fortification of the horse's diet with certain vitamins may prove more detrimental than helpful. Thus, the horseman should avoid harmful imbalances; he should provide vitamins on the basis of recommended allowances. Also, when fortifying with vitamins, consideration should be given to the vitamins provided by the ingredients of the normal ration, for it is the total composition of the feed that counts.

UNIDENTIFIED FACTORS

Since the U.S. foal crop is only around 50 percent, and since horses under stress (racing, showing, etc.) frequently become temperamental in their eating habits, it is obvious that there is room for improvement in the ration somewhere along the line. Perhaps unidentified factors are involved.

Unidentified factors include those vitamins which the chemist has not yet isolated and identified. For this reason, they are sometimes referred to as the vitamins of the future. There is mounting evidence of the importance of unidentified factors for animals, including man. Among other things, they lower the incidence of ulcers in man and swine. For horses, they appear to increase growth and improve feed efficiency and breeding performance when added to rations thought to be complete with regard to known nutrients. The anatomical and physiological mechanism of the digestive system of the horse, plus the stresses and strains to which modern horses are subjected, would indicate the wisdom of adding unidentified factor sources to the ration of the horse. Unidentified factors appear to be of special importance during breeding, gestation, lactation, and growth.

Three highly regarded unidentified factor sources are: dried whey product, corn fermentation solubles, and dehydrated alfalfa meal.

Water

Water is one of the most vital of all nutrients. In fact, horses can survive for a longer period without feed than they can without water. But, fortunately, under ordinary conditions water can be readily provided in abundance and at little cost.

Water is one of the largest single constituents of the animal body, varying in amount with condition and age. The younger the animal, the more water it contains. Also, the fatter the animal, the lower the water content. Thus, as an animal matures, it requires proportionately less water on a weight basis, because it consumes less feed per unit of weight and the water content of the body is being replaced by fat.

Water performs the following important functions in horses:

1. It is essential for the production of saliva.
2. It is necessary to the life and shape of every cell and is a constituent of every body fluid.
3. It acts as a carrier for various substances, serving as a medium in which nourishment is carried to the cells and waste products are removed therefrom.
4. It assists with temperature regulation in the body, cooling the animal by evaporation from the skin as perspiration.
5. It is necessary for many important chemical reactions of digestion and metabolism.
6. It lubricates the joints, as a constituent of the synovial fluid; it acts as a water cushion for the nervous system, in the cerebrospinal fluid; it transports sound, in the perilymph in the ear; and it is concerned with sight and provides a lubricant for the eye.

Surplus water is excreted from the body, principally in the urine, and to a slight extent in the perspiration, feces, and water vapor from the lungs.

The average horse will drink 10 to 12 gallons of water daily, the amount varying according to weather, amount of work done (sweating), rations fed, and size of horse.

Free access to water is desirable. When this is not possible, horses should be watered at approximately the same times daily. Opinions vary among horsemen as to the proper times and method of watering horses. All agree, however, that regularity and frequency are desirable. Most horsemen agree that water may be given before, during, or after feeding.

Frequent, small waterings between feedings are desirable during warm weather or when the animal is being put to hard use. Do not allow a horse to drink heavily when he is hot, because he may founder; and do not allow a horse to drink heavily just before being put to work.

Automatic waterers are the modern way to provide clean, fresh water at all times—as nature intended. Also, frequent but small waterings avoid gorging. All waterers should have drains for easy cleaning, and should be heated to 40° to 45° F during the winter months in cold regions. Waterers should be available in both stalls and corrals.

FEEDS FOR HORSES

Individual feeds vary widely in feeding value. Oats and barley, for example, differ in feeding value according to the hull content and weight per bushel, and forages vary according to the stage of maturity at which they are cut and how well they are cured and stored. Also, the feeding value of certain feeds is materially affected by preparation.

Regardless of the feeds selected, they should be of sound quality, and not moldy, spoiled, or dusty. This applies to both hay and grain. The careful selection of feeds is more important for horses than for any other class of livestock.

More than one kind of hay makes for appetite appeal. In season, any good pasture can replace part or all of the hay unless work or training conditions make substitution impractical.

Good quality oats and timothy hay always have been considered standard feeds for horses. However, feeds of similar nutritive properties can be interchanged in the ration as price relationships warrant; among them, the grains—corn, barley, wheat, and sorghum; the protein supplement—linseed meal, soybean meal, cottonseed meal, and sunflower meal; and hays of many varieties. Feed substitution makes it possible to obtain a balanced ration at lowest cost.

During the winter months, it is well to add a few sliced carrots to the ration, an occasional bran mash, or a small amount of linseed meal. Also a bran mash or linseed meal may be used to regulate the bowels.

The proportion of concentrates must be increased and the roughages decreased as energy needs rise with the greater amount, severity, or speed of work. A horse that works at a trot needs considerably more feed than one that works at a walk. For this reason, riding horses in medium to light use require somewhat less grain and more hay in proportion to body weight than horses that are racing. Also, from an esthetic standpoint, large, paunchy stomachs are objectionable on horses that are used for recreation and sport.

In addition to making for a nutritionally complete ration, the following factors should be considered when choosing horse feeds: cost, palatability, preparation, variety, bulk, and laxative or constipating qualities.

For purposes of convenience in the discussion that follows, the author has classed feeds as (1) pasture, (2) hay, (3) silage, (4) concentrates, (5) protein supplements, (6) special feeds and additives, and (7) treats.

Pasture

Fig. 13-14. Good horsemen, good pastures, and good horses go hand in hand.

The great horse breeding centers of the world—Kentucky, Ireland, and New Zealand, to name three of them—are characterized by good pastures. Yet, it is becoming difficult to provide good pasture for horses, especially in suburban areas. Also, it is recognized that many horsemen are prone to overrate the quality of their grass.

In season and when available, good pastures—pastures that are more than mere gymnasiums for horses—should be provided, especially for idle horses, broodmares, and young stock. In fact, pastures have a very definite place for all horses, with the possible exception of animals at heavy work or in training. Even with the latter, pastures may be used with discretion. Horses in heavy use may be turned to pasture at night or over the weekend. Certainly, the total benefits derived from pasture are to the good, although pasturing may have some laxative effects and produce a greater tendency to sweat.

The use of a temporary or seeded pasture grown in regular crop rotation is recommended instead of a permanent pasture that may become infested with parasites. Legume pasture is excellent for horses because they are less subject to bloat than cattle or sheep.

Horse pastures should be well drained and not too rough or stony. All dangerous places such as pits, stumps, poles, and tanks should be guarded. Shade, water, and suitable minerals should be available in all pastures.

Most horse pastures can be improved by seeding new and better varieties of grasses and legumes and by fertilizing and management. Also, horsemen need to give attention to supplementing some pastures with additional feed. Early in the season, pastures have a high water content and lack energy. Mature, weathered grass is almost always deficient in protein, with as little as three percent or less, and low in carotene, the precursor of vitamin A. However, these deficiencies can be corrected by proper supplemental feeding.

In addition to the nutritive value of the grass, pasture provides invaluable exercise on natural footing—with plenty of sunshine, fresh air, and lowered feeding costs as added benefits. Feeding on pasture is the ideal existence for young stock and breeding animals.

But pastures should not be taken for granted. Again and again, scientists and practical horsemen have demonstrated that the following desired goals in pasture production are well within the realm of possibility:

● To produce higher yields of palatable and nutritious forage.

● To extend the grazing season from as early in the spring to as late in the fall as possible.

● To provide a fairly uniform supply of feed throughout the entire season.

KINDS OF PASTURE

Broadly speaking, all horse pastures may be classified as either (1) permanent pastures, or (2) seeded and temporary pastures.

1. *Permanent pastures*—Permanent pastures, with proper care, last for many years. They are most commonly found on land that cannot be used profitably for cultivated crops, mainly because of topography, moisture, or fertility. The vast majority of U.S. farms have one or more permanent pastures, and most range areas come under this classification.

2. *Seeded and temporary pastures*—Seeded pastures are used as part of the established crop rotation. They are generally used for two to seven years before plowing.

Temporary pastures are those that are used for a short period—like rye, wheat, or oat pasture. They are seeded for the purpose of providing supplemental grazing during the season when the regular permanent or seeded pastures are relatively unproductive.

PASTURE TABLE—ADAPTED GRASSES-LEGUMES

The specific grass or grass legume mixture will vary from area to area, according to differences in soil, temperature, and rainfall. A complete listing of all adapted and recommended grasses and legumes for horse pastures would be too lengthy for this book. However, Table 13-8 shows the most important ones for each of the 10 generally recognized U.S. pasture

areas (Fig. 13-15). In using Table 13-8, bear in mind that many species of forages have wide geographic adaptation, but subspecies or varieties often have rather specific adaptation. Thus, alfalfa, for example, is represented by many varieties which give this species adaptation to nearly all states. Variety then, within species, makes many forages adapted to widely varying climate and geographic areas. The county agricultural agent or state agricultural college can furnish recommendations for the area that they serve. (See page 230 for Table 13-8.)

Five grass species—orchardgrass, reed canarygrass, fescue, smooth bromegrass, and Bermudagrass—account for the major portion of seeded grasses in the United States. The leading legumes are alfalfa, trefoil, lupine, sweet clover, kudzu, and clover.

Sudan and hybrid Sudans in the growing stage should never be grazed by horses, because of the hazard of cystitis. This disease, which occurs more frequently in mares than in stallions or geldings, is characterized by continuous urination, mares appearing to be constantly in heat, and incoordination in the gait. Animals seldom recover after either the incoordination or the dribbling of urine becomes evident. Apparently hay from Sudan or from hybrid Sudans will not produce the same malady.

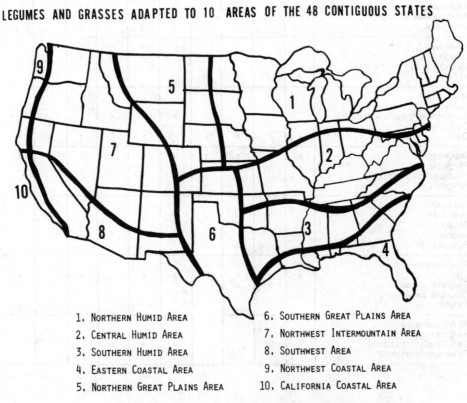

LEGUMES AND GRASSES ADAPTED TO 10 AREAS OF THE 48 CONTIGUOUS STATES

1. Northern Humid Area
2. Central Humid Area
3. Southern Humid Area
4. Eastern Coastal Area
5. Northern Great Plains Area
6. Southern Great Plains Area
7. Northwest Intermountain Area
8. Southwest Area
9. Northwest Coastal Area
10. California Coastal Area

Fig. 13-15. The 10 generally recognized U.S. pasture areas.

TABLE 13-8

ADAPTED GRASSES AND LEGUMES (INCLUDING BROWSE AND FORBS) FOR HORSE PASTURES
BY 10 GEOGRAPHICAL AREAS OF THE U.S. (Fig. 13-15)

	Areas of the U.S.									
	1	2	3	4	5	6	7	8	9	10
Grasses, Shrubs, Forbs										
Alfilaria (filaree)								x	x	
Bahiagrass (a paspalum)			x	x		x				
Beardgrass (a bluestem)								x		
Bermudagrass		x	x	x		x		x		x
Bluegrass	x	x			x		x	x		
Bluestem					x	x		x		
Bristlegrass (a millet)								x		
Brome grass	x				x		x	x		
Buckwheat (wild)								x		
Buffalograss					x	x				
Buffelgrass				x		x				
California coffeeberry								x		
Canarygrass (including reed)	x	x			x		x		x	
Carib grass				x						
Chamiza (fourwing saltbush)								x		
Cottontop								x		
Curly mesquite (a Hilaria)						x		x		
Dallisgrass (a paspalum)			x	x		x		x		x
Digitgrass				x						
Dropseed						x		x		
Fescue, tall	x	x	x		x	x	x	x	x	x
Foxtail						x	x		x	
Galleta (a Hilaria)						x		x		
Grama grass					x			x		
Hardinggrass (a canarygrass)										x
Indiangrass						x				
Indian ricegrass								x		
Indianwheat								x		
Johnsongrass (a sorghum)			x	x		x				
Junegrass					x	x		x		
Kleingrass						x				
Lovegrass						x		x		
Mesquite (vine; a panicum)								x		
Millet	x	x	x	x						
Mormon tea								x		
Muhly								x		
Needlegrass (needle-and-thread)					x		x			
Oatgrass									x	
Oats	x	x	x	x		x		x	x	x
Orchardgrass	x	x	x	x	x		x	x	x	x
Pangolasgrass			x							
Panicgrass (a panicum)						x				
Paragrass				x						
Pea bush								x		
Pearlmillet		x	x	x						
Ratany								x		
Redtop	x						x			
Rescuegrass			x	x						
Rhodesgrass				x						
Rye	x	x	x	x	x	x		x		x
Ryegrass, annual		x	x						x	
Ryegrass, perennial	x								x	
Sacaton								x		
St. Augustine grass			x							
Stargrass			x							
Switchgrass (a panicum)					x	x				
Three-awn (wiregrass)								x		

(Continued)

TABLE 13-8 (Continued)

	Areas of the U.S.									
	1	2	3	4	5	6	7	8	9	10
Timothy	x	x					x		x	
Tobosa (a Hilaria)						x				
Wheat	x	x	x	x	x	x	x	x	x	x
Wheatgrass					x	x	x	x		
Wild-rye					x	x	x			
Wintergrass						x				
Winterfat (white sage)								x		
Legumes										
Aeschynomene			x	x						
Alfalfa (lucerne)	x	x	x	x	x	x	x	x	x	x
Alyceclover			x	x						
Austrian winter peas			x	x					x	
Black medic (yellow trefoil)			x			x		x		
Bur-clover		x	x							x
Clover, alsike	x	x	x		x		x	x	x	
Clover, arrowleaf			x	x						
Clover, crimson	x	x	x	x						
Clover, Hubam								x		
Clover, Ladino	x	x	x	x	x	x	x	x	x	x
Clover, prairie								x		
Clover, red	x	x	x	x	x		x	x	x	
Clover, strawberry					x			x	x	x
Clover, subterranean			x						x	
Clover, white	x	x	x	x	x	x	x	x	x	x
Cowpeas		x	x							
Crown vetch	x									
Hairy andigo				x						
Lespedeza (annual)		x	x	x						
Lespedeza (perennial, sericea)		x	x	x						
Lupine		x	x							
Peas (flat)									x	
Soybeans	x	x	x	x						
Sweet clover	x	x		x	x	x	x	x		
Trefoil, birdsfoot	x	x	x	x	x		x	x	x	x
Velvet beans			x	x						
Vetch			x	x	x	x		x		

SUPPLEMENTING PASTURES

Except for idle horses, it is generally advisable to provide supplemental feed for horses that are on pasture. This is so because (1) horses are usually subjected to considerable stress; (2) show, sale, and pleasure horses should have eye appeal—sleek, bloomy hair coats that attract judges, buyers, and all who see them; and (3) young animals are usually forced for early development. Further, it is important not to jeopardize soundness or lower the reproductive ability of breeding animals. Consequently, the nutritive requirements of horses may be more critical than can be met by pasture alone.

SUPPLEMENTING EARLY SPRING GRASS

Turning horses on pasture when the first sprigs of green grass appear will usually make for a temporary deficiency of energy, due to (1) washy (high water content) grasses, and (2) inadequate forage for animals to consume. As a result, owners are often disappointed in the poor condition of horses.

Fig. 13-16. Supplemental feeding young stock on pasture, using portable feeders. Also, note open shed. (Courtesy, Lee Eaton, Lexington, Ky.)

If there is good reason why grazing cannot be delayed until there is adequate spring growth, it is recommended that early pastures be supplemented with grass hay or straw (a legume hay will accentuate

looseness, which usually exists under such circumstances), preferably placed in a rack; perhaps
with a high-energy concentrate provided, also.

SUPPLEMENTING DRY PASTURE

Dry, mature, weathered, bleached grass characterizes (1) drought periods, and (2) fall-winter pastures. Such cured-on-the-stalk grasses are low in
energy, in protein (as low as 3% or less), in
carotene—the precursor of vitamin A, and in phosphorus and perhaps certain other minerals. These deficiencies become more acute following frost and increase in severity as winter advances. This explains
the often severe loss in condition of horses following
the first fall freeze.

In addition to the deficiencies which normally
characterize whatever plants are available, dry pasture may be plaqued by a short supply of feed.

Generally speaking, a concentrate or supplement
is best used during droughts or on fall-winter pastures. However, when there is an acute shortage of
forage, hav or other roughage should be added, also.

PASTURE SUPPLEMENTS

Horsemen face the question of what pasture supplement to use, when to feed it, and how much of it to
feed.

In supplying a supplement to horses on pasture,
the following guides should be observed:

● It should balance the diet of the horses to
which it is fed, which means that it should supply all
the nutrients missing in the forage.

● It should be fed in such a way that each horse
gets its proper proportion, which generally means (1)
the use of salt blocks, (2) tying up horses during concentrate feeding when more than one animal is fed in
a given pasture, or (3) taking them to their stalls at
feeding time.

● The daily allowance of the supplement should
be determined by (1) the available pasture (quantity
and quality), and (2) the condition of the horse.

Hay

Through mistaken kindness or carelessness,
horses are often fed too much hay or other roughage,
with the result that they breathe laboriously and tire
quickly. With cattle and sheep, on the other hand, it is
usually well to feed considerable roughage. This difference between horses and ruminants is due primarily to the relatively small size of the stomach of the
horse in comparison with the fourfold stomach of the
ruminant.

Usually, young horses and idle horses can be
provided with an unlimited allowance of hay. In fact,

much good will result from feeding young and idle
horses more roughage and less grain. But one should
gradually increase the grain and decrease the hay as
work or training begins.

Hay native to the locality is usually fed. However, horsemen everywhere prefer good quality
timothy. With young stock and breeding animals
especially, it is desirable that a sweet grass-legume
mixture of alfalfa hay be fed. The legume provides a
source of high-quality proteins and certain minerals
and vitamins.

Horses like variety. Therefore, if at all possible, it
is wise to have more than one kind of hay in the stable. For example, timothy may be provided at one
feeding and a grass-legume mixed hay at the other
feeding. Good horsemen often vary the amount of alfalfa fed, for increased amounts of alfalfa in the ration
will increase urination and give a softer consistency to
the bowel movements. This means that elimination
from the kidneys and bowels can be carefully regulated by the amount and frequency of alfalfa feedings.
Naturally, such regulation becomes more necessary
with irregular use and idleness. On the other hand, in
some areas alfalfa is fed as the sole roughage with
good results.

The easily recognizable characteristics of hay of
high quality are:

1. It is made from plants cut at an early stage of
maturity, thus assuring the maximum content of protein, minerals, and vitamins, and the highest digestibility.

2. It is leafy, thus giving assurance of high protein
content.

3. It is bright green in color, thus indicating
proper curing, a high carotene or provitamin A content (provided it is not over a year old), and palatability.

4. It is free from foreign material, such as weeds
and stubble.

5. It is free from must or mold and dust.

6. It is fine stemmed and pliable—not coarse,
stiff, and woody.

7. It has a pleasing, fragrant aroma; it "smells
good enough to eat."

The most important factor affecting hay quality is
the stage of maturity at which it is cut. As the plant
matures, the stem-to-leaf ratio increases, the percentage of digestible nutrients (such as protein and calcium) decreases, and the digestibility and voluntary
intake decrease. Workers at the Pennsylvania Station
cut two hay crops, alfalfa and orchardgrass, on three
different dates—June 3, June 13, and June 23—then
determined the nutritive value of the hays for horses.
Their results are given in Table 13-9.

As shown in Table 13-9, each 10-day delay in the
cutting date of both alfalfa and orchardgrass resulted

TABLE 13-9
EFFECT OF DATE OF CUTTING ON NUTRITIVE VALUE OF HAY FED TO HORSES[1]

Hay	Date	Crude Protein	Crude Fiber	Digestibility of Energy
		(%)	(%)	(%)
Alfalfa	June 3	15.1	28.3	65
	June 13	14.4	32.7	56
	June 23	9.1	38.7	52
Orchardgrass	June 3	14.0	30.9	59
	June 13	10.9	32.3	55
	June 23	6.5	38.0	49

[1]Adapted from Darlington, J.M., and T. V. Herschberger, *Journal of Animal Science*, Vol. 27, No. 6, 1968, p. 1573.

in a decrease in crude protein, an increase in crude fiber, and a lowering of digestibility of energy.

TIMOTHY

Timothy is the preferred hay by most horsemen. Although it may be grown alone, it is commonly seeded in mixtures with medium red or alsike clover.

Timothy is easy to harvest and cure. However, in comparison with hay made from the legumes, it is low in crude protein and minerals, particularly calcium.

As with all other forages, the feeding value of timothy is affected by the stage of growth of the plants at the time of cutting. With increasing maturity, (1) the percentage of crude protein decreases, (2) the percentage of crude fiber increases, (3) the hay becomes less palatable, and (4) the digestibility decreases. However, delaying cutting until timothy has reached the full bloom stage, or later, usually results in the highest yields. When both yield and quality are considered, the best results are obtained when timothy is cut for hay at the early bloom stage.

ALFALFA (Lucerne)

Alfalfa is an important, perennial, leguminous forage plant with trifoliate leaves and bluish-purple flowers. It is grown widely, principally for hay. Alfalfa is capable of surviving dry periods because of its extraordinarily long root system, and it is adapted to widely varying conditions of climate and soil. It yields the highest tonnage per acre and has the highest protein content of the legume hays.

Not too many years ago, alfalfa hay was not considered fit feed for a horse. Today, some horsemen are feeding it exclusively, with good results. It averages 15.3 percent protein, which is of high quality; and it is a good source of certain minerals and vitamins. In addition to being used as a hay, alfalfa is an ingredient of most all-pelleted feeds.

OAT HAY

Oat hay is an excellent feed for horses. It's easy to cure, and horses like it. Early cutting (in the soft dough stage) greatly increases its feeding value, due to the higher protein content. Even though considerable energy is stored in the kernels at maturity, shattering of the grain during harvesting of mature oats results in energy losses and decreased feeding value compared with early-cut hay.

Oat hay is low in protein; hence, its feeding value is greatly enhanced when it is fed with alfalfa or some other legume.

Silage

Well-preserved silage of good quality, free from mold and not frozen, affords a highly nutritious succulent forage for horses during the winter months. *Because horses are more susceptible than cattle or sheep to botulism or other digestive disturbances resulting from the feeding of poor silage, nothing but choice, fresh silage should ever be fed.*

Various types of silages may be fed successfully to horses, but corn silage and grass-legume silage are most common. If the silage contains much grain, the concentrate allowance should be reduced accordingly.

Silage should not be used as the only roughage for horses. Usually it should be fed in such quantity as to replace not more than ⅓ to ½ of the roughage allowance, considering that ordinarily 1 lb of hay is equivalent to approximately 3 lb of wet silage. This means that the silage allowance usually does not exceed 10 to 15 lb daily per head for mature animals, although much larger amounts have been used satisfactorily in some instances. Silage is especially suited for the winter feeding of idle horses, broodmares, and growing foals.

Concentrates

Horses cannot handle as large quantities of roughages as ruminants. When used for heavy work, for pleasure, or for racing they must be even more restricted in their roughage allowance and should receive a higher proportion of concentrates.

Because of less bulk and lower shipping and handling costs, the concentrates used for horse feeding are less likely to be locally grown than the roughages. Even so, the vast majority of grains fed to horses are homegrown, thus varying from area to area, according to the grain crops best adapted.

Of all the concentrates, heavy oats most nearly meet the needs of horses; and, because of the uniformly good results obtained from their use, they have always been recognized as the leading grain for horses. Corn is also widely used as a horse feed, particularly in the central states. Despite occasional prejudice to the contrary, barley is a good horse feed. As proof of the latter assertion, it is noteworthy that the Arabs—who were good horsemen—fed barley almost exclusively. Also, wheat, wheat bran, and commercial mixed feeds are extensively used. It is to be emphasized, therefore, that careful attention should be given to the prevailing price of feeds available locally, for many feeds are well suited to horses. Often substitutions can be made that will result in a marked saving without affecting the nutritive value of the ration. When corn or other heavy grains are fed, it is important that a little linseed meal or wheat bran be used, in order to regulate the bowels.

OATS

Oats are the leading U.S. horse feed. They normally weigh 32 pounds per bushel, but the best horse oats are heavier. The feeding value varies according to the hull content and test weight per bushel.

Because of their bulky nature, oats form a desirable loose mass in the stomach, which prevents impaction.

Oats may be rolled, crimped, or fed whole. Hulled oats are particularly valuable in the ration for young foals.

BARLEY

Barley is the leading horse grain in western United States.

Compared with corn, barley contains somewhat more protein (crude protein: barley 13%; corn 10%) and fiber (due to the hulls) and somewhat less carbohydrate and fat. Like oats, the feeding value of barley is quite variable, due to the wide spread in test weight per bushel. Most horsemen feel that it is preferable to feed barley along with more bulky feeds; for example, 25% oats or 15% wheat bran.

When fed to horses, barley should always be steam rolled or ground coarsely.

CORN (MAIZE)

Corn ranks second to oats as a horse feed. It is palatable, nutritious, and rich in energy-producing carbohydrate and fat, but it has certain very definite limitations. It lacks quality (being especially low in the amino acids, lysine and tryptophane) and quantity of proteins (it runs about 9%), and it is deficient in minerals, particularly calcium.

Corn may be fed to horses on the cob, shelled, cracked, as corn-and-cob meal, or flaked.

WHEAT BRAN

Wheat bran is the coarse outer covering of the wheat kernel. It contains a fair amount of protein (averaging about 16%) and a good amount of phosphorus. Bran is valuable for horses because of its bulky nature and laxative properties. Also, it is very palatable.

Bran Mash

Feeding a bran mash is the traditional way of regulating the bowels of horses on idle days and at such other times as required.

The mash is prepared by filling a 2- to 2 ½-gallon bucket with wheat bran, pouring enough boiling hot water over it to make it the consistency of breakfast oatmeal, covering the bucket with a blanket and allowing it to steam until cool, then feeding it to the horse.

Occasionally, when a horse is offered a bran mash for the first time, he may refuse to eat it. When this occurs, the animal may be enticed to eat the mash by either (1) introducing him to a little of it by hand, or (2) sprinkling some sugar, or some other well-liked feed, over it.

MOLASSES (CANE OR BEET)

Molasses is a by-product of sugar factories, with cane molasses coming from sugarcane and beet molasses coming from sugar beets. Cane molasses is slightly preferred to beet molasses for horses, although either is satisfactory.

For horses, molasses is 80 to 95 percent as valuable as oats, pound for pound. However, molasses is used primarily as an appetizer.

In hot, humid areas, molasses should be limited to 5 percent of the ration; otherwise, mold may develop. Where mustiness is a problem, add calcium propionate to the feed according to the manufacturer's directions.

MILK BY-PRODUCTS

The superior nutritive values of milk by-products are due to their high-quality proteins, vitamins, a good mineral balance, and the beneficial effect of the milk sugar, lactose. In addition, these products are

palatable and highly digestible. They are an ideal feed for young equines and for balancing out the deficiencies of the cereal grains. Most foal rations contain one or more milk by-products, primarily dried skim milk, with some dried whey and dried buttermilk included at times. The chief limitation to their wider use is price.

MILK REPLACER

As indicated by the name, a milk replacer is a replacement for milk. Such replacers generally contain the following composition: animal or vegetable fat, 17-20%; crude soybean lecithin, 1-2%; skimmed milk solids, 78-82% (10-15% dried whey powder can be included in place of an equivalent amount of skimmed milk solids); plus fortification with minerals and vitamins.

Foals suckling their dams generally develop very satisfactorily up to weaning time. But the most critical period in the entire life of a horse is that space from weaning time (about six months of age) until one year of age. This is especially so in the case of young horses being fitted for shows or sales, where condition is so important. Thus, where valuable weanlings or yearlings are to be shown or sold, the use of a milk replacer may be practical.

Protein Supplements

The extent to which the horse's ration is supplemented with proteins depends primarily on the age of the horse and on the quality of the forage fed. Growing or lactating animals require somewhat more protein than horses that are idle, gestating, or working. Also, grass hays and farm grains are generally low in quality and quantity of proteins and require more supplementation than legumes.

In practical horse feeding, foals should be provided with some protein feeds of animal origin in order to supplement the proteins found in grains and forages. In feeding mature horses, a safe plan to follow is to provide plant protein from several sources.

In general, feeds of high protein content are more expensive than those high in carbohydrates or fats. Accordingly, there is a temptation to feed too little protein. On the other hand, when protein feeds are the cheapest—as is often true of cull peas in certain sections of the West—excess quantities of them may be fed as energy feeds without harm, provided the ration is balanced in all other respects. Any amino acids that are left over, after the protein requirements have been met, are deaminated or broken down in the body. In this process, a part of each amino acid is turned into energy, and the remainder is excreted via the kidneys.

The following oil meals are most commonly used as protein supplements for horses: linseed meal, soybean meal, cottonseed meal, and sunflower meal.

LINSEED MEAL

Linseed meal is a by-product of flaxseed following oil extraction by either of two processes: (1) the mechanical process (what is known as the "old process"); or (2) the solvent process ("new process"). If solvent extracted, it must be so designated. Horsemen prefer the mechanical process, for the remaining meal is more palatable, has a higher fat content, and imparts more gloss to the hair coat.

Linseed meal averages about 35 percent protein content. For horses, the proteins of linseed meal do not effectively make good the deficiencies of the cereal grains—linseed meal being low in the amino acids lysine and tryptophane. Also, linseed meal is lacking in carotene and vitamin D, and is only fair in calcium and the B vitamins. Because of its deficiencies, linseed meal should not be fed to horses as the sole protein supplement.

Because of its laxative nature, linseed meal in limited quantities is a valuable addition to the ration of horses. Also, it imparts a desirable "bloom" to the hair of show and sale animals.

SOYBEAN MEAL

Soybean meal, processed from the soybean, is the most widely used protein supplement in the United States. It is the ground residue (soybean oil cake or soybean oil chips) remaining after the removal of most of the oil from soybeans. The oil is extracted by either of three processes: (1) the expeller process; (2) the hydraulic process; or (3) the solvent process. Although a name descriptive of the extraction process must be used in the brand name, well-cooked soybean meal produced by each of the extraction processes is of approximately the same feeding value.

Soybean meal normally contains 41, 44 or 50 percent protein, according to the amount of hull removed; and the proteins are of better quality than the other protein-rich supplements of plant origin. It is low in calcium, phosphorus, carotene, and vitamin D.

Soybean meal is satisfactory as the only protein supplement to grain for mature horses, providing a high-quality ground legume is incorporated in the ration and adequate sources of calcium and phosphorus are provided. For foals, it is best that a dried milk by-product be included.

COTTONSEED MEAL

Among the oilseed meals, cottonseed meal ranks second in tonnage to soybean meal.

The protein content of cottonseed meal can vary

from about 22% in meal made from undecorticated (unhulled) seed to 60% in flour made from seed from which the hulls have been removed completely. Thus, in screening out the residual hulls, which are low in protein and high in fiber, the processor is able to make a cottonseed meal of the protein content desired—usually 41, 44 or 50%.

Cottonseed meal is low in lysine and tryptophane and deficient in vitamin D, carotene (vitamin A value), and calcium. Also, unless glandless seed is used, it contains a toxic substance known as gossypol, varying in amounts with the seed and the processing. But, it is rich in phosphorus.

Some prejudices to the contrary, good grade cottonseed meal is satisfactory for horses. It may be fed in the amounts necessary to balance ordinary rations.

SUNFLOWER MEAL

The development of high oil-yielding varieties by Russian scientists has stirred worldwide interest in the use of sunflowers as an oilseed crop. Some of these varieties yield over 50 percent oil.

Sunflower meal (41% protein or better) can be used as a protein supplement for horses provided (1) it is good quality, and (2) care is taken to supply adequate lysine, for sunflower meal is low in this amino acid. When incorporated in well-balanced rations, properly processed sunflower meal of good quality may supply up to one-third of the protein supplement of horses.

UREA

It is recognized that horses frequently consume urea-containing cubes and blocks intended for cattle and sheep, particularly on the western range. Moreover, it appears that mature horses are able to do so without untoward effects. The latter observation was confirmed in one limited experiment[10] in which 4 horses consumed an average of 4.57 lb per day of a urea-containing supplement, or 0.55 lb/head/day of feed urea (262%), for 5 months. Also, the Louisiana Station[11] did not find urea detrimental or toxic to horses when it constituted up to 5 percent of the grain ration, with up to 0.5 lb per day of urea consumed. There are reports, however, of urea toxicity in foals, in which bacterial action is more limited than in older horses.

Thus, there is some evidence that nonprotein nitrogen (urea) can be substituted for protein in the diet of the horse, but the conversion to protein is inefficient. Up to five percent of urea in the total ration

[10]*Veterinary Medicine*, Vol. 58, No. 12, Dec. 1963, pp. 945-946.

[11]"Non-Toxicity of Urea Feeding to Horses," *Veterinary Medicine/Small Animal Clinician*, Nov. 1965.

does not appear to be harmful to mature horses. Nevertheless, in recognition of the more limited bacterial action in the horse and the hazard of toxicity—especially to young equines, most state laws forbid the use of such nonprotein nitrogen sources as urea in horse rations.

Special Feeds and Additives

Special feeds may be needed from time to time for imparting bloom or gloss to the hair, and for promoting growth of young stock.

FEEDS THAT IMPART BLOOM OR GLOSS

Bloom or gloss is important in horses. But sometimes they lack this desired quality—their hair is dull and dry. Feeding a well-balanced ration will usually rectify this situation. Also, feeding the following products will make for an attractive, shiny coat:

1. *Corn oil or safflower oil*—Feed at the rate of 2 ounces (2 tablespoons) per horse twice per day.

2. *Whole flaxseed soaked*—Put a handful of whole flaxseed in a teacup, cover it with water, let it stand overnight, then pour it over the morning feed. Repeat twice each week.

Unless the horse is afflicted with lice, mange, or some other ailment, either of the above treatments will impart bloom or gloss to the coat.

LYSINE

Protein quality is important for horses. Because of more limited amino acid synthesis in the horse than in ruminants, plus the fact that the cecum is located beyond the small intestine—the main area for digestion and absorption of nutrients, it is generally recommended that high-quality protein rations, adequate in amino acids, be fed to equines. This is especially importnat for young equines, because cecal synthesis is very limited in early life.

Fortunately, the amino acid content of proteins from various sources varies. Thus, the deficiencies of one protein may be improved by combining it with another, and the mixture of the two proteins often will have a higher feeding value than either one alone. It is for this reason, along with added palatability, that a considerable variety of feeds in the horse ration is desirable.

Cornell University reported that the addition of lysine to the diet of growing horses increased weight gains, feed consumption, and feed efficiency. But, this experimental diet contained linseed meal as the major source of protein. Normally, it is much more practical to supply a source of good quality protein, such as milk protein or soybean meal (perhaps along with

some linseed meal), rather than add lysine to linseed meal.

It is not recommended that horsemen spend money on lysine for horses. Instead, a well-balanced ration should be fed to horses of all ages, and especially high-quality proteins should be incorporated in the ration of young equines. There is no experimental evidence that the addition of lysine will improve a good ration.

ANTIBIOTICS

The newer knowledge of antibiotics—products of molds, bacteria, and green plants—dates from the discovery of penicillin by Dr. Alexander Fleming, a British scientist, in 1928.[12] Quite by accident, a stray mold spore floated in on the breeze, and landed on a culture plate of bacteria with which Dr. Fleming was working. It inhibited the growth of the bacteria. Dr. Fleming correctly interpreted his observation—the possible value of the mold in the treatment of disease, thus ushering in the antibiotic era. However, penicillin did not come into prominence until 10 years later, and it was not until 1944 that streptomycin, the second most widely known of the antibiotics, was discovered by Waksman, a soil microbiologist, and his colleagues at the New Jersey station.

Antibiotics are not nutrients; they're drugs. They are a chemical substance, produced by molds or bacteria, which has the ability to inhibit the growth of or to destroy other microorganisms.

The author was a member of the research team that conducted the first U.S. study on feeding antibiotics to foals, which study was subsequently used in obtaining Food and Drug Administration (FDA) approval for feeding Aureomycin to foals. This experiment revealed that an 85 milligram level of Aureomycin, fed to foals from 5 days of age to 5 months, produced 22 pounds more weight.[13]

Certain antibiotics, at stipulated levels, are approved by the FDA for growth promotion and for the improvement of feed efficiency of young equines up to one year of age. Unless there is a disease level, however, there is no evidence to warrant the continuous feeding of antibiotics to mature horses. Such practice may even be harmful. Hence, where antibiotics are needed for therapeutic purposes, it is best to seek the advice of a veterinarian.

It appears that antibiotics may be especially helpful for young foals which suffer setbacks from infections, digestive disturbances, inclement weather, and other stress factors. Also, horses may benefit from an-

tibiotics (1) when being transported from one location to another—for example, when being moved to a new show or track: (2) when there is a low disease level in the herd; or (3) when mares are foaling.

The poorer the feed, the greater the response from antibiotics; and the poorer the management, the greater the response from antibiotics. It follows, therefore, that there is a temptation to use antibiotics as a "crutch," rather than improve the regimen.

When used in feed, the level of antibiotics should be in keeping with the directions of the manufacturer and with the Food and Drug Administration regulations.

Treats

Horses are fed a great variety of treats. On a government horse breeding establishment in Brazil, the author saw a large, well-manicured vegetable garden growing everything from carrots to melons, just for horses. Also, trainers recognize that most racehorses, which are the prima donnas of the equine world, don't "eat like a horse"; they eat like people—and sometimes they're just as finicky. Their menus may include a choice of carrots or other roots, fruit, pumpkins, squashes, or melons, sugar or honey, and innumerable other goodies.

Fig. 13-17. The carrot and the stick.

Ask the average horseman why he feeds treats to his horse and you'll get a variety of answers. However, high on the list of reasons will be (1) as appetizers; (2) as a source of nutrients and as conditioners; (3) as rewards; (4) as a means of alleviating obesity (dieting the horse; or (5) folklore.

TREATS AS APPETIZERS

If a horse doesn't eat his feed, it won't do him any good. Hence, feed consumption is important.

Sooner or later, a horseman is bound to get one of those exasperating equines that just refuses to clean up his feed. Perhaps he'll eat a few bites, then stop; or

---

[12]Actually, the presence of antibiotics was known much earlier than the discovery of penicillin, but no commercial use was made of them.

[13]Wash. Ag. Exp. Sta. Circ. 263, April 1955.

maybe he won't even touch the "stuff." Sometimes this happens to race and show horses that started training in great physical shape, only to lose appetite and have to be taken out of training for rest.

Lots of things can cause finicky eaters; among them, (1) stress and nervousness, (2) an unpalatable and monotonous ration, (3) nutritional deficiencies, (4) poor health, and (5) lack of exercise. Whatever the cause, the condition(s) making for poor feed consumption should be rectified—if it can be determined, and if it is within the power of the caretaker to correct it. Additionally, there should be incorporated in the ration something that the horse really likes—such as carrots or other roots; molasses, sugar, or honey; or sliced fruit.

But treats can be overdone. Hence, a horse should not be permitted to eat too much of any treat, simply because he likes it.

TREATS AS A SOURCE OF NUTRIENTS

Sometimes folks, and even nutritionists, overlook the fact that, when evaluated on a dry matter basis, high water content tubers, fruits, and melons have almost the same nutrient value as the cereal grains. This becomes apparent in the following table which gives the energy value on a moisture-free basis of several horse treats compared with barley, corn, oats, and timothy. (See Table 13-10.)

Generally speaking, horse treats are not a good buy when evaluated on a cost per unit of nutrient content (protein, energy, etc.) basis. This becomes obvious when it is realized that it takes nearly 7 pounds of carrots to equal 1 pound of oats in energy value, primarily because of the difference in water content of the 2 feeds. Occasionally, such products as carrots are in surplus or not suited for human consumption. At such times, they may be available for as little as $2 to $3 per ton, in which case they are a good buy in comparison with grains. Even then, it is best that they not replace more than 10 to 20 percent of the normal

grain ration. For the most part, however, treats are fed to horses because they possess qualities that cannot be revealed by a chemical analysis—because of their values as appetizers, in aiding digestion, and as conditioners.

TREATS AS REWARDS

The training of horses is based on a system of rewards and punishment. This doesn't mean that the horse is fed a tidbit each time he obeys, or that he is beaten when he refuses or does something wrong.

But horses are big and strong; hence, it's best that they want to do something, rather than have to be forced. Also, too frequent or improper use of such artificial aids as whips, spurs, reins, and bits makes them less effective; worse yet, it will likely make for a mean horse.

Horses appreciate a pat on the shoulder or a word of praise. However, better results may be obtained by working on an equine's greediness—his fondness for such things as carrots or a sugar cube. Also, treats may be used effectively as rewards to teach some specific thing such as posing, or to cure a vice like moving while the rider is mounting; but this should not be overdone.

TREATS TO ALLEVIATE OBESITY

Horses are equine athletes; hence, they should be lean and hard, rather than fat and soft. Obese horses should be avoided because (1) they lack agility, (2) excessive weight puts a strain on the musculoskeletal system, (3) it lowers fertility in broodmares and stallions, (4) fat horses are prone to founder, and (5) overweight horses are more susceptible to azoturia.

Such watery feeds as carrots and melons are filling, but low in calories. This becomes obvious when it's realized that (1) it takes more than 8 lb of fresh carrots to produce 1 lb of dried product, and (2) it

TABLE 13-10
ENERGY VALUE OF SEVERAL FEEDS ON A MOISTURE-FREE BASIS

Feed	Water	Dry Matter	Energy Value (TDN)	
			As Fed	Dry Matter Basis
	(%)	(%)	(%)	(%)
Barley	10	90	77	85
Corn	10	90	80	90
Oats	11	89	68	76
Timothy hay, mature	14	86	41	48
Apples	82	18	13	74
Carrots	88	12	10	82
Melons	94	6	5	80
Potatoes	79	21	18	85
Sugar beets	87	13	10	77

takes nearly 7 lb of carrots or over 13 lb of melons to furnish as much energy as 1 lb of oats. Thus, when used as a "salad" for the horse, carrots or melons are as effective as slenderizers for equines as they are for humans.

TREATS FOR FOLKLORE REASONS

Among the bagful of horsemen's secrets, sometimes the claim is made that apple cider will prolong life, increase vigor, and improve sex drive, fertility, and reproduction. However, there isn't a shred of evidence, based on studies conducted by a reputable experiment station, to substantiate such claims. Of course, it's good to have faith in something; and, too, nature is a wonderful thing. It is estimated that 70 to 80 percent of all horses with afflictions would recover even without treatment.

CARROTS AND OTHER ROOTS

Carrots are relished by horses. Additionally, they're succulent, and high in carotene and minerals. Each pound of fresh carrots contains 48 milligrams of carotene, which can be converted into 26,640 IU of vitamin A by the young equine, sufficient vitamin A to meet the daily requirement of a 1,000-lb horse. By contrast, 1 lb of timothy hay (mature) provides only 2.1 milligrams of carotene, or 1,165 IU, which is only 1/26th of the daily vitamin A requirement for a 1,000-lb horse. Also, carrots are a good source of minerals; on a dry basis 1 lb contains 0.42% calcium and 0.34% phosphorus, whereas mature timothy hay as fed contains 0.17% and 0.15% of these elements, respectively. Additionally, carrots are high in sugar; on a dry basis they contain 40% sugar (invert), which explains their sweetness.

Horsemen have long fed carrots, especially during the winter months when green feeds are not available and to horses that are stabled much of the time. They report that 1 to 2 pounds of carrots per horse per day will stimulate the appetite, increase, growth, assist in reproduction, make for normal vision, and improve the health, coat, and attractiveness of the animal.

Carrots should be cleaned, sliced from end to end in small strips, so as to avoid choking, then mixed with the grain.

Other roots such as parsnips, rutabagas, turnips, potatoes, and sugar beets may be fed to horses in small amounts, provided they are first cut finely enough to avoid choking.

PUMPKINS, SQUASHES, AND MELONS

Pumpkins, squashes, and melons are sometimes used as relish for horses. They contain only 6 to 10 percent dry matter; hence, their nutritive value on a wet basis is low in comparison with cereal grains. When fed in the usual amounts, their seeds are not harmful to horses, some opinions to the contrary. However, an entire ration of seeds alone is apt to cause indigestion, because of their high fat content.

APPLES AND OTHER FRUITS

An apple a day is good for a horse, especially when used as a tidbit or reward. They are very palatable because of their sugar content. However, the feeding of apples can be overdone; many a case of colic, or even death, has resulted from old dobbin's stolen visit to the orchard.

Also, peaches, plums, and pears are occasionally used as treats for the horse. The seeds of stone fruits should always be removed prior to feeding.

MOLASSES, SUGAR, AND HONEY

The horse has a "sweet tooth"; or at least he readily cultivates a taste for sweets. Hence, when added to the ration, molasses, sugar, and honey make for a "sweet feed," or appetizer. For this reason, small amounts (usually about 5%) of molasses, sugar, or honey are sometimes added to the concentrate mixtures of racehorses, show horses, and other finicky eaters. Once a horse becomes accustomed to a sweet feed, it is difficult to eliminate it from the ration; in fact, if the sweets are suddenly deleted, the horse may refuse to eat altogether. Thus, if for any reason sweets must be taken out of the ration, the change should be very gradual.

Also, sugar cubes are a good and convenient reward, provided too many of them are not used and the tendency of nipping or biting is avoided.

Palatability of Feed

Palatability is important, for horses must eat their feed if it's to do them any good. But many horses are finicky simply because they're spoiled. For the latter, stepping up the exercise and halving the ration will usually effect a miraculous cure.

Also, it seems possible that well-liked feeds are digested somewhat better than those which are equally nutritious, but less palatable.

Palatability is particularly important when feeding horses that are being used hard, as in racing or showing. Unless the ration is consumed, such horses will not obtain sufficient nutrients to permit maximum performance. For this reason, lower quality feeds, such as straw or stemmy hay, should be fed to idle horses.

Familiarity and habit are important factors concerned with the palatability of horse feeds. For exam-

ple, horses have to learn to eat pellets, and very frequently they will back away from feeds with new and unfamiliar odors. For this reason, any change in feeds should be made gradually.

Occasionally, the failure of horses to eat a normal amount of feed is due to a serious nutritive deficiency. For example, if horses are fed a ration made up of palatable feeds, but deficient in one or more required vitamins or minerals, they may eat normal amounts for a time. Then when the body reserves of the lacking nutrient(s) are exhausted, they will usually consume much less feed, due to an impairment of their health and a consequent lack of appetite. If the deficiency is not continued so long that the horses are injured permanently, they will usually recover their appetites if some feed is added which supplies the nutritive lack and makes the ration complete.

PALATABILITY OF THE PROTEIN SUPPLEMENT

Where a protein supplement lacks palatability, the situation can usually be corrected by increasing the salt content of the supplement to 3%. The reasoning back of increasing the salt is this: Whatever the cause of the unpalatability in a supplement may be (particularly if it is one of the ingredients), it's apt to show up more in the supplement than in other feeds, simply because it is more concentrated. The high salt content usually overcomes the unpalatability and adequate consumption follows. Of course, one should not go higher than 2% in a concentrate or in an all-pelleted ration because higher levels of salt are unpalatable, but up to 3% salt in a supplement fed at a level of 1 to 2 pounds per horse per day will usually work wonders.

PALATABILITY CHECKLIST

Here is a checklist, along with the author's comments, where there appears to be a palatability problem with a horse feed:

☐ 1. *Quality of feeds*—Make very certain on this point. It's almost impossible to detect through a chemical analysis many factors that may lower quality, such as "heated grain" and poor quality hay.

☐ 2. *Mustiness*—Again, check with care. Remember that horses can detect mustiness more quickly and easily than people.

☐ 3. *Hard pellets*—If pellets are too hard, horses will spit them out.

☐ 4. *Flavors*—In some cases, flavors will help in overcoming the lack of palatability due to poor quality feeds, but they will do little to enhance good quality feeds.

☐ 5. *Your premix*—Check on the "carrier" and premix ingredients which your feed manufacturer is using in his horse feeds. The author recalls one incident where dried fish meal was being used in a premix as a source of unidentified factors; and an unpalatable ration resulted because of the poor quality of the fish meal in the premix.

☐ 6. *The formulation*—Of course, some feeds are more palatable to horses than others. Among the well-liked feeds are wheat bran and molasses, both of which are usually incorporated in horse rations.

Distance Lends Enchantment to Feeds

Distance lends enchantment! Many horsemen not only believe that there is something magical about certain horse feeds, but they think that they must be grown in a specific area. For example, timothy hay and oats are frequently extolled on the basis that they are grown in certain "name" areas; they are even referred to as "racehorse oats" or "racehorse timothy hay." Such specialty areas may produce superior products, but their feeding value is generally exaggerated far beyond their price with much of their added cost going for hundreds of miles of transportation and for middlemen.

Chemical Analysis of Feeds

Feed composition tables ("book values"), or average analysis, should be considered only as guides, because of wide variations in the composition of feeds. For example, the protein and moisture content of milo and hay are quite variable. Wherever possible, especially with large operations, it is best to take a representative sample of each major feed ingredient and have a chemical analysis made of it for the more common constituents—protein, fat, fiber, nitrogen-free extract, and moisture; and often calcium, phosphorus, and carotene. Such ingredients as the oil meals and prepared supplements, which must meet specific standards, need not be analyzed so often, except as quality control measures.

Despite the recognized value of a chemical analysis, it is not the total answer. It does not provide information on the availability of nutrients to the animal; it varies from sample to sample, because feeds vary and a representative sample is not always easily obtained; and it does not tell anything about the associated effect of feedstuffs. Nor does a chemical analysis tell anything about taste, palatability, texture, undesirable physiological effects such as digestive disturbances, and laxativeness. Thus, one cannot buy feed for horses on the basis of chemical analysis alone, as is substantiated by the example that follows.

Example: Based on chemical analysis and price, which of the following would you choose?

		#1	#2	#3	#4
Crude protein	(%)	9.06	11.23	7.4	9.8
Fat	(%)		13.59		9.1
Sugar	(%)		0.43	51.2	
Fiber	(%)		16.5		0.3
Moisture	(%)		0.63		5.9
N.F.E.	(%)				72.8
Price/ton	($)	60.00	100.00	40.00	80.00
Cost/cwt	($)	3.00	5.00	2.00	4.00
Cost/lb protein	($)	.33	.445	0.27	0.41

Here's the identity of the samples:

Sample #1 .... soft coal
Sample #2 .... coffee grounds
Sample #3 .... candy
Sample #4 .... crackers

However, a chemical analysis does give a solid foundation on which to start in evaluating feeds. Also, with chemical analysis at hand, and bearing in mind that it's the composition of the total feed (the finished ration) that counts, the person formulating the ration can more intelligently determine the quantity of protein to buy, and the kind and amounts of minerals and vitamins to add.

TERMS USED IN ANALYSES AND GUARANTEES

Knowledge of the following terms is requisite to understanding analyses and guarantees:

Dry matter is found by determining the percentage of water and subtracting the water content from 100 percent.

Crude protein is used to designate the nitrogenous constituents of a feed. The percentage is obtained by multiplying the percentage of total nitrogen by the factor 6.25. The nitrogen is derived chiefly from complex chemical compounds called amino acids.

Crude fat is the material that is extracted from moisture-free feeds by ether. It consists largely of fats and oils with small amounts of waxes, resins, and coloring matter. In calculating the heat and energy value of the feed, the fat is considered 2.25 times that of either nitrogen-free extract or protein.

Crude fiber is the relatively insoluble carbohydrate portion of a feed consisting chiefly of cellulose. It is determined by its insolubility in dilute acids and alkalies.

Ash is the mineral matter of a feed. It is the residue remaining after complete burning of the organic matter.

Nitrogen-free extract consists principally of sugars, starches, pentoses and nonnitrogenous organic acids. The percentage is determined by subtracting the sum of the percentages of moisture, crude protein, crude fat, crude fiber, and ash from 100.

Carbohydrates represent the sum of the crude fiber and nitrogen-free extract.

Calcium and phosphorus are essential mineral elements that are present in feeds in varying quantities. Mineral feeds are usually high in source materials of these elements.

TDN—The digestible nutrients of any ingredient are obtained by multiplying the percentage of each nutrient by the digestion coefficient. For example, dent corn contains 8.9 percent protein of which 77 percent is digestible. Therefore, the percent of digestible protein is 6.9.

The TDN is the sum of all the digestible organic nutrients—protein, fiber, nitrogen-free extract, and fat (the latter multiplied by 2.25).

CALCULATING CHEMICAL ANALYSIS

Most of the larger feed manufacturers maintain strict product control. Among other things, they sample and analyze their feeds from time to time, as a means of satisfying themselves that they are meeting their guarantees.

Smaller manufacturers who do not have their own chemical laboratories usually use a commercial laboratory; or, in some states, the college of agriculture provides a feed testing laboratory service on a nominal charge basis. Horsemen can also check any feed in this same manner.

An actual chemical analysis is always best when it comes to checking on a guarantee. However, where the pounds of each ingredient in a mixed feed are known, the chemical analysis can be calculated. Of course, with closed formula feeds this is not possible.

Table 13-11 and the discussion that follows show how to calculate the chemical analysis of a protein supplement for horses: (See page 242.)

Step by step, here's how the calculation in Table 13-11 was done:

1. The ingredients were listed in the first column, followed in the second column with the pounds of each ingredient in a batch (the size batch need not total 1,000 lb; it could be 100 lb; 1 ton, or any other quantity).

2. By using a feed ingredient table, a calculation

TABLE 13-11
A HORSE PROTEIN SUPPLEMENT

Ingredients	Lb/1,000-Lb Batch	Lb of Crude Protein	Lb of Fat	Lb of Fiber
Linseed meal	80	28	4.8	6.4
Soybean meal	320	146	4.2	18.9
Dried skimmed milk	50	16.5	.5	—
Alfalfa meal, 17% dehy	105	18.4	2.7	26.3
Wheat bran	100	16.4	4.5	10.0
Hominy feed	157.50	16.9	10.2	7.9
Molasses (cane)	100	3.0	—	—
Salt	7.50	—	—	—
Dical	42.50	—	—	—
Vit.-trace min. premix	37.50	—	—	—
	1,000.00	245.2	26.9	69.5

was made of the number of pounds each of protein, fat, and fiber furnished by each ingredient; this was recorded in the proper column. For example, 80 lb of linseed meal × 35.0 percent protein = 28 lb of protein in 80 lb of linseed meal.

3. The sum of each column gives the total number of pounds of protein, fat, and fiber in the particular batch.

4. To obtain the percentages of protein, fat, and fiber, each total was divided by the total pounds in the batch as follows:

a. Protein ... $\dfrac{245.2 \times 100}{1,000} = 24.52\%$ protein

b. Fat ..... $\dfrac{26.9 \times 100}{1,000} = 2.69\%$ fat

c. Fiber .... $\dfrac{69.5 \times 100}{1,000} = 6.95\%$ fiber

For these percentages, the suggested guarantees would be:

	Guarantee	
	(Min.)	(Max.)
Crude protein, %	24	
Fiber %		7.5
Fat %	2.5	

FEED PREPARATION

The physical preparation of cereal grains for horses has been practiced by horsemen for a very long time. Generally speaking, feed is processed in order to increase palatability and digestibility, and to facilitate handling. Basically, grain is either soaked, cooked, ground, rolled (wet or dry), pelleted (cubed), or sprouted; and hay is either fed long, or pelleted (with the grain and hay combined), or cubed.

Pelleted feeds may be prepared from concentrates alone, from forage alone, or from concentrates and forage combined in a complete ration.

A summary relative to each of the common methods of feed preparation for horses follows.

Flaking

Fig. 13-18. Milo properly steam rolled into dustless flakes. (Courtesy, Dr. Al Lane, Extension Livestock Specialist, The University of Arizona; from *Horse Feeding*, Circular 288, The University of Arizona)

Flaking, which is the modification of steam rolling in which the grain is subjected to steam for a longer period of time, is the preferred method of processing grains for horses. It produces light, fluffy particles, which result in fewer digestive disturbances than any other method of feed preparation.

The flaking process varies according to the grain. For example, corn is usually steamed for approximately 20 minutes at a temperature of 200° F, with a moisture content of about 18 percent. The grain that responds the most to flaking is milo, which is generally flaked as follows: the grain is subjected to 20 pounds of steam pressure for 20 to 25 minutes, at approximately 205° F; then, at 18 to 20 percent moisture content, it is run through large rollers operated at ⅓ to ½ capacity and rolled to thin flakes. The end product has a distinct and pleasant aroma, resembling cooked cereal.

Steam Rolling

If properly done, steam rolling of grains is preferred to grinding for horses. However, there is great variation in steam rolling. Altogether too much steam rolling consists in exposing the grain to steam for 3 to 5 minutes, using a temperature of about 180° F, and adding an unknown amount of moisture. Such processing is little better than dry rolling.

Dry Rolling, Crimping, and Grinding

These methods can be and are used in preparing horse feeds. The important thing is to keep the grain as coarse as possible and to avoid fines.

Pelleted Grains-Concentrates

Grains and other concentrates are sometimes pelleted for the purposes of (1) facilitating mechanization in handling; (2) eliminating fines and dust, and increasing palatability; (3) alleviating sifting out and sorting; (4) increasing feed density; (5) reducing storage space; and (6) making it possible to feed on the ground or in windy areas with little loss.

Pelleting is accomplished by (1) grinding the material finely (and usually steaming it, also), then (2) forcing it through a thick die. Pellets can be made into small chunks or cyclinders of different diameters, lengths, and degrees of hardness. Large pellets—especially those large enough to be fed on pasture or range—are commonly called cubes.

The following concentrates may be pelleted: (1) the entire concentrate; (2) the fines only, with the grains flaked; (3) the protein supplement; and (4) pasture supplements.

Hydroponics (Sprouted Grain)

Hydroponics (or sprouted grain), is the growing of plants with their roots immersed in an aqueous solution containing the essential mineral nutrient salts, instead of in soil. This means that sprouted grain for feed is produced with water and chemicals, without dirt.

The Michigan Agricultural Experiment Station made a study of sprouted oats as a feed for dairy cows. As a result of this experiment, the Michigan scientists concluded as follows:[14]

The cost of sprouted oats was over four times that of the original oats or similar grains. This high cost plus (1) the loss in nutrients during sprouting, (2) the decreased digestibility of sprouted oats, and (3) no observed increase in milk production when sprouted oats were added to an

adequate ration indicate that this feed has no justification for being included in any modern dairy ration.

The findings of the Michigan study are likely to be applicable to other classes of livestock.

Without doubt, sprouted grains will give an assist when added to poor rations—and the poorer the ration, the bigger the boost. However, with our present knowledge of nutrition, balanced rations can be arranged without the added labor and expense of sprouting grain.

Pelleted Complete Feed

Currently, horsemen are much interested in complete, all-pelleted feed, in which the hay and grain are combined. Compared to conventional long hay and grain concentrate fed separately, all-pelleted feed has the following advantages:

1. It is less bulky and easier to store and handle, thus lessening transportation, building, and labor costs. Pelleted roughage requires $1/5$ to $1/3$ as much space as is required by the same roughage in loose or chopped form.

2. Pelleting prevents horses from selectively refusing ingredients likely to be high in certain dietary essentials; each bite is a balanced feed.

3. Pelleting practically eliminates waste; therefore, less pelleted feed is required. Horses may waste up to 20 percent of long hay. Waste of conventional feed is highest where low quality hay is fed or feed containers are poorly designed.

4. Pelleting eliminates dustiness and lessens the likelihood of heaves.

5. Pellet-fed horses are trimmer in the middle and more attractive because they consume less bulk.

6. Pellets lessen pollution. Pelleting lessens the manure by about 25 percent, simply because of less wastage and lower feed consumption; hence, it lessens pollution. Since a 1,000-pound horse normally produces about 8 tons of manure, free of bedding, per year, this is an important consideration in the present environment-conscious era. Thus, an all-pelleted ration will result in about 2 tons less manure per horse per year.

The following points are pertinent to the proper understanding and use of all-pelleted rations:

1. ½-inch pellets are preferred for mature horses, and ¼-inch pellets for weanlings and short yearlings. Also, very hard pellets should be avoided; if horses cannot chew them, they will not eat them.

2. The ratio of roughage to concentrates should be higher in all-pelleted rations than when long hay is fed. For most horses, the ratio may range from 60.5% roughage to 39.5% concentrate up to 69% roughage to 31% concentrate.

---

[14]Report from *Quarterly Bulletin*, Vol. 44, No. 4, Michigan State University, East Lansing, May 1962, pp. 654-665.

3. Any horse feed should form a loose mass in the stomach to assure ease of digestion, fewer digestive disturbances, and less impaction. To this end, in a complete all-pelleted ration, such feeds as oats and barley should be crimped or steam rolled but not finely ground. The roughage should be ¼-inch chop or coarser. Otherwise, a couple of pounds of long hay may be fed daily to each horse.

4. Young horses and horses at heavy work need more energy. They should be fed less roughage and more concentrate.

5. When less roughage and more concentrate is fed, horses are likely to be overfed and get too fat if they are idle or at light to medium work. But if the total feed consumption is limited too severely to keep the weight down, the problem of wood chewing is increased because of a lack of physical filling of the digestive tract.

6. When the roughage consists of high-quality legume hay, a higher percentage of roughage may be used than when all or part of the roughage is grass or other nonlegumes.

7. If more energy is needed for racing or young stock on an all-pelleted ration, it can be provided either by increasing the daily allowance of the all-pelleted ration, and/or replacing a portion of the all-pelleted ration with a suitable concentrate or supplement.

8. Because waste is eliminated, less all-pelleted feed is required than conventional feed. For a horse at light work, give 14 to 18 pounds of all-pelleted feed daily per 1,000 pounds of body weight. Use a feed that contains 51 to 58 percent total digestible nutrients (TDN). Increase the feed allowance with the severity of work.

9. As with any change in feed, the switch to an all-pelleted ration should be made gradually, otherwise such vices as wood chewing and bolting (eating feed too rapidly) may be induced. At first, continue to offer all the long hay the horse wants and slowly replace the grain portion of the conventional ration with the complete pelleted feed. Increase the pelleted feed by 1 to 2 pounds daily and begin gradually lessening the hay. After a few days, the horse usually will stop eating the hay and it can be removed completely from the ration.

10. The feces of pellet-fed horses are softer than the feces of those not fed pellets.

ALL-PELLETED RATIONS AND WOOD CHEWING

Among many horsemen, the feeling persists that horses on all-pelleted rations are more prone to wood chewing than those fed long hay. Perhaps this is true—at least to some degree. But wherever there's wood, some horses will chew it, regardless of what they're fed. This stems from the fact that pellet-fed horses have more time to indulge in vices, simply because they can eat an all-pelleted ration more quickly than where long hay is involved. As a result, they get bored; and, to pass the time, they chew wood. (Also, see later section entitled, "Pica—Wood Chewing.")

Hay Cubes

This refers to the practice of compressing long or coarsely cut hay in cubes or wafers, which are larger and coarser than pellets. Most cubes are about 1¼ inch square and 2 inches long, with a bulk density of 30 to 32 pounds per cubic foot. Cubing costs about $5 per ton more than baling.

This method of haymaking is increasing, because it (1) simplifies haymaking, (2) facilitates automation, (3) lessens transportation costs and storage space—cubed roughages require about one-third as much space as when the forage is baled and stacked, and (4) decreases nutrient losses.

From a nutrition standpoint, hay cubes are as satisfactory as hay in any other form (long or baled). However, some horsemen report occasional choking from feeding cubes.

RATIONS

Correctly speaking, a ration is the amount of feed given to a horse in a day, or a 24-hour period. To most horsemen, however, the word implies the feeds fed to an animal without limitation of the time in which they are consumed.

To supply all the needs of horses—maintenance, growth, fitting, reproduction, lactation, and work—the different classes of horses must receive sufficient feed to furnish the necessary quantity of energy (carbohydrates and fats), protein, minerals, vitamins, and water. A ration that meets all these needs is said to be balanced. More specifically, by definition, *a balanced ration is one which provides an animal the proper proportions and amounts of all the required nutrients for a period of 24 hours*. Moreover, the feed must be palatable—horses must like it. The rations listed in Table 13-12 meet these standards. Also, liberal margins of safety have been provided to compensate for variations in feed composition, environment, possible losses of nutrients during storage, and differences in individual animals.

Home Mixed Feeds

A horse feeding guide is given in Table 13-12. In selecting rations, compare them with commercial feeds. If only small quantities are required or little storage space is available, it may be more satisfactory to buy ready-mixed feeds.

The quantities of feeds recommended in Table 13-12, in the column headed "Daily Allowance," are intended as guides only. For example, the caretaker should increase the feed, especially the concentrates, when the horse is too thin and decrease the feed if he gets too fat.

Sudden changes in the diet should be avoided, especially when changing from a less concentrated ration to a more concentrated one. When this rule of feeding is ignored, digestive disturbances result and the horse goes "off feed." In either adding or omitting one or more ingredients, the change should be made gradually. Likewise, caution should be exercised in turning horses to pasture or in transferring them to more lush grazing.

In general, horses may be given as much non-legume roughage as they will eat. But they must be accustomed gradually to legumes because legumes may be laxative.

In feeding horses, as with other classes of livestock, it is recognized that nutritional deficiencies (especially deficiencies of certain vitamins and minerals) may not be of sufficient proportions to cause clear-cut deficiency symptoms. Yet, such deficiencies without outward signs may cause great economic losses because they go unnoticed and unrectified. Accordingly, sufficient additives (especially minerals and vitamins) should always be present, but care should be taken to avoid imbalances.

SUGGESTED RATIONS

Table 13-12 contains some suggested rations for different classes of horses. This is merely intended as a general guide. The feeder should give consideration to (1) the quality, availability, and cost of feeds; (2) the character and severity of the work; and (3) the age and individuality of the animal. (See page 246.)

AMOUNT OF ROUGHAGE

Actually, a horse does not need any hay. Also, more horses receive too much roughage than not enough, as evidenced by hay bellies (distended digestive tracts), quick tiring, and labored breathing.

Under most conditions, the roughage requirement of horses ranges from 0.5 percent to 1.0 percent of body weight, or from 5 to 10 pounds of roughage daily for a 1,000-pound horse.

Racehorses should receive a minimum of roughage, since they need a maximum of energy. Sometimes it is necessary to muzzle greedy horses (gluttons) to prevent them from eating bedding when their roughage allowance is limited.

HOW TO BALANCE A HORSE RATION

Generally speaking, the rations given in Table 13-12 will suffice, especially if similar feeds are substituted in some cases. However, a good horseman should know how to balance a ration. Then, if the occasion demands, he can do so. Perhaps of even greater importance, he will then be able more intelligently to select and buy rations with informed appraisal, to check on how well his manufacturer (or dealer) is meeting his guarantees, aand to evaluate the results.

The author has already made clear his position relative to "nutritive requirements" vs "recommended allowances" for horses (see earlier section under "Nutrient Requirements Vs Allowances"). Hence, the stated allowances given in the two examples that follow are his "recommended allowances," and not "minimum requirements."

Two problems are stated here, followed by their solutions—as an exercise on how to balance a ration.

Problem No. 1: Prepare a balanced ration for a 1,000-pound lactating mare.

Step by step, here is how it's done:

1. *Set down the desired allowances*—In order to balance a ration, it is first necessary to know what allowances we wish to meet. Here they are for a 1,000-pound lactating mare (see Tables 13-3, 13-4, 13-5, and 13-7).

Daily feed[15]	Crude protein[16]	Digestible protein[17]	TDN[16]	Calcium[16]	Phosphorus[16]	Vitamin A[16]	Vitamin D[16]
(lb)	(%)	(%)	(%)	(%)	(%)	(IU)	(IU)
25	13	9.1	50-60	0.6	0.5	50,000	7,000

---

[15]From section on "Amount to Feed" of this chapter.
[16]From Tables 13-3, 13-4, 13-5, and 13-7 of this chapter.
[17]Assuming a 70% digestibility of protein.

2. *Apply the "trial-and-error method"*—Next, let us see if we can meet these desired allowances by using a ration of equal parts of oats and timothy hay.

	Daily feed	Crude protein	Digestible protein	TDN	Calcium	Phosphorus	Vitamin A	Vitamin D
	(lb)	(%)	(%)	(%)	(%)	(%)	(IU)	(IU)
Timothy Hay (late cut)	12.5	6.8	3.1	45	.37	.19	7,333	922
Oats	12.5	11.8	9.4	60	.11	.39	—0—	—0—
	25.0	9.3	6.3	52.5	.24	.29	7,333	922

Upon checking the above with step 1 (the allowances that we wish to meet), it is quite obvious that a ration of equal parts of timothy hay and oats is very unsatisfactory for the 1,000-pound broodmare; it is low in protein, calcium, phosphorus, vitamin A, and vitamin D. The only requisites that it meets are to provide 25 pounds of feed daily and barely enough TDN.

TABLE 13-12

HANDY LIGHT HORSE FEEDING GUIDE[1]

Age, Sex, and Use	Daily Allowance	Kind of Hay	Suggested Grain Rations		
			Rations No. 1	Rations No. 2	Rations No. 3
			lb	lb	lb
Stallions in breeding season (weighing 900 to 1,400 lb)	¾ to 1½ lb grain per 100 lb body weight, together with a quantity of hay within same range.	Grass-legume mixed; or ⅓ to ½ legume hay, with remainder grass hay.	Oats ------- 55 Wheat ------- 20 Wheat bran ------- 20 Linseed meal ------ 5	Corn ------- 35 Oats ------- 35 Wheat ------- 15 Wheat bran ------- 15	Oats ------- 100
Pregnant mares (weighing 900 to 1,400 lb)	¾ to 1½ lb grain per 100 lb body weight, together with a quantity of hay within same range.	Grass-legume mixed; or ⅓ to ½ legume hay, with remainder grass hay (straight grass hay may be used first half of pregnancy).	Oats ------- 80 Wheat bran ------- 20	Barley ------- 45 Oats ------- 45 Wheat bran ------- 10	Oats ------- 95 Linseed meal - 5
Foals before weaning (weighing 100 to 350 lb with projected mature weights of 900 to 1,400 lb)	½ to ¾ lb grain per 100 lb body weight, together with a quantity of hay within same range.	Legume hay.	Oats ------- 50 Wheat bran ------- 40 Linseed meal ------ 10	Oats ------- 30 Barley ------- 30 Wheat bran ------- 30 Linseed meal ------- 10	Oats ------- 80 Wheat bran --- 20
			Rations balanced on basis of following assumption: Mares of mature weights of 600, 800, 1,000, and 1,200 lb may produce 36, 42, 44, and 49 lb of milk daily.		
Weanlings (weighing 350 to 450 lb)	1 to 1½ lb grain and 1½ to 2 lb hay per 100 lb body weight.	Grass-legume mixed; or ½ legume hay, with remainder grass hay.	Oats ------- 30 Barley ------- 30 Wheat bran ------- 30 Linseed meal ------ 10	Oats ------- 70 Wheat bran ------- 15 Linseed meal ------- 15	Oats ------- 80 Linseed meal 20
Yearlings, second summer (weighing 450 to 700 lb)	Good, luxuriant pastures. (If in training or for other reasons without access to pastures, the ration should be intermediate between the adjacent upper and lower groups.)				
Yearlings, or rising 2-year-olds, second winter weighing 700 to 1,000 lb)	½ to 1 lb grain and 1 to 1½ lb hay per 100 lb body weight.	Grass-legume mixed; or ⅓ to ½ legume hay, with remainder grass hay.	Oats ------- 80 Wheat bran ------- 20	Barley ------- 35 Oats ------- 35 Bran ------- 15 Linseed meal ------- 15	Oats ------- 100
Light horses at work; riding, driving, and racing (weighing 900 to 1,400 lb)	*Hard use*—1¼ to 1⅓ lb grain and 1 to 1¼ lb hay per 100 lb body weight. *Medium use*—¾ to 1 lb grain and 1 to 1¼ lb hay per 100 lb body weight. *Light use*—²/₅ to ½ lb grain and 1¼ to 1½ lb hay per 100 lb body weight.	Grass hay.	Oats ------- 100	Oats ------- 70 Corn ------- 30	Oats ------- 70 Barley ------- 30
Mature idle horses; stallions, mares, and geldings (weighing 900 to 1,400 lb)	1½ to 1¾ lb hay per 100 lb body weight.	Pasture in season; or grass-legume mixed hay.	(With grass hay, add ¾ lb of a high-protein supplement daily.)		

[1]With all rations and for all classes and ages of horses, provide free access to a mineral box as follows: (1) *Where the pasture or hay is primarily grass*, use a mixture containing 2 parts of calcium to 1 part of phosphorus; and (2) *where the pasture or hay is primarily a legume*, use a mixture containing 1 part of calcium to 1 part of phosphorus. To each of these mixes, add ⅓ salt (trace mineralized) to improve acceptability. If preferred, a good commercial mineral may be used. Self-feed salt separately.

3. *Let's add some other ingredients*—Oats and timothy hay can be used, provided they are balanced with certain other ingredients. Here's how:

Ingredients	Daily feed	Crude protein	Digestible protein	TDN	Calcium	Phosphorus	Vitamin A	Vitamin D
	(lb)	(%)	(%)	(%)	(%)	(%)	(IU)	(IU)
Timothy (late cut)	12.5	6.8	3.1	45.0	.37	.19		
Oats	.5	11.8	9.4	60.0	.11	.39		
Alfalfa meal sun cured	2.6	15.4	11.1	53.2	1.46	.31		
Corn (Grade No. 2)	.8	9.3	7.2	80.0	.02	.33		
Wheat bran	1.8	16.0	13.0	78.0	.08	.74		
Molasses (cane)	2.5	3.2	—0—	72.0	.89	.08		
Linseed meal (exp.)	1.7	35.3	30.6	75.5	.37	.86		
Soybean meal (exp.)	2.2	43.8	36.8	73.0	.27	.63		
Salt	.1							
Dicalcium phosphate	.2				27.00	19.07		
Premix min.-vit.	.1							
	25.0	13.2	9.3	55.8	.75	.51	57,500[18]	11,250[18]

[18]Obtained in the premix. Vitamin A and D from other sources not computed.

This is an excellent ration. It contains adequate amounts of protein, TDN, calcium, phosphorus, vitamin A, and vitamin D; and the calcium to phosphorus ratio is a very excellent 1.5:1.

Problem No. 2: A horseman grows his own oats and alfalfa-bromegrass hay. He wants to balance these feeds out for a 600-pound weanling, 10 months of age, that is expected to weigh 1,200 pounds when mature—using a commercial protein supplement carrying the following guarantees:

Brand X, 25% Supplement	Guarantee	
	(min.) %	(max.) %
Crude protein	25	
Fiber		8.0
Fat	2.75	
Calcium	1.5	
Phosphorus	1.0	
Salt	0.75	0.75
Ash		12.0
TDN	65.0	
Vitamin A, IU/lb	21,000	
Vitamin D, IU/lb	3,000	

Step by step, here is the answer to Problem No. 2:

1. *Set down the desired allowances*—Here they are for a 600-pound weanling (see Tables 13-3, 13-4, 13-5, and 13-7):

Daily feed[19]	Crude protein[20]	Digestible protein[21]	TDN[20]	Calcium[20]	Phosphorus[20]	Vitamin A[20]	Vitamin D[20]
(lb)	(%)	(%)	(%)	(%)	(%)	(IU)	(IU)
13.1	14	9.8	60.0	0.6	0.5	30,000	4,200

[19]From section on "Amount to Feed," of this chapter.
[20]From Tables 13-3, 13-4, 13-5, and 13-7 of this chapter.
[21]Assuming a 70% digestibility of protein.

2. *Apply the trial and error method*—To start with, let's estimate that about 1½ pounds of the 25 percent supplement would balance this ration:

Ingredients	Daily feed	Crude protein	Digestible protein	TDN	Calcium	Phosphorus	Vitamin A	Vitamin D
	(lb)	(%)	(%)	(%)	(%)	(%)	IU	IU
Alfalfa-brome hay	6	11.8	7.6	47.9	.77	.20		
Oats	6	11.8	9.4	60.0	.11	.39		
25% supplement	1.5	25.0	17.5	65.0	1.50	1.00	31,500	4,500
	13.5	13.2	9.5	55.1	.55	.37	31,500[22]	4,500[22]

[22]Obtained in the premix. Vitamins A and D from other sources not computed.

This is a good ration. However, it could be improved by using alfalfa hay in place of alfalfa-brome hay and by using equal parts of oats and corn instead of oats alone, thereby obtaining more protein and TDN (energy).

FEED SUBSTITUTION TABLE

The successful horseman is a keen student of values. He recognizes that feeds of similar nutritive properties can and should be interchanged in the ration as price relationships warrant, thus making it possible at all times to obtain a balanced ration at the lowest cost.

Table 13-13, Feed Substitution Table for Horses, is a summary of the comparative values of the most common U.S. feeds used for horses. In arriving at these values, chemical composition, feeding value, and palatability have been considered.

In using this feed substitution table, the following facts should be recognized:

1. That, for best results, different ages of animals should be fed differently.

2. That individual feeds differ widely in feeding value. Barley and oats, for example, vary widely in feeding value according to the hull content and the test weight per bushel, and forages vary widely ac-

TABLE 13-13

FEED SUBSTITUTION TABLE FOR HORSES

Feedstuff	Relative Feeding Value (lb for lb) in Comparison with the Designated (underlined) Base Feed Which = 100	Maximum Percentage of Base Feed (or comparable feed or feeds) Which It Can Replace for Best Results	Remarks	Feed Preparation
GRAINS, BY-PRODUCT FEEDS, ROOTS, AND TUBERS:[1] (Low and Medium Protein Feeds)				
Oats	**100**	**100**	The leading horse feed. The feeding value of oats varies according to the hull content and test weight per bushel. Because of their bulky nature, they form a desirable loose mass in the stomach which prevents impaction. Musty oats should never be used because they may cause colic.	Steam rolled, crimped, or fed whole.
Barley	110	100	The Arab, who was a good horseman, fed barley exclusively. It is also the leading horse feed in western U.S. Most horsemen feel that it is preferable to feed barley along with more bulky feeds; for example, 25% oats or 15% wheat bran.	Flaked, steam rolled, or ground coarsely.
Beet pulp, dried	100	33⅓	Not palatable to horses.	
Beet pulp, molasses, dried	100	33⅓	Not palatable to horses.	
Brewers dried grains	100	50		
Carrots	15-25	10	Horses are very fond of carrots.	Fresh or dried.
Corn, No. 2	115	100	Ranks second to oats as a light horse feed. It has a lower value than indicated when forage is of low protein content.	On the cob, shelled, cracked, corn-and-cob meal, or flaked.
Corn, gluten feed (gluten feed)	100	50		
Distillers dried grains	90-100	25		
Distillers dried solubles	90-100	25		
Hominy feed	115	100		
Milo (sorghum, grain)	110-115	85	All varieties have about the same feeding value.	Flaked, steam rolled, or ground coarsely.
Molasses, beet	80-95	10	In hot, humid areas, molasses should be limited to 5%; otherwise, mold may develop. Cane molasses is slightly preferred to beet molasses.	Where mustiness is a hazard, add calcium propionate to the feed according to manufacturer's directions.
Molasses, cane	80-95	10	(Same remarks as for beet molasses.)	
Peas, dried	100	40		
Rice (rough rice)	115	50		Ground.
Rye	115	33⅓	Higher levels, or abrupt changes to rye, may cause digestive disturbances. Not palatable.	
Wheat	115	50	Wheat should be mixed with a more bulky feed in order to prevent colic.	Steam rolled, or crushed.
Wheat bran	100	20	Valuable for horses because of its bulky nature and laxative properties.	May be fed as a wet mash.
Wheat-mixed feed (mill run)	105	20	Excessive quantities will cause colic or other digestive upsets.	
PROTEIN SUPPLEMENTS:				
Linseed meal 35%	**100**	**100**	Linseed meal (old process) is the preferred vegetable protein supplement for horses. It is valued because of its laxative properties, and because of the sleek hair coat which it imparts.	
Brewers dried grains	65-70	50		
Buttermilk, dried	100	100	May be used in place of dried skimmed milk for foals.	
Copra meal (coconut meal)	90-100	50		
Corn gluten feed (gluten feed)	70	100		

Footnotes on last page of table.

(Continued)

TABLE 13-13 (Continued)

Feedstuff	Relative Feeding Value (lb for lb) in Comparison with the Designated (underlined) Base Feed Which = 100	Maximum Percentage of Base Feed (or comparable feed or feeds) Which It Can Replace for Best Results	Remarks	Feed Preparation
Corn gluten meal (gluten meal)	100	50	Somewhat unpalatable to horses.	
Cottonseed meal (41%)	100	100	Satisfactory if limited to amounts necessary to balance ordinary rations. Some prejudices to the contrary, good grade cottonseed meal is satisfactory for horses.	
Peanut meal (41%)	100	100		
Peas, dried	75	50		
Skimmed milk, dried	100	100	Especially valuable for young equines; for creep feeding until past weaning.	
Soybean meal (41%)	100	100		
Soybeans	100	100	Soybeans should be limited to ⅓ of the concentrate ration.	
Sunflower meal	100	33⅓	Sunflower meal should not constitute more than ⅓ of the protein supplement for palatability reasons.	
Whey, dried	50	50	Whey may be laxative.	

Many horsemen prefer commercial protein supplements which are well fortified with vitamins and minerals.

DRY FORAGES AND SILAGES.[2]

Feedstuff	Relative Feeding Value	Maximum Percentage	Remarks	Feed Preparation
Timothy hay	**100**	**100**	The preferred hay of horsemen.	
Alfalfa hay, all analyses	133⅓	100	Good-quality alfalfa is excellent for horses. Alfalfa may be ground and pelleted. It provides high-quality proteins, and certain minerals and vitamins. It is somewhat laxative. Contrary to some "old wives' tales," it will not damage the kidneys.	
Barley hay	100	100	Lower value if not cut at the early dough stage.	
Bromegrass hay	100	100		
Clover hay, crimson	125	100	Crimson clover hay has considerably lower value if not cut at an early stage.	
Clover hay, red	125	100	Clover hay should be well cured and free from dust and mold.	
Clover-timothy hay	110-115	100	Value of clover-timothy mixed hay depends on the proportion of clover present and the stage of maturity at which it is cut.	
Corn fodder	100	50	Preferably fed along with a good legume hay.	Shredded.
Corn silage	45-55	33⅓-50		
Corn stover	60	50	Preferably fed along with a good legume hay.	Shredded.
Cowpea hay	110	100		
Grass-legume mixed hay	110-115	100		
Grass-legume silage	45-50	33⅓-50		
Grass silage	40-45	33⅓-50		
Johnsongrass hay	90-95	100	Johnsongrass thrives in the South.	
Lespedeza hay	115	100		
Oat hay	100	100	Lower value if not cut at the early dough stage.	
Orchardgrass			Should be cut before maturity. It is a safe feed for horses.	
Prairie hay	100	100	Considerable prairie hay is fed in the West.	
Reed canarygrass	90-95	100		
Sorghum fodder	100	50	Preferably fed along with a good legume hay.	Shredded.
Sorghum silage	40-45	33⅓-50		
Sorghum stover	60	50	Preferably fed along with a good legume hay.	Shredded.
Soybean hay	110	100		

Footnotes on last page of table.

(Continued)

TABLE 13-13 (Continued)

Feedstuff	Relative Feeding Value (lb for lb) in Comparison with the Designated (underlined) Base Feed Which = 100	Maximum Percentage of Base Feed (or comparable feed or feeds) Which It Can Replace for Best Results	Remarks	Feed Preparation
Sudangrass hay	90-95	100		
Vetch-oat hay	110-115	100	The higher the proportion of vetch, the higher the value.	
Wheat hay	100	100		

[1]Roots and tubers are of lower value than the grain and by-product feeds due to their higher moisture content.
[2]Well-preserved silage of good quality, free from mold and not frozen, affords a highly nutritious succulent forage for horses during the winter months—especially for idle horses, broodmares, and growing foals. Silages are of lower value than dry forages due to their higher moisture content.

cording to the stage of maturity at which they are cut and how well they are cured and stored.

3. That nonlegume forages may have a higher relative value to legumes than herein indicated provided the chief need of the animal is for additional energy rather than for supplemented protein. Thus, the nonlegume forages of low value can be used to better advantage for wintering mature horses than for young foals.

On the other hand, legumes may have a higher actual value relative to nonlegumes than herein indicated provided the chief need is for additional protein rather than for added energy. Thus, no protein supplement is necessary for broodmares provided a good quality legume forage is fed.

4. That, based primarily on available supply and price, certain feeds—especially those of medium protein content, such as brewers dried grains, distillers dried solubles, and peas (dried)—are used interchangeably as (a) grains and by-products feeds, and/or (b) protein supplements.

5. That the feeding value of certain feeds is materially affected by preparation. The values herein reported are based on proper feed preparation in each case.

For these reasons, the comparative values of feeds shown in the feed substitution table (Table 13-13) are not absolute. Rather, they are reasonably accurate approximations based on average-quality feeds.

Commercial Horse Feeds and Minerals

Commercial horse feeds are feeds mixed by manufacturers who specialize in the feed business. Today, about 60 million tons of commercial feeds are marketed in the United States each year.

Commercial mineral mixes are minerals mixed by manufacturers who specialize in the commercial mineral business, either handling minerals alone or a combination of feeds and minerals.

The commercial manufacturer has the distinct advantages of (1) purchasing ingredients (feeds or minerals) in quantity lots, making possible price advantages, (2) economical and controlled mixing, (3) the hiring of scientifically trained personnel for use in determining the formulations, and (4) quality control. Most horsemen have neither the know-how nor the quantity of business to provide these services on their own. In fact, due to the small quantities of feed and mineral usually involved and the complexities of horse rations and minerals, horsemen have more reason to rely on good commercial products than do owners of other classes of farm animals and poultry. Because of these several advantages, commercial feeds and minerals are finding a place of increasing importance in horse feeding.

The nutritive requirements of horses vary according to age, weight, use or demands, growth, stage of gestation or lactation, and environment. Also, part of the horse ration may be homegrown. It would appear, therefore, that the classes of commercial feeds shown in Table 13-14 are necessary if one is to meet most horse needs.

Good commercial minerals supply only the specific elements that are deficient, and in the quantities necessary. Excesses and mineral imbalances are avoided.

HOW TO EVALUATE A COMMERCIAL FEED OR MINERAL

There is a difference in commercial feeds and minerals! That is, there is a difference from the standpoint of what a horseman can purchase with his feed or mineral dollars. The smart horseman will know how to determine what constitutes the best in commercial feeds or minerals for his specific needs. He will not rely solely on how the feed looks and smells. The most important factors to consider or look for in buying a commercial feed or mineral are:

1. *The specific needs*—Feed needs vary according

TABLE 13-14
COMMERCIAL HORSE FEEDS AND NEEDS

Needed Horse Feeds	Prevailing Conditions	Crude Protein (%)	Used for
Complete (hay and grain combined in a pellet)	For the horseman who must buy all feeds.	13	All horses 10 mo. or older.
Concentrate	For the horseman who has satisfactory hay and/or pasture.	14	All horses 10 mo. or older.
Protein supplement	For supplementing available hay and grain.	25	All horses 10 mo. or older.
Foal ration	For creep feeding.	21	2 wk. or 10 mo. of age.
Protein-salt block	For free-choice feeding in corral or on pasture.	20	All horses 10 mo. of age or older.
Enriched vitamin-trace mineral-unidentified factor supplement.	For the horseman who has hay and grain that meet all needs except vitamin-trace mineral-unidentified factors.		All horses not receiving any of the above feeds.

to (a) the class, age, and productivity of horses, and (b) whether animals are fed primarily for maintenance, growth, fattening (or show-ring fitting), reproduction, lactation or work (running).

The mineral requirements of horses are much the same everywhere, although it is recognized that age, pregnancy, and lactation make for differences. Additionally, there are some area differences. For example, the Northern Great Plains and the Southwest are generally recognized as phosphorus-deficient areas—their grasses and hays are usually low in phosphorus. Accordingly, a high-phosphorus mineral is needed for horses in such areas—one containing 10 to 15 percent phosphorus.

The wise operator will buy different formula feeds and minerals for different needs.

2. *The reputation of the manufacturer*—This may be determined by conferring with other horsemen who have used the particular product and checking on whether or not the commercial feed or mineral under consideration has consistently met its guarantees. The latter can be determined by reading the bulletins or reports published by the respective state departments in charge of enforcing feed laws.

3. *Flexible formulas*—Feeds and minerals with flexible formulas are usually the best buy. This is because the price of ingredients varies considerably from time to time. Thus, a good feed manufacturer will shift his formulas as prices change, in order to give the horseman the most for his money. This is as it should be, for (a) there is no one best ingredient, and (b) if substitutions are made wisely, the price of the feed or mineral can be kept down, and the horseman will continue to get equally good results.

4. *What's on the tag?*—Horsemen should be able to study and interpret what's on the feed or mineral tag. Does the product contain what's needed? Figs. 13-19 and 13-20 show a feed tag taken from a foal ration:

(B R A N D X)

(Net Weight 50 pounds)

GUARANTEED ANALYSIS

Crude Protein, not less than 21.00%
Crude Fat, not less than 2.00%
Crude Fiber, not more than 9.00%
Ash, not more than 9.00%
Added Mineral, not more than 3.00%
Calcium, not less than 1.00%
Phosphorus, not less than .... .75%
Salt, not more than .... .50%
Iodine, not less than 00035%
TDN, not less than 68.00%

Ingredients: Rolled Oats, Dried Whey, Soybean Meal, Cottonseed Meal, Linseed Meal, Dehydrated Alfalfa Meal, Wheat Bran, Wheat Shorts, Wheat Flour, Cane Molasses, Bone Meal, Iodized Salt, Distillers Dried Grains with Solubles, Alfalfa Leaf Meal, Condensed Fish Solubles (Dried), Brewers Dried Yeast, Streptomycin Mycelia Meal, Vitamin A Palmitate with Increased Stability, Fleischman's Irradiated Dry Yeast (Source of Vitamin D-2), d-Alpha-Tocopherol Acetate (Source of Vitamin E), Choline Chloride, Ferrous Carbonate, Niacin, Calcium Pantothenate (Source of d-Pantothenic Acid), Riboflavin Supplement, Copper Oxide, Manganous Oxide, Thiamin, Sulphur, Menadione Sodium Bisulfate (Source of Vitamin K), Calcium Iodate, Folic Acid, Cobalt Carbonate, Vitamin B-12 Supplement, Preserved with Ethoxyquin (1, 2-dihydro-6-ethoxy-2, 2, 4-trimethylquinoline), Anise.

FEEDING DIRECTIONS—SEE OTHER SIDE

Manufactured by
ADAIR MILLING COMPANY
(Address and Phone Number)

Fig. 13-19. Feed tag. (See Fig. 13-20 for reverse side.)

(B R A N D X)

FEEDING DIRECTIONS

	Lb daily/100
	lb weight/foal
Before weaning	½ - 1
After weaning	1¼ - 1½

Plus pasture or hay

Fig. 13-20. Feed tag (reverse side).

An analysis of Fig. 13-19 reveals the following:

a. The "brand" or name of the feed.

b. The net weight.

c. The guaranteed analysis, each stated in percent, in minimum crude protein and crude fat; maximum crude fiber, ash, and minerals; minimum calcium and phosphorus; maximum salt; and minimum iodine and TDN. But guaranteed analysis, within itself, will not suffice. For example, on the basis of chemical composition, soft coal (9.06% crude protein) and coffee grounds (11.23% crude protein) are comparable in protein content to many commonly used grains. Yet, no one would be so foolish as to feed these products to horses.

d. The ingredients, (the constituent material making up the feed) listed in descending order of amounts, by weight. This type of listing aids in making decisions as to the possible quality of the feed. For example, if feather meal, which con-

tains 85% protein by analysis, were listed (which it is not in the above feed), it could be concluded that the horse would obtain little nutritional advantage from this type of ration component. All ingredients listed in the above ration are good, and each one appears to contribute needed nutrients.

e. The name, address, and phone number of the manufacturer.

f. The feeding directions on the reverse side.

Many states have slightly different requirements than indicated by the tag just analyzed. Some require both the minimum and maximum percentage of calcium and salt.

By studying this tag, a knowledgeable user can, readily and easily, see what's in the feed and determine if it will meet the requirements of the horse to which it is to be fed. A similar study and analysis can be made of a mineral tag.

5. *What's the best buy?*—When buying a feed or mineral, the horseman should check price against value received.

● *Best buy in feeds*—One criterion for determining the best buy in horse feeds is the cost per unit protein. (Likewise, one may compare feeds on the basis of cost per unit energy, or on the basis of cost per unit of both protein and energy.)

Example: Two horse feeds are under consideration, which we shall call brand "X" and brand "Y."

Brand X contains 10 percent crude protein and sells at $5 per hundredweight. How much can you afford to pay for brand Y which has 14 percent protein (and other likely plus values that we shall discuss later)?

COMPARATIVE VALUES OF FEEDS—BRANDS X AND Y
(Based on Protein Content Alone)

Brand	Crude protein	Price/cwt	Cost/lb protein
	(%)	($)	(¢)
X	14	7.00	50
Y	10	5.00	50

This shows that if 10 percent crude protein horse feed sells at $5 per cwt, one could afford to pay $7 per cwt for a 14 percent crude protein feed, based on the added value of the protein alone. And that's not all! As a usual thing, if a horse ration is scientifically formulated from the standpoint of quantity of protein, it will also have other plus values, among them:

1. Quality of proteins (the essential amino acids).

2. Energy.

3. Minerals, vitamins, and unidentified factors—which are adequate, without imbalances.

4. Palatability and digestibility. Although horses must like feeds well enough to eat them, it is recognized that—

a. Palatability is, in part, a matter of habit—of being used to a certain feed. For this reason, changes in horse feeds should be made gradually.

b. It does not necessarily follow that everything is good for a horse just because he likes it.

5. The end result—superior performance.

In other words, when a ration is deficient in one category—in protein, for example—you're apt to be short-changed all along the line.

● *Best buy in minerals*—One criterion for determining the best buy in horse minerals is the cost per unit of one or more elements.

Example: Let's assume that the main need is for phosphorus, and that we wish to compare 2 minerals which we shall call brand "X" and brand "Y." Brand X contains 12 percent phosphorus and sells at $8.50 per hundredweight, whereas brand Y contains 10 percent phosphorus and sells at $8.00 per hundredweight. Which is the better buy?

COMPARATIVE VALUE OF MINERALS—BRANDS X AND Y

(Based on Phosphorus Content Alone)

Brand	Phosphorus	Price/cwt	Cost/lb phosphorus
	(%)	($)	(¢)
X	12	8.50	71
Y	10	8.00	80

Hence, brand X is the better buy, even though it costs 50 cents more per hundred.

One other thing is important: As a usual thing, the more scientifically formulated mineral mixes will have plus values in terms of (a) trace mineral (needs and balance), and (b) palatability (horses will eat just the right amount of a good mineral, but they won't overdo it—due to appetizers, rather than needs).

Commercial mineral mixtures costing 60 to 80 cents per pound of phosphorus are not excessively priced. If the average consumption per horse per month of a mineral mix costing $8.50 per hundredweight is 3 pounds, the monthly per head cost will be about 26 cents, or less than 1 cent per horse per day.

RESULTS MORE IMPORTANT THAN COST PER BAG

As is true when buying anything—whether it be a suit of clothes, a dinner, or whatnot—horse feed should be bought on a quality basis, rather than what is cheapest—results are more important than cost per bag. If this were not so, one might well buy and feed many cheap products, including sawdust.

Consideration should be given to meeting the specific needs of the horse, with special attention given to providing adequate quantity and quality proteins, minerals, vitamins, unidentified factors, and palatability.

SWEET FEED

"Sweet feed" refers to a feed to which has been added one or more ingredients that are sweet. Most commonly, it is considerable molasses (approximately 10%); although brown sugar (about 5%) is sometimes used, and occasionally honey.

The horse has a "sweet tooth"; hence, it's not easy to switch him from a sweet feed to what may be a more nutritious ration. Of course, the manufacturer of sweet feed would have it that way. Also, it must be remembered that sweet feeds are a way in which a feed manufacturer may, should he so desire, make poor quality feed ingredients more appetizing.

Further, and most important, not everything is good for a horse just because he likes it. In this respect an analogy may be made to boys and girls. If given a choice between a well balanced diet and candy, most boys and girls will take the latter; yet, few parents or MDs would be so foolish as to say that sweets are good for them. The same can be said relative to many of the "sweet feeds" and concoctions fed to horses.

STATE COMMERCIAL FEED LAWS

Nearly all the states have laws regulating the sale of commercial feeds. These benefit both the horseman and reputable feed manufacturers. In most states, the laws require that every brand of commercial feed sold in the state be licensed, and that the chemical composition be guaranteed.

Samples of each commercial feed are taken each year, and analyzed chemically in the state's laboratory to determine if the manufacturer lived up to his guarantee. Additionally, skilled microscopists examine the sample to ascertain that the ingredients present are the same as those guaranteed. Flagrant violations on the latter point may be prosecuted.

Results of these examinations are generally published, annually, by the state department in charge of such regulatory work. Usually, the publication of the guarantee alongside any "short-changing" is sufficient to cause the manufacturer promptly to rectify the situation, for such public information soon becomes known to both users and competitors.

Additionally, most commercial feed laws stipulate the following:

● *Medicated feed tags and labels*—Medicated feeds (those which contain drug ingredients intended or represented for the cure, mitigation, treatment, or prevention of diseases of animals) must also carry the following information in their labeling: (1) the purpose of the medication; (2) directions for the use of the feed; (3) the names and amounts of all active drug ingredients; (4) a warning or caution statement for a withdrawal period when required for the particular

drug contained in the feed; and (5) warnings against misuse.

● *Vitamin product labels*—When a product is marketed as a vitamin supplement per se, the quantitative guarantees (unit/pound) of vitamins A and D are expressed in USP units; of E in IU; and of other vitamins in milligrams per pound.

● *Mineral product labels*—Some states require that all minerals except salt (NaCl) be quantitatively guaranteed in terms of percentage of the element(s); others require milligrams per pound.

● *Other rules and regulations*—Generally, the following rules and regulations also apply in the different states:

1. The brand or product name must not be misleading.

2. The sliding scale or range (for example, 15% to 18% crude protein) method of expressing guarantees is prohibited.

3. Ingredient names are those adopted by the Association of American Feed Control Officials.

4. The term "dehydrated" may precede the name of any product that has been artificially dried.

5. Urea and ammonium salts of carbonic and phosphoric acids cannot be used in horse feeds.

HOW TO FEED

Feeding horses is both an art and a science. The art is knowing how to feed and how to take care of each horse's individual requirements. The science is meeting the nutritive requirements with the right combination of ingredients.

Amount to Feed

The main qualities desired in horses are trimness, action, spirit, and endurance. These qualities cannot be obtained with large, paunchy stomachs or lack of energy, which may result from excessive use of roughage. Moreover, a healthy condition is desired, but excess fat is to be avoided. The latter is especially true with horses used for racing, where the carrying of any surplus body weight must be avoided.

The quantity of grain and hay required by horses depends primarily upon the following:

1. The individuality—horses vary in keeping qualities, just as people do. Some horses simply utilize their feed more efficiently than others. A hard keeper will require considerably more feed than an easy keeper when doing the same amount of work.

2. The age, size, and condition of the animal.

3. The kind, severity, regularity, amount, and speed of work performed. With greater speed, the horse requires proportionately greater energy; hence, considerably more concentrate is required when performing work at a trot than at a walk.

4. The weather; for example, under ideal October weather conditions in Missouri, a horse may require 14 lb of 60 percent TDN feed daily, whereas in the same area, the same horse may require 16 lb daily of the same feed in July and August, and 20 lb in the winter.

5. Kind, quality, and amount of feed.

6. System of management.

7. Health, condition, and temperament of the animal.

When given all the feed that they will consume, mature horses will generally eat an amount equivalent to about 2.5 percent of their body weight. Growing foals and lactating mares eat more heartily— they'll consume up to 3 percent of their body weight.

Because the horse has a rather limited digestive capacity, the amount of concentrates must be increased and the roughages decreased when the energy needs rise with the greater amount, severity, or speed of work. The following are general guides for the daily ration of horses under usual conditions:

1. *For horses at light work* (1 to 3 hours per day of riding or driving), allow ⅖ to ½ lb of grain and 1¼ to 1½ lb of hay per day per 100 lb of liveweight.

2. *For horses at medium work* (3 to 5 hours per day of riding or driving), allow ¾ to 1 lb of grain to 1 to 1¼ lb of hay per 100 lb of liveweight.

3. *For horses at hard work* (5 to 8 hours per day of riding or driving), allow about 1¼ to 1⅓ lb of grain and 1 to 1¼ lb of hay per 100 lb of liveweight.

The recommended feed allowances on the basis of animal weight are equally applicable to equines of all sizes, including ponies and donkeys; simply vary as necessary according to the work performed and the individuality of the animal.

As will be noted from these recommendations, the total allowance of concentrates and hay should be within the range of 2.0 to 2.5 pounds daily per 100 pounds of liveweight. No grain should be left from one feeding to the next, and all edible forage should be cleaned up at the end of each day.

About 6 to 12 lb of grain daily is an average grain ration for a light horse at medium or light work. Racehorses in training usually consume 10 to 16 lb of grain per day—the exact amount varying with the individual requirements and the amount of work. The hay allowance averages about 1 to 1¼ lb daily per 100 lb liveweight, but it is restricted as the grain allowance is increased. Light feeders should not be overworked.

It is to be emphasized that the quantities of feeds recommended above are intended as guides only. The feeder will increase the allowance, especially the concentrates, when the horse is too thin, and decrease the feed when the horse is too fat.

The regular practice of turning horses to pasture at night, on idle days, and in off-work seasons is good for the health and well-being of the animals and decreases the quantity of grain and hay required. If the horse must be confined to the stall on idle days, the grain ration should be reduced by 50 percent in order to avoid azoturia or other digestive disturbances. When idle, it is also advisable to add some wheat bran to the ration. A mixture of ⅔ grain and ⅓ bran is quite satisfactory. Many good horsemen regularly give a feeding of bran, either dry or as a wet mash, on Saturday night.

OVERFEEDING

Overfeeding may result in two consequences: If done suddenly, it may cause founder (laminitis); if prolonged, it will likely result in obesity (too fat). Both are bad.

Starting Horses on Feed

Horses must be accustomed to changes in feed gradually. In general, they may be given as much nonlegume roughage as they will consume. But they must be accustomed gradually to high-quality legumes, which may be very laxative. This can be done by slowly replacing the nonlegume roughage with greater quantities of legumes. Also, as the grain ration is increased, the roughage is decreased.

Starting horses on grain requires care and good judgment. Usually it is advisable first to accustom them to a bulky type of ration; a starting ration with considerable rolled oats is excellent for this purpose.

The keenness of the appetite and the consistency of the droppings are an excellent index of a horse's capacity to take more feed. In all instances, scouring should be avoided.

Frequency, Order, and Regularity of Feeding

The grain ration usually is divided into 3 equal feeds given morning, noon, and night. Because a digestive tract distended with hay is a hindrance in hard work, most of the hay should be fed at night. The common practice is to feed ¼ of the daily hay allowance at each of the morning and noon feedings and the remaining ½ at night when the animals have plenty of time to eat leisurely.

Usually the grain ration is fed first and then the roughage. This way, the animals can eat the bulky roughages more leisurely.

Horses learn to anticipate their feed. Accordingly, they should be fed at the same time each day. During warm weather, they will eat better if the feeding hours are early and late, in the cool of the day.

Avoid Sudden Changes

Sudden changes in diet should be avoided, especially when changing from a less concentrated ration to a more concentrated one. If this rule of feeding is ignored, horses have digestive disturbances and go "off feed." When ingredients are added or omitted, the change should be made gradually. Likewise, caution should be exercised in turning horses to pasture on in transferring them to more lush grazing.

Sometimes horsemen experience difficulty in switching horses from an overly sweet or highly flavored feed to a more nutritious ration. But the end results usually justify the effort.

Attention to Details Pays

The successful horseman pays great attention to details. In addition to maintaining the health and comfort of animals, he should also give consideration to their individual likes and temperaments.

It is important to avoid excessive exercise to the point of fatigue and undue stress. Also, rough treatment, excitement, and noise usually result in nervousness and inefficient use of feed.

Bolting Feed

Horses that eat too rapidly are said to be bolting their feed. It can be lessened by spreading the concentrate thinly over the bottom of a large grain box, so that the horse cannot get a large mouthful; or by placing in the grain box a few smooth stones about the size of baseballs, so that the horse has to work to get feed.

Eating Bedding

Sometimes gluttonous animals eat their bedding. This is undesirable because (1) most bedding materials are low in nutritional value, and (2) feces soiled bedding adds to the parasite problem. The problem can be alleviated by muzzling the horse.

Self-Feeding

A few caretakers do self-feed high-energy rations, but, sooner or later, those who do usually founder a valuable horse. Except for the use of reasonably hard salt-protein blocks, salt-freed mixes in meal form (never in pellet form), or high-roughage rations, the self-feeding of horses is not recommended.

General Feeding Rules

In addition to the guides already mentioned, observance of the following general rules will help avoid some of the common difficulties:

1. Know the approximate weight and age of each animal.

2. Never feed moldy, musty, dusty, or frozen feed.

3. Inspect the feed box at frequent intervals; by so doing it is easy to detect when a horse goes off his feed.

4. Keep the feed and water containers clean.

5. Make certain that the horse's teeth are sound.

6. Don't feed concentrates to a hot horse; and allow time for digestion following feeding before working him.

7. Feed the horse as an individual—learn the peculiarities and desires of each animal; each one is different, just as people are different.

8. See that the horse gets adequate exercise. It improves its appetite, digestion, and overall well-being.

9. Do not feed from your hand. This can lead to "nibbling."

10. A horse that has been fitted for show or sale should be let down in condition gradually. Experienced horsemen accomplish this difficult task and yet retain strong vigorous animals by (a) cutting down gradually on the feed allowance, and (b) increasing the exercise.

11. Know the signs of a well-fed, healthy horse, any departure from which constitutes a warning signal.

FEEDING PLEASURE HORSES

Keeping pleasure horses—horses used for recreation and sport—in peak condition makes for greater satisfaction when they are used.

It is difficult to feed pleasure horses properly because their use is often irregular. Sometimes they're used moderately; at other times they're idle; at still other times they're worked hard over the weekend or on a trail ride.

Most horses used for pleasure are worked lightly, perhaps 1 to 3 hours of riding per day. Others are worked medium hard, as when ridden 3 to 5 hours per day. Still others are worked very hard, as when raced or when ridden 5 to 8 hours per day. The recommended daily feed allowance per 100 pounds body weight of pleasure horses in light, medium, and hard use follows:

Lb Daily/100 Lb Weight of Horse	Light Use	Medium Use	Hard Use
Hay	1¼ - 1½	1 - 1¼	1 - 1¼
Grain	²/₅ - ½	¾ - 1	1¼ - 1⅓

As shown, the roughage content of the ration decreases and the concentrate content increases as the amount of work increases. This is because the digestibility and the efficiency of conversion are greater for high-energy concentrates than for roughages.

Of course, horses differ in temperament and in ease of keeping. Also, no two horses will perform the same amount of work with an equal expenditure of energy, and no two horsemen will get the same amount of work out of the same horse. So, the feed allowance should be increased if the horse fails to maintain condition, and it should be decreased if the animal becomes too fat.

In season, pasture may replace hay, all or in part, according to the quality of the pasture. But the concentrate allowance of the working horse should remain about the same on pasture as in the stable or dry corral. There is a tendency of the pastured working horse to sweat and tire more easily (be "soft"), probably due to the high water content of green forage.

In addition to forage and grain, pleasure horses should have access to salt and a suitable mineral mix, free choice. The mineral requirements of the working horse differ from the idle horse mainly in the salt requirements, due to the loss of salt in perspiration.

The vitamin requirements of working horses are approximately the same as those of idle horses, except for the increase in the B complex requirements due to the greater carbohydrate metabolism of the working horse.

FEEDING HORSES IN TRAINING

Horses in heavy training for specific purposes—such as training for racing, cutting, roping, jumping, or hunting—have a higher nutritional requirement than most pleasure horses. The younger the animal in training, the higher the level of nutrition needed in order to develop and maintain sound legs and build a strong frame and body. Therefore, the level of work, the temperament of the individual, and the age of the horse determine the nutritional needs.

Horses in training will eat about 1½ lb of grain and 1 lb of hay per 100 lb liveweight.

FEEDING RACEHORSES

It is recognized that some unsoundnesses may be inherited, others may be due to accident and injury, and still others may be due to subjecting horses to stress and strain far beyond the capability of even the best structure and tissue. However, nutritional deficiencies appear to be the major cause of unsoundnesses in racehorses.

Racehorses are equine athletes whose nutritive requirements are the most exacting, but the most poorly met, of all animals. This shocking statement is true because racehorses are commonly handled as follows:

1. Started in training very shortly past 18 months of age, which is comparable to an adolescent boy or girl doing sweatshop labor.

2. Moved from track to track under all sorts of conditions.

3. Trained the year around, raced innumerable times each year, and forced to run when fatigued.

4. Outdoors only a short time each day—usually before sunup, with the result that the sun's rays have little chance to produce vitamin D from the cholesterol in the skin.

5. Without opportunity for even a few mouthfuls of grass—a rich, natural source of the B vitamins and unidentified factors.

6. Fed oats, grass hay, and possibly bran—produced in unknown areas, and on soils of unknown composition. Such an oats-grass hay-bran ration is almost always deficient in vitamins A and D and the B vitamins, and lopsided and low in calcium and phosphorus.

7. Given a potion of some concoction of questionable value—if not downright harmful.

By contrast, human athletes—college football teams and participants in the Olympics, for example—are usually required to eat at a special training table, supervised by nutrition experts. They are fed the best diet that science can formulate and technology can prepare. It's high in protein, rich in readily available energy, and fortified and balanced in vitamins and minerals.

It's small wonder, therefore, that so many equine athletes go unsound, whereas most human athletes compete year after year until overtaken by age.

Indeed, high strung and highly stressed, racehorses need special rations just as human athletes do—and for the same reasons; and, the younger the age, the more acute the need. This calls for rations high in protein, rich in readily available energy, fortified with vitamins, minerals, and unidentified factors—and with all nutrients in proper balance.

A racehorse is asked to develop a large amount of horsepower in a period of one to three minutes. The oxidations that occur in a racehorse's body are at a higher pitch than in an idle or little-worked horse, and, therefore, more vitamins are required.

Also, racehorses are the prima donnas of the equine world; most of them are temperamental, and no two of them can be fed alike. They vary in rapidity of eating, in the quantity of feed that they will consume, in the proportion of concentrate to roughage that they will take, and in response to different caretakers. Thus, for best results, they must be fed as individuals.

During the racing season, the hay of a racehorse should be limited to 7 or 8 pounds, whereas the concentrate allowance may range up to 16 pounds. Heavy roughage eaters may have to be muzzled, to keep them from eating their bedding. A bran mash is commonly fed once a week.

FEEDING BROODMARES

Regular and normal reproduction is the basis for profit on any horse breeding establishment. However, only 40 to 60 percent of mares bred produce foals. There are many causes of reproductive failure, but inadequate nutrition is a major one.

Broodmares should be kept in thrifty condition, but they should not be allowed to become too fat nor too thin. Proper feeding begins with conditioning them prior to the breeding season by providing adequate and proper feed and the right amount of exercise.

Gestating mares need a ration that will meet their own body needs plus (1) the needs of the fetus, or (2) furnishing the nutrients required for milk production. If work is also being performed, additional energy feeds must be provided. Moreover, for the young, growing mare additional proteins, minerals, and vitamins, above the ordinary requirements, must be provided; otherwise, the fetus will not develop normally, or milk will be produced at the expense of the tissues of the dam. Also, protein deficiency may affect undesirably the fertility of the mare.

Most of the growth of the fetus occurs during the last third of pregnancy, thus the reproductive requirements—especially the requirements for proteins, minerals, and vitamins—are greatest during this period.

As with the females of all species, the nutritive requirements for milk production in the mare are much more rigorous than the pregnancy requirements. It is estimated that, 2 months following foaling, mares of mature weights of 600, 800, 1,000, and 1,200 pounds may produce 36, 42, 44, and 49 pounds of milk daily. Thus, it can be appreciated that a mare's feed requirements during the suckling period are not far different from those of a high-producing dairy cow. In general, it is important that the ration of the gestating-lactating mare supply sufficient energy, protein, calcium and phosphorus; and vitamins A and D (the D being provided through the feed if the animal is not exposed to sunlight), and riboflavin.

The correct feeding of a broodmare that is worked is often simpler than the feeding of an idle one, for the condition of the animal can be regulated more carefully under working conditions. In addition to a ration that will meet the maintenance and work requirements largely through high-energy feeds, the working broodmare needs ample protein, calcium, and phosphorus with which to take care of the growth of the fetus and/or milk production.

The broodmare should be fed and watered with care immediately before and after foaling. For the first 24 hours after parturition, she may have a little hay and a limited amount of water from which the chill has been taken. A light feed of bran or a wet bran

mash is suitable for the first feed and the following meal may consist of oats or a mixture of oats and bran. A reasonably generous allowance of good-quality hay is permissible after the first day. If confined to the stable, as may be necessary in inclement weather, the mare should be kept on a limited and light grain and hay ration for about 10 days after foaling. Feeding too much grain at this time is likely to produce digestive disturbances in the mare; and even more hazardous, it may produce too much milk, which may cause indigestion in the foal. If weather conditions are favorable and it is possible to allow the mare to foal on a clean, lush pasture, she will regulate her own feed needs most admirably.

In comparison with geldings or unbred mares, the following differences in feeding gestating-lactating broodmares should be observed:

1. A greater quantity of feed is necessary—usually about 20 to 50 percent more—the highest requirement being during lactation.

2. Dusty or moldy feed and frozen silage should be avoided in feeding all horses, but especially in feeding the broodmare, for such feed may produce complications and possible abortion.

3. More proteins are necessary for the broodmare.

4. More attention must be given to supplying the necessary minerals and vitamins.

5. The bowels should be carefully regulated through providing regular exercise and feeding such laxative feeds as bran, linseed meal, and alfalfa hay.

6. A few days before and after foaling, the ration should be (a) decreased, and (b) lightened by using wheat bran.

7. Regular and ample exercise is a necessary adjunct to proper feeding of the broodmare.

FEEDING STALLIONS

The ration exerts a powerful effect on sperm production and semen quality. In recognition of this fact, the usual advice given worried stallion owners when the stallion is not a sure breeder is to, "reduce the ration and increase the exercise."

In all too many instances, little thought is given to the feeding and caring for the stallion, other than during the breeding season. The program throughout the entire year should be such as to keep the stallion in a vigorous, thrifty condition at all times. Immediately before the breeding season, the feed might very well be increased in quantity so that the stallion will gain in weight. The quantity of grain fed will vary with the individual temperament and feeding ability of the stallion, the work and exercise provided, services allowed, available pastures, and quality of roughage. Usually this will be between ¾ and 1½ pounds daily of the grain mixture per 100 pounds

weight, together with a quantity of hay within the same range.

During the breeding season, the stallion's ration should contain more protein and additional minerals and vitamins than are given in rations fed work horses or stallions not in service. During the balance of the year (when not in service), the stallion may be provided a ration like that of other horses similarly handled. In season, pastures are an excellent source of both nutrients and exercise.

In addition to the grain and roughage, there should be free access to a mineral supplement and salt. These should be placed in separate compartments of a suitable box. During the winter months or when little work or exercise is provided, the stallion should receive a succulent feed, such as carrots. Also, laxative feeds, such as wheat bran or linseed meal, should be supplied at these times. Plenty of fresh, clean water should be provided at all times. Drugs or stock tonics should not be fed in an attempt to increase virility.

Overfitted, heavy stallions should be regarded with suspicion, for they may be uncertain breeders. On the other hand, a poor, thin, run-down condition is also to be avoided.

FEEDING FOALS

Growth is the very foundation of horse production. This is so because horses cannot perform properly or possess the necessary speed and endurance if their growth has been stunted or their skeletons have been injured by inadequate rations during early age. Naturally, these requirements become increasingly acute when horses are forced for early use, such as the training and racing of the two-year-old. Also, unless foals are rather liberally fed when young, they never attain the much desired body form, which is so important where young stock is sold or shown.

As with all young mammals, milk from the dam gives the foal a good start in life. Within 30 minutes to 2 hours after birth, the foal should be up on its feet and getting the colostrum.

But milk is not the perfect food, as once claimed. It is deficient in iron and copper, with the result that suckling young may suffer from anemia. This nutritional deficiency may be prevented, and increased growth, durability, and soundness may be obtained, by feeding foals separate from their dams; either (1) by tying the mare while the foal eats, or (2) by providing a creep for the foals.

The need for a foal feeding program, starting early in life, is due to the decline in mare's milk in both quantity and nutrients following foaling. The Michigan Station[23] reported that the crude protein

---

[23]Ullrey, D. E., et al., *Journal of Animal Science*, Vol. 25, No. 1, February 1966, pp. 217-222.

Fig. 13-21. Foal creep at Saxony Farm, Versailles, Kentucky. With this arrangement, the foal can be fed separately from the dam. (Photo by J. Noye, Versailles, Ky.; courtesy, Dr. W. C. Kaufman, DVM, Claiborne Farm, Lexington, Ky.)

content of the milk dropped from 19.1% within 30 minutes after birth of the foal, to 3.8% 12 hours later, and 2.2% 2 months later. Also, the gross energy, total solids, ash, magnesium, and sodim in mare's milk were relatively high at birth, but dropped rather abruptly 12 hours later, then declined more slowly (see Fig. 13-22).

When the foal is between 10 days and 3 weeks of age, it will begin to nibble on grain and hay. In order to promote thrift and early development and to avoid setback at weaning time, it is important to encourage the foal to eat supplementary feed as early as possible. For this purpose, a low-built grain box should be provided especially for the foal; or, if on pasture, the foal may be creep fed. The choice between individual feeding and creep feeding may be left to the horseman; the important thing is that foals receive supplemental feed.

A creep is an enclosure for feeding purposes, made accessible to the foal(s), but through which the dam cannot pass. For best results, the creep should be built at a spot where the mares are inclined to loiter. The ideal location is on high ground, well drained, in the shade, and near the place of watering. Keeping the salt supply nearby will be helpful in holding mares near the creep.

It is important that foals be started on feed carefully, and at an early age. At first only a small amount of feed should be placed in the trough each day, any surplus being removed and given to other horses. In this manner, the feed will be kept clean and fresh, and the foals will not be consuming any moldy or sour feed.

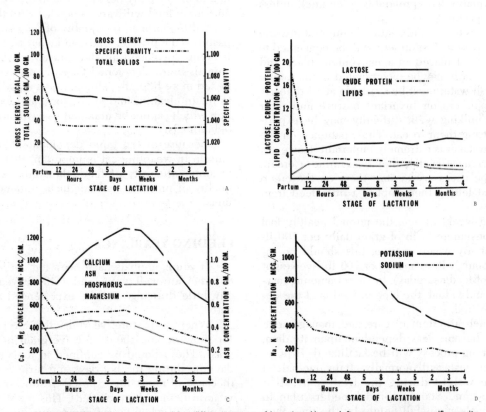

Fig. 13-22. Changes in mare's milk at different stages of lactation: *Upper left*—gross energy, specific gravity, and total solids; *Upper right*—lactose, crude protein, and lipids; *Lower left*—calcium, ash, phosphorus, and magnesium; and *Lower right*—potassium and sodium. (Courtesy, D. E. Ullrey, Dept. of Animal Husbandry, Michigan State University)

Rolled oats and wheat bran, to which a little brown sugar has been added, is especially palatable as a starting ration.

Table 13-15 gives the formulation of an excellent foal ration, which may be either individually fed or creep fed.

TABLE 13-15
FOAL RATION

Ingredients	Percent	Amount in 500-Lb Mix
	(%)	(lb)
Corn (flaked)	37.4	187.0
Soybean meal (41%)	33.0	165.0
Oats (rolled)	23.0	115.0
Brewers' yeast	0.5	2.5
Molasses	3.0	15.0
Dicalcium phosphate	1.0	5.0
Limestone	1.0	5.0
Salt (trace mineralized)	1.0	5.0
Vitamins A and D	0.1	0.5
Total	100.0	500.0

Because of the difficulty in formulating and home mixing a foal ration, the purchase of a good commercial feed usually represents a wise investment.

In addition to its grain ration, the foal should be given good quality hay (preferably a legume), unless it is on good pasture.

Free access to salt and a suitable mineral mixture should be provided. The mineral will be consumed to best advantage if placed in a convenient place and under shelter; or it may be incorporated in the ration. Plenty of fresh water must be available at all times.

When foals are on luxuriant pasture and their mothers are milking well, difficulty may be experienced in getting them to eat. Thus, patience on the part of the caretaker is extremely important. However, foals are curious. Usually, they'll examine a creep. But it may be necessary to start them on the creep ration by first letting them nibble a little feed from the hand.

At 4 to 5 weeks of age, the normal healthy foal should be consuming ½ lb of grain daily per 100 lb of liveweight. By weaning time, this should be increased to about ¾ lb or more per 100 lb liveweight (or 6 to 8 lb of feed/head/day), the exact amount varying with the individual, the type of feed, and the development desired.

Under such a system of care and management, the foal will become less dependent upon its dam, and the weaning process will be facilitated. If properly cared for, foals will normally attain one-half of their mature weight during the first year. Most Thoroughbred and Standardbred breeders plan to have the animals attain full height by the time they are two years of age. However, such results require liberal feeding from the beginning.

It is well recognized that the forced development of race, show, and sale horses must be done expertly if the animals are to remain durable and sound. This calls for particular emphasis on the kind of ration, feed allowance, and exercise.

FEEDING WEANLINGS

The most critical period in the entire life of a horse is that interval from weaning time (about six months of age) until one year of age. Foals suckling their dams and receiving no grain may develop very satisfactorily up to weaning time. However, lack of preparation prior to weaning and neglect following the separation from the dam may prevent the animal from gaining proper size and shape. The primary objective in the breeding of horses is the economical production of a well-developed, sound individual at maturity. To achieve this result requires good care and management of weanlings.

No great setback or disturbances will be encountered at weaning time provided that the foals have developed a certain independence from proper grain feedings during the suckling period. Generally, weanlings should receive 1 to 1½ lb of grain and 1½ to 2 lb of hay daily per each 100 lb of liveweight. The amount of feed will vary somewhat with the individuality of the animal, the quality of roughage, available pastures, the price of feeds, and whether the weanling is being developed for show, race, or sale. Naturally, animals being developed for early use or sale should be fed more liberally, although it is equally important to retain clean, sound joints, legs, and feet—a condition which cannot be obtained so easily in heavily fitted animals.

Because of the rapid development of bone and muscle in weanlings, it is important that, in addition to ample quantity of feed, the ration also provide quality of proteins, and adequate minerals and vitamins.

FEEDING YEARLINGS

If young animals have been fed and cared for so that they are well grown and thrifty as yearlings, usually little difficulty will be experienced at any later date.

When on pasture, yearlings that are being grown for show or sale should receive grain in addition to grass. They should be confined to their stalls in the daytime during the hot days and turned out at night (because of not being exposed to sunshine, adequate vitamin D must be provided). This point needs to be emphasized when forced development is desired; for, good as pastures may be, they are roughages rather than concentrates.

Fig. 13-23. Young stock wintering in an open shed and eating hay from a rack along the wall. (Photo by John C. Wyatt, Lexington, Ky.; courtesy, Lee Eaton, Lexington, Ky.)

The winter feeding program for the rising 2-year-olds should be such as to produce plenty of bone and muscle rather than fat. From ½ to 1 lb of grain and 1 to 1½ lb of hay should be fed for each 100 lb of liveweight. The quantity will vary with the quality of the roughage, the individuality of the animal, and the use for which the animal is produced. In producing for sale, more liberal feeding may be economical. Access to salt and to a mineral mixture should be provided at all times; or the minerals should be incorporated in the ration. An abundance of fresh, pure water must be available.

FEEDING TWO- AND THREE-YEAR-OLDS

Except for the fact that the two- and three-year-olds will be larger, and, therefore, will require more feed, a description of their proper care and management would be merely a repetition of the principles that have already been discussed for the yearling.

With the two-year-old that is to be raced, however, the care and feeding at this time become matters of extreme importance. Once the young horse is placed in training, the ration should be adequate enough to allow for continued development and to provide necessary maintenance and additional energy for work. This means that special attention must be given to providing adequate proteins, minerals, and vitamins in the ration. Overexertion must be avoided, the animal must be well groomed, and the feet must be cared for properly. In brief, every precaution must be taken if the animal is to remain sound—a most difficult task when animals are raced at an early age, even though the right genetic makeup and the proper environment are present.

FITTING FOR SHOW AND SALE

Each year, many horses are fitted for shows or sales. In both cases, a fattening process is involved, but exercise is doubly essential.

For horses that are being fitted for shows, the conditioning process is also a matter of hardening, and the horses are used daily in harness or under saddle. Regardless of whether a sale or a show is the major objective, fleshing should be obtained without sacrificing action or soundness or without causing filling of the legs and hocks.

In fattening horses, the animals should be brought to full feed rather gradually, until the ration reaches a maximum of about 2 lb of grain daily for each 100 lb of liveweight. When on full feed, horses make surprising gains. Daily weight gains of 4 to 5 lb are not uncommon. Such animals soon become fat, sleek, and attractive. This is probably the basis for the statement that "fat will cover up a multitude of sins in a horse."

Although exercise is desirable from the standpoint of keeping the animals sound, it is estimated that such activity decreases the daily rate of gains by as much as 20 percent. Because of the greater cost of gains and the expense involved in bringing about forced exercise, most feeders of sale horses limit the exercise to that obtained naturally from running in a paddock.

In comparison with finishing cattle or sheep, there is more risk in fattening horses. Heavily fed horses kept in idleness are likely to become blemished and injured through playfulness, and there are more sicknesses among liberally fed horses than in other classes of stock handled in a similar manner.

In fitting show horses, the finish must remain firm and hard, the action superb, and the soundness unquestioned. Thus, they must be carefully fed, groomed, and exercised to bring them to proper bloom.

Horsemen who fit and sell yearlings or younger animals may feed a palatable milk replacer or commercial feed to advantage.

SOIL ANALYSIS

For the horseman who produces his own hay, a soil analysis can be very helpful; for example, (1) the phosphorus content of soils affects plant composition, (2) soils high in molybdenum and selenium affect the composition of the feeds produced, (3) iodine deficiency areas are important in horse nutrition, and (4) other similar soil-plant-animal relationships should be considered.

No analysis is any better than the sample taken. So, make sure that you get a representative sample of soil. Ask your county agent (farm advisor) how to take the samples and where to send them. Some colleges of agriculture make soil analyses at nominal cost.

PICA—WOOD CHEWING

Horses, particularly those confined to stalls or lots, sometimes consume such materials as dirt, hair, bones, or feces (the scientific term for the latter is "coprophagy"). Such depraved appetites are known as "pica." This condition is usually caused by one or more of the following conditions:

1. *Boredom*, because they have nothing to do. The more limited the exercise, and the more quickly they consume their feed, the greater the unoccupied time available and the consequent boredom.

By contrast, little *Eohippus* (the dawn horse of 58 million years ago) was a denizen of the swamp. Later, through evolution, he became a creature of the prairies. Although his natural habitat shifted during this long predomestication period, until man confined him he gleaned the feeds provided by nature. Inevitably, this occupied his time and provided exercise.

2. *Nutritional inadequacies*, which may be due to (a) a deficiency of one or more nutrients, (b) an imbalance between certain nutrients, or (c) objection to the physical form of the ration—for example, it may be ground too finely.

3. *Psychological stress and habit*, which contribute to the behavior of horses, and which have been accentuated by the unnatural environment to which man has subjected them.

Whatever the reason(s) for pica, the suspected causative factor(s) should first be rectified. When and where needed, the exercise should be stepped up; the eating time should be prolonged, and the interval between feedings shortened; nutritional deficiencies, imbalances, and physical form of ration should be corrected; and stress should be minimized. Even after these conditions have been rectified, it may be disconcerting to find that wood chewing, and perhaps various other forms of pica, persist among certain horses—perhaps due to habit. Thus, in the final analysis, there is only one foolproof way in which to prevent wood chewing; namely, to have no wood on which they can chew—to use metal, or other similar materials, for fences and barns. Of course, this isn't always practical. So, wood chewing can be lessened, although it cannot be entirely prevented, through one or more of the following management practices:

1. Stepping up the exercise.
2. Feeding three times a day, rather than twice a day, even though the total daily feed allowance remains the same.
3. Spreading out the feed in a larger feed container, and/or placing a few large stones about the size of a baseball in the feed container, thereby making the horse work harder and longer to obtain his feed.
4. Providing 2 to 4 pounds of straw or coarse grass hay per animals per day, thereby giving the horse something to nibble on during his spare time.

NUTRITIONAL DISEASES AND AILMENTS

Nutritional deficiencies may be brought about either by (1) too little feed, or (2) rations that are too low in one or more nutrients. Also, forced production (such as racing two-year-olds) and the feeding of forages and grains which are often produced on leached or depleted soils have created many problems in nutrition. This condition has been further aggravated through the increased confinement of horses, many animals being confined to stalls or lots all or a large part of the year. Under these unnatural conditions, nutritional diseases and ailments have become increasingly common.

Although the cause, prevention, and treatment of most equine nutritional diseases and ailments are known, they continue to plague the horse industry simply because the available knowledge is not put into practice. Moreover, those widespread nutritional deficiencies which are not of sufficient proportions to produce clear-cut deficiency symptoms cause even greater economic losses because they go unnoticed and unrectified.

Unfortunately, there are no warning signals to tell a caretaker when a horse is not getting enough of a certain nutrient. A continuing inadequate supply of any one of several nutrients can produce illness which is very hard to diagnose until it becomes severe, at which time it is difficult and expensive—if not too late—to treat. The important thing, therefore, is to ensure against such deficiencies occurring. But horsemen should not shower a horse with mistaken kindness through using shotgun-type mineral and vitamin preparations. Instead, the quantity of each nutrient should be based on available scientific knowledge.

Table 13-16 contains a summary of the important nutritional diseases and ailments affecting horses. (See page 264.)

SOME COMMON QUESTIONS

Here are some of the most common asked questions by horsemen, along with the answers of the author.

Q. *Do you recommend the prolonged and continuous feeding of antibiotics to mature horses?*

A. No. Unless there is a low disease level, there is no evidence to warrant the continuous feeding of antibiotics to older horses. Such practice may even be harmful. Also, antibiotics are not approved by the Food and Drug Administration for continuous feeding to mature horses.

Q. *If the ration contains minerals, is it also necessary to self-feed them?*

A. Yes, people and horses have many things in common; among them, some individuals require more

Fig. 13-24. Horse with colic. This digestive disturbance may be caused by feed to which the animal is unaccustomed, sudden changes in the ration, rapid eating, imperfectly cured or damaged feeds, the horse's being worked too soon or too hard after feeding, or gorging on water—especially when warm. (Courtesy, Pitman-Moore, Indianapolis, Ind.)

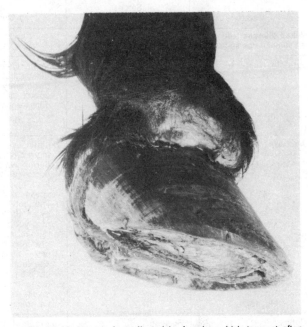

Fig. 13-26. Horse's foot affected by founder, which is most often caused by overeating. (Courtesy, USDA)

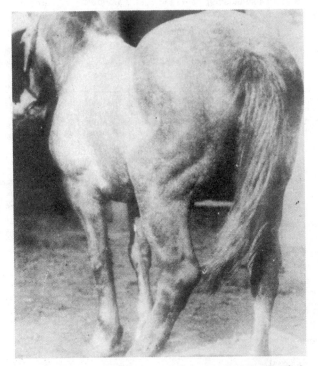

Fig. 13-25. Horse with azoturia, which is generally attributed to faulty metabolism. Prevention lies in restricting the ration and providing daily exercise when the animal is not at work. (Courtesy, Pitman-Moore, Indianapolis, Ind.)

Fig. 13-27. Osteomalacia of the facial bones in a Hackney. This deficiency disease in mature horses may be caused by (1) a lack of vitamin D, (2) a lack of calcium or phosphorus, or (3) an incorrect ratio of calcium to phosphorus. (Courtesy, College of Veterinary Medicine, University of Illinois)

TABLE 13-16

Disease	Species Affected	Cause	Symptoms (and age or group most affected)	Distribution and Losses Caused by
Alkali disease (see selenium poisoning)				
Anemia, nutritional	All warmblooded animals, and man.	Commonly an iron deficiency, but it may be a deficiency of copper, cobalt, or certain vitamins—especially B12.	Loss of appetite, poor performance, progressive emaciation and death. Most prevalent in suckling young.	Worldwide. Losses consist of retarded growth and deaths.
Azoturia (hemoglobinuria, Monday morning disease, blackwater) Fig. 13-28.	Horses.	Sudden exercise, following a day or two of rest during which time the horse has been on full feed, resulting in partial spasm or "tie-up." Thought to be caused by an abnormal amount of glycogen stored in the muscle. As the glycogen breaks down, lactic acid is formed. The lactic acid builds up in the muscle, causing a myocitis which manifests itself as partial spasm, or "tie-up."	Profuse sweating, abdominal distress, wine-colored urine, stiff gait, reluctance to move, and lameness. Finally, animal assumes a sitting position, and eventually falls prostrate on the side.	Worldwide, but the disease is seldom seen in horses at pasture and rarely in horses at constant work.
Colic Fig. 13-29.	Horses.	Improper feeding, working, or watering.	Excruciating pain; and, depending on the type of colic, other symptoms are: distended abdomen, increased intestinal rumbling, violent rolling and kicking, profuse sweating, constipation, and refusal of feed and water.	Worldwide.
Fluorine poisoning (fluorosis)	All farm animals, fish, poultry, and man.	Ingesting excessive quantities of fluorine through either the feed, air, water, or a combination of these.	Abnormal teeth (especially mottled enamel and excessive wear); abnormal bones (bones become thickened, rough, and soft); stiffness of joints; loss of appetite; emaciation; reduction in milk flow; diarrhea; and salt hunger.	The water in parts of Arkansas, California, South Carolina, and Texas has been reported to contain excess fluoride. Occasionally, throughout the U.S., high-fluorine phosphates are used in mineral mixtures. Areas near certain industries which heat earthy materials or burn high-fluoride coal may be a problem.
Founder (laminitis) Fig. 13-30.	Horses. Cattle. Sheep. Goats.	Overeating, (grain; or lush legume or grass—known as "grass founder"), overdrinking, or from inflammation of the uterus following parturition. Also intestinal inflammation. Too rapid change in the ration.	Extreme pain, fever (103° to 106° F), and reluctance to move. If neglected, chronic laminitis will develop, resulting in a dropping of the hoof soles and a turning up of the toe walls.	Worldwide. Actual death losses from founder are not very great, but usefulness may be affected.
Goiter (see Iodine deficiency)				
Heaves Fig. 13-31.	Horses. Mules.	Exact cause unknown, but it is known that the condition is often associated with the feeding of damaged, dusty, or moldy hay. It often follows severe respiratory infection such as strangles. Probably an allergy.	Difficulty in forcing air out of the lungs, resulting in a jerking of flanks (double flank action) and coughing. The nostrils are often slightly dilated and there is a nasal discharge.	Worldwide. Losses are negligible.

Treatment	Prevention	Remarks
Provide dietary sources of the nutrient or nutrients the deficiency of which is known to cause the condition.	Supply dietary sources of iron, copper, cobalt, and certain vitamins—especially B_{12}. Keep suckling animals confined to a minimum and provide supplemental feeds at an early age.	Anemia is a condition in which the blood is either deficient in quality of quantity (a deficient quality refers to a deficiency in hemoglobin and/or red cells). Levels of iron in most feeds believed to be ample, since most feeds contain 40 to 400 mg/lb.
Absolute rest and quiet. While awaiting the veterinarian, apply heated cloths or blankets, or hot-water bottles to the swollen and hardened muscles. The veterinarian should determine treatment. In mild cases, he may use a tranquilizer or sedative. In severe cases, he may use muscle relaxers or sodium bicarbonate in solution to readjust the acid balance in the muscles.	Restrict the ration and provide daily exercise when the animal is idle. Give a wet bran mash the evening before an idle day or turn the idle horses to pasture. Some believe that a diuretic (a drug which will increase the flow or urine) will prevent the tie-up syndrome. This is a common treatment of racehorses. Others feel that increased B vitamins will prevent the lactic acid buildup.	The chances of recovery are good for horses that remain standing, are not forced to move after the signs are noticed, and whose pulse returns to normal within 24 hours.
Call a veterinarian. To avoid danger of inflicting self-injury, (1) place the animal in a large, well-bedded stable, or (2) take it for a slow walk. Depending on diagnosis, veterinarian may use one or more of following: sedatives; laxatives, such as mineral oil; drugs; or surgery.	Proper feeding, working, watering. Control parasites.	Colic is also a symptom of abdominal pain that can be caused by a number of different conditions. For example, bloodworms cause a colic due to damage in the wall of blood vessels. This results in poor circulation to the intestine.
Discontinue the use of feeds, water, or minerals containing excessive fluoride. Any damage may be permanent, but animals which have not developed severe symptoms may be helped to some extent if sources of excess fluorine are eliminated.	Avoid the use of feeds, water or mineral supplements containing excessive fluorine. The National Academy of Sciences (*Effects of Fluorides of Animals*, 1974, p. 55) uses the figure of 60 ppm fluoride as the dietary fluoride tolerance of horses, or dietary level that could be fed without clinical interference with normal performance.	Fluorine is a cumulative poison.
Pending arrival of the veterinarian, the attendant should stand the animal's feet in a cold-water bath. Antihistamines, restricting the diet, use of diuretics, and antiinflammatory agents such as corticosteroids or phenylbutazone, may speed recovery and alleviate serious aftereffects.	Alleviate the causes; namely, (1) overeating, (2) overdrinking (especially when hot), and/or (3) inflammation of the uterus following parturition. Veterinary attention should be given if mares retain the afterbirth longer than 12 hours.	Unless foundered animals are quite valuable, it is usually desirable to dispose of them following a case of severe founder.
Antihistamine granules can be administered in feed to control coughing due to lung congestion. Affected animals are less bothered if turned to pasture, if used only at light work, if fed an all-pelleted ration, or if the hay is sprinkled lightly with water at feeding.	Avoid the use of damaged feeds. Feed an all-pelleted ration, thereby alleviating dust.	Unlike a man, a horse cannot breathe through his mouth. Basically, heaves is a rupture of some of the alveoli in the lungs, of which the specific cause is unknown.

(Continued)

TABLE 13-16

Disease	Species Affected	Cause	Symptoms (and age or group most affected)	Distribution and Losses Caused by
Iodine deficiency (goiter)	All farm animals, and man.	A failure of the body to obtain sufficient iodine from which the thyroid gland can form thyroxine (an iodine-containing hormone). Occasionally, excess iodine causes goiter.	Foals may be weak.	Northwestern U.S. and the Great Lakes region; also reported in California and Texas.
Nitrate poisoning (oat hay poisoning; corn stalk poisoning)	Primarily cattle, but it may affect horses and sheep.	Forages (vegetative part) of most grain crops, Sudan grass, and numerous weeds. Inorganic nitrate or nitrite salts, or fertilizer left where animals have access to them, or where they may be mistaken for salt. Pond or shallow well into which surface runoff from barnyard or well-fertilized soil drain.	Accelerated respiration and pulse rate; diarrhea; frequent urination; loss of appetite; general weakness; trembling and staggering gait; frothing from mouth; abortion; blue color of the mucous membrane and muzzle due to lack of oxygen in blood; death within 4½ to 9 hours after consuming nitrates. A rapid and accurate diagnosis of nitrate poisoning may be made by examining blood. Normal blood is red and becomes brighter when exposed to air, whereas blood from animals toxic with nitrates is a brown color due to formation of methemoglobin.	Excessive nitrate content of feeds is an increasingly important cause of poisoning in farm animals, due primarily to more and more high-nitrogen fertilization. But nitrate toxicity is not new, having been reported as early as 1850, and having occurred in semiarid regions of this and other countries for years.
Osteomalacia	All farm animals.	Inadequate phosphorus (sometimes inadequate calcium). Lack of vitamin D. Inadequate intake of calcium and phosphorus. Incorrect ratio of calcium to phosphorus.	Phosphorus deficiency symptoms are: depraved appetite (gnawing on bones, wood, or other objects; or eating dirt); lack of appetite, stiffness of joints; failure to breed regularly; and an emaciated appearance. Calcium deficiency symptoms are: fragile bones; reproductive failures; and lowered lactations. Mature animals most affected. Most of the acute cases occur during pregnancy and lactation.	Southwestern U.S. is classed as a phosphorus-deficient area whereas calcium-deficient areas have been reported in parts of Florida, Louisiana, Nebraska, Virginia, and West Virginia.
Periodic ophthalmia (moon blindness) Fig. 13-32.	Horses. Mules. Asses.	It may be caused by (1) leptospirosis, (2) localized hypersensitivity or allergic reaction, or (3) lack of riboflavin.	Periods of cloudy vision, in one or both eyes, which may last for a few days to a week or 2 and then clear up; but it recurs at intervals, eventually culminating in blindness in one or both eyes.	In many parts of the world. In the U.S., it occurs most frequently in the states east of the Missouri River.
Rickets	All farm animals, and man.	Lack of calcium, phosphorus, or vitamin D; or an incorrect ratio of the 2 minerals.	Enlargement of the knee and hock joints, and the animal may exhibit great pain when moving about. Irregular bulges (beaded ribs) at juncture of ribs with breastbone, and bowed legs. Rickets is a disease of young animals, including foals.	Worldwide. It is seldom fatal.
Salt deficiency (sodium chloride deficiency)	All farm animals, and man.	Lack of salt (sodium chloride).	Loss of appetite, retarded growth, loss of weight, a rough coat, lowered production of milk, and a ravenous appetite for salt.	Worldwide, especially among grass-eating animals.

Treatment	Prevention	Remarks
At the first signs of iodine deficiency, an iodized salt should be fed to all horses. Once the iodine-deficiency symptoms appear in farm animals, no treatment is very effective.	In iodine-deficient areas, feed iodized salt to all horses throughout the year. Salt containing 0.01% potassium iodide is recommended.	The enlarged thyroid gland (goiter) is nature's way of attempting to make sufficient thyroxine under conditions where a deficiency exists. Large excesses of iodine may cause abortions.
A 4% solution of methylene blue (in a 5% glucose or a 1.8% sodium sulfate solution) administered by a veterinarian intravenously at the rate of 100 cc/1000 lb liveweight.	More than 0.5% nitrate nitrogen (dry basis) may be considered as potentially toxic. Feed should be analyzed when in question. Nitrate poisoning may be reduced by (1) feeding high levels of grains and other high-energy feeds (molasses) and vitamin A, (2) limiting the amount of high-nitrate feeds, (3) ensiling forages which are high in nitrates.	Nitrate form of nitrogen does not appear to cause the actual toxicity. During digestion, the nitrate is reduced to nitrite, a more toxic form, 10 to 15 times more toxic than nitrates. In horses, conversion is in the cecum. When nitrate trouble is expected, contact veterinarian or county agent.
Select natural feeds that contain sufficient calcium and phosphorus. Feed a special mineral supplement. If the disease is far advanced, treatment will not be successful.	Feed balanced rations, and allow animals free access to a suitable calcium and phosphorus supplement. Increase the calcium and phosphorus content of feeds through fertilizing the soils.	Calcium deficiencies are much more rare than phosphorus deficiencies in horses.
Antibiotics administered promptly are helpful in some cases. Immediately (1) change to greener hay or grass, and (2) add riboflavin at the rate of 40 mg/day/animal.	Feed green grass, or well-cured green, leafy hay; or add riboflavin to the ration at the rate of 40 mg per horse per day.	This disease has been known to exist for at least 2,000 years.
If the disease has not advanced too far, treatment may be successful by supplying adequate amounts of vitamin D, calcium, and phosphorus, and/or adjusting the ratio of calcium to phosphorus.	Provide (1) sufficient calcium, phosphorus, and vitamin D, and (2) a correct ratio of the 2 minerals.	Rickets is characterized by a failure of growing bone to ossify or harden properly.
Salt starved animals should be gradually accustomed to salt; slowly increase the hand-fed allowance until the animals may be safely allowed free access to it.	Provide plenty of salt at all times, preferably by free-choice feeding.	Common salt is one of the most essential minerals for grass-eating animals and one of the easiest and cheapest to provide.

TABLE 13-16

Disease	Species Affected	Cause	Symptoms (and age or group most affected)	Distribution and Losses Caused by
Salt poisoning (sodium chloride)	All farm animals, including horses, but swine and sheep most frequently affected.	When excess salt is fed after a period of salt starvation. When salt is improperly used to govern self-feeding of concentrates.	Sudden onset—1 to 2 hours after ingesting salt; extreme nervousness; muscle twitching and fine tremors; much weaving and wobbling, staggering, and circling; blindness; weakness; normal temperature; rapid but weak pulse; and very rapid and shallow breathing; diarrhea; death from a few hours to 48 hours.	Salt poisoning is relatively rare.
Selenium poisoning (alkali disease)	All farm animals, and man.	Consumption of plants grown on soils containing selenium.	Loss of hair from the mane and tail in horses. In severe cases, the hoofs slough off, lameness occurs, feed consumption decreases, and death may occur by starvation.	In certain regions of western U.S.—especially certain areas in South Dakota, Montana, Wyoming, Nebraska, Kansas, and perhaps areas in other states in the Great Plains and Rocky Mountains. Also, in Canada.
Urinary calculi (gravel, stones, water belly)	Horses. Cattle. Sheep. Man.	Unknown, but it seems to be nutritional. Experiments have shown a higher incidence of urinary calculi when there is (1) a high intake of potassium, (2) more phosphorus than calcium in the ration, or (3) a high proportion of beet pulp or grain sorphum in the ration.	Frequent attempts to urinate, dribbling or stoppage of the urine, pain and renal colic. Usually only males affected, the females being able to pass the concretions. Bladder may rupture, with death following. Otherwise, uremic poisoning may set in.	Worldwide. Affected animals seldom recover completely.
Vitamin A deficiency (night blindness and xerophthalmia)	All farm animals, and man.	Vitamin A intake too low. High levels of nitrate intake from hay, silage, and water.	Night blindness, the first symptom of vitamin A deficiency, is characterized by faulty vision, especially noticeable when the affected animal is forced to move about in twilight in strange surroundings. Rough hair coat. Reduced fertility. Xerophthalmia develops in the advanced stages of vitamin A deficiency. The eyes become severely affected, and blindness may follow. Severe diarrhea in young animals and intermittent diarrhea in adult animals.	Worldwide. Especially prevalent where one of the following conditions prevails: (1) extended drought, or (2) winter feeding of bleached grass cured on the stalk, or of bleached hay.

salt and other minerals than others. The ration should contain a reasonable level of minerals. Then, animals and feed differences (due to stage of maturity at harvest, weathering, and length in storage) should be met by free-choice mineral feeding. Allow free access to a double-compartment mineral box as follows: (1) *Where the pasture or hay is primarily grass,* use a mixture containing 2 parts of calcium and 1 part of phosphorus; and (2) *Where the pasture or hay is primarily a legume,* use a mixture containing 1 part of calcium and 1 part of phosphorus. To each of these mixes, add ⅓ salt (trace mineralized) to improve acceptability. If preferred, a good commercial mineral may be used. Self-feed salt separately.

Q. Will alfalfa hay harm a horse?

A. No, many horsemen actually prefer it over grass hay. If fed in large quantities, it may be somewhat laxative and horses may urinate more frequently, but without harm.

Q. Can horses be self-fed on high-energy rations?

A. A few caretakers do self-feed high-energy rations, but, sooner or later, those who do, usually founder a valuable horse. Except for the use of reasonably hard salt-protein blocks, salt-feed mixes in meal form, or high-roughage rations, the self-feeding of horses is not recommended.

(Continued)

Treatment	Prevention	Remarks
Provide large amounts of fresh water to affected animals. Those that cannot and do not drink should be given water via stomach tube, by a veterinarian. The veterinarian may also give (I.V. or intraperitoneally) calcium gluconate to severely affected animals.	If animals have not had salt for a long time, they should be hand fed salt, gradually increasing daily allowance until they leave a little in the mineral box, then self-feed.	Indians and pioneers handed down many legendary stories about huge numbers of wild animals that killed themselves by gorging at a newly found salt lick after having been salt starved for long periods of time.
The use of salt containing 37.5 ppm of arsenic may reduce the incidence of chronic selenium poisoning on seleniferous ranges. Pasture rotation and use of supplemental feeds from nonselenium areas are practical solutions to the problem. There is no known treatment for acute selenium poisoning.	Abandon areas where soils contain selenium, because crops produced on such soils constitute a menace to both animals and man.	Chronic cases of selenium poisoning occur when animals consume feeds containing 8.5 ppm of selenium over an extended period; acute cases occur on 500 to 1,000 ppm. The toxic levels of selenium are in the range of 2.27-4.54 mg/lb of feed (5 to 10 ppm).
Once calculi develops, dietary treatment appears to be of little value. Smooth muscle relaxants may allow passage of calculi if used before rupture of bladder.	Good feed and management appear to lessen the incidence, but no sure preventive is known. Avoid high prosphorus and low calcium. Keep the Ca:P ratio between about 2:1 and about 1:1. One to three percent salt in the concentrate ration may help (using the higher levels in the winter when water consumption is normally lower).	Calculi are stonelike concretions in the urinary tract which almost always originate in the kidneys. These stones block the passage of urine.
Correct the dietary deficiencies and add vitamin A to the ration.	Provide good sources of carotene (vitamin A) through green, leafy hays; silage; lush, green pastures; yellow corn or green and yellow peas; whole milk or fish oil. Add stabilized vitamin A to the ration.	High levels of nitrates interfere with the conversion of carotene to vitamin A.

Q. *Is it possible to control the self-fed consumption of feed of horses through adding salt to a ration, without harm to horses?*

A. Yes, if the feed is in meal form—never pelleted, and if it is carefully and properly done. The practices and precautions are the same as those followed when self-feeding salt-feed mixtures to beef cattle and sheep (see *The Stockman's Handbook*, Sec. "Self-feeding Salt-Feed Mixtures").

Q. *How can one control too rapid eating?*

A. This can be accomplished by spreading the concentrate thinly over the bottom of a large grain box, so that the horse cannot get a large mouthful; or by placing in the grain box a few smooth stones about the size of baseballs, so that the horse has to work to get feed.

Q. *How much roughage must a horse have?*

A. Actually, a horse does not have to have any forage. Also, more horses receive too much roughage than not enough, as evidenced by hay bellies (distended digestive tracts), quick tiring, and labored breathing.

Under most conditions, the roughage requirement of horses ranges from 0.5 percent to 1.0 percent of body weight, or from 5 to 10 pounds of roughage daily for a 1,000-pound horse.

Racehorses should receive a minimum of roughage, since they need a maximum of energy. Sometimes it is necessary to muzzle greedy horses to keep them from eating bedding when their roughage allowance is limited.

Q. *What is meant by the "tying up" syndrome?*

A. The "tying up" syndrome has been observed increasingly in recent years, particularly among racehorses, horses in endurance trials, and other horses in heavy exercise or training. It is characterized by muscle rigidity and lameness affecting the muscles of the croup and loin, accompanied by pain, disinclination to move, a variable temperature, and brownish-colored urine.

Tying up differs from physiologic muscle fatigue in the conspicuous absence of hardness of muscle in the fatigue syndrome.

Some authorities feel that tying up and azoturia are one and the same, differing only in intensity. Both conditions result from exertion and present similar clinical signs and lesions. However, unlike azoturia, tying up seldom is characterized by kidney damage or high mortality.

Tying up appears to be more prevalent in mares than in geldings or stallions, more prevalent in young animals that are in high condition when put in training, and more prevalent following transportation of horses in vans or trailers. Yet, there are exceptions; tying up does occur in older animals and among those that have been in training for some time.

The cause is unknown, although it does seem to be associated with nervousness.

Affected animals usually recover in a short time. Treatment should be by a veterinarian. Among the specific treatments used are steroids, phenylbutazone, and tranquilizers.

The number of treatments within itself indicates a lack of basic knowledge and agreement relative to the disease.

Q. *What can you tell me about (1) "blood testing horses" (hematology), and (2) giving them "shots" or feeding iron?*

A. All body cells require oxygen. With strenuous exercise, as in racing, the oxygen requirement increases.

Oxygen is transported by hemoglobin, the protein-iron coloring matter in blood.

It follows that any reduction in the hemoglobin content, or in total blood volume, will lower the oxygen-carrying capacity of the blood. When this condition is marked, anoxia (lack of oxygen) develops, fatigue sets in, and there is lowered stamina and endurance.

Anoxia may be caused by many conditions. Usually it is due either to (1) nutritional deficiency, or (2) bloodworms—both which may be aggravated by the stress and strain of racing, endurance trials, and showing.

Most trainers accept one or more of the following as indicative of the lack of "fitness": Loss of appetite, loss of weight, excessive "blowing" following work, a dry, harsh cough, rough coat, dull eye, watery instead of beady sweating, and "blowing up" over the loins. In an effort to be more exacting, some veterinarians who attend to racing stables, endurance trials, and show horses now use blood examinations as a means of evaluating physical fitness.

It appears that, although there are breed differences, most horses which show consistent, good racing form have hemoglobin levels between 14 and 16 grams per milliliter, red cell counts between 9 and 11 million per cubic millimeter, and packed cell volumes between 40 percent and 45 percent. Also, other blood determinations are sometimes made. The blood testing approach is interesting and appealing. However, much more information on the subject is needed. Proof of this assertion, if any proof is needed, becomes evident when it is realized that all horses whose blood pictures fall within the above range are not necessarily good performers; neither are horses with blood pictures outside this range incapable of winning. Some horses do respond to treatment, but, generally, the results have been inconsistent and disappointing. One needs to know if horses which have lower blood values, but which do not respond to treatment, carry all of the red cells and hemoglobin that they are capable of developing—whether they have less potential for racing. Even more perplexing is the fact that this blood count can be too high, producing polycythemia. A horse with polycythemia frequently loses appetite, fails to thrive in the stable, performs unsatisfactorily, and may show cyanosis (dark bluish or purple coloration of the skin and mucous membrane due to lack of oxygen). It is also noteworthy that absolute polycythemia occurs at high altitudes or when there is heart disease or fibrosis of the lungs.

Racehorses with anemia are sometimes treated by either (1) injecting iron and/or vitamin B_{12}, or (2) giving orally (in the feed or water) one of several iron preparations. Sometimes folic acid and the other B complex vitamins are added.

At this time, there is insufficient knowledge of equine anemia, or of ways of stimulating hematopoiesis, to make a winner. The true role of therapy, if any, remains unknown.

The most that can be said at this time is that prevailing treatments usually satisfy the owner or trainer who insists that his charges "get the works." Most scientists are agreed, however, that "quickie" miracle shots or concoctions will never replace sound nutrition and parasite control on a continuous basis.

SELECTED REFERENCES

Title of Publication	Author(s)	Publisher
Alternative Sources of Protein for Animal Production	National Research Council	National Academy of Sciences, Washington, D.C., 1973
Animal Feeds	M. Gutcho	Noyes Data Corporation, Park Ridge, N.J., 1970
Animal Growth and Nutrition	E. S. Hafex I. A. Dyer	Lea & Febiger, Philadelphia, Penn., 1969
Animal Nutrition	L. A. Maynard J. K. Loosli	McGraw-Hill Book Company, New York, N.Y., 1969
Applied Animal Feeding and Nutrition	M. H. Jurgens	Kendall/Hunt Publishing Company, Dubuque, Iowa, 1973
Applied Animal Nutrition	E. W. Crampton L. E. Harris	W. H. Freeman and Co. Publishers, San Francisco, Calif., 1969
Atlas of Nutritional Data on United States and Canadian Feeds	National Research Council, U.S.A.; Committee on Feed Composition, Research Branch, Canada Dept. of Agriculture	National Academy of Sciences, Washington, D.C., 1971
Basic Animal Nutrition and Feeding	D. C. Church W. G. Pond	D. C. Church, O & B Books, Corvallis, Ore., 1974
Breeding and Raising Horses, Ag. Hdbk. No. 394	M. E. Ensminger	Agricultural Research Service, USDA, Washington, D.C., 1972
Composition of Cereal Grains and Forages, Pub. 585	National Research Council	National Academy of Sciences, Washington, D.C., 1958
Composition of Concentrate By-Product Feeding Stuffs, Pub. 449	National Research Council	National Academy of Sciences, Washington, D.C., 1956
Effect of Processing on the Nutritional Value of Feeds	National Research Council	National Academy of Sciences, Washington, D.C., 1973
Feed Composition, Tables of, Pub. 1232	National Research Council	National Academy of Sciences, Washington, D.C., 1964
Feed Formulations, Second Edition	T. W. Perry	The Interstate Printers & Publishers, Inc., Danville, Ill., 1975
Feeding Ponies	W. C. Miller	J. A. Allen & Co., London, England, 1968
Feeds and Feeding	A. Cullison	Reston Publishing Company, Inc., Reston, Va., 1975
Feeds and Feeding, 22nd Edition	F. B. Morrison	The Morrison Publishing Company, Ithaca, N.Y., 1956
Feeds and Feeding, Abridged	F. B. Morrison	The Morrison Publishing Company, Ithaca, N.Y., 1956
Feeds for Livestock, Poultry and Pets	M. H. Gutcho	Noyes Data Corporation, Park Ridge, N.J., 1973
Fundamentals of Nutrition	E. W. Crampton L. E. Lloyd	W. H. Freeman and Co. Publishers, San Francisco, Calif., 1959
Handbook of Feedstuffs, The	R. Seiden W. H. Pfander	Springer Publishing Co., Inc., New York, N.Y., 1957
Horse Science Handbook, Vols. 1, 2, and 3	Ed. by M. E. Ensminger	Agriservices Foundation, Clovis, Calif., 1963, 1964, 1966
Horsemanship and Horse Care, Ag. Info. Bull. No. 353	M. E. Ensminger	Agricultural Research Service, USDA, Washington, D.C., 1972

(continued)

Title of Publication	Author(s)	Publisher
International Feed No-menclature and Methods for Summarizing and Using Feed Data to Calculate Diets, An, Bull. 479	L. E. Harris J. M. Asplund E. W. Crampton	Agricultural Experiment Station, Utah State University, Logan, Utah, 1968
Light Horse Management	R. C. Barbalace	Caballus Publishers, Fort Collins, Colo., 1974
Light Horses, Farmers' Bull No. 2127	M. E. Ensminger	U.S. Department of Agriculture, Washington, D.C., 1965
Manual of Clinical Nutrition	R. S. Goodhart M. G. Wohl	Lea & Febiger, Philadelphia, Penn., 1964
Mineral Nutrition of Livestock, The	E. J. Underwood	Food and Agriculture Organization of the United Nations, Rome, Italy, 1966
Mineral Nutrition of Plants and Animals	F. A. Gilbert	University of Oklahoma Press, Norman, Okla., 1948
Nutrient Requirements of Horses, No. 6., Third Revised Edition		National Academy of Sciences, Washington, D.C., 1973
Nutrition of Animals of Agricultural Importance, Parts 1 and 2	Ed. by D. Cuthbertson	Pergamon Press, London, England, 1969
Nutritional Deficiencies in Livestock	R. T. Allman T. S. Hamilton	Food and Agriculture Organization of the United Nations, Rome, Italy, 1952
Proceedings of the Fifth International Congress on Nutrition	Federation of American Societies for Experimental Biology	Waverly Press, Inc., Baltimore, Md., 1961
Processed Plant Protein Foodstuffs	Ed. by A. M. Altschul	Academic Press, Inc., New York, N.Y., 1958
Processing and Utilization of Animal By-Products	I. Mann	Food and Agriculture Organization of the United Nations, Rome, Italy, 1962
Proteins: Their Chemistry and Politics	A. M. Altschul	Basic Books, Inc., Publishers, New York, N.Y., 1965
Selenium in Nutrition	National Research Council	National Academy of Sciences, Washington, D.C., 1971
Shetland Pony	L. F. Bedell	Iowa State University Press, Ames, Iowa, 1959
Single-Cell Protein	Ed. by R. I. Mateles, S. R. Tannenbaum	The M.I.T. Press, Cambridge, Mass., 1968
Stockman's Handbook, The, Fourth Edition	M. E. Ensminger	The Interstate Printers & Publishers, Inc., Danville, Ill., 1970
Stud Manager's Handbook	Ed. by M. E. Ensminger	Agriservices Foundation, Clovis, Calif., annually since 1965
Use of Drugs in Animal Feeds, The, Pub. 1679	National Academy of Sciences	National Academy of Sciences, Washington, D.C., 1969
Vitamins, The: Chemistry, Physiology, Pathology, Methods, Vols. 1-3, Second Edition	Ed. by W. H. Sebrell, Jr., R. S. Harris	Academic Press, Inc., New York, N.Y., 1967, 1968, 1971
Vitamins in Feeds for Livestock	F. C. Aitken R. G. Hankin	Commonwealth Agricultural Bureaux, Farnham Royal, Bucks, England, 1970
Vitamins and Hormones, Vol. 14	Ed. by R. S. Harris, G. F. Marrian, K. V. Thimann	Academic Press, Inc., New York, N.Y., 1957

BUILDINGS AND EQUIPMENT FOR HORSES

The primary reasons for having horse buildings and equipment are (1) to provide a place in which to confine horses and store feed and tack; (2) to modify the environment by controlling temperature, humidity, and other factors; and (3) to provide feed, water, and other facilities for the care of horses. Properly de-signed, constructed, and arranged facilities make for increased horse comfort and performance, greater efficiency in the use of feed, and less expenditure for labor in the care of horses.

The effects of technological progress in horse buildings and equipment are everywhere. Yet, there

Fig. 14-1. Attractive horse barns add to the beauty of the landscape. This shows the headquarters at Windfields Farm, noted Thoroughbred establishment, Chesapeake City, Maryland. (Courtesy, Windfields Farm)

is need for more experimental work pertaining to the basic requirements of such facilities. The most glaring deficiencies pertain to (1) laborsaving devices;[1] (2) flexibility; (3) environmental control—including temperature, humidity, and ventilation; (4) methods of handling excrement; (5) sanitation; (6) safety of animals and caretakers; (7) fire-resistant construction; (8) materials;[2] and (9) cost.

ENVIRONMENTAL CONTROL FOR HORSES

Man achieves environmental control through clothing, vacations in resort areas, and air-conditioned homes and cars.

Wild horses were little affected by environment as long as they roamed pastures and ranges. But the domestication of horses and their confinement into smaller spaces changed all this. Building and equipment design became critical.

Environment may be defined as all the conditions, circumstances, and influences surrounding and affecting the growth, development, and production of a living thing. In horses, this includes the air temperature, relative humidity, air velocity, wet bedding, dust, light, ammonia buildup, odors, and space requirements. Control, or modifications, of these factors offers possibilities for improving animal performance. There is still much to be learned about environmental control, but the gap between awareness and application is becoming smaller.

Properly designed horse barns and other shelters, shades, insulation, ventilation, and air conditioning can be used to approach the environment that we

wish. Naturally, the investment in environmental control facilities must be balanced against the expected increased returns; and there is a point beyond which further expenditures for environmental control will not increase returns sufficiently to justify the added cost. This point of diminishing returns will differ between sections of the country, quality of the horses (the more valuable the animals, the higher the expenditures for environmental control can be), and operators; and labor and feed costs will enter into the picture, also.

Environmentally controlled buildings are costly to construct, but they make for the ultimate in animal comfort, health, and efficiency of feed utilization. Also, they lend themselves to automation, which results in a saving in labor; and, because of minimizing space requirements, they effect a saving in land cost. Today, environmental control is rather common in poultry and swine housing, and it is on the increase for horses.

Environmental control is of particular importance in horse barn construction, because many horses spend the majority of their lives in stalls—for example, race and show horses may be confined as much as 95 percent of the time.

Before an environmental system can be designed for horses, it is important to know their (1) heat production, (2) vapor (moisture) production, and (3) space requirements. This information is as pertinent to designing livestock buildings as nutrient requirements are to balancing rations.

Heat Production of Horses

The heat production of horses varies with age, body weight, ration, breed, activity, barn temperature, and humidity at high temperatures. The heat production of any animal is closely related to size and varies approximately as the 2/3 power of the body weight. Table 14-1 may be used as a guide relative to the heat production of horses.

TABLE 14-1

HEAT PRODUCTION OF A 1,000-POUND HORSE[1]

Temperature	Heat Production, BTU/hr Total	Temperature	Heat Production, Kcal/hr Total
(°F)		(°C)	
70	1,800-2,500[2]	21	453.6-630

[1]Adapted by the author from *Farm Buildings*, by J. C. Wooley, McGraw-Hill Book Company, Inc., 1946, p. 140, Table 24.
[2]Armsby and Kriss, in a paper entitled, "Some Fundamentals of Stable Ventilation," *Journal of Agricultural Research*, Vol. 21, June 1921, p. 343, list the total heat output as follows: A 1,000-lb horse, 1,500 Btu per hour; a 1,500-lb horse, 2,450 Btu per hour.

Heat is measured in British thermal units (Btu). One Btu is the amount of heat required to raise the temperature of 1 pound of water 1 degree Fahrenheit.

[1]Seventy-five percent of horse work is still hand labor, one-third of which could be eliminated by mechanization and modernization.

[2]Many horsemen complain that metal buildings are unsatisfactory; that they must still be protected with wood, that moisture condensation is a problem, and that they are too hot in the summer and too cold in the winter. Some express preference for concrete blocks. However, the vast majority seem to favor conventional wood construction, despite the greater fire hazard.

Vapor (Moisture) Production of Horses

Horses give off moisture during normal respiration; and the higher the temperature the greater the moisture. This moisture should be removed from buildings through the ventilation system. When it's cold and this moisture is not removed, it condenses and forms frost. The latter condition is indicative of lack of ventilation, and it may be indicative of insufficient insulation, also. Most building designers govern the amount of winter ventilation by the need for moisture removal. Also, cognizance is taken of the fact that moisture removal in the winter is lower than in the summer; hence, less air is needed. However, lack of heat makes moisture removal more difficult in the wintertime. Table 14-2 gives the information necessary for determining the approximate amount of moisture to be removed.

TABLE 14-2
VAPOR (MOISTURE) PRODUCTION OF A 1,000-POUND HORSE[1]

Temperature		Vapor Production	Vapor Production
(°F)	(°C)	(lb/hr)	(kg/hr)
70	21	0.729	0.33

[1]Adapted by the author from *Farm Buildings*, by J. C. Wooley, McGraw-Hill Book Company, Inc., 1946, p. 141, Table 25.

As shown in Table 14-2, a horse breathes into the air approximately 17.5 pounds, or about 2.1 gallons, of moisture per day. For 40 horses, there would be given off 700 pounds, or about 84 gallons, of water per day. The removal of such a large quantity of moisture, especially in the winter when the barn is closed, is a difficult problem for the designer to solve.

Since ventilation also involves a transfer of heat, it is important to conserve heat in the building to maintain desired temperatures and reduce the need for supplemental heat. In a well-insulated building, mature horses usually produce sufficient heat to provide a desirable balance between heat and moisture; but in cold areas young animals may require supplemental heat. The major requirement of summer ventilation is temperature control, which requires moving more air than in the winter.

Recommended Environmental Control for Horses

The comfort of animals (or man) is a function of temperature, humidity, and air movement. Likewise, the heat loss from animals is a function of these three items.

The prime function of the winter ventilation system is to control moisture, whereas the summer ventilation system is primarily for temperature control. If air in horse barns is supplied at a rate sufficient to control moisture—that is, to keep the inside relative humidity in winter below 75 percent—then this will usually provide the needed fresh air, help suppress odors, and prevent an ammonia buildup.

Based on currently available information, the author recommends the environmental control given in Table 14-3 for horses.

Thus, until more experimental work is available, based on extrapolating from confinement systems in use for other classes of animals, the author recommends the following environmental conditions for horses:

● *Temperature*—A range of 45° to 75° F (7° to 24° C) is satisfactory, with 55° F (13° C) considered optimum. Until a newborn foal is dry, it should be warmed to 75° to 80° F (24° to 27° C). This can be done with a heat lamp.

● *Humidity*—A range of 50 to 75 percent relative humidity is acceptable, with 60 percent preferred.

● *Insulation and ventilation*—These needs will vary from area to area. Where a wide spread between summer and winter temperature exists, and where horses are confined much of the time, proper insulation and ventilation are of prime importance. Under such circumstances, for moisture control in winter and temperature control in summer, horse barns should have at least 2 inches of insulation on the ceiling or roof, and the sidewalls should be insulated, also.

● *Ventilation*—The barn should have as little moisture and odor as possible, and it should be free from drafts. In a properly ventilated barn, the ventilation system should provide 60 cubic feet per minute (cfm) for each 1,000 pounds of horse (1.7 cu mm/454-kg horse) in winter and 160 cfm per 1,000 pounds of

TABLE 14-3
RECOMMENDED ENVIRONMENTAL CONDITIONS FOR HORSES

Age	Temperature				Acceptable Humidity	Commonly Used Ventilation Rates[1]					Drinking Water			
	Comfort Zone		Optimum			Basis	Winter[2]		Summer		Winter		Summer	
	(°F)	(°C)	(°F)	(°C)	(%)		(cfm)	(cu mm/min.)	(cfm)	(cu mm/min.)	(°F)	(°C)	(°F)	(°C)
Horse, Mature ...	45-75	7-24	55	13	50-75	1,000 lb (or 454 kg)	60	1.7	160	4.5	40-45	4-7	60-75	16-24
Newborn Foal ...	75-80	24-27												

[1]Generally two different ventilating systems are provided; one for winter, and an additional one for summer. Hence, as shown in Table 14-3, the winter ventilating system in a horse barn should be designed to provide 60 cfm (cubic feet/minute) for each 1,000-lb horse. Then, the summer system should be designed to provide an added 100 cfm, thereby providing a total of 160 cfm for summer ventilation.

In practice, in many horse barns, added summer ventilation is provided by opening (1) barn doors, and (2) high-up hinged walls.

[2]Provide approximately ¼ the winter rate continuously for moisture removal.

horse (2.8 cu mm/454-kg horse) in summer. In warm weather, satisfactory ventilation usually can be achieved by opening barn doors and by installing hinged doors or panels near the ceiling that swing open. Then, on extremely hot or quiet days, the natural ventilating system may be augmented with the fan ventilating system.

The design of the barn, and the temperature of the area, will determine the best type of ventilating system to use. Also, the requirements for summer and winter are so different that it is best to use two different ventilating systems—one for winter, and the other for summer.

A professional engineer should always be engaged to design the ventilating system. Generally, summer exhaust fans should be placed high, and winter exhaust fans low. Whatever the ventilating system, drafts on horses should be avoided.

● *Light*—Windows should be provided in the ratio of 1 square foot for each 30 square feet of floor area. They should be protected from horses and screened to keep flies out. Additionally, artificial light should be provided for the convenience of the caretaker. One 60-watt bulb, properly recessed and protected, in each stall, plus lighting in the aisle, should suffice.

● *Water temperature*—In the winter months, water for horses should be warmed to 40° to 45° F (4° to 7° C); in the summer, it should be within the range of 60° to 75° F (16° to 24° C).

HORSE BARN POINTERS

The care of horses differs from the care accorded cattle, sheep, swine, or poultry; they require more individual attention. But just as the needs are unique, meeting them requires greater imagination and creativity.

Area Arrangement

Whether planning a new horse layout or altering an old one, all buildings, fences, corrals, and trees should be added according to a master plan, for once established they are usually difficult and expensive to move. The entire arrangement should make for the best use of the land and require a minimum of walking when caring for horses.

Location

The barn should be located so as to be:

1. *Accessible*—It should be on an all-weather roadway or lane, thereby facilitating the use of horses, delivery of feed and bedding, and removal of manure. Also, it should be adjacent, or in near proximity, to a corral, paddock, or pasture.

2. *High and dry*—It should be on high ground, with drainage away from it, thereby making for dryness.

3. *Expandable*—There should be provision for easy expansion, if and when the time comes. Often a building can be expanded in length provided no other structures or utilities interfere.

4. *Convenient to water and electricity*—Water should be available and plentiful, and electricity should be in near proximity.

Requisites of Horse Barns

All horse barns—regardless of kind, use, and purposes—should meet the following requisites:

1. *Environment control*—Modify winter and summer temperatures for horses; protect them from rain, snow, sun, and wind; and minimize stress.

Also, barns should provide good ventilation. This refers to the changing of air—the replacement of foul air with fresh air. There should be a minimum of moisture and odor, and the barn should be free from drafts. Horse barn ventilation may be achieved through one or more of the following: an opening under the roof, a ridge vent, hinged windows, dutch doors, and/or fans.

2. *Reasonable cost, along with minimum maintenance*—Initial cost is important, but consideration should also be given to durability and maintenance, and to such intangible values as pride and satisfaction, influence on the children, and advertising value.

3. *Adequate space*—Too little space may jeopardize the health and well-being of horses, whereas more space than needed makes for unnecessary expense.

4. *Storage for feed, bedding and tack*—These are generally stored in the same building where used.

5. *Attractiveness*—An attractive horse barn makes for a "heap of living" and enhances the sale value of the property. A horse barn that has utility value, is in good proportions, and is in harmony with the natural surroundings, will have aesthetic value. Good design is never achieved by indulgence in fads, frills, or highly ornamental features.

6. *Minimum fire risk*—The use of fire-resistant materials gives added protection to horses. Also, fire-retarding paints and sprays are available.

7. *Safety*—Safety features should be observed, such as no projections on which horses may become injured, and arrangements for feeding and watering without walking behind horses.

8. *Saving of labor*—This is a must in any commercial horse establishment. Also, where horses are kept for pleasure, it is well to minimize drudgery and eliminate unnecessary labor in feeding, cleaning, and handling.

9. *Horse health protection*—Healthy horses are superior and efficient performers; hence, horse barns should provide healthful living conditions for the occupants.

10. *Rodent and bird control*—Feed and tack storage areas should be rodent-proof and bird-proof.

11. *Suitable corrals and paddocks nearby*—Horse barns should be provided with well-drained, safe, and durably and attractively fenced corrals or paddocks, either adjacent to or in close proximity.

12. *Flexibility*—Both technological development and possible shifts in use make it desirable that horse barns be as flexible as possible—even to the point that they can be, cheaply and easily, converted into cabins, garages, storage buildings, and whatnot. Also, for suburbanites and renters, permanent barns that are portable are advantageous.

Materials

Technology has evolved with new building materials and forced the improvement of old ones. In selecting horse barn building materials, consideration should be given to (1) initial cost, (2) durability and minimum maintenance, (3) attractiveness, and (4) fire resistance.

Among the materials available, and being used, are:

1. Wood, including plywood.
2. Metal.
3. Masonry; including concrete block, cinder, pumice block, brick, and stone.
4. Plastics.

Prefabricated Horse Barns

Preengineered and prefabricated horse barns are finding a place of increasing importance, especially on smaller horse establishments. Fabricators of such buildings have the distinct advantages of (1) price savings due to purchase of materials in quantity lots, (2) economical and controlled fabricating, and (3) well-trained personnel for developing the best in plans and specifications.

Feed and Water Facilities

These are an important part of each barn. They may be either built-in or detached. For sanitary and flexibility reasons, as well as greater suitability, more and more good horsemen favor specialty feed and watering facilities, over old-time wood mangers and concrete or steel tanks. Bulk tank feed storage may well be considered on larger horse establishments, thereby eliminating sacks, lessening rodent and bird problems, and making it possible to obtain more favorable feed prices with larger orders.

KINDS OF HORSE BARNS

The needs for housing horses and storing materials vary according to the intended use of the building. Broadly speaking, horse barns are designed to serve (1) small horse establishments—the owner with one to a few head, (2) large horse breeding establishments, or (3) riding academies and training and boarding stables. A summary of the space requirements of buildings for horses is presented later in this chapter, under the section headed "Space Requirements," in Table 14-5.

Small Horse Establishments

When one or two riding horses or ponies are kept, they are usually stabled close to the house, which makes for greater convenience in their care and use. In most cases, box stalls are built in a row and provision is made for limited feed, bedding and tack storage; usually a combination feed and tack room for units with 1 to 2 stalls, and separate feed and tack rooms with 3 or more stalls. Fig. 14-2 shows an attractive small barn that is used as a private stable.

Fig. 14-2. Stable of Mrs. L. H. French, Hidden Valley, California. Note provision for plenty of fresh air, an essential for healthy horses. (Courtesy, *Sunset Magazine*, Menlo Park, Calif.)

Building plans for a small horse barn are shown in Fig. 14-3. (See page 278.)

Complete working drawings of small horse barns may be obtained through county agricultural agents or from extension agricultural engineers at most state agricultural colleges.

Large Horse Establishments

With large horse breeding establishments, specially designed buildings are generally provided for different purposes. Because of the increasing impor-

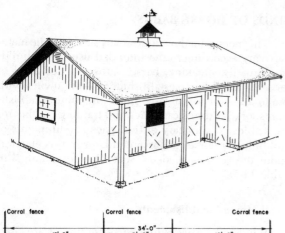

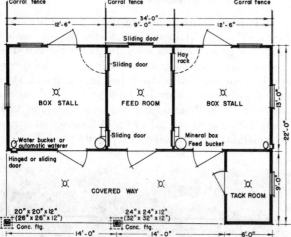

Fig. 14-3. Riding horse barn above and floor plan below. Barn has two box stalls, a feed room, and a tack room.

tance of horses for recreation and sport—and the further fact that the same principles of building construction apply to the one or two riding horse unit and the large breeding establishment—a brief discussion will be presented relative to each of the following types of buildings found on many of the larger breeding establishments throughout America: (1) broodmare and foaling barn, (2) barren mare barn, (3) stallion barn and paddocks, (4) breeding shed, (5) weanling and yearling quarters, and (6) isolation (quarantine) quarters.

BROODMARE AND FOALING BARN

The building designed as the broodmare barn may also be used for mares in foal, mares with suckling foals, weanlings, and barren mares. Whatever their size or style, there are two basic rectangular arrangements of multiple stall barns. The most common is a central aisle with a row of stalls along each side.

The other is the "island" type, which consists of two rows of stalls, back to back, surrounded by an alley or runway. The island type is preferred when an indoor exercising ring is desired.

Fig. 14-4. Broodmare barn and nearby pasture paddock on Domino Farm, Lexington, Kentucky. (Courtesy, Kentucky Department of Public Information, Frankfort, Ky.)

Maternity stalls should be 12 by 12 feet in size, or larger, and located so as to secure the most direct sunlight possible. When feasible, the maternity stalls should be adjacent to an office or some service room, so that at parturition time the caretaker may observe the mare through a peephole without being in sight. With this arrangement, it is preferable that the foaling stall have a double light switch, with one switch at the observation window and the other at the stall door.

For convenience and economy in operation, the broodmare barn should have ample quarters for the storage of a considerable supply of hay, bedding, and grain. Usually, hay and straw are stored in an overhead mow, and grain may be stored either overhead or on the ground-floor level. In the latter case, extra precaution should be taken to prevent animals from taking advantage of an open grain-bin door; otherwise, founder probably will result.

A record or office room, toilet facilities, hot water supply, veterinary supply room, and tack room are usually an integral part of the broodmare barn. In many cases, a reception room for visitors is also provided.

BARREN MARE BARN OR SHED

The same type of barn as used for in-foal mares is entirely satisfactory for barren mares. Generally speaking, however, these mares do not require such careful attention or elaborate quarters. In large breed-

ing establishments, usually they are run in bands of as many as 20 and are required to "rough it" to a considerable extent.

Fig. 14-5. Barren mare shed on the Morgan breeding establishment of Voorhis Farm, Red Hook, New York. (Photo by Fred J. Sass; courtesy, Fred Herrick, Manager, Voorhis Farm, Red Hook, N.Y.)

During inclement weather, a shelter should be available for barren mares. This may consist of either an open shed or a rectangular barn of the required size—allowing approximately 150 square feet per animal—with a combination hay rack and trough down the center or along either wall. If the barn is closed, it should have a large sliding door opening out, away from the direction of the prevailing winds. Ample hay, grain, and bedding should be stored in the barn.

STALLION BARN AND PADDOCK

This barn provides quarters for one or more stallions. It should have a small tack and equipment room, and it may or may not have feed storage. The stalls should be 14 feet square, or larger.

Stallion barns almost always face away from broodmare barns, and preferably in the direction of prevailing winds. Some good horsemen prefer that the topography or plantings be such as to prevent the stallion from seeing mares or other mature horses at a distance. In general, English and French horsemen subscribe to this type of arrangement, keeping their stallions so they cannot see any other horses. On the other hand, many good horsemen in this country insist that such isolation usually makes for a mean, nervous horse. The latter advocates feel that stallions are better satisfied if they can see other horses off at a distance or even fairly close to them.

As in the broodmare barn, it is more practical and convenient to have feed and bedding storage within the stallion barn. Also, a small tack and equipment room should be provided.

Stallion paddocks and the stallion barn are a necessary adjunct to each other. The stallion barn may open directly into the paddock or be separated from it by a runway. The former arrangement is the more convenient and is quite desirable when a vicious stallion must be handled. Many good horsemen insist, however, that a paddock immediately adjacent to the stallion barn—where the horse can go in and out of his quarters at will—encourages the animal to remain

Fig. 14-6. Stallion barn at Domino Stud, Lexington, Kentucky, showing the stallion Dewan. (Courtesy, J. Noye, photographer, Versailles, Ky.)

in the stall too much. These horsemen also believe that merely closing the stall door will not prevent the stallion from unnecessary loitering before the barn. Those subscribing to this school of thought insist that paddocks be located a short distance from the stallion barn and be separated from it by runways.

Regardless of the proximity of the stallion paddock to the barn, a large paddock helps considerably in keeping in fit condition horses that are not otherwise exercised regularly. Although paddock exercise is not so good as that given under saddle or in harness, it helps to guard against filled hocks, azoturia, and other trouble.

Sodded paddocks that provide succulent and nutritious grass are also preferable to barren areas which merely serve as gymnasiums for stallions. A 2- to 4-acre area is desirable. Every effort should be made to build the stallion paddock at least 300 feet on a side.

Care should be taken to see that paddock fences are free from projections that might cause injury. Fences should be constructed of wood or metal, rather than wire. A double fence should separate nearby stallion paddocks, or a stallion paddock from a broodmare pasture. The paddock fence should be a minimum of 6 feet high and should be constructed of 2- by 6-inch lumber or good strong poles.

Water should be available in the stallion paddock at all times. Shade is also very desirable.

BREEDING SHED AND BREEDING CORRAL

The breeding shed is nothing more than a large, roofed enclosure with a high ceiling in which mares may be handled and served under sanitary conditions. Most horsemen prefer to have the breeding shed in close proximity to the stallion barn, thus making for greater ease in handling nervous stallions.

The shed should be dustproof, high and without projections overhead that might possibly injure a rearing horse, well lighted, and should have a clay or tanbark floor (preferably the latter, as it lessens the dust problem). Most breeding sheds are a minimum of 24 feet by 24 feet in size and have a 15- to 20-foot ceiling. The breeding shed should be served by 2 wide doors located on opposite sides of the shed. With this arrangement the stallion and mare can be taken out opposite doors. This will aid in preventing accidents when handling vicious or nervous animals.

The larger establishments generally include the following facilities in addition to the center court which serves as the breeding shed: laboratory for the veterinarian or technician, hot water facilities, and stalls in which mares are prepared for breeding. Formerly, many breeding sheds had a small stall for the young foal that usually accompanied the mare at the time of service. At the present time, however, these

Fig. 14-7. Interior of large and high-ceilinged breeding shed at Westerly Stud, Santa Ynez, California. Note holding cage for foal in the corner. (Courtesy, *The Thoroughbred of California*, Arcadia, Calif.)

Fig. 14-8. Laboratory at Westerly Stud, Santa Ynez, California. (Courtesy, *The Thoroughbred of California*, Arcadia, Calif.)

are seldom used, the foals being left at home.

When the cost of a breeding shed may be excessive, a high and spacious corral built of boards may be used satisfactorily.

WEANLING AND YEARLING QUARTERS

The same type of quarters is adapted to both weanlings and yearlings. In all cases, however, the different age groups should be kept separated from each other, for older animals are likely to crowd the younger ones away from the feed or may inflict injury. It is also best to separate the sexes, at least by the January following foaling. Either small separate barns should be provided for the different age and sex groups of weanlings and yearlings or a larger building and adjacent paddocks may be adapted for such handling.

Fig. 14-9. An open shed for weanlings. This type of building furnishes a desirable place in which to winter young stock and idle horses unless the weather becomes too severe. (Courtesy, USDA)

Weanlings or yearlings may be housed satisfactorily in either a stable or open shed; the main requisites being that the quarters are dry, sanitary, and well bedded and that they provide fairly good protection from winds. When stalls are used, 2 weanlings or 2 yearlings may be kept together. Stalls should be 10 feet square. It must be remembered that in its native environment the horse is hardy and rugged and that diseases and unsoundnesses begin when there is too close confinement, improper feeding, and lack of exercise. This does not imply that such young animals should be neglected. Handling and gentling the animals at an early age is quite desirable.

It must be realized also that such animals will not develop and grow out satisfactorily unless they are well fed. The good horseman, therefore, seeks a happy medium between stabling and ranging in the handling of young stock; he realizes that there are benefits to be derived from each and that losses occur if either is carried to an extreme. The main point to remember is that lots of fresh air and exercise are invaluable. Do not worry about young stock getting cold.

When stalls are used, two weanlings or two yearlings may be placed together.

ISOLATION (QUARANTINE) QUARTERS

New animals that have been brought into a stable should always be kept isolated for a minimum of 21 days before being taken into the herd. This applies to newly purchased animals, boarders, or animals being returned from showing or racing. Mares requiring treatment for infection of the genital tract should be quartered separately and run in special fields or paddocks.

Fig. 14-10. Receiving barn at Gem State Stables, Tipton, California. Each stable opens into a small turnout area. (Courtesy, Harry and Velma Morrison, owners)

A small barn designed for this purpose, with 12 feet by 12 feet stalls and adjacent paddocks is considered an essential part of large breeding establishments. Separate feed and water facilities should also be provided for animals in isolation. Moreover, the caretaker must use discretion in going from the quarantine quarters to the rest of the stables or herd.

The quarters should be cleaned thoroughly and disinfected following the removal of each animal that has been stabled therein.

When possible, the isolation quarters should be so located that horses can be taken to them and removed without either the animals themselves or the vehicles in which they are transported passing through the rest of the breeding farm. It is also desirable that the drainage from the isolation quarters be away from the rest of the farm.

Riding, Training, and Boarding Stables

For this purpose, the quarters may consist of (1) stalls constructed back to back in the center of the barn with an indoor ring around the stalls, (2) stalls built around the sides of the barn with the ring in the center, or (3) stalls on either side of a hallway or alleyway and the ring outdoors. Box stalls should be 10 to 12 ft square and tie stalls should be 5 ft wide and 10 to 12 ft long.

SHEDS

In the wild state (as nature ordained it), the horse augmented his shaggy winter coat by seeking the protection afforded by hills, ravines, and trees. But man changed all this—and not always for the better. Diseases and unsoundnesses began with too close confinement and lack of exercise. Through mistaken kindness, horses are often subjected to lack of ventilation and high humidity.

Fig. 14-11. A horse shed; open to the south, away from the direction of the prevailing winds and toward the sun. (Photo by Ernst Peterson, Hamilton, Mont.; courtesy, Margit Sigray Bessenyey, Hamilton, Mont.)

For broodmares and horses not in constant use, an open shed, with access to a pasture or corral, is preferred. Horses kept in an open shed, even in the colder areas, are healthier and suffer fewer respiratory diseases than horses kept in enclosed barns.

Sheds are usually open to the south or east, preferably opposite to the direction of the prevailing winds and toward the sun. They are enclosed on the

ends and sides. Sometimes the front is partially closed, and in severe weather drop-doors may be used. The latter arrangement is especially desirable when the ceiling height is sufficient to accommodate a power manure loader.

In order that the bedding may be kept reasonably dry, it is important that sheds be located on high, well-drained ground; that eave troughs and downspouts drain into suitable tile lines, or surface drains; and that the structures have sufficient width to prevent rain and snow from blowing to the back end. Sheds should be a minimum of 24 ft in depth, front to back, with depths up to 36 ft preferable. As a height of 8 1/2 ft is necessary to accommodate some power-operated manure loaders, when this type of equipment is to be used in the shed, a minimum ceiling height of 9 ft is recommended. The extra 6 inches allow for the accumulation of manure. Lower ceiling heights are satisfactory when it is intended to use a blade or pitchfork in cleaning the building.

The length of the shed can be varied according to needed capacity. Likewise, the shape may be either a single long shed or in the form of an L or T. The long arrangement permits more corral space. When an open shed is contemplated, thought should be given to feed storage and feeding problems.

Sometimes hayracks are built along the back wall of sheds, or next to an alley, if the shed is very wide or if there is some hay storage overhead. Most generally, however, hayracks, feed bunks, and watering troughs are placed outside the structure.

SHADES

A shade, either trees or man-made, should be provided for horses that are in the hot sun.

The most satisfactory man-made horse shades are (1) oriented with a north-south placement, (2) at least 12 to 15 feet in height (in addition to being cooler, high shades allow a mounted rider to pass under), and (3) open all around.

STALLS

Stalls are of two general types: (1) box stalls; and (2) tie, straight, standing, or slip stalls. As tie stalls differ primarily in the width of the area and their use is less common in breeding establishments, the discussion will be confined to loose or box stalls. The latter are preferred because they allow the horses more liberty, either when standing or lying down.

Adequate quarters for a horse should be (1) ample in size and height for the particular type of animal; (2) properly finished and without projections; (3) dry with good footing; (4) equipped with suitable doors; (5) provided with ample windows for proper lighting; (6) well ventilated; (7) cool in summer and warm in

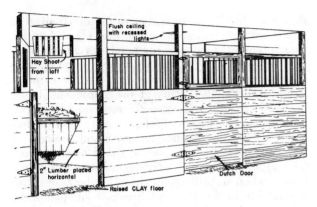

Fig. 14-12. A satisfactory type of box stall for horses. (Drawing by Steve Allured)

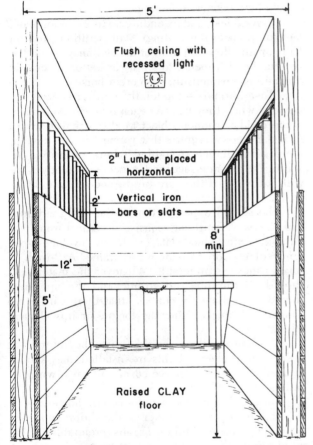

Fig. 14-13. A satisfactory type of tie stall for horses. (Drawing by Steve Allured)

Fig. 14-14. Box stall and door arrangement of the Al Blackburn Stable, Ojai, California. Note concrete footing of partition; walls boarded up solid with smooth, hard 20-inch lumber placed horizontally to a height of 5 feet; and slatted upper portion of partition and alleyway front of vertical iron slats. (Courtesy, *Sunset Magazine*, Menlo Park, Calif.)

Fig. 14-15. Box stalls in the stable of Mr. and Mrs. C. G. Furlong, Ojai, California. (Courtesy, *Sunset Magazine*, Menlo Park, Calif.)

winter; (8) equipped with suitable mangers, grain containers, watering facilities, and mineral boxes; and (9) easy to keep clean.

Floor of Stall

A raised clay floor covered with a good absorbent

bedding, with proper drainage away from the build-ing, is the most satisfactory flooring for horse stables. Clay floors are noiseless and springy, keep the hoofs moist, and afford firm natural footing unless wet; but they are difficult to keep clean and level. To lessen the latter problems, the top layer should be removed each year, replaced with fresh clay, and leveled. Also, a semicircular concrete apron extending into each stall at the doorway will prevent horses from digging a hole in a clay floor at this point. This arrangement is particularly desirable in barns for yearlings, as they are likely to fret around the door.

Rough wooden floors furnish good traction for animals and are warm to lie upon; but they are ab-sorbent and unsanitary, they often harbor rats and other rodents, and they lack durability.

Concrete, asphalt, or brick floors are durable, im-pervious to moisture, easily cleaned, and sanitary; but they are rigid and without resilient qualities, slippery when wet, hazardous to horses, and cold to lie upon. It is noteworthy that concrete and asphalt, generously covered with bedding, are widely used for stable floors throughout eastern and western Europe.

There is great need for an improved stall floor covering material for horses—one which will lessen (1) the amount of bedding needed, and (2) the labor and drudgery of cleaning.

Concrete Footings

Concrete footings and foundation walls are rec-ommended as they are both durable and noncorro-sive. The foundation should be a minimum of 8 in-ches high, so as to be above the manure level.

Size and Height of Stall

Except for foaling mares and for stallions, there is no advantage in having box stalls larger than 12 ft square. The maternity stall should be at least 12 by 12 ft so that the attendant may get about the mare readily to accommodate the foal. Moreover, the stall should be without low hayracks (high hayracks may be used in a foaling stall), feed boxes, or other objects under which the mare might get caught or on which she might otherwise injure herself during parturition. The box stall for the stallion should be at least 14 by 14 ft in size.

It is also important that every part of a stall be of sufficient height so that the animal will not strike its head. A minimum clearance of 8 feet is essential, and it is preferable that the ceiling over all stalls be 9 feet or more in height.

Partitions and Interior of Stall

Regardless of the type of stall or the use made of it, there should be no projections (or ill-advised equipment) on which the horse may injure himself. Rough lumber, such as is commonly used in the con-struction of stables on ordinary farms, has no place in the finishing of stables for breeding establishments.

In general, the walls of the stable should be boarded up solid with smooth, hard lumber placed horizontally to a height of 5 feet, using either (1) dur-able plywood of adequate thickness and strength, or (2) 2-inch, hard lumber (such as oak) placed horizon-tally. Hollow concrete blocks encourage stall kicking; hence, when used they should either be filled with concrete or lined with wood. Breaks in any part of the stall, caused by kicking, create a hazard for the ani-mal. Stallion stalls are sometimes padded to a height of approximately 5 feet. All walls and partitions should be on concrete footings.

Above 5 feet, and extending up to a minimum of 7 feet (or even to the ceiling), stall partitions and the hallway (or alleyway) front of the stall may be slatted, preferably with metal, to allow for better air circula-tion and companionship with other horses.

Most animals—especially stallions—are less nervous when they can see each other in their stalls. Some good horsemen object to slatted partitions for fillies and colts, arguing that young animals develop more self-reliance if stabled where partitions are solid. They cannot see and watch one another and will not worry if they are not turned out simultane-ously.

The slatted upper portion of the stall (partitions and alleyway front) may consist of vertical iron slats, durable vertical wood slats, or a heavy "cyclone-type" fence placed on iron or wood frame. A 2-inch or smaller mesh is preferable. Whatever the material, it should be durable and strong, and the openings should be sufficiently close so that there can be no danger of animals biting the tongue or lips of each other.

A smooth ceiling should finish the interior of every stall. If electric lights are installed, they should be placed under protective cover and flush with the ceiling.

Tailboards are necessary for certain horses.

Stall doors may be either (1) the sliding type sus-pended by overhead rollers or rails (preferably sliding within the stall, so horses cannot push them out), or (2) the swinging Dutch type, with the top part swing-ing down or to the side.

Weather protection over the stall door is impor-tant. It can be easily and simply achieved by an over-hanging roof.

HALLWAYS OR ALLEYWAYS

The hallways or alleyways of light-horse stables

should be a minimum of 8 feet in width[3] and height. Unlike stalls, they are usually not ceiled over, and they are usually higher.

The numerous types of flooring used in stalls are also used in hallways. In general, however, a clay floor is less popular than the hard-surfaced materials for this purpose.

Fig. 14-16. Hallway in the stable of L. Chase Grover, Woodside, California. Note that the traditional wide hallway separates two rows of stables, and that the hallway is not ceiled over. (Courtesy, *Sunset Magazine*, Menlo Park, Calif.)

Usually the hallway separates two rows of stables on either side. In northern areas, however, very often a hallway goes around the outside of the barn with two rows of stalls, back to back, down the center. In this arrangement, the alleyway is a very desirable place in which to exercise horses during inclement weather. This system, however, has one real disadvantage: It is difficult to arrange for direct sunlight in stalls that are located on the interior of the barn.

TACK ROOM

A tack room is an essential part of any barn. With one or two stall units, a combination tack and feed room is usually used, for practical reasons. On large establishments, the tack room is frequently the showplace of the stable. As such, the owner takes great pride in its equipment and arrangement. Also, depending upon the use of the horses, the tack room takes on an air and personality that represents the horses in the stalls.

[3]The width should be increased if wide vehicles are to be accommodated. With wide trucks, 10 to 12 ft may be desirable.

Generally, the tack rooms in stables where there are American Saddle Horses, harness horses, or hunters are rather formal. In the vernacular of the "horsey set," they maintain the "Boston touch." On the other hand, where Western-style riding prevails, generally the formal tack rooms have been replaced by more practical, simple rooms.

Tack rooms should be floored, rodent-proof and bird-proof, and ceiled over.

Figs. 14-17 through 14-21 present some tack rooms that are rather characteristic of stables wherein there are different types and classes of light horses.

Fig. 14-17. The impeccable formal tack room of the J. A. Smith stable, El Monte, California, contains special tack for Hackney and harness show ponies of different sizes and classifications. Since appointments in harness show classes are very important, each set of harness is made for a particular class and rig. The bugle on the table is used to call classes at the shows. (Photo by John H. Williamson, Arcadia, Calif.)

Fig. 14-18. The tack room of the Ella Mae Shofner stable, Montebello, California, is both attractive and practical for serving saddle horses. Note plastic harness cover on the wall, and the convenient saddle cleaning stand that holds all the necessary equipment for saddles, harness, and bridles. (Photo by John H. Williamson, Arcadia, Calif.)

Fig. 14-19. The tack room of the C. M. Deardorff stables, Santa Ana, California. This tack room presents an interesting and attractive display of pictures of winning horses, trophies and ribbons won in shows, and beautiful silver saddles used for parade. This tack room has been in active service for many years. (Photo by John H. Williamson, Arcadia, Calif.)

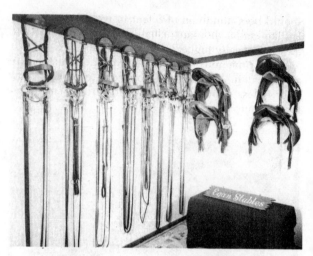

Fig. 14-21. The tack room of the Bob Egan stable, Pacific Palisades, California, is rather typical for owners of hunters, jumpers, and polo ponies. The tack box holds coolers, rub rags, cleaning equipment, hammers, nails, and other gear necessary in taking the horses to the shows. (Photo by John H. Williamson, Arcadia, Calif.)

Fig. 14-20. Tack room of Dwight Murphy's San Marcos Ranch, Santa Ynez Valley, California. Note the large natural color paintings by Nicholas S. Ferfires, depicting the different costumes and saddles of riders and the beautiful silver decorated saddles used in parades on the noted Palominos of San Marcos Ranch. (Photo by John H. Williamson, Arcadia, Calif.)

FIRE PROTECTION

Barns in which valuable horses are stabled should be posted with "no smoking" signs. Additionally, they should be equipped with (1) fire hoses in recessed areas, (2) an automatic fire alarm system, and (3) an automatic sprinkler system. In areas subject to electrical storms, barns should also be equipped with lightning rods.

The fire hazard can also be minimized by storing nothing but properly cured hay and by making sure that all wiring is in accord with strict electrical codes.

HORSE EQUIPMENT

Although the design of horse equipment is likely to be dominated by the fads and fancies of the owner, the basic needs are merely for simple but effective equipment with which to provide hay, concentrates, minerals, and water—without waste, and without hazard to the horse. Whenever possible, it is desirable that feed and water facilities be located so that they can be filled without necessitating that the caretaker enter the stall or corral, from the standpoint of both convenience and safety. In any event, it should not be necessary to walk behind horses in order to feed and water them.

Feed and water equipment may be built in or detached. Because specialty feed and water equipment is more sanitary, flexible, and suitable, many horsemen favor it over old-style wood mangers and concrete or steel tanks. Bulk-tank feed storage may be used to advantage on large horse establishments to eliminate sacks, lessen rodent and bird problems, and make it possible to obtain feed at lower prices by ordering large amounts.

A discussion of each of the common types of horse equipment follows. The specifications of feed and water equipment for horses are given in Table 14-6, under the section headed "Space Requirements."

Hayracks and Mangers

Some authorities advocate feeding the hay from the floor, inasmuch as horses feed from the ground while grazing naturally. This system has the advan-

tage of reducing the cost of construction, economizing in stall space, and enhancing the security of the horse in the stable. But it requires a careful allotment of hay in order to prevent waste. Moreover, some horses acquire the habit of pawing whatever is in front of them, so that they either eat contaminated hay or waste a considerable part of it.

Fig. 14-22. Steel hayrack in paddock at Murrieta Stud, Murrieta, California. (Courtesy, *The Thoroughbred of California*, Arcadia, Calif.)

Fig. 14-23. A good outdoor hayrack. (Courtesy, *Western Horseman*, Colorado Springs, Colo.)

The author favors the use of hayracks because they (1) alleviate the problem of contaminated hay and lessen parasitic infection, and (2) lessen pawing and waste. In barns with haylofts, there should be a chute above each hayrack, so that the hay can be dropped directly from the loft. Racks should open at the bottom so that dirt, chaff, and trash may be removed or will fall out. For stallions and broodmares, high racks should be used to eliminate injury hazards.

A stall rack may be made of metal, fiber, or plas-

Fig. 14-24. A good outdoor hayrack in a well-fenced horse paddock. (Courtesy, *Sunset Magazine*, Menlo Park, Calif.)

tic. A rack for horses should hold 25 to 30 pounds of hay and a rack for ponies, 10 to 15 pounds. It should be in a corner of the stall. The bottom of the rack should be the same height as the horse or pony at the withers.

A wooden manger may be used. It should be 30 in. wide and 24 to 30 in. long for horses and 20 in. square for ponies. Put the manger in the front or in a corner of the stall. The height should be 30 to 42 in. for horses and 20 to 24 in. for ponies.

A corral rack may be made of wood, steel, or aluminum. It should be large enough to hold a one-day supply of hay for the intended number of horses. Put the rack in the fence line of the corral if horses feed from one side only. Put it on high ground if horses feed from both sides. The top of the rack may be 1 to 2 feet higher than the horses at the withers. Corral hayracks that feed from both sides should be portable.

Grain Containers

There is hardly any limit to the number of types of grain containers, both patented and homemade, that are used by horsemen. These containers range all the way from very simple, inexpensive boxes to elaborate and costly equipment. Regardless of the type, the concentrate containers should be removed easily and cleaned by scrubbing. Such cleaning is especially important after a wet mash has been fed. Also, they should not constitute a hazard to horses.

A pail or tub can be made of metal, plastic, or rubber. Usually it has screw eyes and hooks or snaps so it can be suspended. The capacity should be 16 to 20 quarts for horses and 14 to 16 quarts for ponies.

Fig. 14-25. Feed bucket with snap hook, used in the stable of Mr. and Mrs. Edwin Knowles, Montecito, California. (Courtesy, *Sunset Magazine*, Menlo Park, Calif.)

Fig. 14-26. Automatic waterer, placed at one side of manger. (Courtesy, *Sunset Magazine*, Menlo Park, Calif.)

In a stall, the pail or tub should be at the front. The height should be two-thirds the height of the animal at the withers, or 38 to 42 inches for horses and 28 to 32 inches for ponies.

In a corral, put the tub or pail along a fence line and at the same height as in a stall.

A wooden box for horses should be 12 to 16 in. wide, 24 to 30 in. long, and 8 to 10 in. deep. A box for ponies should be 10 to 12 in. wide, 20 to 24 in. long, and 6 to 8 in. deep.

The location and height of a box in a stall are the same as for a pail or tub. Do not use a wooden box in a corral.

If desired, a wedge-shaped metal pan set on a wooden shelf can be mounted in a front corner of the stall and pivoted so it can be pulled out for filling and cleaning and then pushed back into the stall and locked in place.

Watering Facilities

As in feed containers, there is a bountiful supply of types of watering facilities from which to select; some stationary, and other removable. Whatever the type, the water container should be one that can be drained and cleaned frequently. All animals in stalls should be provided with water, and each paddock should have a suitable tank or waterer.

Water pails or automatic waterers are commonly used in stalls. Pails come in different materials— metal, plastic, or rubber. Automatic waterers are made

Fig. 14-27. Steel corral waterer in horse paddock, equipped with a float valve. (Courtesy, California Thoroughbred Assn., Arcadia, Calif.)

of metal. Pails or waterers should be located in a front corner of the stall and, preferably, considerable distance from feed containers. Otherwise, horses will carry feed to the waterer or drip water in the concentrate container. Pails or waterers should be stationed at a height equal to two-thirds the height of the horse at the withers, or about 38 to 42 inches for horses and 28 to 32 inches for ponies.

Automatic waterers or water tanks may be used in corrals. A 2-cup waterer will accommodate 12 horses; a large 20- by 30-inch automatic waterer will accommodate 25 horses.

Water tanks, which may be made of concrete or steel, should be 30 to 36 inches high, with 1 linear foot of tank space allowed for each 5 horses. Tanks should be equipped with float valves that are protected from the horses. When used in a corral, a water tank should be set in the fence line, and there should not be any protruding corners. If a tank is in a pasture and away from a fence, it should be painted white so that horses can see it at night.

The daily water requirements for horses are: mature horse, 12 gallons; foal to 2-year-old, and pony, 6 to 8 gallons. In cold areas, waterers should be heated and equipped with thermostatic controls. A satisfactory water temperature range in winter is 40° to 45° F and in summer 60° to 75° F. Automatic waterers should be checked daily, to make sure that they are working.

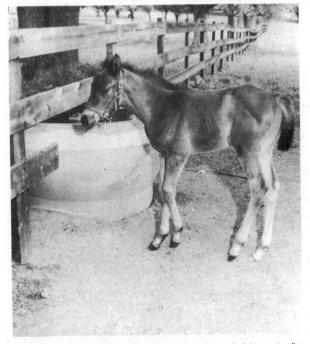

Fig. 14-28. Water tank set in fence line and rounded (no protruding corners), to protect horses from injury. (Courtesy, Kentucky Department of Public Information, Frankfort, Ky.)

Mineral Box or Self-feeder

All horses should have free access to (1) salt, and (2) a suitable mineral mix at all times, with these placed in separate areas of a two-compartment mineral box or self-feeder.

A box may be made of wood and a self-feeder may be made of metal or wood. In a stall, the box or self-feeder should be in a corner and located at the same height as the box or pail used for concentrates.

In a corral, mineral containers should be in a fence corner. The height should be two-thirds the height of the horse at the withers. If a mineral container is in the open, it should be protected from wind and rain.

Other Horse Equipment

In addition to the basic equipment needed for feeding and watering horses, there is hardly any limit to the other kinds of ingenious equipment used in the care and management of horses on breeding establishments. Some of these items of equipment, with illustrated methods of use in some cases, are presented in Fig. 14-29. (See page 290.)

FENCES FOR HORSES

Good fences (1) maintain boundaries, (2) make horse operations possible, (3) reduce losses to both animals and crops, (4) increase property values, (5) promote better relationships between neighbors, (6) lessen accidents from animals getting on roads, and (7) add to the attractiveness and distinctiveness of the premises.

Large pastures, in which the concentration of horses is not too great, may be fenced with woven wire. The mesh of the woven wire fence should be small so that horses cannot get their feet through it. Corrals, paddocks, and smaller pastures require more rigid materials. The deficiencies of board and pole fences are generally recognized. They are chewed by horses; they splinter and break, which may injure a horse; they must be painted and repainted; they're expensive to maintain; and they rot.

Until recently, metal fences—conventional steel, aluminum, wrought iron, chain link, cable, and others—possessed one or more deficiencies; to most people all of them were cold, unimaginative and unattractive in color; some could not be painted; some sagged from side to side; some corroded; some lacked resilience—when bumped they stayed bent; and most of them were difficult to construct. But metal fences have been greatly improved in recent years.

Table 14-4 lists the common materials for horse fences and gives the specifications for their use. (See page 291.)

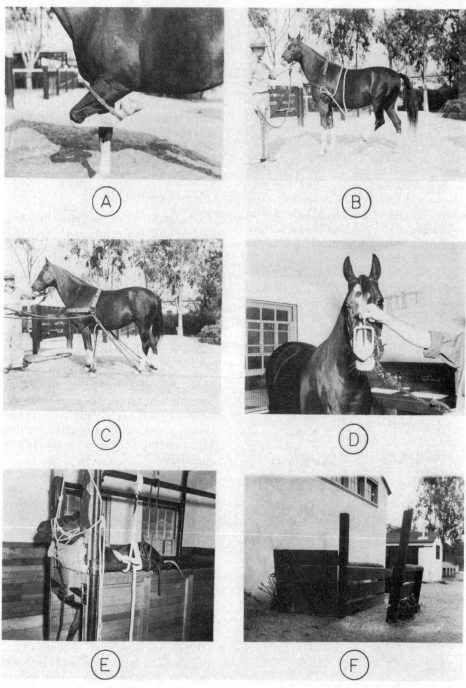

Fig. 14-29. Various means of restraining a horse: A, knee strap; B, side sling; C, casting harness; D, humane nose twitch; E, stocks; and F, a breeding chute. The essential features of such methods and equipment are (1) thorough restraint of the animal, without the hazard of injury, and (2) convenience and protection for the operator. (Courtesy, USDA)

Fig. 14-30. A well-built board fence, painted white, the most common type of fence in horse country. (Courtesy, Kentucky Department of Public Information, Frankfort, Ky.)

TABLE 14-4

HORSE FENCES

Post and Fencing Material	Post Length and Diameter	Size of Rails, Boards, or Poles and Gauge of Wire	Fence Height	Number of Rails, Boards, or Poles and Mesh of Wire	Distance Between Posts on Centers
			(in.)		(ft)
Steel or aluminum posts and rails[1]	7½ ft	10 or 20 ft long	60	3 rails	10
	7½ ft	10 or 20 ft long	60	4 rails	10
	8½ ft	10 or 20 ft long	72	4 rails	10
Wooden posts and boards	7½ ft; 4 to 8 in.	2 × 6 or 2 × 8 in. boards	60	4 boards	8
	8½ ft; 4 to 8 in.	2 × 6 or 2 × 8 in. boards	72	5 boards	8
Wooden posts and poles	7½ ft; 4 to 8 in.	4 to 6 in. diameter	60	4 poles	8
	8½ ft; 4 to 8 in.	4 to 6 in. diameter	72	5 poles	8
Wooden posts and woven wire[2]	7½ ft; 4 to 8 in.	9 or 11 gauge stay wire	55 to 58	12-in. mesh	12

[1]Because of the strength of most metal, fewer rails and posts are necessary than when wood is used.

[2]Locate one strand of barbed wire—with 4 points, 5 in. apart—2 in. to 3 in. above the top of the woven wire. This will prevent horses from breaking down the woven wire by leaning over the fence.

Fig. 14-31. A suitable wire fence for horses where the concentration of animals is not too great. The woven wire should be 55 to 58 inches high, with No. 9 top and bottom wire and No. 9 or 11 stay wire, and 12-inch mesh. One strand of barbed wire—with 4 points, 5 in. apart—2 in. to 3 in. above the top of the woven wire will prevent horses from breaking down the woven wire by leaning over the fence. This type of fence is also satisfactory for all other farm animals except young pigs.

Fig. 14-33. A strong pole fence. Fences for valuable horses should always be constructed of metal, poles, or 2-inch lumber, and there should not be any projections that might cause injury. Barbed wire fence is always hazardous for horses. (Courtesy, *Sunset Magazine*, Menlo Park, Calif.)

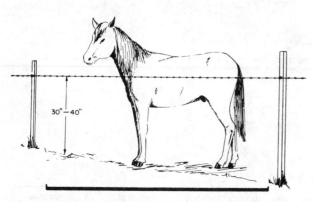

Fig. 14-32. An electric fence for horses, showing the proper height above the ground. Where a temporary enclosure is desired or where existing fences need bolstering from roguish or breachy animals, it may be desirable to install an electric fence, which can be done at a minimum cost. Remember that an electric fence can be dangerous; thus (1) necessary safety precautions should be taken, and (2) one should first check into the state regulations relative to their installation and use.

herewith presented. Table 14-5 shows the space requirements for buildings, and Table 14-6 shows the specifications for feed and water. In general, less space than indicated may jeopardize the health and well-being of animals, whereas more space make make the buildings and equipment more expensive than necessary. (See pages 293-295.)

Recommended Minimum Width of Service Passages

In general, the requirements for service passages are similar, regardless of the kinds of animals. Accordingly, the suggestions contained in Table 14-7 are equally applicable to horse, sheep, cattle, and swine barns. (See page 295.)

Storage Space Requirements for Feed and Bedding

The space requirements for feed storage for horses vary so widely that it is difficult to provide a suggested method of calculating space requirements applicable to such diverse conditions. The amount of feed to be stored depends primarily upon (1) the length of pasture season, (2) the method of feeding and management, (3) the kind of feed, (4) the climate, (5) the proportion of feeds produced on the farm or ranch in comparison with those purchased, and (6) the

SPACE REQUIREMENTS

One of the first, and frequently one of the most difficult, problems confronting the horseman who wishes to construct a building or item of equipment is that of arriving at the proper size or dimensions.

Space Requirements of Buildings and Equipment for Horses

Some conservative average figures of the building and equipment space requirements of horses are

TABLE 14-5

SPACE REQUIREMENTS OF BUILDINGS FOR HORSES

Kinds, Uses, and Purposes	Recommended Plan	Box Stalls or Shed Areas				Tie Stalls (size)
		Size	Height of Ceiling	Height of Doors	Width of Doors	
Smaller Horse Establishments: Horse barns for pleasure horses, ponies, and/or raising a few foals.	12' × 12' stalls in a row; combination tack-feed room for 1- and 2-stall units; separate tack and feed rooms for 3-stall units or more. Generally, not more than a month's supply of feed is stored at a time. Use of all-pelleted rations (hay and grain combined) lessens feed storage space requirements.	Horses: 12' × 12' Ponies:[1] 10' × 10'	8'-9'	8'	4'	5' wide; 10'-12' long
Larger Horse Breeding Establishments: The following specially designed buildings may be provided for different purposes:						
Broodmare and Foaling Barn	A rectangular building, either (1) with a central aisle, and a row of stalls along each side, or (2) of the "island" type, with 2 rows of stalls, back to back, surrounded by an alley or runway. Ample quarters for storage of hay, bedding, and grain. A record or office room, toilet facilities, hot water supply, veterinary supply room, and tack room are usually an integral part of a broodmare barn.	12' × 12' to 16' × 16'	9'	8'	4'	
Stallion Barn	Quarters for one or more stallions, with or without feed storage. A small tack and equipment room. Stallion paddocks, at least 300 ft on a side, adjacent to or in close proximity.	14' × 14'	9'	8'	4'	
Barren Mare Barn	An open shed or rectangular building, with a combination rack and trough down the center or along the wall. Storage space for ample hay, grain, and bedding.	150 sq ft per animal	9'	8'	4'	
Weanling or Yearling Quarters	Open shed or stalls. The same type of building is adapted to both weanlings and yearlings; but different ages and sex groups should be kept separate. When stalls are used, 2 weanlings or 2 yearlings may be placed together.	10' × 10'	9'	8'	4'	
Breeding Shed	A large roofed enclosure with a high ceiling; should include laboratory for the veterinarian, hot water facilities, and stalls for preparing mares for breeding and holding foals.	24' × 24'	15'-20'	8'	9'	
Isolation (quarantine) Quarters	Small barn, with feed and water facilities and adjacent paddock; for occupancy by new or sick animals.	12' × 12'	9'	8'	4'	
Riding Academies; Training and Boarding Stables	Either (1) stalls constructed back to back in the center of the barn, with an indoor ring around the outside; (2) stalls around the outside and a ring in the center; or (3) stalls on either side of a hallway or alleyway, and an outdoor ring.	12' × 12'	9'	8'	4'	5' wide; 10'-12' long

[1]Even for ponies, a 12' × 12' stall is recommended since (1) it costs little more than a 10' × 10', and (2) it affords more flexibility—it can be used for bigger horses when and if the occasion demands.

TABLE 14-6

SPECIFICATIONS OF FEED AND WATER EQUIPMENT FOR HORSES

Equipment for	Kind of Equipment	Materials and Design	Sizes for		In Stall		In Corral		Remarks
			Horses	Ponies	Location	Height	Location	Height	
Concentrates	Pail; tub	Metal, plastic, or rubber; usually with screw eyes, hooks, or snaps for suspending.	16-20 qt	14-16 qt	Front of stall.	⅔ height of animal at withers; or 38″-42″ for horses, and 28″-32″ for ponies.	Along fence line.	Same height as stall.	For sanitary reasons, removable concentrate containers are preferable so that they can be taken out and easily and frequently cleaned—which is especially important after a wet bran mash has been fed.
	Box	Wood	Width 12″-16″ 10″-12″ Length 24″-30″ 20″-24″ Depth 8″-10″ 6″-8″		″	″			If desired, a pie-shaped metal pan set in a wooden shelf can be mounted in a front corner of the stall and pivoted in such manner that it can be pulled outward for filling and cleaning, then returned into the stall and locked in place.
Hay	Stall rack	Metal, fiber, or plastic	25-30 lb	10-15 lb	Corner of stall; in trailer or van.	Bottom of rack same height as horse or pony at withers.			Hayracks (1) eliminate contaminated hay and lessen parasite infestation, and (2) lessen pawing and waste. Racks should open at bottom so that dirt, chaff, and trash may be removed or will fall out. For stallions and broodmares, always use high racks to avoid injury hazards.
	Manger	Wood	Width 30″ 20″ Length 24″-30 20″		Front or corner of stall.	30″-42″ for horses; 20″-24″ for ponies.			
	Corral rack	Wood	Large enough to provide one day's supply of hay for intended number of horses.				In fence line if it feeds from one side only. On high ground if it feeds from both sides.	Top of rack may be 1″ to 2″ higher than height of horse at withers.	Corral hayracks that feed from both sides should be portable.
Mineral	Box	Wood			Corner of stall.	Same height as concentrate box.	Fence corner	⅔ height of horse at withers.	If mineral container is stationed in the open—in a corral, or in a pasture—it should be protected from wind and rain. Mineral containers should have 2 compartments—one for mineral mix, and the other for salt.
	Self-feeder	Metal or wood				″	Fence corner		
Water	Stall, automatic	Metal; 1 cup or 2 cups.			Front corner of stall.	24″-30″			The daily water requirements are: Mature horse, 12 gal; foals to 2-year-olds, 6-8 gal; and ponies 6-8 gal. In colder areas, waterers should be heated, and equipped with thermostatic controls. A satisfactory water temperature range in the winter is 40°-45° F; in summer, 60°-80° F. Watering facilities should be designed so as to facilitate draining and cleaning. Also, they should
	Corral, automatic				In fence corner.	24″-30″			
	Pail	Metal, plastic, or rubber			Front of stall.	⅔ height of horse at withers; or 38″-42″ for horses, and 28″-32″ for ponies.			

(Continued)

TABLE 14-6 (Continued)

Equipment for	Kind of Equipment	Materials and Design	Sizes for		In Stall		In Corral		Remarks
			Horses	Ponies	Location	Height	Location	Height	
									be located proper distance from feed containers; otherwise, horses will (1) carry feed to the waterer, or (2) slobber water into the concentrate container. A 20" × 30" automatic waterer will accommodate about 25 horses, and a 2-cup waterer will serve 12 head. Automatic waterers should be checked daily.
	Tank	Concrete; steel					Set in fence so that there are no protruding corners; or painted white out in corral or pasture.	30"-36"	One linear foot of tank space should be allowed for each 5 horses. Tanks should be equipped with a float valve, which should be protected.

TABLE 14-7
RECOMMENDED MINIMUM WIDTHS FOR SERVICE PASSAGES

Kind of Passage	Use	Minimum Width
Feed alley	For feed cart	4'
Driveway	For wagon, spreader, or truck	9'-12'
Doors and gate	Drive-through	8'- 9'

number of horses. Normally, the storage capacity should be sufficient to handle all feed grown on the farm and to hold purchased supplies.

Table 14-8 gives the storage space requirements for feed and bedding. This information may be helpful to the individual operator who desires to compute the barn space required for a specific horse enterprise. Also, it provides a convenient means of estimating the amount of feed or bedding in storage. (See page 296.)

SHOW-RING

There are no standard specifications relative to size, type of construction, and maintenance of show-rings. Yet, all the better rings meet certain basics.

For most purposes, the author recommends a ring 125 feet by 250 feet in size. It is recognized, however, that many good show-rings are either smaller or larger than these dimensions.

In order to allow plenty of room for such classes as working hunters and jumpers, in which as many as 12 separate jumps may be used, a number of shows have copied the famous Devon Horse Show for ring size. It measures 150 feet by 300 feet. But some horsemen consider it too big.

Those favoring smaller rings point out that the Spanish Riding School ring, in Vienna, in which the famous Lipizzans perform, is only 180 ft long, 59 ft wide, and 56 ft high; and that New York's Madison Square Garden ring, in which the National Horse Show is held, is slightly under 100 ft wide.

In addition to ring size, consideration must be given to proper footing—to achieving resilience, yet firmness and freedom from dust. With an outdoor ring, establishing proper drainage and constructing a good track base are requisite to all-weather use. Drainage is usually secured by (1) locating the ring so that it is high, with the runoff away from it, and (2) installing a perforated steel pipe (with the perforations toward the bottom side), or drainage tile, underneath the track if necessary.

Resilience, with firmness, is usually secured by mixing organic matter with dirt or sand. For example, the entire ring at the Spanish Riding School is covered with a mixture of ⅔ sawdust and ⅓ sand, which is sprinkled at intervals to keep the dust down.

In many indoor rings of the United States, 6 to 8 in. of tanbark on a dirt base are used. Unless tanbark is wet down at frequent intervals, it tends to pulverize and give poor footing. Others mix shavings and/or sawdust with dirt or sand to obtain a covering of 18 to 24 in. of the material. One good ring with which the author is familiar was prepared by laying down 9 in. of wood shavings, 2 in. of sawdust, and 4 in. of sand—all of which were mixed together, then oiled. Still others add a bit of salt, because it holds moisture when wetted down, thereby minimizing dust.

TABLE 14-8

STORAGE SPACE REQUIREMENTS FOR FEED AND BEDDING[1]

Kind of Feed or Bedding	Pounds per Cubic Foot	Cubic Feet per Ton	Pounds per Bushel of Grain
Hay-Straw:			
1. Loose			
Alfalfa	4.4-4.0	450-500	
Nonlegume	4.4-3.3	450-600	
Straw	3.0-2.0	670-1000	
2. Baled			
Alfalfa	10.0-6.0	200-330	
Nonlegume	8.0-6.0	250-330	
Straw	5.0-4.0	400-500	
3. Chopped			
Alfalfa	7.0-5.5	285-360	
Nonlegume	6.7-5.0	300-400	
Straw	8.0-5.7	250-350	
Corn:			
15½% moisture			
Shelled	44.8		56
Ear	28.0		70
Shelled, ground	38.0		48
Ear, ground	36.0		45
30% moisture			
Shelled	54.0		67.5
Ear, ground	35.8		89.6
Barley, 15%	38.4		48.0
ground	28.0		37.0
Flax, 11%	44.8		56.0
Oats, 16%	25.6		32.0
ground	18.0		23.0
Rye, 16%	44.8		56.0
ground	38.0		48.0
Sorghum, grain 15%	44.8		56.0
Soybeans, 14%	48.0		60.0
Wheat, 14%	48.0		60.0
ground	43.0		50.0

[1]*Housing and Equipment Handbook*, MWPS-6, Midwest Plan Service, Iowa State University, Ames, Iowa, 1968, p. 62.

Fig. 14-34. Indoor arena in Rex C. Cauble's Cutter Bill Championship Arena (named after Cutter Bill, the World Champion Cutting Horse, Denton, Texas). This working arena is 360 feet long and 80 feet wide. It is illuminated with Mercury Vapor lights. The floor is made of 4 inches of sand over a hard clay base. (Courtesy, *Quarter Horse Journal*, Amarillo, Tex.)

For outdoor rings, needed organic matter for resilience is sometimes secured by seeding rye, or other small grain, on the track during the off season, then disking the green crop under.

No matter how good the construction, a show-ring must be maintained, both before the show and between events. It must be smoothed and leveled, and holes must be filled; and, when it gets too hard, it must be penetrated. A flexible, chain-type harrow is recommended for show-ring maintenance.

In addition to ring size, construction, and maintenance, consideration must be given to layout for facilitating reversing a performance class in a ring that has turf or other decorative material in the center; attractiveness of the ring; spectator seating capacity, comfort, and visibility; nearby parking; and handling the crowd.

DEPRECIATION ON BUILDINGS AND EQUIPMENT

In 1962, the Treasury issued "useful life" guidelines. If followed, they will not be challenged. For buildings, it's 25 years; for machinery and equipment, it's 10 years.

SELECTED REFERENCES

Title of Publication	Author(s)	Publisher
Agricultural Engineers Yearbook	Ed. by R. H. Hahn, Jr.	American Society of Agricultural Engineers, St. Joseph, Mich., annual
Bibliography of Livestock Waste Management	J. R. Miner D. Bundy G. Christenbury	Office of Research and Monitoring, U.S. Environmental Protection Agency, Washington, D.C., 1972
Breeding and Raising Horses, Ag. Hdbk. No. 394	M. E. Ensminger	Agricultural Research Service, USDA, Washington, D.C., 1972
Facts & Figures for Farmers		Doane Agricultural Service, Inc., St. Louis, Mo., 1972
Farm Builder's Handbook, Second Edition	R. J. Lytle	Structures Publishing Company, Farmington, Mich., 1973
Farm Building Design	L. W. Neubauer H. B. Walker	Prentice-Hall, Inc., Englewood Cliffs, N.J., 1961
Farm Buildings, Third Edition	D. G. Carter W. A. Foster	John Wiley & Sons, Inc., New York, N.Y., 1947
Farm Buildings, Second Edition	J. C. Wooley	McGraw-Hill Book Company, New York, N.Y., 1946
Farm Service Buildings	H. E. Gray	McGraw-Hill Book Company, New York, N.Y., 1955
Farm Structures	H. J. Barre L. L. Sammet	John Wiley & Sons, Inc., New York, N.Y., 1950
Handbook of Livestock Equipment	E. M. Juergenson	The Interstate Printers & Publishers, Inc., Danville, Ill., 1971
Horse Breeding Farm, The	L. C. Willis	A. S. Barnes & Co., Inc., Cranbury, N.J., 1973
Horse Breeding and Stud Management	H. Wynmalen	J. A. Allen & Co. Ltd., London, England, 1950
Horse Science Handbook, Vols. 1-3	Ed. by M. E. Ensminger	Agriservices Foundation, Clovis, Calif., 1963, 1964, 1966
Horsemanship and Horse Care Ag. Info. Bull. No. 353	M. E. Ensminger	Agricultural Research Service, USDA, Washington, D.C., 1972
Light Horses, Farmers' Bull. No. 2127	M. E. Ensminger	Agricultural Research Service, USDA, Washington, D.C.
Livestock Waste Management and Pollution Abatement		American Society of Agricultural Engineers, St. Joseph, Mich., 1971
Livestock Waste Management System Design Conference for Consulting and SCS Engineers		University of Nebraska Cooperative Extension Service, Lincoln, Neb., 1973

(continued)

Title of Publication	Author(s)	Publisher
Principles of Animal Environment	M. L. Esmay	Avi Publishing Co., Westport, Conn., 1969
Stockman's Handbook, The, Fourth Edition	M. E. Ensminger	The Interstate Printers & Publishers, Inc., Danville, Ill., 1970
Structures and Environment Handbook		Midwest Plan Service, Iowa State University, Ames, Iowa, 1972
Stud Managers' Handbook, The	Ed. by M. E. Ensminger	Agriservices Foundation, Clovis, Calif., pub. annually since 1965

* * * * *

Plans and specifications for horse buildings and equipment can also be obtained from the local county agricultural agent, your state college of agriculture, and materials and equipment manufacturers and dealers.

CHAPTER 15

HORSE HEALTH, DISEASE PREVENTION, AND PARASITE CONTROL[1]

[1]The material presented in this chapter is based on factual information believed to be accurate, but is not guaranteed. Where the instructions and precautions given herein are in disagreement with those of competent local authorities or reputable manufacturers, always follow the latter two.

by

DR. ROBERT F. BEHLOW, DVM, Professor and Extension Veterinarian, North Carolina State University, Raleigh, North Carolina,

and

DR. M. E. ENSMINGER, Ph.D., Distinguished Professor, Wisconsin State University; Adjunct Professor, California State University; and Collaborator, U.S. Department of Agriculture,

with

DR. J. H. DRUDGE, DVM and Sc.D., Professor, Department of Veterinary Science, University of Kentucky, Lexington, Kentucky, serving as coauthor of the important section on "Internal Parasites of Horses."

Horses are generally quite valuable and, in the case of horses in training or competition, they must be in top shape. Hence, they merit well-informed owners. When disease is encountered, they require the best of care and treatment that a competent veterinarian can administer.

With the advent of the automobile and truck, most draft horses and mules were automatically quarantined on the farm or ranch where they had less opportunity to rub noses, less need to eat out of contaminated livery stable mangers and feed boxes, and none of the hazards of the community hitching post and the town watering tank. But the rise of light horses for recreation and sport, along with distant travel and rapid transportation, has brought new diseases, parasites, and ailments to plague horses.

In recent years, science has moved with rapid and far-reaching strides in the field of horse health, disease prevention, and parasite control; and new and important advances are being made almost daily. Progressive horsemen and veterinarians will wish to follow these modern developments with care, con-

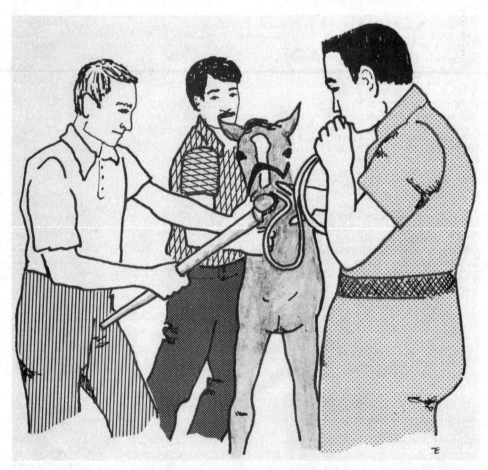

Fig. 15-1. A horse and his friends. The veterinarian and caretakers are ever present to guard against diseases and parasites.

stantly improving upon present information and recommendations.

Currently, some parasites are being used to carry out their own self-destruction. For example, male screwworms are being sterilized by gamma rays from radioactive cobalt; then, when normal screwworm females, which mate only once, mate with these sterile males, their eggs do not hatch. Also, new chemicals are being used in parasite control.

SIGNS OF GOOD HEALTH

The horseman needs to be familiar with the behavioral norms of horses in order to detect and treat abnormalities, especially illnesses.

At the outset, it should be recognized that it is difficult to enumerate all the signs of good health, along with the departures therefrom that constitute ill health. It may be even more difficult to determine whether an illness is due to faulty nutrition or communicable disease. This ability, inborn and honed by experience, sets the expert caretaker apart from the novice. If in doubt, the veterinarian should be called.

The signs of good horse health, any departure from which constitutes a warning signal, follow:

1. *Contentment*—Healthy horses are contented. They look completely unworried when resting.

2. *Alertness*—In horse vernacular, healthy horses are "bright eyed and bushy tailed." They are alert and will prick up their ears on the slightest provocation.

3. *Eating with relish*—In healthy horses, the appetite is good and the feed is attacked with relish (as indicated by eagerness to get to the feed—pawing, nickering, etc.).

4. *Normal productivity*—Healthy horses maintain their normal level of production—in weight and in work.

5. *Sleek coat and pliable and elastic skin*—A sleek, glossy coat of hair and a pliable and elastic skin characterize healthy horses. When the hair coat loses its luster and the skin becomes dry, scurfy, and hidebound, there is usually trouble.

6. *Bright eyes and pink eye membranes*—In healthy horses, the eyes are bright and the membranes—which can be seen when the lower lid is pulled down—are whitish pink in color and moist.

7. *Normal feces and urine*—The consistency of the feces varies with the diet; for example, when horses are first turned on lush grass they will be loose. Normally, they should be firm and not dry; and there should not be large quantities of undigested feed. The urine should be clear. Both the feces and urine should be passed without effort, and should be free from blood, mucus, and pus.

8. *Maintaining the social organization*—Healthy animals whose movements are not restricted by close confinement maintain a normal social organization in the herd—they move about in a certain pattern.

9. *Normal temperature, pulse rate, and breathing rate*—Table 15-1 gives the normal temperature, pulse rate, and breathing rate of animals (for comparative purposes, species other than the horse are listed). In general, any marked and persistent deviations from these norms may be looked upon as a sign of ill health.

Every horseman should provide himself with an animal thermometer, which is heavier and more rugged than the ordinary human thermometer. The temperature is measured by inserting the thermometer full length in the rectum, where it should be left a minimum of three minutes. Prior to inserting the thermometer, a long string should be tied to the end.

In general, infectious diseases are ushered in with a rise in body temperature, but it must be remembered that body temperature is affected by stable or outside temperature, exercise, excitement, age, feed, etc. It is lower in cold weather, in older animals, and at night.

The pulse rate indicates the rapidity of the heart action. The pulse of a horse is taken either at the margin of the jaw where an artery winds around from the inner side, at the inside of the elbow, or under the tail. It should be pointed out that the younger, the smaller, and the more nervous the animal, the higher

TABLE 15-1

NORMAL TEMPERATURE, PULSE RATE, AND BREATHING
RATE OF FARM ANIMALS

| Animal | Normal Rectal Temperature | | Normal Pulse Rate | Normal Respiration Rate |
	Average	Range		
	(degrees F)	(degrees F)	(rate/min.)	(rate/min.)
Horses	100.5	99.0-100.8	32-44	8-16
Cattle	101.5	100.4-102.8	60-70	10-30
Sheep	102.3	100.9-103.8	70-80	12-20
Goats	103.8	101.7-105.3	70-80	12-20
Swine	102.6	102.0-103.6	60-80	8-13
Poultry	100.0	105.0-107.0	200-400	15-36

the pulse rate. Also, the pulse rate increases with exercise, excitement, digestion, and high outside temperature.

The breathing rate can be determined by placing the hand on the flank, by observing the rise and fall of the flank, or, in the winter, by watching the breath condensate in coming from the nostrils. Rapid breathing due to recent exercise, excitement, hot weather, or poorly ventilated buildings should not be confused with disease. Respiration is accelerated in pain and in febrile conditions.

SIGNS OF ILL HEALTH

Most sicknesses, both nutritional and communicable, are ushered in by one or more departures from the signs of good health. They're foretold by signs of poor health, by indicators that tell the expert caretaker that all is not well—that tell him that his horses will go off feed tomorrow, and that prompt him to do something about it today.

Among the signs of horse ill health are: off feed—the animal does not eat and graze normally; listlessness; droopy ears; sunken eyes; humped-up appearance; abnormal dung—either very hard or cow-like dung suggest an upset in the water balance or some intestinal disturbance following infection; abnormal urine—repeated attempts to urinate without success or off-colored urine should be cause for suspicion; abnormal discharges from the nose, mouth, and eyes, or a swelling under the jaw; unusual posture—such as standing with the head down or extreme nervousness; persistent rubbing or licking; dull hair coat and dry, scurfy, hidebound skin; pale, red, or purple mucous membranes lining the eyes and gums; reluctance to move or unusual movements; higher than normal temperature; labored breathing—increased rate and depth; altered social behavior such as leaving the herd and going off alone; and sudden drop in production—weight gains or work.

A PROGRAM OF HORSE HEALTH, DISEASE PREVENTION, AND PARASITE CONTROL

In addition to following a program embracing superior breeding, sound management, and scientific feeding, the good horseman will adhere to a strict sanitation and disease prevention program designed to protect the health of his animals. Although the exact program will differ from farm to farm, the basic principles will remain the same. With this thought in mind, the following program of horse health, disease prevention, and parasite control is presented with the hope that the horseman will use it (1) as a yardstick with which to compare his existing program, and (2) as a guidepost so that he and his local veterinarian,

and other advisors, may develop a similar and specific program for his own enterprise.

I. General Horse Health Program

The following health program is recommended for all horses:

1. Have on hand first aid supplies, and know when and how to use them in case of accident or sudden illness.

2. Vaccinate against the most common diseases (Table 15-2).

3. Avoid public feeding and watering facilities.

4. When signs of infectious disease are encountered, promptly isolate affected animals, provide them with separate water and feed containers, and follow the instructions and prescribed treatment of the veterinatian.

5. Prevent or control parasites by adhering to the following program:

   a. Provide good sanitary practices and a high level of nutrition.

   b. Have adequate acreage; use temporary seeded pasture rather than permanent pasture, and practice rotation grazing.

   c. Pasture young stock on clean pastures, never allowing them to graze on an infested area unless the area has been either plowed or left idle for a year in the interim.

   d. Do not spread fresh horse manure on pastures grazed by horses; either store the manure in a suitable pit for at least two weeks or spread it on fields that are to be plowed and cropped.

   e. When small fields or paddocks must be used, pick up the droppings at frequent intervals.

   f. Keep pastures mowed and harrowed (use a chain harrow).

   g. Prevent fecal contamination of feed and water.

   h. Follow a worming program and schedule to control internal parasites.

   i. When external parasites are present, apply the proper insecticide.

   j. If cattle are on the farm, alternate the use of pastures between cattle and horses, since horse parasites will die in cattle.

   k. Avoid overgrazing, because there are more parasites on the bottom inch of the grass.

II. Breeding and Foaling Health Program

The following health program is recommended where horses are bred and foals are produced.

1. Mate only healthy mares to healthy stallions and observe scrupulous cleanliness at the time of service and examination. Never breed a mare from which there is a discharge.

TABLE 15-2
EQUINE DISEASE VACCINATION PROGRAM AND SCHEDULE

Disease	Type	Initial Immunization			Booster	Age First Given to Foals
Distemper (strangles)	Intramuscular vaccine. (Distemper bacterin causes some complications.)	1st injection.	2nd injection—7 days after the first.	3rd injection—7 days after the second.	One annually.	3 months.
Encephalomyelitis: 1. Eastern and Western	Intradermal vaccine. (Also, there is a new killed virus vaccine which can be used to vaccinate simultaneously against Eastern, Western, and Venezuelan types.)	1st injection—in spring (April-May).	2nd injection—7-14 days after the first.		Both injections should be repeated annually.	2-3 months.
2. Venezuelan (VEE)	Subcutaneous vaccine.	One injection only. (Do not give to pregnant mares.)			One annually.	3 months.
Equine influenza (flu)	Intramuscular vaccine.	1st injection.	2nd injection—4-12 weeks after the first.		One annually.	3-4 months.
Rabies	Intramuscular vaccine. (High egg passage or inactivated tissue culture vaccines only.)	1st injection.	2nd injection—30 days after the first.		One annually.	3 months.
Tetanus (lockjaw)	Toxoid—horse builds immunity lasting for at least 6-18 months after vaccination.	1st injection—intramuscular.	2nd injection—intramuscular, 2-4 weeks after 1st injection.		One annually.	2-3 months.
	Antitoxin—only effective for 10-20 days.	Given to injured animals that have not been previously immunized with tetanus toxoid.				
Viral rhino-pneumonitis (Virus abortion)	Intramuscular vaccine.	Pregnant mares: 1st injection—after 2nd months of pregnancy.	Pregnant mares: 2nd injection—during 5th-7th month of pregnancy.		Both injections should be repeated annually.	
		All other horses should be given initial vaccination in 2 doses (2-4 weeks apart), followed by annual vaccination with a single dose.				
	Intranasal vaccine—not allowed in all states.	1st injection—during July.	2nd injection—during October.		Both doses should be repeated annually to all horses on the farm.	July of birth year.

2. Provide plenty of exercise for the stallion and the pregnant mare, either in harness or under the saddle or in roaming over a large pasture in which plenty of shade and water are available.

3. During the spring and fall months when the weather is warm, allow the mare to foal in a clean, open pasture, away from other livestock. During inclement weather, place the mare in a roomy, well-lighted, well-ventilated box stall—which first should be cleaned carefully, disinfected thoroughly with a lye solution (made by adding 1 can of lye to 12 to 15 gallons of water), and provided with clean straw (not shavings) for the occasion. After foaling, all wet, stained, or soiled bedding should be removed and the floor lightly dusted with lime (excessive lime is irritating to the eyes and nasal passages of foals). The afterbirth should be examined for completeness, and after ascertaining that all of it has been discharged it

should be burned or buried in lime; and the mare should be kept isolated until all discharges have ceased.

4. To lessen the danger of navel infection, promptly treat the navel cord of the newborn foal with tincture of iodine.

5. As a precaution against foaling diseases and other infectious troubles, the veterinarian may administer antibiotics to both the mare and foal on the day of foaling.

III. Health Program for New Horses and Visiting Mares

The following health program is recommended where new horses and visiting mares are brought into the herd.

1. Isolate new animals for a period of three weeks

before adding them to the herd. During this period, the veterinarian may (a) administer sleeping sickness vaccine (in season) and tetanus toxoid, (b) make a thorough general and parasitic examination, and (c) give a genital examination of breeding animals, and treat where necessary.

2. Require that mares brought in for breeding be accompanied by a health certificate issued by a veterinarian. Beware of mares that have had trouble in foaling or have lost foals.

3. If feasible, breed visiting mares near their own isolation quarters, using tack and equipment that is not interchanged with that used for mares kept on the establishment.

Vaccination Schedule

In no case should the vaccination program be used as a crutch for poor management. Likewise, no vaccination program is entirely successful without strict management practices to limit possible spread of infections.

For guidance purposes, a suggested vaccination program and schedule is given in Table 15-2.

FIRST AID FOR HORSES

First aid for horses, as for humans, refers to the immediate and temporary care given in the case of accident or sudden illness before the veterinarian arrives. Its purposes: (1) to prevent accidents, (2) to avoid further injury and unnecessary suffering in case of injury, (3) to recognize serious trouble if and when it strikes, (4) to assist the veterinarian in carrying out the prescribed treatment, and (5) to teach simple remedies and treatments which may be used safely if it is not possible to get a practitioner.

First aid does not alleviate the need for professional assistance; rather, a well thought-out plan in advance of a possible emergency may save the horse's life and usefulness. To this end, the horseman should (1) have on hand first aid supplies and be knowledgeable relative to their use, and (2) know what to do in case of accident or sudden illness.

● *First aid supplies*—First aid supplies should be conveniently available, but they should be stored where neither children nor horses have access to them. The following items are rather basic; but the horseman is admonished to seek the counsel and advice of his local veterinarian relative to these and additional supplies.

Adhesive tape	Epsom salts
Bandages	Eyedropper
Blanket	Germicidal soap
Boric acid	Hoof knife
Bucket	Hot-water bottle
Clippers	Liniment
Disinfectants	Metal syringe

Physiologic saline (sterile solution)	Screwworm preparation
	Splints
Plastic ice bag	Sterile absorbent cotton
Potassium iodide	Stomach tube
Scalpel	Thermometer
Scissors	Tourniquet

● *Liniment for the horse*—A good liniment, properly used, will hasten and assist nature in returning an injured part to normal and relieve fatigue, overexertion, and soreness.

Liniment is an astringent. Its use, along with massage, stimulates circulation, assists the body in removing waste products of muscle metabolism, and hastens nature in returning an injured part to normal.

The use of liniment is recommended for the following conditions: lameness, stiffness, soreness, strained tendons, sore shins, certain types of arthritis, and swellings, bumps, and bruises. It hastens recovery time and helps to prevent everyday injuries from turning into serious problems.

Also, liniment may be used, according to manufacturer's directions, as a body wash or brace after strenuous workouts or transportation, especially on the horse's legs, to relieve fatigue and overexertion, and to prevent soreness.

● *Wounds*—Accidents do happen; horses are more injury prone and subject to a more awesome variety of wounds than any other class of domestic animal. They are thin-skinned; and they cut, tear, and bruise easily. For this reason, maximum wound preventative measures should be an integral part of horse management procedure. Such things as loose wire, sticks, sharp rocks, machinery, loose or broken boards, and trash have no place in horse pastures or corrals; and stables and trailers should be periodically examined for loose boards, protruding nails, or any sharp objects.

Despite all possible precautions, however, as long as there are horses, there will be such things as wire cuts, saddle galls, cinch sores, rope burns, and other abrasions. Hence, it is important that the horseman have on hand at all times a good first aid powder, as an aid in (1) stopping bleeding; (2) killing microbes; (3) drying the wound, thereby discouraging flies and other insects from congregating around it and speeding the healing process; and (4) lessening proud flesh.

The horse, more than any other species of animal, must receive proper care and treatment of wounds. Mistreatment will result in slow healing, excessive scarring, blemishing, and sometimes unsoundness. Wounds below the knees and hocks are especially sensitive; hence, they require careful treatment, and sometimes bandaging, to prevent complications.

Wounds take a variety of forms, sizes, and severity; and, in turn, these determine the treatment. Generally speaking, there are five classes of wounds: (1)

cut wounds (incised) produced by sharp objects, such as glass or sharp metal, where there is a minimum of tissue damage and little bruising; (2) torn wounds (lacerated) produced by irregular objects, such as barbed wire and horn gores, characterized by extensive damage to underlying tissues; (3) puncture wounds (penetrating) produced by sharp objects, such as nails and pitchforks, characterized by small punctures and a considerable amount of deep injury; (4) abrasions caused by such things as rope burns and rubbing against a door or trailer, characterized by oozing of the serum and little bleeding; and (5) bruises (contusions) caused by a blow, such as a kick or fall, which do not break the skin but which cause bleeding and fluid loss deep down.

If the wound is serious, such as a deep puncture wound, or where the swelling or irritation persists, a veterinarian should be consulted. With minor wounds, however, the horseman may administer first aid. At the outset, it should be recognized that only nature can produce living cells and heal a wound; hence, man can merely aid the process.

Although wound treatment will vary according to form and severity, the following steps may be involved:

Step 1—Stop the bleeding. If it is severe, pressure may be applied by tight bandaging above and below the wound, or by placing a pad on the wound and bandaging over it. When a large artery is severed, as evidenced by bright red blood spurting with a pulsing action, it may be necessary to control the loss of blood by applying a tourniquet on the side of the wound nearest the heart, until the arrival of the veterinarian. A tourniquet must be released after about 20 minutes for a minute or two, but it can be reapplied.

Step 2—Clean the wound by washing it with cotton swabs soaked in warm saline (salt) solution. Remove all foreign material (objects and dirt), hair, and torn tissue. Cleanliness is of great importance.

Step 3—Clip or shave long hair (it is often best not to remove short hair, because of the danger of contamination) from around the wound, to a distance of about ½ inch.

Step 4—Apply first aid powder according to the directions on the label.

Step 5—Suture incised and lacerated wounds if necessary, with this decision being left to, and the work done by, a veterinarian. Proper wound drainage should always be established.

Step 6—Protect against tetanus by administering (a) tetanus antitoxin if the animal is not already on a toxoid program, or (b) a toxoid booster when the horse has been immunized previously with this product. Also, the veterinarian may inject an antibiotic(s).

Step 7—Switch from powder to salve. As soon as

a scab has formed over the wound, switch from first aid powder to first aid salve.

It should be recognized that poor nutrition of the horse will delay healing of a wound. Hence, poorly balanced or inadequate rations, bad teeth, and parasitism may contribute to delayed wound healing.

● Bruises and swellings—Blows may produce hemmorages in the tissues under the skin. First aid for such injuries consists in (1) measures to stop the hemorrhage—cold applications together with firm, even pressure, (2) cold-water showers and cold-water bandages until the swelling stops, and (3) heat or liniment applied after the swelling has stopped.

● Fractures—In all cases of fracture, professional assistance should be secured as quickly as possible. Until help arrives, keep the horse as quiet as possible. With leg fractures, it may be necessary to splint the affected limb with wood or pipe to hold the break in place; then wrap it with towels or other padding.

● Colic—When colicky symptoms appear, keep the animal on its feet; walk slowly and quietly, by leading; and apply heat to the abdomen.

● Azoturia—When the characteristic wine-colored urine, sweating distress, and stiffness are noted, (1) stop all exercise, (2) rub the horse dry and blanket him, (3) apply hot-water bottles or heated blankets or cloths to the swollen and hardened muscles, and (4) secure professional help as quickly as possible.

● Founder (laminitis)—Pending the arrival of the veterinarian, pull the shoes if the horse is shod, and stand the animal in a cold-water bath or apply cold bran poultices (preferably using ice water in either treatment).

● Bleeders—Hemorrhage in the nasal cavity occurs in certain families of racehorses. When observed, cease exercise, apply ice packs to the muzzle to help clot the blood, and call the veterinarian.

● Mercury poisoning—Mercury poisoning from consuming grains treated with fungicides is not uncommon. While professional help is on the way, drench the horse with an antidote of a dozen egg whites.

Common sense should always prevail when administering first aid; and the horseman should realize his limitations and consult a professional when he is unsure of himself or of his ability.

DISEASES OF HORSES[2]

Every good horseman knows that keeping animals healthy is a major responsibility. In the discussion that follows, an attempt is made to give a combi-

---

[2]The entire section on "Diseases of Horses" was authoritatively reviewed by the following eminent equine veterinarians: Dr. Jerry Harsch, DVM, Goldendale, Wash.; and Dr. Victor S. Myers, Jr., DVM, Stillwater, Minn.

nation of practical and scientific information relative to the most important diseases affecting horses. It is intended that this should enhance the services of the veterinarian, for the horseman can do a better job in controlling animal diseases if he has enlightened information at his disposal. Effective animal health programs call for full cooperation between the horseman and his veterinarian. Perhaps it is also a fair statement of fact to add that superstition, myth, and secret formulas are used more extensively in treating the diseases of horses than in treating ailments of any other class of livestock.

Disease prevention calls for vaccinating horses against the most common diseases. It calls for establishing and following a vaccination program and schedule, as insurance against heavy losses from certain diseases (see Table 15-2). The program and schedule will vary somewhat from area to area and from herd to herd. Hence, it should be worked out in consultation with the local veterinarian. At the outset, it should be recognized that horsemen should not attempt to vaccinate against every disease for which there is a vaccine. Rather, they should vaccinate against those diseases which are the greatest hazard in a given herd and area, then assume a calculated risk relative to the rest.

Vaccines should always be used according to the instructions of the manufacturer, in both time and method. Also, they should be kept cool before being opened, and they should be used immediately after they are opened.

Anthrax (Splenic Fever, Charbon)

Anthrax, also referred to as splenic fever or charbon, is an acute infectious disease affecting horses and other warm-blooded animals and man; but cattle are most susceptible. It usually occurs as scattered outbreaks or cases, but hundreds of animals may be involved. Certain sections are known as anthrax districts because of the repeated appearance of the disease. Grazing animals are particularly subject to anthrax, especially when pasturing closely following a drought or pasturing land that has been recently flooded. In the United States, human beings get the disease mostly from handling diseased or dead animals on the farm, or from handling hides, hair, and wool in factories.

Historically, anthrax is of great importance. It is one of the first scourges to be described in ancient and Biblical literature; it marks the beginning of modern bacteriology, being described by Koch in 1876; and it is the first disease in which immunization was effected by means of an attenuated culture, Pasteur having immunized animals against anthrax in 1881.

SYMPTOMS AND SIGNS[3]

The mortality is usually quite high. It runs a very short course and is characterized by a blood poisoning (septicemia). The first indication of the disease may be the presence of severe symptoms of colic accompanied by high temperature, loss of appetite, muscular weakness, depression, and the passage of bloodstained feces. Swellings may be observed over the body, especially around the neck region; and in the horse they may appear around the mammary gland or sheath. Milk secretion may turn bloody or cease entirely, and there may be a bloody discharge from all body openings. In very acute anthrax, the animal may die without having shown any noticeable symptoms.

CAUSE, PREVENTION, AND TREATMENT

The disease is identified by a microscopic examination of the blood in which will be found *Bacilli anthracis*, the typical, large rodshaped organism causing anthrax. These bacilli can survive for years in a spore stage, resisting all destructive agents. As a result, they may remain in the soil for extremely long periods.

This disease can be prevented by immunization. In the so-called anthrax regions, vaccination should be performed well in advance of the time when the disease normally makes its appearance. Several types of biologics (serums, bacterins, and vaccines) are available for use in anthrax prevention. The choice of the one to be used should be left to the local veterinarian or state livestock sanitary officials. In infested areas, vaccination should be repeated each year. Herds that are infected should be quarantined, and all milk and other products should be withheld from the market until the danger of disease transmission is past. The horseman should never open the carcass of a dead animal suspected of having died from anthrax; instead, the veterinarian should be summoned at the first signs of an outbreak.

When the presence of anthrax is suspected or proved, all carcasses and contaminated materials should be completely burned or deeply buried, preferably on the spot. This precaution is important because the disease can be spread by dogs, coyotes, buzzards, and other flesh eaters and by flies and other insects.

When an outbreak of anthrax is discovered, all sick animals should be isolated promptly and treated. All exposed healthy animals should be vaccinated; pastures should be rotated; the premises should be

---

[3]Currently, many veterinarians prefer the word "signs" rather than "symptoms," but throughout this chapter the author accedes to the more commonly accepted terminology among horsemen and includes the word "symptoms."

quarantined; and a rigid program of sanitation should be initiated. These control measures should be carried out under the supervision of a veterinarian.

Massive doses (3 to 12 million units) of antibiotics (penicillin or streptomycin) may be effective if used in the early stages of the disease. Likewise, if used at the first signs, 50 to 100 milliliters of antianthrax serum may also be helpful.

Distemper (Strangles)

This is a widespread communicable disease of horses and mules, prevailing especially among young animals. It is also referred to as strangles or infectious adenitis.

Animals that have had the disease are usually immune for life.

SYMPTOMS AND SIGNS

In a week or less following exposure, the disease may manifest itself suddenly in the form of depression and loss of appetite. There will be high fever followed by a discharge of pus from the nose. By the third or fourth day of the disease, the glands under the jaw start to enlarge, become sensitive, and eventually break open and discharge pus. Because the pharynx is also involved, a cough is present that is easily initiated. The disease may spread to other lymph glands of the body, producing the condition known as bastard strangles. As soon as the abscesses are drained, healing usually takes place.

CAUSE, PREVENTION, AND TREATMENT

The disease is caused by the bacterium *Streptococcus equi*, which infects only horses. Transmission is usually by the ingestion or inhalation of the infected discharges. The disease seems to spread rapidly when "green" horses are brought together. The organism is capable of existence outside the animal's body for as long as six months.

Prevention consists in avoiding contact with infected animals or contaminated feeds, premises, or equipment. Public stables and watering troughs are to be avoided. At the first sign of symptoms, the affected animal should be put in strict quarantine. The contaminated quarters and premises should be thoroughly cleaned and disinfected. All excreta and contaminated bedding should be burned or buried.

Vaccination is the best preventative for strangles. Previously unvaccinated horses should receive the vaccine in three 10-milliliter doses at weekly intervals. One "booster" shot is sufficient for horses that are known to have had strangles. Vaccination should be on a yearly basis, with one "booster" dose. The vaccine should not be given to newborn foals.

Good nursing is the most important treatment. This includes clean, fresh water, good feed, and shelter with uniform temperature away from drafts. The veterinarian may prescribe one of the antibiotics or sulfas, or both. Early treatment is of the utmost importance in distemper.

Encephalomyelitis (Sleeping Sickness; or Eastern, Western, or Venezuelan Equine Encephalomyelitis)

This brain disease, which affects both horses and man, is known as equine encephalomyelitis, or sleeping sickness. Both horse and man are "dead-end" hosts, infected only by the mosquito.

Since 1930, the Eastern and Western types of the disease have assumed alarming proportions in the United States. Then, in 1971, Venezuelan equine encephalomyelitis first occurred in the United States, when an outbreak was reported in Texas. The Venezuelan type was first diagnosed in Venezuela in 1936 and was reported in several South and Central American countries prior to appearing in the United States. Equine encephalomyelitis is seasonal in character, extending from early summer until the first sharp frost of fall, when it invariably disappears.

SYMPTOMS AND SIGNS

In the early stages, the horse walks aimlessly about, crashing into objects. Later, the animal may appear sleepy, standing with a depressed head. Grinding of the teeth may be noted. Local paralysis may develop, causing the animal to go down. Inability to

Fig. 15-2. Horse with encephalomyelitis (sleeping sickness). Note the sleepy attitude and the depressed head. (Courtesy, Department of Veterinary Pathology and Hygiene, College of Veterinary Medicine, University of Illinois)

swallow, paralysis of the lips and bladder, and blindness may be observed. If the affected animal does not recover, death usually occurs in two to four days following the onset of symptoms. Those animals which recover, but which are unable to react to normal stimuli, are referred to as "dummies." Some animals make full recovery.

In mild cases, the horse may merely yawn a few times; and this may be the only clinical sign of the disease.

CAUSE, PREVENTION, AND TREATMENT

The disease is caused by several distinct viruses. The three most active types in the United States are: Eastern equine encephalomyelitis, Western equine encephalomyelitis, and Venezuelan equine encephalomyelitis. All three viruses may be spread from animals to man, with mosquitoes serving as the primary means of transport. Wild birds, rodents, and wild animals in all areas of the country are reservoirs of the disease, which enters the body of a mosquito when it feeds on infected creatures. While in the mosquito, the virus multiplies and becomes highly concentrated in the salivary glands. The infected mosquito then transmits the virus to a horse or a man, whichever is handy at its next feeding. In the Venezuelan type, horses can spread the disease directly since the virus is present in their saliva and nasal discharges.

Generally speaking, mortality from the Western type does not exceed 50 percent, whereas that from the Eastern and Venezuelan types is 90 percent or higher.

Prevention entails vaccination of all horses against the 3 separate strains. Vaccination against Eastern and Western encephalomyelitis involves 2 injections, 7 to 14 days apart, given annually in April or May. Protection against Venezuelan equine encephalomyelitis requires one injection only, given annually. Also, there is a new killed virus vaccine which can be used to vaccinate simultaneously against all three types—Eastern, Western, and Venezuelan. A veterinarian should administer the vaccine. Other preventive measures include the isolation of infected animals in screened cages or the application of insect repellent; prompt disposal of all infected carcasses; destruction, if possible, of insect breeding grounds; and discouragement of movement of animals from an epizootic area to a clean one. Fly and mosquito control seems to be very effective, since most outbreaks of the disease do not extend to racetracks and stables where insect control is practiced.

Treatment is not very effective, because of the rapid course of the disease. Since the Western type progresses more slowly and results in a lower mortality rate than the Eastern and Venezuelan types, it lends itself to more supportive treatment. Good nursing is perhaps the best and most important treatment. The maintenance of fluid and electrolyte balance is recommended. No specific therapeutic agent is known to influence the course of the disease.

Equine Abortion

Abortion is the expulsion of the impregnanted ovum at any period prior to the time that the foal can survive out of the uterus. If the foal is advanced enough to live, it is known as premature parturition, and in the mare this may occur as early as the tenth month.

Of all mares that become pregnant, it is estimated that ⅔ will have normal, healthy foals; and ⅓ will either abort or produce weak, infected foals. The financial loss can be readily understood when one realizes that stud fees alone may range from $50 to $50,000, not to mention the investment in the mares and other production factors involved in the breeding establishments.

SYMPTOMS AND SIGNS

Abortion symptoms vary according to the stage of pregnancy in which it occurs, whether it is early or late. Sometimes, especially during the first two months of pregnancy, the mare may miscarry without observable symptoms, and the fact only becomes known by her coming back in heat. At other times, a small clot of blood, containing the rudiments of the foal, may be found behind the mare if she is under close observation. If the occurrence is somewhat later in gestation, there will be some general disturbance, loss of appetite, neighing, and straining; and the small body of the fetus is expelled, enveloped in its membranes. In later stages of pregnancy, abortions are attended by greater constitutional disturbance; and the process resembles normal parturition, with the aggravation that more effort and straining is required to force the fetus through the comparatively undilatable cervix mouth of the uterus. The vulva becomes swollen, with mucus or even bloody discharge; the abdomen droops; the udder fills; the mare paws with the forefeet and kicks with the hind feet, switches the tail, moves around uneasily, lies down and rises, strains, and, as in natural foaling, expels first mucus and blood then "the waters," and finally the fetus. These signs of approaching abortion may last an hour or two, or they may last for a day or more. The symptoms subside for a time, only to reappear with renewed energy.

CAUSE, PREVENTION, AND TREATMENT

Causes of abortion in mares may be grouped into two types: (1) infectious agents, such as viruses, bac-

teria, and fungi; and (2) noninfectious abortions, such as twinning, hormonal deficiencies, congenital anomalies, and miscellaneous causes. Some of the more common causes are discussed in the sections that follow.

● *Infectious causes of abortion*—The effect of infection may be either (1) indirect, where there is destruction of large areas of the placenta causing fetal death through starvation and toxemia; and (2) direct, where the microorganisms invade the fetus.

A discussion of each of the infectious abortions follows:

1. *Virus abortion*—The most common cause of abortion in mares is a herpes virus (the herpes class of viruses commonly affect the cells of the skin and mucous membranes), which produces the disease known as rhinopneumonitis in horses. Rhinopneumonitis gained notoriety as "virus abortion" because abortion often results when pregnant mares are affected with the disease.

Rhinopneumonitis is a mild, usually nonfatal disease of the upper respiratory tract, commonly seen in young horses in the fall or winter. It is characterized by a cough, a nasal discharge, a loss of appetite, and a temperature of 102° - 105° F. As the disease progresses, the temperature returns to normal, but the nasal discharge and cough may persist for several weeks. In older horses, the disease may be so mild as to go unnoticed. Most abortions due to this virus occur between the eighth and eleventh months of gestation, although they may occur as early as the fifth month. Sometimes the foal is born alive at term, but dies at 2 to 3 days of age due to infection by the virus. The fetal membranes are seldom retained; and the genital tract returns to normal as quickly as it does following normal parturition. The abortion rate may approach 100 percent in a herd of susceptible mares. An effective vaccine will prevent rhinopneumonitis and should be used in areas subject to the disease.

The virus of *equine arteritis* may also cause abortion. It produces more obvious signs of illness than equine rhinopneumonitis, including discharges from the eyes and nose, fever (102°-106° F), and filling (edema) of the limbs. A laboratory examination is necessary conclusively to establish the presence of the specific virus. Up to 50 percent of affected pregnant mares may abort. The name "arteritis" is derived from the particular type of arterial damage that this disease inflicts; it results in degeneration of the middle layer of arterial walls, especially in the small arteries. Treatment consists in absolute rest and good nursing, augmented by antibiotics to prevent or combat secondary bacterial infections. An effective vaccine is available and should be used in areas where the disease is a problem.

2. *Bacterial abortion*—Bacterial infection is a common cause of abortion in mares. Several species of bacteria have been incriminated. *Salmonella abortus equi*, which was formerly responsible for abortion storms, still occurs sporadically. However, the most common cause of bacterial abortion at the present time is organisms of the streptococci group. Other bacteria frequently cultured from aborted feti include *E. coli, Klebsiella,* and *Staphylococci.* They may cause abortion at any stage of pregnancy. But, generally *Streptococci* cause abortion during the first five months, whereas *E. coli* are more apt to cause abortion during the last half of pregnancy. Bacteria gain entrance to the reproductive tract at the time of foaling or breeding, thence travel to the uterus, where they cause infection of the fetal membranes, and result in abortion. Bacterial abortion, which may occur at any stage of pregnancy, is often characterized by retention of the placenta, as well as by metritis or inflammation of the uterus. Treatment of the mare may be necessary before she can be rebred successfully. It is a good practice to swab mares before rebreeding, to determine if harmful bacteria are present in the vagina. The latter precaution is especially important where it is the intent to rebreed mares on the ninth day after foaling.

Adherence to the following program will materially reduce bacterial abortions:

a. Breed mares only when the genital tract has returned to normal.

b. Mate only healthy (bacteriologically clean) mares to healthy stallions and be scrupulously clean at the time of breeding.

c. Give a mare foaling abnormally in any respect plenty of time to return to the normal state.

d. Remember that infection is ever present in the filth of the external genitals of both the stallion and the mare.

e. Suturing the lips of the vulva will control this type of abortion in many mares. But this should be done by and on the advice of the veterinarian

When a mare is found to have a severe genital infection, she should be treated properly and should have sexual rest for from six months to a year.

3. *Fungi*—Abortions may result from infection of the placenta by various types of fungi, which are widespread in nature. Fungi probably enter the uterus during the heat period at which conception occurs, or soon after birth—in the case of foaling mares. Another school of thought is that the fungi are inhaled into the lungs, thence enter the blood and go to the pregnant uterus. Fungi do not attack the fetus directly; rather, they cause degeneration of the placenta so that the fetus has insufficient nourishment. For this reason, the aborted fetus is often small and only a

fraction of the normal weight for its gestational age. If abortion does not occur, the foal may be carried to full term and be born in a resaonably vigorous, but undersized and undernourished, state. Most mycotic abortions occur during the second half of pregnancy. There is no vaccine.

● *Noninfectious causes of abortion*—The common noninfectious causes of abortion are:

1. *Twinning*—The birth of healthy twin foals is unusual. The generally accepted theory relative to the inability of the mare to carry twin foals successfully to term is that it is due to placental insufficiency— meaning that there are not enough fetal membranes to accomodate and provide nutrition for two developing fetuses.

2. *Hormone failure*—The hormone progesterone plays a dominant role in the maintenance of pregnancy, preparing the uterus for reception of the fertilized egg and the attachment of the placenta. It is responsible for the necessary changes in the uterus for the continuance of pregnancy and nourishment of the fetus. Other hormones, such as estrogen and cortisone, are also involved in the process and can contribute to abortion. Thus, the maintenance of pregnancy is a matter of hormone balance. Although there are many gaps in our knowledge of reproductive physiology, it appears that some abortions are caused by failure of the glands that control hormonal balance.

3. *Congenital defects*—Early embryonic deaths, which may be mistaken for failure of conception or silent heats, frequently occur. Some of these are presumed to be due to genetic or chromosomal defects resulting in improper development of the embryo, followed by rejection by the dam.

4. *Miscellaneous causes*—This embraces all cases of abortion that cannot be definitely classified in any of the categories discussed above—it includes abortions *not* caused by viruses, bacteria, fungi, twinning, hormonial deficiencies, or congenital anomalies. In the category of miscellaneous causes of abortions are nutritional deficiencies, certain drugs, accidents and injury—such as a severe kick that disturbs the uterus, and noninfectious pathological lesions in the uterus of the mare. Causes of this type are so numerous and general that aside from good breeding, feeding, and management practices not much can be done to prevent them; but these three practices are vital in prevention of abortion as well as other diseases. The mare may abort from almost any cause that very profoundly disturbs the system.

It is important to recognize an impending abortion as early as possible, for sometimes it may be prevented. When a pregnant mare shows any general indefinable illness, she should be examined closely for abortion indications. Any suggestive indications should prompt the horseman to call the veterinarian immediately.

Preventive measures embrace avoidance of all possible causes. It begins with mating only healthy mares to healthy stallions, and with being scrupulously clean at the time of breeding. New horses should always be isolated as a preventive measure, and aborting mares should be quarantined. Where abortions have occurred in the broodmare band, the special cause in the matter of feed, water, exposure to injuries, overwork, lack of exercise, and so forth may often be identified and removed. Avoid constipation, diarrhea, indigestion, bloating, violent purgatives or other potent medicines—including administering cortisones in late pregnancy, painful operations, and slippery roads.

The following points are pertinent in controlling abortion in a band of broodmares:

1. Prevent rhinopneumonitis by following a planned immunization program under the direction of a veterinarian.

2. Prevent equine arteritis in areas where the disease is a problem by administering the vaccine.

3. Prevent *Salmonella* abortion on premises known to be contaminated by vaccinating all pregnant mares each year.

4. Control and prevent bacterial abortion by mating only healthy mares to healthy stallions and observing scrupulous cleanliness at the time of service and examination. Suture mares where necessary.

5. Keep broodmares healthy and in good flesh, and feed a ration that contains all the essential elements of nutrition.

When a case of abortion is encountered, the following procedure is recommended: (1) Gather up the fetus and afterbirth with great care and arrange through the local veterinarian for a diagnosis by the state diagnostic laboratory; (2) isolate the mare in a place where she can be kept in quarantine; (3) burn or bury the bedding; and (4) thoroughly disinfect the stall with a five percent Lysol solution.

One of the most important factors to remember about abortion is that a veterinarian should be called for diagnosis, prevention, treatment, and cure. To forget this is to invite trouble and to pave the way for possible spreading of the infection.

Equine Infectious Anemia—E.I.A. (Swamp Fever)

Equine infectious anemia (E.I.A.) is a very serious blood disease of horses and mules. It is sometimes referred to as swamp fever, mountain fever, slow fever, or malarial fever. Very early, the name swamp fever was given to the disease in the United States because of its prevalence in moist locations— such as on the coastal plains of Texas, and in the lowlands of the Platte and Mississippi Rivers—but it is now known that altitude is not a factor. The disease is

found in the higher altitudes, far removed from any swamps. This infectious disease was first reported in France as early as 1843, and it has existed in the United States for many years. It is characterized by a great variation in symptoms and course. There is a marked tendency for the disease to localize on certain farms or areas, and it does not spread rapidly.

SYMPTOMS AND SIGNS

Symptoms vary, but some of the following are usually seen: high and intermittent fever, depression, stiffness, and weakness (especially in the hindquarters), anemia, jaundice, edema and swelling of the lower body and legs, unthriftiness, and loss of condition and weight—even though the appetite remains good. Affected animals may die within two to four weeks.

Fig. 15-3. Horse with equine infectious anemia (or swamp fever), five days before death. (Courtesy, USDA)

It is an unfortunate truth, however, that neither the symptoms nor the postmortem findings relative to infectious anemia are sufficiently characteristic to make a definite diagnosis possible. Fortunately, a new and reliable test, known as the "Coggins Test," may be employed for identification.

The Coggins Test for diagnosing E.I.A. is accurate—if properly used, fairly simple, and rather inexpensive. The test was developed by Dr. Leroy Coggins of the New York State Veterinary College, Cornell University; hence, the common name. Technically, the correct name for the blood test is the agar gel immunodiffusion (AGID) test. It is valid only if the blood sample is drawn by a veterinarian and submitted to a recognized laboratory. The AGID test is approved by the U.S. Department of Agriculture and is conducted in approximately 100 laboratories.

The Coggins Test is based on detection of antibodies (modified globulins) to E.I.A. virus. Infected horses become positive to this test 2 to 4 weeks after the onset of the initial infection and remain test posi-

tive the rest of their lives. Since foals receive large quantities of antibodies from their dams by way of colostrum, a nursing foal born of an E.I.A. positive dam may be positive for the first 4 to 6 months of its life but not actively infected. Such foals can be considered free from the disease if they test negative at about 7 months of age.

The test is usually repeated to confirm all positive reactions because horses are often destroyed on the basis of the test. Positive reactors are identified with an "A" in a visible body brand or lip tattoo, which stands for anemia. It does not indicate "Grade A" as some buyers have belatedly discovered after acquiring horses at what they thought were bargain prices. Animals branded with an "A" are quarantined and cannot be moved except for slaughter or approved research purposes.

The U.S. Department of Agriculture reported that of the horses tested in 1974 9,089, or 2.56 percent, tested positive.

CAUSE, PREVENTION, AND TREATMENT

Equine infectious anemia is caused by a specific virus. The virus is commonly carried in the blood of infected animals over long periods of time, even though these carrier animals may have made a temporary or even a rather lasting apparent recovery. It is spread chiefly by biting insects, especially flies, but it may also be spread by contaminated hypodermic needles. Studies show that any debilitating factors that lower the animal's resistance not only may predispose the animal to disease but may greatly influence its progress.

There is no vaccination. The following preventive measures are recommended:

1. Use disposable hypodermic needles (one needle to one horse) and sterilize all other skin-penetrating instruments by boiling at least 15 minutes.

2. Practice good sanitation and eliminate or reduce biting insects as much as possible.

3. Be on the alert for sick horses and get a veterinary diagnosis on them.

4. Use tack equipment on one horse only.

5. At racetracks and shows, keep stalls, starting gates, and other facilities clean.

When a positive diagnosis has been made, it is advisable to kill the animal and properly destroy the carcass. Infected mares or stallions should not be used for breeding purposes.

After horse owners test and eliminate all infected animals from their herd, the Coggins Test can be used to protect their stock from reinfection, (1) by buying horses only after they have been tested and found free from the disease, (2) by not allowing untested horses

to be stabled or pastured with their own, and (3) by not taking their horses to any assembly point (show, sale, racetrack, trail ride, etc.) where prior testing is not required.

In 1976, the U.S. Department of Agriculture amended the animal import regulations to require that imported horses pass the Coggins Test to assure that they are free of equine infectious anemia.

The treatment of the disease has been unsuccessful because at the present time no method is known to destroy the virus in the bloodstream.

Equine Influenza (Flu)

Equine influenza is a highly contagious disease which has been recognized for many years and which is widespread throughout the world. It frequently appears where a number of horses are assembled, such as at racetracks, sales, and shows.

While the mortality or death rate from influenza is low, the economic loss is high. The disease may interrupt training programs and racing schedules for weeks or months; and it may force the withdrawal of animals from sales, thereby delaying and/or making for less favorable disposal.

Although both horses and man are subject to influenza and the clinical symptoms are similar in the two species, there appears to be no transmission of the disease between them.

SYMPTOMS AND SIGNS

Young animals (except for very young foals, which have passive immunity from the dam's milk) are particularly susceptible to influenza. For this reason, outbreaks of epidemic proportions are rather common at racetracks where large numbers of yearlings and 2-year-olds are shipped for training and racing purposes. Older animals are usually immune, probably due to repeated exposure to the disease. Symptoms develop as early as 2 days or as late as 10 days after exposure.

The onset of influenza in horses is marked by rapidly rising temperature, which may reach 106° F and persist for 2 to 10 days. Other signs include loss of appetite, extreme weakness and depression, rapid breathing, a dry cough, and water discharges from the eyes and nostrils, which are followed by a white- to yellow-colored nasal discharge.

Since one of the first symptoms of equine influenza is a rapidly rising temperature, it is recommended that the temperature of young horses be taken twice daily under the following circumstances:

1. For a period of 4 to 5 days prior to shipment.
2. For 2 to 10 days after arrival at a new location.

3. When horses are stabled in an area where influenza, coughs, and colds are known to exist.

CAUSE, PREVENTION, AND TREATMENT

Influenza is caused by any one of a group of related viruses.

Conditions incident to shipment, exposure to cold, sudden changes of climate, and fatigue appear to lower the resistance of horses so as to make them more susceptible to the disease.

It is believed that the most common method of transmission of influenza is by way of the respiratory tract, and that the virus itself is carried on contaminated feed, bedding, water, buckets, brooms, on the clothing and hands of attendants, and on transportation facilities.

Effective prevention is obtained by annual vaccination, using 2 doses, with the second injection given 4-12 weeks after the first. For continued protection, each vaccinated animal must receive (1) an annual booster, or (2) a booster when there is exposure or an epizootic condition. Also, all new animals should be isolated for 3 weeks, and sick animals should be quarantined.

Treatment should be handled by the veterinarian. No exercise, no matter how mild, should be permitted during the period of evelated temperature. The early use of antibiotics and/or sulfa drugs will prevent secondary bacterial complications.

Glanders (Farcy)

This is a very old disease, commonly referred to as farcy or *malleus*. It was described as early as 400 B.C., at which time it received the Greek name *malleus* from Aristotle. Glanders is an acute or chronic infectious disease of horses, mules, and donkeys; but it can be transmitted to other animals and to human beings through close contact.

Although glanders was worldwide at one time, it has been eliminated in many countries, including the United States. Nevertheless, horses are now transported widely and quickly, with the result that there is danger of diseased horses being brought in from glanders infected areas. To alleviate the latter hazard, all horses coming from any area where the disease exists are tested.

SYMPTOMS AND SIGNS

The disease usually manifests itself either in the acute or chronic form. The chronic form is most often observed in the horse, while the acute form is seen more in mules and donkeys. The incubation period varies from weeks to months. The chronic symptoms may be manifested in the lungs, skin, or nasal pas-

sages. In the nasal form, there is a nasal discharge which later becomes pus. Hard red nodules, which break down into abscesses and then ulcers, will be seen. When the ulcers heal, they leave a star-shaped scar. The skin form is often seen with the nasal form. It is characterized by the development of nodules and ulcers in the skin and subcutaneous tissue. Both the skin and nasal forms are thought to originate in the lungs. The lungs are the most common location for the lesions of glanders. Evidence of infection consists in a loss in condition and lack of endurance, with sudden bleeding from the nose. Coughing followed by a mucous discharge may be noted. At this stage, there are nodules and abscesses in the lung tissue. In the acute form of the disease, death usually occurs within a week after many or all of the symptoms noted above have been in evidence.

CAUSE, PREVENTION, AND TREATMENT

The cause of this disease is the bacterium *Malleomyces mallei*. It is transmitted by inhalation or ingestion of the exudate containing the causative organism.

Any suspected animal should be subjected to the "mallein test." Positive diagnosis is cause for immediate destruction of the animal and the careful cleaning and disinfection of the contaminated equipment and premises. All exposed animals should be tested at frequent intervals.

No method of immunization is available. Treatment with sulfadiazine, given daily for 20 days, has proven fairly effective.

Navel Ill (Joint Ill, Actinobacillosis)

Navel ill is an infectious disease of newborn foals, calves, and lambs, although it occurs less frequently in calves and lambs than in foals.

SYMPTOMS AND SIGNS

Navel infection is characterized by loss of appetite, by swelling, soreness and stiffness in the joints, by umbilical swelling and discharge, and by general listlessness. There are slowly developing cases that do not become apparent until four to six months of age. These foals usually succumb.

CAUSE, PREVENTION, AND TREATMENT

Navel infection is caused by several kinds of bacteria.

The recommended preventive measures are: sanitation and hygiene at mating and parturition, and dipping the navel of the newborn animal with iodine.

Lack of sanitation is the most important factor in the cause of this disease.

For treatment, the veterinarian may give a blood transfusion, and he may administer a sulfa drug or an antibiotic.

Rabies (Hydrophobia, Madness)

Rabies is an acute infectious disease of horses and all other warm-blooded animals and man. It is characterized by deranged consciousness and paralysis, and it terminates fatally. This disease is one that is far too prevalent, and, if present knowledge were applied, it could be controlled and even eradicated.

When a human being is bitten by a dog that is suspected of being rabid, the first impulse is to kill the dog immediately. This is a mistake. Instead, it is important to confine the animal under the observation of a veterinarian until the disease, if it is present, has a chance to develop and run its course. If no recognizable symptoms appear in the animal within a period of two weeks after it inflicted the bite, it is safe to assume that there was no rabies at the time. Death occurs within a few days after the symptoms appear, and the dog's brain can then be examined for specific evidence of rabies. With this procedure, unless the bite is in the region of the neck or head, there will usually be ample time in which to administer treatment to exposed human beings. As the virus has been found in the saliva of a dog at least five days before the appearance of the clinically recognizable symptoms, the bite of a dog should always be considered potentially dangerous until proved otherwise. In any event, when people are bitten or exposed to rabies, they should see their local doctor, who will select and use the proper vaccine.

SYMPTOMS AND SIGNS

Less than 10 percent of the rabies cases appear in horses, cattle, swine, and sheep. The disease usually manifests itself in 2 forms: the furious, irritable, or violent form, or the dumb or paralytic form. It is often difficult to distinguish between the 2 forms, however. The furious type usually merges into the dumb form because paralysis always occurs just before death.

In comparison with other animals, the horse may resort to more violence and is exceedingly dangerous.

CAUSE, PREVENTION, AND TREATMENT

Rabies is caused by a filtrable virus which is usually carried into a bite wound by the infected saliva. The malady is generally transmitted to farm animals by dogs and certain wild animals such as the fox, skunk, and bat.

Rabies can best be prevented by attacking it at its chief source, the dog. With the advent of an improved antirabies vaccine for the dog, it should be a requirement that all dogs be immunized. This should be supplemented by regulations governing the licensing, quarantine, and transportation of dogs. Also, the control of wild carnivores and bats is of increasing importance in the eradication of rabies.

When horses are bitten or exposed to rabies, they should be seen by a veterinarian. The older vaccine, used for rabies control in all animals, was a killed vaccine of brain origin. Today, several new rabies vaccines are available, and others are being developed and tested experimentally. Thus, the choice of a rabies vaccine for horses should be made by the veterinarian.

Tetanus (Lockjaw)

Tetanus is chiefly a wound-infection disease that attacks horses (and other equines) and man, and less frequently swine, cattle, sheep, and goats. It is generally referred to as lockjaw.

In the United States, the disease occurs most frequently in the South, where precautions against tetanus are an essential part of the routine treatment of wounds. The disease is worldwide in distribution.

SYMPTOMS AND SIGNS

The incubation period of tetanus varies from one to four weeks, but may be from one day to many months. It is usually associated with a wound but may not directly follow an injury. The first noticeable sign of the disease is a stiffness first observed about the head. The animal often chews slowly and weakly and swallows awkwardly. The third eyelid is seen protruding over the forward surface of the eyeball (called "haws"). The animal then shows violent spasm or contractions of groups of muscles brought on by the slightest movement or noise. It usually attempts to remain standing throughout the course of the disease. If recovery occurs, it will take a month or more. In over 80 percent of the cases, however, death ensues—usually because of sheer exhaustion or paralysis of vital organs.

CAUSE, PREVENTION, AND TREATMENT

The disease is caused by an exceedingly powerful toxin (more than 100 times as toxic as strychnine) liberated by the tetanus organism (*Clostridium tetani*). This organism is an anaerobe (lives in absence of oxygen) which forms the most hardy spores known. It may be found in certain soils, horse dung, and sometimes in human excreta. The organism usually causes

Fig. 15-4. Horse with tetanus. Notice the stiff-legged condition and partly raised tail. (Courtesy, Department of Veterinary Pathology and Hygiene, College of Veterinary Medicine, University of Illinois)

trouble when it gets into a wound that rapidly heals or closes over it. In the absence of oxygen, it then grows and liberates the toxin which follows up nerve trunks. Upon reaching the spinal cord, the toxin excites the symptoms noted above.

Immunity against tetanus can be obtained through inoculation with either toxoid or antitoxin. Toxoid is an injection of neutralized tetanus toxin to stimulate the horse to build its own antibodies. Antitoxin is a concentrated serum with tetanus toxin antibodies taken from another horse and administered as a preventive measure following wounds, surgery, or foaling.

Active immunization is achieved through 2 injections of tetanus toxoid at 2- to 4-week intervals, followed by annual booster injections. If an immunized horse is wounded 2 months or more following such immunization, it is recommended that the veterinarian administer another toxoid injection at that time. If a horse not previously immunized is wounded, it is recommended that the veterinarian administer antitoxin, which will give passive protection for up to 2 weeks.

Once the disease develops, the horse should be placed under the care of a veterinarian. Early in the course of the disease, massive doses of antitoxin—100,000 to 200,000 units or more—may be helpful. Also, tranquilizing drugs are effective in reducing the extent and severity of muscular spasma, and antibiotics are helpful.

Horses with tetanus should be confined to darkened box stalls in which the feeding and watering facilities are placed high enough so that the animal is capable of gaining access to them without lowering its head. Support by slinging should be given wherever possible.

PARASITES OF HORSES[4]

The term parasite refers to a form of animal life that lives in or on the body of a host animal, deriving its food therefrom. Parasites kill some horses, but, by and large, the main damage is insidious and results in lowered efficiency—i.e., something less than the best performance of which the animal is capable.

Internal Parasites of Horses[5]

Some 150 different kinds of internal parasites infect horses throughout the world,[6] and probably no individual animal is ever entirely free from them. Although equines are not unique among herbivorous animals in their susceptibility to parasitism, they do harbor many diverse species of pests. Probably this can be attributed to the fact that horses, perhaps more than other domestic animals, have been transported widely for service in war and colonizing enterprises and for racing and breeding purposes. Fortunately, comparatively few of these parasites inflict serious damage upon their host; but those few can be extremely harmful and even deadly.

As would be expected, the kinds of parasites and the degree of infection in horses vary in different parts of the world, and also among individual horses. Then, too, some of the parasites are distributed more or less regionally, primarily because of differences in developmental cycles, climatic conditions, and husbandry practices.

The internal parasites may be located in practically every tissue and cavity of the body. However, most of them locate in the alimentary tract, lungs, body cavity, or bloodstream. Those which inhabit the digestive system usually become localized in specific parts of it. Still others are migratory or wandering in their habits, traveling throughout different parts of the body.

GENERAL SYMPTOMS

Usually the symptoms of parasitism are marked by a slowly progressive chain of events that the owner may overlook entirely or confuse with other conditions. The general symptoms of parasitic infections in the horse are: weakness, unthrifty appearance and emaciation, tucked-up flanks, distended abdomen ("potbelly"), rough coat, paleness of the membranes

Fig. 15-5. Same horse before (upper picture) and after (bottom picture) treatment for internal parasites. Parasites retard the foal's development and lower the efficiency of mature horses. Also, feed is always too costly to give to parasites. (Courtesy, College of Veterinary Medicine, University of Illinois)

of the eyes and mouth, in some cases frequent colic and diarrhea, and stunted growth and development in young animals. Affected animals usually eat well, and the temperature remains normal; but there is always a loss in the functional efficiency of the individual as a working unit.

With certain types of parasitic infections, the specific effects are very pronounced. This is true, for example, of the protozoan parasite *Trypanosoma equiperdum*, which causes dourine.

GENERAL PREVENTIVE AND CONTROL MEASURES

Most parasitic infections of equines may be attributed to the fact that, under domestication, horses (as well as all other animal species) have been forced to sleep and eat in close proximity to their own feces—being either confined and fed in a stall or fenced within limited grazing areas or pastures. By contrast, in the wild state animals roved over vast

[4]The use of trade names of wormers and insecticides in this section does not imply endorsement, nor is any criticism implied of similar products not named; rather, it is recognition of the fact that horsemen, and those who counsel with them, are generally more familiar with the trade names than the generic names.

[5]The material in this section was authoritatively reviewed by Charles B. Duff, President, Farnam Companies, Inc., Phoenix, Ariz.

[6]Some 75 species parasitize horses in this country.

areas, seldom eating, watering, or sleeping in the same spot.

As the feces of the horse are the primary source of infection of internal parasites, it should be obvious that the most important requisite of successful control measures is that they be designed to separate the animal from its own excrement. (See section on "A Program of Horse Health, Disease Prevention, and Parasite Control—Part I. General Horse Health Program.")

COMMON INTERNAL PARASITES AND THEIR CONTROL

Horses are affected by more than 75 internal parasites, which inhabit nearly every organ. These parasites are so widespread that no horse escapes all of them.

Because there are so many kinds of internal parasites, only the most common and damaging ones are summarized in Table 15-3 and discussed at length in the narrative that follows. Strongyles, ascarids, and bots are generally the most injurious of internal parasites, although other kinds are capable of producing severe injury on occasion and generally contribute to the overall picture of parasitism wherever they occur.

● *Choice of drug (anthelmintic)*—Knowing what internal parasites are present within a horse is the first requisite to the choice of the proper drug, or anthelmintic. Since no one drug is appropriate or economical for all conditions, the next requisite is to select the right one; the one which, when used according to directions, will be most effective and produce a minimum of side effects on the animal treated. So, coupled with knowledge of the kind of parasites present, an individual assessment of each animal is necessary. Among the factors to consider are age, pregnancy, other illnesses and medications, and the method by which the drug is to be administered. Some drugs characteristically put horses off performance for several days after treatment, whereas others have less tendency to do so. Some drugs are unnecessarily harsh or expensive for the problem at hand, whereas a safe inexpensive alternative would be equally suitable.

Table 15-4 lists the drug selections, along with the trade name, source, and method of administration of each, for the removal of four important internal parasites of horses—ascarids, bots, pinworms, and strongyles.

Table 15-5 lists the antiparasitic compounds, and gives the recommended dosage level and the efficacy of each, for the removal of ascarids, bots, pinworms, and strongyles. (See page 318.)

It is recommended that wormers be rotated—that several different dewormers be used—combined with

TABLE 15-3
INTERNAL PARASITES OF HORSES

Parasite	Where Found	Damage	Signs
Ascarids (*Parascaris*)	Small intestine.	Irritate intestinal wall, possible obstruction.	Digestive upsets (colic), diarrhea, retarded growth, rough hair coat, pot bellied, death (ruptured intestine), more common in young horses.
Bots (*Gastrophilus*)	Stomach. Gums.	Inflammation, perforation of stomach wall, gums.	Excitement (caused by files), digestive upsets (colic), retarded growth, poor condition, death (stomach rupture).
Pinworm (*Oxyuris*)	Large intestine.	Adults feed on gut contents. Larvae feed on mucosa.	Digestive disturbances, retarded growth, anemia, tail rubbing.
Stomach worm (*Habronema* adult) (*Habronema* larvae)	Stomach. Injured skin.	Causes tumors of wall. Granulomatus ulcers.	Gastritis, digestive disorders, and summer sores—which often heal spontaneously after first frost.
Strongyles, large (Bloodworm)	Large intestine and colon.	Adults suck blood, cause ulcers on mucosa. Larvae cause enlargement and aneurysms of anterior mesenteric artery.	Anemia, rough hair coat, colic, loss of appetite, retarded growth, depression, soft feces with a foul odor. In large infections, legs and abdomen swell.
Strongyles, small (*Triodontophorus, Poteriostomum, Trichonema,* and others)	Large intestine and colon.	Irritate intestinal wall causing thickening and nodules with larvae in them feeding on blood.	Anemia, loss of appetite, retarded growth, dark or black manure, soft feces with a foul odor. In large infections, legs and abdomen swell.
Tapeworm (*Anoplocephala*)	Small intestine.	Ulceration of ileocecal valve, enteritis.	Unthriftiness.
Threadworm (*Strongyloides*)	Small intestine.	Erosion of intestinal mucosa, enteritis.	Loss of appetite, loss of weight, diarrhea, worms disappear by time foals are 6 months old.

TABLE 15-4

DRUG SELECTIONS FOR SPECIFIC PARASITES

Parasite	Active Ingredient	Trade Name	Source	Method of Administration
Ascarids	Piperazine	Various	Various	Tube, feed
		Paravex	Upjohn	Tube
		Equizole-A	Merck	Tube, feed
		Dizan suspension with piperazine	Elanco	Tube
	Trichlorfon	Dyrex	Ft. Dodge	Tube, feed, bolus
		Anthon	Bayvet	Feed
		Combot	Bayvet	Tube
	Butonate of trichlorfon	T-113	Thuron	Tube
	Dichlorvos	Equigard	Shell	Feed
		Equigel	Shell	Intraoral
	Mebendazole	Telmin	Pitman-Moore	Tube, feed
		Telmin-SF	Pitman-Moore	Intraoral
	Carbon disulfide	None	Various	Tube
	Pyrantel	Strongid	Pfizer	Feed
		Strongid T	Pfizer	Tube, feed, drench
	Cambendazole	Camvet	Merck	Tube
	Levamisole and piperazine	Ripercol L-piperazine	American Cyanamid	Tube
Bots	Trichlorfon	Dyrex	Ft. Dodge	Tube, feed, bolus
		Anthon	Bayvet	Feed
		Combot	Bayvet	Tube
		Equizole-B	Merck	Tube, feed
	Butonate of trichlorfon	T-113	Thuron	Tube
	Piperazine-carbon disulfide complex	Parvex	Upjohn	Tube
		Parvex Plus	Upjohn	Tube
	Dichlorvos	Equigard	Shell	Feed
		Equigel	Shell	Intraoral
	Carbon disulfide	None	Various	Tube
Pinworms	Dithiazanine iodide and piperazine citrate	Dizan suspension with piperazine	Elanco	Tube
	Thiabendazole	Equizole	Merck	Tube, feed
		Equizole-A	Merck	Tube, feed
		Equizole-B	Merck	Tube, feed
	Trichlorfon	Dyrex	Ft. Dodge	Tube, feed, bolus
		Anthon	Bayvet	Feed
		Combot	Bayvet	Tube
	Piperazine	Various	Various	Tube, feed
		Parvex	Upjohn	Tube
		Ripercol L-piperazine	American Cyanamid	Tube
	Dichlorvos	Equigard	Shell	Feed
	Pyrantel	Strongid	Pfizer	Feed
		Strongid T	Pfizer	Tube, feed, drench
	Mebendazole	Telmin	Pitman-Moore	Tube, feed
		Telmin-SF	Pitman-Moore	Intraoral
	Cambendazole	Camvet	Merck	Tube
Strongyles	Phenothiazine	Various	Various	Low level in feed
	Phenothiazine and piperazine mixtures	None	Various	Tube
		Parvex Plus	Upjohn	Tube
		Dyrex T.F.	Ft. Dodge	Tube
	Thiabendazole	Equizole	Merck	Tube, feed
		Equizole-A	Merck	Tube, feed
		Equizole-B	Merck	Tube, feed
	Dichlorvos	Equigard	Shell	Feed
	Dithiazanine iodide and piperazine citrate	Dizan suspension with piperazine	Elanco	Tube
	Pyrantel	Strongid	Pfizer	Feed
		Strongid T	Pfizer	Tube, feed, drench
	Mebendazole	Telmin	Pitman-Moore	Tube, feed
		Telmin-SF	Pitman-Moore	Intraoral
	Cambendazole	Camvet	Merck	Tube
	Levamisole and piperazine	Ripercol L-piperazine	American Cyanamid	Tube

TABLE 15-5
DOSAGE LEVEL AND EFFICACY OF ANTIPARASITIC COMPOUNDS USED IN HORSES

Compound	Dose Level[1]			Average Removal Expectancy				
		Ascarids	Bots	Pinworms		Strongyles		
				Mature Oxyurids	Immature Oxyurids	S. vulgaris	S. edentatus	Small
Butonate of trichlorfon	2.0 g/cwt	90-100	90-100	N.D.[2]	N.D.[2]	20-60	5-15	N.D.[2]
Carbon disulfide (CS₂)	2.4 ml/cwt	50-100	90-100	0	0	0	0	0
CBZ	.9 g/cwt	95-100	0	95-100	85-100	95-100	90-100	70-100
Dichlorvos (pellets)	1.6 g/cwt	95-100	80-100	90-100	90-100	95-100	70-80	85-95
Dichlorvos (gel)	.45-.9 g/cwt	90-100	90-100	90-100	N.D.[2]	0-10	0	N.D.[2]
Dithiazanine iodide + PPZ	2.0 + 2.5 g/cwt	95-100	0	90-100	90-100	60-80	10-30	90-100
FBZ	.23 g/cwt	70-90	0	95-100	50-70	95-100	95-100	90-100
Mebendazole	1 g/250 lb	90-100	0	95-100	95-100	95-100	65-95	80-95
Phenothiazine	low-level	0	0	0	0	95-100	95-100	95-100
Phenothiazine (PTZ)	2.5 g/cwt	0	0	0	25-50	50-75	20-40	85-95
Piperazine (PPZ)	4.0 g/cwt	95-100	0	40-60	0-15	40-60	0-10	90-100
PPZ-CS, complex	4.0 g/cwt	95-100	78-85	50-70	10-20	40-60	0-10	90-100
PTZ + PPZ	1.25 + 4.0 g/cwt	95-100	0	50-70	20-40	90-100	40-60	90-100
PTZ + PPZ-CS, complex	.83 + 2.67 g/cwt	95-100	70-80	50-70	20-40	90-100	70-90	90-100
PTZ + PPZ + T	1.25 + 4.0 + 1.8 g/cwt	95-100	90-100	90-100	90-100	95-100	30-50	90-100
Pyrantel	.33 g/cwt	90-100	0	60-70	50-60	95-100	65-75	90-100
TBZ + PPZ	2.0 + 2.5 g/cwt	95-100	0	90-100	30-40	95-100	90-100	90-100
Thiabendazole (TBZ)	2.0 g/cwt	10-30	0	90-100	30-40	95-100	90-100	90-100
Trichlorfon (T)	1.8 g/cwt	95-100	90-100	90-100	N.D.[2]	0-10	0-5	0-30

[1]Piperazine and pyrantel doses expressed as base.
[2]N.D. = No data.

low-level phenothiazine treatment. Preventive (prophylactic) treatment with phenothiazine does not kill worms rapidly. Rather, it interferes with the parasite's capacity to lay fertile eggs, so reinfestation is reduced. Reinfestation occurs constantly because all stages of the parasites are present at all times.

Anthelmintics are constantly being improved, and new ones are becoming available. So, the horseman should consult his local veterinarian relative to the choice of drug to use on his horse(s) at the time.

● *Program and schedule*—Each horse establishment should, in cooperation with the local veterinarian and/or other advisors, evolve with an internal parasite program and schedule. A general understanding of the life cycles of the various parasites is necessary in order to time the treatments to best advantage. Also, it is recommended that an equine practitioner or parasitology laboratory do periodic fecal examinations to help assess the effectiveness of the parasite control program.

A suggested treatment program for (1) foals; and (2) yearlings, two-year-olds, and mature horses follows:

1. *Foals*—For the control of ascarids, foals should be started on Parvex or piperazine at 8 weeks of age, with treatment at 8-week intervals. This treatment will also control pinworms and small strongyles but not large strongyles. For large strongyle control, mares should be maintained on one of the strongyle control programs for mature horses. Addition of thiabendazole to piperazine is commonly practiced to control strongyloides infection, a common concurrent infection in foals. Table 15-6 gives 2 suggested worming programs for foals.

TABLE 15-6
SAMPLE PROGRAMS FOR FOALS

Date	Program "A"	Program "B"
June 1	Parvex	Piperazine
Aug. 1	Parvex	Piperazine
Oct. 1	Parvex	Piperazine
Dec. 1	Parvex, Equigard, or Dyrex T.F.	Parvex, Equigard, or Dyrex T.F.

2. *Yearlings, two-year-olds, and mature horses*[7]—A low-level phenothiazine program has been used for several years. Phenothiazine is fed in the ration at the rate of 2 grams per day for the first 21 days of each month on a year-round basis. One of the bot control drugs (carbon disulfide, Anthon, Dyrex, or Equigard) should be given in late fall or winter. Yearlings may require 1 to 3 treatments with piperazine for ascarids during the first part of the year.

Periodic treatment programs, with the number of treatments varying from twice a year to six times a year, and alternating among the various drugs and combination of drugs, may be used, depending upon the degree of parasitism. Alternating the drugs provides broad spectrum control of strongyles, bots, ascarids, and pinworms. Table 15-7 gives suggested worming programs and schedules for yearlings, two-year-olds, and mature horses.

TABLE 15-7

SAMPLE PERIODIC TREATMENT PROGRAMS FOR YEARLINGS, TWO-YEAR-OLDS, AND MATURE HORSES

Date	Number of Treatments per Year		
	6X	4X	2X
Feb. 1	Parvex Plus, Equigard, or Dyrex T.F.	—	—
Apr. 1	Equizole, or Equizole-A	Parvex Plus, Equigard, or Dyrex T.F.	Parvex Plus, Equigard, or Dyrex T.F.
June 1	Equizole, or Equizole-A	Equizole, or Equizole-A	—
Aug. 1	Parvex Plus, or Phenothiazine/ piperazine mixture	Equizole, or Equizole-A	—
Oct. 1	Equizole, or Equizole-A	—	—
Dec. 1	Dyrex T.F., Equigard, or Parvex Plus	Dyrex T.F., Equigard, or Parvex Plus	Dyrex T.F., Equigard, or Parvex Plus

ASCARIDS (LARGE ROUNDWORMS, WHITE WORMS)

The ascarid, *Parascaris equorum*, is found in the small intestine of equines. The female roundworm varies from 6 to 22 inches in length and the male from 5 to 13 inches. When full grown, both are about the diameter of a lead pencil.

Distribution and Losses Causes by Ascarids

Roundworms are fairly widely distributed throughout the United States. They especially affect

[7]*Do not treat mares within one month of foaling.*

foals and young animals, but are rarely important in horses over two years of age. This decreased susceptibility as age increases is credited to an acquired immunity resulting from earlier infections. Roundworms are particularly damaging to their equine host because of the destruction that the migrating larvae inflict upon the liver and lungs and the partial or complete obstruction and possible rupture of the small intestine caused by the large size and numbers of worms.

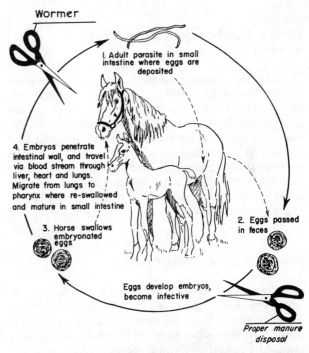

Fig. 15-6. Diagram showing the life history and habits of the ascarid (large roundworm). As noted (see scissors), effective control and treatment (cutting the cycle of the parasite) consist in (1) proper manure disposal, and (2) administering an effective wormer. (Drawing by Prof. R. F. Johnson)

Although it pursues a migratory route in the host, the roundworm usually comes to rest in the upper part of the small intestine; but sometimes it is found in the middle and terminal portions of the small intestine. The complete life cycle of this parasite may be summarized as follows:

1. In the small intestine, each female worm may deposit 100,000 eggs per day which pass to the outside with the feces. Ascarid eggs are very resistant to environmental conditions and may live for years in stalls, paddocks, and pastures. Thus, the source of infection for young horses is the contaminated ground that was seeded down by ascarid eggs by preceding crops of infected foals.

2. Under favorable conditions—warm weather and dampness—the eggs develop embryos and are infective to horses in 10 to 14 days.

3. The infective eggs are swallowed with feed and water, especially by grazing horses, and the larvae are liberated in the stomach and intestine.

4. The larvae then take the following migratory route: They penetrate the gut wall and enter the bloodstream, thence travel via the blood through the liver, heart, and lungs, leave the bloodstream in the lungs and migrate up the trachea to the pharynx, and finally are again swallowed and develop to maturity in the small intestine.

Damage Inflicted; Symptoms and Signs of Affected Animals

The injury produced by ascarids covers a wide range, from light infections producing moderate effects to heavy infections which may be the essential cause of death. Death from ascarid infection is usually due to a ruptured intestine. Serious lung damage caused by migrating ascarid larvae may result in pneumonia. More common, and probably more important, are retarded or impaired growth and development manifested by potbellies, rough hair coats, and digestive disturbances.

Prevention, Control, and Treatment

Prevention consists primarily in sanitary measures. The foaling barn and paddocks must be kept clean, manure must be disposed of properly, and clean feed and water must be supplied. Young foals should be placed on clean pasture.

Tables 15-4 and 15-5 give the drug selections and recommended dosage levels for the control of ascarids.

In addition to selecting the particular drug(s) for ascarid control, the horseman should set up a definite treatment schedule, then follow it. The advice of the veterinarian should be sought on both points. Then, the drug of choice should be given according to the manufacturer's directions. Also, to preclude the possibility that worms may become resistant to a drug that is used continuously, the veterinarian may recommend a rotation of drugs.

The first ascarid infections in foals mature when the foals are about 11 weeks of age; hence, the first treatment should be given at 8 to 10 weeks of age so as to remove the initial infection just before the ascarids mature. If ascarids are allowed to mature, and the foal is subsequently treated with an effective wormer, intestinal blockage and death may result. In most areas, treatments for ascarid control should be repeated at 8-week intervals, at least during the summer months.

BOTS

Horse bots are highly specialized parasites—attacking horses, mules, asses, and perhaps zebras, but not molesting other classes of livestock.

Three species of horse bot flies are pests of horses in the United States: the common horse bot or nit fly (*Gastrophilus intestinalis*), the throat bot or chin fly (*G. nasalis*), and the nose bot or nose fly (*G. hemorrhoidalis*).

Fig. 15-7. The nose bot fly. *G. hemorrhoidalis*. (Courtesy, USDA)

Fig. 15-8. Horses rubbing their noses on each other in an effort to avoid the nose bot fly (*G. hemorrhoidalis*). Though the bot fly does not sting the animal, deposition of the eggs on the lips causes a tickling sensation. (Courtesy, USDA)

As horse bots are found in different sections of the world, it is reasonable to surmise that they were introduced to this country with the first horses imported from Europe. The common horse bot and the throat bot are now distributed throughout the United States wherever horses are found, but the nose bot fly is usually found only in northwestern United States and in the midwestern states.

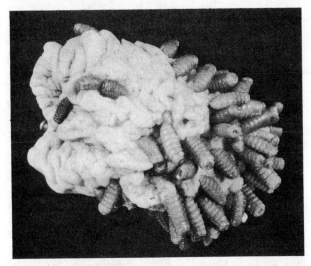

Fig. 15-9. Bots attached to the stomach wall of a horse. At this stage they remain attached to the lining of the stomach and intestines for several months, feeding on blood until they are about ¾ inch in length, after which they release their hold and pass out with the feces. (Courtesy, Department of Veterinary Pathology and Hygiene, College of Veterinary Medicine, University of Illinois)

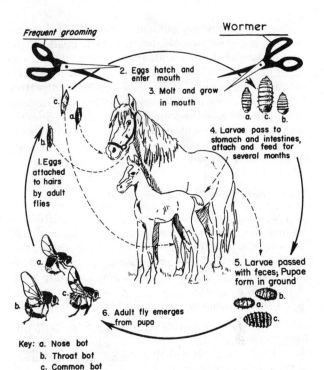

Fig. 15-10. Diagram showing the life history and habits of horse bots, of which three species are serious pests. As noted (see scissors), effective control and treatment (cutting the cycle of the parasite) consist in (1) frequent grooming, washing, and clipping to remove the eggs that are attached to the hairs of the host; and (2) administering an effective wormer. (Drawing by Prof. R. F. Johnson)

Broadly speaking, the losses inflicted by horse bots are of three types: (1) the annoyance to the animal caused by the flies at the time they deposit the eggs, (2) the burrowing of the bots into the lining of the stomach and duodenum, resulting in irritation and a place of entry for microorganisms, and (3) interfering with the passage of food materials through the gastrointestinal tract. Contrary to the common belief of many persons, bot flies do not sting the animal.

Life History and Habits

Like other flies, the four distinct stages of the horse bot are: the egg, the larva (bot), the pupa, and the adult fly. It requires one year in which to complete the entire life cycle of the horse bot. Further details concerning the habits and life histories of the bot are as follows:

1. The eggs are attached to the hairs of the host. The common bot fly may deposit its eggs on various parts of the animal, but particularly about the fetlocks and on the inside of the knees; the throat bot fly attaches its eggs on the hairs beneath the jaws; and the nose bot fly deposits its eggs on the short hairs of the lips. Usually only a single egg is laid at each strike.

2. Although varying somewhat according to the particular species of bot fly, the eggs usually hatch within two to seven[8] days' time, and the young larvae soon enter the horse's mouth.

3. Again varying according to species, the larvae remain in the mouth from two to four weeks, during which time they molt and grow.

4. Next the larvae pass to the stomach and intestine where they attach themselves to the lining for several months, feeding until they are about ¾ inch in length.

5. When grown, the bots release their hold on the lining of the alimentary canal and pass out with the feces; the nose bots reattach themselves to the rectum for a few days before dropping to the ground.

6. The larvae, or bots, then enter the pupal or resting stage for a period of 20 to 70 days, the exact time varying according to the species. Finally, they change into the adult or fly stage at which time they are again ready to lay eggs. The adult fly is unable to take food, but enough is stored in its body in the bot stage to develop 150 to 300 eggs to be deposited during its short life, the sole purpose of which is reproduction. The flies are smaller than honeybees, which they somewhat resemble.

Damage Inflicted; Symptoms and Signs of Affected Animals

Even though the bot fly does not sting the animal, cementing of its eggs to the hairs causes a tickling

---

[8]As the eggs of the common bot fly must be rubbed first by the warm lips of the horse in order to hatch, they may lie quietly in the egg stage for as long as 90 days.

sensation, particularly evident in the case of the nose bot fly. Attacked animals may toss their heads in the air, strike the ground with their front feet, and rub their noses on each other or on any convenient object.

Infected animals may show frequent digestive upsets and even colic, lowered vitality and emaciation, and reduced work output. The most serious effect is general debility of the animal caused by toxic excretions from the parasites. Occasionally, heavy infections have caused rupture of the stomach.

Prevention, Control, and Treatment

Working animals may be given fair protection against the annoyance resulting from the deposition of eggs by throat and nose bots through the application of a cover to the jaws and nose, respectively. Frequent grooming, washing, and clipping are also helpful control measures.

Horses should be treated for bots as follows:

1. In the late fall or early winter, at least one month after the first killing frost, administer one of the recommended drugs according to manufacturer's directions.

2. Thirty days prior to administering a drug, the eggs of the common bot fly, which may be clinging to the body, should be destroyed by either (a) vigorously applying warm water at 120° F, or (b) clipping the hair of the horse. The insides of the knees and the fetlocks especially should be treated in this manner.

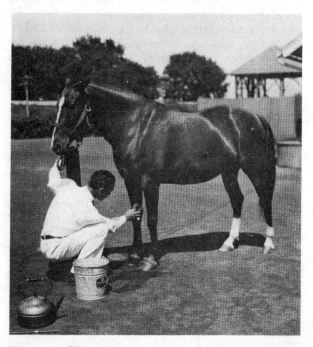

Fig. 15-11. Washing to remove the eggs of adult bot flies attached to the hairs of the horse. (Courtesy, USDA)

3. Prevention of reinfection is best assured through community campaigns in which all horses within the area are thus treated.

Tables 15-4 and 15-5 give the drug selections and recommended dosage levels for the control of bots. The horseman should seek the advice of his local veterinarian, county agent, extension entomologist, or consultant in arriving at the wormer of choice. Also, the horseman is admonished to follow the labeled directions of the manufacturer.

DOURINE

This is a chronic venereal disease of horses and asses, caused by the microscopic parasite *Trypanosoma equiperdum*. It is also referred to as "mal du coit" or equine syphilis, because it is similar to syphilis in man.

Distribution and Losses Caused by Dourine

It is still quite frequent in many countries, but now rare in the United States.

Life History and Habits

The causative parasite is transmitted from animal to animal by the act of copulation. Following an incubation period of eight days to two months, the characteristic symptoms appear in infected animals.

Damage Inflicted; Symptoms and Signs of Affected Animals

There are two stages usually described for the disease. The primary symptoms are a redness and swelling of the external genitalia of both the mare and stallion. There are frequent attempts at urination, and increased sexual excitement is observed in both sexes. A pussy discharge may be noted. The secondary stage is initiated by the appearance of firm, round, flat swellings (dollar plaques) on the body and neck. In the advanced stages, nervous symptoms may also be manifest. They consist of paralysis of the face, knuckling of the joints of the hind limbs, and dragging of the feet.

Prevention, Control, and Treatment

The infective agent is a protozoan. It is spread mostly through mating, but may be transmitted by biting insects. The complement fixation test is used in diagnosis.

The most effective method of eradication is the prompt destruction of all the infected animals. Often in areas of heavy infection, the castration of stallions and spaying of mares is practiced with only a small

degree of success. The most effective prevention consists in avoiding coition with infected animals, and in the application of modern hygiene.

No successful treatment is known.

EQUINE PIROPLASMOSIS (BABESIASES)

This disease is tick-borne and caused by either of two protozoans, *Babesia caballi* or *B. equi*, which invade the red blood cells.

Distribution and Losses Caused by Equine Piroplasmosis

The disease is worldwide. It was first diagnosed in the United States in 1961, in Florida. The death rate is between 10 and 15 percent.

Life History and Habits

Horses usually acquire the infection from ticks, although occasionally it is introduced through intrauterine infection.

After the tick attaches itself to the host horse, the protozoan leaves it, enters the bloodstream, invades a red blood cell, multiplies (by simple division) and destroys the invaded red blood cell, following which each new protozoan invades different blood cells and repeats the performance.

Damage Inflicted; Symptoms and Signs of Affected Animals

The signs are very similar to equine infectious anemia (or swamp fever), but a positive diagnosis can be made by demonstrating the presence of the protozoa in the red blood cells or by an antigen-antibody serum test. Clinical signs include fever (103° to 106° F), anemia, depression, thirst, tears, and swelling of the eyelids. Constipation and colic may occur. The urine is yellow to reddish colored. The incubation period is 1 to 3 weeks.

Prevention, Control, and Treatment

Tick control is the most effective approach to the prevention of equine piroplasmosis. The tropical horse tick, *Dermacentor nitens*, is the vector in the United States.

Also, extreme caution should be exercised in the use of all syringes, needles, and medical instruments. Recovered animals remain carriers for 10 months to 4 years, unless treated; hence, they should be isolated.

In the past, a number of treatments were used, each with varying degrees of success. A new and promising treatment, developed by the University of Florida, consists in 2 successive treatments of Diam-

pron, 4 milligrams per pound body weight, given intramuscularly 48 hours apart. This will eliminate the positive carrier state.

PINWORMS (RECTAL WORMS)

Two species of pinworms are frequently found in horses; namely, *Oxyuris equi* and *Probstmyria vivipara*. The former are whitish worms with long, slender tails, whereas the latter are so small as to be scarcely visible to the naked eye.

Distribution and Losses Caused by Pinworms

Pinworms are quite widely distributed in horses throughout the United States. The large species, *Oxyuris equi*, are the most damaging to the host.

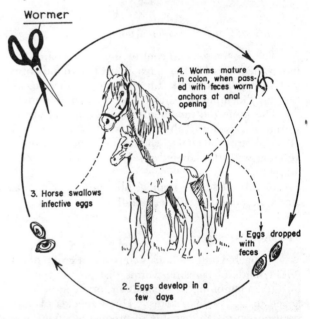

Fig. 15-12. Diagram showing the life history and habits of the pinworm. As noted (see scissors), the common treatment for the removal of pinworms consists in administering a suitable wormer, thus cutting the cycle of the parasite. Prevention and control involve sanitation and keeping the animal separated from its own excrement. (Drawing by Prof. R. F. Johnson)

The life history of the larger of the two species of pinworms, *Oxyuris equi*, may be summarized as follows:

1. The female worms pass out with the feces, either depositing their eggs with the droppings or around the anal region. The latter type of deposition results when the female worms of *O. equi* anchor themselves at the anal opening and deposit their eggs.

2. Outside the body, the eggs develop and reach the infective stage in a few days.

3. Horses become infected by swallowing the eggs with feed or water.

4. The worms mature in the large intestine, principally in the dorsal colon.

The small pinworm, *Probstmyria vivipara*, are—as the name indicates—viviparous worms. Their young are produced alive, and presumably they can complete their entire cycle of development within the ventral colon of the host.

Damage Inflicted; Symptoms and Signs of Affected Animals

Frequently the best evidence of the presence of the larger pinworms is that the worms are seen in the feces of heavily infected animals. Irritation of the anus and tail rubbing are also symptoms. Heavy infections may also cause digestive disturbances and produce anemia.

Prevention, Control and Treatment

The prevention and control of pinworms are similar to measures for the large intestinal roundworms and strongyles. Chiefly, this involves sanitation and keeping the animal separated from its own excrement.

The preferred treatments for the removal of pinworms are given in Tables 15-4 and 15-5.

The drug of choice should be administered in keeping with the labeled directions of the manufacturer.

In case of severe itching, blue ointment may be applied around the tail beneath the anus.

STOMACH WORMS

Stomach worms of horses consist of a group of different kinds of parasitic worms that are responsible for inflammation in the stomach or for a condition referred to as "summer sores." Three species of large stomach worms are capable of producing severe gastritis in horses. Diagnosis is difficult because the eggs are not ordinarily detected by flotation examination of feces, thus the importance of these worms tends to be minimized.

The minute stomach worm (*Trichostrongylus axei*) is a common parasite of cattle, sheep, and a number of other hosts, in addition to the horse; and there is cross infection between different species of animals.

Distribution and Losses Caused by Stomach Worms

Workers in both Europe and the United States have expressed the opinion that probably no other ailment of horses is so regularly associated with a sudden loss of condition as is infection with stomach worms. Wasted feed and lowered efficiency are the chief losses when horses are infected with stomach worms.

Life History and Habits

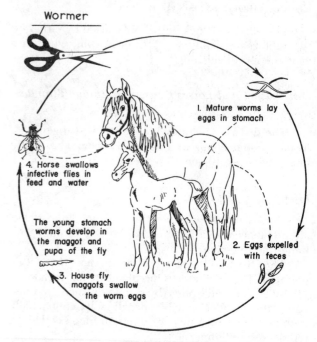

Fig. 15-13. Diagram showing the life history and habits of the large stomach worm. As noted (see scissors), a suitable wormer may be used for removal of stomach worms, thus cutting the cycle of the parasite. (Drawing by Prof. R. F. Johsnon)

The life history of the horse stomach worm varies somewhat, according to the particular kind. The cycle of the large stomach worm, *Habronema muscae*, is as follows:

1. The mature worms in the stomach lay many eggs.

2. The eggs containing young worms are expelled from the digestive tract with manure.

3. The eggs are swallowed by fly maggots; the young worms develop in the maggot and in the pupa and are infective when the adult fly emerges.

4. Horses become infected after swallowing infected flies or the larvae that escape from flies while the latter are feeding on the moisture of the lips.

Damage Inflicted; Symptoms and Signs of Affected Animals

Sometimes, the larvae of the larger stomach worms are responsible in part for a relatively common skin disease of horses called summer sores.

Heavy infections may cause a rapid loss of condi-

tion associated with extensive and severe catarrhal gastritis. Long-standing infections result in chronic inflammatory changes.

Prevention, Control, and Treatment

Houseflies and stable flies are the vectors. Hence, the control of flies is the best method of preventing and controlling stomach worms.

Carbon disulfide and levamisole (Tramisol) are effective treatments, when used according to manufacturer's directions.

Dilute formaldehyde or ronnel and astrigents are commonly used in the treatment of summer sores.

STRONGYLES (LARGE STRONGYLES, SMALL STRONGYLES)

Of the several hundred parasites affecting horses, without question the most serious threat to the health and life of the horse kept under conditions found on breeding farms the world over is the strongyle.

Of a total of 140 horses autopsied by Dr. Robert F. Behlow, DVM (one of the coauthors of this chapter), at the University of Kentucky, 22 died of verminous aneurysm, the most harmful effect of parasitism in the horse, caused by the bloodworm parasite *Strongylus vulgaris*. Most of the 22 losses were young animals (sucklings and weanlings), and one of them might have been a million dollar horse.

There are approximately 40 different species of strongyles. Although not all of these kinds have ever been found in any one horse, almost every animal that has had access to pasture, and has not been treated at intervals for their removal, harbors several of them. The different species vary considerable in size, some being scarcely visible to the naked eye; whereas others reach a length of 2 inches.

The large strongyle—also variously referred to as palisade worms, bloodworms, sclerostomes, and red worms—include only three species, but these forms are the most injurious parasites of the horse. The balance of the species—the vast majority of strongyles—are the small strongyles. The latter are generally regarded as being much less pathogenic than the large strongyles. In a heavily infected animal, 1 or more of the 3 species of large strongyles may be present, along with 15 to 25 species of small strongyles.

Distribution and Losses Caused by Strongyles

Strongyles are found throughout the United States wherever horses are pastured. Naturally, the degree of infection varies according to the extent of exposure; and this in turn depends upon the sanitation, feeding, medication, season, and climate. Heavy infections with strongyles may result in marked un-

thriftiness, loss in capacity to perform work, and even death. The harmful effects are greatest with younger animals.

As a single deposit of manure from an infected horse may contain hundreds of thousands of strongyle eggs, and with the life cycle of the parasite being what it is, it is easy to understand why pastured horses are almost always infected.

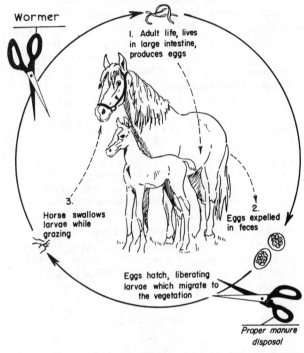

Fig. 15-14. Diagram showing the life history and habits of strongyles. As noted (see scissors), a wormer may be used for removing strongyles, thus cutting the cycle of the parasite. First and foremost, however, it is important that there be a barrier between the horse and its excrement. (Drawing by Prof. R. F. Johnson)

The life cycle of *Strongylus vulgaris* follows:

1. The eggs are passed in the feces.
2. The eggs embryonate on the ground or herbage.
3. The eggs hatch into the first stage larvae, thence they develop to second stage larvae, and finally to third stage infective larvae. This process takes about seven days under favorable temperature and moisture conditions.
4. The larvae crawl onto vegetation.
5. The infective larvae are ingested in feed and water.
6. After years of divergent opinions, there is now general agreement relative to the migratory route of the parasite. The larvae penetrate the wall of the small intestine, cecum, and ventral colon; thence they invade the walls of the small arteries and migrate toward the anterior mesentric artery, and produce thrombosis and aneurysm. Thence the larvae break

out of the thrombus and are carried by the bloodstream to the ventral colon and cecum, where they migrate back through the walls to become adult worms attached to mucosa of the cecum and colon. All this migration and development takes six months, during which time the larvae are inaccessible to ordinary doses of anthelmintics.

The small strongyles migrate to a lesser extent, passing directly to the large intestine after being swallowed. After becoming adult worms, some of them attach themselves to the wall of the large intestine, much in a manner as the large strongyles. Most of them, however, are found free and unattached in the contents of the large intestine or cecum.

Damage Inflicted; Symptoms and Signs of Affected Animals

Severe infections with large and small strongyles—and such infections are especially common with animals grazed on permanent pastures—result in lack of appetite, anemia, progressive emaciation, a rough hair coat, sunken eyes, digestive disturbances including colic, a tucked-up appearance, and sometimes posterior incoordination or weakness. Collectively, these diverse and severe symptoms constitute the disease known as strongylosis.

Fig. 15-15. Horse with strongyle infection. (Courtesy, Department of Veterinary Pathology and Hygiene, College of Veterinary Medicine, University of Illinois)

The presence of the characteristic eggs in the feces is evidence of strongyle infection, and, combined with the marked symptoms indicated above, should be considered as evidence of strongylosis.

Prevention, Control, and Treatment

Unfortunately, the infective larvae of the strongyle can withstand unfavorable environmental influences to a remarkable degree. Neither low temperatures nor air drying will harm them. As a result, when pastures are infested, they will so remain for a year or more, even when held idle or grazed by some other class of livestock. For these and other reasons, the control of strongyles involves more than average difficulties.

All the general control measures previously recommended for parasites of all kinds may well be applied to the control of strongyles. First and foremost, it is important that there be a barrier between the horse and its excrement. Gathering up manure daily from pastures and barns and storing it in a pit for two or three weeks, allowing it to be subjected to its own generated heat, is a sure way to reduce infections. Moist pastures and overstocking should be avoided. Pasture rotation or rotation of stocks is effective, as these parasites are not transmissible to ruminants or swine. Medication should supplement rather than replace wholesome feed and water and clean surroundings.

The commonly used treatments for the removal of strongyles are given in Tables 15-4 and 15-5.

TAPEWORMS

There are three species of horse tapeworms, but *Anoplocephala perfoliate* is both the most common and most damaging of the three. It tends to form clusters at the ileocecal valve region of the cecum and produce ulcerative lesions, which may perforate.

Treatment is not ordinarily suggested, primarily because only light infections are encountered. Yomesan or lead arsenate (Bi-forma), used according to the manufacturer's directions, are the common treatments.

THREADWORMS (STRONGYLOIDES)

Infections by the small intestinal threadworm (*Strongyloides westeri*) are quite common in foals. Recent observations indicate that foals are infected by larvae shed in the milk of their dams. Little is known of the actual effects of this worm on foals other than the association of diarrhea with infection and the self-limiting aspects in which the worms disappear by the time the foals are six months of age. Thiabendazole (Equizole), Thiabendazole-trichlorfon (Equivet-14), and Thiabendazole-piperazine (Equizole-A), used according to manufacturer's directions, are effective in removing intestinal threadworms.

External Parasites (Ectoparasites) of Horses[9]

Horses are subject to infestation by a number of external parasites. Their effects vary according to the kind of parasite, the degree of infestation, and the health of the horse. Generally speaking, they cause irritation, restlessness, and rubbing; result in a dull coat, loss of hair, and a harsh skin; make for a loss in weight; lower the vitality and spirit of the horse; and produce a general unthrifty condition. In extreme cases, they may even cause death.

External parasites are also responsible for the spread of several serious diseases of horses which exact a heavy toll each year in sickness and death. Thus, equine piroplasmosis (or babesiases) is transmitted by a tick (*Anocentor nitens*); and mosquitoes (*Culicidae*) are vectors of equine infectious anemia (swamp fever) and equine encephalomyelitis (sleeping sickness).

INSECTICIDES

In the sections that follow, pertinent information is presented relative to the forms, application, precautions in the use, and drug withdrawal of insecticides. This is followed by a discussion of each of the common external parasites of horses. Strengths and application directions are not given for the recommended insecticides because of (1) the diversity of environments and management practices represented by this group; (2) the varying restrictions on the use of insecticides from area to area; (3) the fact that registered uses of insecticides change from time to time; and (4) the fact that the final choice of a specific insecticide will probably be made on the basis of what the local merchant, supplier, or veterinarian has available. Additional information about the choices and registered uses of insecticides in a particular area may be obtained from the local county agent, extension entomologist, or livestock consultant.

FORMS OF INSECTICIDES

Insecticides for use on horses may be purchased in several forms. The most common are emulsifiable concentrates, dusts, wettable powders, and oil solutions.

● *Emulsifiable concentrates (EC)*—Emulsifiable concentrates, perhaps the most common type of formulation, are solutions of insecticides in petroleum oils or other solvents. An emulsifier has been added so that the solution will mix well with water. On occa-

sion, usually after extended storage, an EC may separate into its various parts. If this happens, it should not be used—it should be discarded. An emulsion may also separate if it is allowed to stand after the concentrate has been added to the water; periodic agitation will help prevent the latter.

● *Dusts*—Dusts are applied directly to animals in dry form and cannot be used as sprays.

● *Wettable powders*—Wettable powders are also dry, but the addition of a dispersing and wetting agent allows them to be suspended in water for application to horses. Continuous agitation of the mixture is important when treating with wettable powders.

● *Oil solutions*—Oil solutions are insecticides dissolved in oil; no emulsifier is added. These materials are usually ready for use and should not be added to water.

APPLICATION OF INSECTICIDES

The type of application for treating horses may be based upon (1) the target pest; (2) the management and use of the horses; and (3) the available product and formulation. Horses tend to be more excitable than cattle, so when insecticides are applied as sprays, especially with high-pressure sprayers, care should be taken to avoid startling animals. For this reason, many horse owners prefer to apply insecticides by hand, either as dusts or as dilute sprays wiped on with a sponge (wipe-on).

When sprays are used, wettable powder formulations are usually preferred because the oils and solvents in emulsifiable concentrates may cause hair damage and skin irritation to some horses.

In addition, insecticides may be purchased in aerosol applicators, and some insecticides may be added to the feed (feed additive) for treatment of some pests (horse bots).

Another problem peculiar to insecticidal treatment of horses, one not usually encountered with other livestock, is that the excessive sweating of horses being ridden or exercised may render the insecticide ineffective and greatly shorten its residual life on the animal.

Timing of the application of insecticides is very important. Treatment should begin when the parasite is in a weak stage, not when the animal is in a weakened stage. Control measures should be initiated at the beginning of the season of the pest, before populations become annoying and more harmful. The objective is to break the life cycle of the pest early in life, before it becomes an adult.

PRECAUTIONS ON THE USE OF INSECTICIDES

Certain basic precautions should be observed when insecticides are used because, when used im-

---

[9]The material in this section was authoritatively reviewed by Dr. Charles D. Schmidt, Research Entomologist, U.S. Livestock Insect Laboratory, Agricultural Research Service, USDA, Kerrville, Tex.; and Charles B. Duff, President, Farnam Companies, Inc., Phoenix, Ariz.

properly, they can be injurious to man, animals, wildlife, and beneficial insects. Follow the directions and heed all the precautions on the labels.

● *Selecting insecticides*—Always select the formulation and insecticide labeled for the purpose for which it is to be used.

● *Storing insecticides*—Always store insecticides in original containers. Never transfer them to unlabeled containers or to food or beverage containers. Store insecticides in a dry place out of reach of children, animals, or unauthorized persons.

● *Disposing of empty containers and unused insecticides*—Properly and promptly dispose of all empty insecticide containers. Do not reuse. Break and bury glass containers. Chop holes in, crush, and bury metal containers. Bury containers and unused insecticides at least 18 inches deep in the soil in a sanitary landfill or dump, or dump in a level isolated place where water supplies will not be contaminated. Check with local authorities to determine specific procedures for the area.

● *Mixing and handling*—Mix and prepare insecticides in the open or in a well-ventilated place. Wear rubber gloves and clean dry clothing (respirator device may be necessary with some products). If any insecticide is spilled on clothing, wash with soap and water immediately and change clothing. Avoid prolonged inhalation. Do not smoke, eat, or drink when mixing and handling insecticides.

● *Applying*—Use only amounts recommended. Although horses are usually not considered for human consumption, the recommended insecticide may cause harmful residues in food or feed products if not handled in full accordance with the label. Avoid retreating more often than label restrictions. Avoid prolonged contact with all insecticides. Do not eat, drink, or smoke until all operations have ceased and hands and face are thoroughly washed. Change and launder clothing after extensive use of an insecticide.

DRUG WITHDRAWAL

The insecticide recommendations given in this chapter are for horses not used for food. Where horses are to be slaughtered for food, the tolerance levels and withdrawal period given on the manufacturer's label should be followed with care.

GENERAL PREVENTIVE AND CONTROL MEASURES

Effective prevention and control of external parasites of horses involves both the animals and their surroundings. It calls for good nutrition and grooming, avoiding too heavy concentration of horses, and the selection of the right insecticide and its application on the animals in accordance with the manufacturer's di-

rections. It calls for sanitary stalls and paddocks, augmented by the choice of the right insecticide(s) for the control of flies, chiggers, and ticks, and its proper use—as a bait, dust, emulsifiable concentrate, spray, and/or wettable powder—in barns and holding areas.

COMMON EXTERNAL PARASITES

Flies and lice are the most common external parasites of horses, although some of the others are capable of producing more severe injury when they occur.

BLOWFLIES

The flies of the blowfly group include a number of species that find their principal breeding ground in dead and putrifying flesh, although sometimes they infest wounds or unhealthy tissues of live animals and fresh or cooked meat. All the important species of blowflies except the flesh flies, which are grayish and have three dark stripes on their backs, have a more or less metallic luster.

Distribution and Losses Caused by Blowflies

Although blowflies are widespread, they present the greatest problem in the Pacific Northwest and in the South and southwestern states. Death losses from blowflies are not excessive, but they cause much discomfort to affected animals, and they lower production.

Life History and Habits

With the exception of the group known as gray flesh flies, which deposit tiny living maggots instead of eggs, the blowflies have a similar life cycle to the screwworm, although the cycle is completed in about one-half the time.

Damage Inflicted; Symptoms and Signs of Affected Animals

The blowfly causes its greatest damage by infesting wounds and the soiled hair of living animals. Such damage, which is largely limited to the black blowfly (or wool-maggot fly), is similar to that caused by screwworms. The maggots spread over the body, feeding on the dead skin and exudates, where they produce a severe irritation and destroy the ability of the skin to function. Infested animals rapidly become weak and fevered; and, although they recover, they may remain in an unthrifty condition for a long period.

Prevention, Control, and Treatment

Prevention of blowfly damage consists of eliminating the pest and decreasing the susceptibility of animals to infestation.

As blowflies breed principally in dead carcasses, the most effective control consists in promptly destroying all dead animals by burning or deep burial. The use of traps, poisoned baits, and electrified screens is also helpful in reducing trouble from blowflies.

Daily dusting of the irritated or infested area with coumaphos (Co-Ral, etc.) or ronnel (Korlan) will control the flies. Puff-bottle applicators containing these insecticides are available and provide an effective means of application.

FLIES AND MOSQUITOES

Flies and mosquitoes are probably the most important insect pests of horses. They lower the vitality of horses, mar the hair coat and skin, produce a general unthrifty condition, lower performance, and make for hazards when riding or using horses. Also, they may temporarily or permanently impair the development of foals and young stock. Even more important, they can be the vector (carrier) of serious diseases. Because of their varying habits, along with different materials and methods required for their control, flies have been classed as either biting or nonbiting in the discussion that follows.

Biting Flies and Mosquitoes

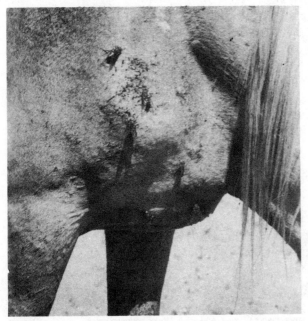

Fig. 15-16. Horse fly (*Tabanus americanus*) feeding on a horse. (Courtesy, USDA)

Several species of biting (bloodsucking) flies and mosquitoes attack horses, but the following are the most common: horse flies (*Tabanus* spp.), deer flies (*Chrysops* spp.), stable flies (*Stomoxys calcitrans*), horn flies (*Haematobia irritans*), mosquitoes (species of the genera *Aedes, Anopheles, Culex, and Psorophora*), black flies (family *Simuliidae*), and biting midges (genus *Culicoides*). Because these flies suck blood, several of them may transmit such diseases as anthrax, encephalomyelitis, (Eastern, Western, and Venezuelan), swamp fever, vesicular stomatitis, and anaplasmosis. All of them are pests—that is, they cause considerable annoyance to horses.

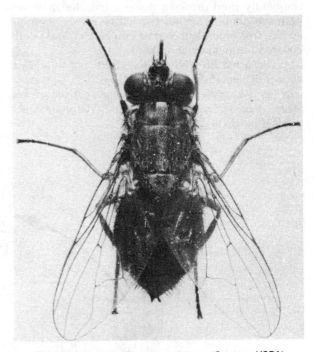

Fig. 15-17. Stable fly, *Stomaxys calcitrans*. (Courtesy, USDA)

Distribution and Losses Caused by Biting Flies and Mosquitoes

Biting (bloodsucking) flies and mosquitoes are found wherever there are horses, with the highest population occurring during warm weather and where there is lack of sanitation. They annoy horses—on pastures, in stalls, and in paddocks. They cause pain and discomfort to the animal, and, at times, they make them unmanageable when they are being worked.

Horse and deer flies attack horses pastured in or near areas with a marsh, swamp, creek, or irrigation ditch.

Stable flies are found wherever there are horses, people, or other mammals—their usual victims.

Horn flies are found near cattle. So, horses are attacked when they are pastured with cattle, kept in areas near cattle, or ridden near cattle.

Mosquitoes cause special discomfort to horses, particularly during early spring and wet years.

Life History and Habits

Horse flies and deer flies breed in standing water that is fairly shallow and has an abundance of organic matter. Stable flies breed in horse manure, soiled bedding, feed wastes, decomposed fruit and vegetable matter, and compost piles and clippings. Horn flies breed in single, fresh droppings of cow manure. Mosquitoes breed on water, in such places as water-holding low spots in corrals and paddocks, infrequently used drinking troughs, irrigated pastures, drainage ditches, natural flooded meadows, swamps, creeks, tree holes, leaf choked rain gutters, and poorly covered septic tanks and drains.

The usual life cycle of flies from egg to adult is shown in Fig. 15-18.

The life cycles of all mosquitoes consist of four stages: egg, larva ("wiggler"), pupa ("tumbler"), and adult (Fig. 15-19).

Damage Inflicted, Symptoms and Signs of Affected Animals

Horse flies and deer flies possess sharp, scissor-like mouthparts, which slice into the skin and make for a good flow of blood.

The stable fly sucks blood and is a vicious biter, especially in the early evening hours when the weather is warm and humid. Severe attacks irritate horses and cause restlessness and the stamping of feet. Because stable flies crawl over horse manure and then suck blood from the horse, they readily transmit stomach worms (*Habronema*).

Horn flies feed primarily on the back of the head, the sides of the neck, shoulders, withers, along the back, around the navel, and on the legs. They remain on the horse day and night.

In addition to their vicious biting habits, mosquitoes are of particular concern to horsemen because they transmit the viruses causing encephalomyelitis (Eastern, Western, and Venezuelan).

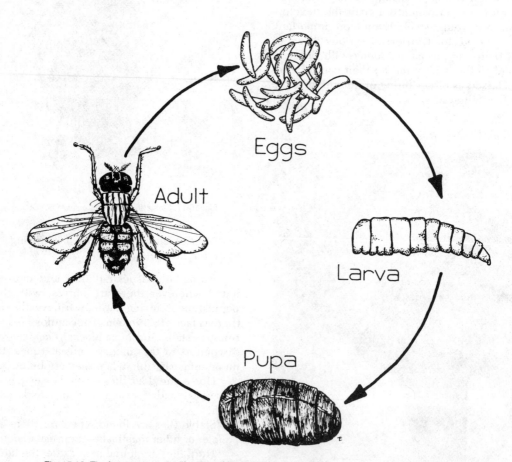

Fig. 15-18. The four stages in the life cycle of flies: egg, larva (maggot), pupa, and adult. Under optimum conditions during warm weather, the various species complete their life cycles in the following number of days: housefly, 7; stable fly, 21; face fly, 8; black blowfly, 11; green blowfly, 8; screwworm fly, 14.

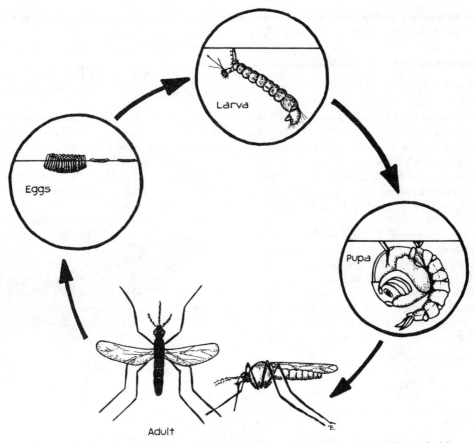

Fig. 15-19. The four stages in the life cycle of mosquitoes: egg, larva (wiggler), pupa (tumbler), and adult.

Prevention, Control, and Treatment

Sanitation—the destruction of the breeding areas of the pests—is the key to the control of biting flies and mosquitoes. Do not allow manure or other breeding areas to accumulate. Spread manure in fields (to dry) every day or two. Control horse flies, deer flies, and mosquitoes by filling low spots in corrals or paddocks and draining all water-holding areas.

As a supplement to sanitation, use insecticide (of which there are several) according to manufacturer's directions. Treat manure piles and buildings for fly control; and treat wet areas that harbor mosquitoes.

Fly repellents containing pyrethrins which last four to eight hours after application have been developed for the control of horse flies and deer flies on horses.

Nonbiting Flies

Horses may be annoyed by the face fly (*Musca autumnalis*) and the housefly (*M. domestica*), neither of which suck blood.

Distribution and Losses Caused by Nonbiting Flies

Face flies are serious pests of horses (and cattle) in the eastern, midwestern and certain western states.

Houseflies are widely distributed throughout the world and are one of the principal pests around horse stables.

Life History and Habits

The face fly breeds only in single, fresh animal droppings, and only from cattle on rangeland or pasture. The life cycle from egg to adult takes 8 days during warm summer months (Fig. 15-18) and up to 2 to 3 weeks in cooler weather.

Houseflies are attracted to waste materials, where they feed and deposit their eggs. This includes stacked horse manure, soiled bedding, wet feed, and decomposed plant material (grass clippings, vegetable and fruit wastes). Houseflies do not normally develop in single manure droppings; rather, they use piles of manure or other organic matter. Under favorable

conditions—warm weather and plenty of food—the usual life cycle from egg to adult fly is one week (Fig 15-18).

Damage Inflicted, Symptoms and Signs of Affected Animals

Face flies congregate about the nose and eyes of horses, where they sponge up liquids. The feeding of face flies causes excessive flow of tears and saliva—and irritation. Infested horses usually stand about restlessly switching their tails and not grazing naturally. Almost complete freedom from face flies can be obtained by keeping horses confined to stables during the daytime.

The housefly, which feeds twice daily, regurgitates liquid through its proboscis while depositing fecal matter as it crawls over its food. In this manner, it can transmit human and animal diseases, and it transmits stomach worms (*Habronema*) to horses. The dark spots on walls, ceilings, corral fences, etc, are the characteristic "fly specks" of vomit or fecal material.

Houseflies are attracted to the moist areas of the horse's face.

Prevention, Control, and Treatment

Good face fly control is difficult to achieve. Pyrethrin repellents applied to the horse's face and head will repel nonbiting flies for 8 to 12 hours. A mask or net can be made and attached to the halter so that its movements protect the horse's eyes from face flies when on pasture. Residual sprays, when applied to the sunny surfaces of barns, shelters, and fences where face flies congregate reduce populations.

Sanitation is the most efficient method of reducing populations of houseflies. Sanitation may be additionally important if the horses are located near an urban area, in order to avoid complaints from neighbors. Residual sprays will eliminate many houseflies. Also, houseflies are attracted to baits (insecticides mixed with sugar or other attractive material), which are effective housefly killers.

LICE

The louse is a small, flattened, wingless insect parasite of which there are several species. Horses are commonly infested with two species of lice, the horse-sucking louse (*Haematopinus asini*) and the horse-biting louse (*Bovicola equi*). The sucking louse obtains blood and lymph from horses by puncturing the skin with piercing-sucking mouthparts. The biting louse feeds on scales, hair, and skin exudate and does not pierce the skin or suck blood. Of the two groups, sucking lice are the most injurious. Most species of lice are specific for a particular species of animals.

Lice are always more abundant on weak, unthrifty animals and are more troublesome during the winter months than during the rest of the year.

Distribution and Losses Caused by Lice and Ticks

The presence of lice upon animals is almost universal, but the degree of infestation depends largely upon the state of animal nutrition and the extent to which the owner will tolerate parasites. The irritation caused by the presence of lice on horses retards growth, gains, and/or production of milk.

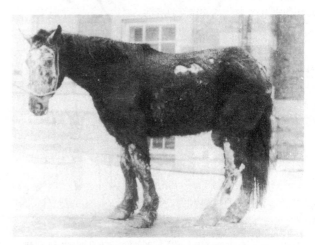

Fig. 15-20. Horse with a severe infestation of lice. Note the rough coat and loss of hair caused by gnawing and rubbing. Infestation shows up most commonly in winter and in poorly fed and neglected animals. (Courtesy, Department of Veterinary Pathology and Hygiene, College of Veterinary Medicine, University of Illinois)

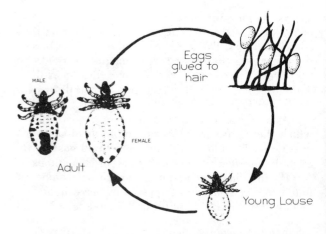

Fig. 15-21. Life cycle of long-nosed, bloodsucking lice showing nits (eggs) glued to hair, young louse, female with developing egg, and male.

Life History and Habits

Lice spend their entire life cycle—eggs (nits),

nymphs, and adults—on the host's body. They attach their eggs or "nits" to the hair near the skin where they hatch in about two weeks. Two weeks later the young females begin laying eggs, and after reproduction they die on the host. Lice do not survive more than a week when separated from the host; but, under favorable conditions, eggs clinging to detached hairs may continue to hatch for two or three weeks.

Damage Inflicted; Symptoms and Signs of Affected Animals

Lice infestation shows up most commonly in winter on illnourished and neglected animals. There is intense irritation, restlessness, and loss of condition. As many lice are bloodsuckers, they devitalize their host. There may be severe itching and the animal may be seen scratching, rubbing, and gnawing at the skin. The hair may be rough and thin, and lack luster; patches of hair may be rubbed off; and scabs may be evident. In horses, favorite locations for lice are the root of the tail, on the inside of the thighs, over the fetlock region, and along the neck and shoulders. In some cases, the symptoms may resemble those of mange; and it must be kept in mind that the two may occur simultaneously. With the coming of spring, when the hair sheds and the animals go to pasture, lousiness is greatly diminished.

Prevention, Control, and Treatment

Lice are easily controlled by periodic applications, according to the directions on the label, of one of the following insecticides: crotoxyphos, coumaphos (Co-Ral), dioxathion, malathion, or rotenone.

MITES (MANGE)

Mites produce a specific contagious disease known as mange (or scabies, scab, or itch). These small insectlike parasites, which are almost invisible to the naked eye, constitute a very large group. They attack member of both the plant and animal kingdom.

Each species of domesticated animals has its own peculiar species of mange mites; and, with the exception of the sarcoptic mites, the mites from one species of animals cannot live normally and propagate permanently on a different species. The sarcoptic mites are transmissible from one class of animals to another and, in the case of the sarcoptic mite of the horse and cow, from animals to man. There are two chief forms of mange: sarcopic mange, caused by burrowing mites, and psoroptic mange, caused by mites that bite the skin and suck blood but do not burrow. The sarcoptic form is most damaging; for, in addition to their tunneling, the mites secrete an irritating poison. This combination results in severe itching.

Horses may become infested with three species of mange mites—*Sarcoptes scabiei equi*, *Psoroptes equi*, and *Chorioptes bovis equi*. These minute parasites live on the skin of horses; and each species produces a particular type of mange.

Mites are responsible for the condition known as mange (scabies) in horses, sheep, cattle, and swine. The disease appears to spread most rapidly among young and poorly nourished animals.

Distribution and Losses Caused by Mites

Injury from mites is caused by irritation and blood sucking and the formation of scabs and other skin affections. In a severe attack, the growth of young animals may be retarded.

Life History and Habits

All stages of the life cycle of mange mites are found on the host—the horse. The mites will live for only 2 or 3 weeks when removed from the animal. The female mite which produces sarcopic mange—the most severe form of scabies—lays from 10 to 25 eggs during the egg-laying period, which lasts about 2 weeks. At the end of another 2 weeks, the eggs have hatched and the mites have reached maturity. A new generation of mites may be produced every 15 days.

The disease is more prevalent during the winter months, when animals are confined and in close contact with each other.

Damage Inflicted; Symptoms and Signs of Affected Animals

Heavy infestations of mites, which are a source of constant annoyance to horses, result in a characteristic hairless, scaly appearance.

When the mite pierces the skin to feed on cells and lymph, there is marked irritation, itching, and

Fig. 15-22. Horse with a severe infestation of sarcoptic mites, producing a condition commonly known as mange (or scabies, scab, or itch). The only certain method of diagnosis is to demonstrate the presence of mites. (Courtesy, USDA)

scratching. Exudate forms on the surface, and this coagulates, crusting over the surface. The crusting is often accompanied or followed by the formation of thick, tough, wrinkled skin. Often there are secondary skin infections. The only certain method of diagnosis is to demonstrate the presence of the mites.

Prevention, Control, and Treatment

Prevention consists in avoiding contact with diseased animals or infested premises. In the case of an outbreak, the local veterinarian or livestock sanitation officials should be contacted.

Any of the following insecticides, used as a spray or dip, will meet the federal regulations for the control of mites on horses: lime-sulfur (2% "sulfide sulfur"), lindane (0.05 - 0.06%), or toxaphene (0.5 - 0.6%); using 2 applications of each insecticide, 10-14 days apart.

RINGWORM

Ringworm, or barn itch, is a contagious disease of the outer layers of skin. It is caused by certain microscopic molds or fungi (*Trichophyton, Achorion, or Microsporon*). All animals and man are susceptible.

Distributions and Losses Caused by Ringworm

Ringworm is widespread throughout the United States. Though it may appear among animals on pasture, it is far more prevalent as a stable disease. It is unsightly, and affected animals may experience considerable discomfort; but the actual economic losses attributed to the disease are not too great.

Life History and Habits

The period of incubation for this disease is about one week. The fungi form seed or spores that may live 18 months or longer in barns and elsewhere.

Damage Inflicted; Symptoms and Signs of Affected Animals

Round, scaly areas almost devoid of hair appear mainly in the vicinity of the eyes, ears, side of the neck, or the root of the tail. Crusts may form, and the skin may have a gray, powdery, abestoslike appearance. The infested patches, if not checked, gradually increase in size. Mild itching usually accompanies the disease.

Prevention, Control, and Treatment

The organisms are spread from animal to animal or through the medium of contaminated fence posts, currycombs, and brushes. Thus, prevention and control consists of disinfecting everything that has been in contact with infested animals. The affected animals should also be isolated. Strict sanitation is an essential in the control of ringworm.

The hair should be clipped, the scabs removed, and the area sandpapered and washed with soap. The diseased parts should be painted with tincture of iodine or salicylic acid and alcohol (1 part in 10) every 3 days until cleared up. Copper napthenate or dichlorphene are also effective in treatment of ringworm.

SCREWWORM (FLIES)

Among all the insect pests on this earth, those which raise their maggots in the living flesh of animals—such as the screwworm fly (*Cochliomyia hominivorax*)—are peculiarly loathsome. True screwworms seldom get through the unbroken skin, but will penetrate moist pockets like the prepuce of a gelding. They are not found in cold-blooded animals such as turtles, snakes, and lizards.

Man-made wounds resulting from branding and castrating horses afford a breeding ground for this parasite. Add to this the wounds from some types of vegetation, from fighting, and from bloodsucking insects; and ample places for propagation are provided.

Distribution and Losses Caused by Screwworms

The screwworm fly was eradicated from southeastern United States in the late 1950s. Today, infestations occur occasionally in certain areas of Arizona, New Mexico, and Texas; and infestations frequently occur in Mexico. Sometimes under exceptionally favorable weather conditions or through the shipping of infested animals from further south, destructive outbreaks of the pest occur in areas to the north and east.

The screwworm fly may infest horses through wounds, or through lesions caused by ticks, horse flies, or horn flies. In infested areas, it is undoubtedly the greatest enemy of all the insect species with which the livestock owner must contend. For example, in the Southwest, prior to the use of sterile flies for eradication, many ranchers reported that 50 percent of their normal annual livestock losses were caused by this parasite.

Life History and Habits

The primary screwworm fly is bluish green in color, with three dark stripes on its back and reddish or orange color below the eyes. The fly generally deposits its eggs in shinglelike masses on the edges on the dry portion of wounds. From 50 to 300 eggs are

laid at one time, with a single female being capable of laying about 3,000 eggs in a lifetime. Hatching of the eggs occurs in 11 hours, and the young whitish worms (larvae or maggots) immediately burrow into the living flesh. There they feed and grow for a period of 4 to 7 days, shedding their skin twice during this period.

When the larva has reached its full growth, it assumes a pinkish color, leaves the wound, and drops to the ground, where it digs beneath the surface of the soil and undergoes a transformation to the hard-skinned, dark brown, motionless pupa. It is during the pupa stage that the maggot changes to the adult fly.

After the pupa has been in the soil from 7 to 60 days, the fly emerges from it, works its way to the surface of the ground, and crawls up on some nearby object (bush, weed, etc.) to allow its wings to unfold and otherwise to mature. Under favorable conditions, the newly emerged female fly becomes sexually mature and will lay eggs 5 days later. During warm weather, the entire life cycle is usually completed in 21 days, but under cold, unfavorable conditions, this cycle may take as many as 80 days or longer.

Damage Inflicted; Symptoms and Signs of Affected Animals

The injury caused by this parasite is inflicted chiefly by the maggots. Unless proper treatment is administered, the great destruction of tissues kills the host in a few days.

Prevention, Control, and Treatment

Prevention in infested areas consists mainly of keeping animal wounds to a minimum and of protecting those that do materialize.

As the primary screwworm must have living warm-blooded animals in which to breed and so that it may survive, it must produce a new generation during each four-month period. It is evident, therefore, that the most effective control measures can be effected during the winter months. During this season, the life cycle is slowed down, and it is difficult for the fly to live and breed. Thus, the most effective control consists in preventing infestation of wounds and of killing all possible maggots during the winter and spring months. Additional control is effected through timing, as much as possible, those farm and ranch operations that necessarily produce wounds. The winter season is preferable, being the time when the flies are least abundant and least active. The eradication of plants that cause injuries, breeding so that young will arrive during the season of least fly activity, and avoidance of anything else that might produce wounds will all aid greatly in screwworm control. In brief, the elimination of wounds or injuries to the host constitutes effective control.

The screwworm eradication program, by sterilization, has been very effective. This consists in sterilizing male screwworms, in the pupal stages with gamma rays. Male screwworms mate repeatedly, but females mate only once. Thus, when a female mates with a sterilized male, only infertile eggs are laid. The release of millions of sterilized males has led to the near eradication of screwworms from most of the United States.

When maggots (larvae) infest the flesh of an animal, a sample of the larvae should be sent to proper authorities for identification, and the animal should be treated with a proper insecticide. Additional treatment or control measures will be supervised by inspection personnel if the larvae are screwworms.

The application of dusts of coumaphos (Co-Ral) and ronnel (Korlan) will provide relief.

Ticks

The numbers and species of ticks infesting horses varies with the geographical area. Each region has its own group of ticks.

Basically, ticks can be classified into two groups: the "hard" ticks, and the "soft" ticks. Horses are parasitized by a number of hard ticks, most of which are three-host ticks (they utilize three hosts during the life cycle) that detach after feeding as larvae and as nymphs and molt on the ground.

Distribution and Losses Caused by Ticks

Ticks are particularly prevalent on horses in the southern and western parts of the United States. In severe infestation, they reduce the vitality of horses through constant irritation and loss of blood.

Life History and Habits

All ticks have life cycles that are generally similar; that is, the females lay eggs, and the six-legged larvae (or seed ticks) hatch, engorge on a host, and molt to eight-legged nymphs; the nymphs also engorge and then molt to adults. The adults usually mate on a host. The females engorge, drop off, and lay eggs, and the males remain on the host to mate with other females.

The lone star tick (*Amblyomma americanum*), the Gulf Coast tick (*Amblyomma maculatum*), the Pacific Coast tick (*Dermacentor occidentalis*), the American dog tick (*D. variabilis*), and the Rocky Mountain wood tick (*D. andersoni*) are all three-host ticks, and all are limited in distribution to certain areas. Immature stages (larvae and nymphs) engorge on small mammals and birds, and adults are usually found on

horses in the spring and summer. Another three-host species, the blacklegged tick (*Ixodes scapularis*), is found on horses in the late winter and early spring.

Of special interest to horse owners are two species of one-host ticks, the winter tick (*D. albipictus*) and the tropical horse tick (*Anocentor nitens*). These ticks are called one-host ticks because they molt from larva to nymph to adult while still attached to the same host. Thus, they utilize only one host during the life cycle.

The winter tick is found throughout the northern tier of states and in the Rocky Mountain States south of Texas. The winter tick, as the name indicates, is found on horses and other large animals in the fall and winter months. Females lay eggs in the winter and spring, and the larvae hatch, remain quiet through the summer, and then become active and attach to hosts in the fall. Winter ticks are often found in large numbers on horses.

The tropical horse tick is found in Florida, Georgia, and the southern tip of Texas. It is unusual because all the parasitic stages are found in the ears of horses. However, in cases of heavy infestation, they may also be found in the nasal diverticulae and on the mane and belly. The engorging female eliminates large amounts of wastes so the ears of horses may become full of ticks and their excrement. *Anocentor nitens* is of considerable importance to horse owners because it is the vector of equine piroplasmosis.

Two other one-host ticks are the closely related cattle tick (*Boophilus annulatus*) and the southern cattle tick (*B. microplus*). They have been eradicated from the United States and are subjects of stringent quarantine to prevent reintroduction from Mexico.

The only soft tick found on horses is the ear tick (*Otobius megnini*). The ear tick is a one-host species commonly found deep in the ears of livestock in the southwestern states though it is widely distributed in the United States and is established as far north as British Columbia, Canada. Larvae engorge in the ears of livestock and molt there to nymphs. After feeding slowly in the ear for as long as six months, nymphs engorge fully and leave the host. (The stage most commonly seen is the engorging spiny nymphs.) Fed nymphs seek shelter under sheds, salt troughs, and other cover where they molt to the adult stage. Unlike the other tick species, the adults do not feed. After mating off the host, the female lays small batches of eggs intermittently for more than six months. Newly hatched larvae seek hosts and make their way to the animal's ears.

*Damage Inflicted; Symptoms and Signs
of Affected Animals*

Ticks are important to horsemen because they may transmit diseases such as equine piroplasmosis

(carried by *Anocentor nitens*) or cattle fever (carried by the *Boophilus* species). Also, most of the ticks mentioned may be vectors of anaplasmosis, and several species can cause tick paralysis in hosts. Massive infestations may cause anemia, loss of weight, and even death. "Head heaviness" is often associated with massive infestations of ear ticks. Other losses may result from the simple presence of the ticks on the animals, a factor called "tick worry."

Prevention, Control, and Treatment

Because most species of ticks, except the ear tick and the tropical horse tick, attach to the external surfaces of horses, an application of the recommended insecticide by spray or wipe-on will give effective control. Ear ticks and tropical horse ticks should be treated by applying the chemical into the ears of the horses. Since horses are often confined to rather small areas, treatments of the premises may also help control heavy infestations of ticks.

Recommended insecticides for control of ticks (except ear tick) are: crotoxyphos, coumaphos (Co-Ral), dioxathion, malathion, and pyrethrins.

The recommended insecticides for control of ear ticks are: lindane and ronnel (Korlan).

SWIMMING HORSES THERAPEUTICALLY

Horsemen have long known that horses can swim. The Romans swam their battle steeds to give them endurance. Napoleon's troops swam their horses in competitive events. Some tribes of American Indians swam their mounts for sport. In the late 1920s, Golden Prince, a Thoroughbred, swam his way from an injury back to the track. His trainer used California beaches for his swim to health. In his first start following swimming therapy, Golden Prince won the

Fig. 15-23. Horse swimming in pool. This pool is 40 feet in diameter and 13 feet deep and is equipped with a complete filtering system. (Courtesy, El Rancho, Murrieta, Calif.)

$100,000 added Coffroth Handicap at Tijuana, setting a new track record and collecting $98,250. Following this success, therapeutic swimming was here to stay.

Swimming pools have a place, and their use will increase. But they are expensive to construct and operate, and they're not a panacea. Thus, the therapeutic value of horse swimming should be placed in perspective. We need to know more about physiologic effect, injuries in the pool, health hazards, therapeutic value, and special needs in pool design and engineering; and we need more research on therapeutic horse swimming. Based on presently available information, the following points are pertinent to horse swimming pools and therapeutic swimming:

1. *Pool "broke"*—It takes 2 to 4 days to train a horse to enter the pool and to swim in the proper direction.

2. *Wash before swim*—Most pool operators wash (or hose) horses off before putting them into the pool. It keeps the pool cleaner and prepares the horse for the swim.

3. *Usefulness*—Training by swimming is especially useful for horses with minor leg injuries; it allows exercising them back to condition without placing premature strain on the injury or ailment. Also, it is reported that many chronic cases of "tying up" improve after swimming exercise.

4. *Pool construction*—Special construction is required for man-made horse pools.

Pools may be either circular or canal type (linear). Circular pools range from 25 to 66 ft in diameter and average about 10 ft deep. Canal-type pools are usually about 100 ft long, 10 ft wide, and 10 ft deep. Each pool has advantages and disadvantages.

The main advantage of a circular pool with a tangential entry chute is that horses may exit without turning if they swim clockwise. The disadvantages: Some horses will swim only in one direction, regardless of lameness or track experience; and, too, a sharp turn must be negotiated after the animal enters the pool. In circular pools with a radial entry chute, horses must make turns both on entry and exit. With a center island in a round pool, the attendant does a minimum of walking.

Canal-type pools are most useful for stationary swimming.

Where a pond or lake is used, horses are usually led by motorboat, by the attendant swimming, or by the attendant standing on a floating dock, with the horse swimming around it.

Entry pens and chutes must be properly constructed and swimming horses must be kept away from the edge of the pool to avoid leg injury. The latter may be accomplished either by having an overhanging ledge—walkway, or by using a head pole to hold the animal away from the edge of the pool.

5. *Filter—Chlorination—heating*—A special filtration system is required for an equine pool, since horses routinely defecate during swimming. Floating manure must be removed with long-handled nets. Other contamination—hair, skin excretions, and debris carried on the hoofs—must also be removed. Vacuum cleaning and special filters are necessary.

A pH of 7.2 to 7.4 is recommended, with muriatic acid (hydrochloric acid) used for this purpose. Chlorine levels are held at 2 to 4 parts per million by most pool operators. Insufficient chlorine will result in infectious dermatoses; excessive chlorine may cause dermatitis.

During the winter months in colder climates, a water heater is necessary. Most horse pools are held at about 70° F.

6. *Leg movement*—The leg movements of most equine swimmers are similar to a three-beat gait—much like the gallop. However, it is noteworthy that many Standardbred horses mimic their gaits—they either trot or pace in the pool. All horses can stay afloat, but some are better swimmers than others.

7. *Stationary swimming*—When a horse is held in one spot, slightly more exertion is required than when free swimming; hence, it's a way in which to increase the exercise.

8. *Length of swim*—The usual plan is to swim 1 to 3 minutes the first day, then increase the swim by 1 minute daily up to 15 to 25 minutes per day per swim. Many combinations of swimming, track work, and "hot-walking" are used.

9. *After the swim is over*—After the swim, horses are usually scraped, then walked for 20 to 30 minutes.

10. *Stifle lameness*—It is reported that stifle lameness is worsened by swimming.

11. *Maintain fitness*—Swimming offers a way in which to maintain fitness during convalescence.

12. *Psychosomatic therapy*—Swimming constitutes psychosomatic therapy for "track-sour" horses; following two to three weeks of swimming, they're ready to run and win.

13. *Physiologic effect*—Pool advocates feel that a portion of a horse's training can be achieved in a swimming pool, but there is general agreement that the training of a racehorse must be finished on the track.

From the above, it may be concluded that swimming exercise is not a panacea, nor is it a totally trial-and-error lameness therapy. Further, it is obvious that much research is needed, particularly in the areas of pool design, filtration, chlorination, safety, and effect on the horse. It would appear, however, that equine swimming pools may come to mean to horses what swimming pools have always meant to people—a fine way in which to condition, or exercise, especially where there are minor leg weaknesses.

DISINFECTANTS

A disinfectant is a bactericidal or microbicidal agent that frees from infection (usually a chemical agent which destroys disease germs or other microorganisms, or inactivates viruses).

The high concentration of horses and continuous use of horse barns often results in a condition referred to as disease buildup. As disease-producing organisms—viruses, bacteria, fungi, and parasite eggs—accumulate in the environment, disease problems can become more severe and be transmitted to each succeeding group of horses raised on the same premises. Under these circumstances, cleaning and disinfection become extremely important in breaking the life cycle. Also, in the case of a disease outbreak, the premises must be disinfected.

Under ordinary conditions, proper cleaning of barns removes most of the microorganisms, along with the filth, thus eliminating the necessity of disinfection.

Effective disinfection depends on five things:

1. Thorough cleaning before application.
2. The phenol coefficient of the disinfectant, which indicates the killing strength of a disinfectant as compared to phenol (carbolic acid). It is determined by a standard laboratory test in which the typhoid fever germ often is used as the test organism.
3. The dilution at which the disinfectant is used.
4. The temperature; most disinfectants are much more effective if applied hot.
5. Thoroughness of application, and time of exposure.

Disinfection must in all cases be preceded by a very thorough cleaning, for organic matter serves to protect disease germs and otherwise interferes with the activity of the disinfecting agent.

Sunlight possesses disinfecting properties, but it is variable and superficial in its action. Heat and some of the chemical disinfectants are more effective.

The application of heat by steam, by hot water, by burning, or by boiling is an effective method of disinfection. In many cases, however, it may not be practical to use heat.

A good disinfectant should (1) have the power to kill disease-producing organisms, (2) remain stable in the presence of organic matter (manure, hair, soil), (3) dissolve readily in water and remain in solution, (4) be nontoxic to animals and humans, (5) penetrate organic matter rapidly, (6) remove dirt and grease, and (7) be economical to use.

The number of available disinfectants is large because the ideal universally applicable disinfectant does not exist. Table 15-8 gives a summary of the limitations, usefulness, and strength of some common disinfectants.

When using a disinfectant, *always read and follow the manufacturer's directions.*

TABLE 15-8
HANDY DISINFECTANT GUIDE

Kind of Disinfectant	Usefulness	Strength	Limitations and Comments
Alcohol (ethyl-ethanol, isopropyl, methanol)	Primarily as skin disinfectants and for emergency purposes on instruments.	70% alcohol—the content usually found in rubbing alcohol.	They are too costly for general disinfection. They are ineffective against bacterial spores.
Boric acid[1]	As a wash for eyes, and other sensitive parts of the body.	1 oz in 1 pt water (about 6% solution).	It is a weak antiseptic. It may cause harm to the nervous system if absorbed into the body in large amounts. For this and other reasons, antibiotic solutions and saline solutions are fast replacing it.
Chlorines (sodium hypochlorate, chlormine-T)	Used for dairy equipment and as deodorants. They will kill all kinds of bacteria, fungi, and viruses, providing the concentration is sufficiently high.	Generally used at about 200 ppm for dairy equipment and as a deodorant.	They are corrosive to metals and neutralized by organic materials.
Cresols (many commercial products available)	A generally reliable class of disinfectant. Effective against brucellosis, shipping fever, swine erysipelas, and tuberculosis.	Cresol is usually used as a 2 to 4% solution (1 cup to 2 gal. of water makes a 4% solution).	Cannot be used where odor may be absorbed, and, therefore, not suited for use around milk and meat.
Formaldehyde (gaseous disinfectant)	Formaldehyde will kill anthrax spores, TB organisms, and animal viruses in a 1 to 2% solution. It is often used to disinfect buildings following a disease outbreak.	As a liquid disinfectant, it is usually used as a 1 to 2% solution. As a gaseous disinfectant (fumigant), use 1½ lb of potassium permanganate plus 3 pt of formaldehyde. Also, gas may be released by heating paraformaldehyde.	It has a disagreeable odor, destroys living tissue, and can be extremely poisonous. The bactericidal effectiveness of the gas is dependent upon having the proper relative humidity (above 75%) and temperature (above 30° C and preferably near 60° C).

(Continued)

TABLE 15-8 (Continued)

Kind of Disinfectant	Usefulness	Strength	Limitations and Comments
Heat (by steam, hot water, burning, or boiling)	Heat is used in burning rubbish or articles of little value, and in disposing of infected body discharges. The steam "Jenny" (which produces steam) is effective for disinfection, particularly if used in conjunction with a phenolic germicide.	10 minutes' exposure to boiling water is usually sufficient.	Exposure to boiling water will destroy all ordinary disease germs but sometimes fails to kill the spores of such diseases as anthrax and tetanus. Moist heat is preferred to dry heat, and steam under pressure is the most effective. Heat may be impractical or too expensive.
Iodine[1] (tincture)	Extensively used as skin disinfectant, for minor cuts and bruises.	Generally used as tincture of iodine, either 2% or 7%.	Never cover with a bandage. Clean skin before applying iodine. It is corrosive to metals.
Idophore (tamed iodine)	Effective against all bacteria (both gram-negative and gram-positive), fungi, and most viruses.	Usually used as disinfectants at concentrations of 50-75 ppm titratable iodine, and as sanitizers at levels of 12.5 ppm titratable iodine, they can be used as an antiseptic in drinking water.	They are inhibited in their activity by organic matter. They are quite expensive.
Lime (quicklime; burnt lime; calcium oxide)	As a deodorant when sprinkled on manure and animal discharges; or as a disinfectant when sprinkled on the floor or used as a newly made "milk of lime" or as a whitewash.	Use as a dust; as "milk of lime"; or as a whitewash, but use *fresh*.	Not effective against anthrax or tetanus spores. Wear goggles, when adding water to quicklime.
Lye (sodium hydroxide; caustic soda)	On concrete floors. In strong solution (5%), effective against anthrax.	Lye is usually used as either a 2% or 5% solution. To prepare a 2% solution, add 1 can of lye to 5 gal. of water. To prepare a 5% solution, add 1 can of lye to 2 gal. of water. A 5% solution is necessary to destroy the spores of anthrax.	Damages fabrics, aluminum, and painted surfaces. Be careful, for it will burn the hands and face. Lye solutions are most effective when used hot. **Diluted vinegar can be used to neutralize lye.**
Lysol (the brand name of a product of cresol plus soap)	For disinfecting surgical instruments and instruments used in castrating and tattooing. Useful as a skin disinfectant before surgery, and for use on the hands before castrating.	0.5 to 2.0%.	Has a disagreeable odor. Does not mix well with hard water. Less costly than phenol.
Phenol (carbolic acid): 1. Phenolics-coal tar derivatives 2. Synthetic phenols	They are ideal general-purpose disinfectants. Effective and inexpensive. They're very resistant to the inhibiting effects of organic residue; hence, they are suitable for barn disinfection, and foot and wheel dip-baths.	Both phenolics (coal tar) and synthetic phenols vary widely in efficacy from one compound to another. So, note and follow manufacturer's directions. Generally used in a 5% solution.	They are corrosive, and they're toxic to animals and humans. Ineffective on fungi and viruses.
Quaternary ammonium coupounds (QAC)	Very water soluble, ultrarapid kill rate, effective deodorizing properties, and moderately priced. Good detergent characteristics and harmless to skin.	Follow manufacturer's directions.	They can corrode metal. Not very potent in combatting viruses. Adversely affected by organic matter.
Sal soda	It may be used in place of lye against certain diseases.	10½% solution (13½ oz to 1 gal. water).	
Sal soda and soda ash (or sodium carbonate)	They may be used in place of lye against certain diseases.	4% solution (1 lb to 3 gal. water). Most effective in hot solution.	Commonly used as cleaning agents, but have disinfectant properties, especially when used as a hot solution.
Soap	Its power to kill germs is very limited. Greatest usefulness is in cleansing and dissolving coatings from various surfaces, including the skin, prior to application of a good disinfectant.	As commercially prepared.	Although indispensable for sanitizing surfaces, soaps should not be used as disinfectants. They are not regularly effective; staphylococci and the organisms which cause diarrheal diseases are resistant.

[1]Sometimes loosely classed as a disinfectant but actually an antiseptic and practically useful only on living tissue.

SELECTED REFERENCES

Title of Publication	Author(s)	Publisher
Animal Agents and Vectors of Human Disease	E. C. Faust	Lea & Febiger, Philadelphia, Penn., 1956
Animal Disease and Human Health	J. H. Steele	Food and Agriculture Organization of the United Nations, Rome, Italy, 1962
Animal Diseases: Yearbook of Agriculture, 1956	Ed. by A. Stefferud	U.S. Department of Agriculture, Washington, D.C., 1956
Animal Parasitism	C. P. Read	Prentice-Hall, Inc., Englewood Cliffs, N.J., 1972
Animal Sanitation and Disease Control, Sixth Edition	R. R. Dykstra	The Interstate Printers & Publishers, Inc., Danville, Ill., 1961
Control of Ticks on Livestock, The	S. F. Barnett	Food and Agriculture Organization of the United Nations, Rome, Italy, 1968
Diseases of the Horse	Bureau of Animal Industry	U.S. Department of Agriculture, Washington, D.C., 1942
Diseases of Livestock, Sixth Edition	T. G. Hungerford	Angus & Robertson, Ltd., Sydney, Australia, 1967
Diseases Transmitted from Animals to Man Fifth Edition	T. G. Hull	Charles C Thomas, Publisher, Springfield, Ill., 1963
Disinfection, Sterilization, and Preservation	C. A. Lawrence S. S. Block	Lea & Febiger, Philadelphia, Penn., 1968
Emerging Diseases of Animals	Veterinary Research Laboratory, Onderstepoort, South Africa	Food and Agriculture Organization of the United Nations, Rome, Italy, 1968
Equine Medicine & Surgery, Second Edition	Ed. by E. J. Catcott, J. F. Smithcors	American Veterinary Publications, Inc., Wheaton, Ill., 1972
First Aid Hints for the Horse Owner	W. E. Lyon	Collins, St. James's Place, London, England, 1971
Hagan's Infectious Diseases of Domestic Animals, Sixth Edition	D. W. Bruner J. H. Gillespie	Cornell University Press, Ithaca, N.Y., 1973
Handbook of Veterinary Procedures and Emergency Treatment	R. W. Kirk S. I. Bistner	W. B. Saunders Company, Philadelphia, Penn., 1975
Horse Owner's Vet Book, The	E. C. Straiton	J. B. Lippincott Co., New York, N.Y., 1973
Horsemen's Veterinary Adviser	J. B. Davidson	Horse Publications, Columbus, Ohio, 1966
Horses' Injuries	C. L. Strong	Arco Publishing Co., Inc., New York, N.Y., 1973
Illustrated Veterinary Encyclopedia for Horsemen, The	Staff	Equine Research Publications, Grapevine, Tex., 1975
Infectious Diseases of Domestic Animals, Third Edition	W. A. Hagan D. W. Bruner	Comstock Publishing Associates, Ithaca, N.Y., 1957
Lameness in Horses	O. R. Adams	Lea & Febiger, Philadelphia, Penn., 1962
Livestock Health Encyclopedia, Third Edition	R. Seiden	Springer Publishing Co., Inc., New York, N.Y., 1968

(continued)

Title of Publication	Author(s)	Publisher
Merck Veterinary Manual, The, Fourth Edition	Ed. by O. H. Siegmund	Merck & Co., Inc., Rahway, N.J., 1973
Nationwide System for Animal Health Surveillance, A	National Research Council	National Academy of Sciences, Washington, D.C., 1974
New Zealand Farmers' Veterinary Guide	D. G. Edgar et al.	The New Zealand Dairy Exporter, Wellington, New Zealand, 1962
Practical Parasitology: General Laboratory Techniques and Parasitic Protozoa	C. J. Price J. E. Reed	United Nations Development Programme, and Food and Agriculture Organization of the United Nations, Rome, Italy, 1970
Preventive Medicine and Public Health, Ninth Edition	Ed. by P. E. Sartwell	Appleton-Century-Crofts, New York, N.Y., 1965
Principles of Veterinary Science, Fourth Edition	F. B. Hadley	W. B. Saunders Company, Philadelphia, Penn., 1949
Progress in Equine Practice, Vol. I	Ed. by E. J. Catcott, J. F. Smithcors	American Veterinary Publications, Inc., Santa Barbara, Calif., 1966
Progress in Equine Practice, Vol. II	Ed. by E. J. Catcott, J. F. Smithcors	American Veterinary Publications, Inc., Wheaton, Ill., 1970
Some Diseases of Animals Communicable to Man in Britain	Ed. by O. Graham-Jones	Pergamon Press, Ltd., London, England, 1968
Some Important Animal Diseases in Europe: Papers Presented at the Animal Disease Meeting, Warsaw, 1948	K. V. Kesteven	Food and Agriculture Organization of the United Nations, Rome, Italy, 1952
Stockman's Handbook, The, Fourth Edition	M. E. Ensminger	The Interstate Printers & Publishers, Inc., Danville, Ill., 1970
The Vet Horse Book	TV Vet	Farming Press Ltd., Ipswich Suffolk, England, 1972
Veterinary Medicine	D. C. Blood J. A. Henderson	The Williams & Wilkins Co., Baltimore, Md., 1960
Veterinary Notes for Horse Owners	Rev. by J. F. Tutt	Arco Publishing Company, Inc., New York, N.Y., 1972
Veterinary Parasitology, Second Edition	G. Lapage	Charles C Thomas, Publisher, Springfield, Ill., 1968

In addition to the above selected references, valuable publications on different subjects pertaining to animal diseases, parasites, disinfectants, and poisonous plants can be obtained from the following sources:

1. Division of Publications
   Office of Information
   U.S. Department of Agriculture
   Washington, D.C. 20250

2. Your state agricultural college.

3. Several biological, pharmaceutical, and chemical companies.

CHAPTER 16

HORSE BEHAVIOR AND TRAINING

Contents   **Page**

Each animal species has characteristic ways of performing certain functions and rarely departs therefrom. The horse is no exception. A good understanding of horse behavior enhances horse training.

PART I. HORSE BEHAVIOR

Fig. 16-1. Horses at play. (Photo by Mrs. Buddy Banner, Willow Springs Ranch, Oracle, Ariz.)

The marvels and mysteries of horse behavior are ages old, yet 20th Century new. Modern domestic horses paw the ground when excited in much the same manner as did Przewalsky's horse. During the last round of the barn at night, horses keep up a running conversation with the caretaker as he gives a handful of hay to one still-hungry horse or treats a favorite mount to an apple. In a sign language that speaks louder than words, they tell him how they feel and what they want. Every movement and every sound conveys a message of well-being, distress, or disease. Lack of interest, dull eyes, sluggishness, rough coat, poor appetite, and/or abnormal droppings spell trouble. Alertness, stretching, yawning, vocalizing, eating with relish, and frisking are good omens and tell him that all is well in the barn.

Written observations of animal behavior date to the writings of the ancient Greeks, Aristotle in particular, about 350 B.C.

Prior to animal domestication, the very survival of the human race depended upon knowledge of animal habits and habitats as man hunted for his food. Primitive man understood the behavior of the wild horse; he knew where to find him, how to get close enough to kill him, and where he would run when frightened. But the behavioral information needed—first to hunt game, and later to domesticate animals—did not assume primary scientific significance for many years after the writings of Aristotle and of subsequent hunters, explorers, naturalists, and agriculturalists. Finally, in two classical books—*The Origin of Species by Means of Natural Selection*, published in 1859; and *The Descent of Man and Selection in Relation to Sex*, published in 1871, Charles Darwin laid the foundation for modern animal behavior. For many years thereafter, however, conditions were ripe for unscrupulous "animal behavior practitioners" to turn a "quick buck" as they made all sorts of claims for the reasoning powers of their charges. The most notable show on the road of this type involved "Clever Hans," a horse in Germany, about 1900, billed as the wonder horse who could add, multiply, divide, and even spell out words and sentences. Hans would stand in front of his trainer, and by pawing the ground with his hoof the appropriate number of times, answer questions put to him. If asked "How much is 2 + 2?" he would paw the ground 4 times. If asked to spell out words or sentences, he would paw the proper number of times for each letter of the alphabet. Finally, a committee of scientists was appointed to study the celebrated horse. They found that Hans did, indeed, paw out the correct answers. But, close observation revealed that the trainer cued the horse through a slight movement of his head. Hence, by watching his trainer, the horse would always stop when he observed the head signal. Both horse and trainer were amply rewarded; the horse by treats and affection, and the trainer by another stellar performance before a large and satisfied audience. Both maintained their behavior.

Despite some charlatans along the way, man applied his knowledge of horse behavior from the remote day of their domestication forward. It required knowledge of basic behavior patterns to capture, confine, and herd horses; and to breed, feed, water, and shelter them. Without this understanding, domestication would have failed and horses would not have survived. By 1900, the groundwork had been laid for the scientific work that followed; and the study of animal behavior became a distinct discipline. In recent years, it has advanced rapidly.

Horse behavior may be defined as the reaction of horses to certain stimuli or the manner in which they react to their environment. Modern horse breeding, feeding, and management have brought renewed interest in horse behavior, especially as a factor in their training, performance, and efficiency. Also, with increased confinement, or stabling, of horses, many abnormal behaviors have evolved to plague those who raise them, including finicky appetites, degenerate sexual behavior, cribbing, and a host of other behavioral disorders. Confinement has not only limited space, but it has interfered with the habitat and social

organization to which, through thousands of years of evolution, the species became adapted and best suited.

We now know that controlled environment must embrace far more than an air-conditioned chamber, along with ample feed and water. The horseman needs to concern himself more with the natural habitat of horses. Nature ordained that they do more than eat, sleep, and reproduce. Evidently, environmental deficiencies are manifested by abnoraml behaviors.

What can be done about it? Preventing cribbing by using choke collars on horses is not unlike trying to control malaria fever in humans by the use of drugs without getting rid of mosquitoes. Rather, we need to recognize these disorders for what they are—warning signals that conditions are not right. Correcting the cause of the disorder is the best solution. Unfortunately, this is not easy. Rectifying the cause may involve trying to emulate the natural conditions of the species, such as altering space per animal and group size, providing training and experience at opportune times, promoting exercise, and gradually changing rations. Over the long pull, selection provides a major answer to correcting confinement and other behavioral problems; we need to breed horses adapted to man-made environments.

This chapter is for the purpose of presenting some of the principles and applications of behavior in horse care and training. Those who have grown up around horses and dealt with them in practical ways have already accumulated substantial workaday knowledge about horse behavior. Those who are less familiar with horses may need to familiarize themselves with their behavior, better to feed, care for, and train them, and to recognize the early signs of illness. To all, the principles and applications of horse behavior depend on understanding, which is the intent of this chapter.

CAUSES OF HORSE BEHAVIOR

Horse behavior is caused by, or is the result of, three forces: (1) heredity, (2) training and experience, and (3) intelligence.

Heredity

Genes determine all the hereditary characteristics of horses, from the body type to the color of the hair. Heredity has already made its contribution at the time of fertilization, whereas environment (including training) works ceaselessly away until death.

Progressive horse breeders influence horse behavior by propagating genetically superior animals. They locate such horses by observing their type and performance (individuality), along with the type and performance of their relatives.

Simple Learning

No horse—whether he be used for saddle, race, or other purposes—reaches a high degree of proficiency without an education. Thus, if the offspring of Man o' War and six of the fastest mares ever to grace the tracks had merely worked on laundry trucks until six years old, then if they were suddenly—without warning or other preparation—placed upon a racetrack, the immediate results would have been disappointing. Their natural aptitude and conformation in breeding would not have been enough. Schooling and training would still have been necessary in order to bring out their inherent abilities.

In general, the behavior of animals depends upon the particular reaction patterns with which they were born. These are called *instincts* and *reflexes*. They are unlearned forms of behavior. Thus, all horses instinctively like to run. But how well and how fast they run depends upon the training to which they are subjected. They learn by experience. However, the training is only as effective as the inherited neural pathways. Several types of learned behavior are known; among them are those that follow.

● *Trial and error (rewards and punishment)*— This is a method by which horses learn. It is reinforced through the judicious employment of rewards and punishments. This doesn't mean that a horse is rewarded each time he obeys, or that he is beaten when he refuses to do something. But horses are big and strong; hence, it's best that they want to do something, rather than have to be forced. Also, too frequent or improper use of such artificial aids as whips, spurs, reins, and bits makes them less effective; worse yet, it will likely make for a mean horse. However, horses appreciate a pat on the shoulder or a word of praise. Even better results may be obtained by working on an equine's greediness—his fondness for such things as carrots or a sugar cube. Also, treats may be used effectively as rewards to teach some specific thing such as posing, or to cure a vice like moving while the rider is mounting; but this should not be overdone.

Another example of the application of the trial-and-error method to the learning and experience of horses is the use of an electric fence. When an electric fence is installed, the immediate instinct of horses is to investigate—to touch it with their noses. Upon receiving a shock, they back off and let it alone. Thereafter, the electricity can be shut off for a considerable period of time before some horse again tests it.

● *Imprinting (socialization)*—This is a form of early learning which occurs in foals. It is the phenomenon that causes newborn foals to follow any

moving object, including humans. (Also see section on "Care-Giving and Care-Seeking (Mother-Young) Behavior.")

Complex Learning

Complex learning is the capacity to acquire and apply knowledge—the ability to learn from experience and to solve problems. It is the ability to solve complex problems by something more than simple trial-and-error, habit, or stimulus-response modifications. In man, we recognize this capacity as the ability to develop concepts, to behave according to general principles, and to put together elements from past experience into a new organization.

Animals learn to do some things, whereas they inherit the ability to do others. The latter is often called instinct. Thus, ducks do not have to learn to swim—instinctively, they take to water.

Some folks judge the intelligence of animals by the size of their brain in relation to body size. Others rank them according to their ability to solve a maze (a pathway complicated by at least one blind alley, used in learning experiments and intelligence tests) in order to get food.

Generally speaking, behavioral scientists are agreed that each species has its own special abilities and capacities, and that it should only be tested on these. For example, the dog, pig, and rat, are more adept at solving a maze test than the horse. Hence, solving a maze in order to find food favors the scavangers (and the dog, the pig, and the rat are all scavangers)—they have connived for their food since the beginning to time. However, the horse, whose natural feed was the grass that lay around him, never had to develop this kind of intelligence. He was a plains-living animal, highly specialized for speed as a means of escape from his enemies and with almost no powers of manipulation. Thus, a horse should be good at any problem that can be solved by running, including racing, polo, pole bending, calf roping, etc. Indeed, had equines not been smart and adapted to their particular environment, they would never have made it through 58 million years. Thus, each species is uniquely adapted to only one ecological niche. Moreover, a niche is filled by the particular species that can solve food finding therein, and that is best adapted under the conditions that prevail. It follows that intelligence comparisons between species are not meaningful, and that it is absurd to say that one species is smarter than another.

● *Insight learning (reasoning)*—This type of learning is most prevalent in the higher mammals. It refers to the ability to respond correctly the first time that an animal encounters a certain situation or experience. It alleviates trial and error.

The most important single factor to remember in training animals is that none of them (horses included) can reason things out. An animal's mind functions by intuition, not logic. Moreover, it has no conscious sense of right and wrong. Thus, it is one of the trainer's tasks to teach a horse the difference between right and wrong—between good and bad. Although the horse cannot utilize pure reason, it can remember, and it has the ability to use the memory of one situation as it applies to another.

Of course, man's intelligence is generally recognized. In fact, were it not for his superior mental facilities, along with his limited muscular force, he might find himself under the saddle or between the shafts, instead of the horse.

The horse's intelligence has been tested by two methods: (1) the detour method (Fig 16-2), and (2) the reading signs method (Fig 16-3).

Fig. 16-2. Testing a horse for detour problem-solving ability. Horse X has been separated from its companions, Y and Z. Faced with this problem, X will not likely find his way back to his companions through the open gates, unless he accidentally encounters the gaps in his excitement and galloping. Instead, he will probably try to jump the fence at the point separating them. It is difficult to know whether X's failure to find the detour is due to his lack of intellect or because of his good training.

Fig. 16-3. Horse reading a sign. Two cards are used; one with a cross on it, the other with a triangle (other symbols, such as a square or a circle may be used if desired). The cross is placed in front of an open bucket with grain. The triangle is placed in front of a bucket about 10 feet away that has grain covered with a screen. The horse is allowed to walk to the buckets. If he selects the right one, he is rewarded with feed; it he selects the wrong one, he goes hungry. An intelligent horse soon learns to look for and "read" the cross.

The following additional points are submitted in support of the intelligence of the horse:

● *The horse has primeval instincts and a highly developed, but very specialized, degree of intelligence*—The horse learned to be ever alert—to interpret the slightest rustle of a leaf and the faintest whiff of an unknown scent. He remembered the best grazing areas, the freshest waterholes, and the most protected areas; these he returned to with the seasons. He learned to free himself when trapped in boggy or craggy country. He learned to communicate warnings concerning danger and movement, so that the herd could stick together in its flight and fight.

● *The horse has the intelligence to untie knots and open latches*—Horses will figure out how to undo knots and latches of the most intricate kinds.

● *The horse has an excellent memory*—To a very considerable degree the horse's aptitude for training is due to his memory, for he remembers or recognizes the indications given him, the manner in which he responded, and the rewards or punishments that followed his actions. Many examples substantiating the excellent memory of horses could be cited, but only one will be related.

In the days of Mohammed, intelligence and obedience were the main requisites of the Arab's horse. For war purposes, only the most obedient horses were used, and they were trained to follow the bugle. Legend has it that the Prophet himself had need for some very obedient horses, so he inspected a certain herd to make personal selections. The horses from which he wished to make selections were pastured in a large area bordering on a river. The Prophet gave orders that the animals should be fenced off from the river until their thirst became very great. He then ordered the fence removed, and the horses rushed for the water. When they were just about to dash into the river to quench their thirst, a bugle was sounded. All but 10 of the horses ignored the call of the bugle. The obedient 10 turned and answered the call of duty, despite their great thirst. The whimsical story goes on to say that these 10 head constituted the foundation of the "Prophet Strain."

HOW HORSES BEHAVE

Horses exhibit the following nine general behavioral systems, each of which will be discussed:

1. Protective behavior.
2. Ingestive (eating and drinking) behavior.
3. Eliminative behavior.
4. Sexual behavior.
5. Care-giving and care-seeking (mother-young) behavior.
6. Agonistic behavior (combat).
7. Allelomimetic behavior.
8. Shelter-seeking behavior.
9. Investigative behavior.

Protective Behavior

The basic behavior of modern horses reflects the millions of years that they survived as creatures of the prairies, where they often grazed long distances from water and fled from their enemies in their struggle to survive.

Even today, horses retain their built-in environmental control—their self-protection from the elements. In cold weather, they augment their shaggy coats by seeking the protection of such natural windbreaks as trees, hills, and valleys. Also, they will turn their rear ends toward a storm. The latter instinct makes it difficult to ride a horse into a driving rain or snowstorm, because he wants to protect his eyes and ears by facing away from the elements.

Following a frosty night, horses will stand broadside to the sun, so as to expose as much of their bodies as possible to the sun's warmth. In hot weather, they will seek shade; they may even travel to the top of a hill or ridge to benefit from a cooling breeze. If no shade is to be had on a hot day, they will usually line up with the sun, thereby exposing a minimum of their bodies to the sun's heat.

Most wild animals respond to predator attack in one or two ways—by fight or flight. The wild horse was almost totally dependent upon flight. He fought only when cornered. The evolution in length and structure of the foot (see Table 1-1) made for greater speed, agility, and endurance for escape. This explains much of his behavior today. He has well-developed senses of hearing, sight, and smell to warn him of the approach of danger. He is fearful of any type of confinement or restraint, because this meant death to his ancestors. This explains why untrained horses are skeptical about entering a barn or being loaded on a trailer for the first time. It's why unbroken horses are frightened by halters, foot ropes, and hobbles. It's why a gentle horse will even mutilate a foot in order to free himself from a wire fence.

The wild horse had an additional, and even greater, fear—the fear of something on his back. This stems from the fact that anything that jumped on his back was there to kill him (see Fig. 16-4). During the opening up of the western range of the United States, it was not uncommon for mountain lions to kill horses, particularly foals, in this manner. Even today, it occurs in remote parts of the world. This innate fear of something on his back explains the natural instinct of horses to buck off a rider. Even after 5,000 years of domestication, and almost constant association with man, an untrained horse is apt to revert to the wild and try to dislodge a rider. Today, training is designed to keep a horse from bucking. To accomplish this, the

trainer must assure the horse that a saddle and a man on his back are friends—not mortal enemies.

Fig. 16-4. The lion, a mortal enemy of the horse, has preyed on him for millions of years.

Fig. 16-5. He remembers! The horse must be assured that the saddle and the man on his back are friends—not mortal enemies.

Ingestive (Eating and Drinking) Behavior

This type of behavior includes eating and drinking; hence, it is characteristic of animals of all species and all ages. It is very important because animals cannot live without feed and water.

The first ingestive behavior trait, common to all young mammals, including foals, is suckling.

Each animal species is distinct in its eating and drinking habits. The following points are unique to horses and pertinent to an understanding of their eating and drinking habits:

1. As the horse was transformed to a creature of the prairie, his teeth grew longer, stronger, and more roughened—suited for grinding grasses. Thus, the modern horse has teeth that are well suited to masticating his common feeds.

2. As the horse's legs lengthened in the evolutionary process, it was necessary that his head and neck also become longer in order to enable him to feed on low-growing plants. This process of proportionate elongation of the legs and of the head and the neck is not always perfect. Thus, a foal may have dif-

Fig. 16-6. A long-legged foal with a short head and neck standing with front legs spread apart in order to reach the ground.

ficulty in getting his head to the ground. As a result, he may have to spread his front legs in order to get his mouth to the grass. As the foal grows, his head and neck grow faster than his legs with the result that the anatomy problem is soon solved.

3. The horse possesses incisor teeth in both the upper and lower jaws. But the mobile upper lip is used in gathering in grass and other feed, in the same way that a cow uses her tongue or an elephant uses his trunk. The upper lip is very sensitive. So, in addition to being well adapted to ingesting food, the application of a twitch to the upper lip of the horse provides a way in which to restrain him.

4. When snow covers the pasture or range, horses will paw (with either their right or left front foot) through the snow and clear an area so that they can reach the grass. (Buffalo and elk also feed in this manner.) This behavior of horses allows them to winter in northern range areas without supplemental feed.

5. The horse has a blind spot that extends in front of his nose. Thus, he cannot see the feed as he eats it.

6. Horses rarely browse; that is, they will not eat the leaves of trees or shrubs provided grass is available.

7. Strange as it may seem, horses can injure themselves by eating a natural feed; they will founder on lush grass, particularly when confined to small areas.

8. Horses prefer grazing in an open area, where they can watch for enemies. Also, they prefer young tender grass to coarse-stemmed plants, a preference which often causes them to overgraze certain areas.

9. The horse evolved to graze small amounts almost continuously, rather than large amounts infrequently. This explains why modern horses do better if fed in small amounts—often. An understanding of ingestive behavior allows the horse owner to approach natural feeding. Irregular and inadequate hand feeding is directly related to such abnormal behavior patterns as wood chewing, stall weaving, pawing, and kicking.

10. The habit of foals to nibble the feces or droppings of older horses is usually condemned as unsanitary. However, it has been postulated that nature ordained this behavior as a means of inoculating the digestive tract (colon) of the foal with microorganisms. Apparently there is little danger of parasitism in this manner because most parasite eggs must go through an incubation period of about two weeks before they can infest a foal.

11. In areas where water is scarce, wild horses usually graze 6 to 8 miles from water and come to water every other night. Horses prefer clean, clear water from deep pools. A thirsty horse may lower his head deep enough to cover the nostrils, but there is no danger of drowning because he won't draw water into his lungs.

12. Grazing horses will meet their water needs by eating snow in the wintertime.

13. Where water is supplied to horses, it is best to use fountains or troughs with fresh running water available at all times. If horses are hand watered in buckets, they should be given water at least twice daily.

Eliminative Behavior

In recent years, elimination has become a most important phenomenon, and pollution has become a dirty word. Nevertheless, nature ordained that if animals eat, they must eliminate.

A full understanding of the eliminative behavior will make for improved animal building design and give a big assist in handling manure. Right off, it should be recognized that the eliminative behavior in farm animals tends to follow the general pattern of their wild ancestors; but it can be influenced by the method of management.

Horses tend to deposit their feces and urine in certain areas, then graze in other areas. This is particularly noticeable in small pastures where some areas may be grazed quite closely with few droppings present, whereas other areas have tall, rank grass with a greater concentration of droppings.

Stallions are much more prone to deposit droppings on the same old mound than mares or geldings. Mares and geldings are inclined to use the border of their defecating area, with the result that they enlarge it each time.

The defecating behavior of horses probably evolved for two reasons:

1. As a means of stallions marking their area or territory, much as dogs stake out their area with urine scent posts. Apparently, such markings serve to warn rival stallions that they are encroaching on the territory of another stallion.

2. To provide some protection for horses from infestation by internal parasites. Because many internal parasites are spread from one horse to another by grazing pastures contaminated with parasite eggs from the droppings of infested horses, it is conjectured that wild horses may have reduced this opportunity for the spread of internal parasites by defecating in certain areas and grazing in others. Horses in confinement cannot effectively employ this type of protection from parasites; hence, horse owners must use other methods to keep parasites under control (see Chapter 15).

Sexual Behavior

Reproduction is the first and most important requisite of horse breeding. Without young being born

and born alive, the other economic traits are of academic interest only. Thus, it is important that all those who breed horses should have a working knowledge of sexual behavior.

Sexual behavior involves courtship and mating. It is largely controlled by hormones, although stallions that are castrated after reaching sexual maturity (known as stags) usually retain considerable sex drive and exhibit sexual behavior. This suggests that psychological, or learned, as well as hormonal factors may be involved in sexual behavior.

Each animal species has a special pattern of sexual behavior. As a result, interspecies matings do not often occur. There is a notable exception, however: The best-known cross between animal species is the mule, a hybrid, which is a cross between the horse family and the ass family.

Stallions detect females in heat by sight or smell. Also, it is noteworthy that courtship is more intense on pasture or range than under confinement, and that captivity has the effect of producing many distortions of sexual behavior in wild animals. Perhaps this explains the high-percentage foal crop of wild bands of mares, where conception and foaling rates of 90 percent or better were commonplace, in comparison with the average 50 percent foaling rate under domestication.

The signs of estrus in the mare are (1) the relaxation of the external genitalia; (2) frequent urination in small quantities; (3) the teasing of other mares; (4) the apparent desire for company; (5) a slight mucous discharge from the vulva; (6) allowing the stallion to smell and bite her; (7) spreading the hind legs; and (8) lifting the tail sideways. But many mares are shy breeders. Thus, when there is any question about a mare being in season, she should be tried with the stallion. When possible, it is usually good business regularly to present mares to the teaser every day or every other day as the breeding season approaches. A systematic plan of this sort will save much time and trouble.

Horses (both mares and stallions) tend to be seasonal breeders, with the greatest sexual activity in the spring and early summer, although they will breed and are fertile any time of the year. This is due to hormone levels, which are influenced by the length of day (see Chapter 12, "Breeding Horses," for artificially lengthening the length of day by use of electric lights). This nature ordained phenomena of spring breeding and spring foaling was a biological necessity for wild horses. It meant that mares foaled in the spring when conditions were favorable (1) for the newborn, because of the mild climate; (2) for milk production, for which nutritious green grass was available; and (3) for flushing and rebreeding the mare.

The courtship (teasing) of the stallion, which pre-

Fig. 16-7. Sexual behavior in the stallion, showing extended head and upcurled upper lip. The stallion is trying to detect an odor indicating estrus in a mare.

pares him physically and mentally for mating, is characterized by neighing; smelling the external genitalia of the mare, followed by extended head and upcurled upper lip; and pinching the mare with his teeth by grasping the folds of her skin in the loin-coup area. Wild stallions, and range stallions, always carefully approach the mare from the front to avoid being kicked or struck.

Care-Giving and Care-Seeking (Mother-Young) Behavior

The care-giving behavior is largely confined to females among domestic animals, where it is usually described as "maternal." The care-seeking behavior is normal for young animals. This type of behavior begins at birth and extends until the young are weaned.

The preference of the mare to foal away from other horses apparently evolved in their evolution for two reasons: (1) to provide the foal with the opportunity to identify or imprint itself with its mother, and (2) to protect against predators.

Imprinting occurs in many species of animals. At the time of birth, a newborn foal will follow any moving object, including humans. If other horses are present, a foal may follow a mare other than its own mother. Conditions are ripe for a dominant mare without a foal of her own to steal the new foal. So, by going off alone to give birth, foal stealing is alleviated and the foal will imprint or learn to identify its mother in a short time.

The other reason that mares instinctively prefer to foal alone is that the chances of being found by predators is far less where a single mare is involved than where there is a group.

At birth, a mare identifies her foal partly by odor.

As the foal grows older, recognition by sight and sound become more important.

Mares show the same maternal behavior toward their young as is exhibited by females of other species of farm animals. Thus, a mare calls for her foal with a neigh or whinny and exhibits nervousness and distress when her young is disturbed. When mares are separated from their foals, such as sometimes happens when they are worked or taken away for rebreeding, there is usually a noisy exchange of whinnying between mother and foal when they are put back together again and the foal is allowed to nurse.

It is noteworthy that mares and foals will never willingly lose sight of each other. Thus, a mare will not leave her foal sleeping while she grazes at a distance, as cows do. This is due to the fact that there is no effective means for reuniting the two following a separation. Thus, if a wild mare is away from her foal, and if during her absence the foal is disturbed by a predator and runs off, the mare and foal are not likely to find each other again—except by chance. Of course, domesticated mares and foals in fenced pastures will eventually locate each other.

It is noteworthy that a mare will devote as much attention and affection to a mule colt—a hybird (ass X horse) as she will to a horse foal.

All healthy foals exhibit an amazing ability to get on their feet and travel within a short time after birth. No other young of farm animals are as precocious. The newborn foal nurses frequently, usually once or twice each hour. If another horse or person approaches, the foal will seek the protection of the mare by moving to her side opposite the approacher.

Agonistic Behavior (Combat)

This type of behavior includes fighting, flight, and other related reactions associated with conflict. Among all species of farm mammals, males are more likely to fight than females. Nevertheless, females may exhibit fighting behavior under certain conditions. Castrated males are usually quite passive, which indicates that hormones, (especially testosterone) are involved in this type of behavior. Thus, horsemen have for centuries used castration as a means of producing docile males (geldings or stags).

Stallions that are run together from a very young age seldom fight. Perhaps they have already settled their social rank. On the other hand, bringing together sexually mature strange stallions almost always results in a vicious fight. Stallions fight by biting, kicking, and striking. Generally they fight head to head and most of the biting is on the neck, shoulders, and front legs. Although fighting rarely results in death, it usually continues until one gives up—battle scarred by teeth and hoof marks.

Fighting among mares is less vicious than be-

Fig. 16-8. Agonistic behavior (combat), showing two stallions fighting viciously with teeth and feet.

tween stallions. Body biting and kicing are used as a means of establishing social order. Geldings may fight much like mares.

Jacks are unusually vicious fighters. They rely on their teeth, rather than kicking. Sometimes wild jacks killed a rival by cutting his windpipe or jugular vein. Also, it is reported that the dominant jack occasionally castrated the weaker jacks with his teeth.

Agonistic behavior is of practical importance when strange horses are first put together. One way or another, a social order must be established. Hence, there is always the potential of injury until rank is settled. Also, agonistic behavior may create a potentially dangerous situation to both horses and riders in group riding. To reduce the hazard of such accidents, all horses should be spaced well apart when standing or moving.

Wild bands of horses and bands of domestic horses on the range behave very much alike. The stallions have keen sight, hearing and smell; and each stallion leader is very good at protecting his harem, which usually includes 10 to 20 mares. When frightened or facing danger, the stallion warns his band with snorting and restless movements and takes his place ready for battle if necessary.

Allelomimetic Behavior

Allelomimetic behavior is mutual mimicking behavior. Thus, when one member of a group does something, another tends to do the same thing; and because others are doing it, the original individual continues. Horses moving across a pasture toward water often display allelomimetic behavior. One horse starts toward the water, and the others follow. Because the rest of the herd is following, the first horse proceeds on. Even a timid horse will follow behind the group, in order not to be left behind.

In the wild state, this trait was advantageous in detecting the enemy, and in providing protection therefrom. Under domestication, animals are usually protected from predators.

For animals that normally live in herds (like

horses), the presence of other animals also provides companionship and has a quieting effect. When kept alone, such animals may become lonely, depressed, frightened, and/or irritated. The best-known animal companionship of all pertains to high-strung racehorses and stallions, in which all sorts of companions are used—a goat, a sheep, a chicken, a duck, or a pony. Such companions are commonly referred to as "mascots." The expression "to get his goat" was born of the common custom of having goats for mascots. Back in the days when skulduggery was as important as form in winning races, the men of one stable sometimes plotted to kidnap the goat mascot of a rival's horse. By "getting the goat" of a favorite, they cleaned up by betting against a horse that was odds-on to win, but too upset to run at his best.

The great Stymie, Thoroughbred winner of $918,485, became attached to a hen of nondescript breeding who came to dinner one day and never left.

Probably the most publicized mascot of all times was the pony, Peanuts, constant companion to the Thoroughbred racehorse Exterminator. Peanuts died three years ahead of the great old gelding. When his pony pal failed to appear in the stall the next morning, Exterminator stopped eating. He would likely have died of a broken heart had his handlers not acted wisely. They left the remains of Peanuts in the Thoroughbred's stall one night, to demonstrate to him that his mate was dead. All night long, Exterminator lay with his head over the pony's body. By morning he was resigned to the situation. A new pony was brought to him, and the old warrior carried on.

Shelter-Seeking Behavior

All species of animals seek shelter—protection from the sun, wind, rain and snow, insects, and predators.

Horses are not very sensitive to either heat or cold. In the wild state, they developed a shaggy coat of hair in the wintertime and sought shelter from storms under trees and in the valleys. They even pawed to get their feed supply when the ground was covered with snow. Like cattle, horses face away from the direction of a severe storm.

Investigative Behavior

Investigative behavior is closely related to fear— to self-protective behavior.

All animals are curious and have a tendency to explore their environment. Investigation takes place through seeing, hearing, smelling, tasting, and touching. Whenever an animal is introduced into a new area (stall, paddock, or pasture), its first reaction is to explore it. When a horse that is being ridden is spooked, he should be made to go near the spooky object where he can smell it. Usually this will cause him to lose his fear of it.

Foals are more curious than older horses. Young equines spend much of their time looking at and sniffing objects in their pastures or stalls. As the foal grows older, it may exhibit fear of certain objects. At this stage, it may even move away from its caretaker. When this happens, the horseman should never run after the foal. Rather, stand still; very soon the foal's curiosity will get the best of it, and it will return. A mare frequently becomes very nervous as she watches her offspring investigate, fearful that it may get hurt in the process.

SOCIAL RELATIONSHIPS

Each of the general behavioral systems listed under "How Horses Behave" has a tendency to draw horses together, with the exception of agonistic behavior, which has the effect of keeping them at a distance or driving them apart.

Fig. 16-9. Horses need other horses. This shows two horses massaging each other over the withers.

Through millions of years of evolution, horses have developed a very strong need for the company of each other, primarily for protective reasons. A group of horses has many more eyes, ears, and nostrils to detect danger than one lone horse. Thus, a group imparts a feeling of security, whereas one individual feels insecure.

A horse's desire for companionship with other horses is deep seated and may create many problems in training and handling. Thus, the separation of a foal from its dam is a trying experience. Taking a mature horse away from his mates may be even more traumatic. Basically, the lone animal fears for its life. It may not eat, and it almost always becomes nervous and uneasy. Fortunately, most horses soon calm down after they learn that they have nothing to fear from being alone.

Although horses prefer the company of other members of their species, when no other horses are available they will accept other species as friends (see section entitled "Interspecies Relationship"). They

will even replace the security of horse company with the security of the barn. Their feeling of security around the barn may be so strong that a horse in an adjacent corral or paddock may lose his life by running into a barn that is on fire.

Group living—in a herd or band—has resulted in the development of a form of social structure in horses, the unique features of which are discussed under the following headings: (1) social order; (2) leader-follower; (3) interspecies relationship; and (4) man-animal relationship.

Social Order

Most species of animals which live in groups establish a social order, based on dominance and submissive relationships. This explains why one horse in a group seems to be the boss and will bite and kick others, always with authority—and sometimes with ferocity. By studying any group of horses, it is possible to rank them, numerically, by dominance, or social order. One method of accomplishing this is to place a tub of grain in a corral and remove one horse at a time as it is determined which of the remaining horses eats from the tub first. Thus, with a group of 10 horses, it will be found that Number 1 is dominant over the other 9; Number 2 is dominant over all the horses from 3 to 10, and so on down the line. Number 10 is at the bottom of the "totem pole" and is not dominant over any horse. Depending on their disposition, some horses will inflict injury as they enforce their social strata; others merely lay back their ears or push a lower horse out of the feed box with their nose.

Fig. 16-10. Dominant mare using her teeth to put a submissive mare in her proper place.

Sometimes a horse high in the dominance order pairs up with a horse near the bottom of the scale. As long as the dominant horse is present, other horses will not be aggressive toward its partner. If the dominant horse is removed, however, the partner will very promptly be put in its proper place in the social order.

Animals respect the order in their relationship just as carefully as protocol demands that it be observed at a "Department of State" dinner. In chickens, in which this phenomenon was first observed, the social order is called the "peck order."

Among wild horses, social order is nature's way of giving mating priority to the top ranking stallions. Hence, they leave behind more of their progeny than do the less dominant (bachelor) males. In domesticated horses, the social rank order is usually important only in mares and young stock, because mature stallions are seldom run together in groups.

Social order among horses is of little consequence as long as they are on pasture or range and there is plenty of feed and water, but it becomes of very great importance when animals are placed in confinement. It is doubly important if feed is limited. Under the latter circumstances, the dominant individuals crowd the subordinate ones away from the feed, with the result that they may go hungry.

● *Establishing social order*—When unacquainted (strange) horses are brought together, they engage in some form of aggression (kicking, biting, etc.) until one submits and the other becomes the socially dominant one. After all have had their contacts, the dominance order is initiated. Each must now be able to recognize all the others and remember the dominance relationships. The larger the group of horses and the greater the space (as on the range), the less frequently the pairs meet and the longer it takes to reduce the strife—that is, to firm up the social relationship. Once the social order is established, it results in a peaceful coexistence of the herd. Thereafter, when the dominant animal merely threatens by some trait or stance, the subordinate animal submits and avoids conflict. The usual posture and signals of horses are kicking, attempting to bite with bared teeth, and ears laid back. Of course, there are some pairs that fight every time they chance to meet. Also, if strange animals are introduced into such a group, social disorganization results in the outbreak of new fighting, as a new social rank order is established.

Several factors influence social rank; among them, (1) age—both young animals and those that are senile rank toward the bottom; (2) early experience—once a subordinate, usually always a subordinate; (3) weight and size; and (4) aggressiveness or timidity.

It is noteworthy that a mature horse (be it mare, gelding, or stallion) will seldom fight a foal or short yearling to establish dominance. They appear to recognize that the foal is no threat to their position and, therefore, disregard it.

● *Maintaining social order*—The more frequent the meeting of pairs of horses under noncompetitive situations, the better the memory of individuals, and, it follows, the better the social dominance relationships. Too many individuals in the group stress the memory and lessen individual recognition. Too large a space (individual distances and personal spaces) re-

duces the chances of competitive encounters and the enforcement of social relationships. Too small a space (extreme density) restricts social activity, creates stress, and promotes boredom.

● *Stability in social order*—The ideal horse group is socially stable because procedures in activities (called mannerisms in people) are well developed. Hunger increases sensitivity to stimuli and results in threats and fights; hence, adequate and available feed facilitates stability. Adding strange horses to a group is always disruptive.

Leader-Follower

For a group of horses to function effectively, there must be a leader. This implies that there are followers, too.

Fig. 16-11. Lead mare taking off for a new area, with the stallion bringing up the rear. When on the move, horses always follow the leader in Indian file—never abreast. (Courtesy, Wild Horse Research Farm, Porterville, Calif.)

In wild bands, the stallion was not the leader. He was the defender-protector of his harem of mares from rival stallions and predators. He herded and kept the mares together, fought off other studs and chased other horse groups from his territory, and brought up the rear. But he was not the leader. Generally, a dominant mare, with special qualities of leadership, served as the leader of the band. She possessed an intimate knowledge of the area in which the group lived; she knew the location of the best grass and water; she knew where to seek protection from storms and predators; and she knew the trails and the best escape routes.

The lead mare in wild bands established and maintained her position by ample use of her teeth and feet. When a new mare was added to the band, a test of dominance ensued and the winner became the leader. In this manner, a new leader evolved from time to time. Thus, in wild bands, the best fighter (the dominant mare) was always the leader, but the lead-

ers was not necessarily the mare with the most knowledge of the area and the greatest ability to lead the band safely.

Domesticated groups of horses also exhibit the leader-follower relationship. But there may be one great difference. The leader of a domestic band is not always the dominant mare. The leader may be one of the smaller or younger mares. Taking a page from history and people, it is noteworthy that one of the world's greatest leaders, Napoleon, was small in stature, but he was adventuresome and smart. So it is with the leader of domestic horses; the leader may not be the strongest, but she must be adventuresome and smart.

Fig. 16-12. Leader or follower—winner or loser?

The leader-follower relationship may be important in racehorses. At least, it merits further study. There is some evidence that a horse's natural inclination to be a leader or a follower is involved in winning or losing a race. It appears that the leader has a driving urge to take the lead out of the starting gate and never to relinquish it. If not held back, he may use up too much energy—spend himself—early in the race and fade in the stretch. If he can be taught (without fighting the jockey) to stay off the lead at the start and conserve his energy for a drive to the front at the end of the race, he may be a great racehorse. On the other hand, if he is a natural follower, he may lack the heart to win—he may be reluctant to pass horses. Such a horse usually brings up the rear. Some trainers feel that follower-type horses must be in the lead all the way in order to win—that they must be frontrunners.

Interspecies Relationships

Social relationships are normally formed between members of the same species. However, they can be developed between two different species. In domestication this tendency is important (1) because it permits several species to be kept together in the same

pasture or corral (horses and cattle, for example), and (2) because of the close relationship between man and animals. Such interspecies relationships can be produced artificially, especially by taking advantage of the maternal instinct of females and using them as foster mothers.

Man-Animal Relationships

Social relationships can also be transferred to human beings. Thus, an animal caretaker usually forms a care-dependency relationship with the animals under his care. This is particularly true with horses.

One of the best-known stories of a man-horse relationship pertained to groom Will Harbut and the great Thoroughbred, Man o' War (Big Red). When training, Man o' War's morning came early. Will Harbut gave him his first meal at 3:30 a.m.; at 7:30 a.m., he was groomed. Big Red was very fond of his caretaker; he liked to snatch his hat and carry it around as he showed off for visitors. Will Harbut, who had quite a way with words as well as with horses, never tired of telling the thousands of visitors who came to see Man o' War that, "He was the mostest horse that ever was."

Without doubt, the most fantastic man-animal relationship of all time is the story pertaining to Romulus and Remus, who were suckled by a wolf. Anulius, who was on the throne of Alban, ordered a mother to be buried alive (because she had broken her vestal vows) and her two children to be thrown into the Tiber River. The legendary story goes on to say that the river received the babies kindly and bore them to a little bank, where they were cast ashore at the foot of a fig tree. Here they were found by a she-wolf, who cared for them until they were discovered by the shepherd Faustulus, who took them into his home and reared them. Romulus later became the legendary first king of Rome and the founder of the city.

COMMUNICATION

Although horses cannot speak like people, they do communicate with each other very effectively. Without doubt, this trait accounts, in part at least, for the foundation stock of the American Indians and the hardy bands of Mustangs—the feral horses of the Great Plains. In some mysterious manner, the abandoned and stray horses of the expeditions of de Soto and Coronado communicated with and found each other; otherwise, they would not have reproduced.

Vocal Signals

Horses can detect sounds above and below the frequencies that a human is capable of hearing. They have a very acute sense of hearing, perceiving higher and fainter noises than the human ear.

Horses use sounds in many ways; among them, (1) feeding, in sounds of hunger by young, or food finding, and of hunting cries; (2) distress calls, which announce the approach or presence of an enemy and the all-clear signal following the departure of a predator; (3) sexual behavior, courting songs, and related fighting; (4) mother-young interrelations to establish contact and evoke care behavior; and (5) maintaining the group in its movements and assembly. An experienced horseman always listens for such sounds and knows how to interpret them. For example, if he hears a horse squealing, he will investigate to see what horses are fighting and if there is any real danger of one of them being injured.

Horses use a variety of vocal, or voice, communications, of which the following are most common:

1. *Snort*—This is a warning signal, used to alert a group of horses of impending danger. It is made by blowing air out through the nostrils. A horse will snort when he sees something that frightens him. In wild horses, the snort was used primarily as a warning of the presence of predators.

2. *Neigh or whinny*—This is a distress call. It is a loud piercing sound used by a horse to express great concern, anxiety, and even terror. It is never used to express pain or anger. The neigh is the call made by a horse when he finds himself unexpectedly alone.

3. *Nicker*—This is a greeting, used to greet other horses, other animal friends, the barn, and even people. It is the sound of pleasure emitted upon seeing an old friend.

4. *Squeal*—This is a sound of anger, most often heard when horses are fighting. Sometimes horses squeal when bucking. Also, stallions and mares may squeal during the breeding season.

5. *Stallion or mating call*—This is the sound of a stallion. It is loud, shrill, and threatening. Wild stallions used it as a challenge or warning to other stallions. In domestic horses, it is considered a mating call, made by a stallion when he sees or hears another horse.

6. *Mare talk*—A mare talks to her foal in soft nickers, probably to reassure it that all is well.

Visual Signals

The horse makes visual signals with his ears, tail, mouth and lips, eyes, and nostrils. A brief description of each of these follows:

1. *Ears*—The ears of a horse are the most easily understood visual signal with which the horse communicates his feelings to humans (see Fig. 16-13). The eyes and ears of a horse function together. Thus,

the direction that he is looking can be determined by his ears. It is noteworthy, too, that a horse can, simultaneously, look and listen to the front with the ear and eye on one side and to the back with the ear and eye on the other side.

Fig. 16-13. Ear signals of horses.

Good horsemen always watch the ears of a horse as a means of being aware of his moods.

2. *Tail*—The tail of a horse may be used as a signal (see Fig. 16-14).

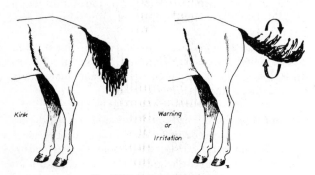

Fig. 16-14. Tail signals of horses.

If a horse has a kink in his tail on a cold morning, you better beware—he will likely test your riding ability.

When the tail is held high, it indicates that the horse is gay and feeling good. When the tail is tucked between the legs, it indicates that the horse is badly frightened or is preparing to kick. Tail switching is a sign of irritation about something, such as flies or the actions of the rider.

3. *Mouth and lips*—Foals communicate their immaturity by mouth. It will cautiously approach a strange horse with its head extended and rapidly open and close its mouth. Usually this signal avoids attack and a test of dominance.

The lips are used to express the following three emotions which reflect the feelings of a horse: (1) A raised upper lip of a horse that is eating may express displeasure at the taste or odor of the feed; (2) a raised upper lip may express discomfort or pain in the digestive tract; or (3) a stallion's curled upper lip with the head held high and extended is part of his mannerism in smelling horse droppings or in determining if a mare is in estrus.

4. *Eyes*—The eyes are not too communicative. The only visible change is in the opening of the eyelids; a frightened horse has his eyelids wide open.

5. *Nostrils*—When excited or frightened, the nostrils of a horse will flare out to allow greater intake of air into the lungs. Sometimes this is accompanied by a snort.

Chemical Indicators

Females in estrus secrete a substance that attracts males. Hence, stallions locate mares that are in heat by the sense of smell.

On the range, it has been observed that each stallion usually stakes out a territory for himself and his harem of mares, with the outside boundary thereof marked by his feces.

SPECIAL SENSES

Horses are endowed with some special senses of importance in their behavior and training. These are listed in the sections that follow.

Sight

In its natural habitat, the adult horse keeps a sharp lookout for its enemies, even while grazing. It is rare to see all members of a herd lying down together; one horse is almost always on the lookout.

Horses have monocular vision; that is, each eye is independent of the other and can see different pictures. This gives them a panoramic view—to the sides, the front, and the back—virtually at the same time. When a horse wants to see an object very clearly, it will face the object and use both eyes in a binocular manner. By contrast, humans have binocular vision and see the same picture with both eyes.

The lens of the horse's eye is nonelastic, but the retina is arranged on a slope, the bottom part being nearer the lens than the top part. Thus, in order to focus on objects at different distances, the horse has to raise or lower his head so that the image is brought on to that part of the retina at the correct distance to achieve a sharp image.

Because of its monocular vision, it is difficult for a horse to judge distance accurately. In its evolution, it was more important that the horse see a wide area around him as he watched for predators than to judge distance. With domesticated horses, however, being able to judge distances is very important in certain types of performance. Thus, a rope horse must accurately judge the distance between himself and the animal he is following; a barrel racing horse must accurately judge the distance to the barrel as he prepares for the turn; and a jumping horse must accurately determine distance to the jump in order to select the take-off point, and he must determine the height and spread of the jump. Of course, top performing horses used for these purposes possess the ability to learn to judge distances, and they receive expert training.

Also, it is noteworthy that the horse has good vision in darkness. It's not as good as a cat's night vision, but it is considerably better than that of man. Thus, a horse may be ridden at night with reasonable safety, particularly if he is familiar with the area.

Color

Most authorities maintain that color vision in horses has not been established. However, color tests conducted at Montana State University by one of the author's former students showed that horses are able to recognize colors with considerable accuracy. The Montana workers devised a very simple test consisting of two buckets of equal size, but different colors. One had oats in it, the other was empty. The buckets were placed about 10 feet apart in a corral, and the horses were allowed to walk toward the buckets from a distance of 30 feet. It was found that all the horses tested had the ability to recognize colors, although some horses learned faster than others.

Hearing

The horse has excellent hearing, which undoubtedly evolved as a part of his protective mechanism during his long evolution. Today, the acute hearing of the horse is very useful in training. The horse can be taught to respond to such commands as walk, trot, canter (lope), as well as the conventional start and stop cues.

Smell

The horse has a good sense of smell. However, it is not as well developed in the horse as it is in some of his enemies.

Wild horses used smell for protection, to identify companions that may have been separated from the group, and to identify the home range. Stallions, in particular, smell fecal deposits, apparently to determine if they are on their home range and if there are any trespassers.

Domestic horses use the sense of smell in the following ways: (1) to identify each other, (2) to recognize humans, (3) to detect when mares come in heat, and (4) to avoid drugs and other additives in feeds. Mares also use odor to identify their newborn foals.

Touch

Like all higher animals, the horse has a well-developed sense of touch. Certain areas of its body are more sensitive to touch than others. Among the most sensitive areas are: the nose, eyes, and ears, all of which are very essential parts; the legs; the rear flank; the withers; and the frog.

Touch is the most important sense used in cueing horses; it is used far more extensively than sight and sound. Thus, the rider touches the horse through its mouth and neck; and he touches the horse with his legs in the rib area and with his weight at its withers. Almost all horses will learn to respond to lighter and lighter touch cues. Response to light cues of the hands, legs, and weight is the ultimate in both training and horsemanship.

TRAITS OF HORSES

Certain traits of horses are pertinent in their behavior and training; among them, those listed in the sections which follow.

Homing or Backtracking

The mystery of pathfinding is possessed by many species, great and small. The homing pigeon is noted for its ability to find its way home from great distances. Ants that go in groups usually travel a narrow trail that is chemically saturated by their passing; when one of them comes upon such a trail it is easily identified as the right roadway. When baby green turtles hatch from their eggs, they must dig upward through the sand in which the mother deposited the eggs, and head for water. Then, there are the migrating birds for which no single explanation is really satisfying. But it is the wide-roaming salmon whose navigational feats are the most fantastic. Horses also possess this trait. Through sound, scent, a photographic memory, or some sense of which we do not know, they often find their way back home when moved to very distant places.

The wild horse's best defense from predators was flight. In the escape, it was often necessary for them to run for miles—to leave the home range far behind. If the home range possessed some definite survival advantages—in such things as feed, water, and

shelter—it was in the best interest of the horses to return, thus necessitating a homing instinct. This behavioral instinct was usually most pronounced in the
lead mare; hence, she was the one most determined
to return to the home range.

Domestic horses have little opportunity to test
the homing instinct. Today, most land areas are
fenced, with the result that it is impossible for a stray
horse to make his way for any distance. Also, most
horses are hauled to new locations, rather than
trailed; hence, they have no way of knowing which
way is home.

Sometimes a riding horse exhibits the homing
instinct—the urge to return to the home range by
wanting to return to the barn, where he will feel safe
and secure. Such behavior is commonly called "barn
sour."

A horse's homing or backtracking ability can be
easily tested as follows: Ride for a considerable distance into an area that is new and unfamiliar to your
horse. Take the most winding route possible, preferably not over distinct trails. When it is time to start
back, give the horse his head and see what happens.
Most horses will head back in the right direction. A
few will backtrack almost step by step.

Sleeping and Resting

The mature horse sleeps and rests standing up.
This is made possible by a system of ligaments, which
do not get tired like muscles, and which take the
weight off muscles during rest. When asleep, the head
droops, the eyes are closed, and the horse invariably
stands on three legs. One hind leg is cocked, while
the other three legs carry the weight. Unless a horse
is lame, it will alternate the hind legs between resting
and carrying weight. Most mature horses do not lie
down regularly, although a few will sleep and rest in
this position.

Foals sleep lying flat and stretched out on one
side. They spend a good part of their time sleeping.
As they grow older, they lie down and sleep less.

In contrast to cattle and sheep which sleep very
little, the horse may sleep soundly for as much as 7
hours out of each 24 hours, mostly during the warmest
part of the day. But not all of the 7 hours of sleep are
taken at one time; rather, it is short and irregular, depending on the degree of hunger and the climatic
conditions.

In a wild band, not all horses will sleep at the
same time, either day or night. Domestic horses are
different; all of them will eat at the same time, and all
of them will sleep at the same time.

Rolling (Grooming)

The horse grooms himself by rolling in the dust.

Unlike the cat or the cow, the horse's tongue is not
suited to grooming. Instead, he rolls, preferably in
dry, soft dirt—the dustier the better. After rolling, a
horse shakes himself vigorously to remove as much
dust as possible. Horses particularly like to roll after a
hard day's work and much sweating. In additon to re-
laxing the horse, rolling gives an assist in controlling
external parasites and in removing winter hair.

Other species groom themselves, too. Chickens
and buffalo take dust baths, whereas pigs and elk wal-
low in the mud.

ABNORMAL BEHAVIOR

Abnormal behaviors of domestic animals are not
fully understood. As with human behavior disorders,
more experimental work is needed. However, we
have learned from studies of captured wild animals
that when the amount and quality, including variabil-
ity, of the surroundings of an animal are reduced,
there is increased probability that abnormal behaviors
will develop. Also, it is recognized that confinement
of animals makes for lack of space which often leads
to unfavorable changes in habitat and social interac-
tions for which the species have become adapted and
best suited over thousands of years of evolution.

Few animals have undergone such drastic change
through evolution as equines. Little *Eohippus* (the
dawn horse of 58 million years ago) was a denizen of
the swamp. Later, through evolution, the horse became a creature of the prairie. Even though his
natural habitat shifted during this long predomestication period, until man confined him he gleaned the
feeds provided by nature. Inevitably, this occupied
his time and provided exercise. But domestication
wrought many changes—changes which spawned abnormal behaviors, including balking, bolting feed,
cribbing, halter pulling, kicking, tail rubbing, weaving, wood chewing (pica), backing, rearing, shying,

Fig. 16-15. Abnormal behavior. A cribber in action. This is the vice of
biting or setting the teeth against some object, such as a post or manger,
while sucking in air. (Also called wind sucker or stump sucker.)

striking with the front feet, a tendency to run away, and objection to harnessing, saddling, and grooming. Many of these vices originate with incompetent handling; nevertheless, they may be difficult to cope with or to correct. This is especially true in older animals, thus lending credence to the statement, "You can't teach an old horse new tricks."

BEHAVIOR SUMMARY

Gradually, man adopted a more settled mode of life, and with this came the desire to safeguard his food supply for times when hunting was poor and to have his food close at hand; at this stage, nearly all our modern animals were tamed or confined, or, as we say, domesticated.

In domesticating animals, man recognized the importance of behavior; he selected those species which could both be tamed and used to satisfy his own needs. However, in the breeding, care, and management that followed, behavior received less attention than the quantity and quality of meat, milk, eggs, fiber, and power produced. The race was on for greater rate and efficiency of production. Animals in forced production were confined and automated. Then, suddenly, animals told us that all was not well in the barnyard. They told us that something was missing—something as vital to them as an essential amino acid, mineral, or vitamin—something as important as disease prevention and environmental control. They told us that consideration of their habitat and social organization had not kept pace with advances in genetics, nutrition, environmental control, and other areas of animal care. They told us what was wrong and what they wanted through a whole host of abnormal behaviors, including cannibalism, loss of appetite, poor parental care, overaggressiveness, dullness, degenerate sexual behavior, tail biting, and cribbing. These warning signals are being heeded. Today, there is renewed interest in the study and application of animal behavior; we are trying to make it right with animals by correcting the causes of the disorders. For the time being, this calls for emulating the natural conditions of the species.

At the outset of this chapter, it was stated that the application of animal behavior depends upon understanding. The presentation to this point (Part I) has been for the purpose of understanding. Part II, which follows, pertains to the practical applications of animal behavior—the training of horses.

PART II. TRAINING

A well-mannered horse may be said to be the combined result of desirable heredity, skillful training, and vigilant control. Once conception has taken

Fig. 16-16. Training a yearling on "how to be a racehorse." Learning to gallop beside a lead pony is one of the first lessons.

place, it is too late to change the genetic makeup—the native intelligence—of the animal. However, the eventual training and control of the horse are dependent upon how well the trainer understands equine behavior and mental faculties as well as methods of utilizing them so that the desired performance may be obtained.

There are as many successful ways to train horses as there are to train children. The author has observed several top professional trainers. Each used a different technique, yet all ended up with the same result—a champion. Most of them follow the basic principles given herein.

The good horseman who has followed a program of training and educating the foal from the time it was a few days old has already eliminated the word "breaking." To him, the saddling and/or harnessing of the young horse is merely another step in the training program, which is done with apparent ease and satisfaction.

CONTROLLING THE HORSE

The horse has whims and ideas of his own. Always, however, the rider should be the boss, with the mount promptly carrying out his wishes. With the experienced horseman, this relationship is clear-cut, for the rider is able to relay his feelings to the horse instantly and unmistakably.

Purebred horse breeding establishments have long been aware, consciously or unconsciously, of the equine mental faculties. As a result, most breeders have substituted gradual and early training programs for the so-called breaking of animals at 3 to 5 years of age. Even on some of the more progressive ranches, the cowboy and the bucking bronco are fast passing into permanent oblivion. The owners of the famous King Ranch in Texas report that they have discarded the former method of breaking 3-year-olds in favor of starting training at 3 months of age. It has been their experience that the latter method has materially re-

duced injuries to both men and horses, has resulted in more really gentle mounts, and has cost less in time, labor, and money.

For complete control and a finished performance, the horse should have a proud and exalted opinion of himself; but at the same time he should subjugate those undesirable traits that make a beast of his size and strength so difficult to handle by a comparatively frail and small man. Complete control, therefore, is based on mental faculties rather than muscular force.

The faculties of the horse that must be understood and played upon to obtain skillful training and control at all times are summarized briefly in this chapter.

Memory

To a considerable degree, the horse's aptitude for training is due to his memory; for he remembers or recognizes the indications given him, the manner in which he responded, and the rewards or punishments that followed his actions. These facts must be taken into consideration both in training the young horse and in retaining control of the trained animal.

Discipline and reward must be administered very soon after the act (some competent horsemen say that it should be within three seconds) in order for the horse to associate and remember.

Confidence and Fear

In the wild state, the horse was his own protector; and his very survival was often dependent upon rapidity of escape. In a well-mannered horse, it is necessary that confidence in the rider replace fear. Thus, it is best to approach the horse from the front. He should be spoken to in a quiet, calm voice and should be patted by using comparatively slow movement of the hands to avoid exciting him. Above all, when one is approaching a horse, he should make certain that the animal knows of his presence. Startling a horse often causes accidents for which the animal is blameless.

During moments of fright, the good horseman utilizes the means by which the horse is calmed. However, when the horse is voluntarily and knowingly disobedient, the proper degree of punishment should be administered immediately.

Association of Ideas

Horses are creatures of habit; for example, when the grain bin door is heard to open, the horse regularly anticipates his feed. For this reason, the schooling of a horse should be handled by the same competent horseman, who allows the animal an opportunity to associate the various commands with the desired response. A well-trained horse may become confused and illmannered when poorly handled by several persons.

Willingness

A willing worker or performer is to be desired. Some animals submit to the horseman's subjugation with little trouble and hesitation, whereas others offer resistance to the point of being stubborn. Complete control over the mount at all times is achieved through the judicious employment of rewards and punishments.

Rewards

The two most common rewards given horses are a praising voice and a gentle stroking with the hand. Satisfying the horse's greediness for such things as a lump of sugar is also most effective, but this may make for great disappointment if the reward is not available at all times. To be effective, rewards must not be given promiscuously but only when deserved. It is also important that the same word always be used for the same thing and that the horseman means what he says.

Punishment

The two common types of equine punishment are the spur and the whip. Punishment should be administered only when the horseman is certain that the animal is being disobedient and not when the horse lacks sufficient training, has not understood some command, or has done something wrong because of the rider. When necessary, however, the punishment should be administered promptly, so that the animal understands why it is given; and it should be given with justice and with the horseman retaining a cool head at all times. Following punishment, the animal should be made to carry out the original command that he failed to follow, and then he would be properly rewarded.

TRAINING THE FOAL

The foal should be given daily lessons of 15 to 30 minutes each, for 7 to 10 days. If trained early in life, it will be a better disciplined, more serviceable horse. Give it one lesson at a time, and in sequence; that is, be sure the pupil masters each learning experience before it is given the next one.

Put a well-fitted halter on the foal when it is 10 to 14 days old. When it has become accustomed to the halter, in a day or so, tie it securely in the stall beside the mare. Try to keep the foal from freeing itself from the rope or from becoming tangled up in it.

Fig. 16-17. Teaching the foal to lead. After the foal has been gentled to a halter, a nonskid loop slipped over the hindquarters will teach him to move forward promptly.

Leave the foal tied 15 to 30 minutes each day for 2 or 3 days. Groom the animal carefully while it is tied. Rub each leg and handle each foot so that the foal becomes accustomed to having its feet picked up. After it has been groomed, lead it around with the mare for a few days and then lead it by itself. Lead it at both the walk and the trot. Many breeders teach a foal to lead simply by leading it with the mare from the stall to the paddock and back again.

At this stage of the training, be sure the foal executes your commands to stop and go as soon as you give them. When halted, make it stand in show position—squarely on all four legs with its head up.

Use all your patience, gentleness, and firmness in training the foal. Never let your temper get the best of you.

TRAINING THE YEARLING

The yearling should be given daily lessons of 30 minutes each, repeated until each learning experience is mastered. The horse learns by repetition. Thus, teach only one thing at a time, and repeat it in the same manner daily until mastered; then proceed to the next learning experience. Teach the yearling the following, in order:

1. *The meaning of "Whoa" and his name*—The yearling should be taught that "whoa" means stop. Always give the command, then call his name, as "Whoa, Duke."

2. *To stand when hobbled*—Next the young horse should be hobbled; first the two front feet, then "sideline" (tie a front foot and a hind foot on the same side together). Hobbling is for the purpose of teaching the horse to stand still (as if tied) and not get excited if he gets caught in a fence. Many a valuable horse has mutilated himself for lack of this kind of training.

Fig. 16-18. Front feet of a yearling hobbled with a large, soft cotton rope. This training lesson is designed to teach the young horse to stand still (as if tied) and not get excited if he gets caught in a fence.

3. *To become accustomed to the saddle blanket*—Gently put the saddle blanket on the young horse's back, and move it from head to tail, until he is not afraid of having an object on his back. Repeat this training for two days.

4. *To get used to the saddle*—Next, ease a saddle on him. Put it on and off several times. Then tighten the girth moderately and lead him around. Repeat this procedure for five or six days.

Thus, the gentling of the yearling is for the purposes of teaching him the meaning of the word "whoa"; to stand patiently when hobbled or caught in a wire fence; and to get used to the saddle blanket and the saddle. After a few days of gentling like this, the yearling may be turned to pasture for a time.

TRAINING AT 18 MONTHS OF AGE

At 18 months of age, the young horse should receive additional training. At this stage, each lesson should be for 30 minutes daily, with each step mastered before moving on to the next. The trainer should always be gentle, but firm; and should not make a pet out of the horse. Let him know who is boss. When he must be punished for wrongdoing, use the whip—one time only; and do so immediately after the horse commits the act. Never discipline a horse by gouging him with spurs. When he does well, reward him by stroking his neck or shoulder and calling his name: "That's a good boy, Duke." At 18 months of age, teach the following:

1. *To drive, turn, stop, and back up, by using plowlines*—Tie the stirrups together under the horse, then run plowlines through them. Stand behind the horse and use the plowlines to drive, turn, stop, and back up.

Fig. 16-20. When the horse is about 18 months of age, teach him to flex his neck and set his head. This shows rubber reins, made from strips of an old inner tube, being used for this purpose.

Fig. 16-19. When the horse is approximately 18 months of age, use plowlines to teach him to drive, turn, stop, and back up.

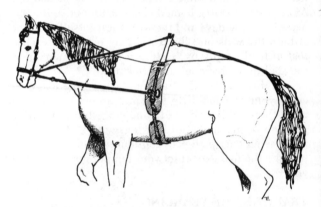

Fig. 16-21. Dumb jockey, a bitting contrivance for training a young horse to place his head in the desired position.

2. *To flex his neck and set his head*—This may be accomplished either by (a) tying the reins to the stirrups, or (b) using rubber reins made from strips of old inner tube. Then turn the young horse loose in the corral or training ring for 30 minutes (he can't hurt himself).

Also, a dumb jockey bitting rig—a contrivance fastened on a young horse—may be used to train him to place his head in the desired position. The rigging consists of surcingle, back strap, crupper, side reins, overcheck or sidecheck, standing martingale, and some sort of projection above the top of the surcingle to which reins may be attached.

3. *The respond to the bosal, ride him; introduce leg pressure*—During the first few months of riding, use a bosal; it will alleviate the hazard of hurting his mouth with bits. Do some light riding; introduce leg pressure.

TRAINING THE TWO-YEAR-OLD

At this stage, each lesson should be of 30 minutes' duration daily, repeated until mastered. The two-year-old is ready for the following advanced training:

1. *To respond to the aids*—Mount the horse and put him in motion by use of the aids—the legs, hands and reins, and voice. After riding him for 5 or 6 days at the walk and trot, move him into the lope or canter, always on the proper lead—a right foot lead when going clockwise, a left foot lead when moving counterclockwise.

2. *To back*—From the ground, teach the horse to back. Hold the reins near the bosal or bit; push back (push and release) and command "Back, Duke." If necessary, push on his shoulder and/or switch him on the forelegs. Next, mount the horse and, from his back, teach him to stop and back up. If he won't back when you're mounted, have a friend stand in front of him and switch him back while you pull (pull and release) on the reins and command "Back, Duke." Backing teaches the horse to get his feet under him, which is essential for pivots and sharp turns.

3. *To pivot (Western horse)*—Each time the horse is stopped and backed up, pause for a few seconds, then collect him, (with the reins, and apply a little leg pressure) and pivot. Always teach the young horse to turn on his hind feet; pull him back until his hind feet are under him, then pull diagonally on the reins.

4. *To make a sliding stop (Western horse)*—Teach the horse to make a proper sliding stop—to "stick his tail in the ground." When properly done, the rider's reining hand is low, the horse's head is low and his front feet are near the ground. Most judges prefer a stop with 3 or 4 feet on the ground, rather than the more spectacular 2-hind-leg stop. If the stop is on 3 feet, one forefoot is up slightly, ready to run or roll back either way. Most expert Western horsemen don't like a sliding stop with both front feet up in the air because the horse is not balanced and can fall over backward.

Fig. 16-22. A good stop. Note that the reining hand is low, the horse's head is low, and three of the feet are on the ground.

It takes months of training to get a horse to do the sliding stop right. First he should be stopped at the walk, then the trot, next the short lope, and finally when wide open.

In executing the sliding stop, the Western rider uses his aids as follows: (a) squeezes with his legs; (b) says "Ho"; (c) sits back deep in the saddle; and (d) pulls up on the reins. The leg pressure is to alert the horse. Throwing the rider's weight back when properly timed, drives the horse's hind feet up under him. The reins are pulled no harder than necessary, then the pressure is released so that the horse can use his head to maintain his balance.

Proper timing is important. The rider squeezes when the lead foot is off the ground and the hind feet are getting ready to come off. As his hind feet come up, he shifts his weight back and starts making contact with the horse's mouth. He does not jerk, for jerking hurts the horse's mouth, and makes his head fly up and his mouth gape open. Another important thing relative to timing is this: If the rider "applies the brakes" when the horse is stretched out and his front feet are in the air, he forces the horse to throw all his weight on his front feet and he'll bounce.

The really good sliding stop is performed with rhythm and balance, and is easy and smooth.

Some good horsemen train horses on the longe line—a light strap of webbing or leather 30 feet long. When the author visited the Spanish Riding School of Vienna, where the famed Lipizzaner stallions perform, he learned that all basic training—including gaits, leads, stops, rollbacks, etc.—is given on the longe. Starting at age four, these horses are worked from the ground for one year before they are ever mounted.

The only exception to use of the longe line in training is a roping horse, because, when on the end of a rope, a roping horse is taught to run straight back from the trainer, rather than around him.

SORING HORSES

Soring is the use of painful methods and devices to enhance a horse's gait in the show-ring. It involves the use of caustic liquid, commonly called "scooter juice," along with chains or shackles, to make a walking horse's front ankles sore. This process, combined with feet 7 or more inches long, heavy shoes, and some drastic training, creates the desired show-ring gait. Both the Horse Protection Act of 1970 and the rules of the American Horse Shows Association prohibit soring.

Soring evolved as a means of producing a fast, flashy gait in Tennessee Walkers, for the show-ring.

A true running walk is executed at a speed of 6 to 8 miles per hour and will not exceed 10 miles per hour. It is done with economy of effort to both the horse and the rider and is not very showy. In an effort to increase the speed to 15 to 18 miles per hour and obtain high action in front, yet keep the gait from being classed as a rack, horses are sometimes sored by means of blisters, chains, and whatnot, so that they scoot their hind feet far under them in order to keep

the weight off their sore front feet. The soreness, along with accompanying long toes and heavy shoes (secured by bands over the feet, in addition to nails), cause the horse to pick his front feet up very high as he leaps through the air. Actually the fast, artificial gait that results more nearly resembles a rack than a running walk.

The U.S. Department of Agriculture, Animal and Plant Health Inspection Service, is charged with enforcing the Horse Inspection Act. The regulations provide that—

1. Boots and collarlike devices of any weight may be used so long as they are properly constructed and do not sore the feet of the horse that wears them.

2. Bracelets made of properly constructed chains may be used as long as they don't weigh more than 10 ounces, including the fastener.

3. Rollers may be used if made from hardwood or aluminum as long as they don't weigh more than 14 ounces.

4. All other devices, including beads and bangles, are outlawed.

5. No substance may be applied to a horse's leg above the hoof and below the fetlock when the horse is brought for preshow inspection. After inspection, a clear, transparent lubricant (like glycerine, petrolatum, or mineral oil) may be applied, but only under supervision of horse show management.

Any person violating any provision of the Act or the regulations is subject to a civil penalty of up to $1,000 or criminal penalties up to $2,000 and 6 months' imprisonment for each violation.

BLOOD TESTING FOR FITNESS

Blood testing (hemotology) is a means of evaluating physical fitness.

All body cells require oxygen. With strenuous exercise, as in racing, the oxygen requirement increases. Oxygen is transported by hemoglobin, the protein-iron coloring matter in blood. It follows that any reduction in the hemoglobin content, or in total blood volume, will lower the oxygen-carrying capacity of the blood. When this condition is marked, anoxia (or anemia) develops, fatigue sets in, and there is lowered stamina and endurance.

Anoxia may be caused by many conditions. Usually it is due either to (1) nutritional deficiency, or (2) bloodworms—both of which may be aggravated by the stress and strain of racing, endurance trials, and showing.

Most trainers accept one or more of the following as indicative of the lack of "fitness": loss of appetite; loss of weight; excessive "blowing" following work; a dry, harsh cough; rough coat; dull eyes; watery instead of beady sweating; and "blowing up" over the loins. In an effort to be more exacting, some veterinarians who attend to racing stables, endurance trials, and show strings now use blood examinations as a means of evaluating physical fitness.

It appears that, although there are breed differences, most horses which show consistent, good racing form have hemoglobin levels between 14 and 16 grams per milliliter, red cell counts between 9 and 11 million per cubic millimeter, and packed cell volumes between 40 percent and 45 percent. Also, other blood determinations are sometimes made. The blood testing approach is interesting and appealing. However, much more information on the subject is needed. Proof of this assertion becomes evident when it is realized that all horses whose blood pictures fall within the above range are not necessarily good performers; neither are horses with blood pictures outside this range incapable of winning. Some horses do respond to treatment, but, generally, the results have been inconsistent and disappointing. One needs to know if horses which have lower blood values, but which do not respond to treatment, carry all of the red cells and hemoglobin that they are capable of developing—whether they have less potential for racing. Even more perplexing is the fact that this blood count can be too high, producing polycythemia. A horse with polycythemia frequently loses appetite, fails to thrive in the stable, performs unsatisfactorily, and may show cyanosis (dark bluish or purple coloration of the skin and mucous membrane due to lack of oxygen). It is also noteworthy that absolute polycythemia occurs at high altitudes or when there is heart disease or fibrosis of the lungs.

Racehorses with anemia are sometimes treated by either (1) injecting iron and/or vitamin B_{12}, or (2) giving orally (in the feed or water) one of several iron preparations. Sometimes vitamin C (ascorbic acid), folic acid, and other B complex vitamins are added.

At this time, there is insufficient knowledge of equine anemia, or of ways of stimulating the making of blood (hematopoiesis), to make a winner. The true role of therapy, if any, remains unknown.

The most that can be said at this time is that prevailing treatments usually satisfy the owner or trainer who insists that his charges "get the works." Most scientists are agreed, however, that "quickie" miracle shots or concoctions will never replace sound nutrition and parasite control on a continuous basis.

SELECTED REFERENCES

Title of Publication	Author(s)	Publisher
Animal Agriculture: The Biology of Domestic Animals and Their Use by Man	Ed. by H. H. Cole, M. Ronning	W. H. Freeman and Co., Publishers, San Francisco, Calif., 1974
Animal Behavior	V. G. Dethier E. Stellar	Prentice-Hall, Inc., Englewood Cliffs, N.J., 1970
Behavior of Domestic Animals, The, Third Edition	E. S. Hafez	The Williams & Wilkins Co., Baltimore, Md., 1975
Care and Training of the Trotter and Pacer	J. C. Harrison et al.	The United States Trotting Association, Columbus, Ohio, 1970
First Horse	R. Hapgood	Chronicle Books, San Francisco, Calif., 1972
Marvels & Mysteries of Our Animal World		Reader's Digest Association, Pleasantville, N.Y., 1964
Our Friendly Animals and Whence They Came	K. P. Schmidt	M. A. Donohue & Co., Chicago, Ill., 1938
Saddle Up!	C. E. Ball	J. B. Lippincott Co., Philadelphia, Penn., 1970
Science of Animals That Serve Mankind, The, Second Edition	J. R. Campbell J. F. Lasley	McGraw-Hill Book Company, New York, N.Y., 1975
Training the Arabian Horse	H. H. Reese	The Cruse Publishing Company, Inc., Fort Collins, Colo., 1961
Training Horses for Races	G. W. Meredith	Constable and Company Ltd., London, England, 1926
Training the Quarter Horse Jumper	H. P. Levings	A. S. Barnes & Co., Inc., Cranbury, N.J., 1968
Training Tips for Western Riders	L. N. Sikes	The Texas Horseman Company, Houston, Tex., 1960
Understanding and Training Horses	A. J. Ricci	J. B. Lippincott Co., Philadelphia, Penn., 1964
Western Equitation, Horsemanship and Showmanship	D. Stewart	Vantage Press, New York, N.Y., 1973
Western Horse Behavior & Training	R. W. Miller	Doubleday & Company, Inc., Garden City, N.Y., 1975

SELECTED REFERENCES

Title of Publication	Authors	Publisher

HORSEMANSHIP

Fig. 17-1. Horsemanship. The "mounties"—Royal Canadian Mounted Police of Canada. (Courtesy, RCMP, Ottawa, Canada)

Riding has become increasingly popular in recent years because it offers pleasant and healthful outdoor recreation, beneficial to both body and mind. Furthermore, it is a sport that can be indulged in at any time by those who like it. Also, it can be enjoyed alone or with groups. Nor is it confined to any age, rank, or profession. Businessmen value riding because they can get vigorous exercise and obtain relaxation from professional troubles. A good horse is companion enough, is always good humored, and has no worries or business troubles to talk about.

Women can ride at such times as may suit their convenience. For the housewife, this may be an important consideration.

Children build character through riding, automatically acquiring confidence, self-control, and patience—all through companionship with their good friend and stout companion, the horse.

For greatest enjoyment, one should learn to ride correctly. It is an unfortunate truth that many people think they can ride if only they can stick on a horse. Although these same people may pay well for instruction in golf, swimming, tennis, and other sports, it never occurs to them that a competent riding master may be essential in learning to ride. The word competent is used with reference to riding masters; for, what is even more tragic, many people think that they are qualified to instruct others as soon as they have learned a few things about riding.

Equitation is a very difficult subject to teach. In the first place, no two horses nor two riders are alike. Then there is hardly any limit to the types of available equipment, and there are the different gaits; and, in addition, riding to hounds and riding on a city bridle path present entirely different problems. Moreover, riding cannot be taught by merely reading a set of instructions. It can be mastered only after patient practice under a competent instructor. The amateur, there-

fore, should be under no illusions about achieving horsemanship and horsemastership merely through reading what follows. Rather, it is proposed to present here some of the basic principles of equitation and information pertaining to equipment, with the hope that the beginner may better understand the why and wherefore of the instructions given him. Also, through reading this presentation it is hoped that the experienced equestrian may be less likely to suffer relapse.

It must be recognized also that there are many schools of riding, and each riding master will proceed along different lines. Yet, the end result will always be the same—training the rider to get the maximum pleasure with the least exertion to himself and his mount. Regardless of the method of instruction, the first requisite is that of instilling confidence in the amateur. Confidence is usually obtained through first becoming familiar with the horse and equipment and then by riding a gentle and obedient horse at the walk in an enclosed ring, while keeping the mount under control at all times.

In instructing the beginner, the author favors a simple approach of first becoming familiar with the horse and equipment and then learning to use that equipment properly. Knowledge of correct grooming and care of the horse, care of equipment, saddling, bridling, and leading is also essential.

SELECTION OF THE MOUNT

Fig. 17-2. The mount should be selected carefully for the individual rider—keeping in mind (1) the purchase price that the rider can afford, (2) the skill of the rider, (3) the size of the rider, and (4) the type of work to be performed. (Photo by Mrs. Joan S. Byrne; courtesy, American Saddle Horse Breeders Assn., Louisville, Ky.)

The mount should be carefully selected by a competent horseman. In addition to obtaining a sound horse of desirable conformation, one should give the following points careful consideration:

1. The mount should be purchased within a price range that the rider can afford.

2. The amateur or child should have a quiet, gentle, well-broken horse that is neither headstrong nor unmanageable. The horse should never be too spirited for the rider's skill. It is best that the beginner select a horse (a) with manners, rather than looks, and (b) that is older, rather than a two- or three-year-old.

3. The size of the horse should be in keeping with the size and weight of the rider. Very small children should have a small horse or pony, whereas a heavy man should have a horse of the weight-carrying type. An exceedingly tall man or woman also looks out of place if not mounted on a horse with considerable height.

4. Usually the novice will do best to start with a 3-gaited horse and first master the 3 natural gaits before attempting to ride a horse executing the more complicated 5 gaits, should a 5 gaited horse be desired.

5. Other conditions being equal, the breed and color of horse may be decided on the basis of preference.

6. When one wants a horse that is to be used for business purposes—an animal such as is desired by ranchers—the mount should be well suited to the type of work to be performed.

7. Before buying, take every possible precaution to avoid a horse that has undesirable traits or vices; question the owner, and observe the horse in its stall and when being ridden.

After the horse has been selected, it is important that he and the rider become acquainted with each other. Just as every automobile driver knows the major parts of a car—the steering wheel, tires, wheels, hood, fenders, windows, etc.—the horseman should be familiar with the important parts of a horse. This information may be secured by studying Fig. 4-2 in Chapter 4.

TACK

Each horse should have his own saddle, bridle, halter, and lead shank. Then, the equipment can be adjusted to fit the particular horse.

Equipment should be selected so as to suit the intended purpose, as well as to fit both the horse and the rider. As in buying almost anything—food, a suit of clothes, and whatnot—you generally get what you pay for. In the long run, it is usually cheaper to buy superior quality tack. Then, by taking good care of it, one can derive satisfaction for many years.

The sections that follow give pertinent facts about some common tack items.

Fig. 17-3. Parade horse, showing elaborate tack. (Courtesy, Willard Beanland, Canoga Park, Calif.)

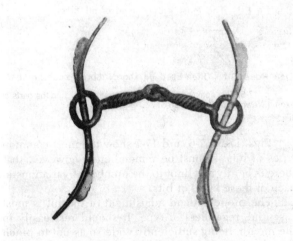

Fig. 17-4. Gold-gilded, winged snaffle bit, made and used 113 B.C., in Western Han Dynasty. On display in the Exhibit of Cultural Relics, Peking, China. (Photo by A. H. Ensminger)

Bits

The bit is the most important part of the bridle; in fact, the chief use of the bridle is to hold the bit in its place in the horse's mouth. There are more types of bits than of any other article of horse equipment. In this connection, it is interesting to note that the snaffle bit—which is still the most widely used of all varieties—was the first type to which historians make reference, having been developed by the early Greek horsemen. The bit provides communication between the hands of the rider or driver and the mouth of the horse.

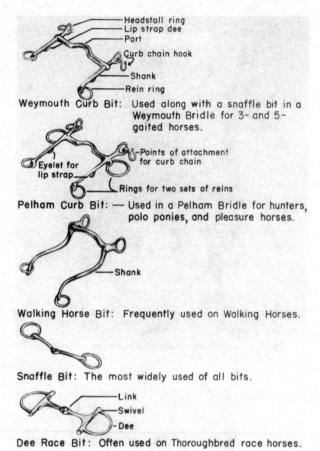

Weymouth Curb Bit: Used along with a snaffle bit in a Weymouth Bridle for 3- and 5-gaited horses.

Pelham Curb Bit: — Used in a Pelham Bridle for hunters, polo ponies, and pleasure horses.

Walking Horse Bit: Frequently used on Walking Horses.

Snaffle Bit: The most widely used of all bits.

Dee Race Bit: Often used on Thoroughbred race horses.

Fig. 17-5. Five common types of English riding bits, and the parts of each. (Drawings by Steve Allured)

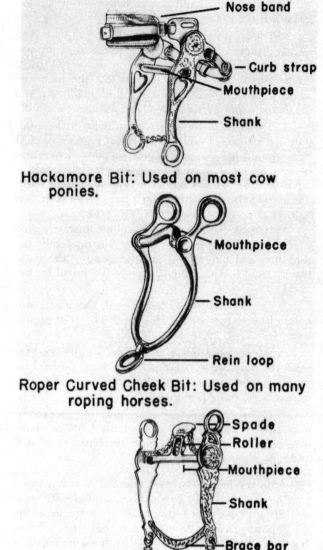

Hackamore Bit: Used on most cow ponies.

Roper Curved Cheek Bit: Used on many roping horses.

Spade Mouth Bit: Used on many stock horses.

Fig. 17-6. Three common types of Western riding bits, and the parts of each. (Drawings by Steve Allured)

Figs. 17-5, 17-6, and 17-7 show the most common types of bits. It must be remembered, however, that there is hardly any limit to the number of variations in each of these kinds of bits.

The proper fit and adjustment of the bit is most essential, regardless of type. It should rest easily in the mouth, being sufficiently wide so as not to pinch the cheeks or cause wrinkles in the corners of the mouth. As a rule, curb-type bits rest lower in the mouth than the snaffle. All bits should be supplied with large rings or other devices to prevent them from passing through the mouth when either rein is drawn in turning.

The following additional points are pertinent to bits:

1. The snaffle bit is usually used when starting a horse in training.

2. The hunting (or egg butt) snaffle is used on hunters and jumpers.

3. The curb bit is a more severe bit, which may be used either alone or with the snaffle bit.

4. The Pelham bit is one bit, which is used with two reins and a curb chain. It is a combination of a snaffle and a curb bit and is used in park or pleasure riding and hunting.

5. The Weymouth bit along with a snaffle bit is known as a bit and bradoon.

6. Western bits are made similar to the curb bit, but they have longer shanks and are larger. They are usually used with a leather curb strap, although a leather curb strap with a small amount of chain in the middle is sometimes used.

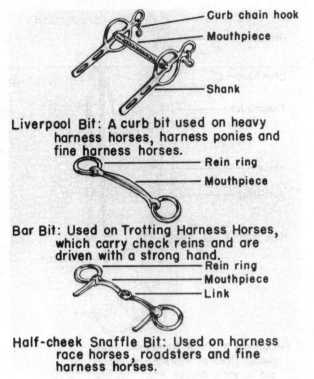

Liverpool Bit: A curb bit used on heavy harness horses, harness ponies and fine harness horses.

- Curb chain hook
- Mouthpiece
- Shank

Bar Bit: Used on Trotting Harness Horses, which carry check reins and are driven with a strong hand.

- Rein ring
- Mouthpiece

Half-cheek Snaffle Bit: Used on harness race horses, roadsters and fine harness horses.

- Rein ring
- Mouthpiece
- Link

Fig. 17-7. Three common types of driving bits, and the parts of each. (Drawings by Steve Allured)

Bridles and Hackamores

Light bridles and bits usually indicate competent horsemen and well-mannered horses. Bridles may be either single or double. A single bridle is equipped with one bit, whereas a double bridle is ordinarily equipped with both a snaffle bit and a curb bit, two headstalls, and two pairs of reins. Only one rein is used with Western bridles.

All bridles should be properly fitted, and the headstall should be located so that it neither slides back on the horse's neck nor pulls up against his ears. The cheek straps should be adjusted in length so that the bit rests easily in the mouth without drawing up the corners; and the throat latch should be buckled loosely enough to permit the hand, when held in a vertical position, to pass between it and the horse's throat.

Both the bosal hackamore and the hackamore bit bridle are used as a training device for Western horses and on horses with tender mouths. The bosal hackamore consists of an ordinary headstall which holds in place a braided rawhide or rope noseband knotted under the horse's jaw, and a pair of reins. It is an excellent device for controlling and training a young horse without injuring its mouth. The hackamore is used extensively on the western ranges in the training

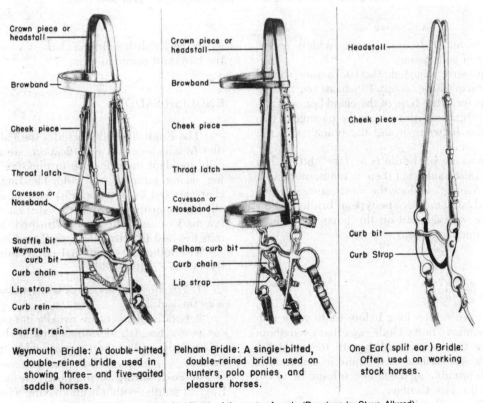

Weymouth Bridle: A double-bitted, double-reined bridle used in showing three- and five-gaited saddle horses.

- Crown piece or headstall
- Browband
- Cheek piece
- Throat latch
- Cavesson or Noseband
- Snaffle bit
- Weymouth curb bit
- Curb chain
- Lip strap
- Curb rein
- Snaffle rein

Pelham Bridle: A single-bitted, double-reined bridle used on hunters, polo ponies, and pleasure horses.

- Crown piece or headstall
- Browband
- Cheek piece
- Throat latch
- Cavesson or Noseband
- Pelham curb bit
- Curb chain
- Lip strap

One Ear (split ear) Bridle: Often used on working stock horses.

- Headstall
- Cheek piece
- Curb bit
- Curb Strap

Fig. 17-8. Three types of bridles, and the parts of each. (Drawings by Steve Allured)

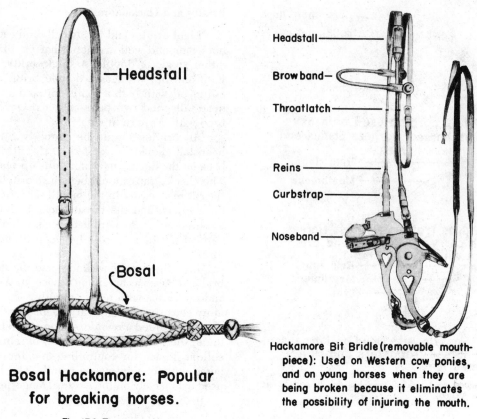

—Headstall

—Bosal

Bosal Hackamore: Popular for breaking horses.

Headstall————

Browband—

Throatlatch————

Reins ————

Curbstrap————

Noseband————

Hackamore Bit Bridle (removable mouth-piece): Used on Western cow ponies, and on young horses when they are being broken because it eliminates the possibility of injuring the mouth.

Fig. 17-9. Two types of hackamores, and the parts of each. (Drawings by Steve Allured)

of cow ponies, and it is used equally widely in the early training of polo ponies.

When properly adjusted, the hackamore should rest on the horse's nose, about 4 inches from the top of the nostrils (or at the base of the cheekbones of the horse's head). It should also permit the passage of two finger breadths between it and the branches of the jaw.

The hackamore bit bridle is a "fake" bit—it has the shanks on each side, but there is no mouthpiece.

Figs. 17-8 and 17-9 show the most common types of bridles and hackamores. The type of bridle and bit or hackamore will depend on the horse's previous training and intended use.

Saddles

Horses were ridden long before there were saddles. The so-called "horse cloth" was first used about 800 B.C., but the use of saddles with trees did not exist until the 4th Century A.D. Anne of Bohemia is credited with introducing the ladies' sidesaddle in the latter part of the 14th Century.

Although considerable styling and individuality

exist, the English saddle and the Western saddle are the two most common types.

ENGLISH SADDLE

The English saddle includes the flat types of saddles in which certain modifications are made specifically to adapt them for use in pleasure riding, training, racing, jumping, and polo. The English saddle is characterized by its relatively flat seat and its generally light construction. Its advocates claim that its use is a mark of distinction of the finished rider, as it permits the best in riding form, skill, and balance.

The following additional points are pertinent to the use of English saddles:

1. For show horses, use a white web or linen girth with the saddle.

2. Saddle blankets are usually not necessary.

3. For English pleasure riding or showing, select an English saddle; then use a double bit or Pelham bridle.

4. For hunting or jumping, use a forward seat English saddle, with a bridle having a hunting snaffle or Pelham bit.

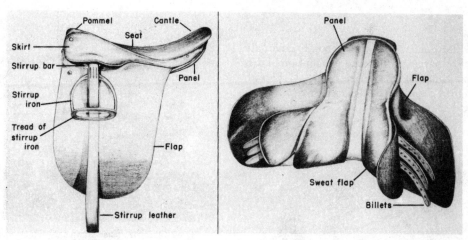

Fig. 17-10. An English saddle, and its parts. Left, upright position; right, underside. (Drawings by Steve Allured)

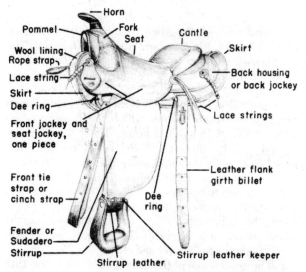

Fig. 17-11. A Western saddle, and its parts. (Drawings by Steve Allured)

WESTERN SADDLE

Western saddles were first developed and used by the Spaniards in Old Mexico. They constructed them with horns, and they liked them roomy, heavy, and ornate. Subsequently, American ranchers made some changes; they lightened them and made them less cumbersome, and they added the high pommel and swelled fork—better to provide extra leg grip should the horse buck or rear.

The Western saddle is the common saddle used by the cowboy. The essential features are: a steel, light metal, or wooden tree; a pommel varying in height and surmounted with a horn for roping; a comparatively deep seat; a cantle varying in height (the variation in the height of the pommel and cantle is determined by the uses to which the saddle is to be put and the personal preference of the rider); heavy

square, or round, skirts; double cinch (though a single cinch may be used); and heavy stirrups that may be either hooded or open. This is primarily a work saddle and is designed to afford comfort for all-day riding and to provide enough strength to stand up under the strain of calf roping. The Western saddle often has strong appeal to the novice because it is the saddle of the romantic, adventurous cowboy and because its deep seat and heavy construction impart a feeling of security. Some riders claim that for pleasure riding, the Western saddle is too heavy, is hot in summer, and offers too much temptation to "pull leather" as a substitute for skill and balance. The average Western saddle weighs from 35 to 40 pounds.

Additional pertinent facts about Western saddles are:

1. They're used for Western riding of all kinds, both work and pleasure.
2. Western saddles are utilitarian. They're designed to provide all-day comfort, and the horn is a convenient and secure post around which the lariat can be tied or quickly wound when handling cattle.
3. The design of Western saddles—especially height of pommel and cantle—is determined by use and personal preference.

Westerners take pride in their saddles. To them, they're much more than something to throw over a horse's back, or to use in working cattle. They're symbolic of the development of the range, of trailing, and of the transition from the Texas longhorn to the prime bullock. Most makes and styles of Western saddles are accorded meaningful names, with such selections suggestive of their historical significance, their construction, and/or their use.

To reputable manufacturers and proud owners alike, the names of Western saddles are symbols of service, pledges of integrity, and assurances of courage, character, and wisdom.

Harness

It is not within the scope of this book to cover all types and parts of harness. But some conception of the subject may be obtained by studying Figs. 17-12 and 17-13, showing the standard harness and rigging used on trotters and pacers.

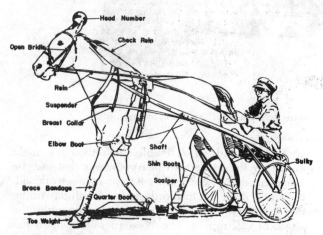

Fig. 17-12. Trotter's harness and rigging. (Courtesy, The United States Trotting Assn., Columbus, Ohio)

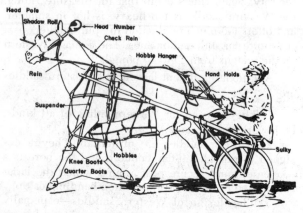

Fig. 17-13. Pacer's harness and rigging. (Courtesy, The United States Trotting Assn., Columbus, Ohio)

Horse-Drawn Vehicles

Man made much use of saddle horses and pack-horses before the carriage came into general use. Also, primitive sliding vehicles preceded the use of wheels. The coming of the wheel made as big an impact on civilization as did the internal combustion engine years later. The Egyptians are believed to have been the original makers of wheels; the first vehicles were probably the wagons and chariots referred to in the Old Testament.

The earliest carriage, still in perfect condition, to

Fig. 17-14. Bronze horse-drawn cart, with umbrella over man, taken from a tomb of the late Eastern Han Dynasty (25 A.D.-220 A.D.) now on display in Peking, People's Republic of China. (Photo by A. H. Ensminger)

be found today is the State Chariot of Tutankhamen (1361-1352 B.C.) in the Cairo Museum, in Egypt. The first known carriage to be built in Great Britain was made by William Rippon for the second Earl of Rutland in 1555.

Originally, horse-drawn vehicles evolved to meet practical needs, following which they were embellished to meet individual tastes. There was the dignified family carriage with fringe on top; the buckboard with its jump seat—the pickup truck of grandfather's time; the governess cart, with its door at the rear and two seats facing eath other; the high two-wheeled dog cart, for transporting hounds to the hunt; the high-seated rig of the society matron; the old-fashioned top buggy of the country doctor; and the roadster of the young gallant.

The golden age of the carriage arrived in the 18th Century. Many different styles of vehicles were built. The high phaeton was a popular vehicle of the period. Later, it was succeeded by the pony phaeton—a long, low vehicle. The names of different types of carriages often came from the name of the builder or the place in which they were made. Although carriages were built throughout the world, it was generally accepted that French and British carriage builders were the masters of their craft.

Even hitches evolved for practical reasons. Tandem driving, for example, was originated by the hunting men of Old England. Wishing to spare their hunting mount as they traveled to and from the meet, these ingenious huntsmen devised the method of driving him ahead, where he trotted between slack traces, while the horse to the rear did all the work.

Today, most horse-drawn vehicles either are used for recreation and sport—drawn by heavy harness horses, fine harness horses, roadsters, or ponies, or are of historical significance only—they are reminiscent of the horse-and-buggy era.

KINDS OF VEHICLES

There are many kinds of horse-drawn vehicles. Table 17-1 shows some appropriate vehicles for dif- ferent uses. Other types of vehicles are illustrated and described in Figs. 17-15 through 17-19. Note that Figs. 17-15, 17-16, and 17-17 are embellished with the

TABLE 17-1
APPROPRIATE HORSE-DRAWN VEHICLES

Use	Breed	Appropriate Vehicle	Comments
Racing	Standardbred Shetland	Sulky; a light vehicle with bicycle wheels. 	The pneumatic tire racing sulky was first introduced in 1892. Sulkies weigh from 29 to 37 lb, and usually have hardwood shafts, although aluminum and steel sulkies have been introduced in recent years.
Roadster: Horses	Standardbred, predominately; although other breeds may be used.	Cart or bike; buggy or road wagon. 	Roadster vehicles must be attractive and light, but strong.
Ponies		(same as above)	
Hackney (or heavy harness horses): Horses	Hackney	Viceroy, miniature side rail buggy of type used for fine harness horses, or gig. Tandem Hackneys may be shown with either a 2- or 4-wheeled vehicle; a gig or viceroy.	The vehicles pulled by Hackneys are of heavy construction, elegant design, and devoid of shiny parts.
Ponies	Hackney	(same as above)	
Fine Harness: Horses	American Saddle Horses, predominately; although other breeds are so used.	Preferably a small side rail buggy with 4 wire wheels, but without a top.	A fine harness horse is exactly what the name implies—a fine horse presented in fine harness. The entire ensemble is elegant and represents the ultimate in grace and charm.
Ponies	Hackney, Welsh, Shetland	(same as above)	
Pleasure Driving	Any Breed.	Any 2-wheeled or 4-wheeled vehicle. 	In olden times, the buckboard was usually a one-seater with a bed behind.
Breaking or Training Cart	Any Breed.	2-wheeled training cart. 	When training green horses, 2-wheeled training carts should be used, because (1) they are strong and (2) they will not tip over easily.

Fig. 17-15. Four-wheeled dogcart. Dogcarts were so named because they were used for carrying sporting dogs, under the seat. They carried 4 passengers, back to back, plus the hounds. At first they were 2-wheeled. Later, they were built with 4 wheels. Usually they were pulled by one horse, but the bigger 4-wheeled dogcarts sometimes required 2 horses.

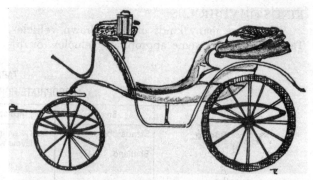

Fig. 17-18. The Victoria. Introduced from the Continent by the Prince of Wales in 1869, where it was known as a milord, the Victoria quickly achieved popularity. Essentially a summer vehicle (it has no doors) the Victoria was much favored by ladies of fashion because of the ease with which the carriage could be entered and the elegant setting for the display of finery. Initially designed for two passengers facing the front, the Victoria was later modified to accommodate four; sometimes there is a rumble seat for a groom. The Victoria is coachman-driven to a single horse or to a pair.

Fig. 17-16. Landau, the convertible of great grandfather's time. It was named after Landau, Germany, where it was first manufactured about 1790. It was a 4-wheeled covered carriage with the top divided into 2 sections. The back section could be let down or thrown back while the front section could be removed or left stationary. Landaus held 4 people and were usually drawn by 2 horses. This vehicle was very popular in England from mid-Victorian times onward.

Fig. 17-19. Stagecoach, a heavy, enclosed, four-wheeled vehicle, usually drawn by four horses, formerly used for carrying passengers and goods.

Fig. 17-17. The park phaeton. The phaeton was a four-wheeled vehicle of which there were many varieties. The early phaetons were built very high. But those of the 19th Century were considerably lower and were made in many different shapes and sizes. There was the pony phaeton made in 1824 for King George IV. Then in 1828 came the massive male phaeton driven exclusively by men. Elegant ladies' phaetons followed.

Ensminger coat of arms (the author's ancestors) as was the custom of the day.

DRIVING CUSTOMS

The history of some driving customs follows.

● *Heavy harness vehicles*—Heavy harness horses

(Hackneys) in horse shows are harnessed with heavy leather and hitched to heavy vehicles. The heavy leather used on these animals was first decreed by fashion in England, where it stemmed from the idea that to drive handsomely one had to drive heavily. In this country, heavy harness horses are reminiscent of the Gay Nineties, when bobtailed Hackneys hitched to high-seated rigs made a dashing picture as they pranced down the avenue.

Vehicles for Hackneys must be of heavy construction, elegant design, and devoid of shiny parts (the latter tends to blind spectators).

● *Driving to the right*—The American custom of driving to the right on the road, instead of to the left as is the practice in some parts of the world, originated among the Conestoga (named after the Conestoga Valley, a German settlement in Pennsylvania) wagon drivers of the 1750s, who transported freight

Fig. 17-20. Handsome and heavy. A Hackney heavy harness horse in action. (Courtesy, Mrs. Dean J. Briggs, Garden Plain, Kan.)

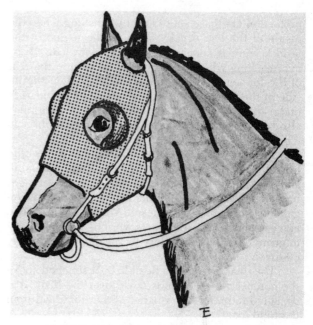

Fig. 17-21. Racing blinkers—a hood with leather cups.

overland to and from river flatboats and barges along the Ohio, Cumberland, Tennessee, and Mississippi Rivers. The drivers of these 4- and 6-horse teams either sat on the left wheel horse or on the left side of the seat, the better to wield their whip hand (the right hand) over the other horses in the team. Also, when 2 Conestoga drivers met, they pulled over to the right so that, sitting on the left wheel horse or on the left side of the seat, they could see that the left wheels of their wagons cleared each other. Lighter vehicles naturally followed the tracks of the big Conestoga wagons. Even with the development of highways and automobiles, the American custom of driving to the right persisted.

Other Tack

There is hardly any limit to the number of items and adaptations of tack. No attempt is made herein to describe, or even to mention, all of them. However, the most generally used types, in addition to those already described, are covered in the sections that follow.

BLINKERS (BLINDERS OR WINKERS)

Blinkers are an attachment to the bridle or hood, designed to restrict the vision of the horse from the sides and rear and to focus the vision forward. Driving blinkers (or winkers) are made of leather, often with a crest or embellishment on the outside. Racing blinkers are in the form of a hood with leather cups that act as shields.

BOOTS (FOR HORSES)

Boots are used to protect the legs or feet against injuries. The most common injuries requiring such

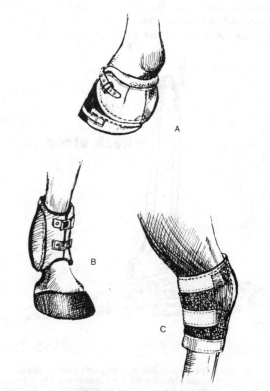

Fig. 17-22. Three types of boots: A, Quarter Boot; B, Ankle Boot; and C, Hock Boot.

protection are those caused (1) by brushing when the inside of the leg, usually on or in the region of the fetlock joint, is knocked by the opposite foot, (2) by overreaching when the hind toes strike into the rear of the foreleg, or (3) by speedy cutting when the inside of the leg is struck high above the joint, usually under the hock. The shins (either front or hind) may also be endangered as a result of striking an obstacle when jumping.

Various types of boots are available to protect the horse from the different kinds of injuries listed above—among them, the quarter boots to prevent bruising of a front heel from a hind toe, worn by five-gaited saddle horses, Tennessee Walking Horses, and harness horses; the shin boots worn by the polo pony to guard cannons from injury by the mallet; and many others.

The quarter boot is a flexible boot attached above the coronet which extends down over the hoof. It is designed to protect the quarter of the front heel from the hind toe.

BREASTPLATE; BREAST COLLAR

The breastplate usually consists of a short, wide strap that passes over the neck in front of the withers, two adjustable straps that run from each end of the short strap back to the saddle, two adjustable straps that run down the shoulders to a ring on the breastplate, and another adjustable strap that runs from this ring and attaches to the girth after passing between

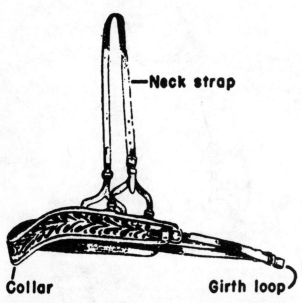

Fig. 17-23. The breast collar. It is frequently used on slender-bodied horses and on horses which require some special security to prevent the saddle from slipping to the rear (such as racehorses). The breastplate may be used for the same purposes as the breast collar. (Drawing by Steve Allured)

the forelegs. Sometimes this type is equipped with a strap that runs from the ring on the breastplate to the neckband, and acts as a martingale.

The breast collar serves the same purpose as the breastplate. Fig. 17-23 shows a breast collar.

Either the breastplate or the breast collar is frequently used on slender-bodied horses and on horses which require some special security to prevent the saddle from slipping to the rear (such as racehorses). With both articles, it is important that they be adjusted as loosely as possible consistent with holding the saddle in place, with proper allowance made for motion and movement of the horse's neck.

CAVESSON

The breaking or longeing cavesson consists of a heavy headstall, except that it has an additional strap known as the "jowl strap"—and a hinged, jointed, heavily padded, metal noseband with a ring at the top for the attachment of the longe. The cavesson (with the longe) is used for exercising, disciplining, and training horses.[1]

HALTER (HEAD COLLAR)

A halter is used for leading a horse or tying him. There are many types of halters made from a number of different materials. The rope halter (formerly made of cotton, now made of nylon) is very strong and inexpensive. It will outlast most leather halters, and it is easy to put on and take off. But care must be taken to fit it loosely, otherwise it will rub the cheekbones.

Leather halters are also widely used. The better ones are mounted with brass. Show halters are of finer, lighter leather than the ordinary stable halter, and usually they have brow bands.

Sometimes the novice has difficulty in figuring out how to put on a halter. The following procedure will alleviate this problem: Take the buckle in the left hand and the strap in the right hand, making sure that the three short parallel straps are on the bottom; slip the horse's nose through the noseband; swing the strap over from the far side, place it behind the ears, catch it with the left hand, bring the right hand back, and buckle the strap snugly enough to prevent the horse from getting it over his head.

Never leave a halter on a horse in the pasture. Although a haltered horse may be easier to catch, there is risk of the halter getting caught on some object and the animal not being able to free himself.

---

[1]Another type of cavesson is used on many bridles. It consists of a narrow strap around the nose which is held in place by another strap which goes over the head and behind the ears. The cavesson-type bridle was originally designed to prevent the horse from opening its mouth too wide when the reins are pulled, thereby getting away from the discipline of the bit.

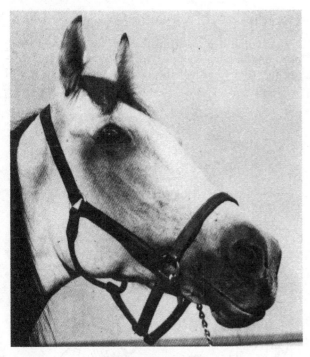

Fig. 17-24. A leather halter.

noseband and a light neck strap to keep the martingale from getting under the horse's feet when the head is lowered. When properly adjusted, it has the effect of preventing the elevation of the head beyond a certain level without cramping the horse. The standing martingale is most generally employed on saddle horses that rear and on polo ponies and stock horses that endanger their riders by throwing their heads up

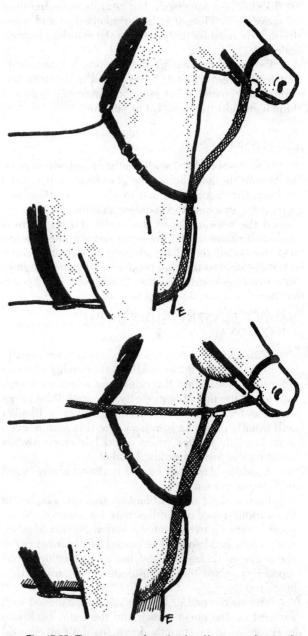

LONGE (LUNGE)

The longe is a strong light strap (usually made of webbing or leather) about 30 feet long, one end of which is attached by a swivelled snap to the noseband of the cavesson. The young horse can begin training at an early age by means of the longe line. He can be circled to the left and to the right; made to walk, trot, canter, and halt; and trained to get used to and obey words of command. The longe is especially useful for urban raised foals, who are limited in space for exercising on natural footing.

Although a young horse can do all kinds of gymnastics without injury when running loose in a corral or pasture, he can be injured by improper use of the longe line. If his head is pulled at the wrong time, or too quickly or too severely, his balance will be destroyed and he may injure a foreleg or foot, throw a curb, or be stifled.

LONGEING WHIP

A typical longeing whip has a stock about 4 feet long and a lash 6 to 8 feet long. It is used when exercising and disciplining the horse in longeing.

MARTINGALES

Martingales are of two types: standing (or sometimes called a tie-down) and running (or ring). The standing martingale consists of a strap which extends from around the girth, between the forelegs, to the

Fig. 17-25. The two types of martingales. *Upper*: standing martingale; also called a tie-down. It is sometimes used on saddle horses that rear and on polo ponies and stock horses that endanger their riders by throwing their heads up in response to a severe curb when pulled up sharply. *Lower*: a running martingale. It is used for the same purposes as the standing martingale, but permits more freedom of movement; thus it may be used on jumpers.

in response to a severe curb when pulled up sharply. On the other hand, some competent horsemen prefer to use the running martingale on horses that habitually rear. They feel that the standing martingale sets the head too high.

The running martingale is not attached to the horse's head but terminates in two rings through which the reins pass. It is used for the same purpose as the standing martingale but permits more freedom of movement. Thus, it is better adapted to and more frequently used for jumping than the standing martingale.

Proper adjustment of the running martingale is obtained when, with the horse's head in a normal position, the snaffle reins stretched from the pommel form a straight line from bit to pommel.

NOSEBAND

The noseband is a wide leather band which passes around the nose below the cheekbones. It is used to keep the mouth shut and the bit in position, as a means for attaching the standing martingale, or to enhance the appearance of the bridle. Heavy harness and most riding bridles are equipped with nosebands. The noseband should be adjusted so that it is about 1½ inches below the cheeckbone and loose enough so that two fingers may be placed under it.

SADDLE BLANKET (NUMNAH, PAD, OR CORONA)

With English saddles, saddle blankets are usually not necessary when the saddle is thoroughly cleaned after each ride, when the rider uses a balanced seat, and when the mount is properly groomed. When kept clean and when properly used, however, a blanket will usually prevent a sore back. For this reason, even with English saddles, many good horsemen always insist on the use of a saddle blanket.

A saddle blanket or corona is almost always used with Western saddles.

Felt, mohair, or pad blankets that are adapted to the various types of saddles may be secured. Many good horsemen even prefer a folded Navajo blanket, with a hair pad inside. The corona is a blanket cut to the shape of the saddle and has a large colorful roll around the edge that is quite showy for use with a stock saddle.

The saddle pad or blanket should be placed well forward on the horse's neck and then slid back into position so as to smooth down the hair. It should come to rest smoothly and in such manner that 2½ to 4 inches of it will show in front of the saddle. After being used, the blanket or pad should be hung up to dry. It then should be brushed thoroughly to eliminate hair and dried sweat.

TWITCH

A twitch is a rope run through the end of a stick, used on the horse's upper lip; it is tightened by twisting in order to attract the horse's attention so it will stand still.

Fig. 17-26. Twitch, used in restraining a horse.

CLOTHES FOR RIDERS

There is hardly any limit to the variety or cost of clothes that may be and are worn by riders. In general, riding attire is utilitarian. Close fitting legs eliminate wrinkles that might cause chafing, and chamois leather lining inside the knees and calves prevents pinching of the muscles of the leg under the stirrup leathers and increases the firmness of the leg grip. Boots or jodhpurs protect the ankle from the stirrup iron; and high boots also protect the breeches from being snagged on objects along the trail, shield the trouser legs from the saddle straps and the horse's sides, and protect the legs from rain and cold. For the

most comfortable ride, breeches (either regulation or jodhpur type) should be made to order.

Appropriate clothes for riding for the most common occasions are shown in Fig. 17-27 and described in Table 17-2. The time of day, the type of riding horse, and the class in which shown determine the riding attire. In addition to selecting proper clothes, well-groomed and experienced riders place emphasis on fine tailoring, good materials, and proper fit. Also,

when saddle horses are being ridden, gaudy colors, excess jewelry, and sequins are to be discouraged except in parade classes.

Western Boots

Western boots are more than a handsome trademark of the range. They're practical. The high heel is designed to give the wearer protection against

Fig. 17-27. Proper riding attire.

| | Western Riding | Pleasure Classes | | Gaited Show Horse Classes | |
		Informal Park or School Riding, Morning or Afternoon Classes	Semiformal, Afternoon, or Evening Classes	Five-gaited	Three-gaited
Coat	Coats and jackets not usually worn, except in inclement weather. Tailored western suits may be worn (matching shirt and pants).	Any conservative color, tweeds or checks, usually light in weight.	Gabardine, wool gabardine, or dress worsted, or other menswear materials. Inverted pleats in back. Dark colors preferred. Summer—linen or tropical worsted.	One button, inverted pleats, black or midnight blue tuxedo style riding coat. Gentlemen usually wear a dark suits instead of a tuxedo. Conservative colors are required; in addition to black and midnight blue, the rider may wear gray, green, beige, or brown.	Tuxedo style in black, dark gray, dark brown, or midnight blue. Soft pastel-colored coats can be worn. White coat in summer. Shawl collar with satin lapels. *Equitation classes:* Must wear (1) dark tuxedo style with silk top hat in evening and (2) matched suit with derby in daytime.
Jodhpurs or breeches	Western cut, bell-bottom pants of gabardine, cotton twill, cavalry twill, or wool; with chaps, shotgun chaps, or chinks. Conservative in color and well tailored.	Jodhpurs of stretch gabardine, whipcord, corduroy, or stretch twill in colors to match or in contrast to coat. Kentucky style—no flare at hip and with bell-bottoms.	Jodhpurs of same material as coat (riding habit). Kentucky style—bell-bottom, no flare at hip and no cuff.	Material and color to match coat.	Material and color to match coat (riding habit). Satin stripe down outside of jods.
Vest	Leather or cloth (optional).	Optional. Light, solid color or tattersall check.	Solid color or tattersall check, to match outfit or to contrast.	Solid colors to match habit.	White pique or commerbund (optional).
Shirt	Western type; color to match or contrast with Western pants (solid or patterned fabric acceptable). It is trim fitting with long sleeves.	Man's shirt, white or colored, broadcloth or oxford cloth, or a long-sleeved sweater.	Man's shirt in white or light color to match suit.	Man's shirt.	Formal style, white stiff front tuxedo. Shirt with wing collar and pleated front.
Neckwear	Knotted kerchief; dogger-type tie; choker; or silk scarf tied ascot style and tucked into open neck of shirt.	Contrasting 4-in-hand tie, or bow tie.	Matching or contrasting color man's 4-in-hand tie.	4-in-hand tie, or bow tie.	Black, white, or midnight blue bow tie.
Hat	Western hat; felt or straw; wide brimmed.	A soft, "Panama" hat.	Saddle derby to match suit.	Saddle derby or soft hat.	Silk top hat.
Boots	Western boots.	Black or brown strap or elastic jodhpur boots, casual style.	Black or brown jodhpur boots.	Black patent jodhpur boots with tuxedo; brown or black with a suit.	Black leather or patent leather jodhpur boots.
Gloves:	Leather (optional).	Leather gloves to blend with habit (optional).	Leather in a natural shade or to match suit (optional).	Leather to match habit.	Leather to match habit.
Jewelry or other accessories:	Hand carved belt and Western belt buckle. Carry a rope or riata. If closed reins are used in trail and pleasure horse classes, hobbles must be carried. Spurs (optional).	Cuff links, tie pin, belt. Spurs of unrowelled type, whip or crop (optional).	Tie clasp, cuff links, belt. Spurs and riding whip (optional).	Cuff links, tie pin, gaited riding whip and spurs (optional).	Formal shirt studs. Walk, trot stick, (optional).

Other Occasions:

1. *Side Saddle Forward Seat for Hunting*—Hunting silk hat, hat guard required. Dark melton habit with matching skirt, black boots without tops. Spurs (optional). White or colored rain gloves, neckwear, coat collar, vest, sandwich case and flask same as member of a hunt.

¹For information on the subject of clothes for riders for specific show classes, see the current (issued yearly) *Rule Book* of the American Horse Shows Association.

CLOTHES FOR RIDERS[1]

	Hunting and Jumping		
Hunting (informal)	Hunt Seat Equitation	Member of a Hunt (formal)	Jumping
Black oxford or English tweed.	Black (or conservative color) oxford or tweed hunt coat. Conservative wash jacket in season.	Black hunt coat of melton or Engligh cavalry twill. May wear black or midnight blue coat of shadbelly or other cutaway-type scarlet hunt livery. Collar: Same material and color as coat, unless rider has been invited to wear hunt-club colors, in which case collar should conform to hunt livery.	Any color of hunt coat in solid or checks. Jumping attire can be of any informal forward seat type.
Brick, tan, beige, or canary breeches or jods, with peg and cuff.	Buff, brick, or canary breeches.	No-flare, in beige, brick, white, or canary with black coat. Men: White breeches with scarlet coat.	No-flare breeches of a contrasting color to coat.
Hunting yellow or tattersal (optional).	Canary with black coat (optional).	Buff or yellow, or hunt colors if member.	Checkered or solid color.
Stock shirt or ratcatcher in white, light blue, maize, mint, pink, gray, or rust.	Stock shirt.	White stock shirt.	Ratcatcher shirt with stock. Man's shirt.
Choker, stock, or ratcatcher tie.	White stock or choker.	White stock, fastened with plain gold safety pin worn straight across stock.	4-in-hand tie, or stock.
Brown or black hunting derby; hunting cap if 18 years or under, with head harness and sponge rubber head cushion.	Hunting derby; hunting cap if 18 years or under.	Silk or velveteen hunting hat; hat guard required with scarlet coat or black shadbelly. Hunt caps for staff members and juniors. Derby with hat guard with black coat for adults.	Hunting derby, or hunt cap.
Black or brown boots, high or jodhpur.	Black or brown hunt boots.	Regular hunting boots with tabs; black calf. Black patent tops permissible for ladies; brown tops for men on staff.	Black or brown hunting boots.
Brown leather or rain gloves of string.	Optional.	Brown leather or rain gloves of white or yellow string.	Optional.
Stock or choker pin, belt, hunting crop, and spurs with straps to match boots.	Spurs of unrowelled type (optional). Crop or hat (optional). Stock pin worn straight across on stock tie or choker.	Sandwich case and flask. Regulation hunting whip. Spurs of heavy pattern with moderately short neck. Preferably without rowels. Worn high on heel. Boot garter: Plain black or black patent leather with patent leather boot tops. Brown with brown boot tops. White with white breeches.	Stock pin, belt, jumping bat, spurs optional.

2. Side Saddle Show Seat—Habit of dark blue, black, or oxford gray with matching or contrasting skirt. Black jodhpur boots. Bow tie or 4-in-hand. White shirt. Hard derby. White or pigskin gloves.
3. Plantation Walking Horses (Tennessee Walking Horse)—Attire should be same as listed for 3- or 5-gaited. Ladies seldom wear hats; men can wear soft felt.

losing his stirrups at critical moments; it prevents the foot from slipping through when pressure is applied for quick stops and turns. The top protects the ankles and calves of the legs against inclement weather, brush, insects, and snakes.

Modern Western boots possess two added features; namely, (1) comfort, and (2) adaptation for walk-ing, so that the wearer can walk without it being a painful experience.

BRIDLING THE HORSE

Bridling is made easy by the procedure that follows.

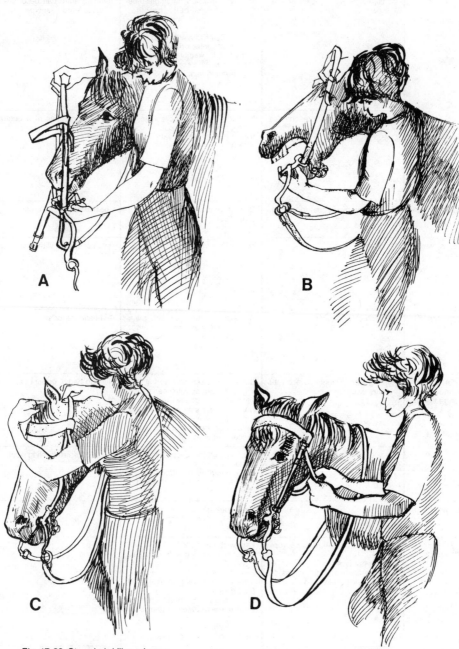

Fig. 17-28. Steps in bridling a horse:

A. Bridle in position—with the nose between the cheek pieces, the crownpiece in front of the ears, and the bit dangling against the teeth.
B. Mouth open.
C. Bridle on, with the bit in mouth and crownpiece over ears.
D. Throatlatch buckled.

Take the crownpiece of the bridle in the left hand and the reins in the right. Approach the horse from the left side opposite the shoulder. With your right hand slip the reins over his head, allowing them to rest on the crest directly behind the ears. Remove the halter—if there is one. Place yourself just behind the horse's head, facing front. Then, step by step, bridle him as follows:

● *Step A*—Take the crownpiece of the bridle in your right hand and slip the horse's nose between the cheek pieces (and in the cavesson or noseband, if the bridle is so equipped). Raise the bridle with the right hand, until the crownpiece of headstall is just in front of the ears and the bit is dangling against the teeth. With your left hand, cup the horse's chin firmly, holding the bar of the bit across the palm and keeping it against the teeth with your thumb.

● *Step B*—Slip the ends of your fingers between the horse's lips on the far side and into the animal's mouth. Thereupon, he will open his mouth and curl back his lips.

● *Step C*—With a quick pull on the crownpiece, bring the bridle into position—that is, the bit in his mouth and the crownpiece slipped over his ears.

● *Step D*—Buckle the throatlatch.

From these steps and the accompanying figure, the novice should not get the impression that in bridling a horse each step is so distinct and different as to be marked by intermittent pauses. Rather, when properly executed, bridling is a series of rhythmic movements, and the entire operation is done so smoothly and gracefully that it is difficult to discern where one stage ends and the next one begins.

SADDLING THE MOUNT

Regardless of the type of saddle—English or Western—it should be placed on the horse's back so that the girth will come about 4 inches to the rear of the point of the horse's elbow.

When first adjusted, the girth should be loose enough to admit a finger between it and the horse's belly. After tightening the saddle, it is always a good practice to "untrack" the horse—that is, to lead him ahead several paces before mounting. This procedure serves two purposes: First, if the horse is the kind that "blows up" so that he cannot be cinched snugly, the "untracking" will usually cause him to relax; and second, if a horse has any bad habits, he will often get them out of his system before the rider mounts.

After the horse has been ridden a few minutes, the girth should always be reexamined and tightened if necessary. The saddle should always be cinched tightly enough so that it will not turn when the horse is being mounted, but not so tight as to cause discomfort to the horse.

The length of stirrups will depend upon the type of riding. It may vary from very short on running horses to quite long on stock horses. The stirrup leather on English saddles should always be turned so that the flat side of the leather comes against the leg of the rider.

For correct posting, the stirrup straps or stirrup leathers must be adjusted to the right length. If stirrups are too short, posting will be high and exaggerated. For English riding, the stirrups can be adjusted to the approximate correct length before mounting by making them about 1 inch shorter than the length of the rider's arm with fingers extended. When the rider is sitting in the saddle, with the legs extended downward and the feet out of the stirrups, the bottom of the stirrup iron should touch just below the ankle bone. For Western riding, the length of stirrups may be considered as about right when there is approximately a 3-inch clearance between the saddle tree and the crotch of the mounted rider standing in the stirrups.

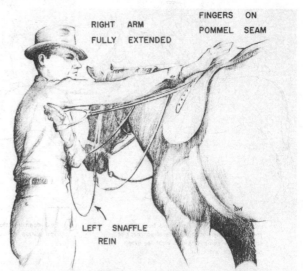

RIGHT ARM FULLY EXTENDED
FINGERS ON POMMEL SEAM
LEFT SNAFFLE REIN

STIRRUP SHOULD JUST REACH INTO RIGHT ARMPIT....... ADJUST ACCORDINGLY......... REVERSE ARM ARRANGEMENT WHEN ADJUSTING RIGHT, OR OFF STIRRUP.

Fig. 17-29. Method of checking the stirrup straps of an English saddle for proper length.

MOUNTING AND DISMOUNTING ENGLISH

Before mounting, two precautions should be taken: always check the cinch (or saddle girth) for tightness and the stirrup straps or leathers for length. A loose girth may let the saddle slip down on the horse's side or belly, especially when one is mounting and dismounting. When the girth is adjusted properly, one should be able to get only the first half of the fingers under it without considerable forcing.

When all precautions have been taken, the steps in mounting and dismounting a horse English style are as follows (see Fig. 17-30):

① Mount from left or "near" side, gather reins in left hand, and place left hand on or just in front of withers.

② Turn stirrup iron one-quarter turn, steady stirrup with right hand and shove left foot into it.

③ Hop off the right foot, swing around to face the horse, grasp the cantle (horn in Western riding) with right hand, and spring upward until standing position is reached.

④ Lean on left arm, shift right hand from cantle to pommel (usually right-hand side of pommel) of saddle; then swing extended right leg over horse's back and croup.

⑤ Ease down into the saddle; then shove right foot into right stirrup without looking down.

⑥ Sit easily, be alert and keep head up, and allow legs to hang comfortably with heels well down and toes turned out slightly.

⑦ Dismounting - Gather reins in left hand, place left hand on horse's withers and right hand on pommel, stand up in the stirrups. Then proceed as instructed in point number 7 of the narrative.

Fig. 17-30. Diagrams showing the steps in mounting and dismounting a horse English style. (Drawings by artist Steve Allured, based on photos made especially for this book by Mrs. Fern P. Bittner, Instructor in Horsemanship, Lindenwood College, St. Charles, Mo.)

1. Always mount from the left or "near" side of the horse. Stand beside the horse's left front leg and face diagonally twoard the croup.[2] Then gather the reins in the left hand, adjusting them so that a gentle pressure (restraining but not backing the animal) is applied equally on each side of the horse's mouth, and place the left hand on or immediately in front of the horse's withers. Without letting go of the reins, open the fingers of your left hand and get a handful of the horse's mane; this will give you more stability and avoid jerking the horse's mouth.

2. Turn the stirrup iron one-quarter turn toward you, steady the stirrup with the right hand and shove the left into it.

3. Hop off the right foot, swing around to face the horse, grasp the cantle (rear) of the saddle (in Western riding, the right hand is usually placed on the horn instead of the cantle) with the right hand, and spring upward until a standing position is reached, with the leg straight and facing the saddle and the left knee against the horse.

4. Lean on the left arm, shift the right hand from the cantle to the pommel (usually right-hand side of pommel) of saddle. Then, at the same time, swing the fully extended right leg slowly over the horse's back and croup, being careful not to kick him.

5. Ease down into the saddle; avoid punishing or frightening the horse by suddenly dropping the entire weight of the body into the saddle. Then shove the right foot into the right stirrup without looking down. Adjust both stirrups under the balls of the feet, and simultaneously, gather the reins. Hold the reins as indicated in the section entitled "Holding the Reins."

6. Sit easily in the saddle, be alert and keep the head up, and allow the legs to hang comfortably with the heels well down and the toes turned out slightly. This position permits proper leg contact with the horse and a more secure seat.

7. Essentially, correct *dismounting* is just the reverse of mounting. In succession, the rider should carefully gather the reins in the left hand, place the left hand on the horse's withers and the right hand on the pommel of the saddle, stand up in the stirrups, kick the right foot free from the stirrup, transfer the weight to the left foot as the right leg is swung backward across the horse's back and croup, shift the right hand to the cantle of the saddle (or in Western riding, grasp the horn with the right hand), descend to the ground, and remove the left foot from the stirrup.

Another accepted way of dismounting from the

[2]Another common method of mounting begins with facing the front of the horse while standing opposite the left stirrup. The method given in Point 1 above is considered safer for the beginner, however; for if the horse should start to move as he is being mounted, the rider is automatically swung into the saddle and is not left behind. Also, the person mounting is out of the way of a horse that "cow kicks."

English saddle consists in removing the left foot from the stirrup and sliding down with relaxed knees. The rider will never get hung in the stirrups when dismounting in this manner and, small children can get off a horse easily and without assistance.

From the above outline the novice should not gain the impression that in mounting and dismounting each step is so distinct and different as to be marked by intermittent pauses. Rather, when properly executed, mounting or dismounting is a series of rhythmic movements, and the entire operation is done so smoothly and gracefully that it is difficult to discern where one stage ends and the next one begins.

MOUNTING AND DISMOUNTING WESTERN

Fig. 17-31. Mounting Western.

The steps in mounting a horse in Western riding are as follows:

(1) Take the reins in the left hand and place the left hand on the horse's neck in front of the withers; (2) keep the romal or end of the reins on the near side; (3) grasp the stirrup with the right hand and place the left foot in the stirrup with the ball of the foot resting securely on the tread; (4) brace the left knee against the horse, grasp the saddle horn with the right hand, and spring upward and over; and (5) settle into the saddle and slip the right foot into the off stirrup. Dismounting is the same as described for dismounting English (see Point 7), except that, in Western riding, the horn is grasped with the right hand.

HOLDING THE REINS

In English riding, the rider may hold the reins either in the left hand alone or in both hands. In Western riding, only one hand, usually the left, is permitted, and the hands cannot be changed.

When holding the reins with both hands—as is usual in English show-ring riding and training—toss the "bight" (ends) of the reins to the right (off) side of the horse's neck; in hunting and jumping, toss the bight to the left.

When holding the reins in one hand, the left for example—as in English style, cross-country riding, or in Western riding—the bight should fall to the left side of the horse's neck and the right hand should be dropped loosely down the side or placed comfortably on the thigh of the right leg. The free hand should never be placed on the pommel of an English saddle or on the pommel or horn of a Western saddle.

Figs. 17-32 and 17-33 illustrate better than words the correct methods of holding the reins.

In no case should the rein pressure be more vigorous than absolutely necessary, nor should the reins be used as a means of staying on the horse. A horse's mouth is tender, but it can be toughened by unnecessary roughness. Good hands appear to be in proper rhythm with the head of the horse. Beginners are likely to let the hands bob too much, thus jerking the horse's mouth unnecessarily and using the reins as a means of "hanging on" the horse. The desired "light hands" exist when a light feeling extends to the horse's mouth via the reins.

SEAT

As in any type of sport, correct riding must include rhythm and balance. The rider's movements must be in complete harmony with the horse's movements, for this assures greater security of the rider and freedom of action of the horse.

The balanced seat may be defined as that position of the mounted rider that requires the minimum of muscular effort to remain in the saddle and which interferes least with the horse's movements and equilibrium. In essence, it means that the rider must be "with the horse," rather than ahead of or behind him. When a balanced seat is maintained, the center of gravity of the rider is directly over the center of

Methods of Holding the Reins English Style

DOUBLE - REIN BRIDLE

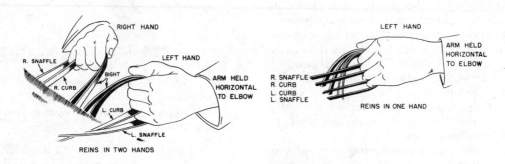

SINGLE - REIN BRIDLE

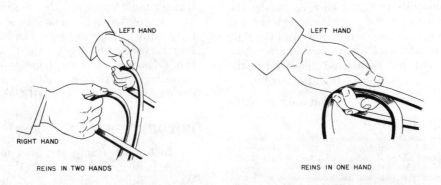

Fig. 17-32. Holding the reins English style. *Top*: double-rein bridle; *bottom*: single-rein bridle.

Holding The Reins Western Style

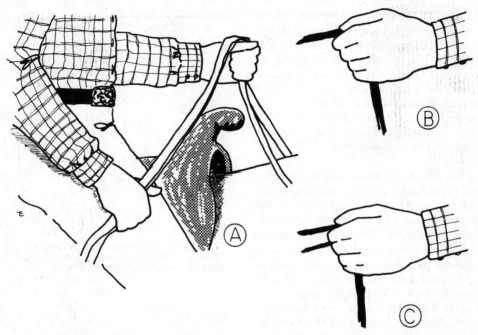

Fig. 17-33. In Western reining, (1) only one hand can be used and hands cannot be changed, and (2) the hand is to be around the reins (as shown in A and B above). When using split reins, one finger between the reins is permitted (as shown in C above).

gravity of the horse. With the proper seat, the minimum use of the aids will be necessary to get immediate and correct response from the horse at any gait.

The balanced seat is obtained largely through shifting the point of balance of the upper body from the hips up; the knees, legs, ankles, and to a great extent the thighs remain in fixed position. Thus, the

Line of body ● ● ● ● ● ● ● ● ● ● ● ●

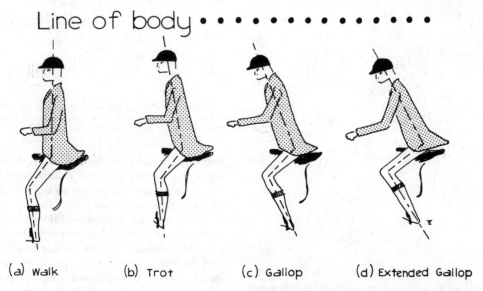

(a) Walk   (b) Trot   (c) Gallop   (d) Extended Gallop

Fig. 17-34. The balanced seat, obtained by shifting the center of gravity of the rider over the center of gravity of the horse. The greater the forward speed of the horse, the greater the forward inclination of the rider.

degree of forward inclination of the upper body will vary according to the speed and gait of the horse; but always the rider should remain in balance over his base of support. The eyes, chin, and chest are lifted, thus permitting clear vision ahead and normal posture of the back. It must also be remembered that the greater the speed and the inclination of the body forward, the shorter the stirrups. The jockey, therefore, rides his mount with very short stirrups and reins and a pronounced forward position. He rises out of his saddle and supports himself almost entirely with the stirrups, knees, and legs. In steeplechasing, the position of the rider is less extreme than in flat racing; for in this type of riding, it is necessary to combine speed with security.

From what has been said, it can be readily understood that there are different seats or positions for different styles of riding. Fashion, particularly in the show-ring, also decrees that certain form be followed.

When riding a 3- or 5-gaited horse, at all gaits and either on the bridle path or in the show-ring, the rider assumes the show or park seat—sitting erect and well back in the saddle (leaving a space of at least a hand's breadth between the back of his jodhpurs and the cantle). The ball of the foot rests directly over the stirrup iron; knees are in; heels are lower than the toes; and his hands and reins are in such position that the horse will carry his head high and his neck arched. In this position, the body is easily erect and balanced on a base consisting of seat, thighs, knees, and stirrups; the chest is high and just forward of the true vertical; and the back is hollow, the waist relaxed, the head erect,

Fig. 17-36. Correct show seat and riding attire for a five-gaited horse. (Drawing by Steve Allured; based on illustrations provided especially for this book by Mrs. Claud H. Drew, Columbia, Mo.)

Fig. 17-37. Correct show seat and riding attire at the running walk. (Drawing by Steve Allured; based on illustrations provided especially for this book by Mrs. Claud H. Drew, Columbia, Mo.)

and the shoulders square. Figs. 17-35 through 17-37 show the correct seat and riding attire for a 3-gaited horse, a 5-gaited horse, and a Plantation Walking Horse, respectively.

When using a stock saddle and riding Western style, the rider should sit straight, keep the legs fairly straight—or bent slightly forward at the knees—and rest the balls of the feet on the stirrup treads with the heels down. The left hand with the reins should be carried in a relaxed manner slightly above and ahead of the horn. The right hand should be placed on the

Fig. 17-35. Correct show seat and riding attire for a three-gaited horse. (Drawing by Steve Allured; based on illustrations provided especially for this book by Mrs. Claud H. Drew, Columbia, Mo.)

thigh, or it may be dropped loosely down the side, or held about waist high without resting it on anything. In cutting horses or in barrel racing, the left hand may rest on the saddle horn. "Sitting" the saddle is required at all gaits. Neither posting the trot (jog) nor standing in the stirrups at the trot or gallop (lope) is accepted in Western style riding. Because speed and agility are frequently required of stock horses, a firm seat and superior balance are important. Fig. 17-38 shows the correct Western Seat and riding attire.

Fig. 17-38. Correct Western seat and riding attire. (Drawing by Steve Allured)

Fig. 17-39. Correct hunter seat. The eyes should be up and the shoulders back. The toes should be out at an angle best suited to the rider's comfort; ankles flexed in, heels down, calf of leg in contact with horse and slightly behind girth. Iron may be either on toe, ball of foot, or "home." Rider is wearing a metal-lined black velvet hunting cap.

In riding hunters (including cross-country riding) and jumpers, the stirrups are shortened; the foot is shot home farther than when working at slower gaits (but with some portion of the ball of the foot still resting on the stirrup, and with the heel slightly down); the upper part of the rider's body is thrust forward, giving the "forward seat"; and a comparatively loose rein is kept. The higher the jumps are, the shorter the stirrups should be and the more pronounced the forward inclination of the body. Fig. 17-39 shows the correct saddle position for hunting and jumping.

Most polo players prefer to use medium-length stirrups, with feet shot home in the stirrups. This permits a good grip when turning at full speed. The stirrups are also sufficiently short to allow the player to stand up in the stirrup irons when making a long reach for the ball.

Each of these styles of riding differs in appearance, but the end result is the same—balanced riding. An accomplished horseman or horsewoman can and does change the seat to meet the style of riding.

PUTTING THE HORSE IN MOTION

After the rider is properly mounted, he is ready to put the horse in motion. This is accomplished by means of "the aids," which are really the only mutual language between the horse and rider.

Natural Aids

The natural aids to retaining equilibrium and controlling the horse's movements are the legs, the hands and reins, the weight of the rider, and the voice. When necessary, these may be assisted by the artificial aids: spurs and crop. For a finished performance, all of the natural aids must be invoked in unison, and the artificial aids must be used sparingly—if at all.

ACTION OF THE LEGS

The rider's legs are used primarily for the purposes of producing impulsion (forward movement) and increasing the gait. These results are obtained by a simple pressure on the horse by the inner calf muscles of the rider. Should this prove inadequate, it is proper to resort to the use of the spurs or the whip. One of the rider's legs may be used with greater force than the other, thus displacing the horse's hindquarters laterally to prevent it from sidestepping, to straighten it, or to change direction in a cramped space.

ACTION OF THE REINS

The reins are an intermediary between the rider

and the mount; they afford direct contact between the hands and the horse's mouth. The reins regulate the impulsion—slowing, stopping, or backing the horse. The reins, acting through the mouth and the neck, are also used to change direction of travel or to turn the horse to either the right or the left.

ACTION OF THE WEIGHT

By shifting the position of his body from the hips up—a weight of approximately 100 pounds in the average person—the rider can contribute materially to variations in the balance of the horse. When moving, stopping, or turning, the rider may facilitate and hasten the obedience of the mount by slightly displacing his weight in the direction of desired movement.

Artificial Aids

Ingenious man has devised many artificial aids which, when judiciously used by an experienced horseman, may supplement effectively the natural aids. In addition to the whip and spur, the following equipment may be listed under this category: longeing whip, link straps, martingales, nosebands, various types of reins, and innumerable types of bits.

Such artificial aids should be used sparingly— particularly the spur and whip. Perhaps for the most part, they should be used only when there has been disobedience to the natural aids.

Starting

In starting the horse, the rider should simultaneously invoke the use of the natural aids. He should slightly tighten the reins to awake the mount to attention, bring slight pressure with the inner calf muscles, and incline the body forward. Finally, as a last resort, he may use judiciously one or more of the artificial aids.

Stopping

The rider stops the horse by pulling back on the reins in slow and repeated movements, by releasing the pressure the instant the animal shows signs of obedience, and by repeating the action as often as necessary to bring him to a dead stop. At the same time, the rider, without standing up, puts his weight evenly into both stirrups and leans slightly backward.

Turning

In turning, the rider must pull the rein on the side toward which it is desired that the horse shall go; at the same time he must slacken off the pressure on the opposite side. Simultaneously, more weight is shifted to the stirrup on the side of the turn. Adequate rein pressure should be applied, but it is not necessary to jerk or pull hard.

Executing the Gaits

After the rider has mastered the art of starting, stopping, and turning the mount, attention may be given to the gaits. The amateur had best use only the three natural gaits: the walk, trot, and canter. A description of these gaits, together with additional gaits and defects in the way of going, is found in Chapter 7. Knowledge of the different gaits should be mastered before one attempts to execute them.

WALK

Before trying the faster gaits, it is wise that the beginner first "learn to walk." The balanced seat and correct posture must be mastered. The back should be erect, but the waist should be supple. Often it is helpful to have the beginner walk the horse with the feet out of the stirrups while keeping the knee and hip joints relaxed, the shoulders square, the head back, the legs down, and the ankles relaxed.

TROT

Trotting is the roughest of all gaits to the beginner, but correct riding at this gait must be acquired. There are two ways of riding at the trot: the "close" or "cowboy seat," in which the rider remains firmly seated in the saddle at all times; and the "posting seat," in which the rider's body goes slightly up in the air in unison with the horse.

The beginner should not attempt to fast trot or to post until the balanced seat has been thoroughly mastered at the slow trot. Moreover, the slow trot (about 6 miles per hour) is not, as a rule, ridden by posting, nor do riders post when riding Western. The "posting seat" is used by most park-riding civilians and horse-show folks and by practically all calvalry services.

POSTING THE TROT

Posting may be described as the rising and descending of the rider with the rhythm of the trot. This action reduces the shock or jar of the trot for both horse and rider. Posting is accomplished by rising easily in the saddle in rhythm at one beat, of the two-beat trot, and settling back at the next beat. In posting, the rider inclines the upper part of the body slightly forward (while at the same time keeping the shoulders back, the chin up, and the legs under the body, with the heels down); supports himself by pressing the knees inward against the horse; and then permits his body to be impelled upward by the thrust

of one of the hind legs (the left, for example). The rider remains up during the stride of the other hind leg (the right) and returns the seat nearly to the saddle only to be impelled upward again by the next thrust of the left hind leg. Sitting back in the saddle each time the right forefoot strikes the ground is known as posting on the right diagonal; whereas returning to the saddle when the left fore strikes the ground is known as posting on the left diagnal.

Some competent and experienced equitation instructors[3] report that they prefer to teach posting the correct diagonal as follows:

1. Watch the horse's shoulder and knee.

2. Rise in the saddle as the shoulder and knee of the outside foreleg come forward. The rider will then be posting to the outside foreleg or the one nearest the rail.

To change diagonals, the rider should learn to sit 1, 3, or 5 beats of the trot—preferably 1 beat; to sit even beats puts the rider back where he was.

The rider should frequently alternate the diagonals used in posting as this makes for greater ease on the horse. When riding in a ring, the rider should post on the outside diagonal so that the work of the hindquarters will be equalized. For correct posting, the stirrups should be sufficiently short to permit the rider to carry most of the weight on the ball of the foot. Only a small portion of the weight should be carried on the inside of the thighs and knees. Correct posting is one of the most difficult phases of riding.

CANTER (LOPE)

The canter is a slow, restrained gallop. In the show-ring or on the bridle path, this gait is started from the walk rather than from the trot, although some horsemen—especially army personnel—recommend that the canter be demanded from the trot.

The horse is made to canter (1) by drawing his head up and his nose in with the reins, and with the nose held slightly to the opposite direction of the desired lead (thus, the nose should be slightly to the left for a right lead), (2) by shifting the weight of the rider slightly to the front and to the side of the desired lead, and (3) by applying the legs in such a manner as to urge the horse to go forward. When cantering, the rider should stay with the saddle and keep the knees and calves of the legs close to the horse. When cantering in a circular ring, the horse should "lead" or step out with the right forefoot when traveling to the right and with the left forefoot when traveling to the left. A well-trained animal should be capable of and willing

to take either lead upon command. Moreover, to avoid tiring the animal, the lead should be shifted at intervals.

The lope is the western adaptation of a very slow canter. It is a smooth, slow gait in which the head is carried low.

ADDITIONAL GAITS

In addition to the 3 natural gaits (walk, trot, and canter) 5-gaited horses are expected to take one of the slow gaits—running walk, fox-trot, or stepping pace (the stepping pace is the preferred slow gait in the show-ring)—and the rack. The amateur should not attempt to ride the added gaits until the 3 basic gaits have been mastered.

SOME RULES OF GOOD HORSEMANSHIP

Good riders observe the following rules:

1. Approach a horse from his left. Never walk or stand behind a horse unannounced; let him know that you are there by speaking to and placing your hand on him. Otherwise, you may get kicked.

2. Pet a horse by first placing your hand on his shoulder or neck. Do not dab at the end of his nose.

3. Grasp the reins close to the bit on the left side when leading a horse.

4. Walk the horse to and from the stable; this prevents him from running home and from refusing to leave the stable.

5. See that the saddle blanket, numnah, pad, or corona is clean and free from dried sweat, hair, caked dirt, or any rough places—any of which will cause a sore back.

6. Check the saddle and bridle (or hackamore) before mounting. The saddle should fit and be placed just back of the withers; it should not bear down on or rub the withers, nor should it be placed too far back. The girth should be fastened snugly and should not be too close to the forelegs. Be sure that the bridle (or hackamore) fits comfortably and that the curb chain or strap is flat in the chin groove and fastened correctly.

7. Mount and dismount from the left side. Make the horse stand until the rider is properly seated in the saddle or has dismounted.

8. Assume the correct seat for the style of riding intended.

9. Retain the proper tension on the reins; avoid either tight or dangling reins.

10. Keep the hands and voice quiet when handling your horse. Avoid "clacking" to the horse, loud laughing or screaming (never scream—no matter how excited or frightened you may be; it will only make matters worse), and slapping him with the ends of the reins; such things are unnecessary and in poor taste.

---

[3]This is the system used by Mrs. Claud H. Drew, Columbia, Mo., and Mrs. Fern P. Bittner, Lindenwood College, St. Charles, Mo.—noted equestriennes, instructors, and judges—who very kindly reviewed this book.

11. Warm up the horse gradually; walk him first, then jog him slowly.

12. Keep to the right side of the road except when passing, and never allow your horse to wander all over the road. Give right-of-way courteously.

13. Walk the horse across bridges, through underpasses, and over pavements and slippery roads.

14. Slow down when making a sharp turn.

15. Walk the horse when going up or down hill; running may injure his legs and wind. Do not race horses; when so handled, they form bad habits and may get out of control.

16. Keep the horse moving when a car passes. If you stop, he may act up or back into the passing vehicle.

17. Anticipate such distractions as cars, stones, paper, trees, bridges, noises, dogs, children, etc.; in other words, think ahead of your horse.

18. Vary the gaits; and do not force the horse to take a rapid gait—canter, rack, or trot—for more than a half mile at a time without allowing a breathing spell in the interim.

19. Keep the horse under control at all times. If you are riding a runaway horse, try to stop him by sawing the bit back and forth in his mouth so as to break (a) his hold on the bit and (b) his stride; if in an open space, pull one rein hard enough to force him to circle.

20. Practice firmness with the horse and make him obey your wishes; he will have more respect for you. At the same time, love and understand him and he will reward you with the finest friendship and the grandest sport.

21. Never lose your temper and jerk a horse; a bad-tempered person never makes for a good-tempered horse.

22. Lean forward and loosen the reins if a horse rears. If you lean back and pull, the horse may fall over backwards.

23. Pull up the reins of a bucking horse; keep his head up.

24. Loosen the reins and urge the horse forward with your legs if he starts backing. Don't hold the reins too tightly when the horse is standing still.

25. Bring the horse in cool; walk him at the end of the ride.

26. Do not allow the horse to gorge on water when he is hot; water a warm horse slowly—just a few swallows at a time.

27. Do not turn the horse loose at the stall entrance. Walk into the stall with him, turn him around, so that he is facing the door, then depart. In a tie stall, make certain that the horse is tied securely with proper length rope.

28. Groom the horse thoroughly after each ride.

29. Wash the bit off carefully before it is hung in the tack room; remove hair and sweat from the saddle and girth before putting them on the rack; and wash all leather equipment with saddle soap at frequent intervals, thereby preserving the leather and keeping it pliable.

In addition to observing the above rules, good riders show consideration for other riders by observing the following additional practices—whether on the bridle path or on the trail, in the show-ring, or under other circumstances:

1. Keep abreast (about 5 feet apart), or keep a full horse's length behind other mounts, to prevent kicking.

2. Never dash up to another horse or group of horses at a gallop; to do so invites injury to yourself and the horses.

3. Never rush past riders who are proceeding at a slower gait; this may startle both horses and riders and cause an accident. Instead, approach slowly and pass cautiously on the left side.

4. Wait quietly when one person has to dismount, as when closing a gate. Do not run off and leave that person.

5. Never race after a mounted runaway horse—to do so will only make him run faster; instead, if possible, another rider should circle and come up in front of him. In case a rider is thrown, stop the other horses and keep quiet; generally the loose horse will return to the group where he may be caught.

6. Do not trespass on private property.

7. Leave gates the way you found them; otherwise, livestock may get out.

HOW TO CLEAN AND CARE FOR TACK

As used herein, tack, gear, and equipment embrace all articles used on, or attached to, riding and driving horses.

Good tack, gear, and equipment are expensive; hence, they merit good care. If properly cared for, they will last for years.

Ideally, each article should be cleaned thoroughly every time it is used on the horse. However, the owner and/or caretaker of pleasure horses may not be able to devote this amount of time. For the busy person, therefore, it is recommended that the vital parts be cleaned following each use—that the bottom of the saddle and the inside of the bridle be cleaned, that the bit be washed, and that the pad or blanket (if used) be brushed after drying out and before reusing. Then a thorough cleaning should be administered to all tack and equipment once each week.

The tack, gear, and equipment used on race and show horses, where maximum performance is all-important, should be thoroughly cleaned after each usage.

The general principles presented in the accompanying discussion also apply to the equipment used on race or show horses, with the following changes:

Do not use soap (or cream) on leather boots used on horses; it tends to deteriorate the stitching and catch a film of dirt. Instead, brush (preferably with a circular brush) to eliminate the sweat, dirt, and grime; wipe dry with a cloth; rub in petroleum jelly or liquid preservative; and, before using, dust with talcum powder or cornstarch, either of which will absorb moisture and smooth out minor rough or chafing spots.

Fig. 17-40. Cleaning the saddle. (Courtesy, *Western Horseman*, Colorado Springs, Colo.)

Why Clean

Good tack is expensive. Proper cleaning will do the following:

1. Extend the life of leather and metal.
2. Impart softness and pliability to leather.
3. Make for comfort to the horse. It will lessen saddle and harness sores from the use of dirty, crusted, and stiff leather; and avoid irritation and infection from a rusty, moldy, and dirty bit.

4. Assure that minor tack defects will be noticed and repaired promptly, before they become serious.
5. Protect the user, by minimizing the breaking of a rein or line, girth, girth straps, stirrup leathers, or other vital parts.
6. Impart pride and pleasure in the ownership and use of equipment. Your equipment, your horse, and you will look smart and feel smart.

Cleaning Equipment

The following items of cleaning equipment are commonly used:

1. A saddle rack on which to rest the saddle when it's being cleaned. Preferably, the rack should be designed so that it will also hold the saddle upside down, to facilitate cleaning the underside as well as the top.
2. A bridle rack, peg, or hook on which to hang the bridle for cleaning.
3. A harness rack for cleaning (if you have harness).
4. A bucket for warm water.
5. Three sponges, preferably (although one sponge will suffice if rinsed properly):

    a. One for washing—for cleaning off sweat, dirt, mud, etc.

    b. The second for applying leather preservative or glycerine soap.

    c. The third for occasional application of neatsfoot or other similar oil.

6. A chamois cloth for drying off leather.
7. Cheesecloth (about a yard) for applying metal polish.
8. A flannel rag for polishing metal.

Cleaning Materials

The usual cleaning materials are:

1. Saddle soap, or a bar of castile soap, for cleaning.
2. A leather preservative, or bar of glycerine soap, for finishing.
3. Neatsfoot oil.
4. Metal polish.
5. Petroleum jelly.

Order of Cleaning

To assure that all tack and all parts are cleaned (that none is overlooked), it is important that some logical, practical, and regular order be followed, automatically and routinely. Any order that accomplishes this purpose will be satisfactory.

The following is suggested for articles used in riding, and is perhaps most common:

1. Clean the saddle:

   a. Remove and clean girth.
   b. Clean underside of saddle.
   c. Get topside of saddle.
   d. Clean nearside (left).
   e. Clean offside (right).

2. Clean the bridle.
3. Clean the martingale, etc. if used.
4. If a saddle pad or blanket is used, brush it after it has dried.

A similar procedure should be used for articles used in driving.

How to Clean Tack

Once a week, wash with saddle soap or with castile soap as described and apply light neatsfoot oil or other leather dressing to all leather parts. Avoid excess oil, which will darken new leather and soil clothing.

SADDLE

1. Remove girth; clean as described under Point 3 below.
2. Turn saddle upside down.
3. Wash panel (that part of saddle in contact with horse's back) and gullet (underside center). With sponge wetted in warm water and wrung out, apply saddle soap to leather, and rub to work up a stiff lather to remove sweat and dirt before it hardens. The amount of dirt will determine how much soap, water, and elbow grease are necessary.
4. Wash rest of saddle in same manner, following the order given under "Order of Cleaning."
5. Dry entire saddle with chamois.
6. Take second sponge, dampen slightly, and apply leather preservative or glycerine soap without suds to all parts of saddle, following the order given.

BRIDLE

Wash the bit in warm water.

On the leather part, follow exactly the same procedure given for the saddle; wash thoroughly with warm water and saddle soap or castile soap, dry with chamois, and apply either preservative or glycerine soap with slightly damp sponge.

Using cheesecloth, apply metal polish to all metal parts; then polish with flannel. If the bridle is not to be used for a time, clean and dry the bit, and apply a light coat of petroleum jelly, to prevent pitting or rusting.

HARNESS

Follow the same procedure as given for saddle and bridle.

BLANKETS AND PADS

Hang up or spread out to dry; then brush off hair and dried sweat.

VEHICLES

Carts, sulkys, buckboards, and viceroys should be kept clean at all times. If vehicles are to be used in the show-ring, they should be washed a few hours ahead. Then apply metal polish to chrome, and wipe enamel wood finish with soft, dry flannel. Upholstering should be brushed, vacuumed, or washed—according to the material.

After Cleaning

After cleaning, tack should be handled as follows:

1. Store in a cool, dry place.
2. Hang the bridle on its rack, neatly and so that all parts drape naturally without bending.
3. Place the saddle on its rack.
4. Hang the harness on a rack.
5. Cover the saddle, bridle, and harness.
6. Protect vehicles from the weather, and use dust covers.

GROOMING AND WASHING

Proper grooming is necessary to (1) make and keep the horse attractive, and (2) maintain good health and condition. Grooming cleans the hair, keeps the skin functioning naturally, lessens skin diseases and parasites, and improves the condition and fitness of the muscles.

Wild horses groomed themselves by rolling and taking dust baths. Domesticated horses will do the same thing when turned into a corral.

How to Groom a Horse

Grooming should be rapid and thorough, but not so rough or severe as to cause irritation, either to the horse's skin or temper.

Horses that are stabled or in small corrals should be groomed thoroughly at least once daily. Those that are worked or exercised should be groomed both before leaving the stable and immediately upon their return. Heated, wet, or sweating animals should be handled as follows:

1. Remove the equipment as fast as possible; wipe it off, and put it away.

2. Remove excess perspiration with a sweat scraper; then rub briskly with a grooming or drying cloth to dry the coat partially.

3. Blanket and walk the horse until cool.

4. Allow a couple of swallows of water every few minutes while cooling out.

The needed articles of grooming equipment, and instructions on how to use them, are given in Table 17-3.

TABLE 17-3
GROOMING EQUIPMENT AND HOW TO USE IT

Article	What It is: How to Use It	Used for	Grooming Procedure: How to Do It
Hoof pick	A metal pick for cleaning the feet.	To clean out the feet.	To assure that the horse will be groomed thoroughly and that no body parts will be missed, follow a definite order. This may differ according to individual preference, but the following procedure is most common: 1. *Clean out the feet*—Use the hoof pick. Work from the heel toward the toe. Clean throughly the depressions between the frog and the bars. Inspect for thrush and loose shoes.
Curry comb (rubber or metal)	Use gently and in small circles, rather than with pressure and in long strokes. Do not use the metal curry comb below the knees or hocks, about the head, or over bony predominences. Nor should it be used on horses that have been clipped recently, or that have a thin coat of hair.	To groom horses that have long thick coats. To remove caked mud. To loosen matted scurf and dirt in the hair. To clean the brush.	2. *Groom the body*—Hold the curry comb in the right hand and the brush in the left hand, and proceed as follows: a. Start with the left side. b. Follow this order: the neck, breast, withers, shoulders, foreleg down to the knee, back, side, belly, croup, and hind legs down to the hock. Then brush from the knee and hock down toward the hoofs. At frequent intervals, clean the dust and hair from the brush with the curry comb, and knock the curry comb against your heel or the back of the brush to free it from dirt.
Body brush	The body brush is the principal tool used for grooming.	To brush the entire body.	Curry gently, but brush vigorously. Brush the hair in the direction of its natural lay. Brush with care in the regions of the flanks, between the fore and hind legs, at the point of the elbows, and in the fetlocks. After grooming the left side, transfer the brush to the right hand and the curry comb to the left hand; then groom the right side in the same order as described above.
Dandy brush	The dandy brush is made of stiff fiber usually about 2 inches in length.	To remove light dirt from the skin. To brush the mane and tail.	3. *Brush the head; comb and brush the mane and tail*—Use the body brush on the head. Groom the mane and tail as follows: a. Brush downward, using either the body brush or the dandy brush. b. Clean the tail by: (1) Brushing upward, a few strands of hair at a time; or by (2) Picking or separating out a few hairs at a time by hand. (3) Occasionally, washing with warm water and soap.
Mane and tail comb	Use as directed in last column.	To comb out matted mane and tail.	
Sweat scraper	A metal or wood scraper for removing sweat or water.	To remove excess perspiration from heated, wet, and sweating animals.	

(Continued)

TABLE 17-3 (Continued)

Article	What It is: How to Use It	Used for	Grooming Procedure: How to Do It
Grooming cloth	The grooming cloth can be made from old toweling or blankets. It should be about 18 to 24 inches square.	To remove dirt and dust from the coat. To wipe out the eyes, ears, nostrils, lips and dock. To give the coat a final sheen or polish. To dry or ruffle the coat before brushing.	4. *Wipe with the grooming cloth*—Use the grooming cloth to: a. Wipe about the ears, face, eyes, nostril, lips, sheath, and dock, and b. Give a final polish to the coat. 5. *Check the grooming*—Pass the fingertips against the natural lay of the hair. If the coat and skin are not clean, the fingers will be dirtied and gray lines will show on the coat where the fingers passed. Also inspect the ears, face, eyes, nostrils, lip, sheath, and dock. 6. *Wash and disinfect grooming equipment*—Wash with soap and warm water often enough to keep clean. Disinfect as necessary as precaution against the spread of diseases.

How to Clip and Shear

In addition to routine grooming, horses should be sharpened up by shearing and clipping at such intervals as necessary.

Show-ring custom decrees certain breed differences in "haircuts" and "hairdos." These are illustrated in Fig. 17-41. (See opposite page.)

1. *Protect inside of ears*—Place a wad of cotton in the ears, to cut down on noise from clippers and prevent hair from falling into ears.

2. *Clip long hairs*—Remove long hairs from about the head, the inside of the ears, on the jaw, and around the fetlocks.

How to Wash (Shampoo) a Horse

Following strenuous exercise, the horse should receive a welcome and refreshing bath. Washing will make him look better and feel better. Horses like to be clean.

Shampooing (1) cleans the animal—it removes the dirt, stains, and sweat that cannot be removed by grooming; (2) makes for a fine hair coat with a good sheen; and (3) keeps the skin smooth and mellow.

Formerly, there was strong prejudice against washing horses, perhaps stemming from the use of old-fashioned, harsh detergents and strong soaps, followed by poor rinsing. But "baths" are good for horses, just as they are good for people; and horses like to be shampooed.

Shampoo the horse as frequently as necessary, as determined by soiling, work, and weather conditions. For example, always wash him following use on a sloppy, muddy ring, trail, or track—when he comes back covered with mud from head to tail; or after using him when it's hot and muggy, and he's all lathered up with sweat.

In preparation for shampooing, (1) groom the horse carefully, (2) secure the animal for washing either by having someone hold him by the shank or by tying, and (3) have shampoo concentrate, warm water, buckets, and sponges available.

Step 1—Wet the animal thoroughly all over with water alone. For this purpose, fill one bucket with warm water (and refill it as necessary), then apply the water to the horse by means of a large sponge which may be dipped into the bucket as fast and frequently as desired.

To assure that the horse will be washed thoroughly and that no body parts will be missed, follow a definite order. This may differ somewhat according to individual preference, but the following procedure is most common: Start with the head, wetting between the ears and on the foretop (but do not get water in the ears; either hold them down or shut them off with the hand as the head is washed), over the face and cheeks, and around the eyes, muzzle and nostrils.

Next, proceed to the left side. While carrying the bucket in your left hand and holding the sponge in your right hand, with long strokes wet the neck, withers, shoulder, back, side, and croup. Return to the front, and with sponge in left hand, wash the chest. Return the sponge to the right hand and wash under the elbow and down the foreleg. Then, take the sponge in the left hand, set the bucket down as near as possible, and sponge the belly thoroughly. Hold onto the hind leg on the outside above the hock (this precaution will keep a restive horse from pawing, kicking, or stepping on your foot) while sponging the sheath (of stallions and geldings) and the inside of the hind leg down to the hoof.

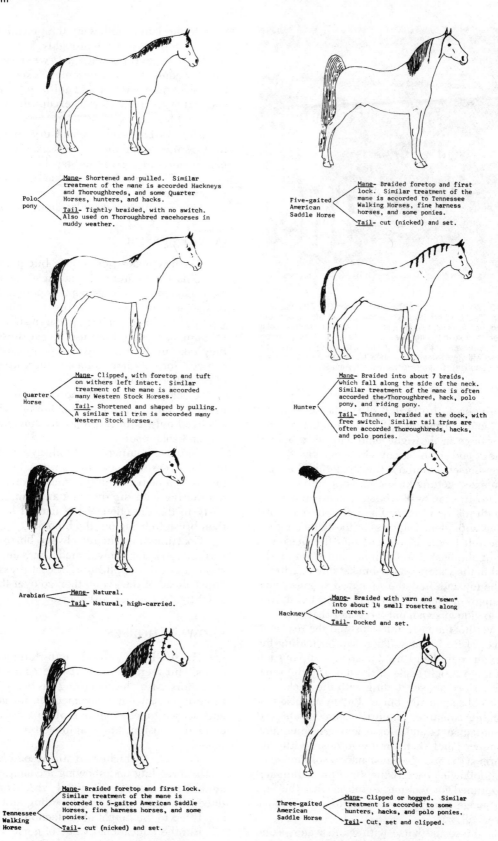

Mane- Shortened and pulled. Similar treatment of the mane is accorded Hackneys and Thoroughbreds, and some Quarter Horses, hunters, and hacks.

Tail- Tightly braided, with no switch. Also used on Thoroughbred racehorses in muddy weather.

Polo pony

Mane- Braided foretop and first lock. Similar treatment of the mane is accorded to Tennessee Walking Horses, fine harness horses, and some ponies.

Tail- cut (nicked) and set.

Five-gaited American Saddle Horse

Mane- Clipped, with foretop and tuft on withers left intact. Similar treatment of the mane is accorded many Western Stock Horses.

Tail- Shortened and shaped by pulling. A similar tail trim is accorded many Western Stock Horses.

Quarter Horse

Mane- Braided into about 7 braids, which fall along the side of the neck. Similar treatment of the mane is often accorded the Thoroughbred, hack, polo pony, and riding pony.

Tail- Thinned, braided at the dock, with free switch. Similar tail trims are often accorded Thoroughbreds, hacks, and polo ponies.

Hunter

Mane- Natural.

Tail- Natural, high-carried.

Arabian

Mane- Braided with yarn and "sewn" into about 14 small rosettes along the crest.

Tail- Docked and set.

Hackney

Mane- Braided foretop and first lock. Similar treatment of the mane is accorded to 5-gaited American Saddle Horses, fine harness horses, and some ponies.

Tail- cut (nicked) and set.

Tennessee Walking Horse

Mane- Clipped or hogged. Similar treatment is accorded to some hunters, hacks, and polo ponies.

Tail- Cut, set and clipped.

Three-gaited American Saddle Horse

Fig. 17-41. Common haircuts and hairstyles for different breeds and uses of horses.

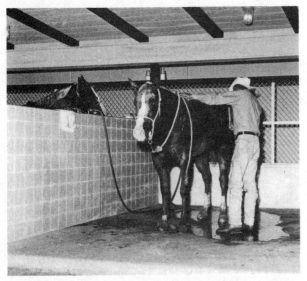

Fig. 17-42. Wash stall in Rex Cauble's Cutter Bill Championship Arena, Denton, Texas, where horses may be washed after a workout. When washing, use lukewarm water and a mild soap, rinse thoroughly with cool water, then keep the horse out of drafts while rubbing him dry with a clean cloth. Except for the mane and tail, it is usually not advisable to wash a horse within two weeks of a show because washing removes the natural oil. (Courtesy, *Quarter Horse Journal*, Amarillo, Tex.)

Station yourself to the left of the horse near the hind leg, facing to the rear. Set the bucket nearby. Take the sponge in the right hand and wash behind the hind legs and in the groove between the thighs. Since many horses fuss about this operation, be careful so as to avoid getting kicked or stepped on.

Hold up the tail with the left hand and wash under it with the right hand. The tail is best washed by sponging with plenty of water at the tailhead, then putting the full length of the tail into the bucket of water, lifting the bucket to the bone and sloshing the tail around in the water. Set the bucket down, grip the tail near the top and draw the squeezed sponge down the full length of the hair; then give the tail a snap from side to side to swish out the water that is left.

After wetting the near (left) side and the rear end, get a bucket of fresh water. Then, while holding the bucket in your right hand and the sponge in your left hand, wet the off (right) side of the horse in the same order as described above, starting with the neck.

Step 2—Shampoo the horse. Put in a bucket or other suitable container shampoo concentrate and water in the amounts and proportions recommended on the shampoo label, then stir it vigorously with your hand to form suds. Sponge the shampoo solution over the animal, following exactly the same procedure and order as outlined for wetting. Scrub against the hair with the sponge and your hands until a rich, thick lather covers all parts.

Step 3—Rinse the horse with warm water, using either a bucket and sponge or a hose (if the horse is

used to the latter), following the procedure and order given in Step 1. Rinse thoroughly.

Step 4—Scrape with a "sweat scraper" held snugly against the hair to remove excess water, using long sweeping strokes and following the procedure and order given in Step 1, except do not scrape the head and legs.

Step 5—Dry with a clean dry sponge or coarse towel, squeezing it out at intervals; following the procedure and order given in Step 1.

Step 6—Blanket the horse and walk him until he is completely dry.

Step 7—Apply a coat dressing if desired.

COAT DRESSING

"Trifles make perfection, but perfection is no trifle," is an old and well-known adage among horsemen. This philosophy prompts experienced caretakers to use a good coat dressing to achieve the all-important "bloom" or eye appeal in show, parade, and sale animals. Also, they use a coat dressing because they take pride in the everyday appearance of their charges, for how horses look is indicative of the kind of caretakers back of them.

A coat dressing will not take the place of the natural conditioning of the horse, which can be achieved only through proper feeding, health, grooming, and shampooing.

Proper grooming should always precede the use of coat dressing. Coat dressing is best applied by means of a heavy cloth (preferably terry cloth). Moisten the rag with the dressing and rub the coat vigorously in the direction of the natural lay of the hair; then brush to bring out the bloom.

Coat dressing should always be used following washing, and for show, parade, or sale. It is best to apply a heavier application of coat dressing 12 to 24 hours ahead of the event, then go over the horse with a lightly dressed rag just ahead.

SHOWING HORSES

Horse shows provide entertainment for spectators, and recreation, sport, and competition for the exhibitors. Also, the show-ring has been, and will continue to be, an important medium for getting horses and people together in one place and at one time to compare, design, and engineer the most desirable models.

There is no higher artistic accomplishment than that of breeding and showing a champion horse—an animal representing an ideal which has been produced through intelligent breeding and then trained and fitted to the height of perfection.

But the educational value of horse shows has not been exploited. Many people who attend a horse

show for the first time are bewildered by the procedure and the many breeds and classes that they see. Others have never gone to a horse show because they feel that their lack of knowledge would prevent them from enjoying it. It is the author's fond hope that this book will result in more people enjoying more horse shows with informed appraisal.

Horse shows have increased in recent years, on all levels—local, state, and national. Also, they have grown in terms of quality and prize money.

In addition to spectator entertainment, horse shows stimulate improved breeding, for winning horses (and their relatives) bring good prices.

The American Horse Shows Association (A.H.S.A.) regulates the rules and schedules of all the big shows. Recognized shows include all regular shows, local shows, combined training events, and dressage competitions which are members of the A.H.S.A.

The successful showman knows the rules of the classes and follows the correct showing techniques. Broadly speaking, this calls for knowledge of both performance and breeding (in hand) divisions, as well as of the several classes within each division.

Showing in Hand (at Halter)

Breeding classes are discussed here. They are shown "in hand," which means the horses are exhibited wearing a halter, preferably, or a bridle. The halter should be clean, properly adjusted, and fitted with a fresh looking leather or rope lead. If the horse is shown wearing a bridle, the exhibitor should not jerk on the reins hard enough to injure the mouth.

Many horsemen lack knowledge of the correct showing technique for breeding classes, even though they may be quite professional in exhibiting in performance classes.

The following practices are recommended for showing in hand, or at halter:

1. Train the horse early.
2. Groom the horse thoroughly.
3. Dress neatly for the show.
4. Enter the ring promptly and in tandem when the class is called. Line up at the location indicated by the ringmaster or judge unless directed to continue around the ring in tandem.
5. Stand the horse squarely on all 4 feet with the forefeet on higher ground than the hind feet if possible. The standing position of the horse should vary according to the breed. For example, Arabians are not stretched, but American Saddlers are trained to stand with their front legs straight under them and their hindlegs stretched behind them. Other breeds generally stand in a slightly stretched position, somewhat intermediate between these 2 examples. When stand-

ing and facing the horse, hold the lead strap or rope in the left hand 10 to 12 inches from the halter ring. Try to make the horse keep his head up.

6. Unless the judge directs otherwise, the horse should first be shown at the walk and then at the trot. Move the horse as follows:

a. Reduce the length of the lead strap or rope by a series of "figure 8" folds or by coils held in the left hand. Hold the upper part of the lead strap or rope in the right hand and lead from the left side of the horse. If the horse is well-mannered, give him 2 to 3 feet of lead so he can keep his head, neck, and body in a straight line as he moves forward. But keep the lead taut so the horse is always under control. Do not look back.

Fig. 17-43. Correct method of leading when showing "in hand."

b. The exhibitor should keep the horse's head up and briskly move him forward in a straight line for 50 to 100 feet as directed.

c. At the end of the walk, turn to the right. That is, the exhibitor should turn the horse away from himself and walk around the horse. If the horse is turned toward the exhibitor, the horse is more likely to step on the exhibitor. Make the turn in as small a space as practical, and as effortless as possible. When showing at the trot, bring the horse to a walk and move him slightly in the direction of the exhibitor before turning.

d. The exhibitor should lift his knees a little higher than usual when he is showing in the ring.

e. Trail the horse with a whip if it is permitted and desired. Most light horses are given early training by trailing with the whip but usually they are shown without this aid. If a "trailer" is used, he should follow at a proper distance. The distance should not be so near he might get kicked but not so far he would be ineffective. The trailer should keep the animal moving in a straight line, avoid getting between the judge and

the horse, and always cross in front of the horse at the turn.

7. Walk the horse down about 50 feet and walk back; then trot down about 100 feet and trot back. To save time, the judge may direct that horses be walked down and trotted back, which is a proper procedure. After the horse has been walked and trotted, stand him promptly in front of the judge. After the judge has made a quick inspection, move to the location in the line indicated by the ringmaster or judge.

8. Keep the horse posed at all times; keep one eye on the judge and the other on the horse.

9. When the judge signals to change positions, the exhibitor should back the horse out of line, or if there is room, turn him to the rear of the line and approach the new position from behind.

10. Try to keep the horse from kicking when he is close to other horses.

11. Keep calm; a nervous showman creates an unfavorable impression.

12. Work in close partnership with the horse.

13. Be courteous and respect the rights of other exhibitors.

14. Do not stand between the judge and the horse.

15. Be a good sport; win without bragging and lose without complaining.

Showing in Performance Classes

Performance classes for horses are so numerous and varied that it is not practical to describe them here. Instead, the showman should refer to the official rule book of the American Horse Shows Association and to the rules printed in the programs of local horse shows.

COMBINED TRAINING (THREE-DAY EVENT)

Combined training, or three-day event, is the modern English term for what the French have always known as "concours complet"—the complete test. It is perhaps the most demanding and rewarding of any equestrian activity. In order to do well, a horse must combine speed, stamina, obedience, and considerable jumping ability; and the rider must be knowledgeable and expert in three distinct branches of horsemanship—dressage, cross-country riding, and show-jumping. The object of combined training is to test the all-around quality and versatility of the horse.

Through the centuries, the great horsemasters evolved systems of training and riding horses which were adopted in whole or in part by cavalrymen, who placed emphasis upon endurance.

In Sweden, a military three-day event was held at the cavalry school at Stronsholm in 1907; Belgium followed suit in 1910; and Switzerland held its first

Fig. 17-44. Jumper in performance class. (Courtesy, American Quarter Horse Assn., Amarillo, Tex.)

event in 1921. The growing international interest was partly responsible for the introduction, at the 1912 Olympic games, of equestrian events. All the competition at this time was still drawn from military sources. It was not until after World War II that civilian participation in three-day events began.

Combined training competitions are usually held over three days, though the various phases of the competition have been modified to produce one-day events.

In any combined training competition, there are the following three phases:

1. *Dressage*—This test is designed to show that the horse is educated, balanced, supple, and obedient. Although many of the movements included in the test form part of the schooling program of any horse, others set out to demand from the horse and rider a greater degree of schooling and a more polished performance than the average hunter, for example, would acquire.

2. *Speed and endurance test*—The second part of the competition in 3-day events, the speed and endurance test, consists of several phases. There are 2 on roads and tracks, with these separated by a steeplechase course. Finally, there is the greatest test of all—the cross-country phase, a gruelling course of some 30 obstacles spread over 4 to 5 miles of open country. The whole speed and endurance section of the competition will cover some 20 miles; the roads and tracks being taken at a brisk trot or easy canter, the steeplechase course at a good gallop, and the cross-country to be ridden at speed—allowing for the individual horse's ability over solid, and sometimes tricky, obstacles. Only bold, clever horses with con-

fidence in and obedience to their riders, and at the peak of fitness, can hope to compete successfully in the second day—and without undue exhaustion.

3. *Show-jumping*—The third day involves a show-jumping course designed as a final test of fitness for both horse and rider.

Any good hunter who is temperate enough to perform a dressage test and jump a course of artificial fences in addition to galloping across country tackling big fences at speed can succeed in combined training, provided he has sufficient quality and heart.

In all countries where horses and riding are featured, the demands of versatility in achievement of combined training are a particularly popular challenge. Each year, the sport is becoming more popular all over the world.

CAPARISONED HORSE WITH BOOTS IN REVERSE POSITION

In the funeral processions of both President Dwight (Ike) Eisenhower and President John (Jack) Kennedy there was a riderless horse, led by a man in uniform. The horse was properly saddled, but the stirrups held in reverse position a pair of polished cavalry boots with spurs. Also, a glittering saber was hanging to the right side of the saddle. The significance of this follows.

A riderless horse, decked out with the ornamental trappings described above, accompanies the bodies of general officers and former cavalry officers. Also, this consideration may be accorded to a U.S. President, as Commander-in-Chief.

The practice of having the caparisoned (or decked out) charger of the deceased military officer led in the funeral procession stems from an ancient custom surrounding the burial of warriors. The horse bore a saddle with the stirrups inverted and a sword through them to symbolize that the warrior had fallen and would ride no more. Also, the horse was sacrificed at the time, because it was believed that the equine spirit would find his master in the hereafter; otherwise, the departed warrior would have to walk. Horses are no longer sacrificed. But a riderless horse, with the boots and spurs reversed, is still led in the funeral procession to symbolize that the warrior has fallen.

SELECTED REFERENCES

Title of Publication	Author(s)	Publisher
Bit by Bit	D. Tuke	J. A. Allen & Co. Ltd., London, England, 1965
Breeding and Raising Horses, Ag. Hdbk. No. 394	M. E. Ensminger	Agricultural Research Service, USDA, Washington, D.C., 1972
Carts and Wagons	J. Vince	Spurbooks Ltd., Buckinghamshire, England, 1975
Cavalletti	R. Klimke, trans. by D. M. Goodall	J. A. Allen & Co. Ltd., London, England, 1973
Elegant Carriage, The	M. Watney	J. A. Allen & Co. Ltd., London, England, 1969
English Pleasure Carriages	W. B. Adams	Adams & Dart, Bath, Somerset, England, 1971
First Horse	R. Hapgood	Chronicle Books, San Francisco, Calif., 1972
Grooming Horses	R. W. Collins	*The Blood Horse,* Lexington, Ky., 1959; reprinted under special arrangement by *The Thoroughbred Record,* Lexington, Ky., 1971
Grooming Your Horse	N. Haley	A. S. Barnes & Co., Inc., Cranbury, N.J., 1974
Guide to American Horse Shows, A	D. A. Spector	Arco Publishing Co., Inc., New York, N.Y., 1973
Horse, The	J. M. Kays	A. S. Barnes & Co., Inc., Cranbury, N.J., 1969
Horse, The	P. D. Rossdale	The California Thoroughbred Breeders Association, Arcadia, Calif., 1972

(continued)

Title of Publication	Author(s)	Publisher
Horse Psychology	M. Williams	A. S. Barnes & Co., Inc., Cranbury, N.J., 1969
Horse Show, At the	M. C. Self	Arco Publishing Co., Inc., New York, N.Y., 1973
Horse Shows	A. N. Phillips	The Interstate Printers & Publishers, Inc., Danville, Ill., 1956
Horsemanship	A. W. Jasper	Boy Scouts of America, New Brunswick, N.J., 1963
Horsemanship and Horse Care, Ag. Info. Bull. No. 353	M. E. Ensminger	Agricultural Research Service, USDA, Washington, D.C., 1972
Horsemanship and Horsemastership	Ed. by G. Wright	Doubleday & Company, Inc., Garden City, N.Y., 1962
Horses	M. C. Self	A. S. Barnes & Co., Inc., Cranbury, N.J., 1953
Horses and Horsemanship	L. E. Walraven	A. S. Barnes & Co., Inc., Cranbury, N.J., 1970
Horses, Horses, Horses	M. E. Ensminger	M. E. Ensminger, Clovis, Calif., 1969
Horses, Horses, Horses	S. Wilding	Van Nostrand Reinhold Company, New York, N.Y., 1970
Horses: Their Selection, Care and Handling	M. C. Self	A. S. Barnes & Co., Inc., Cranbury, N.J., 1943
Leg at Each Corner, A	N. Thelwell	E. P. Dutton & Co., Inc., New York, N.Y., 1963
Light Horse Management	R. C. Barbalace	Caballus Publishers, Fort Collins, Colo., 1974
Light Horses, Farmers' Bull. No. 2127	M. E. Ensminger	Agricultural Research Service, USDA, Washington, D.C., 1965
Manual of Horsemanship of The British Horse Society and The Pony Club		The British Horse Society, Warwickshire, England, 1968
Practical Dressage for Amateur Trainers	J. M. Ladendorf	A. S. Barnes & Co., Inc., Cranbury, N.J., 1973
Rule Book		The American Horse Shows Association, Inc., New York, N.Y., annual
Saddle Up!	C. E. Ball	J. B. Lippincott Co., Philadelphia, Penn., 1970
Saddlery	E. H. Edwards	A. S. Barnes & Co., Inc., Cranbury, N.J., 1963
Selecting, Fitting and Showing Horses	J. E. Nordby H. E. Lattig	The Interstate Printers & Publishers, Inc., Danville, Ill., 1963
Shetland Pony, The	L. F. Bedell	Iowa State University Press, Ames, Iowa, 1959
Shetland Pony, The	M. C. Cox	A & C Black Ltd., London, England, 1965
Spanish Riding School, The	H. Handler	McGraw-Hill Book Company, Ltd., Maidenhead, England, 1972
Stagecoaches & Carriages	I. Sparkes	Spurbooks Ltd., Buckinghamshire, England, 1975
Western Equitation, Horsemanship and Showmanship	D. Stewart	Vantage Press, Inc., New York, N.Y., 1973
Western Horse, The	J. A. Gorman	The Interstate Printers & Publishers, Inc., Danville, Ill., 1967

CHAPTER 18

MANAGEMENT

Contents

Fig. 18-1. The eye of the caretaker watches over the horse, for horses are prone to get hurt. Carefully wrapped bandages sometimes prevent a bumped shin or a cut ankle, or protect an old injury.

Good horsemen practice good management. To be sure, horse management practices vary from area to area, according to the size of the enterprise—whether one horse or several are involved—and between horsemen. In a general sort of way, however, the principles of good management are the same under all conditions.

SOME MANAGEMENT PRACTICES

Without attempting to cover all management practices, some facts relative to, and methods of accomplishing, common horse management practices follow.

Marking or Identifying Horses

The method of marking or identifying animals varies according to the class of animals and the objectives sought. Thus, some methods of marking are well adapted to one class of animals but not to another; ear notches, for example, are commonly used for identify-

ing swine, but should not be used for horses. On the western range, marking by branding is primarily a method of establishing ownership.

Until the 16th Century (and even later in some parts of England), the ears of horses were cut in various ways as a means of identification. For example, a "bitted" ear was bitten (a piece was cut out) from the inner edge, and a cropped ear was cut straight across halfway down the ear. Eventually, cropped ears became fashionable, much as they are with certain breeds of dogs today, with the result that the practice persisted into the 18th Century. This explains why early paintings of horses frequently showed the animals with tiny ears, scarcely 2 inches long.

With a purebred herd of horses, marking is a means of ascertaining ancestry or pedigree. This is particularly important where one person only knows the individuals in a given herd, and, suddenly and without warning, that person is no longer available. Under such circumstances, many a valuable registered horse has been sold as a grade, simply because positive identity could not be established.

In racehorses, an infallible means of identification is necessary in order to prevent "ringers." A *ringer is a horse that is passed off under false identity, with the idea of entering him in a race below his class where he is almost certain to win.* In the early 1920s the most common camouflage for a ringer was a coat of paint—hence the terms "dark horse" and "horse of another color." Formerly, the ringer's nemesis was rain; today, it is the lip tattoo system, which must accompany horses of most breeds to every major racing meet.

One of the duties of a steward, through his horse identification assistant, is that of assuring that each starter in a race is actually the horse named in the entry. This is necessary because only a relatively small percentage of the more prominent racehorses are fondly recognized on sight by the public; the vast majority of racehorses are known only by names and past performances.

A lip tattoo method of identifying horses was developed by the old Army Remount Service (now extinct) at Pomona, California. The Thoroughbred Racing Protective Bureau (TRPB), Inc., perfected this method and utilizes it so that the member tracks of the Thoroughbred Racing Association (TRA) are able to guarantee to the public the identity of each and every horse running at their tracks. The system consists of tattoo branding, with forgery-proof dyes, The Jockey Club serial number (the registry number) under the upper lip of the horse, with a prefix letter added to denote the age of the horse (see Fig. 18-2). The process is both simple and painless. It is applied by expert crews of the TRPB to two-year-olds as they come to each TRA track.

Pinkerton's National Detective Agency, The Joc-

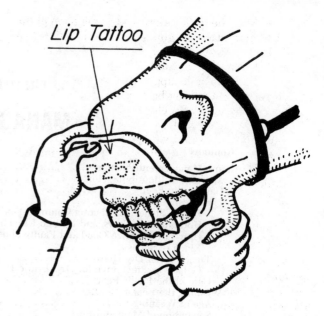

Fig. 18-2. A drawing showing the lip tattoo under the upper lip of a horse. The prefix letter denotes the age of the horse, and the number denotes The Jockey Club registry number. (Drawing by Prof. R. F. Johnson)

key Club, and others have also developed a method of identifying horses which corresponds to the human system of fingerprinting employed by the FBI and police departments throughout the world. A horse can be identified by its "chestnuts" or "night-eyes"; these consist of a horny growth on each of the four legs.[1] Studies reveal (1) that no two chestnuts are exactly alike, and (2) that from the yearling stage on, these chestnuts retain their distinctive sizes and shapes. The chestnuts are photographed, and then classified according to (1) size, and (2) distinctive pattern.

"Fingerprinting" horse chestnuts is both costly and complex. Also, except as a means of establishing herd ownership on range horses (where all animals in a specific herd are given the owner's registered brand), hot-iron hide brands are seldom used as a means of marking or identifying horses because they tend to damage the appearance of the animal and decrease its salability. However, the following two methods of individual identification are available for use by horse owners:

1. *The lip tattoo*—Lip tattoo equipment and ink similar to that used by the Thoroughbred Racing Protective Bureau is manufactured and sold commercially. The manufacturer's step-by-step instructions relative to the use of the Wilmot Tattoo Gun (distributed by Stone Mfg. & Supply Company, 1212 Kansas Ave., Kansas City, Missouri) read as follows:

---

[1]Chestnuts occur on the inside of each front leg above the knee and on the back legs below the hock. In rare instances, a horse lacks a chestnut on one or both hind limbs.

a. After the digits are placed in the head of the tattoo gun, place the gun head with the digits in a dish of antiseptic (such as Zephiran chloride, available at any drugstore).

b. Roll and hold upper lip back with fingers; do not place anything back of lip.

c. Wipe upper lip clean with cotton saturated with rubbing alcohol.

d. Shake gun to dry off excess antiseptic.

e. Apply tattoo gun, making sure gun and digits are square with lip. Hold gun rigidly and with sufficient pressure to withstand recoil action of gun.

f. Apply ink and rub into perforations with thumb. Use more ink if bleeding persists. Leave any excess ink on lip.

2. *Freeze marking (cold branding)*—This new method of identifying horses, known as freeze marking (cold branding), was developed by Dr. R. Keith Farrell, Washington State University. Called the Angle System, it is derived from the ancient Arabic numeral system. It utilizes the basic principle that straight lines are easy to make with crude instruments. It offers simplicity, preciseness, universal application, and good visual communication. Also, it lends itself to a computerized data retrieval system. Freeze marking is now used to identify horses in the United States (Arabians and Appaloosas), New Zealand, Sweden, and Egypt.

Called freeze marking to escape painful associations with the term "branding," the technique utilizes heavy copper stamps, or marking rods, chilled in either liquid nitrogen or dry ice, and 95 percent alcohol. The area to be marked is shaved and scrubbed with a 95 percent alcohol wetting solution to aid in conducting the intense cold and to withdraw body heat.

Placing the copper stamp against the animal's body for 10 to 20 seconds destroys pigment-producing cells (melanocytes) and produces a pigment-free skin area. Hairs growing back in this area will be white. Longer application times result in more balding, a condition necessary for producing legible marks on white or light-colored animals.

A freeze mark that produces white hair causes only minimal changes in the hide and does not seriously impair leather properties. Freeze marks that produce baldness cause some permanent scarring and hide damage. Severe freeze mark damage, however, is minimal compared to fire brand damage.

Freeze marking is more legible than fire branding. Marks are much more distinct, and last just as long. No open wound is produced, which eliminates disease and insect infestations, and freeze marking is relatively painless.

Because some horsemen, particularly those who

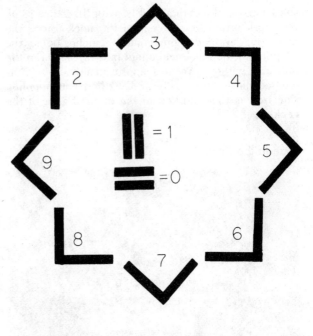

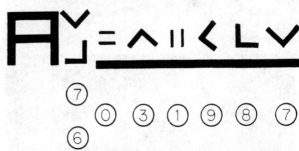

Above is the series of right angles developed by Dr. R. Keith Farrell to replace the present Arabic numerals. The number that each angle represents is written inside the angle.

Below is a freeze brand as it would actually appear under the mane of a horse. The encircled numbers do not appear in the brand; they are used in this illustration and caption merely to enhance readability. The first symbol, the capital A, denotes that the horse is a purebred Arabian. The stacked symbols in the second position indicate that the horse was born in 1976. The remaining symbols are the horse's registration number: 031987.

Fig. 18-3. Freeze marking.

Fig. 18-4. Cold (freeze) branded horses. Note numbers on their right shoulders. (Courtesy, Louisiana State University)

show horses, object to a visible mark (like Fig. 18-4), the mark is usually placed on the neck under the mane. It is applied approximately 2 inches below the eruption of the mane and about midway between the poll and withers. An area approximately 2″ × 7″ is clipped close to the skin and washed with alcohol. The iron is then applied to the clipped area of the neck.

Care of the Feet

Fig. 18-5. Peter Pan, a Shetland Pony, before and after foot trimming. *Top*: Hoofs turned grotesquely upward like wooden shoes—the results of three years' neglect while confined to a small corral. *Bottom*: Six months later, following trimming by master farrier, M. I. Rasmussen, New Mexico State University, Las Cruces, New Mexico. (Courtesy, Mr. Rasmussen)

The value of a horse lies chiefly in its ability to move; hence, good feet and legs are necessary. The Greeks alluded to this in the age-old axiom: "no foot, no horse."

Of course, nature didn't intend that the horse be used on hard surfaces or have a person on his back. When it is realized that he has been transplanted from his natural roving environment and soft, mother-earth footing to be used in carrying and drawing loads over hard, dry-surfaced topography by day and then sta-

bled on hard, dry floors at night, it is not surprising that foot troubles are commonplace. Thus, when man domesticated the horse, he assumed certain responsibilities for his care in an unnatural environment—including trimming, shoeing, and caring for his feet.

The important points in the care of a horse's feet are to keep them clean, prevent them from drying out, trim them so they retain proper shape and length, and shoe them correctly when shoes are needed.

Each day, the feet of horses that are shod, stabled, or used should be cleaned and inspected for loose shoes and thrush. Thrush is a disease of the foot, caused by a necrotic fungus, and characterized by a pungent odor. It causes a deterioration of tissues in the cleft of the frog or in the junction between the frog and bars. This disease produces lameness and, if not treated, can be serious.

Fig. 18-6. Correct way to pick up and examine the front foot.

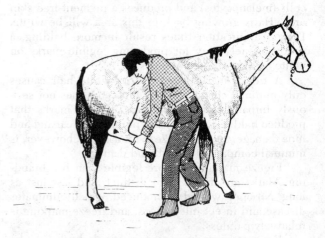

Fig. 18-7. Correct way to pick up the hind foot.

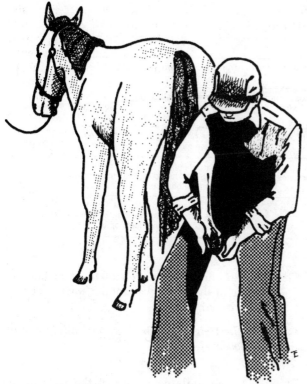

Fig. 18-8. Correct way to examine the hind foot.

HORSESHOEING

Horseshoeing is a time-honored profession. In the golden age of the horse, which extended from the Gay Nineties to the mechanization of American agriculture, every schoolboy knew and respected the village blacksmith who plied his trade "under the spreading chestnut tree."

It is not necessary that horse owners and managers be expert farriers. Yet, they should be knowledgeable relative to (1) the anatomy and nomenclature of the foot (see Figs. 3-4 and Table 3-1, Chapter 3), (2) what constitutes proper stance and motion, and how to correct some common faults through trimming, (3)

the basic horseshoeing tools and how to use them, (4) how to recognize good and faulty shoeing, (5) kinds of shoes, and (6) the treatment of dry hoofs.

PROPER STANCE; CORRECTING COMMON FAULTS

Before trimming the feet or shoeing a horse, it is important to know what constitutes both proper and faulty conformation. This is pictured in Chapter 4, Figs. 4-16 and 4-17.

Fig. 18-9 shows the proper posture of the hoof and incorrect postures caused by hoofs grown too long in either toe or heel. The slope is considered normal when the toe of the hoof and the pastern have the same direction. This angle should always be kept in mind and changed only as a corrective measure. If it should become necessary to correct uneven wear of the hoof, the correction should be made gradually over a period of several trimmings.

Prior to the trimming of the feet, the horse should be inspected while standing squarely on a level area—preferably a hard surface. Then it should be seen in action, both at the walk and the trot.

The hoofs should be trimmed every month or six weeks, whether the animal is shod or not. If shoes are left on too long, the hoofs grow out of proportion. This may throw the horse off balance and place extra stress upon the tendons. Hence, the hoofs should always be kept at the proper length and the correct posture. They should be trimmed near the level of the sole; otherwise, they will split off if the horse remains unshod. The frog should be trimmed carefully, with only ragged edges removed that allow the filth to accumulate in the crevices, and the sole should be trimmed sparingly, if at all. The wall of the hoof should never be rasped.

Table 18-1 shows the common faults and how to correct them through proper trimming. (See page 410.)

HORSESHOEING TOOLS, AND HOW TO USE THEM

Horses are shod to protect the foot from breaking

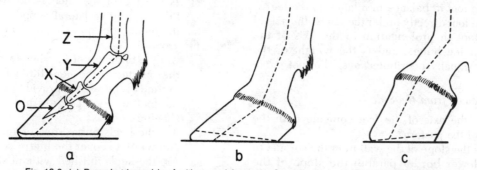

a   b   c

Fig. 18-9. (a) Properly trimmed hoof with normal foot axis: O—coffin bone; X—short pastern bone; Y—long pastern bone; Z—cannon bone. (b) Toe too long, which breaks the foot axis backward. Horizontal dotted line shows how hoof should be trimmed to restore normal posture. (c) Heel too long, which breaks the foot axis forward. Horizontal dotted line shows how trimming will restore the correct posture.

TABLE 18-1
COMMON FOOT FAULTS, AND HOW TO CORRECT THEM

Fault	How It Looks	How to Trim
Splayfoot	Front toes turned out, heels turned in.	Trim the outer half of the foot.
Pigeon-toed	Front toes turned in, heels turned out—the opposite of splayfoot.	Trim the inner half of foot more heavily; leave the outer half relatively long.
Quarter crack	Vertical crack on side of hoof.	Keep the hoof moist, shorten the toes, and use a corrective shoe.
Cocked ankles	Standing bent forward on fetlocks—most frequently the hind ones.	Lower the heels to correct. However, raising the heels makes for more immediate horse comfort.
Contracted heels	Close at the heels.	Lower the heels and allow the frog to carry more of the weight, which tends to spread the heels apart.

and wearing away faster than the growth of the horn. Also, shoes may be used to change gaits and action, to correct faulty hoof structure or growth, and to protect the hoof itself from such conditions as corns, contraction, or cracks. When properly done, shoes should interfere as little as possible with the physiological functions of the different structures of the foot or with the gaits of the horse.

Just as do-it-yourself woodworkers, mechanics, and whatnot usually have a shop and some tools, so the horseman should have certain basic horseshoeing tools, and know how to use them. Table 18-2 may be used as a guide in selecting tools.

HOW TO RECOGNIZE GOOD AND FAULTY SHOEING

The following checklist may be used as a means by which to evaluate a shoeing job, whether plied by the caretaker or owner, or by a professional farrier:

1. *As Viewed from the Front—*

Yes No

☐ ☐ Are the front feet the same size, the toes the same length, and the heels the same height?
☐ ☐ Is the foot in balance in relation to the leg?
☐ ☐ Is the foot directly under the leg, is the axis of the foot in prolongation to the axis of the upper leg bones, and is the weight of the body equally distributed over the foot structure?

2. *As Viewed from the Side—*

☐ ☐ Does the axis of the foot coincide with the axis of the pastern?
☐ ☐ Does the slope of the wall from the coronet to the lower border parallel the slope of the pastern?
☐ ☐ Has the lower outer border of the wall been rasped?

☐ ☐ Does the conformation of the foot and the type of shoe used warrant the amount of rasping done?

3. *As the Height and Strength of Nailing Are Inspected Closely—*

Yes No

☐ ☐ Do the nails come out of the wall at the proper height and in sound horn?
☐ ☐ Are the nails driven to a greater height in the wall than necessary?
☐ ☐ Is the size of the nail used best suited for the size and condition of the foot and the weight of the shoe?
☐ ☐ Are the clinches of sufficient thickness where the nail comes out of the wall to ensure strength?
☐ ☐ Are the clinches smooth and not projecting above the surface of the wall?

4. *As the Outline and Size of the Shoe Are Scrutinized—*

Yes No

☐ ☐ Is the toe of the shoe fitted with sufficient fullness to give lateral support to the foot at the moment of breaking over and leaving the ground?
☐ ☐ Are the branches of the shoe from the bend of the quarter to the heel fitted fuller than the outline of the wall to provide for expansion of the foot and normal growth of horn between shoeing periods?
☐ ☐ Are the heels of the shoe of sufficient length and width to cover the buttresses?
☐ ☐ Are the heels finished without sharp edges?
☐ ☐ Does the shoe rest evenly on the bearing surface of the hoof, covering the lower border of the wall, white line, and buttresses?

□ □ Is the shoe concaved so that it does not rest upon the horny sole?

□ □ Are the nail heads properly seated?

□ □ Is the shoe the correct size for the foot?

□ □ Will the weight of the shoe provide reasonable wear and protection to the foot?

□ □ Have the ragged particles of the horny frog been removed?

KINDS OF SHOES

A number of factors should be considered when selecting the shoes for a given horse; among them:

1. *The proper size*—The shoe should fit the hoof, rather than any attempt being made to trim the hoof to fit the shoe. (Continued next page)

TABLE 18-2

HORSESHOEING TOOLS AND THEIR USE

Tools	Use
Anvil	As a block to shape shoes, and as the farrier's work bench.
Forge	To heat steel or shoes in preparation for shaping them for the horse being shod.
Vise	To finish shoes, and to hold metal.
Knife	To remove dirt and trim excess frog and sole from the foot. The hook on the end is used to trim the frog and clean the crevice between the bar and frog.
Nippers or Parers	To trim the wall of the hoof and other parts that are too hard for the knife. There is hardly any limit to the sizes and descriptions of these items; some are one-sided, others are two-sided.
Hoof Level	To determine the angle of the hoof relative to the ground surface.
Clinch Cutter	To cut clinches prior to pulling shoes.
Rasp	To level the foot after trimming; one side is coarse, and the other side fine.
Driving Hammer	To drive nails into hoof.
Hardy	As a wedge in the anvil hole, in cutting steel of the desired length and in cutting off shoes.
Hammers	To shape shoes. Various kinds of hammers may be used.
Tongs	To hold hot metal.
Nails	Assorted sizes of nails are available for different types of horseshoes.
Apron	To protect the horseshoer from sparks, from cuts that might otherwise be inflicted by slips of the knife or rasp, and from possible nail injury of nervous horses.

Shoes come in sizes. The old and new sizes follow:

Old Standard Shoe	New Multiproduct Shoe
(Size)	(Size)
00	3
0	4
1	5
Half size	6
2	7
Half size	8
3	9

2. *Front vs hind shoes*—Front shoes are more nearly circular and wider at the heels than hind shoes.

3. *The individual horse*—His weight, the shape and texture of his hoof, and the set of his legs should be considered.

4. *The use to which the horse is put, and the kind of ground*—A plain shoe or a rim shoe is satisfactory for most horses used for pleasure, cutting, roping, barrel racing, polo, and jumping; whereas racing plates, to aid in gripping the track, are needed on running horses. Also there are many corrective shoes, a few of which are listed in Table 18-3.

TABLE 18-3

SOME CORRECTIVE SHOES, AND THEIR USE

Kind of Corrective Shoe	Purpose or Use
Bar shoe	To apply pressure to the frog of the foot, or to relieve pressure on any part of it.
Rocker toe shoe	For use on horses that stumble, that forge, or that have ringbone or sidebones.
Squared toe shoe with trailer	For cow-hocked horses.
Lateral extension toed shoe	For horses that either toe out or toe in.

Shoes may be either handmade or ready-made (factory-made). The latter are becoming increasingly popular because they (1) require a minimum of work, and (2) are ideal for the do-it-yourselfer. Both steel and aluminum shoes are available. Fig. 18-10 shows four common types of horseshoes.

TREATMENT OF DRY HOOFS

In the wild state, horses roved over the prairies and moistened their hoofs frequently as they drank deep from the streams and lakes. But man changed all this. Today, the vast majority of horses spend much of their time in a dry stall or corral; stand dry footed as they water from a bucket, fountain, or tank; are shod; and are exercised on a hard, dry surface—conditions which make for dry, brittle hoofs. With the domestication of the horse, therefore, man entered into an unwritten contract with him—to replace nature's way of keeping the hoofs moist.

A ready-made shoe is suited for most riding and driving horses.

Ready-Made Shoe

A self-cleaning rim shoe is suited for horses used for riding, cutting, roping, barrel racing, polo, and jumping.

Rim Shoe

A hot shoe is one that must be heated and shaped prior to being used.

Hot Shoe

A racing plate meets the exacting needs of racehorses—it is light in weight, and it grips the track.

Racing Plate

Fig. 18-10. Common types of horseshoes.

When hoofs become dry and brittle, they sometimes split and cause lameness. The frogs lose their elasticity and are no longer effective shock absorbers. If the dryness is prolonged, the frogs shrink and the heels contract.

Dry hoofs usually can be prevented by keeping the ground wet around the watering tank, attaching wet burlap sacks around the hoofs, or applying a hoof dressing.

A good hoof dressing will restore and maintain necessary flexibility and elasticity of the hoof. It will (1) penetrate the hoof structure readily, (2) allow the hoof to "breathe"; (3) regulate the absorption and evaporation of moisture; and (4) accentuate the natural luster of the hoof, without leaving a sticky residue or sealing off the hoof wall. When applied daily, a hoof dressing will provide added moisture which will penetrate the hoof and prevent evaporation of the moisture that is already within the hoof, thereby imparting suppleness (elasticity). Several satisfactory

commercial hoof dressings are on the market. Also, a good homemade product may be made as follows:

> 6 parts fish oil (cod liver oil)
> 1 part pine tar oil
> 1 part Creolin
> 2 parts glycerin

The above mix should be stirred well before using and applied daily. If fish oil is not available, raw linseed oil may be substituted.

When it comes to preventing dry hoofs, "an ounce of prevention is worth a pound of cure"—then some. Each day, the feet of shod horses that are confined to a stable (or corral) should be cleaned thoroughly, then treated with hoof dressing. By means of a brush or cloth, apply the hoof dressing to the coronet, the wall, and the bottom surface (including the frog), of freshly cleaned feet. Because most of the moisture within the hoof rises through the sole (like sap rises in a tree), be sure to apply plenty of hoof dressing to the bottom area.

The telltale symptoms of too dry feet are: hardness and drying of the horny frog, contracted heels, corns, brittle hoofs, and sometimes cracks and lameness. When any one of these conditions prevails, good nursing and first aid treatment are essential. The first step is to correct any errors in shoeing and trimming, and the second is to restore and maintain the normal moisture content of the horn. Treating the wall and bottom of the feet daily with hoof dressing will accomplish the latter.

Hoof dressing is not designed to take the place of proper trimming and shoeing by an experienced farrier; rather, it should go hand in hand with them.

Gelatin as Preventive for Dry, Brittle Hoofs

Although it is true that the major protein in the hoofs of horses is gelatin, the author is not aware of any experimental evidence that the feeding of gelatin as such will improve the structure, toughness, and moisture of the hoof.

Hoof tissue is synthesized in the body primarily from the amino acids contained in the bloodstream, and these can be derived from any good source of protein for horses, such as linseed meal and soybean meal. Of course, a deficiency of protein in the horse's ration would tend to produce poor hoofs, but this protein can be furnished from sources other than gelatin and the same results obtained.

From the standpoint of other tissues in the body, gelatin is a rather incomplete protein, notably deficient in the amino acids lysine and tryptophan. From an overall metabolism standpoint, therefore, gelatin would appear to be a poorer source of protein than the oilseed proteins—linseed, soybean, cottonseed, and peanut meal.

For the above reasons, before buying and feeding gelatin instead of one of the oilseed proteins, the horseman is admonished to see research data, conducted by a reputable independent research laboratory, in support of the "gelatin theory."

CARE OF THE FOAL'S FEET

Foals may become unsound of limb when the wear and tear is not equally distributed due to an unshapely hoof. On the other hand, faulty limbs may be helped or even corrected by regular and persistent trimming. Such practice also tends to educate the foal and make shoeing easier at maturity. If the foal is run on pasture, trimming of the feet may be necessary long before weaning time. A good practice is to check the feet regularly every month or six weeks and to trim a small amount each time if trimming is needed, rather than trim too much at any one time. Tendons should not receive undue strain by careless trimming of the feet. Usually, only the outer rim should be trimmed, though sometimes it is necessary to cut down the heel or frog to shorten the toes. The necessary trimming may be done with the rasp, farrier's knife, and nippers (using the rasp for the most part).

Before the feet are trimmed, the foal should be inspected first while standing squarely on a hard surface. Then it should be seen in action, both at the walk and the trot.

Weaning the Foal

Weaning of the foal is more a matter of preparation than of absolute separation from the dam. The simplicity with which it is accomplished depends very largely upon the thoroughness of the preparation.

AGE OF WEANING

Foals are usually weaned at 4 to 6 months of age, depending on conditions. When either the foal or the mare is not doing well, when the mare is being given heavy work, or when the dam has been rebred on the ninth day after foaling, it may be advisable to wean the foal at a comparatively early age. On the other hand, when both the mare and the foal seem to be doing well, when the mare is idle, when breeding has been delayed following foaling, or when it is desirable to develop the foal to the maximum, the weaning may very well be delayed until 6 months of age.

If by means of the creep or a separate grain box, the foal has become accustomed to the consumption of considerable grain and hay (about ¾ lb of grain per each 100 lb liveweight daily), weaning will result in

very little disturbance or setback. Likewise, if the ration of the dam has been decreased (lessened by ½) a few days before the separation, usually her udder will dry up with no difficulty.

SEPARATION OF MARE AND FOAL

When all preliminary precautions and preparations for weaning have been made, the separation should be accomplished. This should be complete and final with no opportunity for the foal to see, hear, or smell its dam again. Otherwise, all which has been gained up to this time will be lost, and it will be necessary to begin all over again. Perhaps the best arrangement is to shut the foal in the stall to which it has been accustomed and to move the mare away to new quarters, making certain that all obstructions have first been removed so that there is no possibility of injury to the foal while it is fretting over the separation.

After the weanlings have remained in the stable for a day or two and have quieted down, they should be turned out on pasture. Where a group of weanlings is involved, undue running and possible injury hazard may be minimized in this transition by the following procedure: First turn two or three of the least valuable animals out and let them tire themselves out, and then turn the rest of the weanlings out and they will do very little running.

With a great number of weanlings, it is advisable to separate the sexes, and even to place some of the more timid ones to themselves. In all cases, it is best not to run weanlings with older horses.

DRYING UP THE MARE

The following procedure for drying up mares is recommended:

1. Rub an oil preparation (such as camphorated oil or a mixture of lard and spirits of camphor) on the bag. Take the mare from the foal and place her on less lush pasture or grass hay.

2. Examine the udder and rub oil on it at intervals, but do not milk it out for 5 to 7 days. It will fill up and get tight, *but do not milk it out.* At the end of 5 to 7 days, when the bag is soft and flabby, milk out what little secretion remains (perhaps not more than a half a cup).

Castration

Regardless of age or time, the operation is best performed by an experienced veterinarian. A colt may be castrated when only a few days old, but most horsemen prefer to delay the operation until the animal is about one year of age. Although there is less

real danger to the animal and much less setback with early altering, the practice results in imperfect development of the foreparts. On the other hand, leaving the colt entire for a time will result in more muscular, bold features and better carriage of the foreparts. Therefore, weather and management conditions permitting, the time of altering should be determined by the development of the individual animal. Thus, underdeveloped colts may be left entire six months or even a year longer than overdeveloped ones. Breeders of Thoroughbred horses usually prefer to have the horses first race as an entire.

There is less danger of infection if colts are castrated in the spring of the year soon after they are turned out on a clean pasture. Naturally, this should be done sufficiently early so as to avoid hot weather and fly time.

Exercise

Regular exercise is essential to strong, sound feet and legs and to health.

Fig. 18-11. Correct method of longeing a horse, with a longeing cavesson and long web tape longe line in use.

Except during times of inclement weather and when being worked heavily, horses should be out in the open where they can romp and play on natural footing as much as possible. For this purpose, pastures are ideal, especially for young animals.

Where exercise on pastures is not feasible, mature animals should be exercised for an hour daily under saddle or hitched to a cart.

When handled carefully, the broodmare should be exercised within a day or two of foaling. Above all, when not receiving forced exercise or on idle days, she should not be confined to a stable or a small, dry lot.

Frequently, in light horses, bad feet exclude exercise on roads, and faulty tendons exclude exercise under saddle. Under such conditions, one may have to depend upon (1) exercise taken voluntarily in a

large paddock, (2) longeing or exercising on a 30- to 40-foot rope, or (3) leading.

Transporting Horses

Horses are transported via trailer, van, truck, rail, boat, and plane. Today, transportation by motor (trailer, van, or truck) is most common because of the distinct advantage of door-to-door movement. Regardless of the method, however, the objectives are the same: to move them safely, with the maximum of comfort, and as economically as possible. To this end, selection of the equipment is the first requisite. But equipment alone, no matter how good, will not suffice.

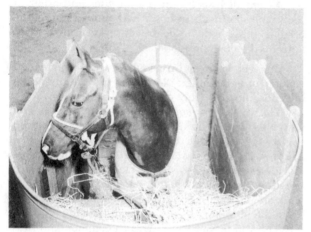

Fig. 18-12. Front view of a horse in a trailer, showing animal properly blanketed, double tied, and with hay in the manger. Trailers are a very popular means of transporting one or two horses. (Courtesy, USDA)

Fig. 18-13. Horse van of Gem State Stables, Thoroughbreds, Tipton, California. (Courtesy, Velma V. Morrison, owner)

The trip must be preceded by proper preparation including conditioning of horses; and horses must receive proper care, including smooth movement, en route.

The discussion which follows presents, in summary form, the requisites of good transportation, with special emphasis on motor transportation. The same principles also apply to plane, boat, and rail ship-

ments, although each method of transportation has certain peculiarities and presents special problems.

• *Provide good footing*—The floor of the vehicle should be covered with heavy coco matting made for the purpose, sand covered with straw or other suitable bedding material, or rubber mats. Clean the floor covering at frequent intervals while in transit to avoid ammonia and heat.

• *Drive carefully*—Drive at a moderate, constant speed as distinguished from fast or jerky driving, which causes added stress and tiring. If weather conditions make the roads unsafe, the vehicle should be stopped.

• *Make nurse stops*—Nurse stops should be made at about three-hour intervals when mares and foals are transported together.

• *Provide proper ventilation*—Provide plenty of fresh air without drafts.

• *Teach horses to load early in life*—When horses will be transported later in life, they should be accustomed to transportation as youngsters before they get too big and strong. This can be done by moving them from one part of the farm to another.

• *Provide health certificate and statement of ownership*—A health certificate signed by a licensed veterinarian is required for most interstate shipments. Foreign shipments must be accompanied by a health certificate that has been approved by a government veterinarian. The latter takes several days. Branded horses must be accompanied by a brand certificate, and all horses should be accompanied by a statement of ownership.

• *Schedule properly*—Schedule the transportation so that animals will arrive on time. Show, sale, and race animals should arrive a few days early.

• *Have the horses relaxed*—Horses ship best if they are relaxed and not overtired before they are moved.

• *Clean and disinfect public conveyance*—Before using any type of public conveyance, thoroughly clean and disinfect it. Steam is excellent for this purpose. Remove nails or other hazards that might cause injury.

• *Have a competent caretaker accompany horses*—Valuable horses should not be shipped in the care of an inexperienced person.

• *Use shanks except on stallions*—When animals are tied, use a ⅝-inch cotton rope shank that is 5 feet long and has a big swivel snap at the end. Chain shanks are too noisy. Always tie the shank with a knot that can easily and quickly be released in case of an emergency.

• *Feed lightly*—Allow horses only a half feed of grain before they are loaded for shipment and at the first feed after they reach their destination. In transit, horses should be fed alfalfa, to keep the bowels open, but no concentrates should be fed. Commercial hay

nets or homemade burlap containers may be used to hold the hay in transit, but they should not be placed too high.

● *Water liberally*—When transporting horses, give them all the fresh, clean water they will drink at frequent intervals unless the weather is extremely hot and there is danger of gorging. A tiny bit of molasses may be added to each pail of water, beginning about a week before the horses are shipped, and the addition of molasses to the water may be continued in transit. This prevents any taste change in the water.

● *Pad the stalls*—Many experienced shippers favor padding the inside of the vehicle to lessen the likelihood of injury, especially when a valuable animal is shipped. Coco matting or a sack of straw properly placed may save the horse's hocks from injury.

● *Take along tools and supplies*—The following tools and supplies should be taken along in a suitable box: pinch bar, hammer, hatchet, saw, nails, pliers, flashlight, extra halters and shanks, twitch, canvas slapper or short piece of hose, pair of gloves, fork and broom, fire extinguisher, and medicine for colic and shipping fever provided by a veterinarian.

● *Check shoes, blankets, and bandages*—Whenever possible, ship horses barefoot. Never allow them to wear calked shoes during a long shipment. They may wear smooth shoes. In cool weather, horses may be blanketed if an attendant is present in case a horse gets entangled. The legs of racehorses in training should be bandaged to keep the ankles from getting scuffed or the tendons bruised. Bandages are not necessary on breeding stock except for valuable stallions and young animals. When bandages are used, they should be reset often.

● *Be calm when loading and unloading*—In loading and unloading horses, always be patient and

Fig. 18-14. Easy does it! This shows an easy way in which to load a "green" horse into a trailer.

never show anger. Try kindness first; pat the horse and speak to him to reassure him. If this fails, it may be necessary to use one of the following techniques:

1. Sometimes the use of the twitch at the right time is desirable, especially if the horse is tossing his head about.

2. When a horse must be disciplined, a canvas slapper or a short rubber hose can be used effectively; these make a lot of noise without inflicting much hurt.

3. If a horse gets very excited and is about to break out, dash a bucket of water in his face; usually he will back off and calm down.

4. A nervous, excitable horse may be calmed by a tranquilizer, which should be administered by a veterinarian.

5. If a horse will not move or is kicking, grab his tail and push it over his back. In this position, he cannot kick but can be pushed along.

● *Control insects*—In season, flies and other insects molest animals in transit. When necessary, use a reliable insecticide to control insects. Follow directions on the container label.

Trailers, vans, and trucks have the very great advantage of being able to load from in front of one stable and unload in front of another.

The trailer is usually a one- or two-horse unit, which is drawn behind a car or truck. Generally speaking, this method of transportation is best adapted to short distances—less than 500 miles. Horses are trailered to shows, races, endurance rides, breeding establishments, to new owners, from one work area to another on the range; in fact, it may well be said that today's horses are well traveled.

The van or vanlike trailer is a common and satisfactory method of transportation where three to eight horses are involved. There is hardly any limit to the kinds of vans, ranging from rather simple to very palatial pieces of equipment.

Most experienced horse shippers frown upon shipping horses in an open truck.

Rail shipments are seldom used anymore. But during the heyday of the draft horse and mule—until the 1930s—rail shipments were the common mode of horse transportation. Old-time horsemen, who have used various methods of transportation, are generally agreed that horses ship more comfortably by rail, either by freight or express, than in any other way.

Like rail shipments, boat shipments have declined in importance in recent years. Where valuable horses are involved, they have given way to the greater speed and flexibility of plane transportation.

Plane shipments are a specialty, the details of which had best be left in the hands of an experienced person or agency, such as an importing or exporting company or the representative of the airline. At the present time, such shipments are largely confined to valuable racehorses, polo ponies, and breeding horses, with both national and international movements involved.

Fig. 18-15. An Appaloosa loaded in a jet cargoliner, ready for flight. With this arrangement, loading in the stall is accomplished on the ground. The stall containing the horse is then lifted into the airplane door by forklift and maneuvered into position and tied down by the loading crew. (Courtesy, *Western Horseman*, Colorado Springs, Colo.)

Bedding Horses

A soft, comfortable bed will ensure proper rest and make for a cleaner animal and easier grooming. But bedding has the following added values from the standpoint of manure:

1. It soaks up the urine, which contains about one-half the total plant food of manure.
2. It makes manure easier to handle.
3. It absorbs plant nutrients, fixing both ammonia and potash in relatively insoluble forms that protect

them against losses by leaching. This characteristic of bedding is especially important in peat moss, but of little significance with sawdust and shavings.

KIND AND AMOUNT OF BEDDING

The kind of bedding material selected should be determined primarily by (1) availability and price, (2) absorptive capacity, (3) cleanness (this excludes dirt or dust which might cause odors or stain horses), (4) ease of handling, (5) ease of cleanup and disposal, (6)

TABLE 18-4

WATER ABSORPTION OF BEDDING MATERIALS

Material	Lb of Water Absorbed per Cwt of Air-Dry Bedding	Material	Lb of Water Absorbed per Cwt of Air-Dry Bedding
Barley straw	210	Sand	25
Cocoa shells	270	Sawdust (top quality pine)	250
Corn stover (shredded)	250	(run-of-the-mill hardwood)	150
Corncobs (crushed or ground)	210	Sugar cane bagasse	220
Cottonseed hulls	250	Tree bark (dry, fine)	250
Flax straw	260	(from tanneries)	400
Hay (mature, chopped)	300	Vermiculite[1]	350
Leaves (broadleaf)	200	Wheat straw (long)	220
(pine needles)	100	(chopped)	295
Oat hulls	200	Wood chips (top quality pine)	300
Oat straw (long)	280	(run-of-the-mill hardwood)	150
(chopped)	375	Wood shavings (top quality pine)	200
Peanut hulls	250	(run-of-the-mill hardwood)	150
Peat moss	1,000		
Rye straw	210		

[1]This is a micalike mineral mined chiefly in South Carolina and Montana.

nonirritability from dust or components causing allergies, (7) texture or size, and (8) fertility value or plant nutrient content. In addition, a desirable bedding should not be excessively coarse, and should remain well in place and not be too readily kicked aside.

Table 18-4 lists some common bedding materials and gives the average water absorptive capacity of each. Cereal straw and wood shavings are the favorite bedding materials for horses.

Naturally, the availability and price per ton of various bedding materials vary from area to area, and from year to year. Thus, in the New England states shavings and sawdust are available, whereas other forms of bedding are scarce, and straws are more plentiful in the central and western states.

Other facts of importance, relative to certain bedding materials and bedding uses, are:

1. *Wood products (sawdust, shavings, tree bark, chips, etc.)*—The suspicion that wood products will hurt the land is rather widespread but unfounded. It is true that shavings and sawdust decompose slowly, but this process can be expedited by the addition of nitrogen fertilizers. Also, when plowed under, they increase soil acidity, but the change is both small and temporary.

Softwood (on a weight basis) is about twice as absorptive as hardwood, and green wood has only 50 percent the absorptive capacity of dried wood.

2. *Cut straw*—Cut straw will absorb more liquid than long straw; cut oats or wheat straw will take up about 25 percent more water than long straw from comparable material. But there are disadvantages to chopping—chopped straws may be dusty.

From the standpoint of the value of plant food nutrients per ton of air-dry material, peat moss is the most valuable bedding and wood products the least valuable.

The minimum desirable amount of bedding to use is the amount necessary to absorb completely the liquids in manure. For 24-hour confinement, the minimum daily bedding requirements of horses, based on uncut wheat or oats straw, is 10 to 15 pounds. With other bedding materials, these quantities will vary according to their respective absorptive capacities (see Table 18-4). Also, more than minimum quantities of bedding may be desirable where cleanliness and comfort of the horse are important.

In most areas, bedding materials are becoming scarcer and higher in price, primarily because (1) geneticists are breeding plants with shorter straws and stalks, (2) there are more competitive and numerous uses for some of the materials, and (3) the current trend toward more confinement rearing of livestock requires more bedding.

Horsemen may reduce bedding needs and costs as follows:

1. *Chop bedding*—Chopped straw, waste hay, fodder, or cobs will go further and do a better job of keeping horses dry than long materials.

2. *Ventilate quarters properly*—Proper ventilation lowers the humidity and keeps the bedding dry.

3. *Provide exercise area*—Where possible and practical, provide for exercise in well-drained, dry pastures or corrals, without confining horses to stalls more than necessary.

Stable Management

The following stable management practices are recommended:

1. Remove the top layer of clay floors yearly; replace with fresh clay, and level and tamp. Also, keep the stable floor higher than the surrounding area, thereby making for dryness.

2. Keep stalls well lighted.

3. Use properly constructed hayracks to lessen waste and contamination of hay, with the possible exception of maternity stalls.

4. Scrub concentrate containers at such intervals as necessary, and after feeding a wet mash.

5. Work over bedding daily, removing excrement and wet, stained or soiled material, and provide fresh bedding.

6. Practice rigid stable sanitation to prevent fecal contamination of feed and water.

7. Lead foals when taking them from the stall to the paddock and back, as a way in which to further their training.

8. Restrict the ration when horses are idle, and provide either a wet bran mash the evening before an idle day or turn idle horses to pasture.

9. Provide proper ventilation at all times—by means of open doors, windows that open inwardly from the top, or stall partitions slatted at the top.

10. Keep stables in repair at all times, so as to lessen injury hazards.

MANURE

The term manure refers to a mixture of animal excrements (consisting of undigested feeds plus certain body wastes) and bedding.

The rise in light horse numbers, along with the shift of much of the horse population from the nation's farms and ranches to stables and small enclosures in suburban areas, created disposal problems. Surplus manure came during an era when chemical fertilizers were relatively abundant and cheap, with the result that most horsemen forgot that horses can provide manure for the fields.

No doubt, the manure pollution problem, suspicioned or real, will persist. However, the energy

crisis, accompanied by high chemical fertilizer prices, has caused manure to be looked upon as a resource and not a waste that presents a disposal problem. At 1976 fertilizer prices (per pound: nitrogen (N) = 20¢; phosphorus (P) = 24¢; and potassium (K) = 8¢), 1 ton of average horse manure is worth $4.20 (Table 18-5). As a result, a growing number of American farmers are returning to organic farming—they're using more manure—the unwanted barnyard centerpiece of the past 40 years. They are discovering that they are just as good reapers of the land and far better stewards of the soil.

In the future, as fertilizer and feed become increasingly scarce and expensive, the economic value of horse manure will increase.

From the standpoint of soils and crops, barnyard manure contains the following valuable ingredients:

● *Organic matter*—It supplies valuable organic matter which cannot be secured in chemical fertilizers. Organic matter—which constitutes three to six percent, by weight, of most soils—improves soil tilth, increases water-holding capacity, lessens water and wind erosion, improves aeration, and has a beneficial effect on soil microorganisms and plants. It is the "lifeblood" of the land.

● *Plant food*—It supplies plant food or fertility—especially nitrogen, phosphorus, and potassium. In addition to these three nutrients, manure contains calcium, and trace elements such as boron, manganese, copper, and zinc. A ton of well-preserved horse manure, free of bedding, contains plant food nutrients equal to about 100 pounds of 13-2-12 fertilizer (see Table 18-5). Thus, spreading manure at the rate of 8 tons per acre supplies the same amounts of nutrients as 800 pounds of a 13-2-12 commercial fertilizer.

Amount, Composition, and Value of Manure Produced

The quantity, composition, and value of horse manure produced vary according to weight of animal, kind and amount of feed, and kind and amount of bedding. The author's computations in Table 18-5 are on a fresh manure (exclusive of bedding) basis and per 1,000 pounds liveweight. As indicated, a 1,000-pound horse will produce about 8 tons of manure, free of bedding, per year.

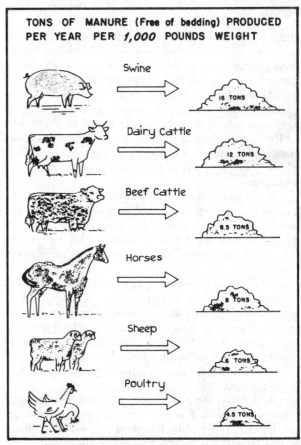

Fig. 18-16. On the average, each class of stall confined animals produces per year per 1,000 pounds' weight the tonnages shown above. (Drawing by Prof. R. F. Johnson)

TABLE 18-5

QUANTITY, COMPOSITION, AND VALUE OF FRESH HORSE MANURE
(FREE OF BEDDING) EXCRETED PER 1,000 POUNDS LIVEWEIGHT

Tons Excreted/Year/1,000 Lb Liveweight[1]	Composition and Value of Manure on a Tonnage Basis[2]						
	Excrement	Lb/Ton[3]	Water	N	P[4]	K[4]	Value/Ton[5]
			(%)	(lb)	(lb)	(lb)	($)
8	Liquid	400					
	Solid	1,600					
	Total	2,000	60	13.8	2.0	12.0	4.20

[1]*Manure Is Worth Money—It Deserves Good Care*, University of Illinois Circ. 595, 1953, p. 4.
[2]Last 5 colums on the right from *Farm Manures*, University of Kentucky Circ. 593, 1964, p. 5, Table 2.
[3]From Reference Material for 1951 Saddle and Sirloin Essay Contest, p. 43, compiled by M. E. Ensminger; data from *Fertilizers and Crop Production*, by Van Slyke, published by Orange Judd Publishing Co.
[4]Phosphorus (P) can be coverted to P_2O_5 by multiplying the figure given above by 2.29, and potassium (K) can be converted to K_2O by multiplying by 1.2.
[5]Calculated on the assumption that nitrogen (N) retails at 20¢, phosphorus (P) at 24¢, and potassium (K) at 8¢ per pound in commercial fertilizers.

The data in Table 18-5 are based on animals confined to stalls the year around. Actually, the manure recovered and available to spread where desired is considerably less than indicated because (1) animals are kept on pasture and along roads and lanes much of the year, where the manure is dropped, and (2) losses in weight often run as high as 60 percent when manure is exposed to the weather for a considerable time.

Fig 18-16 shows the tons of manure (free of bedding) produced by different species per year per 1,000 pounds weight. As noted, on comparable body weight basis, horses rank fourth in manure production, being exceeded by swine, dairy cows, and beef cattle.

About 75% of the nitrogen, 80% of the phosphorus, and 85% of the potassium contained in horse feeds are returned as manure. In addition, about 40% of the organic matter in feeds is excreted as manure. As a rule of thumb, it is commonly estimated that 80% of the total nutrients in feeds are excreted by horses as manure.

The urine makes up 20% of the total weight of the excrement of horses. Also, it is noteworthy that the nutrients in liquid manure are more readily available to plants than the nutrients in the solid excrement. These are the reasons why it is important to conserve the urine.

The actual monetary value of manure can and should be based on (1) increased crop yields, and (2) equivalent cost of a like amount of commercial fertilizer. Numerous experiments and practical observations have shown the measurable monetary value of manure in increased crop yields. Tables 18-5 and 18-6 give the equivalent cost of a like amount of commercial fertilizer.

Currently, we are producing horse manure (exclusive of bedding) at the rate of 64 million tons annually (see Table 18-6). Based on equivalent fertilizer prices (see Table 18-5, right-hand column), and horse numbers (Table 18-6), the yearly horse manure crop is worth 268.8 million dollars.

Of course, the value of manure cannot be measured alone in terms of increased crop yields and equivalent cost of a like amount of commercial fertilizer. It has additional value for the organic matter which it contains, which almost all soils need, and which farmers and ranchers cannot buy in a sack or tank.

Also, it is noteworthy that, due to the slower availability of its nitrogen and to its contribution to the soil humus, manure produces rather lasting benefits which may continue for many years. Approximately ½ of the plant nutrients in manure are available to and effective upon the crops in the immediate cycle of the rotation to which the application is made. Of the unused remainder, about ½, in turn, is taken up by the crops in the second cycle of the rotation; ½ of the remainder in the third cycle, etc. Likewise, the continuous use of manure through several rounds of a rotation builds up a backlog which brings additional benefits, and a measurable climb in yield levels.

Horsemen sometimes fail to recognize the value of this barnyard crop because (1) it is produced whether or not it is wanted, and (2) it is available without cost. Most of all, no one is selling it. Whoever heard of a traveling manure salesman?

Modern Ways of Handling Manure

Clay floors cannot be cleaned by flushing with water, and hard stable floors of concrete, asphalt, or wood require considerable bedding to provide softness and comfort. These conditions make it impractical to handle horse manure as a liquid. But horse manure is relatively dry and well adapted to handling as a solid.

Modern handling of manure involves maximum automation and a minimum loss of nutrients. Among the methods of handling manure being used are: scrapers; power loaders; conveyors; industrial-type vacuums; slotted floors; storage vats; spreaders; dehydrators; and lagoons. Actually, there is no one best manure management system for all situations; rather, it is a matter of designing and using that system which will be most practical for a particular set of conditions.

Both small and large horse establishments face the problem of what to do with horse manure, once it is removed from the stable. Because the feces of

TABLE 18-6
TONNAGE AND VALUE OF MANURE (EXCLUSIVE OF BEDDING)
EXCRETED BY U.S. HORSES IN 1976[1]

No. of Horses in U.S.[2]	Average Liveweight	Tons Manure Excreted/Year/ 1,000 Lb Liveweight[3]	Total Manure Production	Total Value of Manure[4]
	(lb)	(tons)	(tons)	($)
8,000,000	1,000	8	64,000,000	268,800,000

[1]In these computations, no provision was made for animals that died or were slaughtered during the year. Rather, it was assumed that their places were taken by younger animals, and that the population was stable throughout the year.
[2]Estimate made by the author.
[3]*Manure Is Worth Money—It Deserves Good Care*, University of Illinois Circ. 595, 1953, p. 4.
[4]Computed on the basis of the value per ton given in the right-hand column of Table 18-5.

horses are the primary source of infection of internal parasites, fresh horse manure should never be spread on pastures grazed by horses. The following alternatives for disposing of horse manure exist:

1. Spread fresh manure on those fields that will be plowed and cropped, where there is sufficient land and this is feasible.

2. Contract with a nearby mushroom or vegetable grower, on a mutually satisfactory basis.

3. Store the manure in a suitable tightly constructed pit for at least a two-week interval prior to spreading, allowing the spontaneously generated heat to destroy the parasites.

4. Compost it in an area which will neither pollute a stream nor be offensive to the neighbors; then spread it on the land.

HOW MUCH MANURE CAN BE APPLIED TO THE LAND?

With today's heavy animal concentration in one location, the question is being asked: How much manure can be applied to the land without depressing crop yields, making for salt problems in the soil, making for nitrate problems in feed, or contributing excess nitrate to groundwater or surface streams?

Based on earlier studies in midwestern United States, before the rise of commercial fertilizers, it would appear that one can apply from 5 to 20 tons of manure per acre, year after year, with benefit.

Heavier applications can be made, but probably should not be repeated every year. With rates higher than 20 tons per annum, there may be excess salt and nitrate buildup. Excess nitrate from manure can pollute streams or groundwater and result in toxic levels of nitrate in crops. Without doubt the maximum rate at which manure can be applied to the land will vary widely according to soil type, rainfall, and temperature.

Objectionable Features of Manure

Despite the recognized value of horse manure, it does possess the following objectionable features:

1. *It may propagate insects*—Unless precautions are taken, often manure is the preferred breeding place for flies and other insects.

2. *It may spread diseases and parasites*—Where animals are allowed to come in contact with their own excrement, there is always danger of infections from diseases and parasites.

3. *It may produce undesirable odors*—Where manure is stored improperly, there may be a nuisance from odors.

4. *It may scatter weed seeds*—Even when fermented, manure usually contains a certain quantity of viable weed seeds which may be scattered over the land.

MANAGEMENT OF SUBHUMID, HUMID, AND IRRIGATED PASTURES

Many good pastures have been established only to be lost through careless management. Good pasture management in the subhumid, humid, and irrigated areas involves the following practices:

Fig. 18-17. Standardbred mares and foals on pasture in Kentucky. Good horsemen, good pastures, and good horses go hand in hand. (Courtesy, United States Trotting Assn., Columbus, Ohio)

1. *Controlled grazing*—Nothing contributes more to good pasture management than controlled grazing. At its best, it embraces the following:

a. *Protection of first year seedings*—First year seedings should be grazed lightly or not at all in order that they may get a good start in life. Where practical, instead of grazing, it is preferable to mow a new first year seeding about 3 inches above the ground and to utilize it as hay or silage, provided there is sufficient growth to justify this procedure.

b. *Rotation or alternate grazing*—Rotation or alternate grazing is accomplished by dividing a pasture into fields (usually two to four) of approximately equal size, so that one field can be grazed while the others are allowed to make new growth. This results in increased pasture yields, more uniform grazing, and higher quality forage.

Generally speaking, rotation or alternate grazing is (1) more practical and profitable on rotation and supplemental pastures than on permanent pastures, and (2) more beneficial where parasite infestations are heavy than where little or no parasitic problems are involved.

c. *Shifting the location of salt, shade, and water*—Where portable salt containers are used, more uniform grazing and scattering of the droppings may be obtained simply by the practice of shifting the location of the salt to the less grazed areas of the pasture. Where possible and practical, the shade and the water should be shifted likewise.

d. *Deferred spring grazing*—Allow 6 to 8 inches of growth before turning horses out to pasture in the spring, thereby giving grass a needed start. Anyway, the early spring growth of pastures is high in moisture and washy.

e. *Avoiding close late fall grazing*—Pastures that are grazed closely late in the fall start late in the spring. With most pastures, 3 to 5 inches of growth should be left for winter cover.

f. *Avoiding overgrazing*—Never graze more closely than 2 to 3 inches during the pasture season. Continued close grazing reduces the yield, weakens the plants, allows weeds to invade, and increases soil erosion. The use of temporary and supplemental pastures, may "spell off" regular pastures through seasons of drought and other pasture shortages, and alleviate overgrazing.

g. *Avoiding undergrazing*—Undergrazing seeded pastures should also be avoided, because (1) mature forage is unpalatable and of low nutritive value, (2) tall-growing grasses may drive out such low-growing plants as white clover due to shading, and (3) weeds, brush, and coarse grasses are more apt to gain a foothold when the pasture is grazed insufficiently. It is a good rule, therefore, to graze the pasture fairly close at least once each year.

2. *Clipping pastures and controlling weeds*—Pastures should be clipped at such intervals as necessary to control weeds (and brush) and to get rid of uneaten clumps and other unpalatable coarse growth left after incomplete grazing. Pastures that are grazed continuously may be clipped at or just preceding the usual haymaking time; rotated pastures may be clipped at the close of the grazing period. Weeds and brush may also be controlled by chemicals, by burning, etc.

3. *Topdressing (Fertilizing)*—Like animals, for best results grasses and legumes must be fed properly throughout a lifetime. It is not sufficient that they be fertilized (and limed if necessary) at or prior to seeding time. In addition, in most areas it is desirable and profitable to topdress pastures with fertilizer annually, and, at less frequent intervals, with reinforced manure and lime (lime to maintain a pH of about 6.5). Such treatments should be based on soil tests, and are usually applied in the spring or fall.

Properly used, inorganic fertilizers will make for more sound horses. Of course, improper fertilization of pasture or hayland can result in an imbalance of the mineral content of the forage, which, in turn, will affect the animal. But when soil samples are properly taken and analyzed, then used as a guide for fertilizer application, the mineral content of the forage will be improved.

Remember that it's the total mineral intake of the horse that counts. This calls for (1) soil testing, with the fertilizer application based thereon, (2) forage testing, and (3) ration testing, with the mineral supplement balancing out the needs of the horse.

4. *Scattering droppings*—The droppings should be scattered three or four times each year and at the end of each grazing season in order to prevent animals from leaving ungrazed clumps and to help them fertilize a larger area. This can best be done by the use of a brush harrow or chain harrow.

5. *Grazing by more than one class of animals*—Grazing by two or more classes of animals makes for more uniform pasture utilization and fewer weeds and parasites, provided the area is not overstocked. Different kinds of livestock have different habits of grazing; they show preference for different plants and graze to different heights. Also, horse parasites die in cattle. For these reasons, horses and cattle are commonly grazed on the same pastures in the great horse breeding centers of the world.

6. *Irrigating where practical and feasible*—Where irrigation is practical and feasible, it alleviates the necessity of depending on the weather.

7. *Supplementing to provide needed nutrients*—Although the horse ration should be as economical as

Fig. 18-18. A chain harrow is ideal for scattering droppings; controlling parasites; seeding, maintaining, or renovating pastures; and/or maintaining a show-ring or track.

possible, condition and results in show, sale, and use are the primary objectives, even at somewhat added expense. Generally, this calls for supplemental feeding on pasture—for providing added energy, protein, minerals, and vitamins.

Extending the Grazing Season

In the South and in Hawaii, year-round grazing is

a reality on many a successful farm. By careful planning and by selecting the proper combination of crops, other areas can approach this desired goal.

In addition to lengthening the grazing season through the selection of species, earlier spring pastures can be secured by avoiding grazing too late in the fall and by the application of a nitrogen fertilizer in the fall or early spring. Nitrogen fertilizers will often stimulate the growth of grass so that it will be ready for grazing 10 days to 2 weeks earlier than unfertilized areas.

Pointers on Caring for Horse Pastures and Recreational Areas

There is a paucity of information on the care of horse pastures, turfs, and recreational areas. Few college courses even mention them, and precious little authoritative literature has been published on the subject.

Table 18-7 tells how successful operators maintain, renovate, and seed horse pastures, and how they care for racetracks, show-rings, bridle paths, and other like areas. These areas can no longer be taken for granted. They're big and important—and they'll get bigger. Hence, they merit the combined best recommendations of scientists and practical operators.

TABLE 18-7

GUIDE FOR CARING FOR HORSE PASTURES AND RECREATIONAL AREAS

For	When	How to Do It	Comments
Pasture maintenance	Spring and fall. Scatter droppings in spring and fall, plus 3 to 4 times during the grazing season.	Use a chain-type tine harrow to— 1. Tear out the old, dead material. 2. Stimulate growth through gentle cultivating action. 3. Prevent a sod-bound condition. 4. Increase moisture penetration. 5. Scatter animal dropping to— 　a. Help control parasites. 　b. Fertilize a larger area. 　c. Prevent animals from leaving ungrazed clumps.	Altogether too many horse pastures are merely gymnasiums or exercising grounds. This need not be so. Through improved pasture maintenance, horsemen can— 1. Produce higher yields of nutritious forage. 2. Extend the grazing season from early in the spring to late in the fall. 3. Provide a fairly uniform supply of feed throughout the entire season.
Pasture renovation	Spring or fall.	Use a chain-type tine harrow to work the fertilizer and seed into the soil, and yet destroy a minimum of the existing sod.	Run-down pastures can be brought back into production without plowing and reseeding.
Preparing new pasture seedbed	Spring or fall.	Use a chain-type tine harrow to— 1. Level 2. Smooth down 3. Pack	When properly prepared, a seedbed should be so firm that you barely leave a footprint when you walk across it. The firmer the better from the standpoint of moisture conservation and small seeds.
Racetracks; show-rings	Whenever the track or ring becomes bedded. Just before the race or show; and between races or show events.	Set a chain-type tine harrow for maximum or light penetration, depending on the condition of the track or ring. Use a chain-type tine harrow as a drag mat to smooth and fill holes.	Good racetracks and show-rings must be firm, yet resilient. Because it's flexible, this harrow can be pulled at good speed, as is necessary between races or show events, and yet do an excellent job of smoothing and filling holes.
Bridle paths; farm lanes; dirt roads	Whenever they become rough or uneven.	Use maximum penetration of chain-type tine harrow to put in shape; then turn harrow over to level and fill up holes.	

SELECTED REFERENCES

Title of Publication	Author(s)	Publisher
Art and Science of Horseshoeing, The	R. G. Greeley	J. B. Lippincott Co., Philadelphia, Penn., 1970
Breeding and Raising Horses, Ag. Hdbk. No. 394	M. E. Ensminger	Agricultural Research Service, USDA, Washington, D.C., 1972
Care and Training of the Trotter and Pacer	J. C. Harrison et al.	The United States Trotting Association, Columbus, Ohio, 1970
Complete Horseshoeing Guide, The	R. F. Wiseman	University of Oklahoma Press, Norman, Okla., 1968
Elements of Farrier Science	D. M. Canfield	Enderes Tool Co., Inc., Albert Lea, Minn., 1966
First Horse	R. Hapgood	Chronicle Books, San Francisco, Calif., 1972
Horse Science Handbook, Vol. 1-3	Ed. by M. E. Ensminger	Agriservices Foundation, Clovis, Calif., 1963, 1964, 1966
Horsemanship and Horse Care,	M. E. Ensminger	Agricultural Research Service, USDA, Washington, D.C., 1972
Horsemanship and Horsemastership, Vol. II		The Cavalry School, Fort Riley, Kan., 1946
Horses: Their Selection, Care and Handling	M. C. Self	A. S. Barnes & Co., Inc., New York, N.Y., 1943
Horseshoeing	A. Lungwitz, trans. by J. W. Adams	Oregon State University Press, Corvallis, Ore., 1966
Introduction to Light Horse Management, An	R. C. Barbalace	Caballus Publishers, Fort Collins, Colo., 1974
Light Horses, Farmers' Bull. No. 2127	M. E. Ensminger	Agricultural Research Service, USDA, Washington, D.C., 1965
Master Farrier, The	B. Beaston	Oklahoma Farrier's College, Sperry, Okla., 1975
Principles of Horseshoeing, The	D. Butler	D. Butler, Ithaca, N.Y., 1974
Saddle Up!	C. E. Ball	J. B. Lippincott Co., Philadelphia, Penn., 1970
Selecting, Fitting and Showing Horses	J. E. Nordby H. E. Lattig	The Interstate Printers & Publishers, Inc., Danville, Ill., 1963
Stable Management and Exercise, Sixth Edition	M. H. Hayes	Stanley Paul & Co., Ltd., London, England, 1968
Stockman's Handbook, The, Fourth Edition	M. E. Ensminger	The Interstate Printers & Publishers, Inc., Danville, Ill., 1970
Stud Managers' Course (Lectures)		Stud Managers' Course, Lexington, Ky., intermittent since 1951
Stud Managers' Handbook	Ed. by M. E. Ensminger	Agriservices Foundation, Clovis, Calif., annually since 1965
Top Form Book of Horse Care	F. Harper	Popular Library, New York, N.Y., 1966

CHAPTER 19

Business Aspects of Horse Production

In the present era, many horse enterprises are owned and operated as businesses, with a profit motive—just as other stockmen have cattle, sheep, or swine enterprises. These horsemen must treat their operations as businesses and become more sophisticated; otherwise, they won't be in business very long. Other horsemen keep horses as a hobby—for much the same reason that some folks play golf, hunt, fish, or go boating. When kept for the latter purpose, their cost should be looked upon much like that of any other hobby or an evening's entertainment; that is, decide in advance how much you can afford to spend, then stop when that amount has been spent.

There was a time when horsemen-hobbyists operated much like most fishermen and hunters, who do not wish to be reminded of the cost per pound of their catch or quarry. The guiding philosophy of these hobbyists is very similar to that of the story attributed to J. Pierpont Morgan, who once admonished an inquiring friend that, "If you have to ask what it costs to maintain a yacht, you can't afford it." But this attitude among horsemen-hobbyists has changed, primarily because of (1) inheritance taxes making it increasingly difficult to pass wealth from one generation to the next, and (2) closer scrutiny of tax write-offs. Also, even when horses are kept primarily for the fun of it, most owners derive more pleasure therefrom when the operation pays, or nearly pays, its way—it's a matter of pride and a challenge. For these reasons, more and more folks who keep horses primarily for pleasure, like those who keep horses for profit, are interested in improving the business aspects of their enterprises.

CAPITAL

Horsemen who are in business to make a profit should never invest money, either their own or borrowed, unless they are reasonably certain that it will make money. Capital will be needed for land, buildings, machinery and equipment, horses, feed, supplies, labor, and miscellaneous items.

Whether establishing or enlarging a horse enterprise, the most common question, a two-pronged one, is—how much money will it take, and how much will it make? This information is needed by both horsemen and lenders. Unfortunately, a simple answer cannot be given. However, the following guides will be helpful:

1. *Land, buildings, machinery and equipment, and horse and labor costs*—Generally speaking, it is not too difficult to arrive at these costs.

The horseman can easily determine the prevailing price of land in the area under consideration, either by inquiring of local land owners or reputable realtors. Where new buildings must be constructed, local architects can quote approximate costs on a square foot basis. Likewise, dealers can give prices on major items of machinery and equipment.

Horse prices vary widely, by breed and age, and according to quality. Nevertheless, auction or private treaty sales, or a knowledgeable horseman, will aid one in establishing the prevailing price for the breed, age, and quality desired. Also, going wages can usually be determined rather easily for a particular area.

2. *Feed, tack, and drug costs*—Where no pasture whatsoever is available, a 1,000-lb horse will consume about 30 lb of feed (hay and grain) daily, or about 5½ tons per year. Where an all-pelleted ration is used, 20 percent less feed will suffice, primarily because there is practically no wastage; hence, the allowance of a 1,000-lb horse on an all-pelleted ration may be computed on the basis of 25 lb per day, or 4½ tons per year.

Based on a study made by the author, on the average and for the United States as a whole, it appeared that the annual expenditure per horse for feed, tack, and drugs in 1976 was approximately $1,000.

Certainly, feed, tack, and drug costs will vary widely, some being more and others less than the above figures.

3. *Size of horse enterprise*—Generally speaking, larger horse enterprises contribute to increased profits for the following reasons:

a. They result in fewer hours of labor per horse.

b. They are more apt to be used to capacity. For example, if for an establishment producing 20 foals per year the depreciation, interest, repairs, insurance, and taxes cost $12,000 annually, that's $600 per foal. If the same facilities were used to produce 40 foals per year, the cost would be lessened to $300 per foal. This shows how increased numbers can reduce the building and equipment cost per foal.

Guidelines Relative to Facility and Equipment Costs

Overinvestment is a mistake. Some horsemen invest more in land and buildings than reasonably can be expected to make a satisfactory return; others invest too much in feed mills and equipment. Sometimes operators of small establishments fail to recognize that it may cost half as much to mechanize for 10 horses as it does for 60.

In order to lessen the hazard of overinvestment, guidelines are useful. Here are two:

Guideline No. 1—The break-even point on how much you can afford to invest in equipment to replace hired labor can be arrived at by the following formula:

Annual saving in hired
labor from new equipment
―――――――――――――――――――――― = amount you can af-
(divide by) .15   ford to invest.

Example:

If hired labor costs $6,000 per year, this be-
comes—

$\dfrac{\$6,000}{.15}$ = $40,000, the break-even point on new
            equipment

Since labor costs are going up faster than machinery and equipment costs, it may be good business to
exceed this limitation under some circumstances.
Nevertheless, the break-even point, $40,000 in this
case, is probably the maximum expenditure that can
be economically justified at the time.

Guideline No. 2—Assuming an annual cost plus
operation of power machinery and equipment equal
to 20 percent of new cost, the break-even point to justify replacement of one hired man is as follows:

Example:

If annual cost of one hired man is[1]	The break-even point on new investment is
$5,000 (20%) × 5	$25,000
6,000 (20%) × 5	30,000
7,000 (20%) × 5	35,000

[1]This is assuming that the productivity of men at different
salaries is the same, which may or may not be the case.

Assume that the new cost of added equipment
comes to $3,000, that the annual cost is 20 percent of
this amount, and that the new equipment would save
one hour of labor per day for 6 months of the year.
Here's how to figure the value of labor to justify an
expenditure of $3,000 for this item:

$3,000 (new cost) × 20% = $600
    600 (annual ownership use cost) ÷ 180 hrs. (labor
    saved) = $3.33 per hour.

So, if labor costs less than $3.33 per hour, you
probably shouldn't buy the new item.

CREDIT IN THE HORSE BUSINESS

In 1974, U.S. agricultural assets totaled $478.8
billion, while total farm debt was $84.1 billion. This
means that, in the aggregate, farmers had 82 percent
equity in their business, and 18 percent borrowed
capital. Perhaps they have been too conservative, for
it is estimated that ¼ to ⅓ of American farmers could
profit from the use of more credit in their operations.

Credit is an integral part of today's horse business. Wise use of it can be profitable, but unwise use
of it can be disastrous. Accordingly, horsemen should
know more about it. They need to know something
about the lending agencies available to them, the

types of credit, how to go about obtaining a loan, and
methods of computing interest.

The common lending sources of farm credit
are: commercial banks, production credit associations, Federal land banks, individuals and other private lenders, life insurance companies, merchants and
dealers, and the Farm Home Administration.[2] Grain
companies, feed companies, and various other
suppliers are also important sources of credit to
horsemen.

Types of Credit or Loans

Following are the three general types of agricultural credit to consider, based on length of life and
type of collateral needed:

1. *Short-term or production loans*—These loans
are for up to one year. They are used for purchase of
feed and for operating expenses.

2. *Intermediate-term loans*—These loans may be
for one to seven years. They are used for the purchase
of breeding stock, machinery, equipment, and
semipermanent investments. Repayment is made
from the profits over several production periods.

3. *Long-term loans*—These loans are used for
land and major farm building, and for physical plant
construction. They may be for as long as 40 years.
Usually they are paid off in regular annual or semian-
nual payments. The best source of long-term loans
are: an insurance company, the Federal Land Bank,
the Farm Home Administration, or an individual.

Credit Factors Considered and
Evaluated by Lenders

Potential money borrowers sometimes make their
first big mistake by going in "cold" to see a lender—
without adequate facts and figures—with the result
that they already have two strikes against them regarding their getting the loan. Moreover, horsemen
should realize that bankers have a long-standing fear
of loans on horses and feathers (poultry).

When considering and reviewing horse loan requests, the lender tries to arrive at the repayment
ability of the potential borrower. Likewise, the borrower has no reason to obtain money unless it will
make money.

Lenders need certain basic information in order
to evaluate the soundness of a loan request. To this
end, the following information should be submitted:

1. *Analysis and feasibility study*—Lenders are
impressed with a borrower who has a written down

[2]Information relative to each of these credit sources is given in
The Stockman's Handbook, a book by the same author and the same
publisher as *Horses and Horsemanship*.

feasibility study, showing where he is now, where he's going, and how he expects to get there. In addition to spelling out the goals, this report should give assurance of the necessary management skills to achieve them. Such an analysis of the present and projection into the future is imperative in big operations.

2. *The applicant, farm, and financial statement*—It is the borrower's obligation, and in his best interest, to present the following information to the lender:

a. *The applicant:*

(1) Name of applicant and wife; age of applicant.

(2) Number of children (minors, legal age).

(3) Partners in business, if any.

(4) Years in area.

(5) References.

b. *The farm:*

(1) Owner or tenant.

(2) Location; legal description and county, and direction and distance from nearest town.

(3) Type of enterprise: breeding, racing, riding stable, etc.

c. *Financial statement*: This document indicates the borrower's financial record and current financial position, his potential ahead, and his liability to others. The borrower should always have sufficient slack to absorb reasonable losses due to such unforeseen happenstances as storms, droughts, diseases, and poor markets, thereby permitting the lender to stay with him in adversity and to give him a chance to recoup his losses in the future. The financial statement should include the following:

(1) Current assets:

(a) Horses and other animals.

(b) Feed.

(c) Machinery.

(d) Cash—There should be reasonable cash reserves, to cut interest costs, and to provide a cushion against emergencies.

(e) Bonds or other investments.

(f) Cash value of life insurance.

(2) Fixed assets:

(a) Real property, with estimated value.

(b) Farm property.

(c) City property.

(d) Long-term contracts.

(3) Current liabilities:

(a) Mortgages.

(b) Contracts.

(c) Open account—to whom owed.

(d) Cosigner or guarantor on notes.

(e) Any taxes due.

(f) Current portion of real estate indebtedness due.

(4) Fixed liabilities—amount and nature of real estate debt:

(a) Date due.

(b) Interest rate.

(c) To whom payable.

(d) Contract or mortgage.

3. *Other factors*—Shrewd lenders usually ferret out many things, among them:

a. *The potential borrower*—Most lenders will tell the potential borrower that he is the most important part of the loan. Lenders consider his:

(1) Character.

(2) Honesty and integrity.

(3) Experience and ability.

(4) Moral and credit rating.

(5) Age and health.

(6) Family cooperation.

(7) Continuity, or line of succession.

Lenders are quick to sense the "high-liver"—the fellow who lives beyond his income; the poor manager—the kind who would have made it except for hard luck, and to whom the hard luck happened many times; and the dishonest, lazy, and incompetent.

In recognition of the importance of the man back of the loan, "key man" insurance on the owner or manager should be considered by both the lender and the borrower.

b. *Production records*—This refers to a good set of records showing efficiency of production. On a horse breeding establishment, for example, such records should show prices of horses sold, percent foal crop, filly replacement program, depreciation schedule, average crop yield, and other pertinent information. Lenders will increasingly insist on good records.

c. *Progress with previous loans*—Has the borrower paid back previous loans plus interest? Has he reduced the amount of the loan, thereby giving evidence of progress?

d. *Profit and loss (P & L)*—This serves as a valuable guide to the potential ahead. Preferably, this should cover the previous three years. Also, most lenders prefer that this be on an accrual basis (even if the horseman is on a cash basis in reporting to the Internal Revenue Service).

e. *Physical plant*—

(1) Is it an economic unit?

(2) Does it have adequate water, and is it well balanced in feed and horses?

(3) Is there adequate diversification?

(4) Is the right kind of horse enterprise being conducted?

(5) Are the right crops and varieties grown; and are approved methods of tillage and fertilizer practices being followed?

(6) Is the farmstead neat and well kept?

f. *Collateral (or security)*—

(1) Adequate to cover loan, with margin.

(2) Quality of security:

(a) Grade and age of horses.

(b) Type and condition of machinery.

(c) If grain storage is involved, adequacy of protection from moisture and rodents.

(d) Government participation.

(3) Identification of security:

(a) Tattoo or brand on horses.

(b) Serial numbers on machinery.

4. *The loan request*—Horsemen are in competition for money with other agriculturalists and with urban businessmen. Hence, it is important that their request for a loan be well presented and supported. The potential borrower should tell the purpose of the loan, how much money is needed, when it's needed, the soundness of the venture, and the repayment schedule.

Credit Factors Considered by Borrowers

Credit is a two-way street; it must be good for both the borrower and the lender. If a borrower is the right kind of person and on a sound basis, more than one lender will want his business. Thus, it is usually well that a borrower shop around a bit; that he be familiar with several sources of credit and what they have to offer. There are basic differences in length and type of loan, repayment schedules, services provided with the loan, interest rate, and the ability and willingness of lenders to stick by the borrower in emergencies and times of adversity. Thus, interest rates and willingness to loan are only two of the several factors to consider. Also, if at all possible, all borrowing should be done from one source; a one-source lender will know more about the borrower's operations and be in a better position to help him.

Helpful Hints for Building and Maintaining a Good Credit Rating

Horsemen who wish to build up and maintain good credit are admonished to do the following:

1. *Keep credit in one place, or in few places*—Generally, lenders frown upon "split financing." Shop around for a creditor (a) who is able, willing, and interested in extending the kind and amount of credit needed, and (b) who will lend at a reasonable rate of interest; then stay with him.

2. *Get the right kind of credit*—Don't use short-term credit to finance long-term improvements or other capital investments.

3. *Be frank with the lender*—Be completely open and aboveboard. Mutual confidence and esteem should prevail between borrower and lender.

4. *Keep complete and accurate records*—Complete and accurate records should be kept by enterprises. By knowing the cost of doing business, decision-making can be on a sound basis.

5. *Keep annual inventory*—Take an annual inventory for the purpose of showing progress made during the year.

6. *Repay loans when due*—Borrowers should work out a repayment schedule on each loan, then meet payments when due. Sale proceeds should be promptly applied on loans.

7. *Plan ahead*—Analyze the next year's operation and project ahead.

Calculating Interest

The charge for the use of money is called interest. The basic charge is strongly influenced by the following:

1. The *basic cost* of money in the money market.

2. The *servicing costs* of making, handling, collecting, and keeping necessary records on loans.

3. The *risk* of loss.

Interest rates vary among lenders and can be quoted and applied in several different ways. The quoted rate is not always the basis for proper comparison and analysis of credit costs. Even though several lenders may quote the same interest rate, the effective or simple annual rate of interest may vary widely. The more common procedures for determining the actual annual interest rate, or the equivalent of simple interest on the unpaid balance, follow.

1. *Simple or true annual interest on the unpaid balance*—A $1,200 note payable at maturity (12 months) with 8% interest:

Interest paid	$.08 \times \$1,200 = \$96$
Average use of the money	$1,200 for the entire year
Actual rate of interest	$\dfrac{96 \text{ (interest)}}{1,200 \text{ (used for one year)}} = 8\%$

2. *Installment loan (with interest on unpaid balance)*[3]—A $1,200 note payable in 12 monthly installments with 8% interest on the unpaid balance:

---

[3]This method is used for amortized loans.

Interest paid ranges from:

First month .... $\dfrac{.08 \times \$1,200}{12}$ = \$8.00

to

Twelfth month .... $\dfrac{.08 \times 100}{12}$ = \$ .67

Total for 12 months is \$52.00

Average use of the money ranges from \$1,200 for the first month down to \$100 for the twelfth month, an average of \$650 for 12 months.

Effective rate of interest .. $\dfrac{\$ 52}{\$650}$ = 8%

3. *Add-on installment loan (with interest on face amount)*—A \$1,200 note payable in 12 monthly installments with 8% interest on face amount of loan:

Interest paid .... .08 × \$1,200 = \$96

Average use of the money ranges from \$1,200 for the first month down to \$100 for the twelfth month, an average of \$650 for 12 months.

Effective rate of interest .. $\dfrac{\$ 96}{\$650}$ = 14.77%

4. *If interest is not stated, use this formula to determine the effective annual interest rate:*

Effective rate of interest—

$$\dfrac{2 \;\times\; \begin{array}{c}\text{Number of}\\ \text{Payment periods}\\ \text{in one year}[4]\end{array} \;\times\; \begin{array}{c}\text{Finance}\\ \text{charges}[5]\end{array}}{\text{Balance owed}[6] \;\times\; \begin{array}{c}\text{Number of payments in}\\ \text{contract plus one}\end{array}}$$

For example, a store advertises a refrigerator for \$250. It can be purchased on the installment plan for \$30 down and monthly payments of \$20 for 12 months. What is the actual rate of interest if you buy on the time payment plan?

Effective rate of interest—

$$\dfrac{2 \times 12 \times \$20}{\$220 \times (12 \text{ plus } 1)} = \dfrac{\$480}{\$1,860} = 16.8\%$$

BUDGETS IN THE HORSE BUSINESS

A budget is a projection of records and accounts and a plan for organizing and operating ahead for a specific period of time. A shorttime budget is usually

[4]Regardless of the total number of payments you will make, use 12 if the payments are monthly, use 6 if payments are every other month, or use 2 if payments are semi-annual.

[5]Use either the time payment price less the cash price, or the amount you pay the lender less the amount you received if negotiating for a loan.

[6]Use cash price less down payment or, if negotiating for a loan, the amount you receive.

for one year, whereas a longtime budget is for a period of years. The principal value of a budget is that it provides a working plan through which the operation can be coordinated. Changes in prices, droughts, and other factors make adjustments necessary. But these adjustments are more simply and wisely made if there is a written budget to use as a reference.

How to Set Up a Budget

It's unimportant whether a printed form (of which there are many good ones) is used or a form is made up on an ordinary ruled 8½" × 11" sheet placed sidewise. The important things are that (1) a budget is kept, (2) it be on a monthly basis, and (3) the operator be "comfortable" with whatever form or system is to be used.

An important part of any budget, or any system of accounting, is that there shall be a listing, or chart, of classifications or categories under which the owner wants the transactions accumulated. In a horse operation that both breeds and races, there may be 150 or more such classifications. From the standpoint of facilitating record keeping, each classification is usually given a number for identification purposes. Then the farm bookkeeper, or the farm manager, codes or classifies each transaction into proper category.

No budget is perfect. But it should be as good an estimate as can be made—despite the fact that it will be affected by such things as droughts, diseases, markets, and many other unpredictables.

A simple, easily kept, and adequate budget can be evolved by using forms such as those shown in Tables 19-1, 19-2 and 19-3.

The Annual Cash Expense Budget should show the monthly breakdown of various recurring items—everything except the initial loan and capital improvements. It includes labor, feed, supplies, fertilizer, taxes, interest, utilities, etc.

The Annual Cash Income Budget is just what the name implies—an estimated cash income by months.

The Annual Cash Expense and Income Budget is a cash flow chart obtained from the first two forms. It's a money "flow" summary by months. From this, it can be ascertained when money will need to be borrowed, how much will be needed, and the length of the loan along with a repayment schedule. It makes it possible to avoid tying up capital unnecessarily, and to avoid unnecessary interest.

How to Figure Net Income

Table 19-3 shows a gross income statement. There are other expenses that must be taken care of before net profit is determined, namely:

1. *Depreciation on buildings and equipment*—It

TABLE 19-1
ANNUAL CASH EXPENSE BUDGET

For _____ (date)
_____ (name of farm)

Item	Total	Jan.	Feb.	Mar.	Apr.	May	June	July	Aug.	Sept.	Oct.	Nov.	Dec.
Labor hired													
Feed purchased													
Stud fees													
Gas, fuel, grease													
Taxes													
Insurance													
Interest													
Utilities													
Etc.													
Total													

TABLE 19-2
ANNUAL CASH INCOME BUDGET

For _____ (date)
_____ (name of farm)

Item	Total	Jan.	Feb.	Mar.	Apr.	May	June	July	Aug.	Sept.	Oct.	Nov.	Dec.
30 yearlings													
30 stud fees, @ $500 each													
490 bu. wheat													
Etc.													
Total													

TABLE 19-3
ANNUAL CASH EXPENSE AND INCOME BUDGET (Cash Flow Chart)

For _____ (date)
_____ (name of farm)

Item	Total	Jan.	Feb.	Mar.	Apr.	May	June	July	Aug.	Sept.	Oct.	Nov.	Dec.
Gross income	25,670					1,000	1,000	etc.					
Gross expense	13,910					575	2,405	etc.					
Difference	11,760					425	1,405	etc.					
Surplus (+) or Deficit (−)	+					+	−						

is suggested that the "useful life" of horse buildings and equipment be as follows, with depreciation accordingly:

Buildings—25 years.
Machinery and equipment—10 years.

Sometimes a higher depreciation, or amortization, is desirable because it produces tax savings and is protection against obsolescence due to scientific and technological developments.

2. *Interest on owner's money invested in farm and equipment*—This should be computed at the going rate in the area, say 8 percent.

Here's an example of how these work:

Let's assume that on a given horse establishment there was a gross income of $100,000 and a gross expense of $60,000, or a surplus of $40,000. Let's further assume that there are $40,000 worth of machinery, $30,000 worth of buildings, and $175,000 of the owner's money invested in farm and equipment. Here is the result:

```
Gross profit ............................. $40,000
Depreciation—
  Machinery:  $ 40,000 @ 10% = $ 4,000
  Buildings:  $ 30,000 @  4% =   1,200
                                 $ 5,200
  Interest:   $175,000 @  8% =  14,000
                     Total ........  19,200
Return to labor and management .......... $20,800
```

Some people prefer to measure management by return on invested capital, and not wages. This approach may be accomplished by paying management wages first, then figuring return on investment.

Enterprise Accounts

When one has a diversified horse enterprise—for example when producing yearlings for sale, having a racing or showing stable, standing stallions for public service, and growing corn—enterprise accounts should be kept; in this case four different accounts for four different enterprises. The reasons for keeping enterprise accounts are:

1. It makes it possible to determine which enterprises have been most profitable, and which least profitable.

2. It makes it possible to compare a given enterprise with competing enterprises of like kind, from the standpoint of ascertaining comparative performance.

3. It makes it possible to determine the profitableness of an enterprise at the margin (the last unit of production). This will give an indication as to whether to increase the size of a certain enterprise at the expense of an alternative existing enterprise when both enterprises are profitable in total.

ANALYZING A HORSE BUSINESS; IS IT PROFITABLE?

Most people are in business to make money—and horsemen are people. In some areas, particularly near cities and where the population is dense, land values may appreciate so as to be a very considerable profit factor. Also, a tax angle may be important. But neither of these should be counted upon. The horse operation should make a reasonable return on the investment; otherwise, the owner should not consider it a business.

The owner or manager of a horse establishment needs to analyze his business—to determine how well he's doing. With big operations, it's no longer possible to base such an analysis on the bank balance statement at the end of the year. In the first place, once a year is not frequent enough, for it is possible to go broke, without really knowing it, in that period of time. Secondly, a balance statement gives no basis for analyzing an operation—for ferreting out its strengths and weaknesses. In large horse enterprises, it is strongly recommended that progress be charted by means of monthly or quarterly closings of financial records.

Also, a horseman must not only compete with other horsemen down the road, but he must compete with himself—with his record last year and the year before. He must work ceaselessly at making progress and lowering costs of production.

To analyze a horse business, three things are essential: (1) good records, (2) enterprise accounts—that is, with such categories as boarding horses, racing stable, breaking and training yearlings, etc., and (3) profit indicators.

Through enterprise accounts, the owner or farm manager can get answers to such questions as the following:

1. How much does it cost me to board horses of different ages each month during the year?

2. How much is it costing to run a racing stable (or show stable)?

3. What is the actual cost of breaking and training a yearling?

4. Are grooms producing at or below standard rates of performance?

5. Is it profitable for me to produce crops along with my breeding operation?

6. Should I let out my crop land on a cash rental or sharecropping arrangement, or should we do the farming ourselves?

7. Should I produce or buy hay?

Profit indicators are a gauge for measuring the primary factors contributing to profit. In order for a horseman to determine how well he's doing, he must be able to compare his own operation with something else, for example: (1) his own historical five-year average, (2) the average for the United States or for his particular area, or (3) the top five percent. The author favors the latter, for high goals have a tendency to spur superior achievement.

Admittedly, profit indicators are not perfect, simply because no two horse enterprises are the same. Nationally, there are wide area differences in climate, feeds, land costs, salaries and wages, and other factors. Nevertheless, indicators as such serve as a valuable yardstick. Through them, it is possible to measure how well a given operation is doing—to ascertain if it is out of line in any one category, and, if so, the extent to which it is out of line.

After a few years of operation, it is desirable that a horse operator evolve his own yardstick and profit indicators, based on his own historical records and averages. Even with these, there will be year-to-year fluctuations due to seasonal differences, horse and feed price changes, disease outbreaks, changes in managers, wars and inflation, and other happenstances.

COMPUTERS IN THE HORSE BUSINESS

Accurate and up-to-the-minute records and controls have taken on increasing importance in all agriculture, including the horse business, as the investment required to engage therein has risen. Today's successful horsemen must have, and use, as complete records as any other business. Also, records must be kept current.

Big and complex enterprises have outgrown hand record keeping. It's too time consuming, with the result that it doesn't allow management enough time for planning and decision making. Additionally, it does not permit an all-at-once consideration of the complex interrelationships which affect the economic success of the business. This has prompted a new computer technique known as linear programming.

Linear programming is similar to budgeting, in that it compares several plans simultaneously and chooses from among them the one likely to yield the highest returns. It is a way in which to analyze a great mass of data and consider many alternatives. It is not a managerial genie, nor will it replace decision-making managers. However, it is a modern and effective tool in the present age, when just a few dollars per head or per acre can spell the difference between profit and loss.

There is hardly any limit to what computers can do if fed the proper information. Among the difficult

Fig. 19-1. Computers have a place in large and sophisticated horse operations. (Courtesy, IBM)

questions that they can answer for a specific operation are:

1. *How is the entire operation doing so far?* It is preferable to obtain quarterly or monthly progress reports, often making it possible to spot trouble before it's too late.

2. *What enterprises are making money; which ones are freeloading or losing?* By keeping records by enterprises—breeding horses, racing stable, wheat, corn, etc.—it is possible to determine strengths and weaknesses, then either to rectify the situation or shift labor and capital to a more profitable operation. Through "enterprise analysis," some operators have discovered that one part of the business may earn $10, or more, per hour for labor and management, whereas another may earn only $5 per hour, and still another may lose money.

3. *Is each enterprise yielding maximum returns?* By having profit or performance indicators in each enterprise, it is possible to compare these (a) with the historical average of the same establishment, or (b) with the same indicators of other operations.

4. *How does this operation stack up with its competition?* Without revealing names, the computing center (local, state, area, or national) can determine how a given operation compares with others—either the average, or the top (say 5%).

5. *How can you plan ahead?* By using projected prices and costs, computers can show what moves to make for the future—they can be a powerful planning

tool. They can be used in determining when to plant, when to schedule farm machine use, etc.

6. *How can income taxes be cut to the legal minimum?* By keeping accurate record of expenses and figuring depreciations accurately, computers make for a saving in income taxes on most establishments.

7. *What is the least-cost ration formulation and the best buy in ingredients?* Many large horse breeding establishments, and most commercial feed companies, now use computers for ration formulation and as a buying and selling aid of feed ingredients. An electronic computer can't do a thing that a good mathematician can't, but it can do it a lot faster and check all possible combinations. It alleviates the endless calculations and hours common to hand calculations. For example, it is estimated that there may be as many as 500 practical solutions when as many as 6 quality specifications and 10 feedstuffs are considered. For these reasons, the use of computers in horse ration formulation and in the buying and selling of feed ingredients will increase.

For providing answers to these questions, and many more, computer accounting costs an average of one percent of the gross income.

There are three requisites for linear programming a horse establishment, namely:

1. Access to a computer.
2. Computer know-how, so as to set the program up properly and be able to analyze and interpret the results.
3. Good records.

The pioneering computer services available to farmers were operated by universities, trade associations, and government; most of them were on an experimental basis. Subsequently, others have entered the field, including commercial data processing firms, banks, machinery companies, feed and fertilizer companies, and farm suppliers. They are using it as a "service sell," as a replacement for the days of "hard sell."

Programmed farming is here to stay, and it will increase in the horse business.

Computers in Horse Breeding Operations

In the past, the biggest deterrent to adequate records on a horse breeding establishment has been the voluminous and time-consuming record keeping involved. Keeping records as such does not change what an animal will transmit, but records must be used to locate and propagate the genetically superior animals if genetic improvement is to be accomplished.

Performance testing has been covered elsewhere in this book (see Chapter 12); thus, repetition at this point is unnecessary.

In addition to their use in performance testing, computerized records can be used for breeding record purposes—as a means of keeping management up-to-date and as an alert on problems to be solved or work to be done. Each animal must be individually identified. Reports can be obtained at such intervals as desired, usually monthly or every two weeks. Also, the owner can keep as complete or as few records as desired. Here are several of the records that can be kept by computer:

1. Pedigrees.
2. Records of animals that need attention, such as:

    a. Animals 4 months old that are unregistered.
    b. Animals ready for inspection or scoring.
    c. Mares that have been bred 2 consecutive times.
    d. Mares that have not conceived 2 months after foaling.
    e. Mares due to foal in 30 days.
    f. Foals 7 months of age that haven't been weaned.
    g. Animals that have not received their seasonal vaccinations; for example, that have not been vaccinated against sleeping sickness by May 1.
    h. Animals that have not been treated for parasites at the scheduled time.
3. A running or cumulative inventory of the herd, by sex; including foals dropped, foals due, and purchases and sales—in number of animals and dollars.
4. The depreciation of purchased animals according to the accounting method of choice.

MANAGEMENT

According to Webster, *management is "the act, art, or manner of managing, or handling, controlling, directing, etc."*

Three major ingredients are essential to success in the horse business: (1) good horses, (2) a sound feed and care program, and (3) good management.

Management gives point and purpose to everything else. The skill of the manager materially affects how well horses are bought and sold, the health of the animals, the results of the rations, the stresses of the horses, the growth rate of young stock, the performance of labor, the public relations of the establishment, and even the expression of the genetic potential of the horses. Indeed, a manager must wear many hats—and he must wear each of them well.

The bigger and the more complicated the horse operation, the more competent the management required. This point merits emphasis because, cur-

rently, (1) bigness is a sign of the times, and (2) the most common method of attempting to "bail out" of an unprofitable horse venture is to increase its size. Although it's easier to achieve efficiency of equipment, labor, purchases, and marketing in big operations, bigness alone will not make for greater efficiency as some owners have discovered to their sorrow, and others will experience. Management is still the key to success. When in financial trouble, owners should have no illusions on this point.

In manufacturing and commerce, the importance and scarcity of top managers are generally recognized and reflected in the salaries paid to persons in such positions. Unfortunately, agriculture as a whole has lagged; and altogether too many owners still subscribe to the philosophy that the way to make money out of the horse business is to hire a manager cheap, with the result that they usually get what they pay for—a "cheap manager."

Traits of a Good Manager

There are established bases for evaluating many articles of trade, including hay and grain. They are graded according to well-defined standards. Additionally, we chemically analyze feeds and conduct feeding trials. But no such standard or system of evaluation has evolved for managers, despite their acknowledged importance.

The author has prepared the Manager Checklist given in Table 19-4, which (1) employers may find

TABLE 19-4

MANAGER CHECK LIST

□ CHARACTER
Has absolute sincerity, honesty, integrity, and loyalty; is ethical.

□ INDUSTRY
Has enthusiasm, initiative, and aggressiveness; is willing to work, work, work.

□ ABILITY
Has horse know-how and experience, business acumen—including ability systematically to arrive at the financial aspects and convert this information into sound and timely management decisions, knowledge of how to automate and cut costs, common sense, and growth potential; is organized.

□ PLANS
Sets goals; prepares organization chart and job description; plans work and works plans.

□ ANALYZES
Identifies the problem, determines pros and cons, then comes to a decision.

□ COURAGE
Has the courage to accept responsibility, to innovate, and to keep on keeping on.

□ PROMPTNESS AND DEPENDABILITY
Is a self-starter; has "T.N.T.," which means that he does it "today, not tomorrow."

□ LEADERSHIP
Stimulates subordinates and delegates responsibility.

□ PERSONALITY
Is cheerful; not a complainer.

useful when selecting or evaluating a manager, and (2) managers may apply to themselves for self-improvement purposes. No attempt has been made to assign a percentage score to each trait, because this will vary among horse establishments. Rather, it is hoped that this checklist will serve as a useful guide (1) to the traits of a good manager, and (2) to what the boss wants.

Organization Chart and Job Description

It is important that every worker know to whom he is responsible and for what he is responsible; and the bigger and the more complex the operation, the more important this becomes. This should be written down in an organization chart and a job description.

The next page shows how an organization chart and job description look.

Incentive Basis for the Help

Big horse establishments must rely on hired labor, all or in part. Good help—the kind that everyone wants—is hard to come by; it's scarce, in strong demand, and difficult to keep. And the farm-horse manpower situation is going to become more difficult in the years ahead. There is need, therefore, for some system that will (1) give a big assist in getting and holding top-flight help, and (2) cut costs and boost profits. An incentive basis that makes hired help partners in profit is the answer.

Fig. 19-2. A good incentive basis makes hired help partners in profit.

Many manufacturers have long had an incentive basis. Executives are frequently accorded stock option privileges, through which they prosper as the business prospers. Common laborers may receive bonuses based on piecework or quotas (number of units, pounds produced). Also, most factory workers get overtime pay and have group insurance and a retirement plan. A few industries have a true profit-sharing arrangement based on net profit as such, a specified percentage of which is divided among employees. No two systems are alike. Yet, each is designed to pay more for labor, provided labor improves production and efficiency. In this way, both owners and laborers benefit from better performance.

Family-owned and family-operated horse enter-

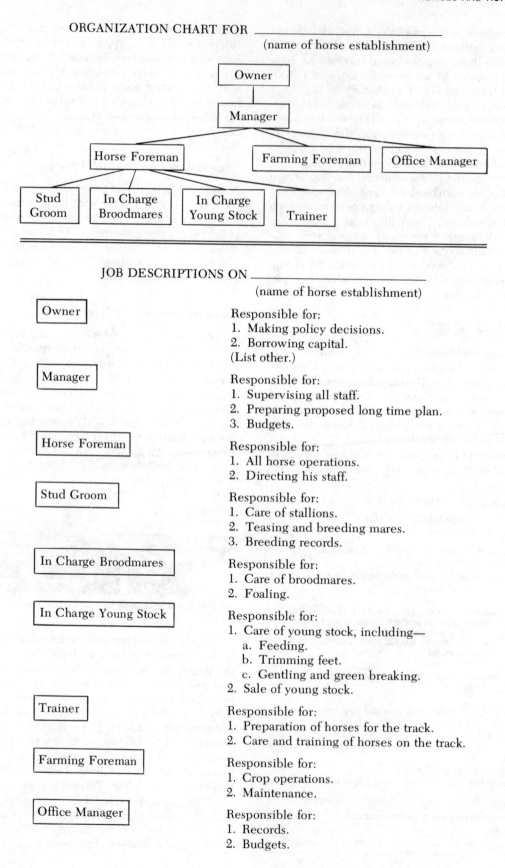

ORGANIZATION CHART FOR _____
(name of horse establishment)

JOB DESCRIPTIONS ON _____
(name of horse establishment)

Owner

Responsible for:
1. Making policy decisions.
2. Borrowing capital.
(List other.)

Manager

Responsible for:
1. Supervising all staff.
2. Preparing proposed long time plan.
3. Budgets.

Horse Foreman

Responsible for:
1. All horse operations.
2. Directing his staff.

Stud Groom

Responsible for:
1. Care of stallions.
2. Teasing and breeding mares.
3. Breeding records.

In Charge Broodmares

Responsible for:
1. Care of broodmares.
2. Foaling.

In Charge Young Stock

Responsible for:
1. Care of young stock, including—
   a. Feeding.
   b. Trimming feet.
   c. Gentling and green breaking.
2. Sale of young stock.

Trainer

Responsible for:
1. Preparation of horses for the track.
2. Care and training of horses on the track.

Farming Foreman

Responsible for:
1. Crop operations.
2. Maintenance.

Office Manager

Responsible for:
1. Records.
2. Budgets.

prises have a built-in incentive basis; there is pride of ownership, and all members of the family are fully cognizant that they prosper as the business prospers. Also, there is an incentive basis in racehorses; both trainers and jockeys share in winnings. However, few horse breeding establishments or riding stables have evolved with an incentive basis for the help. They should give serious consideration to doing so.

Sometimes employers erroneously conclude that providing an incentive basis means that they are giving up a portion of their normal net. For a brief period of time, this may be true. But with the right kind of help, and over a period of time, it will make money for both owners and employees.

Many different incentive plans can be, and are, used. There is no best one for all operations. The various plans given in Table 19-5 are intended as guides only. (See page 438.)

The incentive basis chosen should be tailored to fit the specific operation, with consideration given to kind and size of operation, extent of owner's supervision, present and projected productivity levels, mechanization, and other factors.

HOW MUCH INCENTIVE PAY?

After (1) reaching a decision to go on an incentive basis, and (2) deciding on the kind of incentive, it is necessary to arrive at how much the incentive should be. Here are some guidelines that may be helpful in determining this:

1. Pay the going base, or guaranteed, salary; then add the incentive pay above this.

2. Determine the total stipend (the base salary plus incentive) to which you are willing to go.

3. Before making any offers, always check the plan on paper to see (a) how it would have worked out in past years based on your records, and (b) how it will work out as you achieve the future projected production.

REQUISITES OF AN INCENTIVE BASIS

Owners who have not previously had experience with an incentive basis are admonished not to start with any plan until they are sure of both their plan and their help. Also, it is well to start with a simple plan; then a change can be made to a more inclusive and sophisticated plan after experience is acquired.

Regardless of the incentive plan adopted for a specific operation, it should encompass the following essential features:

1. Good owner (or manager) and good workers. No incentive basis can overcome a poor manager. He must be a good supervisor and fair to his help. Also, on big establishments, he must prepare a written-down organization chart and job description so the help knows (a) to whom they are responsible, and (b) for what they are responsible. Likewise, no incentive basis can spur employees who are not able, interested, and/or willing. This necessitates that employees must be selected with special care where they will be on an incentive basis. Hence, the three—good owner (manager), good employees, and good incentive—go hand in hand.

2. It must be fair to both employer and employees.

3. It must be based on and make for mutual trust and esteem.

4. It must compensate for extra performance, rather than substitute for a reasonable base salary and other considerations (house, utilities, and certain provisions).

5. It must be as simple, direct, and easily understood as possible.

6. It should compensate all members of the team, from top to bottom.

7. It must be put in writing, so that there will be no misunderstanding.

8. It is preferable, although not essential, that workers receive incentive payments (a) at frequent intervals, rather than annually, and (b) immediately after accomplishing the extra performance.

9. It should give the hired help a certain amount of responsibility, from the wise exercise of which they will benefit through the incentive arrangement.

10. It must be backed up by good records; otherwise, there is nothing on which to base incentive payments.

11. It should be a two-way street. If employees are compensated for superior performance, they should be penalized (or, under most circumstances, fired) for poor performance. It serves no useful purpose to reward the unwilling, the incompetent, and the stupid. No overtime pay should be given to an employee who must work longer because of slowness or correcting mistakes of his own making. Likewise, if the reasonable break-even point on an operation is not reached because of obvious neglect (for example, not being on the job at foaling time), the employee(s) should be penalized (or fired).

INDIRECT INCENTIVES

Normally, we think of incentives as monetary in nature—as direct payments or bonuses for extra production or efficiency. However, there are other ways of encouraging employees to do a better job. The latter are known as indirect incentives. Among them are (1) good wages; (2) good labor relations; (3) an adequate house plus such privileges as the use of the farm truck or car, payment of the electric bill, use of a swimming pool, hunting and fishing, and the furnish-

TABLE 19-5

INCENTIVE PLANS FOR HORSE ESTABLISHMENTS

Types of Incentives	Pertinent Provisions of Some Known Incentive Systems in Use	Advantages	Disadvantages	Comments
Bonuses	A flat, arbitrary bonus; at Christmas time, year-end, or quarterly or other intervals. A tenure bonus such as (1) 5 to 10% of the base wage or 2 to 4 weeks' additional salary paid at Christmas time or year-end, (2) 2 to 4 weeks' vacation with pay, depending on length and quality of service or (3) $3.00 to $20.00 per week set aside and to be paid if employee stays on the job a specified time.	It's simple and direct.	Not very effective in increasing production and profits.	
Equity-building plan	Employee is allowed to own a certain number of horses. These are usually fed without charge.	It imparts pride of ownership to the employee.	The hazard that the owner may feel that employee accords his animals preferential treatment; suspicioned if not proved.	
Production sharing	$50 for every mare conceiving above 75%. $100 for every live foal born (foal standing and nursing) above 60%, based on mares bred.	It's an effective way to achieve higher conception and foal crop.	Net returns may suffer. If a high performance level already exists, further gains or improvements may be hard to come by.	
Profit sharing:		It's an effective way to get hired help to cut costs.		
1. Percent of gross income in cash.	1% to 2% of the gross, with each employee sharing on a prorata of salary basis.	It's a good plan for a hustler.	Percent of gross does not impart cost of production consciousness. Controversy may arise (1) over accounting procedure; e.g., from the standpoint of the owner a fast tax write-off may be desirable on new equipment, but this reduces the net shared with the worker; and (2) because some owners are prone to overbuild and overequip, thereby decreasing net.	There must be prior agreement on what constitutes gross or net receipts, as the case may be, and how it is figured. Generally, a working owner should accord himself a salary as part of the operating expense of the business, just as he allows salaries to other help. Then, all operating costs, including interest on the owner's money, should be deducted as expenses. Books should not be opened to all employees. Access to books should be limited to supervisory personnel and the bookkeeper. Most laborers do not understand accounting principles; hence, opening up the books to them may lead to gossip, suspicion, and distrust.
2. Percent of net income in cash.	10% to 20% of the net after deducting all costs, with each employee sharing on a prorata of salary basis.		There may not be any net some years.	
3. Percent of net income as investment in the business.	Giving employees an investment (stock) in the future growth and expansion of the business in an amount equal to 20% of the yearly net profit, with each employee sharing on a prorata of salary basis.	Employees stand to profit if the business grows and prospers.		

(Continued)

TABLE 19-5 (Continued)

Types of Incentives	Pertinent Provisions of Some Known Incentive Systems in Use	Advantages	Disadvantages	Comments
4. Percent of net income placed in trust account.	A certain percent (say 20%) of the net earnings placed in a trust account, and (1) divided among the employees on a prorata of salary basis, and (2) paid to employees upon retirement or completion of a specified number of years' service.	Provides for retirement income and encourages continuity of service. There is a considerable saving in income tax paid.	Some employees do not wish to wait so long for their added compensation.	
Production sharing and prevailing price	Table 19-6 gives a proposed incentive basis for a breeding establishment that derives most of its income from the sale of yearlings. Table 19-7 gives a proposed incentive basis for a riding stable.	It embraces the best features of both production and profit sharing, without the major disadvantages of each. It (1) encourages high productivity and likely profits, (2) is tied in with prevailing prices, (3) does not necessitate opening the books, and (4) is flexible—it can be split between owner and employee on any basis desired, and the production part can be adapted to a sliding scale or escalator arrangement.	It is a bit more complicated than some other plans, and it requires more complete records.	When properly done, and all factors considered, this is the most satisfactory incentive basis for a horse establishment selling yearlings or operating a riding stable. Also, it can be adapted to any other type of horse enterprise.
Using a scorecard (rating)	The score is the basis for bonus, salary raise, and other considerations. The score method involves the preparation of a score card listing desired traits and performance, with a numerical value assigned to each according to its relative importance (see Fig. 19-3).	This method works well in an office in which the personnel are carefully selected.		

ing of meat, milk, and eggs; (4) good buildings and equipment; (5) vacation time with pay, time off, sick leave; (6) group health; (7) security; (8) the opportunity for self-improvement that can accrue from working for a top man; (9) the right to invest in the business; (10) an all-expense-paid trip to a short course, show, or convention; and (11) a year-end bonus for staying all year. Such indirect incentives will be accorded to the help of more and more establishments, especially the big ones.

INCENTIVE BASIS FOR A HORSE BREEDING ESTABLISHMENT

On horse breeding establishments there is need for some system which will encourage caretakers to (1) get a high conception rate; (2) be good nursemaids to newborn foals, though it may mean the loss of sleep; and (3) develop and sell surplus animals advantageously.

From the standpoint of the owner of a horse breeding establishment, production expenses remain practically unchanged regardless of the efficiency of the operation. Thus, the investment in land, buildings and equipment, stallion and broodmares, feed, and

labor differs very little with a change (up or down) in the percent foal crop; and income above the break-even point is largely net profit. Yet, it must be remembered that owners take all the risks; hence, they should benefit most from profits.

On a horse breeding establishment, the author recommends that profits beyond the break-even point (after deducting all expenses, including the salary of the owner) be split on an 80:20 basis. This means that every dollar made above a certain level is split, with the owner taking 80 cents and the employees getting 20 cents. Also, there is merit in an escalator arrangement, with the split changed to 70:30, for example, when a certain plateau of efficiency is reached. Moreover, that which goes to the employees should be divided on the basis of their respective contributions, all the way down the line; for example, 25% of it might go to the manager, 25% might be divided among the foremen, and 50% of it divided among the rest of the help; or that which goes to the employees may be divided on a prorata of salary basis.

Gross income in horse breeding operations is determined primarily by (1) percent conception on mares bred, (2) percent foal crop, and (3) prices on horses sold. The first two factors can easily be deter-

TABLE 19-6

A PROPOSED INCENTIVE BASIS FOR A BREEDER WHO SELLS YEARLINGS

Yearling Crop Sold Based on 100 Mares Bred to Produce	Price of Yearlings	How It Works
(no. of yearlings sold)	($)	
30	200	On this particular establishment, 100 mares are bred annually, and each year 15 top fillies are retained as herd replacements. Over and above this, the break-even point is 50 yearlings marketed annually. Thus, if 100 mares were bred in 1975 to break even there would have to be 65 yearlings in 1976, out of which 15 would be kept and 50 marketed.
35	300	
40	400	
45	500	
50 ◄–(break-even)–►	600	Moreover, the historical records of this establishment show that $600/head is the break-even point, provided 50 yearlings are sold—or a total gross of $30,000.
55	700	The sale of each yearling in excess of 50 head involves only $300 expense, primarily for added feed.
60	800	
65	900	
70	1,000	Thus, if 60 yearlings are marketed at an average of $1,000, that's a gross of $60,000. The break-even point is $30,000 (50 yearlings @ $600) plus the added cost of $3,000 to produce 10 more yearlings (10 × $300), or a total of $33,000. Hence, the net is $27,000. With an escalator arrangement, there might be an 80:20 split on a net up to $27,000; a 70:30 split of a net from $27,000 to $40,000; and a 65:35 split of a net in excess of $40,000.
75	1,100	
80	1,200	It is recommended that division among employees be on a prorata of salary basis.

mined. Usually, enough horses are sold to establish prices or values; otherwise, the going price can be used.

The incentive basis proposed in Table 19-6 for horse breeding operations is simple, direct, and easily applied. As noted, it is based on the number and price of yearlings sold.

BREAK-EVEN POINT

Whenever possible, the break-even point on a horse establishment—the dollars gross necessary in order to break even—should be arrived at from actual records accumulated by the specific horse establishment, preferably over a period of years. Perhaps, too, break-even points should be moving averages, based on 5 to 10 years, with older years dropped out and more recent years added from time to time, thereby reflecting improvements in efficiency due primarily to changing technology, rather than to the efforts of the caretakers.

With a new horse operation, on which there are no historical records from which to arrive at a break-even point, it is recommended that the figures of other similar operations be used at the outset. These can be revised as actual records on the specific enterprise become available. It is important, however, that the new operation start on an incentive basis, even though the break-even point must be arbitrarily assumed at the time.

INCENTIVE BASIS FOR A RIDING STABLE

An incentive basis for riding stable help is needed for motivation purposes, just as it is in racing or breeding horses. It is the most effective way in which to lessen absenteeism; make for superior training, teaching, and public relations; and improve housekeeping.

A proposed incentive basis for a riding stable is shown in Table 19-7. For this incentive basis to work at its best, the organization should have each Instructor-Trainer under the supervision of the Director of Riding Stable, and responsible for a specific unit of 40 to 80 horses. This includes serving as a working foreman in their care, and handling all the instruction and training therewith.

This unit-responsibility-and-care arrangement is patterned after Grosbois in France, and Newmarket in England, where it has been highly successful for many years. It will require that the facilities be developed with the unit type of operation in mind. But it has the very great virtue of making each Instructor-Trainer responsible for the success of his (or her) division—horses, facilities, keep of premises, and instruction—thereby minimizing supervision and avoiding "passing the buck." In addition, each Instructor-Trainer is responsible for such assignments as delegated by the Director, including record keeping.

In the operation of a riding stable, where teaching equitation and training horses are the two primary sources of income, there is need for Instructors-Trainers who are able to (1) keep their stables filled with horses in training, and (2) keep their classes filled with students; for, here again, the overhead cost is little different between well-filled and empty classrooms and stables. The incentive basis proposed in Table 19-7 will accomplish these objectives.

THE SCORECARD INCENTIVE BASIS

As the name implies, the scorecard method involves the preparation of a scorecard. In the scorecard, each major desired trait and performance is given a numerical value according to its relative importance.

TABLE 19-7

A PROPOSED INCENTIVE BASIS FOR EACH
INSTRUCTOR-TRAINER IN A RIDING STABLE

Yearly Gross from Boarding-Training Horses (@ $200/mo., $2,400/yr.)	Yearly Gross from Conducting Riding Classes (@ $10/student/2-hr. lesson)	How It Works
(no. horses; $ gross/yr.)	*(students, class days; gross)*	
2 horses; $4,800/yr.	One class of 6 students/day; 300 days/yr. instruction = $18,000 gross.	Each Instructor-Trainer is responsible for his own unit. He receives a basic salary of $600/mo. plus living quarters.
3 horses; $7,200/yr. ◄—(break-even)—►	One class of 12 students/day; 300 days/yr. instruction = $36,000 gross.	To cover all expenses—the Instructor-Trainer's salary, grooms, horses, facilities, equipment, feed, insurance, and overhead, requires 3 horses being boarded-trained and one class of 12 students receiving 300 days instruction, or a total gross of $43,200 ($7,200 + $36,000). That's the break-even point.
5 horses; $12,000/yr.	Two classes of 12 students/day; 300 days/yr. instruction = $72,000 gross.	With 5 horses boarded-trained and two classes instead of one, the gross would be increased to $84,000. The added expense to generate $84,000 instead of $43,200 is small—only $1,200 more for keeping 2 horses. Hence, the net on the $84,000 is: $84,000—($43,200 + 1,200), or $39,600.
		With an 80:20 division, $31,680 would go to the owner, and $7,920 would be distributed among the employees. Or, if desired, the split could be on an escalator arrangement, with the employees getting a higher percentage as the net increases. Whatever the division, it is suggested that it be divided among them on a prorata of salary basis.

A scorecard which the author developed and has used is herewith presented as Fig. 19-3. (See page 442.)

Based on the average of two scores per year (Fig. 19-3), the following considerations are suggested for staff:

1. *Christmas Bonus.*

Score	Grade	Employee Should:	Christmas Bonus[7]
59 or under	. Poor	Improve, work longer hours, and/or look for a job elsewhere	None
60-74	. Fair	Improve and work longer hours	None
75-79	. Good	Keep Improving	$ 50
80-84	. Good	Keep Improving	$100
85-89	. Good+	Keep Improving	$150
90-94	. Excellent	Keep Improving	$200
95-100	. Superior	Keep on keeping on	$250

2. *Health insurance; extra vacation time*—Full-time employees on appointment (not on hourly basis) exceeding (and maintaining) a minimum score of 75 after 6 months' service or 80 after 2 years' service, will be accorded the following added considerations:

After Years' Service	Consideration
½ year (6 mos.)	Health insurance[8] for employee (not family), with employer and employee each paying 50% of premiums. (Employer will terminate health insurance upon termination of employment of employee.)
2 years	Health insurance for employee (not family), with employer paying premiums. (Employer will terminate health insurance upon termination of employment of employee.)
3 years	Added workday of paid vacation.[9]
4 years	Added workday of paid vacation.
5 years	Added workday of paid vacation.
6 years	Added workday of paid vacation.
7 years	Added workday of paid vacation.

[7]Based on full-time employees and 12 months' prior service; regular half-time employees are accorded half these amounts. Those not on the job 12 months are accorded consideration on a proportion to 12 months' basis.

[8]Health insurance is not accorded employees who already have such protection via the spouse.

[9]Thus, at the end of 7 years, employees meeting the stipulated score requisite will have health insurance and 3 weeks, (15 work days) vacation with pay.

PERSONAL SCORE CARD For _____	Pts. or %	1977 June 30	1977 Dec. 31	1978 June 30	1978 Dec. 31	1979 June 30	1979 Dec. 31
USE: This score card is applied by the owner-manager to each staff member every 6 months, then the results are discussed with each person in a private conference. PURPOSE: To provide staff with an evaluation which they may use as a basis for self-improvement, and to recognize and reward superior preformance.							
CHARACTER: Absolute sincerity, honesty, integrity, loyalty; ethical	10						
INDUSTRY: Works hard; has enthusiasm, initiative, and aggressiveness; a desire to get the job done, and a willingness to let the boss worry about raises; not afraid of long hours when necessary, not a clock watcher	15						
ABILITY AND PERFORMANCE: Skilled and competent in area of work; is neat and accurate; turns out adequate work; has know-how, clarity, common sense, good judgment, and maturity; is organized; shows growth potential and self-improvement; not a know-it-all; accepts responsibility, masters the job assignments without being told "what to do next"; plans work, organizes, and keeps on top; efficient and cuts costs; recognizes that the "boss" must make decisions and give directions	40						
INTEREST: Genuine interest in work—not just payday and 5 o'clock	10						
COURAGE: To innovate—to try the new, and to keep on keeping on	5						
PROMPTNESS AND DEPENDABILITY: A self-starter, does it today and not tomorrow	10						
PERSONALITY AND APPEARANCE: Cheerful; not a complainer; a member of the team	10						
	100						

Fig. 19-3. Scorecard and incentive basis for staff.

3. *Merit increases*—Salary increases on a merit basis only, and determined by (a) average annual score of the employee, (b) how well the business is doing, and (c) going wages of the area for the particular assignment. Whatever salary increase is accorded will be on a January 1 basis only, following the second six months' review.

SYNDICATED HORSES

Reduced to simple terms, a syndicated horse is one that is owned by several people. Most commonly, it's a stallion; although an expensive yearling or broodmare is sometimes syndicated. Also, any number of people can form a syndicate. However, there is a tendency to use the term "partnership" where two to four owners are involved, and to confine the word "syndicate" to a larger group of owners.

Each member of the syndicate owns a certain number of "shares," depending on how much he purchased or contributed. It's much like a stock market investor, who may own one or several shares in General Electric, IBM, or some other company. Some-

times one person may own as much as a half-interest in a horse. Occasionally, half-shares are sold.

Generally speaking, the number of shares in a stallion is limited to the number of mares that may reasonably be bred to him in one season—usually 30 to 35, with Thoroughbred stallions.

Why and How Owners Syndicate

The owner of a stallion that has raced successfully usually has the opportunity to choose between (1) continuing as sole owner of the horse, and standing him for service privately or publicly, or (2) syndicating him. In recent years, more and more owners of top stallions have elected to syndicate. The most common reasons for so doing are:

1. The stallion owner does not have a breeding farm or an extensive band of broodmares.
2. The owner believes that the stallion under consideration may not nick well with many of his mares; or perhaps the stallion is closely related to the mares.

3. The owner has need for immediate income. Moreover, the profit, according to a tax court ruling, is subject to the frequently advantageous capital gains treatment on income tax. By contrast, if sole ownership is retained, considerable promotional and advertising expenses will be involved for approximately three years—until the stallion's get make their debut on the tracks; and, in the meantime, practically no income can be expected until about a year from entering stud, at which time the usual "live foal" guarantee is met. Until this condition is fulfilled, any stud fees that are collected are generally held in escrow, as protection if they should have to be returned.

4. Syndicating spreads the risk, should the stallion get injured or die, or prove unsuccessful as a sire.

The owner may arrange the syndication himself, usually with competent legal advice; or, if preferred, the syndication can be turned over to a professional manager, who will generally take a free share as his organization fee.

The following pointers are pertinent to successful syndication of stallions:

1. *Check fertility*—Before syndicating, it is a good idea to check the fertility by test-mating to a coldblood (draft) mare. Of course, if the stallion is still racing, and has not been retired to stud, this is impossible.

2. *Establish stud fee*—A common rule of thumb is that each syndicate share is worth four times the stud fee. Hence, if it is decided that the stallion under consideration will command a $10,000 stud fee, each share would be worth $40,000. If 30 shares are involved, the horse would have a value of $1,200,000 for syndication purposes.

3. *Determine time of Payment*—In most cases, payment is due upon the signing of the syndicate contract, although some contracts (a) allow 30, 60, or 90 days, or (b) provide that the price of a share may be paid on the installment plan over a 2- or 3-year period.

4. *Put it in writing*—Syndication agreements should be clear, detailed, and in writing. In addition to identifying the horse, the agreement should state (a) the shareholder's proportionate interest (say 1/32); (b) the breeding rights of a shareholder (for example, the right to breed one mare per season to the horse, so long as he is in good health and able to breed); (c) the method of distributing services by lot, should it be necessary to limit the number of mares bred during any given season; (d) the method of disposing of, and the price to charge for, any extra services (over and above one per share, for example) during a given season; (e) the place where the horse shall stand, or how such determination will be made (usually by majority vote of the shareholders); and (f) how other policy matters not covered in the agreement will be determined (usually by majority vote).

Generally, such routine matters as the feed, care, and health of the stallion, and the scheduling of mares are left to the discretion of the syndicate manager, at a stated fee per month, with each shareholder billed proportionate to his number of shares. The manager also handles the promotion and advertising, insurance, and unusual veterinary expenses, as stipulated by the syndicate, with the costs prorated among its members.

Normally, a shareholder can barter his breeding service to another stallion. However, he cannot sell his share without prior approval of the manager and giving the other shareholders the right to buy it at the price offered; and, normally, this same stipulation applies to the sale of a service during any season.

Also, provision is usually made for sale of the horse should the majority of the shareholders so desire, with them also determining, at the time of sale, the price and whether sale shall be at private treaty or auction. Further, the contract usually provides for "pensioning," or otherwise disposing of, a sire should he become sterile or be overtaken by old age before dying.

In short, a syndicate agreement, like any good legal contract, attempts to spell out every foreseeable

Fig. 19-4. The thoroughbred stallion, Nashua, syndicated by Leslie B. Combs II, Spendthrift Farm, Lexington, Kentucky, for $1,251,200—a total of 32 shares, each at $39,100. Nashua was the winner of $1,288,565. (Courtesy, Mr. Combs)

contingency that may arise during the stud's career, and to arrange for majority vote of the shareholders to settle any unforeseen contingencies.

The Nashua Syndicate Agreement, used by Mr. Leslie B. Combs II, Spendthrift Farm, Lexington, Kentucky, who has probably contributed more than any other person to stallion syndication, follows. It is also noteworthy that, when Mr. Combs syndicated Nashua, he sold all but one share of a total of 32, each at $39,100 (for a total of $1,251,200), over the telephone in one afternoon; and the only reason that the one share was not sold until the next morning was that he couldn't reach one of his regular clients on the telephone that afternoon.

Sample Syndicate Agreement

The syndicate agreement for the noted Thoroughbred stallion, Nashua, is given in Fig. 19-5.[10]

---

[10]This agreement was provided through the courtesy of Mr. Leslie B. Combs II and published by Agriservices Foundation in *Stud Manager's Handbook*, Vol. I, beginning on p. 45.

STALLION BREEDING CONTRACTS

Stallion breeding contracts should always be in writing; and the higher the stud fee, the more important it is that good business methods prevail. Neither "gentlemen's agreements" nor barn door records will suffice.

From a legal standpoint, a stallion breeding contract is binding to the parties whose signatures are affixed thereto. Thus, it is important that the contract be carefully read and fully understood before signing.

A sample stallion breeding contract is presented in Fig. 19-6.[11] (See page 446.)

In addition to the provisions made in the sample stallion breeding contract presented here, and in most other similar contracts, the author suggests that the following matters be covered in the stallion breeding contract:

1. *Facts about the mare*—There should be record of the mare's temperament; thereby lessening danger

---

[11]Sample prepared by the author of this book.

SYNDICATION AGREEMENT
(prepared for Thoroughbred stallion, Nashua)

THIS AGREEMENT, made as of December 15, 19__, between the several persons whose names and addresses are set out in the Schedule hereto attached as the original Subscribers, and being referred to collectively as "the Shareholders."

WITNESSETH:

WHEREAS, Leslie Combs II, Spendthrift Farm, Ironworks Pike, Lexington, Kentucky, has purchased the Thoroughbred horse NASHUA (B. c., 1952), by *NASRULLAH-SEGULA, by JOHNSTOWN from the Estate of William Woodward, Jr. and has formed a Syndicate to acquire the ownership thereof upon the following terms and conditions:

1. The ownership of NASHUA shall be divided into thirty-two (32) shares, and the purchasers of said thirty-two (32) shares have paid the total purchase price of One Million, Two Hundred and Fifty-One Thousand, Two Hundred Dollars, ($1,251,200.00), or the sum of Thirty-Nine Thousand, One Hundred Dollars, ($39,100.00) per share.

2. Each of the thirty-two (32) shares shall be on an equal basis with the others and shall be indivisible, and only a full share shall have any of the rights hereunder; provided, however, that there is expressly reserved, and the within sale is made subject to one (1) free nomination to NASHUA each year during his life for each of the following named persons, their heirs and assigns: John W. Hanes, 460 Park Avenue, New York City, C. J. Devine, 48 Wall Street, New York City, and Leslie Combs II, Spendthrift Farm, Lexington, Kentucky.

3. NASHUA shall be returned to training as soon as practicable and shall race under the personal management and supervision of a Committee consisting of John W. Hanes, C. J. Devine, and Leslie Combs II, as agents for the shareholders. The Committee shall have full charge of and complete control over the future racing career of NASHUA, including but not limited to (a) the employment of a trainer, (b) the selection of tracks at which he will be trained and raced, (c) the races to which he will be nominated and in which he will be actually started, (d) the selection and employment of a jockey or jockeys, (e) the name and colors under which he will be raced, and (f) how long NASHUA shall race and when he shall be retired from racing, and the actions, decisions and judgments of the Committee with respect to any and all of the foregoing matters shall be final, conclusive and binding upon all of the Shareholders and shall not give rise to any liability upon the Committee or the individual members thereof so long as they act in good faith.

All expenses incurred by the Committee in training and racing NASHUA shall be paid by the Shareholders in proportion to the number of shares owned by each of them, and the earnings of NASHUA shall likewise be divided amongst the Shareholders proportionately. The Committee shall furnish each Shareholder periodically with a statement showing the expenses and earnings.

The Committee is authorized to execute such leases or other instruments as may be required under the rules of The Jockey Club and/or the various Racing Commissions and other governmental bodies having jurisdiction of the premises to qualify NASHUA to race.

If a member of the Committee should die, resign or be unable to serve for any reason, then the remaining members of the Committee shall select his successor from amongst the Shareholders.

4. Upon retirement to the stud, NASHUA shall stand and shall be kept and maintained at Spendthrift Farm, Ironworks Pike, in Fayette County, Kentucky, under the sole personal managment and supervision of Leslie Combs II, and he shall be entitled to charge and receive the prevailing rates for stallion keep. Leslie Combs II shall have complete charge of advertising the stallion and shall have the authority to select a veterinarian. Owners of shares shall pay all charges, costs and expenses incurred in connection with said stallion in the proportion that their respective shares bear to the whole number of shares.

(Continued)

5. Each Shareholder in each breeding season shall be entitled to one (1) free nomination to said stallion for each share owned by him, subject to the payment of his share of the Syndicate expenses and the provisions of Paragraph 6; provided, however, that in NASHUA's first full season in the stud he shall be limited to a book of twenty-five (25) mares, and the owners of the thirty-two (32) nomination shall be determined by lot at a drawing to be held at such time and place as the aforesaid Committee may determine, and notice of which shall be sent by registered mail or by telegram to each Shareholder at least five (5) days prior thereto. Each share and each free nomination shall be regarded as if it were the subject of separate ownership and shall be on an equal basis, the one with the other.

Thereafter, if the veterinarian attending said stallion and the Syndicate Manager, Leslie Combs II, shall certify that in their opinion NASHUA's book may be increased without injury to him, then additional yearly nominations may be sold by the Syndicate Manager at the regular stud fee and the yearly proceeds thereof shall be divided among the Shareholders in proportion to the number of shares owned by each.

Each mare bred to NASHUA must be in sound breeding condition and free from infection or disease, and no mare shall be covered more than six (6) times in any breeding season.

6. If Leslie Combs II, with the advice and approval of the veterinarian, shall determine that NASHUA shall be bred to less than thirty-five (35) mares in any stud season, then the Shareholders and those persons holding the three (3) free nominations in each year (as provided in Paragraph 2 herein) who collectively shall be entitled to such reduced number of nominations shall be determined by lot, and any Shareholder or holder of said free nominations who has suffered by reason of the drawing of lots in any season shall not be submitted to the risk of drawing in any subsequent season unless and until all other Shareholders and holders of said free nominations, have suffered as the result thereof; and for the purpose of this clause each share and free nomination shall be regarded as if it were the subject of separate ownership and shall be on an equal basis, the one with the other. Notice of the decision to reduce NASHUA's book to less than thirty-five (35) nominations and of the time and place of the drawing shall be sent by the Syndicate Manager to each Shareholder and holder of a free nomination by registered mail or by telegram at least five (5) days prior to said drawing.

7. Leslie Combs II shall employ the usual care customarily employed in Fayette County, Kentucky, in the management of NASHUA, but shall not be responsible for any injury, disease or death of said stallion, nor for any injury, disease or death of any mare resulting from breeding or attempted breeding to said stallion.

8. Leslie Combs II shall have and is hereby granted the right and option to purchase any share or shares which any owner desires to sell, and such owner shall first offer the same to Leslie Combs II with the price requested for the same. If Leslie Combs II is unwilling to pay the price requested by the owner, then such owner may secure a written offer elsewhere for such share or shares, and if the owner is willing to accept such written offer he shall present the same to Leslie Combs II, who shall have the right to purchase, within forty-eight hours thereafter, such share or shares for the price so offered in writing and which the owner was willing to accept. In the event Leslie Combs II fails to purchase such share or shares within the time specified, then such owner may accept such written offer. This option shall apply in the same manner and under the same conditions to such share or shares in the new ownership. This option shall apply to and have priority over any hypothecation, distraint or other alienation of said share or shares or any interest therein, and any and all transfers of any share or shares are expressly subject to said option.

9. All notices required hereunder shall be effective and binding if sent by prepaid registed mail, telegram, cable, or delivered in person to the address of the respective Shareholders set out in the Schedule attached or such address as shall hereafter be designated in writing to the Syndicate Manager.

10. The Shareholders accept delivery of NASHUA without examination as to his fertility and breeding soundness, as no veterinary examination with reference thereto has been made or will be made prior to his retirement from racing.

11. The undersigned hereby subscribes for _____ shares in the Syndicate for the total sum of $ _____, payable in cash upon the execution of this Agreement, and in consideration thereof Leslie Combs II has sold and conveyed _____ Shares to undersigned, subject to all of the terms and conditions herein.

This Agreement may be executed in several counterparts, and when executed by the Shareholders the several counterparts shall constitute the agreement between the parties as if all signatures were appended to one original instrument.

WITNESS the hand of the undersigned as of the day and date first above written.

_____

Name

_____

_____

Address

Approved:

_____

Syndicate Manager

Fig. 19-5. Syndication agreement.

to her, to the stallion, and to the personnel. Also, historical information should be included about the mare's breeding record and peculiarities, and her health—preferably with the health record provided by the veterinarian who has looked after her.

2. *Some management understandings*—The parties to the contract should reach an understanding relative to the mare's veterinary care, parasite control, seasonal injections, foot trimming, etc., and then put it in writing.

3. *An incentive basis*—Generally, stallion owners guarantee a live foal, which means that the foal must stand and nurse; otherwise, the stud fee is either refunded or not collected, according to the stipulations. Of course, it is in the best interests of both parties that a strong, healthy foal be born. One well-known Quar-

STALLION BREEDING CONTRACT

(To be executed in duplicate for each mare; one copy to be retained by each party.)
This Contract for the breeding season of _____ made and entered into by and between
(year)

_____   _____
(owner of stallion)   (address)

herinafter designated Stallion Owner, and

_____   _____
(owner of mare)   (address)

herinafter designated Mare Owner.
This contract covers _____

The stallion, _____, whose service fee is $ _____,
(name of stallion)

$_____ of which is paid with this contract, and the balance of

$_____ will be paid before the mare leaves _____
(name of farm or ranch)

and
The mare, _____, Reg. No. _____, by _____
(sire)

out of _____, age _____, color _____.
(dam)

I. *The Mare Owner agrees that—*

Upon arrival, the mare will (a) be halter-broken, (b) have the hind shoes removed, and (c) be accompanied by a health certificate signed by a veterinarian, certifying that she is healthy and in sound breeding condition.
Stallion Owner will not be responsible for accident, disease, or death to the mare, or to her foal (if she has a foal).
Stallion Owner may, at his discretion, have his veterinarian (a) check and treat the mare for breeding condition or diseases, and (b) treat her for parasites if needed; with the expenses of such services charged to Mare Owner's account and paid when the mare leaves the farm or ranch.
He will pay the following board on his mare at the time the mare leaves the farm or ranch: Feed and facilites $ _____/day.
Should the mare prove barren, or should the foal die at birth, he will send notice of same, signed by a licensed veterinarian, within five days of such barren determination or death.
Should he fail to deliver the above mare to Stallion Owner's premises on or before _____,
(date)
Stallion Owner shall be under no further obligation with respect to any matter herein set forth.
This contract shall not be assigned or transferred. In the event the mare is sold, any remaining unpaid fee shall immediately become due and payable and no refund shall be due anyone under any circumstances.

II. *The Stallion Owner agrees that—*

He will provide suitable facilities for the mare and feed and care for her in a good and husbandlike manner.
Mare owner will not be responsible for any disease, accident, or injury to Stallion Owner's horses.
A live foal is guaranteed—meaning a foal that can stand up alone and nurse.

III. *The Stallion Owner and Mare Owner mutually agree that—*

This contract is not valid unless completed in full.
Should the above-named stallion die or become unfit for service, or should the above-named mare die or become unfit to breed, this contract shall become null and void and money paid as part of this contract shall be refunded to Mare Owner.

Should the mare prove barren, or should the foal die at birth, with certification of same provided to Stallion Owner within the time specified, Stallion Owner has the option either to (a) rebreed the mare the following year, or (b) refund the $_____ portion of the breeding fee, thereby cancelling this entire contract.

The mare will not receive more than _____ covers during the breeding season; and she will not be
(no.)

bred before _____ 19 _____
(date)
or after _____ 19 _____
(date)

_____   _____   _____
(date)   (signature; Mare Owner or Rep.)   (address)

_____   _____   _____
(date)   (signature; Stallion Owner or Rep.)   (address)

Fig. 19-6. Stallion breeding contract.

ter Horse establishment reports that their records reveal that of all mares settled during a particular 3-year period, 19% of them subsequently either resorbed or aborted feti, or the foal or mare died. Further, their investigation of these situations showed that the vast majority of these losses could have been averted by better care and management. They found many things wrong—ranging from racing mares in foal to turning them to pastures where there was insufficient feed. To alleviate many, if not most, of these losses—losses that accrue after the mare has been examined and pronounced safe in foal, then taken away from the stallion owner's premises—the author suggests that an incentive basis be incorporated in the stallion breeding contract. For example, the stallion owner might agree to reduce the stud fee (1) by 10, 15, or 20% (state which), provided a live foal is born; or (2) by 25 to 33⅓% provided the mare owner's veterinarian certifies that the mare is safe in foal 30 days after being removed from the place where bred, with payment made at that time and based on conception rather than on birth of a live foal.

BOARDING AGREEMENT

Today's tough zoning laws and antipollution campaigns are making it increasingly difficult to keep horses in towns and suburban areas. As a result, more and more horses are being stabled and cared for in boarding establishments out in the country, to which owners commute. This prompts the need for an agreement.

Boarding agreements should always be in writing, rather than verbal, "gentlemen's agreements." From a legal standpoint, a boarding agreement is binding to the parties whose signatures are affixed thereto. Thus, it is important that the agreement be carefully filled out, read, and fully understood before signing. A sample boarding agreement is given in Fig. 19-7. (See page 448.)

HORSEMEN AND INCOME TAXES[12]

The 1976 Tax Reform Law affects horsemen in the areas of (1) income tax, and (2) estate and gift taxes; hence, horsemen should be aware of the provisions thereof. Also, they are admonished to consult a conpetent tax authority before embarking upon any business operation involving horses.

Cash Vs Accrual Method

There are two standard methods of reporting, the cash basis and the accrual basis. Most horsemen use the cash basis, in which income is reported when it is actually received and expenses are recorded when actually paid. It does not include the value of products sold or services performed for which payment was not actually received during the taxable year. In addition to being simple and easy, the cash basis has the advantage of allowing the horseman partially to control his income for tax purposes by timing year-end payment of expenses.

From a management standpoint, however, the accrual basis is preferred because it more nearly reflects the income of a particular period. Under it, income is accounted for when it is earned and expenses are recorded when incurred rather than when paid. Also, the accrual basis necessitates that complete annual inventories be kept, with taxes paid on increases of inventory, and deductions made for any decreases in inventory.

On large horse establishments, it is recommended that both record systems be used—the cash basis for tax purposes, and the accrual basis for management purposes. A competent accountant can set up such a system with the same set of records simply by adding a few memo accounts that are removed at the end of the year when closing the books for tax purposes.

Hobby or Business

The first real hazard is that participation in the horse business—whether in breeding, racing, training, and/or showing—may be regarded by the Internal Revenue Service (IRS), as indulgence in a hobby or diversion rather than a true business venture, with the result that any losses accruing therefrom are disallowed in their entirety. This should cause no concern to those who derive their entire living from the horse business or to those successful horsemen who normally operate at a profit. Rather, it is the person of independent means, or one who is profitably engaged in another enterprise or other enterprises, who is likely to be challenged when he or she has an unbroken string of loss years accruing from breeding, racing, and/or showing operations. Also, IRS does not automatically take cognizance of the fact that breeding programs designed to develop a new breed of horses, or even to build up a herd, take many years. It is essential, therefore, that the horseman establish a profit-making motive and a reasonable chance of achieving this aim. Then, he must conduct his operations in a business-like manner throughout, and refrain from anything that may cause his actions even to be suspicioned as pursuit of a hobby rather than the conducting of a business.

In breeding, racing, training, and/or showing horses, a fine line often separates a hobby from a

---

[12]This section was authoritatively reviewed by Kenneth A. Wood, Attorney at Law and author of *The Business of Horses*, 315 Fourth Ave., Suite S, Chula Vista, California; and Dale E. Rose, CPA and author of *Depreciation for the Horse Industry*, Campbell-Rose & Company, Mansfield, Ohio. In addition to being tax authorities, both reviewers are engaged in the horse business.

BOARDING AGREEMENT

(To be executed in duplicate; one copy to be retained by each party.)
This agreement made and entered into by and between _____, _____,

                                                  (owner of horse)   (address)

hereinafter designated "Horse Owner," and _____, _____, hereinafter

                                                 (owner of stable)   (address)

designated, "Stable Owner." This agreement covers the horse described as follows:

_____ _____ _____ _____
       (Name)   (Sex)   (Age)   (Color)

I. *Stable Owner agrees that—*

    1. He will keep the horse in a stall and/or paddock described as follows:

    2. He will feed, water, and care for the horse in a good and husbandlike manner; feeding horse as follows:

	Amount of Feed		
Kind of Feed	Morning	Noon	Night
	(lbs)	*(lbs)*	*(lbs)*

    3. He will perform the following additional services:

        a. *Grooming (specify):* _____

        b. *Exercising (specify):* _____

        c. *Parasite treatments (specify):* _____

_____

_____

        d. *Others (list):* _____

_____

_____

II. *Horse Owner agrees that—*

    1. He will make all arrangements for the periodic shoeing of the horse, and assume the cost thereof. Any exception to this shoeing arrangement shall be given in the space that follows:

    2. He will pay Stable Owner (a) for the foregoing facilities, feed, and services the sum of $ _____ per month, payable on the _____ day of each month in advance; and (b) for drugs and medications, at cost, the first of each month following invoicing.

    3. Stable Owner shall be entitled to a lien against the boarded horse for the value of services rendered, and shall be entitled to enforce said lien according to the appropriate laws of the state, *provided* (a) Stable Owner performs the services herein specified, and (b) Horse Owner fails to make a scheduled payment.

III. *Horse Owner and Stable Owner mutually agree that—*

    1. In the event the horse shall require the services of a Veterinarian, Stable Owner will immediately contact Horse Owner. In the event Horse Owner cannot be reached, Stable Owner is hereby authorized, as agent for Horse Owner, (a) to call Dr. _____, DVM; and, should he be unavailable, (b) to call any other licensed veterinarian of his choice. All fees charged by said veterinarian shall be the sole and exclusive responsibility of the Horse Owner, with no liability whatsoever on the part of Stable Owner for such fees.

    2. This document constitutes the entire agreement between the parties and there are no other agreements between them except as noted below.

_____ _____
           (Signature of Horse Owner)   (date)

_____ _____
           (Signature of Stable Owner)   (date)

Fig. 19-7. Boarding agreement.

business. Moreover, a hobby sometimes turns out to be a profitable venture to the point that the taxpayer may turn it into a business. In any event, once the question is raised, the burden of proof—whether the horse enterprise shall be classed as a hobby or a business by IRS and the court—is with the taxpayer. In various cases, the courts have noted the following factors as indicative that the enterprise is a business rather than a hobby:

1. That the taxpayer is able to show that serious study went into the initial planning and long-range development of the horse enterprise (breeding, racing, training, and/or showing); for example, that a recognized and qualified consultant was employed to make a feasibility study, following which he was retained to guide the proposed program.

2. That the farm or stable is being directed by an able manager, whose credentials give evidence of both technical training and business ability.

3. That the taxpayer is giving personal attention to all phases of the operation and exhibiting good and sound business judgment. That there has been a practical, common-sense approach—that the enterprise has been run like a business, rather than like a plaything.

4. That the farm, ranch, or stable is located in an area adapted to the type of horse enterprise being conducted.

5. That the facilities are functional in design, rather than like a "country estate." For example, it's difficult to justify a situation where the principal improvements to a horse farm consist of a swimming pool, tennis court, and guest house.

6. That good and complete records are available, showing all transactions. Although good records as such will not establish the enterprise as a business, the absence of such records may constitute adverse evidence.

7. That there is ample evidence that a profitable breeding and marketing program takes several years. Horse breeding may be likened to (a) the beginning orchardist who plants young trees, then cultivates, sprays, waters, prunes, and replaces for a number of years before he harvests the first crop; or (b) the producer of a timber crop, where it takes up to 25 years to get into production. It doesn't seem unreasonable, therefore, that it should require 8 to 12 years in which to get a horse breeding establishment on a profitable basis, for in that period of time, only 2 to 3 generations of horses can be produced.

8. That the enterprise is of such magnitude that it can conceivably make a profit, considering all the circumstances of the particular situation.

9. That the advertising and promotion programs have been sound, and in keeping with those followed by other similar businesses that have been successful.

10. That there has been proper and rigid culling of horses.

11. That the taxpayer has exhibited evidence of keeping abreast of the latest developments in the horse field through such things as attending recognized short courses, acquiring a technical library in the field, and subscribing to related periodicals—all of which indicate the intent of the taxpayer to conduct a sound business enterprise.

It is emphasized that the matter of INTENT is paramount. Generally speaking, taxpayers who meet, to a reasonable degree, these 11 points can, if necessary, prove to the courts their "intent to show a profit from a business venture."

Proof of INTENT is especially difficult if (1) the taxpayer is wealthy and over a period of years has sustained heavy losses sufficient to put an average horseman out of business, or (2) there is some interest connected with the horse enterprise of greater importance in the taxpayer's scheme of life than making a profit. Indeed, these two points tend to indicate an expensive hobby, rather a business.

Tax Guidelines

The sections that follow present some guidelines pertinent to horsemen in dealing with the Internal Revenue Service. Because tax provisions change from time to time, the horseman should always seek and follow the advice of a tax expert.

PROFIT TWO YEARS OUT OF A CONSECUTIVE SEVEN YEARS

Under the tax laws, an activity is presumed not to be a hobby if profits result in two out of seven consecutive years, unless IRS proves otherwise. To take advantage of this provision, in principal loss years the horseman must file an election on forms provided by IRS.

HOLDING PERIOD (TIME OWNED) ON BOUGHT HORSES

To be eligible for capital gain treatment, purchased (or gift) horses, including race and show horses, must be held 24 months. (Cattle must be held 24 months, also. Swine and sheep need to be held only 12 months.)

RAISED HORSES

Raised horses for cash method taxpayers have a "zero" tax basis. Hence, all proceeds on disposition of eligible animals are a gain to be treated as capital gain.

CAPITAL GAIN

Since capital gain is not taxed nearly so heavily as ordinary income, it behooves horsemen to report the maximum thereunder permitted by law. For an individual horseman with up to $50,000 long-term capital gain, the tax rate is 25%; for over $50,000 is is 35%. For corporations, capital gain tax is 30%.

TRANSPORTATION COSTS

Transportation costs incurred in the acquisition of breeding animals are capital expenditures and should be added to the cost of the animal for depreciation purposes.

LIMITATIONS ON LOSSES

The basic rule that hobby or pleasure losses cannot be deducted from non-farm income beyond the income generated from the horse business prevails, and the general rule that a person must enter into the horse business "to make a profit" before deductions for his expenses beyond income from the horse business was left intact by the 1976 Tax Reform Law.

Under the prior law, the amount that could be written off was without limitation until the losses exceeded $25,000, and the nonfarm income or non-horse business income exceeded $50,000. This was referred to as the "farm loss recapture" rules or the "excess deductions account" (EDA). After 1975, no further additions to EDA were required or permitted, but the rules applied to existing accounts.

Under the 1976 Tax Reform Law, the $25,000 limitation was eliminated and the amount of loss that a horseman can deduct from nonhorse income is limited to the amount that he has "at risk." A taxpayer is generally considered "at risk" with respect to an activity to the extent of his cash and the adjusted basis of the property contributed to the activity, plus any amounts borrowed for use in the activity with respect to which the taxpayer has personal liability for payment from his personal assets. Further, his net fair market value of personal assets which secure nonrecourse borrowings is included in the definition of "at risk." "Nonrecourse" means the taxpayer has no personal liability for the payment of a debt.

These "at risk" provisions apply to losses attributable to amounts paid, incurred, depreciated, or amortized in taxable years after December 31, 1975.

In summary, the horseman will be limited to those dollars he has put out of his pocket, plus contracts or loans for monies or property put into the horse business that carries his personal liability or responsibility.

If the loss in any year is less than the amount "at risk," the full amount of the loss is deductible and the "at risk" amount is reduced by the loss deducted. The reduced "at risk" amount is then carried over to the next year to determine any limit deductions lost under that year.

If the loss is greater than the amount "at risk," the deductible loss is limited to the amount "at risk" at the end of the year. The amount "at risk" is reduced to "0." In this case, the nondeductible portion of the loss is carried over to the next year and is available for deduction then, if not prevented by application by the "at risk" rule.

If the risk amount has been reduced to "0," no further losses may be deducted until such time as the taxpayer places additional amounts of investment through borrowings or additional cash investment.

HORSES OF DIFFERENT SEXES CANNOT BE EXCHANGED "TAX-FREE"

Horses of different sexes are not considered "like kind" and cannot be exchanged on a tax-free basis. Neither do geldings qualify as "like kind" for exchange for stallions. However, mares for mares, and stallions for stallions, are eligible for "tax-free" exchange.

STUD AND TRAINING FEES DEDUCTIBLE

Both stud fees and training fees are tax deductible in the year paid by a cash basis taxpayer.

EDUCATING THE HORSEMAN

Increasingly, horsemen have opportunities to enroll in sophisticated stud managers' courses, short courses, and equine seminars. This prompts the question as to whether such educational costs can be deducted from the horseman's tax returns.

The general rule under the tax law is that expenditures made to maintain or improve skills required in a taxpayer's employment or other trade or business, or to meet his job requirements, are deductible. However, costs incurred in education to qualify the taxpayer for entrance to his profession or employment are not deductible personal expenses.

PREPAYMENT OF FEED PURCHASES

Sometimes cash basis horsemen buy feed for use the next year(s). To get a deduction for prepaid feed bills, a cash basis horseman must show that such prepayment (1) is a payment and not a deposit, (2) has a business purpose, and (3) is not a distortion of income. Acceptable business purposes include guaranteeing prices and/or making certain of supply.

RECAPTURE OF DEPRECIATION ON HORSES BOUGHT

Depreciation on horses bought (horses raised have no depreciation basis for a horseman on a cash basis) for breeding and racing purposes is subject to depreciation recapture as are all other similar business assets. Thus, gain realized on the sale of such horses is taxed at ordinary income rates to the extent of depreciation claimed or allowable on such animals after 1969; and the remainder of the gain, if any, is taxed as capital gain, provided the holding period of two years has been satisfied.

APPRAISAL, SALVAGE, AND DEPRECIATION

If the "useful" life guidelines issued by the Treasury are followed, the taxpayer will not be challenged. They are:

Buildings .... 25 years
Machinery and equipment .... 10 years
Breeding and work horses .... 8-12 years

Definitions of "appraisal, salvage, and. depreciation" as applied to horses follow:

● *Appraisal* refers to the act of establishing the worth of the horse.

● *Salvage* refers to the remaining value, if any, of an animal after it has served its intended purpose—for example, at the end of usefulness as a breeding animal, or at the end of a racing or showing career.

● *Depreciation* refers to the amortization or write-off of the cost of a horse over the period of its useful life.

In each of the above, the horseman, or the specialist to whom such matters are entrusted, should apply rates which he can justify.

On purchased animals, the price paid establishes value for depreciation purposes. Inherited or gift horses can also be depreciated, with their value established by a qualified appraiser or on the basis of current sales of similar animals. Raised horses cannot be depreciated, for the cost of raising them has been deducted as an annual expense.

Breeding animals have no appreciable salvage value at the end of their reproductive life. On the other hand, the salvage value of a racehorse that is retired to stud is a matter of opinion.

Depreciation figures on horses are difficult to come by, and they vary according to source, use, and breed. Unfortunately, the Internal Revenue Service has not stipulated any depreciation rates other than suggesting that horses used for breeding or work purposes should have an 8- to 12-year life.

The accounting firm of Owens, Potter and Hisle, Lexington, Kentucky, which specializes in accounting for horse establishments, has developed Table 19-8 as a depreciation guide for the useful lives of race and breeding horses.

The author suggests that the depreciation schedule on show horses be the same as those given for racehorses in Table 19-8.

Horsemen have claimed and been allowed rates widely at variance with the figures given in Table 19-8. For example, some owners claim depreciation on yearlings from date of acquisition, whereas others date it from the time they are placed in training; but such practices might prove difficult to defend in a well-fought tax case. If the return is filed in a district where there are few horsemen, the examiner may fail to challenge the method simply because he is unfamiliar with the peculiarities of the industry. Inconsistent practices are likely to continue unless the horse industry itself takes initiative and accumulates more and more factual studies, made by independent agencies, which horsemen can present. Without doubt, the results of such a research studies would more than justify the cost.

Any one of the following three methods may be used in computing depreciation of horses:

1. *The straight line method*, in which annual depreciation on the horse is determined by dividing its purchase price when acquired, less its estimated salvage value, if any, by the total number of years of useful life remaining (see Table 19-8). For example, according to Table 19-8, a racehorse acquired at age 3 has an expected useful race life of 4 years. Hence, a

TABLE 19-8
HORSE DEPRECIATION GUIDE[1]

Age When Acquired	Years of Useful Life Remaining		
	Racehorses	Broodmares	Stallions
1	6		
2	5		
3	4		
4	3	10	10
5	3	9	9
6	2	9	9
7	2	8	8
8	2	7	7
9		7	7
10		6	6
11		5	5
12		5	5
13		5	5
14		4	4
15		4	4
16		4	4
17		3	3
18		3	3
19		2	2
20		2	2
21		2	2

[1]From: *The Blood-Horse*, Dec. 2, 1967, p. 3747, with the permission of Mr. John C. Owens and Mr. Rex B. Potter, of the firm of Owens, Potter and Hisle, Lexington, Ky.

depreciation of 25 percent would be taken each year under the straight line method.

The following example will serve to illustrate how the straight line method works:

Example: A mare costing $8,000 was purchased at age 4, at which age she also dropped her first foal. For purposes of computing depreciation, it is estimated that she has 10 more years of useful life remaining (Table 19-8). Further, it is estimated that her salvage value at the end of this period (at age 14) will be $100. How much depreciation may be taken each year by the straight line method?

Answer: $8,000 − $100=$7,900, the depreciation which may be taken over a 10-year period; hence—100÷10=10%, annual percentage write-off.

$7,900×10%=$790, annual dollars write-off.

2. *The declining balance method*, in which the largest depreciation is taken during the early years of life, and a gradually smaller allowance is taken in later years. The amount of depreciation taken each year is subtracted before figuring the next year's depreciation, so that the same depreciation rate is applied to a smaller or declining balance each year. The maximum rate under this method may not exceed twice the rate that would be used under the straight line method. For example, if *new* tangible property has an estimated useful life of 5 years remaining, the depreciation rate under the straight line method is 20 percent; but under the declining balance system, depreciation may be figured at any rate that does not exceed 40 percent.

Horses that are purchased are usually considered "*used property*," and, therefore, limited to 150 percent of the straight line rate. Salvage value is not deducted before figuring depreciation under this method, but depreciation must stop when the unrecovered cost is reduced to salvage value.

3. *The sum of the years digit method*, in which a different fraction is applied each year to the basis of the property less its estimated salvage value. The denominator, or bottom of the fraction, which remains constant, is the total of the numbers representing the years of useful life of the horse. For example, if the useful life is 5 years, the denominator is 15 (1 plus 2, plus 3, plus 4, plus 5, equals 15). The numerator, or top of the fraction, is the number of years of life remaining at the beginning of the year for which the computation is made. For the first year of an estimated 5 year life, the numerator would be 5, the second year 4, etc. Thus, for a horse with a useful life of 5 years, the fraction to be applied to the cost minus salvage to figure depreciation for the first year is $5/15$; the fraction for the second year is $4/15$, etc.

In addition to the 3 methods of depreciation given above, there's Section 179, "bonus" depreciation. This permits the taxpayer to write off 20 percent of the cost, or portion of the cost, of a purchased horse during the first taxable year for which a depreciation deduction is allowable, provided (1) the horse has an estimated useful life of at least 6 years, (2) the horse was acquired from an unrelated person, and (3) the maximum write-off is $2,000 for the year, or $4,000 on a joint return. This "bonus" depreciation applies to both new and used property; hence, young broodmares, young stallions, and purchased yearlings put into training will so qualify.

Before a horseman adopts any method of depreciation, competent tax assistance should be sought. Many factors must be considered.

RECAPTURE OF CERTAIN FARMLAND EXPENDITURES

This rule is for the purpose of alleviating the practice of purchasing a farm or ranch with the intention of engaging in land development and speculation through (1) deducting land improvement costs against nonfarm income, and (2) selling the improved land in a few years and claiming capital gains on the profit. It applies to land that has been held less than 10 years and pertains to deductions for land improvement—for soil and water conservation and land clearance. The act stipulates that—

1. If held for 5 years or less, deductions for land improvement will be recaptured as ordinary income and at 100 percent.

2. If held longer than 5 years, but less than 10 years, the percentage is scaled down 20 percent per year in excess of 5 years. The following example shows how it works:

A taxpayer acquired land in 1970 and sells in 1978. In 1972, taxpayer expended $30,000, in land improvements. Hence, the recapture will be 40 percent, or $12,000 ($30,000 × 40%) because the land was sold in the eighth year following purchase. This means that $12,000 of the total expenditures will be recapturable and taxed as ordinary income.

In the Event of a Court Case

In the event of a court case, it is usually advisable that the taxpayer appear in person and testify, rather than expect that his attorney and accountant handle the matter entirely. This is especially important from the standpoint of establishing intent, for no one knows the original intent better than the owner. Additionally, it is usually advisable that the testimony of

recognized experts in the field be used to substantiate the fact that there was, or is, a reasonable expectation of making a profit. However, whether or not the taxpayer and/or experts testify in a particular case should be left to the decision of the lawyer, for nothing is worse for the taxpayer than not giving the lawyer free rein to develop the case.

ESTATE PLANNING

Human nature being what it is, most horsemen shy away from suggestions that someone help plan the disposition of their property and other assets. Also, many of them have a long-standing distrust of lawyers, legal terms, and trusts, and, to them, the subject of taxes seldom makes for pleasant conversation.

If no plans are made, estate taxes and settlement costs often run considerably higher than if proper estate planning is done and a will is made to carry out these plans. Today, the horse business is big business; many horsemen have well over $500,000 invested in land, horses, and equipment. Thus, it is not a satisfying thought to one who has worked hard to build and maintain a good horse establishment during his lifetime to feel that his heirs will have to sell the facilities and horses to raise enough cash to pay federal estate and inheritance taxes. By using a good estate planning service, a horseman can generally save thousands of dollars for his family in estate and inheritance taxes and in estate settlement costs. For assistance, horsemen should go to an estate planning specialist—an individual or company specializing in this work, or to the trust department of a commercial bank.

A limited discussion of some of the revisions in the estate and gift tax laws resulting from the Tax Reform Act of 1976 follows.

● *Farm valuation*—One very important aspect of the new law for the benefit of the horseman's estate is the formula to be used for valuing farms. Many heirs of farmers have been faced with the problem of a farm being valued at its highest and best use, which in many cases was substantially higher than its farming use value and resulted in substantial estate taxes.

Under the 1976 Act, if certain conditions are met, real property used for farming may be valued on the basis of its existing use instead of the highest and best use as under the old law. In no case, however, may the alternate method reduce the gross estate by more than $500,000.

In general, the formula for valuing farms is the actual value based on the average annual gross cash rental for comparable farm purpose of land located in the same locality, less the average annual state and local real estate taxes for such comparable land, divided by the average annual effective rate for all new federal land bank loans. The general result of the law

change is expected to reduce the amount of estate taxes due on farms.

● *Longer time to pay estate taxes*—To lessen the need for forced sales of farms or ranches in order to pay estate taxes, the estate will be able to pay the taxes in up to ten (10) annual installments, provided the horse business is a closely held business and the business value exceeds 35 percent of the value of the gross estate, or 50 percent value of a taxable estate.

This is a great benefit to a farmer's estate that is short on cash, and it alleviates a forced sale of horses or ranch in order to pay taxes.

If more than 65 percent of a decedent's adjusted gross estate is an interest in a closely held business, an executor may elect to pay all or part of the estate taxes, in up to 10 equal annual installments. Moreover, he may elect, for the first installment for a period up to 5 years, with interest limited to a special 4 percent rate on the estate taxes attributable to the first $1 million of the farm, or other closely held business property.

However, if there is a disposition of the horse business or aggregate withdrawals of one-third of its money or property, there will be an acceleration of the taxes that would have been due.

It should be noted that these new liberalized provisions apply not only to closely held horse businesses, but to any type of business.

● *Higher exemptions*—One of the significant benefits of the new tax law was the increase in the exemption for estate taxes. Although the exemption was a "tax credit," in 1977 the equivalent exemption was approximately double the former $60,000 exemption.

The credit (or exemption) will increase through 1981 until the ultimate credit of $47,000 or equivalent exemption of $175,625.

It should be noted that the present annual $3,000 per donee exclusion is retained by the law.

● *"Basis" for sales of property received from estate*—One method to reduce estate taxes prior to the new law was to arrange that property with a low acquisition cost ("basis") compared to its current value, so it would be held in such a manner that upon the death of one of the spouses, or the owner of the property, would receive a "stepped-up basis," meaning that the property would be given a value as of the date of death. The advantage resulting would be that if the property was subsequently sold, the income would be the difference between the selling price and the new basis at the time of death, rather than the original purchase price. Obviously, this resulted in less income to the seller and reduced tax collections by the IRS.

Under the new law, for property acquired before 1977, the stepped-up basis will be that value as of December 31, 1976, rather than the value at the time

of death after that date. For property acquired after 1977, the basis will be the same as the decedent's.

For pre-1977 property, the market value will be determined based on the assumption that appreciation has occurred on a uniform basis from the date of acquisition. Thus, the basis and the market value on the date of death will be the only figures needed to determine the value on December 31, 1976.

Irrespective of the above, a new provision provides that there will be a minimum carry over basis of $60,000 for each estate so at least that amount of protection is retained beyond the law valuing estate property as of December 31, 1976.

● *Unified Rate Schedule for Estate and Gift Taxes*—The gift and estate tax systems were completely changed by the Tax Reform Act of 1976. In the past, the most anyone could leave entirely free of federal or estate tax was $120,000, and at least $60,000 of that had to go to the surviving spouse. Also, there were 2 separate tax systems: (1) a gift tax with its own rate schedule and its own $30,000 lifetime exemption for every donor (and also a $3,000 annual exclusion per donee not changed by the '76 Act); and (2) an estate tax with its own schedule of rates and with its own $60,000 exemption. Both of these taxes also provided for a marital deduction whereby half of a lifetime gift to a spouse was free from gift tax and up to half of the estate could be left to the surviving spouse free of estate tax. To get maximum benefits, family estate planning often had to be based on the best combination of lifetime gifts and estate bequests. The '76 Tax Reform Act changed all this. In place of the $30,000 lifetime gift exemption and the $60,000 estate exemption, there is a single "unified" credit against both estate and gift taxes and a single "unified" gift and estate tax rate schedule (Table 19-9). The result is that gifts made during life are taxed at the same rate as transfers made after death by will, joint tenancy or otherwise. The amount of tentative tax in either case is figured from the unified gift and estate tax schedule and the credit subtracted to find the tax payable. The credit can be used against gift tax, entirely or in part, or it may be used against estate taxes. But whatever amount is used against gift tax is not available for use against estate tax. The credit is phased in over a 5-year period. It will be $30,000 in 1977, $34,000 in 1978, $38,000 in 1979, $42,500 in 1980, and $47,000 in 1981 and thereafter.

● *Summary*—The 1976 Tax Reform Law provided substantial benefits to the horsemen in many areas. It made for more advantages than disadvantages to the horseman. However, with the nonhorse law changes—especially the adjusted basis for long-term capital gains—in specific situations the tax reform law may have an adverse impact on a particular horseman.

The new law covers many areas of taxes and is a very complex bill. With the significant changes affect-

TABLE 19-9
UNIFIED GIFT AND ESTATE TAX SCHEDULE

If Tentative Tax Base Is More Than:	But Not Over:	Tentative Tax Is:	Of Excess Over:
0	$10,000	18% of such amount	
$10,000	20,000	$1,800 + 20%	$10,000
20,000	40,000	3,800 + 22%	20,000
40,000	60,000	8,200 + 24%	40,000
60,000	80,000	13,000 + 26%	60,000
80,000	100,000	18,200 + 28%	80,000
100,000	150,000	23,800 + 30%	100,000
150,000	250,000	38,800 + 32%	150,000
250,000	500,000	70,800 + 34%	250,000
500,000	750,000	155,800 + 37%	500,000
750,000	1,000,000	248,300 + 39%	750,000
1,000,000	1,250,000	345,800 + 41%	1,000,000
1,250,000	1,500,000	448,300 + 43%	1,250,000
1,500,000	2,000,000	555,800 + 45%	1,500,000
2,000,000	2,500,000	780,800 + 49%	2,000,000
2,500,000	3,000,000	1,025,800 + 53%	2,500,000
3,000,000	3,500,000	1,290,800 + 57%	3,000,000
3,500,000	4,000,000	1,575,800 + 61%	3,500,000
4,000,000	4,500,000	1,880,800 + 65%	4,000,000
4,500,000	5,000,000	2,205,800 + 69%	4,500,000
5,000,000	—	2,550,800 + 70%	5,000,000

ing the horseman, he should seek competent tax counsel so as to take advantage of the new laws and be well prepared for future tax planning.

STRAY HORSES ON HIGHWAYS

Although state, county, and/or township laws vary, and it is not possible to predict with accuracy what damages, if any, may be recovered in particular instances, the following general rules apply:

● If a horse owner is negligent in maintaining his fences and allows his horse(s) to get on the road, he can be held liable for damage or injury resulting to persons using the highway.

● If a horse owner has good fences that are well maintained, but has a horse(s) which he knows is in the habit of breaking out, he may be held liable for damages caused by such horse(s).

● If a horse(s) gets onto the highway, despite the facts that there are both good fences and the horse(s) is not known habitually to get out, the owner may be held liable for any damage inflicted provided he knew that the horse(s) was out and made no reasonable effort to get him in.

● If the horse owner is not negligent in any way, he may or may not be judged liable for the damage inflicted by his horse(s), depending on the state law

● If a horseman is driving a horse(s) along or across a highway, he is not likely to suffer liability for any damage unless it can be proved that he was negligent. Stock-crossing signs usually increase the caution exercised by motorists, but such signs do not excuse a horse owner from exercising due care.

● In some states, laws provide that a horse owner may, under the supervision of and with varying amounts of assistance from highway authorities, construct an underpass for his horse(s) and for general farm use.

INSURANCE

Few horsemen examine closely or understand the insurance coverage that they buy, either on their horses or in the area of liability. To the end that they may be more knowledgeable on this subject, sections on horse insurance and liability follow.

Horse Insurance

The ownership of a fine horse constitutes a risk, which means that there is a chance of financial loss. Unless the owner is in such strong financial position that he alone can assume this risk, the animal should be insured.

Several good companies write horse insurance; and, in general, the policies and rates do not differ greatly. The provisions and rates quoted in Table 19-10 approximate those used by most underwriters.

In 1977, it was reported that the owners of Seattle Slew carried a $3.5 million insurance policy on the Triple Crown winner (Kentucky Derby, Preakness, and Belmont Stakes), and that premiums ran $2,000 per week.

It is noteworthy that the two major causes of death to horses (other than old age) are fire and colic. Fire claims more lives, but the value of horses dying from colic is greater. This is because valuable horses are more often stabled in fireproof buildings.

In order to obtain insurance, the following information is generally required: identification (markings and/or tattoo) of animal, age, individual valuation, and a statement of health from the local veterinarian.

It is recommended that the person desiring or having insurance confer with a broker who makes a specialty of horse insurance, read the policy with care, and change the provisions of the policy at such intervals as required or when special circumstances arise.

Liability Insurance; Workmen's Compensation Insurance

Most horsemen are in such financial position that they are vulnerable to damage suits. Moreover, the number of damage suits arising each year is increasing at an almost alarming rate, and astronomical damages are being claimed. Studies reveal that about 95 percent of the court cases involving injury result in damages being awarded.

Several types of liability insurance offer a safeguard against liability suits brought as a result of injury suffered by another person or damage to their property.

TABLE 19-10

HORSE INSURANCE; COVERAGE AND RATES

Type of Coverage	Annual Rate	Comments
	(%)	
Full mortality. This pays the policy holder the insured value of the horse upon death from any cause or when an injury is so severe as to justify death to relieve pain and suffering.		Value usually set by purchase price. But, value may be reappraised on basis of horse's accomplishments. Rates given to the left apply to age 12. From 13 on, insured value of animal decreases 20%/year and premium rate increases 1%/year. Rate decreases as value increases.
a. For broodmare or stallion	4½	
b. For show horse or hunter	5½	
c. For flat racing:		
(1) Mare or stallion	7¾	
(2) Gelding	8½	
d. For steeplechase horse	9	
Limited mortality. It does not pay for death attributable to disease; but covers death losses due to other causes.	3	Not a popular insurance. Sometimes used where animals are exposed to such hazards as heavy traffic or game hunters.
Loss of use. Available for show horses (not racehorses). Covers inability to perform, due to injury or disease, that does not result in death.	2½	Animals must first have full coverage; hence, the rate is added thereto. With loss of use, owner collects 60% of insured value and keeps the horse.
Fire, lightning, and transportation.	1½	Public carriers are insured, but only up to $200 per horse.
Stallion fertility. Pays if stallion is unable to breed because of infertility or physical injury.	2½	Available to owner or syndicate members.
Unborn foal. Covers from time pregnancy examination shows mare in foal until 30 days after birth.	17	Value of foal is calculated at 3 times stud fee if stud fee is under $10,000; or 2½ times if stud fee is over $10,000.

Comprehensive personal liability insurance protects an operator who is sued for alleged damages suffered from an accident involving his property or family. The kinds of situations from which a claim might arise are quite broad, including injuries caused by animals, equipment, or personal acts.

Both workmen's compensation insurance and employer's liability insurance protect operators against claims or court awards resulting from injury to hired help. Workmen's compensation usually costs slightly more than straight employer's liability insurance, but it carries more benefits to the worker. An injured employee must prove negligence by his employer before the company will pay a claim under employer's liability insurance, whereas workmen's compensation benefits are established by state law and settlements are made by the insurance company without regard to who was negligent in causing the injury. Conditions governing participation in workmen's compensation insurance vary among the states.

CAREERS WITH HORSES

The author receives numerous letters from boys and girls asking about training and job placement in horse work. Here is what he tells them.

The first and most important requisite for a successful career in the equine field is that the person must possess a great love for horses. This appears to be an inborn trait, for some people never acquire a natural ability to work with horses—no matter how long or how hard they try. When such love for horses exists, the animals are more docile and easier to handle, for the caretaker's feelings are relayed to his charges. Also, a great love for horses appears to be essential if the caretaker is to feed them regularly and cheerfully, with enjoyment and without regard to long hours and Sundays or holidays; if he is to provide clean, dry bedding, despite the fact that a driving storm may make it necessary to repeat the same operation the next day; if he is to serve as nursemaid to a newborn foal or a sick horse, though it may mean loss of sleep and working with cold, numb fingers; and if he is to remain calm and collected, though striking an animal or otherwise giving vent to his feelings might at first appear to be warranted.

Next to having a great love for horses, to be successful in the equine field it is important that the person have adequate knowledge, both scientific and practical. Also, owners and managers of large operations, must have skill in money management and knowledge of the business aspects. A college education is important. If they are good students, serious consideration should also be given to completing a veterinary or Ph.D. degree. Additionally, those who have not grown up with horses should learn the rudiments of the business by working two years on a good horse establishment. Most young folks entering the horse field aspire higher than being a groom and mucking out stalls. Nevertheless, this is a good place to start.

Finally, industry and good judgment are very necessary requisites for success in the horse business. These words carry the same connotation in all industries and are self-explanatory.

When it comes to hiring girls for horse work, some employers still think Victorian and sidesaddle. But if girls meet the requisites outlined above, they should be able to find, or to make, employment opportunities.

Among the professional opportunities in the multimillion dollar horse industry are the following:

- Owning, managing, or working on a horse breeding establishment.
- Training horses.
- Operating a boarding stable.
- Veterinarians in private practice, or with drug manufacturers, or with large horse establishment.
- In research, sales, and public relations with companies that manufacture and distribute feed, tack, and other products for the horse industry.
- As farriers (horseshoers).
- On the staffs of horse magazines and breed registry associations.
- In college teaching.
- As riding school instructors.
- With racing stables; and as racing officials and jockeys.
- With hunt clubs.
- With summer camps.
- Horse shows.
- Buying and selling horses.
- Rodeo riding.
- As secretaries, office managers, and executive assistants, to administrators and associations engaged in the horse field.
- Consultants.

SELECTED REFERENCES

Title of Publication	Author(s)	Publisher
Business of Horses, The	K. A. Wood	Wood Publications, P.O. Box 963, Rancho Santa Fe, Calif., 1973
Depreciation for the Horse Industry	D. E. Rose	Equine Publications, Ltd., Lexington, Ohio, 1975
Doane's Agricultural Report		Doane Agricultural Service, Inc., St. Louis, Mo., kept current
Farm Management Economics	E. O. Heady H. R. Jensen	Prentice-Hall, Inc., Englewood Cliffs, N.J., 1955
Introduction to Agri-Business Management, An	W. J. Wills	The Interstate Printers & Publishers, Inc., Danville, Ill., 1973
Kiplinger Agricultural Letter, The		The Kiplinger Washington Editors, Washington, D.C., bi-weekly
Law and Your Horse	E. H. Breene	A. S. Barnes & Co., Inc., Cranbury, N.J., 1971
Midwest Farm Handbook		Iowa State University, Ames, Iowa, 1964
Stockman's Handbook, The, Fourth Edition	M. E. Ensminger	The Interstate Printers & Publishers, Inc., Danville, Ill., 1970
Stud Managers' Handbook	Ed. by M. E. Ensminger	Agriservices Foundation, Clovis, Calif., annually since 1965

CHAPTER 20

Glossary of Horse Terms

A mark of distinction of a good horseman is that he "speaks the language"—he uses the correct terms and knows what they mean. Even though horse terms are used glibly by people in the horse and pony business, often they are baffling to the newcomer.

Many terms that are defined or explained elsewhere in this book are not repeated in this chapter. Thus, if a particular term is not listed herein, the reader should look in the Index or in the particular chapter and section where it is discussed.

A

Across the board: A combination pari-mutuel (race) ticket on a horse is known as "across the board," meaning that you collect something if your horse runs first, second, or third.

Actinobacillosis: See Navel infection.

Action: Movement of the feet and legs—should be straight and true.

Aficionado: Ardent follower, supporter, or enthusiast; a fan.

Age: The age of horses is computed from the first of January.

Aged horse: Correctly speaking, a horse 8 years of age or over; but the term is often used to indicate a horse that is smooth mouthed—that is, 12 years of age or older. Since one year of a horse's life corresponds to approximately 3 of a man's, it follows that at age 7 a horse "comes of age," or attains maturity.

Aids: The legs, hands, weight, and voice, as used in controlling a horse.

Alter: To castrate a horse; to geld.

American Horse Council, Inc.: The American Horse Council, which represents all sectors of the U.S. horse industry, was formed in 1969. It is dedicated to the development of the American equine industry. It seeks a fair tax consideration for horse producers (farmers) and develops educational programs and activities designed to meet the needs of the horse industry. The address follows:

American Horse Council, Inc.
1776 "K" Street, N.W.
Washington, D.C. 20006

Anatomy: The science of the structure of the animal body and the relation of its parts.

Anthrax (splenic fever, charbon): An acute, infectious disease caused by *Bacillus anthracis*, a large, rod-shaped organism.

Antihistamines: A drug used to neutralize and treat allergic conditions in the body.

Antiseptic: An agent used in the treatment of wounds or disease to prevent the growth and development of germs.

Appointments: Equipment and clothing used in showing.

Arab: Used interchangeably with Arabian; hence, a breed of horses.

Ascarids: See Roundworms, large.

Aseptic: Refers to something being free from the living germs of disease.

Asterisk: Used in front of a horse's name, an asterisk (*) indicates "imported." Used in front of a jockey's name, it indicates that he is an apprentice rider.

Astringent: A drug, such as tannic acid, alum, and zinc oxide or sulphate, that causes contraction of tissues.

At the end of the halter: Sold with no guarantee except title.

Azoturia (Monday morning disease, blackwater): A metabolic disease of unknown origin. It usually appears when the horse is worked following a period of idleness on full feed.

B

Babesiasis: See Equine piroplasmosis.

Back: The command to move backward.

Balanced seat: That position of the mounted rider that requires the minimum of muscular effort to remain in the saddle and which interferes least with the horse's movements and equilibrium.

Bald face: A white face, including the eyes and the nostrils, or a portion thereof.

Balk: Refuse to go.

Balky horse: Any horse that stands still—refuses to go. This vice was not uncommon in the draft horse and horse-and-buggy era. The causes of balking were numerous; among them, too severe punishment when overloaded, and sore shoulders. The legendary cures (none recommended by the author) included (1) pounding on one shoe to divert the balky horse's attention; (2) pouring sand in one ear, which was supposed to shake the idea of balking out of his head; and (3) building a fire under him.

In the old days, when selling a balky horse at auction, it was generally announced that he "sells at halter." Belatedly, some uninformed buyer learned that this meant that the horse was prone to balk, and that he wouldn't pull the hat off your head.

Banged: Hair of the tail cut off in a straight line.

Bangtail: Slang term for a racehorse, as in the old days running horses usually had banged tails, often banged close to the dock, or docked and banged. Also, a wild horse.

Barefoot: Unshod.

Barrel racing: The only woman's event in rodeo. It is an excellent test of combined speed and agility of horseflesh, for it is a race against time coupled with ease of maneuverability. Each contestant must ride a cloverleaf pattern around three barrels. Women and girls are particularly suited to barrel racing; in colorful attire, they contribute much to spectator appreciation of the sport.

Fig. 20-1. Well-trained and well-ridden barrel racing horse. (Courtesy, McLaughlin Photography, Morrison, Colo.)

Barren: A mare that is not in foal.

Bars: May refer either to the bars of the mouth, or of the hoof.

Base narrow: Standing with front or rear feet close together, yet standing with legs vertical.

Base wide: Standing with front or rear feet wide apart, yet with legs vertical.

Bean-shooter: A horse that throws its front feet violently forward at the trot, with little flexion, "landing" about 12 inches above the ground. A very undesirable trait.

Beefy hocks: Thick meaty hocks, lacking in quality.

Bell boots: Rubber protective boots that are bell-shaped, fitting over the coronet bands and down on the hoof.

Bellerophon: The Prince of Corinth in Greek mythology who tamed the winged horse, Pegasus. According to legend, Bellerophon used a golden bridle to coax the curious animal from his favorite meadow, then made him captive and rode him off to destroy the dragonlike monster, the Chimera. Success encouraged him to try to fly to Olympia to live with the gods. However, Zeus, angered by this mortal's ambition, sent a gadfly to sting Pegasus, causing him to unseat his venerable and conceited master, who fell to earth crippled and blinded.

Big hitch: A "heavy hitch" of draft horses in 4s, 6s, 8s, or even more.

Bight of the reins: The part of the reins passing between thumb and fingers and out the top of the hand.

Bishoping: The practice of artificially altering the teeth of older horses in an attempt to make them sell as young horses.

Blaze: A broad white marking covering almost all of the forehead, but not including the eyes or nostrils.

Blemishes: Those abnormalities that do not affect the serviceability of the horse, including such things as wire cuts, rope burns, nail punctures, shoe boils, and capped hocks.

Blindness: Partial or complete loss of vision.

Blinker: An attachment to the bridle or hood, designed to restrict the vision of the horse from the sides and rear and to focus the vision forward.

Blister: An irritant applied as a treatment for unsoundnesses and blemishes.

Blistering: Blistering consists in applying an irritating substance such as Spanish fly and iodide of mercury (one common preparation consists of 15 parts Spanish fly, 8 parts iodide of mercury, and 120 parts of lard) as treatment for a blemish or unsoundness. Before applying a blister, the hair should be closely clipped from the affected area, the scurf brushed from the skin, and the animal tied so that it cannot rub, lick, or bite the treated area. The blistering agent is then applied by rubbing it into the pores of the skin with the palm of the hand. Three days later the blistered area should be bathed with warm water and soap, dried, and treated with sweet oil or Vaseline to prevent cracking of the skin. Blistering increases the blood supply to the site of the blister and induces more rapid healing.

Blood-horse: A pedigreed horse. To most horsemen, the term is synonymous with the Thoroughbred breed.

Blood spavin: A varicose vein enlargement which appears on the inside of the hock but immediately above the location of bog spavin.

Bloodworms: See Strongyles.

Bloom: Hair that is clean and of healthy texture.

Blow: To blow wind after strenuous exercise.

Blowfly: A blowfly group consists of several species of flies that breed in animal flesh.

Blow out: To walk or exercise a horse either to loosen its muscles for further exercise, or to prevent chilling and stiffening after a hard workout.

Blue eye: An unsound eye with a blue appearance; the sight may or may not be entirely gone.

Bog spavin: A filling of the natural depression on the inside and front of the hock. A bog spavin is much larger than a blood spavin.

Bolting: 1. The name given to the habit that ravenous horses have of eating too fast. This condition may be controlled by adding chopped hay to the grain ration or by placing some large, round stones, as big or bigger than baseballs, in the feed box.

2. An animal breaking out of control or trying to run away is said to be bolting.

Bone: The measurement of the circumference around the cannon bone about halfway between the knee and fetlock joints. Eight inches of bone is average for the Thoroughbred. "Flat bone" indicates that the cannon and the back tendon are parallel, with the tendon clean-cut and standing well away from the cannon bone. The word "flat" refers to the appearance of the cannon, which is wide and flat when viewed from the side although narrow from the front, and does not mean that the bone itself is flat.

Bone spavin (or jack spavin): Bone spavin is a bony enlargement that appears on the inside and front of the hind leg(s) below the hock at the point where the base of the hock tapers into the cannon part of the leg.

Boots: Protective covering for the legs or feet, generally used when exercising. Some types of boots are used for balance and perfection in gait.

Bosal: The braided rawhide or rope noseband of a bosal hackamore. The bosal is knotted under the horse's jaw.

Bots: The larva stage of highly specialized parasites that attack horses, mules, and perhaps zebras.

Bowed tendons: Enlarged tendons behind the cannon bones, in both the front and hind legs. Descriptive terms of "high" or "low" bow are used by horsemen to denote the location of the injury; the high bow appears just under the knee and the low bow just above the fetlock. This condition is often brought about by severe strains, such as heavy training or racing. When bowed tendons are pronounced, more or less swelling, soreness, and lameness are present. Treatment consists in blistering or firing. The object of blistering and firing is to convert a chronic into an acute inflammation. This hastens nature's processes by bringing more blood to the part, thus inducing a reparative process which renders the animal suitable for work sooner than would otherwise be the case.

Bowlegged: Wide at the knees, close at the feet.

Brace bandages: Resilient bandages on the legs of horses worn in some cases in an effort to support lame legs, and worn in other cases to protect a horse from cutting and skinning its legs while racing.

Brand: A mark used as means of identification.

Break: To teach a young horse to obey commands, and accept direction and control.

Breaking: A horse's leaving its gait and "breaking" into a gallop. A trotter or pacer must remain on gait in a race. If it makes a break, the driver must immediately pull it back to its gait.

Breeder: Owner of the dam at the time of service who was responsible for the selection of the sire to which she was mated.

Breeding: An attempt to regulate the progeny through intensive selection of the parents.

Breedy: Smart and trim about the head and front part of body.

Breezing: A race workout in which a horse is running at a controlled speed.

Bridoon: The correct name for the little snaffle bit in the full bridle.

Brittle hoofs: Hoofs that are abnormally dry and fragile.

Broke: Tamed and trained to a particular function, as halter-broke. Also, to leave or alter gait; e.g., the trotter broke stride.

Broken crest: A heavy neck which breaks over and falls to one side.

Broken knees: Knees with scars on them, indicating that the horse has fallen. Often scars are an indication that the horse is awkward and inclined to stumble.

Bronchitis: A condition of the respiratory system, characterized by the inflammation of the bronchial tubes, with signs similar to heaves.

Broodmare: A mare kept for breeding or reproductive purpose.

Broomtail: A wild and untrained western range horse of inferior quality.

Brothers (or sisters):

Full brothers: By the same sire and out of the same dam.

Half brothers: Out of the same dam, by different sires. This is one of the most frequently misused terms. Horses by the same sire and out of different dams are referred to as "by the same sire," or else the name of the sire is used, as "by Man o' War." This distinction is for a definite purpose, for only a few horses can be half brothers (or half sisters) to a famous horse, but hundreds can be by the same sire. This restricted definition tends to give a little of the credit to good broodmares instead of leaving the meaning ambiguous.

Brothers in blood: By the same sire out of full sisters, or by full brothers out of the same dam, or any combination of exactly the same blood.

Three-quarter brothers: For example, horses having the same dam and whose sires have identical sires but different dams.

Seven-eighths brothers: The progeny of a horse and his son produced by the same mare, or similar combinations of lineage.

Brush: To force a horse to top speed over a short distance.

Brushing: Striking the fetlock with the other hoof, which may result in either roughing the fetlock hair or in an actual injury.

Bucked shins: A temporary racing unsoundness characterized by a very painful inflammation of the periosteum (bone covering) along the greater part of the front surface of the cannon bone, caused by constant pressure from concussion during fast works or races.

Bucking: Springing with a quick leap, arching the back, and descending with the forelegs rigid and the head held as low as possible.

Buck-kneed: Standing with the knees too far forward.

Bug boy: An apprentice jockey.

Bull pen: Auction ring.

C

Calcium lactate: A calcium salt of lactic acid, used to induce thickening and more rapid clotting of the blood.

Calf-kneed: Standing with knees too far back; directly oppostie to buck-kneed or knee-sprung. This condition causes more trouble than knee-sprung or buck-kneed.

Calico-pinto: A multicolored or spotted pony.

Calk: Grips on the heels and the outside of the front shoes of horses, designed to give the horse better footing and prevent slipping.

Calking: Injury to the coronary band by the shoe of the horse. Usually incurred by horses whose shoes have calks, or by horses that are "rough-shod," as for ice.

Canter: A slow, restrained, three-beat gait in which the two diagonal legs are paired, thereby producing a single beat which falls between the successive beats of the other unpaired legs.

Capped elbow: See Shoe boil.

Capped hock: An enlargement at the point of the hock; it is usually caused by bruising.

Capriole: An intricate movement performed by the Lipizzan horses in the Spanish Riding School in Vienna. It is considered the ultimate of all high school and classical training. The horse leaps into the air, and, while in the air, kicks out with the hind feet. The Capriole also, like so many other forms of high school work, belongs to the Medieval methods of combat, in which, by means of such jumps by the horse, the surrounded rider could rid himself of adversaries. By the horse's kicking out with the hind legs, the enemy was prevented from getting within striking distance with sword and lance.

Cast: Refers to a horse's falling or lying down close to a wall or fence so that it cannot get up without assistance.

Cat-hammed: Having long, relatively thin thighs and legs.

Cavesson: Head stall with a noseband (often quite large) used for exercising and training horses.

Centaurs: The centaurs were an ancient mythical Greek race dwelling in the mountains of Thessalay. They were imagined as men with the bodies of horses and half-bestial natures.

Champing: A term that describes the horse's playing with the bit. Its development is encouraged in bitting a young horse by using a bit with "keys" attached to the mouthpiece, which tends to make the saliva flow and keep the mouth moist—an aid in producing a "soft" mouth.

Charbon: See Anthrax.

Check: Short for checkrein.

Checkrein: A strap coupling the bit of a bridle to the harness back band to keep the head up and in position.

Cheek: A cheek strap, a part of the bridle.

Chestnut: The horny growth on the inside of the horse's legs, above the knees and below the hocks.

Chukker: A seven-and-one-half-minute period in a polo game. (From the Hindu language, meaning "a circle.")

Cinch: Girth of a Western saddle.

Claiming race: A race in which all the horses are entered at stated prices and may be claimed (purchased) by any other owner or a starter in the race. In effect, all horses in a claiming race are offered for sale.

Clean legs: A term indicating that there are no blemishes or unsoundnesses on the legs.

Clicking: Striking the forefoot with the toe of the hind foot on the same side. Also known as forging.

Cluck: To move the tongue in such a way as to produce clucks. The command to go, proceed; the signal to increase speed.

Coarse: Lacking in quality—shown in texture of hair, hairy fetlocks, all-over lack of refinement, common head; flat and shelly feet, and gummy legs.

Cob: A close-knit horse, heavy boned, short coupled and muscular, but with quality, and not so heavy or coarse as to be a draft animal. A cob is usually small, standing under 15 hands.

Cobby: Close coupled, stoutly built. Like a cob.

Cocked ankles: A horse that stands bent forward on the fetlocks in a cocked position.

Cockhorse: An extra horse used with English stagecoaches, ridden behind the coach in ordinary going, but hitched before the team for added draft when approaching steep hills or heavy going. The cockhorse was usually of a flashy color.

Coffin bone: The bone of the foot of a horse, enclosed within the hoof.

Coggins test: A test for diagnosing equine infectious anemia. It was developed by Dr. Leroy Coggins, Cornell University, from whom it takes its common name.

Cold-backed: Describes a horse that humps his back and does not settle down until the saddle has been on a few minutes. Some "cold-backed" horses will merely tuck their tails and arch their backs when first mounted, but others will take a few crow hops until warmed up.

Coldblood: A horse of draft horse breeding.

Cold-jawed: Tough-mouthed.

Colic: A severe indigestion, which causes abdominal discomfort.

Collected: The term applied to a horse when ridden well up to its bit with its neck flexed, jaw relaxed, and hocks well under it. A collected horse has full control over its limbs at all gaits and is ready and able to respond to the signals or aids of its rider.

Colt: A young stallion under three years of age; in Thoroughbreds, the age is extended to include four-year-olds.

Combination horse: One used for saddle and driving.

Combined training: Competitions of this type are usually held over three days and involve dressage, speed and endurance test, and show-jumping. In order to do well, a horse must com-

bine speed, stamina, obedience, and considerable jumping ability; and the rider must be knowledgeable and expert in the three branches of horsemanship upon which the mount is tested.

Condition: The state of health, as evidenced by the coat, state of flesh, and general appearance.

Conformation: Body shape or form.

Congenital: Acquired during development in the uterus and not through heredity.

Contracted feet: A condition characterized by a drawing in or contracting at the heels.

Cool out: To cause a horse to move about quietly after heavy exercise.

Coon footed: Having long low pasterns and shallow heels.

Corn: A bruise to the soft tissue underlying the horny sole of the foot which manifests itself in a reddish discoloration of the sole immediately below the affected area.

Corticosteroids: An organic compound, used to stimulate the proper functioning of the adrenal gland.

Coupling: The section between the point of the hip and the last rib. A short-coupled horse is considered to be an easy keeper, while a long-coupled horse is said to "take a bale of hay a day." The width of four fingers is considered to constitute a short coupling.

Cow hocks, cow-hocked: Standing with the joints of the hocks bent inward, with the toes pointing outward.

Crab bit: Bit with prongs extending at the horse's nose. Purpose is to tip the horse's head up and help prevent him from ducking his head, bowing his neck, and pulling hard on the rein.

Cracked heels, scratches: An inflamed state of the skin at the back of the pastern joint.

Cradle: A device made of wood or aluminum worn around the neck of the horse which prevents him from chewing at sores, blankets, bandages, etc.

Crest: The top part of the neck. This is very well developed in stallions.

Cribber (wind sucker, or stump sucker): A horse that has the vice of biting or setting the teeth against some object, such as the manger, while sucking air.

Crop: A riding whip with a short, straight stock and a loop.

Crop-eared: Refers to an animal which has had the tips of its ears either cut off or frozen off.

Crossbred: The offspring of a sire and dam of differing breeds.

Cross-firing: Cross-firing, a defect in the way of going, generally confined to pacers, which consists of a scuffing on the inside of the diagonal forefeet and hind feet.

Crow hops: Mild or playful bucking motions.

Crupper: A leather strap with a padded semicircular loop. The loop end goes under the tail and the strap end is affixed at the center of the back band of a harness or the cantle of a saddle to prevent the saddle from slipping over the withers.

Cryptorchid: A stallion with one or both testicles retained in the abdomen.

Curb: 1. An enlargement at the rear of the leg and below the point of the hock.

  2. A bit mouthpiece, designed to bring pressure to bear on the horse's bars.

Curry: Cleaning (grooming) with currycomb, dandy brush, body brush, sponge, rub rag, hoof pick, etc.

Cutback saddle: A long, flat saddle that rests low on the horse's back and is designed to place the rider's weight toward the rear. The name is derived from the U-shaped cutaway slot for the withers. It is used primarily for showing.

Cut-out: The cutting out of certain animals in a herd.

Cutting horse: A cow horse used in cutting cattle from the herd. To promote the cutting horse and establish uniform rules for his exhibition, cutting horse enthusiasts are banded together in the following association:

National Cutting Horse Assn.
P. O. Box 12155
Fort Worth, Texas 76116

D

Daisy-cutter: A horse that seems to skim the surface of the ground at the trot. Such horses are often predisposed to stumbling.

Dam: The female parent of a horse.

Dapple: Small spots, patches, or dots contrasting in color or shade with the background, such as dapple-gray.

Dash: Race decided in a single trial.

Dead heat: A racing term referring to two or more contestants that arrive simultaneously at the finish line.

Deerfly: A biting insect that inflicts a painful bite.

Denerving: The removal of part of the nerve trunk and/or nerves in certain areas.

Dental star: A marking on the incisor teeth of horses, used in judging their age. It first appears on the lower central and intermediate incisors when the horse is about eight years of age.

Derby: A word that stems from a classic race exclusively for three-year-olds which was initiated at Epsom Downs, in England, in 1780, by the twelfth Earl of Derby. This race became so famous that, today, the word "derby" is considered synonymous with any well-known race; hence, there is the Kentucky Derby, the Japan Derby, etc. In England, the word is pronounced "darby,"

whereas in the United States it is pronounced "derby."

Diagonal: Refers to the forefoot moving in unison with its opposite hindfoot at the trot. If it is the left forefoot, it is called the left diagonal.

Dish-faced: A term used if the face is concave below the eyes, and, especially in Arabians, if the profile shows a definite depression below the level of the eyes. This term is also applied to some horses and many ponies that have flat or concave foreheads with prominent temples, but this type is the absolute opposite to the "dish" of the Arab, which has a prominent forehead.

Dishing: Carrying the foot forward in a lateral arc in a trot, but advancing the knee in a straight line.

Disqualification: A fault so serious that is disqualifies a horse for registry or show.

Distaff side: The female side, as in a pedigree.

Distemper (strangles): A widespread contagious disease of horses, especially among young animals, caused by *Streptococcus equi*, a bacterium.

Dock: The solid portion of the tail.

Docked: A tail in which part of the dock has been removed.

Docking and setting: Removing part of the dock of the tail, cutting the tendons, and "setting" the tail to make the horse carry it high.

Doping: The administering of a drug to a horse to increase or decrease his speed in a race. Racecourse officials run saliva tests, urine tests (urinalyses), etc., in order to try to detect any horses that have been doped. Usually such tests are conducted on the winners of every race and on the first three to finish in stakes races. Where doping is proved, the horse may be banned from the track for a period of time; the owner may have his entire stable banned from racing for a period of time; and/or the trainer or jockey may lose his license, with the penalty determined by the circumstances.

Double-gaited: A term applied to a horse that can both trot and pace with good speed.

Drafty: Having the characteristics of a draft horse. Heavy and lacking in quality.

Drag hunt: A hunt staged on horseback with hounds following a laid trail, made by dragging a bag containing anise seed or litter from a fox's den.

Dressage: The guiding of a horse through natural maneuvers without emphasis on the use of reins, hands, and feet.

Drover: A word reminiscent of one of the most thrilling chapters in American history. Prior to the advent of railroads and improved highways, great herds of cattle, sheep, and hogs were driven on horseback over famous trails, often many hundreds of miles long. The crew of "drovers" usually consisted of the boss (often the owner of the herd), a man to ride along each side, and a fourth man to lead.

The "drovers"—those who did the driving—were rugged, and their lives were filled with adventure. The work was accompanied by an almost ceaseless battle with the elements, clashes with thieves, and no small amount of bloodshed.

Dutchman's team: It is customary to hitch the smaller horse of a team on the left side. When a careless horseman hitches his larger horse on the near side, he is said to be driving a "Dutchman's team."

Dwelling: A noticeable pause in the flight of the foot, as though the stride were completed before the foot reaches the ground. It is most noticeable in trick-trained horses.

E

Ear down: To restrain an animal by biting or twisting its ear.

Eastern: Applied to horses of Arab, Barb, or similar breeding.

Eczema: A condition involving the skin, inflammation of the skin with lesions of either a dry or weeping nature. Allergies are probably the most common cause.

Encephalomyelitis (sleeping sickness): A virus, epizootic (epidemic) brain disease which affects both horses and man. It is caused by several distinct viruses. The three most common types in the United States are: Eastern equine encephalomyelitis, Western equine encephalomyelitis, and Venezuelan equine encephalomyelitis.

Endurance rides: Trials of speed and endurance. Eleven 300-mile endurance rides were held, 7 in New England and 4 in Colorado, but these were discontinued in 1926. Today, there are several well-known 50- to 100-mile competitive endurance rides in the United States. The time for the different courses varies according to the topography, elevation, and footing, but it is approximately 17 hours for 100 miles and 6 hours for 50 miles.

Entire: An ungelded male.

Equestrian: One who rides horseback.

Equestrienne: A female equestrian.

Equine: A horse. Correctly speaking, the term includes all the members of the family *Equidae*—horses, zebras, and asses.

Equine abortion: The premature expulsion of the fetus.

Equine infectious anemia (swamp fever): An infectious virus disease.

Equine influenza: An infectious disease caused by a myxovirus that has properties of the Type A influenza viruses.

Equine piroplasmosis (babesiasis): Caused by *Babesia caballi* or *B. equi*, protozoan parasites that invade the red blood cells.

Equitation: The act or art of riding horseback.

Ergot: The horny growth at the back of the fetlock joint; the spurs of a horse's hoofs.

Estrus: The period of sexual excitement (heat) during which the female will accept the male in the act of mating.

Ewe neck: A neck like that of a sheep, with a dip between the poll and the withers. Also termed a "turkey neck" and "upside-down neck."

Extended trot: Moving the horse at a very rapid, but collected, gait at the trot. To achieve this, the rider applies pressure with the calves of legs as he or she comes down into the saddle while posting.

Exudate: Refers to the discharge of fluid and tissue material from an ozzing sore or wound. This is usually characterized by a dry, crusty state of scabbylike sores.

F

Face fly: Flies that gather in large numbers on the faces of horses, especially around the eyes and nose.

Fallen neck: See Broken crest.

Family: The lineage of an animal as traced through either the males or females, depending upon the breed.

Farcy: See Glanders

Farrier: A horseshoer.

Far side: The right side of a horse.

Favoring a leg: To favor one leg; to limp slightly.

Feather: The long hairs that grow at the back of the pastern or fetlock.

Feather in eye: A mark across the eyeball, not touching the pupil; often caused by an injury, it may be a blemish or some other defect.

Feral: Describes a wild horse—one that has escaped from domestication and become wild, as contrasted to one originating in the wild.

Fetlock joint: The connection between the cannon and the pastern bones.

Fetus: The unborn animal as it develops in the uterus.

Figure-eight bandage: A style of bandaging, applied in a figure-eight fashion, which allows for expansion at the flexing of hocks and knees.

Filly: A young female horse under three years of age; in Thoroughbreds, it includes four-year-olds.

Film patrol: The practice of recording a race on film.

Firing: Applying a hot iron or needle to a blemish or unsoundness as a treatment.

First lock: The first lock of the mane on or in back of the poll (when the poll is clipped). The first lock is sometimes braided with a ribbon, as is the foretop.

Fistulous withers: An inflamed condition in the region of the withers, commonly thought to be caused by bruising.

Flat bone: See Bone.

Flat foot: A foot of which the angle is less than 45°, or one in which the sole is not concave, or one with a low, weak heel.

Flat race: A race without jumps.

Flat-sided: Lacking spring in ribs.

Flaxen: A light-colored mane or tail.

Flea-bitten: Describes a white horse covered with small, brown marks, or any "mangy-looking" animal.

Floating: Filing off the sharp edges of a horse's teeth.

Foal: A young, unweaned horse of either sex.

Foaling: Giving birth to a foal.

Follicle: A bubblelike structure on the ovary which contains an egg.

Foot-lock or feather: Long hair which grows back of the fetlock.

Forage: Vegetable material in a fresh, dried, or ensiled state which is fed to livestock (pasture, hay, silage).

Forehand: The "front" of the horse, including head, neck, shoulders, and forelegs—in other words, that portion of the horse in front of the center of gravity.

Foretop, forelock: The lock of hair falling forward over the face.

Forging: See Clicking.

Form: The past performance of a racehorse; often a table giving details relating to a horse's past performance.

Founder: See Laminitis.

Four-in-hand: A hitch of four horses, consisting of two pairs, with one pair in front of the other.

Fox hunt: A hunt with hounds, staged on horseback, after a live fox. The fox may have been released from captivity or tracked and flushed out of hiding by the hounds.

Fox-trot: A slow, short, broken type of trot in which the head usually nods. In executing the fox-trot, the horse brings each hind foot to the ground an instant before the diagonal forefoot.

Frog: A triangular-shaped, elasticlike formation in the sole of the horse's foot.

Full bridle: Another term for either a Weymouth or show bridle.

Full brothers (or sisters): Horses having the same sire and the same dam.

Funeral procession horse(s): U.S. Armed Service horse(s) used in funeral processions, either as a team to draw a caisson or as a riderless horse.

Fungi: Certain vegetable organisms such as molds, mushrooms, and toadstools.

Furlong: A racing distance of 1/8th mile, or 40 rods, or 220 yards, or 201.17 meters.

Futurity race: A race in which the horses entered were nominated before birth. As in any other stake race, a fee must accompany the entry of the mare's unborn produce, and further payments must be made to keep the youngster eligible. All these fees go into the winner's kitty.

G

Gait: A particular way of going, either natural or acquired, which is characterized by a distinctive rhythmic movement of the feet and legs.

Gallop: See Run.

Galloping boot: A protective leg support, put on the front legs covering the tendon, cannon bone, and upper portion of the ankle joint.

Galton's law: The theory of inheritance expounded by Sir Francis Galton (1822-1911). According to this genetic theory, the individual's inheritance is determined as follows: 1/4 by its sire and 1/4 by its dam; 1/16 by each of the 4 grandparents; 1/64 by each of the 8 great grandparents; and on and on, with each ancestor contributing just 1/4 as much to the total inheritance as did the one a generation nearer to the individual. "Galton's law" is correct in the sense that the relationship between ancestor and descendant is halved with each additional generation which intervenes between them. It is not correct in the sense that the individual's heredity is completely determined by the heredity of its ancestors. Rather, in a random-bred population, the individual is 1/4 determined by each parent and 1/2 determined by chance in Mendelian segregation. Determination by more remote ancestors is included in the determination by the parent. Galton's law is often used as a stamina index by Thoroughbred breeders.

Gamete: A mature sex cell (sperm or egg).

Gaucho: The South American cowboy. In particular, the term is used in the Pampas area of Argentina. The gaucho is considered by many to be the world's finest roughrider.

Gear: The equipment and accessories used in harness driving (except the vehicle) and in polo playing (except the bridles and saddles). See Tack.

Gee: The teamster's term signaling a turn to the right.

Geld: To cut or castrate a male horse.

Gelding: A male horse that was castrated before reaching maturity.

Genotype selection: Selection of breeding stock not necessarily from the best appearing animals but from the best breeding animals, according to genetic makeup.

Germ plasm: Germ cells and their precursors, bearers of hereditary characters.

Get: Progeny or offspring.

Get-up: The command to go; proceed; move forward. When repeated, it means to increase speed. "Giddap," slang.

Girth: The strap or webbing that holds the saddle or backband in place.

Girth-place: The place for the girth, as the name implies, it is marked by a depression in the underline just in back of the front legs.

Glanders (or farcy): An acute or chronic infectious disease caused by *Malleomyces mallei*, a bacterium.

Glass-eyed: The term applied to an eye that is devoid of pigment.

Good mouth: Said of an animal 6 to 10 years of age.

Goose-rumped: An animal having a short, steep croup that narrows at the point of the buttocks.

Grade: An animal of unknown ancestry. If it shows some specific breed characteristics, it may be suffixed with the name of that breed; e.g., grade Shetland.

Grain: Harvested cereals or other edible seeds, including oats, corn, milo, barley, etc.

Granulation: The formation of excess or scar tissue in early wound healing and repair.

Gravel: A condition which is usually caused by penetration of the protective covering of the hoof by small bits of gravel or dirt. Access to the sensitive tissue is usually gained by the "white line" or junction of the sole and wall, where the horn is somewhat softer. Once in the soft tissue inside the wall or sole, bacterial infection carried by the foreign material develops rapidly, producing pus and gas that create pressure and intense pain in the foot. In untreated cases, it breaks out at the top of the coronary band and the pus and gas are forced out through this opening.

Grease heel (or scratches): A low-grade infection affecting the hair follicles and skin at the base of the fetlock joint, most frequently the hind legs. It is similar to scratches, but in a more advanced stage.

Green broke: A term applied to a horse that has been hitched or ridden only one or two times.

Groom: A person who tends and cares for horses; an attendant, horseman, hostler, swipe (not preferred).

Gummy-legged: Having legs in which the tendons lack definition, or do not stand out clearly.

Gymkhana: A program of games on horseback.

H

Hack: A horse used for riding at an ordinary gait over roads, trails, etc.

Hair: A slender outgrowth of the epidermis which performs a thermoregulatory function, to protect the animal from cold or heat. It becomes long and shaggy during the winter months in cold areas, especially if the horse is left ouside. Then, during the warm season, or when the animal is blanketed, the horse sheds and the coat becomes short.

Hair colors: The five basic horse coat colors are bay, black, brown, chestnut, and white. Additionally, there are five major variations of these colors: dun (buckskin), gray, palomino, pinto (calico or paint), and roan.

Half-bred: When capitalized, this denotes a horse sired by a Thoroughbred and registered in the Half-Bred Stud Book.

Half stocking: White extends from the coronet to the middle of the cannon.

Halter puller: A horse that pulls back on the halter rope.

Hammerhead: A coarse-headed animal.

Hamstrung: Disabled by an injury to the tendon above the hock.

Hand: A 4-inch unit of measurement.

Hand-canter: A semiextended canter, midway between a promenade canter and a gallop.

Hand gallop: An extended canter, but the horse remains collected, unlike the flat-out run when the horse's gait almost returns to a four-beat status.

Handicap: A race in which chances of winning are equalized by assigned weights; heaviest weights are given to the best horses, and lightest weights to the poorest.

Hard-mouthed: Term used when the membrane of the bars of the mouth where the bit rests have become toughened and the nerves deadened because of the continued pressure of the bit.

Hat-rack: An emaciated animal.

Haute école: "High school," the highest form of specialized training of the riding horse.

Haw: The teamster's term signaling a turn to the left.

Hay belly: Having a distended barrel due to the excessive feeding of bulky rations, such as hay, straw or grass. Also called "grass belly."

Heat: 1. One trip in a race that will be decided by winning two or more trials.

2. A common term for estrus.

Heaves: Difficulty in forcing air out of the lungs. It is characterized by a jerking of the flanks (double-flank action) and coughing after drinking cold water.

Height: Tallness of a horse as measured from the withers to the ground. It is expressed in hands, each hand being 4 inches.

Heredity: Characteristics transmitted to offspring from parents and other ancestors.

Hernia (or rupture): The protrusion of any internal organ through the wall of its containing cavity, but it usually means the passage of a portion of the intestine through an opening in the abdominal muscle.

Herring gutted: Lacking depth of flank, which is also termed "single gutted."

Heterozygous: Having like genes which can be present for any of the characteristics such as coat color, size, etc.

Hidebound: A tight hide over the body.

High school: The highest form of specialized training of riding horses.

Hippology: The study of the horse.

Hitch: 1. To fasten a horse; e.g., when hitched to a rail.

2. A connection between a vehicle and a horse.

3. A defect in gait noted in the hind legs, which seem to skip at the trot.

Hitching: 1. Having a shorter stride in one hind leg than in the other.

2. Fastening a horse to an object or vehicle.

Hives: Small swellings under or within the skin similar to human hives. They appear suddenly over large portions of the body and can be caused by a change in feed.

Hobbles: Straps which encircle the pasterns or fetlock joints on the front legs of the horse and are connected with a short strap or chain, to prevent it from roaming too far when turned out to graze. Another type of hobble is used on the hind legs (often around the hocks) of a mare in breeding, to prevent her from kicking the stallion.

Hogged mane: A hogged mane is one that has been clipped short.

Homozygous: Having like genes in a horse which can be present for any of the characteristics of the animal such as coat color, size, etc.

Homozygous dominant: A dominant character that produces only one kind of gamete.

Homozygous recessive: A recessive character that produces two kinds of gametes; one carries the dominant gene, while the other carries the recessive gene.

Honda: A ring of rope, rawhide, or metal on a lasso through which the loop slides.

Hopples: The term applied to hobbles (leather or plastic straps with semicircular loops) used in harness racing, which are placed on the gaskin and forearm, connecting the fore and hind legs of

the same side in pacers, and running diagonally in trotters, connecting the diagonal fore and hind legs. Such hopples, which were invented by a railroad conductor named John Browning in 1885, are used to keep a horse on gait; i.e., to prevent trotters from pacing and pacers from trotting.

Hormone: A body-regulating chemical secreted by a gland into the bloodstream.

Horn fly: Primarily pests of cattle, but they sometimes seriously annoy horses.

Horse: In the restricted sense this applies to an entire, not a gelding or mare.

Horsemanship: The art of riding horseback.

Horsemeat: In France and Belgium, and other parts of the world, horsemeat is considered a delicacy for human consumption. In this country, many horses that have outlived their usefulness or that are less valuable for other purposes are processed in modern, sanitary slaughtering plants for pet food.

Horsepower: Originally, "horsepower" was a measure of the power that a horse exerts in pulling. Technically speaking, a horsepower is the rate at which work is accomplished when a resistance (weight) of 33,000 pounds is moved 1 foot in 1 minute, or 550 pounds is moved 1 foot in 1 second. Despite their sophistication, modern motors are rated in horsepower, based on tests made on a machine known as the dynamometer.

Hot-blooded: Of Eastern or Oriental blood.

Hot-walker: One employed to cool out horses.

House fly: Nonbiting, nuisance insect.

Hunt: Pursuit of game. As used by horsemen, the term usually implies a hunt on horseback with hounds.

Hunt seat saddle: Much like the jump saddle, but with less incline to the cantle.

Hybrids: Crosses of species, not breeds. The mule is a hybrid, cross between the horse family and the ass family. Most mules are infertile.

I

Import: To bring horses from another country.

Importing: In registering horses from another country in the U.S. stud book of their respective breeds, the certificates of registration issued bear the abbreviation Imp. and the country of export; e.g., Imp. Hydroplane (Eng.). When a name, such as Hydroplane has been previously granted to a horse foaled (born) in this country, a symbol is added; e.g., Imp. Hydroplane II (Eng.). Imported is also denoted by an asterisk in front of the name; e.g., *Hydroplane II (Eng.).

Indian broke: Horses trained to allow mounting from the off side.

Indian pony: A horse of pinto color.

Influenza: A contagious virus disease, characterized by respiratory inflammation, fever, muscle soreness, and often a loss of appetite.

In hand: Refers to horses shown in halter classes.

Interfering: The striking of the fetlock or cannon by the opposite foot that is in motion is known as interfering. This condition is predisposed in horses with base-narrow, toe-wide, or splay-footed standing positions.

Iodoform: A light yellow crystallin compound, used as an antiseptic medicine.

Itch: See Mange.

J

Jack spavin: See Bone spavin.

Jennet: Female of the ass family.

Jerk line: A single rein, originally used in western United States. It was fastened to the brake handle and ran through the driver's hand to the bit of the lead animal.

Jockey Club: Probably the most exclusive club in America, limited to about 80 members. The Jockey Club is custodian of the American Stud Book, registry of Thoroughbred horses.

Jockeys: Professional riders of horses in races. Jockeys are both born and made. They were born to be small people; and they are made as jockeys if they possess courage and intelligence. Jockeys weigh anywhere from 94 to 116 pounds, with an average of about 105 pounds. A famous observation, which the author once overhead in a jockeys' room before a race, was "What would we all be if it weren't for racing? We'd all be bellhops." But, the jockey might well have added that they would be bellhops anyway if they didn't have the courage to ride down a track at 40 miles an hour, delicately balanced in a pair of short stirrups, amid 48 flying steel plates (shoes) and 6 thundering tons of horseflesh—calmly, but in a split second, planning every move as they ride.

Jockey stick: A stick fastened to the hame of the near horse and the bit of the off horse for use in driving with a single rein to prevent crowding.

Jog cart: A cart longer and heavier than a racing sulky, used in warm-up miles because it's more comfortable for the driver than a sulky.

Jogging: A slow warm-up exercise of several miles with the horse going the wrong way of the track.

Joint ill: See Navel infection.

Jughead: A stupid horse. Also one with a large, ugly head.

Jump seat saddle: A saddle with a high cantle (back) which inclines the rider's weight forward to keep

in balance with the horse when going over jumps. It usually has knee rolls to help maintain balance.

K

Kick: Movement by a horse of the back or front leg, or legs, with intent to hit a person or other object.

Knee-sprung: See Buck-kneed.

L

Lameness: A defect that can be detected when the affected foot is favored when standing. In action, the load on the ailing foot is eased, and there is a characteristic bobbing of the head of the horse as the affected foot strikes the ground.

Laminae: The flat tissue in the sole or base of the hoof.

Laminitis (or founder): An inflammation of the sensitive laminae under the horny wall of the hoof. All feet may be affected, but the front feet are most susceptible. It is characterized by ridges running around the hoof.

Lampas: Referring to the membranes of the upper hard plate of the mouth, just behind the upper incisor teeth.

Lead: The leading foot (leg) of a horse under saddle. When cantering circularly, the foot to the inner arc of the circle—clockwise, a right foot lead; and counter clockwise, a left foot lead.

Leaders: The head team in 4-, 6-, or 8-horse hitch.

Lead line: A chain, rope, or strap, or combination thereof, used for leading a horse.

Leathers: The straps running from the saddle to the irons on an English saddle.

Left lead: Left front foot and left rear foot lead on the canter.

Leg bracer: A solution, lotion, or liniment, containing a large amount of alcohol used as a stimulant for the legs, causing increased blood circulation to the applied area.

Legs out of the same hole: Very narrow-fronted. Such horses usually stand basewide; i.e., the feet stand wider apart than the distance across the legs at the chest.

Levade: An exercise of the *haute école,* especially as performed in the Spanish Riding School at Vienna. In the Levade the horse is in a half rearing position, with the forelegs well bent and the hind legs in a crouching position.

Lice: Small, flattened, wingless insect parasites.

Lineback: An animal having a stripe of distinctive color along the spine.

Lines, reins: A leather, webbing, or rope attached to the bit or bits for control and direction. In driving, lines are sometimes called reins. In riding, reins are never called lines.

Lip strap: The small strap running through the curb chain from one side of the bit shank to the other. Its primary function is to keep the horse from taking the shank or the bit in its teeth.

Live foal: A foal that must stand and nurse.

Lockjaw: See Tetanus.

Long-coupled: Too much space between the last rib and the point of the hip.

Longe: See Lunge.

Lope: The western adaptation of a very slow canter. It is a smooth, slow gait in which the head is carried low.

Lop-neck, fallen-neck, or broken-crest: A heavy neck that breaks over or falls to one side.

Lugger: A horse that pulls at the bit.

Lugging and pulling: Some horses pull on the reins, "lug" on one rein, or bear out or in with the driver, making it hard to drive them and to rate the mile at an even clip.

Lunge (longe): The act of exercising a horse on the end of a long rope, usually in a circle.

Lungworms (Dictyocaulus arnfieldi): Parasites which may be found in the air passages of the horse and other equines. The male worm reaches a length of about 1 inch and the female may be about 2 inches long. The equine lungworm is very rare in the United States.

M

Maiden: 1. A mare that has never been bred.
2. On the racetrack, it refers to a horse (stallion, mare, or gelding) that has not won a race on a recognized track. In the show-ring, it refers to a horse that has not won a first ribbon in a recognized show in the division in which it is showing.

Mane: Long hair on the top of the neck.

Mange (scabies, scab, or itch): A specific contagious disease caused by mites.

Manners: A way of behaving.

Mare: A mature female four years or older; in Thoroughbreds, five years or older.

Mascot: A companion for a horse. The most common mascots are ponies, goats, dogs, cats, and chickens.

Matron: A mare that has produced a foal.

Mites: Very small parasites that cause mange (scabies, scab, or itch).

Mixed-gaited: Said of a horse that will not adhere to any one true gait at a time.

Mohammed's ten horses: In the days of Mohammed, intelligence and obedience were the main requisites of the Arab's horse. For war purposes, only the most obedient horses were used, and they were trained to follow the bugle.
Legend has it that the Prophet himself had need for some very obedient horses, so he in-

spected a certain herd to make personal selections. The horses from which he wished to make selections were pastured in a large area bordering on a river. The Prophet gave orders that the animals should be fenced off from the river until their thirst became very great.

He ordered the fence removed, and the horses rushed for the water. When they were just about to dash into the river to quench their thirst, a bugle was sounded.

All but 10 of the horses ignored the call of the bugle. The obedient 10 turned and answered the call of duty, despite their great thirst. The whimsical story goes on to say that these 10 head constituted the foundation of the "Prophet Strain."

Moon-blindness (periodic ophthalmia): An eye disease which causes a cloudy or inflamed condition of the eyes.

Morning glory: A horse that works out in record time in the morning, but that does not live up to its promise in the afternoon race.

Mosquito: A biting insect.

Mottled: Marked with spots of different colors: dappled, spotted.

Mounting: The act of getting on a horse.

Mouthing: Determining the approximate age of a horse by examining the teeth.

Mudder: A horse that runs well on a track that is wet, sloppy, or heavy.

Mustang: Native horse of the western plains.

Mutation: A sudden variation which is later passed on through inheritance and which results from changes in a gene or genes.

Mutton-withered: Being low in the withers, with heavy shoulder muscling.

Muzzle: The lower end of the nose which includes the nostrils, lips, and chin.

N

Narragansett pacer: A fast type of pacer, descended from the indigenous horse of the Narragansett Bay area of Rhode Island, which evolved during the time of the Revolutionary War (1775-1781). During this period, racing was illegal except in Rhode Island.

Navel ill: See Navel infection.

Navel infection (joint ill, navel ill, actinobacillosis): An infectious disease of newborn animals caused by several kinds of bacteria.

Navicular disease: An inflammation of the small navicular bone and bursa of the front foot. It is often impossible to determine the exact cause of the disease. Affected animals go lame; have a short stubby stride; and usually point the affected foot when standing. Few animals completely recover from the disease. Treatment consists in

special shoeing. In cases of persistent and severe lameness, unnerving may be performed by a veterinarian to destroy the sensation in the foot.

Near side: The left side of a horse. The custom of working from the left side of the horse evolved quite logically in two ways:

1. In the days when horsemen wore swords, they hung to the left. Hence, the sword would have interferred with the rider by hanging between his legs had he tried mounting from the right.

2. In England, traffic keeps to the left. Therefore, when working around horses the coachman stood on the left side if possible in order to be on the side of the road and out of the line of traffic.

In both the above situations horsemen were most often on the left side of horses: hence, logically it became known as the "near" side, and the right side became the "off" side. With a team of horses, the one on the left is the "near" horse, the one of the right is the "off" horse.

Neck rein: To guide or direct a horse by pressure of the rein on the neck.

Neigh: The loud, prolonged call of a horse.

O

Off side: The right side of a horse.

Open bridle: Bridle without blinds or blinkers covering the eyes. Some bridles are rigged with blinds that shut off vision to the rear and side and a few horses are raced with goggles or "peekaboo" blinds.

Open-hocked: Wide apart at the hocks with the feet close together.

Oriental: See Eastern.

Orloff trotter: A breed of horses originating in the USSR in the 18th Century, principally through the interest of Count Alexis Gregory Orloff Chesminski. Used in the Soviet Union for light work, pleasure driving and riding, exhibition at fairs in various forms of competition including dressage, and extensively in harness racing.

Osselets: A rather inclusive term used to refer to a number of inflammatory conditions around the ankle joints. Generally it denotes a swelling that is fairly well defined and located slightly above or below the actual center of the joint, and, ordinarily, a little to the inside or outside of the exact front of the leg. When touched, it imparts the feeling of putty or mush, and it may be warm to hot. The pain will be in keeping with the degree of inflammation as evidenced by swelling and fever. Afflicted horses travel with a short, choppy stride and show evidence of pain when the ankle is flexed.

Outlaw: A horse that cannot be broken.

Ovary: The female organ that produces eggs. There are two ovaries.

Overreach: The hitting of the forefoot with the hind foot.

Overshot jaw: The upper jaw protruding beyond the lower jaw. Same as "parrot mouth."

Ovulation: The time when the follicle bursts and the egg is released.

Ovum: Scientific name for egg, the female reproductive cell.

P

Pace: A fast, two-beat gait in which the front and hind feet on the same side start and stop simultaneously.

Paddling: Throwing the front feet outward as they are picked up. This condition is predisposed in horses with toe-narrow or pigeon-toed standing positions.

Pair: Two horses hitched abreast. Also, used in reference to two horses ridden side by side, together as in pair classes.

Palisade worms: See Strongyles.

Pari-mutuels: Machine-controlled pool betting, invented in France in 1865, by a perfume shop proprietor named Pierre Oller, who, embittered by a losing streak with the bookies, worked out the idea of the betting pool and began selling tickets over his store counter. His take was five percent; the rest was divided equally among the winners.

Parrot mouth: See Overshot jaw.

Passage: A movement of the *haute école.* This is a slow, cadenced, rather high trot with a fairly long period of suspension, giving the impression that the horse is on springs, or "trotting on air." Also a term for diagonal movement of the horse while facing straight forward, at the walk or trot.

Pastern: That part of the leg between the fetlock joint and the coronary band of the hoof.

Pedigree: A record of the ancestry of an animal.

Pedigree breeding: Selection on the combined bases of the merits of the individual and the average merits of its ancestry.

Pegasus: A word of Greek origin, meaning strong. Legend has it that the winged horse, Pegasus, was fashioned from the body of Medusa, daughter of a sea god who, in her youth, was as mortal as she was beautiful. At his birth, the frisky colt flew to Mount Helicon, where he created a fountain (Horsewell) with one swift blow of his hoof. Using a golden bridle, Bellerophon coaxed the curious animal from his favorite meadow, made him captive, and rode him off. Later, Pegasus unceremoniously dumped his venerable and con-

Fig. 20-2. Pegasus, the strong, fleet, winged horse of Greek mythology.

ceited master and flew into outer space where he became the constellation that bears his name.

Pelham bit: A one-piece bit equipped to handle four reins. Two are snaffle reins, used for guiding the horse and lifting the head; and two are curb reins, used for control and for setting the head. Snaffle reins are always heavier than curb reins.

Periodic ophthalmia: See Moon blindness.

Piaffe: A dressage movement in which the horse does a cadenced trot in place, without moving from the spot. It is the foundation of all high school movements.

Piebald: Refers to black-and-white coat color.

Pigeon-toed: Pointing toes inward and heels outward.

Pig-eyed: Having small, narrow, squinty eyes, set back in the head; also, having thick eyelids.

Pin-firing: A method of using an electric needle to insert into an injured area. This induces healing at the site.

Pinto: A multicolored, spotted horse.

Pinworms (Oxyuris equi, Probstmyria vivipara): Two species of pinworms, or rectal worms, frequently are found in horses. *Oxyuris equi* are whitish worms with long, slender tails. *Probstmyria vivipara* are so small they are scarcely visible to the eye.

Pirouette: A dressage exercise in which the horse holds its forelegs more or less in place while it moves its hindquarters around them.

Pivot: A movement in dressage in which the horse pivots around its hindquarters, holding one hind

leg more or less in place and side-stepping with the other hind foot.

Place: To finish second in a race.

Placenta: The membrane by which the fetus is attached to the uterus. Nutrients from the mother pass into the placenta and then through the navel cord to the fetus. When the animal is born, the placenta is expelled. It is commonly called the "afterbirth."

Plug: A horse of common breeding and poor conformation.

Point: The team in back of the leaders in an eight-horse hitch.

Pointing: 1. Perceptible extension of the stride with little flexion is called pointing. This condition is likely to occur in the Thoroughbred and Standardbred breeds—animals bred and trained for great speed with a long stride.

2. Referring to a standing position when one of the front legs is extended ahead of the other. This occurs when a horse with a sore foot places the ailing foot ahead in order to take the weight off it.

Points: Black coloration from the knees and hocks down, as in most bays and browns, and in some buckskins, roans, and grays.

Poll evil: An inflamed condition in the region of the poll (the area on top of the neck and immediately behind the ears), usually caused by bruising the top of the head.

Polo pony: A "pony" used for polo. Polo ponies of today are mostly of Thoroughbred breeding. They must be fast, and tough and courageous enough to stand the bumping, riding-off, and the many quick stops and turns.

Pop-eyed: Refers to a horse whose eyes are generally more prominent or bulge out a little more than normal; also to a horse that is "spooky" or attempts to see everything that goes on.

Popped knee: A general term describing inflammatory conditions affecting the knees, so named because of the sudden swelling that accompanies it.

Post: The starting point of a race.

Posting: The rising and descending of the rider with the rhythm of the trot.

Post position: Refers to race starting position. Beginning with position No. 1 nearest the rail, horses line up at the starting gate according to number.

Poultice: A moist, mealy mass, applied hot to a sore or inflamed part of the body.

Pounding: A "heavy foot" contact with the ground, common in high-going horses.

Prepotency: Refers to breeding power, as measured by the degree in which parent likeness is transmitted to offspring.

Produce: Offspring.

Progenitor: One that originates or precedes.

Progeny: Refers to offspring or descendants of one or both parents.

Puffs: Windgalls, bog spavins, or thoroughpins.

Pulled tail: A tail thinned by hairs being pulled.

Pulling record, world: The world's record in a pulling contest was established at the 1965 Hillsdale County Fair, in Michigan. It is held jointly by Frank Vurckio, Sun Down, New York; and Fowler Bros., Montgomery, Michigan. It was made on a dynamometer with a tractive pull of 4,350 pounds (equal to 56,493 pounds, or over 28 tons, on a wagon).

Purebred: An animal descended from a line of ancestors of the same breed but not necessarily registered. This should not be confused with "Thoroughbred," a breed of horses.

Purse: Race prize money to which the owners of horses in the race do not contribute.

Q

Quality: Refinement, as shown in a neat and well-chiselled head, fine texture of hair with little or no fetlock, clean bone, good texture of hoof, etc.

Quarter crack (sand crack): A vertical split in the horny wall of the inside of the hoof (in the region of the quarter), which extends from the coronet or hoof head downward.

Quittor: A deep-seated running sore which occurs on the coronet band or hoof head. It is caused initially by an injury or puncture wound in the area of the sole of the foot.

R

Rack (single-foot): A fast, flashy, unnatural, four-beat gait in which each foot meets the ground separately at equal intervals; hence, it was originally known as the "single-foot," a designation now largely discarded.

Random: Three horses hitched in single file, usually to a dogcart.

Rangy: Elongated, lean, muscular, of slight build.

Rat tail: A tail with a short-hair coat.

Rattlers: Rattlers (wooden, rubber, or plastic balls) or links of light chain fastened about the pasterns of high-going harness and saddle horses and ponies. Weighted boots are also used to enhance action.

Reata: Spanish for lariat.

Recessive character: A characteristic which appears only when both members of a pair of genes are alike. Opposite of dominant.

Red worms: See Strongyles.

Reins: See Lines.

Remuda: A collection of riding horses at a roundup from which are chosen those used for the day. A relay of mounts.

Ribbed-up: Said of a horse on which the back ribs are well arched and incline well backwards, bringing the ends closer to the point of the hip and making the horse shorter in coupling.

Ridgeling: A horse with at least one testicle in the abdomen. A ridgeling is difficult to geld, and often retains the characteristic of a stallion.

Right lead: Right front foot and right rear lead on the canter.

Ringbone: A bony growth on the pastern bone in the area of the coronet. It is generally on the forefoot, although occasionally the hind foot is affected.

Ringer: A horse passed off under false identity, with the idea of entering it in a race below its class where it is almost certain to win. With today's lip tattoo system of identification, ringers are a thing of the past.

Ringworm: This is a contagious infection of the outer layers of skin caused by an infestation of microscopic fungi.

Roach-backed: Arched-backed, razorbacked.

Roached mane: A mane that has been cut short and tapered so that it stands upright. It is not so short as a clipped mane.

Roarer: A wind-broken animal that makes a loud noise in drawing air into the lungs.

Rollers, rattlers: Wooden balls on a cord, encircling a horse's pastern to give the horse more action.

Rolling: Excessive lateral shoulder motion, characteristic of horses with protruding shoulders, is known as rolling.

Roman-nosed: Refers to a horse having a profile that is convex from poll to muzzle.

Rope-walking: See Winding.

Roundworms, large (ascarids; Parascaris equorum): The female varies from 6 to 22 inches long and the male from 5 to 13 inches. When full-grown, both are about the diameter of a lead pencil.

Rubdown: A rubbing of the body with a rough towel, usually given after exercise to promote circulation and remove fatigue.

Run (gallop): The run, or gallop, is a fast, four-beat gait where the feet strike the ground separately—first one hind foot, then the other hind foot, then the front foot on the same side as the first hind foot, then the other front foot which decides the lead.

Running walk: A slow, four-beat gait, intermediate in speed between the walk and rack. The hind foot oversteps the front foot from a few to as many as 18 inches, giving the motion a smooth gliding effect. It is characterized by a bobbing or nodding of the head, a flopping of the ears, and a snapping of the teeth in rhythm with the movement of the legs.

Rupture: See Hernia.

S

Saline: Consisting of or containing salt.

Saliva test: The testing of saliva for the presence of drugs or narcotics.

Sand crack: See Quarter crack.

Scab: See Mange.

Scabies: See Mange.

Scalping: That condition in which the hairline at the top of the hind foot hits the toe of the forefoot as it breaks over.

Schooling: Training and developing natural characteristics in a pony.

Sclerostomes: See Strongyles.

Scoring: Preliminary warming up of horses before the start. The horses are turned near the starting point and hustled away as they will be in the race.

Scotch collar: Housing over the collar of draft show harness.

Scraper: A metal or wooden, slightly concave, tool shaped like a hook at the upper end and used with one hand for scraping sweat and liquid from the body. Also, a thin metal strip with handles affixed at either end, used with both hands for scraping sweat and liquid from the body.

Scratches: See Grease heel.

Screwworm: Maggots of the screwworm fly, which require living flesh of animals on which to feed.

Scrotum: The saclike pouch that suspends the testicles outside the male animal.

Scrub: A low-grade animal.

Self-colored: A term applied to the mane and tail when they are the same color as the body coat.

Sell at halter: To sell with no guarantee except the title.

Semen: Sperm mixed with fluids from the accessory glands.

Serviceably sound: Said of a horse that has nothing wrong that will materially impair its value for the intended use.

Sesamoid fractures: The fracture of one or both of the two pyramidlike bones that form a part of the fetlock or ankle joints (on both front and rear legs) and articulate with the posterior part of the lower end of the cannon bone.

Set tail: A tail in which the cords have been cut or "nicked" and the tail put in a set.

Sex cells: The egg and the sperm, which unite to create life. They transmit genetic characteristics from the parents to the offspring.

Shadbelly: See Herring gutted.

Shipping fever (distemper, strangles): An infectious, febrile disease. Frequently abscesses will develop under the lower jaw, along the neck or anywhere on the body. To begin with, similar

signs are shown as with a cold and later the abscesses develop. One should be most cautious and observant of the disease developing in young horses.

Shoe-boil (capped elbow): A soft, flabby swelling at the point of the elbow; hence, the other name "capped elbow." It is usually caused by contact with the shoe when the horse is lying down.

Short-coupled: Describes a horse having a short distance (usually not more than four fingers' width) between the last rib and the point of the hip.

Show: Finishing third in a race.

Show bridle: Same as Weymouth bridle, but the leather usually is cut finer and the bits often are more severe.

Sickle-hocked: The hind legs set too far forward, giving the impression of a sickle when viewed from the side.

Sidebones: Ossified lateral cartilages immediately above and toward the rear quarter of the hoof head. They occur most commonly in the forefeet.

Sidestep: See Traverse.

Sign: The word used when speaking of animal symptoms. Animals show "signs" of abnormality, whereas people can relate their symptoms of ill health. In horses, one must observe these signs.

Single-foot: Now called a "rack." See Rack.

Sire: The male parent.

Sisters: See Brothers.

Skewbald: Refers to coat color other than black—such as bay, brown, or chestnut—combined with white.

Skirt: That part of the saddle against which the knees and calves of the rider are placed.

Slab-sided: Flat-ribbed.

Sleeping sickness: See Encephalomyelitis.

Sloping shoulders: Shoulders properly angulated and laid back.

Slow gait: A slow, animated, four-beat gait, similar to the rack.

Slow pace: See Stepping pace.

Smoky eye: A whitish-clouded eye. See Wall eye.

Smooth: Unshod, "barefoot."

Smooth coat: Short, hard, close-fitting coat of hair.

Smooth-mouthed: No cups in the teeth. Indicates a horse is 12 years of age or older.

Snaffle bit: A mouthpiece with a joint in the center. The ring may be either circular or D-shaped. The most widely used of all bits.

Snip: A white mark between the nostrils or on the lip.

Snorter: An excitable horse.

Soft: Easily fatigued.

Solid color: Having no white markings.

Sound: Said of a horse free from injury, flaw, mutilation, or decay; also one that is guaranteed free from blemishes and unsoundness.

Spavin: See Blood spavin, Bog spavin, and Bone spavin.

Spay: To remove a mare's ovaries.

Speck in eye: A spot in the eye, but not covering the pupil. It may or may not impair the vision. See Feather in eye.

Speedy cutting: A condition of a horse at speed in which a hind leg above the scalping mark hits against the shoe of a breaking-over forefoot. In trotters, legs on the same side are involved. In pacers, diagonal legs are involved.

Sperm, sperm cell: Male sex cell produced in the testicles.

Spider bandage: A style of bandaging, using a tying method which resembles a spider lock. Applied to either the hocks or knees, allowing expansion at the flexing points.

Splenic fever: See Anthrax.

Splints: Abnormal body growths found on the cannon bone, usually on the inside surface, but occasionally on the outside. They are most common on the front legs.

Spooky: Nervous.

Sprinter: A horse who performs best at distances of a mile or under.

Spurs: The artificial aid worn over a boot, used to achieve a desired result when riding.

Stable fly: Biting insect that bites principally on the legs.

Stag: A male horse that was castrated after reaching maturity.

Stake race: A stake race, short for sweepstake, is just what the name implies. Each owner puts up an equal amount of money (nominating fees, fees for keeping them eligible, and starting fees) and the winner takes all. Also, the track usually puts up added money. Actually, few stake races are run on a winner-take-all basis; rather, the money is divided among the first four horses.

Stall: Space or compartment in which an animal is placed or confined. It may be a straight stall with the animal tied at the front end (a tie stall) or a compartment with the animal loose inside (a box stall).

Stallion: A male horse four years old or over; in Thoroughbreds, five years old or over.

Standing halter: Similar to a martingale, it is a strap that runs from the girth to a tight halter on the horse's head. It helps keep the horse from throwing its head up and going into a break.

Star: Any white mark on the forehead located above a line running from eye to eye.

Stargazer: A horse that holds its head high in an awkward position.

Steeplechaser: A horse used in cross-country racing with jumps.

Stepping pace (slow pace): A modified pace in which the objectionable side or rolling motion of the true pace is eliminated because the 2 feet on each side do not move exactly together. Instead, it is a 4-beat gait with each of the 4 feet striking the ground separately.

Sterile: A term used to designate a stallion that is infertile.

Stifle: The counterpart of the knee joint in man. The junction of the horse's tibia and patella in the hind leg.

Stifled: A horse is said to be stifled when the patella (or kneecap) slips out of place and temporarily locks in a location above and to the inside of its normal location.

Stirrup iron: The metal D-shaped device on the saddle through which the leather runs and on which the foot rests.

Stock horse: 1. In the West this term designates a cow horse.
　　2. In some places, it refers to a stallion used as a stud.

Stocking: White extends from the coronet to the knee. When the white includes the knee, it is known as a full stocking.

Stomach worms (Habronemia spp., Trichostrongylus axei): A group of parasitic worms that produce inflammation of the stomach.

Straight shoulder: Said of shoulder lacking sufficient angulation.

Strangles: See Distemper.

Stride: The distance covered by one foot when in motion. Greyhound, holder of the world's trotting record at 1:55¼, had a stride of more than 27 feet.

Stringhalt: A condition characterized by excessive flexing of the hind legs. It is most easily detected when backing a horse.

Stripe: A narrow white marking that extends from about the line of the eyes to the nostrils.

Strongyles, large and small (Strongylus spp. and others): There are about 60 species of strongyles. Three are large worms that grow up to 2 inches long. The rest are small and some are barely visible to the eye. Large strongyles are variously called bloodworms (*Strongylus vulgaris*), palisade worms, sclerostomes, and red worms.

Stud: 1. A male horse (stallion) kept for breeding.
　　2. An establishment or farm where animals are kept for breeding.

Stud book: The permanent book of breeding records.

Stump sucker: See Cribber.

Substance: A combination of good bone, muscularity, and width and depth of body.

Suckling: A foal that is not weaned.

Sulky or bike: Light racing rig with bicycle-type wheels used in harness races. The sulkies weigh from 29 to 37 pounds, and usually have hardwood shafts, although aluminum and steel sulkies have been introduced recently.

Summer sores: These are irritated spreading sores which develop from a wound. The sore may be as small as a dime but will enlarge rapidly within a week's time.

Surcingle: A belt, band, or girth passing over a saddle or over anything on a horse's back to bind the saddle fast.

Suspensory ligament sprain: The suspensory ligament is situated over the back of the leg and passes over the fetlock or ankle joint, both in the forelegs and hind legs. Its principal function is to support the fetlock. This ligament is frequently the object of severe strain; the swelling begins just above the ankle and extends obliquely downward and forward over the sides of the ankle. Should the injury be further up on the leg, the exact location at first may appear obscure as the ligament is covered by the flexor tendons.

When the suspensory ligament is affected, the swelling will be found right up against the bone. If it is the flexor tendons that are involved, the swelling will be further back near the surface on the back of the leg.

Swamp fever: See Equine infectious anemia.

Swan neck: A long, slim, swanlike neck.

"Swap horses in midstream": The origin of the saying, "Don't swap horses in midstream," appears to be clouded in obscurity.

Upon being congratulated when renominated for the presidency, Lincoln said: "I do not allow myself to suppose that either the convention or the league have concluded to decide that I am either the greatest or the best man in America, but rather they have concluded it is not best to swap horses while crossing the river, and have further concluded that I am not so poor a horse that they might not make a botch of it in trying to swap." One historian of that period credited the utterance to a Dutch farmer; and H. L. Mencken reports that the phrase was used some 24 years earlier than when Lincoln used it.

Swaybacked: Having a decided dip in the back. Also termed "easy-backed" and "saddle-backed."

Sweat scraper: An instrument for removing excess sweat from a hard worked horse.

Sweeney: A depression in the shoulder due to atrophied muscles.

Sweet feed: Refers to horse feed which is characterized by its sweetness due to the addition of molasses, usually a commercial horse feed mixture.

Swing team: The middle team in a six-horse hitch, or the team in front of the wheelers in an eight-horse hitch.

Swipe: Racetrack slang for a groom, stable hand, or exercise boy.

Synovial fluid: The fluid that lubricates the joint.

T

Tack: Equipment used in riding and driving horses, such as saddles, bridles, etc.

Tack room: Place for storage of bridles, saddles, other equipment and accessories used in horseback riding. Also a display room for pictures, prizes, ribbons, trophies, and the like.

Tail (banged or thinned): A tail is banged if the hair is cut off in a straight line below the dock; it is thinned if it is shortened; and it is thinned and tapered if the hairs are pulled and broken.

Tail female: The female, or bottom line of a pedigree.

Tail male: The sire line, or top line in a pedigree.

Tail rubbing: Persistent rubbing of the tail against the side of the stall or other objects.

Tail-set: A crupperlike contrivance, with a shaped section for the tail, which brings the tail high so that it can be doubled and tied down, to give it an "arch" and extremely high carriage; but a tail so set must first be "nicked" to give such results. The set is worn most of the time while the horse is in the stable, and until a short time before the horse is to be shown. Horses with "set" tails are usually "gingered" (an herb which is used as a stimulant) before entering the ring, in order to assure high tail carriage while being shown.

Tally ho: The cry of the hunt once the fox is sighted.

Tandem: Said of two horses, one hitched in front of the other.

Tapadera: A long, decorative covering over the stirrup used in parade classes.

Tapeworms (Anoplocephala magna, A. perfoliata, Paranoplocephala mamillana): Internal parasites of horses, of which there are three species. *Anoplocephala perfoliata* is the most common and most damaging.

Teaser: A horse, usually a stallion or a ridgeling, used to test the response of a mare prior to breeding, or used to determine if a mare is in heat and ready to breed.

Temperament: Refers to the horse's suitability for the job it is to perform.

Temperature: Normal rectal temperature for the horse is 100.5° F.

Testicle: A male gland which produces sperm. There are two testicles.

Tetanus (lockjaw): Chiefly a wound-infection disease caused by a powerful toxin, more than 100 times as toxic as strychnine, that is liberated by the bacterium *Clostridium tetani*, an anaerobe.

Thick wind: Difficulty in breathing.

Thoroughpin: A puffy condition in the web of the hock. It can be determined by movement of the puff, when pressed, to the opposite side of the leg. The swelling is more or less rounded or oval in shape and can be observed from both sides.

Threadworms (Strongyloides westeri): They are known as strongyloides.

Three-day event: See Combined training.

Thrifty condition: Healthy, active, vigorous.

Throat latch: The narrow strap of the bridle, which goes under the horse's throat and is used to secure the bridle to the head.

Throng: The lash of the whip.

Thrush: A disease of the foot, caused by a necrotic fungus characterized by a pungent odor. It is most commonly found in the hind feet and is caused by unsanitary conditions in the animal's stall. Thrush causes a deterioration of tissues in the cleft of the frog or in the junction between the frog and bars. This disease produces lameness and, if not treated, can be serious.

Ticks: External insects, several kinds of which may be found on horses. The most common ones are the winter tick, *Dermacentor albipictus*; the lone star tick, *Amblyomma americanum*; and the spinose ear tick, *Otobius megnini*.

Tie: To attach or fasten by use of a halter and a shank.

Tie weight (drop weight, ground weight): An iron weight formerly used for ground-tying a horse. They were either (1) rounded, but flat on the ground side, or (2) square; and they usually weighed about 8 pounds.

Toe weight: A metal weight (knob) fitted to a spur previously placed on the front hoof to induce a change or balance in motion. Used extensively in the training and racing of harness horses.

Tongue-loller: A horse whose tongue hangs out.

Tooth rasp: A file with a long handle, used for floating or removing sharp edges from the teeth.

Totalisator: The mechanical "brains" of the pari-mutuel system.

Tote board: The indicator board of the totalisator on which is flashed all pari-mutuel information before or after a race.

Tout: A low-order con man who peddles tips, betting systems, etc. to the unwary racegoer.

Traces: The parts of a harness which run from the collar to the single-tree.

Tracheotomy: An operation on the throat to cure roaring, or to keep a horse from suffocating in an emergency.

Trappy action: A short, quick stride.

Traverse (sidestep): The traverse or sidestep is simply a lateral movement of the animal to the right or left as desired, without moving forward or backward.

Troika: The word "troika" is a Russian word meaning trio or 3. A troika hitch is a 3-horse combination team hitched to a vehicle; e.g., a carriage, wagon, sleigh, or sled. The carriage is the vehicle of common use and it is known as a charaban. It is a light 4-wheeled 2-passenger vehicle with an elevated seat for the driver.

Trot: A natural, rapid, two-beat, diagonal gait in which the front foot and the opposite hind foot take off at the same split second and strike the ground simultaneously.

Tucked-up: Having the belly under the loin. Refers also to a small-waisted horse. Differs from "herring gutted" and similar conditions, in that a horse may be "tucked-up" temporarily due to hard work, lack of water, lack of bulk in the diet, etc. Also, called "gaunted-up" or "ganted-up."

Twitch: A rope run through the end of a stick, used on the horse's upper lip; it is tightened by twisting in order to attract the horse's attention so it will stand still.

Two-track: The horse moves forward and diagonally at the same time.

"Tying up": The "tying up" syndrome is characterized by muscle rigidity and lameness affecting the muscles of the croup and loin, accompanied by pain, disinclination to move, a variable temperature, and brownish-colored urine. The cause is unknown, although it does seem to be associated with nervousness.

Type: Type may be defined as an ideal or standard of perfection combining all the characteristics that contribute to the animal's usefulness for a specific purpose.

U

Underpinning: The legs and feet of the horse.

Undershot jaw: The lower jaw is longer than the upper jaw.

Unicorn: An unusual three-horse hitch with two horses hitched as a pair and a third hitched in front of the pair.

Unsoundnesses: Those more serious abnormalities that affect the serviceability of the horse.

Utility saddle: A saddle that is between the jump seat and the show seat and is designed for general purpose use, except jumping.

V

Vesicular stomatitis: A contagious disease of the mouth caused by a virus.

Veterinarian: One who treats diseases or afflictions of animals medically and surgically; a practitioner of veterinary medicine or surgery.

Vice: Any of the multitude of bad habits that a horse may acquire.

Viceroy: A lightweight, cut under, wire-wheeled show vehicle with curved dash, used for some heavy harness classes, and especially for Hackney ponies, Shetlands, and harness show ponies.

W

Walk: A natural, slow, flatfooted, four-beat gait, the latter meaning that each foot takes off from and strikes the ground at a separate interval.

Wall-eye: Also termed glass, blue, china, or crockery eye; refers to lack of color in a horse's eye.

Warm-up, warming up: The process or routine of graduated exercise until the horse is properly conditioned for a strenuous effort.

Weanling: A weaned foal.

Weaving: A rhythmical swaying back and forth while standing in the stall. The prevention and cure are exercise, with ample room and freedom from stress.

Weymouth bridle: A bridle in which the snaffle bit and the curb bit are separate.

Wheelers: The team on the pole or tongue, hitched directly in front of a rig or wagon in a four or more horse hitch.

Whinny: The horse's sound that denotes happiness, or anticipation of more pleasure.

Whip: An instrument or device of wood, bone, plastic, leather, fiberglass, metal, or combination thereof with a loop or cracker of leather or cord at the upper end; used for disciplining or goading an animal. Sometimes a required accessory when exhibiting (driving), as in a horse show. Also, one who handles a whip expertly, one who drives a horse in harness other than racing, or one who "whips in" or manages the hounds of a hunt club.

Whip in the Senate: The term "whip" is derived from the British fox hunting term "whipper-in," the Huntsman's principal assistant whose job is to keep the hounds from leaving the pack. The principal job of the whip in the U.S. Senate is to round up the party's Senators for important votes and to try to make sure that they vote in keeping with the wishes of the party leaders.

White line: The union between the sole and the wall of the foot.

Whoa: The command to stop; stand. When repeated softly, means to slow down, but may also mean attention.

Windgall: See Wind-puffs.

Winding (rope-walking): A twisting of the striding leg around in front of the supporting leg so as to make contact in the manner of a "rope-walking"

artist is known as winding or rope-walking. This condition most often occurs in horses with very wide fronts.

Wind-puffs (windgall): An enlargement of the fluid sac (bursa) located immediately above the pastern joints on the fore and rear legs. They are usually the result of too fast or too hard road work, especially on hard surfaces.

Wind sucker: See Cribber.

Windy, or wind-broken: Said of an animal that whistles or roars when exerted.

Winging: Winging is an exaggerated paddling, particularly noticeable in high-going horses.

Wrangling: Rounding up range horses.

Y

Yearling: A horse between one and two years of age.

Appendix

SECTION I—ENERGY TERMS AND FEED COMPOSITION[1]

In chart form, Fig. I-1 shows the conventional energy system. Apparent digestible energy (DE), metabolizable energy (ME), and net energy (NE) are usually calculated by the conventional system.

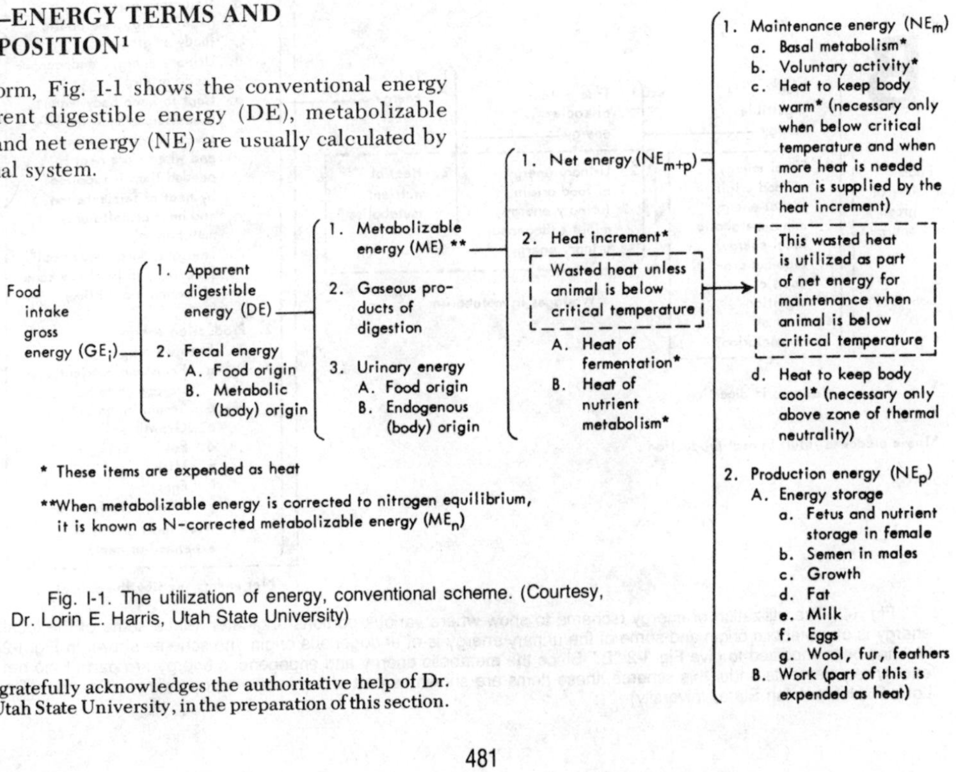

Food intake gross energy (GE_i)—

1. Apparent digestible energy (DE)—
   1. Metabolizable energy (ME) **—
      1. Net energy (NE_{m+p})—
         1. Maintenance energy (NE_m)
            a. Basal metabolism*
            b. Voluntary activity*
            c. Heat to keep body warm* (necessary only when below critical temperature and when more heat is needed than is supplied by the heat increment)
         2. Production energy (NE_p)
            A. Energy storage
               a. Fetus and nutrient storage in female
               b. Semen in males
               c. Growth
               d. Fat
               e. Milk
               f. Eggs
               g. Wool, fur, feathers
            B. Work (part of this is expended as heat)
      2. Heat increment*
         | Wasted heat unless animal is below critical temperature |
         A. Heat of fermentation*
         B. Heat of nutrient metabolism*
         | This wasted heat is utilized as part of net energy for maintenance when animal is below critical temperature |
         d. Heat to keep body cool* (necessary only above zone of thermal neutrality)
   2. Gaseous products of digestion
   3. Urinary energy
      A. Food origin
      B. Endogenous (body) origin
2. Fecal energy
   A. Food origin
   B. Metabolic (body) origin

* These items are expended as heat

**When metabolizable energy is corrected to nitrogen equilibrium, it is known as N-corrected metabolizable energy (ME_n)

Fig. I-1. The utilization of energy, conventional scheme. (Courtesy, Dr. Lorin E. Harris, Utah State University)

[1]The author gratefully acknowledges the authoritative help of Dr. Lorin E. Harris, Utah State University, in the preparation of this section.

Fig. I-2 shows where the various energy fractions originate. Since some of the fecal energy is of metabolic origin and some of the urinary energy is of endogenous origin, the scheme shown in Fig. I-2"A" has been modified to give Fig. I-2"B" which gives true digestible energy (TDE), true metabolizable energy (TME), and true net energy (TNE). Since the metabolic energy and endogenous energy are part of the net energy requirements under this scheme, these items are shown as part of the maintenance energy.

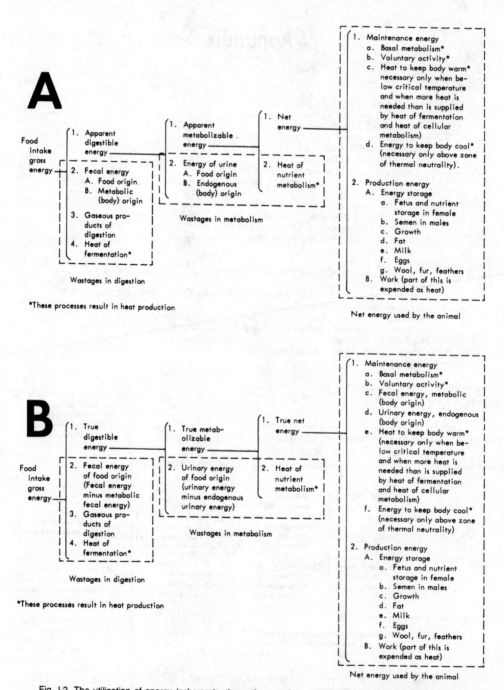

Fig. I-2. The utilization of energy (scheme to show where various portions originate). Since some of the fecal energy is of metabolic origin and some of the urinary energy is of endogenous origin, the scheme shown in Fig. I-2 "A" has been modified to give Fig. I-2 "B." Since the metabolic energy and endogenous energy are part of the net energy requirements under this scheme, these items are shown as part of the maintenance energy. (Courtesy, Dr. Lorin E. Harris, Utah State University)

APPENDIX

ENERGY TERMS

A part of the confusion and disagreement over the calorie system stems from a lack of understanding of terms, and from the coining of numerous "pet" names. For this reason, under the heading, "Glossary of Energy Terms" the author has elected to present the terms, and brief definitions of each, after the monumental work of Harris.[2] Additionally, use of the calorie system necessitates a working knowledge of the metric system (see Appendix Section III).

Glossary of Energy Terms

Abbreviation	Term—Definition
DE	**Digestible Energy** (or apparent absorbed energy, or apparent energy of digested feed) is the feed intake gross energy minus fecal energy.
TDE	**True Digestible Energy** is the feed intake gross energy minus fecal energy of feed origin (FE minus FE_m) minus energy in gaseous products of digestion minus heat of fermentation.
BM	**Basal Metabolism** is the chemical change which occurs in the cells of an animal in the fasting and resting state when it uses just enough energy to maintain vital cellular activity, respiration, and circulation as measured by the basal metabolic rate.
CB	**Carbon Balance** is the relation between the feed intake carbon and the carbon output.
cal	A **calorie** (cal, always written with a small c) is the amount of heat required to raise the temperature of one gram of water one degree centigrade.
EB	**Energy Balance** is the relation between the feed intake gross energy and the energy output.
FHP	**Fasting Heat Production** is the heat produced by the animal while fasting.
FE	**Fecal Energy** is the gross energy of the feces. It consists of the energy content of the undigested feed and the metabolic (body) fraction of the feces.
FE_m	**Fecal Energy, Metabolic,** is the amount of energy contained in the metabolic (body) fraction of feces (i.e., abraded intestinal mucosa, digestive fluids) that is not obtained from unabsorbed ration residues.
GPD	**Gaseous Products of Digestion** includes the combustible gases produced in the digestive tract incident to the fermentation of the ration. Methane makes up by far the major proportion of the combustible gases produced.
GE	**Gross Energy** (or heat of combustion) is the amount of heat, measured in calories, that is released when a substance is completely oxidized in a bomb calorimeter containing 25 to 30 atmospheres of oxygen. The gross energy of a feed, feces, urine, tissue, eggs, or other material is determined by burning them in a bomb calorimeter (see Fig. 13-5).
GE_i	**Gross Energy Intake** is the gross energy of the feed consumed.
HF	**Heat of Fermentation** is the heat produced in the digestive tract as a result of microbial action.
HI	**Heat Increment** is the increase in heat production following consumption of feed when the animal is in a thermo-neutral environment.
HBC	**Heat to Keep Body Cool** is the extra energy expended by the animal when the temperature of the environment is above the animal's zone of thermal neutrality.
HBW	**Heat to Keep Body Warm** is the additional heat needed to keep the animal's body warm when the temperature of the environment is below the critical temperature.
HNM	**Heat of Nutrient Metabolism** is the heat produced as a result of the utilization of absorbed nutrients.
HP	**Heat Production (Total)** of an animal consuming feed in a thermo-neutral environment is composed of the heat increment (heat of fermentation plus heat of nutrient metabolism) plus heat used for maintenance (basal metabolism plus voluntary activity). It can be estimated by 3 procedures; namely, (1) by measuring the quantity of oxygen an animal consumes (open circuit method), (2) by measuring directly the amount of heat produced by the animal (direct method), and (3) by the comparative slaughter technique. For the latter, 2 comparable animals are slaughtered, one at the beginning of the test period and the other at the end of the test period, and the energy content of each is determined. Then, the difference between these 2 values represents the amount of energy gained. The total heat production and energy utilization of a lactating mare are illustrated in Fig. I-3.
kcal	A **kilocalorie** is 1,000 small calories.

(Continued)

---

[2]Harris, L. E., *Biological Energy Interrelationships and Glossary of Energy Terms*, Pub. No. 1411, National Academy of Sciences.

Glossary of Energy Terms (Continued)

Mcal	A **Megacalorie,** or a therm, is equivalent to 1,000 kilocalories or 1,000,000 calories.
$W^{0.75}$	**Metabolic Body Size** is defined as the weight of the animal raised to the three-fourths power.
ME	**Metabolizable Energy** is the feed intake gross energy minus fecal energy, minus urinary energy, minus energy in the gaseous products of digestion.
TME	**True Metabolizable Energy** is the feed intake gross energy minus fecal energy of feed origin (FE minus FE_m), minus energy in gaseous products of digestion, minus heat of fermentation energy, minus urinary energy of feed origin (UE minus UE_e).
ME_n	**N-Corrected Metabolizable Energy** is the feed intake gross energy minus fecal energy, minus energy in the gaseous products of digestion, minus urinary energy; the total is then corrected for nitrogen retained or lost from the body.
TME_n	**N-Corrected True Metabolizable Energy** is the feed intake gross energy minus fecal energy of feed origin (FE minus FE_m), minus energy in gaseous products of digestion, minus heat of fermentation energy, minus urinary energy of feed origin (UE minus UE_e); the total is then corrected for nitrogen retained or lost from the body.
NE or NE_{m+p}	**Net Energy** is the difference between metabolizable energy and heat increment and includes the amount of energy used either for maintenance only or for maintenance plus production.
NE_m	**Net Energy for Maintenance** is the fraction of net energy expended to keep the animal in energy equilibrium.
NE_p	**Net Energy for Production** is the fraction of net energy required in addition to that needed for maintenance that is used for work or for tissue gain (growth and/or fat production) or for the synthesis of a fetus, milk, eggs, wool, fur or feathers.
NE_{egg}	**Net Energy for Egg Production.**
NE_{fat}	**Net Energy for Fat Production.**
NE_{fur}	**Net Energy for Fur Production.**
NE_{growth}	**Net Energy for Growth.**
NE_{milk}	**Net Energy for Milk Production.**
$NE_{preg.}$	**Net Energy for Pregnancy.**
NE_{wool}	**Net Energy for Wool Production.**
NE_{work}	**Net Energy for Work.**
	Note: These abbreviations could be used in feed composition tables or where more than one kind of production is being discussed.
TNE	**True Net Energy** is the intake gross energy minus the fecal energy of feed origin (FE—FE_m) minus energy in gaseous products, minus heat of fermentation energy, minus urinary energy or direct feed origin (UE—UE_e), minus heat of nutrient metabolism.
TNE_m	**True Net Energy for Maintenance** is the sum of the energy required for basal metabolism, voluntary activity, metabolic fecal energy (body origin), and endogenous urinary energy (body origin).
NB	**Nitrogen Balance** is the nitrogen in the feed intake (NI) minus the nitrogen in the feces (FN), minus nitrogen in the urine (UN).
NCR	**Nutrient to Calorie Ratio.** There is acceptable evidence that the energy needs of animals and their requirements of the several nutrients are quantitatively correlated. This does not necessarily mean a direct cause-and-effect relation, but it does mean that there is an optimum balance between them. For those nutrients that are needed to metabolize energy, it is logical to consider that the amount of energy metabolized "determines" their requirements. Hence, it is logical to express nutrients in weight per unit of energy needed. For example, it is suggested that the protein to calorie ratio should be expressed as grams of protein per 1000 kcal metabolizable energy (g protein/1000 kcal ME). If the ME is corrected for nitrogen retained or lost from the body, then the abbreviation should be g protein/1000 kcal ME_n. This same dimension may easily be extended to other nutrients as g calcium/1000 kcal or mg riboflavin/1000 kcal, etc.
PFV	**Physiological Fuel Values** expressed in calories, are units used in the United States to measure food energy in human nutrition. It is similar to metabolizable energy.
UE	**Urinary Energy** is the gross energy of the urine.
UE_e	**Urinary Energy, Endogenous** is the amount of energy contained in the endogenous (body) fraction of the total urine.
VA	**Energy of Voluntary Activity** is the amount of energy needed by an animal to provide the energy required in getting up, standing, moving about to obtain food, grazing, drinking, lying down, etc.

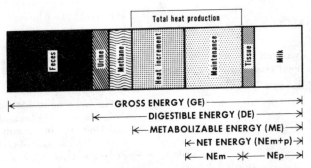

Fig. I-3. The total heat production and energy utilization of a lactating mare, modified by the author from data of W. P. Flatt. (Courtesy, Dr. Lorin E. Harris, Utah State University)

FEED COMPOSITION

Nutrient compositions of feedstuffs are necessary for intelligent ration preparation, animal health, and feed efficiency. Table I-1 contains the most commonly used feeds for horses. It was adapted for this book by Dr. Lorin E. Harris, and it is being reproduced through the courtesy of the National Research Council, National Academy of Sciences.

It contains data, if available, for proximate composition, gross energy (GE), mineral, vitamin, and amino acid contents of feeds. Where available, apparent digestible protein, apparent digestible energy (DE), metabolizable energy (ME), and total digestible nutrients (TDN) are listed.

NRC Nomenclature

The nomenclature of the feeds under which the analytical data are shown is based on the National Research Council (NRC) scheme.[3] It is designed to give (to the extent that the information is available or applicable) a qualitative description of the product as to its (1) origin or parent material, (2) species, variety, or kind, (3) the part actually eaten, (4) the process(es) and treatment(s) to which it has been subjected, (5) the stage of maturity, (6) cutting or crop, (7) grade or quality designations, and (8) classification.

Feeds of the same origin or parent material (and the same species, variety, or kind, if designated) have been subgrouped into the following feed classes: (1) dry forages and roughages, (2) pasture, range plants, and forages fed green, (3) silages, (4) energy feeds, (5) protein supplements, (6) minerals, (7) vitamins, and (8) additives. Classes are coded as indicated above and are included in parentheses following the NRC names. Within each origin (and species, variety, or kind, if given) there may be feeds that belong to several classes. These classes are grouped in ascending numerical order of their class code number with origin or within origin and species. The scientific name precedes each group of feeds with the same scientific name.

Feeds in the dry state which contain more than 18% crude fiber are classified as forages and roughages. Products that contain 20% or more of protein are classified as protein supplements. Products with less than 20% protein are classified as energy feeds. (These guidelines are approximate and there is some overlapping.) The feeds have been classified in this way because each class has certain properties that are considered in balancing a ration. Fruits, nuts, and roots, have been classified as energy feeds because most of the by-product feeds from these subclasses are used primarily as energy feeds.

To reduce the names to minimum printing or punch-card space requirement, a system of abbreviations has been devised covering many of the terms involved in the eight components of the name. These are listed in this section under the heading, "Feed Term Abbreviations."

The system of naming is illustrated as follows:

COMPONENTS

1. Origin .... Clover
2. Variety .... red
3. Part eaten .... aerial pt
4. Process .... s-c
5. Maturity .... pre-blm
6. Cutting .... cut 1
7. Grade .... leafy
8. Classification .... (1)

The NRC name is written out in linear form with the components of the name separated by commas and without other punctuation. Commas are not included within the eight components so that the reader may readily recognize the entire component. The name would appear as:

Clover, red, aerial pt, s-c, pre-blm, cut 1, leafy, (1)

This example would be read:

Clover, red, aerial part, sun-cured, prebloom, first cutting, leafy. It is a dry roughage.

The Association of American Feed Control Officials (AAFCO) names, Canada Feeds Act (CFA) names and other common names appear after the NRC names. Cross references (where necessary) have been included so the NRC name may be readily located.

Although care has been taken to include cross references, it is suggested that the entire list of feeds under a given origin be checked so that a feed is not missed.

An example of a feed which has different names is as follows:

Components
1. Origin .... Barley
3. Part .... flour by-prod mil-rn
8. Classification .... (4)

[3]Harris, L. E., "Symposium on Feeds and Meats Terminology: III. A System for Naming and Describing Feedstuffs, Energy Terminology, and the Use of Such Information in Calculating Diets," *Journal of Animal Science*, Vol. 22, No. 2, 1963, pp. 535-547.

Other names:
    Barley mill by-product (AAFCO)
    Barley mixed feed (CFA)

Each feed has been given a six-digit reference number, the first of which indicates the feed classification. For the above example the Names and Feed reference number would appear as follows:

Barley, flour by-prod mil-rn, (4)
    Barley mill by-product (AAFCO)
    Barley mixed feed (CFA)
Ref no 4-00-523

The analytical data are expressed in the metric system (with the exception of the bushel weights of the cereal grains) and are on an "as fed" as well as a "dry" basis. The NRC reference feed number may be used as an identification on electronic computers for linear programming.

It has not been possible to obtain apparent digestible energy (DE) and metabolizable energy (ME) values for all feedstuffs. In some of these cases, values have been estimated using the following formulas:

$$\text{DE (kcal/kg)} = \frac{\text{TDN\%} \times 4409.2}{100}$$

$$\text{ME (kcal/kg) for horses} = \text{DE (kcal)} \times 0.82$$

Where energy data were lacking for individual feeds, cattle data were used.

The International Standards for vitamin A activity based on vitamin A and beta-carotene are as follows: One International Unit (IU) of vitamin A = one USP unit = vitamin A activity of 0.300 mcg of crystalline vitamin A alcohol, corresponding to 0.344 mcg of vitamin A acetate or 0.550 mcg of vitamin A palmitate. Beta-carotene is the standard for provitamin A. One International Unit of vitamin A activity is equivalent to 0.6 mcg of beta-carotene or 1 mg of beta-carotene = 1667 IU of vitamin A. International Standards for vitamin A are based on the utilization by the rat of vitamin A and/or beta-carotene.

The vitamin A equivalent for carotene was calculated by assuming that 0.6 mcg of beta-carotene = one IU of vitamin A.

Because the various species do not convert carotene to vitamin A in the same ratio as rats, it is suggested that the following conversion rate be used:

CONVERSION OF BETA-CAROTENE TO VITAMIN A FOR DIFFERENT SPECIES[1]

Species	Conversion mg beta-carotene to IU vitamin A		IU vitamin A activity (calculated from carotene)
	(mg)	(IU)	(%)
Standard	1 =	1,667	100.
Horses			
Growth	1 =	555	33.3
Pregnancy	1 =	333	20.0
Sheep	1 =	400-500	24.0-30.0
Swine	1 =	500	30.0
Beef cattle	1 =	400	24.0
Dairy cattle	1 =	400	24.0
Poultry	1 =	1,667	100.
Rat	1 =	1,667	100.
Man	1 =	556	33.0

[1]Beeson, W. M., "Relative Potencies of Vitamin A and Carotene for Animals," *Federation Proc.*, Vol. 24, 1965, pp. 924-926.

Individual feed samples may vary widely from indicated averages because of such influencing factors as crop, variety, harvesting and storage conditions, and climate and soil pertinent to the locality where the feed was produced. Therefore, the values given should be used with judgment, often in conjunction with more specific information on hand about the feed.

APPENDIX

FEED TERM ABBREVIATIONS

Abbreviation	Feed Term
AAFCO	Association of American Feed Control Officials
by-prod	by-product
Ca	calcium
Can	Canadian
c-bolt	coarse bolted
CFA	Canada Feeds Act
chop	chopped
c-sift	coarse sifted
comm	commercial
cond	condensed
CW	Canadian Western
dehy	dehydrated
dig	digestibility, digestible
distil	distillation, distillers
dry-mil	dry milled
dry-rend	dry rendered
equiv	equivalent
F	fluorine
fbr	fiber
f-grnd	fine ground
fm	foreign material (including seeds other than the principal product or grain)
f-scr	fine screened
f-sift	fine sifted
g	gram
gr	grade
grnd	ground
hydro	hydrolyzed
ICU	International Chick Unit
insol	insoluble
IU	International Units
kcal	kilocalories
kg	kilogram
mech-extd	mechanically extracted, expeller extracted, hydraulic extracted, or old process
mcg	microgram
mg	milligram
mil-rn	mill run
mn	minimum
mx	maximum
N	nitrogen
No	Northern
P	phosphorus
precip	precipitated
proc	processed, processing
prot	protein
pt	part(s)
res	residue
s-c	sun-cured
shred	shredded
skim	skimmed
sol	solubles
solv-extd	solvent extracted
US	United States
w	with
wet-rend	wet rendered
wo	without
wt	weight

Formulas for Adjusting Moisture Content

The majority of feed composition tables are on an "as fed" basis, while most of the National Research Council nutrient requirement tables are on an "approximate 90 percent dry matter" basis. Also, feeds contain varying amounts of dry matter. Hence, it would be much simpler if both feed composition and nutrient requirement tables were on a dry basis.

The significance of water content of feeds becomes obvious in the following examples. When using Total Digestible Nutrients (TDN) as a measure of energy value, some of the high-moisture tubers show almost the same feeding value per unit of their dry matter content as the cereal grains:

Feed	Water	Dry Matter	Energy Value (TDN)	
			As Fed	Dry Matter Basis
			%	
Corn, grain	10	90	80	90
Barley, grain	10	90	77	85
Melons, whole	94	6	5	80
Potatoes, tuber	79	21	18	85
Apples, fruit	82	18	13	74

As shown, dry matter becomes a common denominator for the comparison for feeds, particularly as to energy value; but this applies to other nutrients, also.

The following formulas may be used for adjusting moisture contents:

From Dry to as Fed

To be used in converting the amounts of ingredients of a dry diet[4] to a wet diet having a given percent of dry matter.

Formula 1

$$\text{Parts of ingredient in wet diet} = \frac{\text{\% ingredient in dry diet} \times \text{\% dry matter wanted in diet}}{\text{\% dry matter in ingredient}}$$

Total the parts and add enough water to make 100 parts (or 100%).

From Wet to Dry

To be used in calculating the amount of an ingredient that should be contained in a dry diet if the amount required in a wet diet having a given percent of dry matter is known.

Formula 2

$$\text{\% of ingredient in wet diet} = \frac{\text{\% of ingredient in wet diet}}{\text{\% dry matter wanted in diet} \times \text{\% dry matter of ingredient}} = \text{\% of ingredient in dry diet}$$

From Wet to Dry

To be used if the diet is on an as fed basis and it is desired to change the amounts of the ingredients to a dry basis.

Formula 3

Parts on wet basis = % ingredient in wet diet × % dry matter of ingredient

Perform this calculation for each ingredient; then add the products and divide each product by the sum of the products.

From Wet to Dry

To be used if the diet is on an as fed basis and it is desired to compare the nutrient content of the diet with dry basis requirements.

Formula 4

$$\text{\% nutrient in dry diet (total)} = \frac{\text{\% nutrient in wet diet (total)}}{\text{\% dry matter in diet (total)}}$$

Composition of Some Common Horse Feeds

Refer to Table I-1, which follows.

---

[4]The term "dry diet" means a diet calculated on a dry (moisture-free) basis; "as fed" means a diet calculated to contain the amount of dry matter as it is fed to the animal.

APPENDIX

TABLE I-1
COMPOSITION OF SOME COMMON HORSE FEEDS[a]

ALFALFA. Medicago sativa

Alfalfa, aerial pt, dehy grnd, mn 17 prot, (1)

Ref no 1-00-023

Feed name or analyses		As fed	Dry
Dry matter	%	93.0	100.0
Ash	%	9.0	9.7
Crude fiber	%	24.3	26.1
Ether extract	%	3.0	3.2
N-free extract	%	38.9	41.8
Protein (N×6.25)	%	17.9	19.2
Horses	dig prot %	14.0	15.0
Energy			
Horses	DE kcal/kg	2543.	2734.
Horses	ME kcal/kg	2085.	2242.
Horses	TDN %	58.	62.
Calcium	%	1.33	1.43
Chlorine	%	.46	.49
Iron	%	.046	.049
Magnesium	%	.29	.31
Phosphorus	%	.24	.26
Potassium	%	2.49	2.68
Sodium	%	.09	.10
Cobalt	mg/kg	.360	.390
Copper	mg/kg	9.9	10.6
Iodine	mg/kg	.150	.161
Manganese	mg/kg	29.0	31.2
Selenium	mg/kg	.600	.645
Zinc	mg/kg	16.0	17.2
Carotene	mg/kg	161.2	173.3
Choline	mg/kg	1518.	1632.
Folic acid	mg/kg	2.10	2.26
Niacin	mg/kg	45.8	49.2
Pantothenic acid	mg/kg	30.0	32.2
Riboflavin	mg/kg	12.3	13.2
Thiamin	mg/kg	3.5	3.8
a-tocopherol	mg/kg	128.0	137.6
Vitamin B6	mg/kg	6.30	6.77
Vitamin K	mg/kg	8.70	9.35
Vitamin A equiv	IU/g	268.7	288.9
Alanine	%	.90	.97
Arginine	%	.70	.75
Aspartic acid	%	1.90	2.04
Glutamic acid	%	1.70	1.83
Glycine	%	.90	.97
Histidine	%	.40	.43
Isoleucine	%	.70	.75
Leucine	%	1.30	1.40
Lysine	%	.80	.86
Methionine	%	.20	.22
Phenylalanine	%	.80	.86
Proline	%	.90	.97
Serine	%	.70	.75
Threonine	%	.80	.86
Tryptophan	%	.40	.43
Tyrosine	%	.50	.54
Valine	%	.90	.97

Alfalfa, aerial pt, dehy grnd, mn 20 prot, (1)

Ref no 1-00-024

Feed name or analyses		As fed	Dry
Dry matter	%	93.1	100.0
Ash	%	10.3	11.1
Crude fiber	%	20.2	21.7
Ether extract	%	3.6	3.9
N-free extract	%	38.4	41.2
Protein (N×6.25)	%	20.6	22.1
Horses	dig prot %	16.0	17.2

(Continued)

Feed name or analyses		As fed	Dry
Energy			
Horses	DE kcal/kg	2545.	2734.
Horses	ME kcal/kg	2087.	2242.
Horses	TDN %	58.	62.
Calcium	%	1.52	1.63
Chlorine	%	.58	.62
Iron	%	.040	.043
Magnesium	%	.35	.38
Phosphorus	%	.27	.29
Potassium	%	2.52	2.71
Sodium	%	.86	.92
Cobalt	mg/kg	.320	.344
Copper	mg/kg	10.6	11.4
Iodine	mg/kg	.140	.150
Manganese	mg/kg	34.0	36.5
Selenium	mg/kg	.500	.537
Zinc	mg/kg	18.0	19.3
Carotene	mg/kg	216.4	232.4
Choline	mg/kg	1618.	1738.
Folic acid	mg/kg	2.67	2.87
Niacin	mg/kg	54.7	58.7
Pantothenic acid	mg/kg	32.8	35.2
Riboflavin	mg/kg	15.5	16.6
Thiamin	mg/kg	3.9	4.2
a-tocopherol	mg/kg	147.0	157.9
Vitamin B6	mg/kg	7.90	8.48
Vitamin K	mg/kg	14.70	15.79
Vitamin A equiv	IU/g	360.7	387.4
Alanine	%	1.10	1.18
Arginine	%	.90	.97
Aspartic acid	%	2.10	2.26
Glutamic acid	%	2.10	2.26
Glycine	%	1.00	1.07
Histidine	%	.40	.43
Isoleucine	%	.80	.86
Leucine	%	1.50	1.61
Lysine	%	.90	.97
Methionine	%	.30	.32
Phenylalanine	%	1.10	1.18
Proline	%	1.00	1.07
Serine	%	.90	.97
Threonine	%	.90	.97
Tryptophan	%	.50	.54
Tyrosine	%	.70	.75
Valine	%	.10	.11

Alfalfa, hay, s-c, immature, (1)

Ref no 1-00-050

Feed name or analyses		As fed	Dry
Dry matter	%	89.1	100.0
Ash	%	8.6	9.7
Crude fiber	%	23.4	26.3
Ether extract	%	2.4	2.7
N-free extract	%	35.5	39.8
Protein (N×6.25)	%	19.1	21.5
Horses	dig prot %	13.4	15.0
Energy			
Horses	DE kcal/kg	2239.	2513.
Horses	ME kcal/kg	1836.	2061.
Horses	TDN %	51.	57.
Calcium	%	1.89	2.12
Chlorine	%	.30	.34
Iron	%	.020	.020
Magnesium	%	.23	.26
Phosphorus	%	.27	.30
Potassium	%	2.01	2.26
Sodium	%	.20	.22
Sulfur	%	.56	.63
Manganese	mg/kg	34.4	38.6
Carotene	mg/kg	446.6	501.2
Vitamin A equiv	IU/g	744.5	835.5

Alfalfa, hay, s-c, pre-blm, (1)

Ref no 1-00-054

Feed name or analyses		As fed	Dry
Dry matter	%	84.5	100.0
Ash	%	6.0	7.1
Crude fiber	%	24.1	28.5
Ether extract	%	2.7	3.2
N-free extract	%	35.3	41.8
Protein (N×6.25)	%	16.4	19.4
Horses	dig prot %	9.9	11.7
Energy			
Horses	DE kcal/kg	2347.	2778.
Horses	ME kcal/kg	1925.	2278.
Horses	TDN %	53.	63.
Calcium	%	1.06	1.25
Phosphorus	%	.19	.23

Alfalfa, hay, s-c, early blm, (1)

Ref no 1-00-059

Feed name or analyses		As fed	Dry
Dry matter	%	90.0	100.0
Ash	%	8.5	9.4
Crude fiber	%	26.8	29.8
Ether extract	%	2.0	2.2
N-free extract	%	36.2	40.2
Protein (N×6.25)	%	16.6	18.4
Horses	dig prot %	11.4	12.7
		1.8	2.0
Cellulose	%	.8	.9
Lignin			
Energy	GE kcal/kg	4050.	4500.
Horses	DE kcal/kg	2262.	2513.
Horses	ME kcal/kg	1855.	2061.
Horses	TDN %	51.	57.
Calcium	%	1.12	1.25
Chlorine	%	.34	.38
Iron	%	.020	.020
Magnesium	%	.27	.30
Phosphorus	%	.21	.23
Potassium	%	1.87	2.08
Sodium	%	.14	.15
Sulfur	%	.27	.30
Cobalt	mg/kg	.080	.090
Copper	mg/kg	12.1	13.4
Manganese	mg/kg	28.4	31.5
Carotene	mg/kg	114.5	127.2
Vitamin A equiv	IU/g	190.9	212.0

Alfalfa, hay, s-c, mid-blm, (1)

Ref no 1-00-063

Feed name or analyses		As fed	Dry
Dry matter	%	89.2	100.0
Ash	%	7.6	8.5
Crude fiber	%	27.6	30.9
Ether extract	%	1.8	2.0
N-free extract	%	37.0	41.5
Protein (N×6.25)	%	15.2	17.1
Horses	dig prot %	10.8	12.1
Cellulose		2.4	2.7
Lignin		.7	.8
Energy			
Horses	DE kcal/kg	2281.	2557.
Horses	ME kcal/kg	1870.	2097.
Horses	TDN %	52.	58.
Calcium	%	1.20	1.35
Iron	%	.010	.010
Magnesium	%	.31	.35
Phosphorus	%	.20	.22
Potassium	%	1.30	1.46

(Continued)

---

(1) dry forages and roughages
(2) pasture, range plants, and forages fed green
(3) silages
(4) energy feeds
(5) protein supplements
(6) minerals
(7) vitamins
(8) additives

[a]Data and feed names were arranged for this book by Dr. Lorin E. Harris, Utah State University.

TABLE I-1 (Continued)

Feed name or analyses		Mean	
		As fed	Dry
Copper	mg/kg	13.7	15.4
Manganese	mg/kg	14.7	16.5
Carotene	mg/kg	29.7	33.3
Vitamin A equiv	IU/g	49.5	55.5

Alfalfa, hay, s-c, full blm, (1)

Ref no 1-00-068

		As fed	Dry
Dry matter	%	87.7	100.0
Ash	%	7.8	8.9
Crude fiber	%	29.7	33.9
Ether extract	%	1.6	1.8
N-free extract	%	34.6	39.5
Protein (N×6.25)	%	14.0	15.9
Horses	dig prot %	10.0	11.4
Energy			
Horses	DE kcal/kg	2204.	2513.
Horses	ME kcal/kg	1807.	2061.
Horses	TDN %	50.	57.
Calcium	%	1.13	1.28
Iron	%	.010	.020
Magnesium	%	.31	.35
Phosphorus	%	.18	.20
Potassium	%	.48	.55
Copper	mg/kg	11.8	13.4
Manganese	mg/kg	29.6	33.7
Carotene	mg/kg	32.4	37.0
Vitamin A equiv	IU/g	54.0	61.7

Alfalfa, hay, s-c, mature, (1)

Ref no 1-00-071

		As fed	Dry
Dry matter	%	91.2	100.0
Ash	%	7.1	7.8
Crude fiber	%	34.2	37.5
Ether extract	%	1.5	1.7
N-free extract	%	35.9	39.4
Protein (N×6.25)	%	12.4	13.6
Horses	dig prot %	8.7	9.5
Energy			
Horses	DE kcal/kg	2212.	2425.
Horses	ME kcal/kg	1813.	1988.
Horses	TDN %	50.	55.

Alfalfa, leaves, dehy grnd, (1)
Alfalfa leaf meal, dehydrated (AAFCO)

Ref no 1-00-137

		As fed	Dry
Dry matter	%	92.2	100.0
Ash	%	11.0	11.9
Crude fiber	%	19.6	21.3
Ether extract	%	3.0	3.2
N-free extract	%	38.0	41.2
Protein (N×6.25)	%	20.6	22.4
Horses	dig prot %	15.3	16.6
Energy			
Horses	DE kcal/kg	2276.	2469.
Horses	ME kcal/kg	1866.	2024.
Horses	TDN %	52.	56.
Calcium	%	1.64	1.78
Chlorine	%	.31	.34
Iron	%	.036	.039
Phosphorus	%	.23	.25
Potassium	%	2.07	2.25
Cobalt	mg/kg	.199	.216
Copper	mg/kg	10.6	11.5
Manganese	mg/kg	36.8	39.9
Carotene	mg/kg	149.0	161.6
Niacin	mg/kg	36.4	39.5
Pantothenic acid	mg/kg	32.9	35.7
Riboflavin	mg/kg	18.1	19.6

(Continued)

(1) dry forages and roughages

(2) pasture, range plants, and forages fed green

Feed name or analyses		Mean	
		As fed	Dry
Thiamin	mg/kg	5.5	6.0
Vitamin D₂	IU/g	.4	.4

Alfalfa, aerial pt, fresh, (2)

Ref no 2-00-196

		As fed	Dry
Dry matter	%	27.2	100.0
Ash	%	2.4	9.0
Crude fiber	%	7.4	27.4
Ether extract	%	.8	3.0
N-free extract	%	11.2	41.3
Protein (N×6.25)	%	5.2	19.3
Horses	dig prot %	4.1	15.0
Energy			
Horses	DE kcal/kg	732.	2690.
Horses	ME kcal/kg	600.	2206.
Horses	TDN %	16.	61.
Calcium	%	.47	1.72
Chlorine	%	.13	.47
Iron	%	.010	.030
Magnesium	%	.07	.27
Phosphorus	%	.08	.31
Potassium	%	.55	2.03
Sodium	%	.05	.20
Sulfur	%	.11	.39
Cobalt	mg/kg	.020	.090
Copper	mg/kg	2.7	9.9
Manganese	mg/kg	13.7	50.5
Zinc	mg/kg	4.8	17.6
Carotene	mg/kg	54.1	198.9
Vitamin A equiv	IU/g	90.2	331.6
Vitamin D₂	IU/g		.2

ALFALFA-BROME, SMOOTH. Medicago sativa, Bromus inermis

Alfalfa-brome, smooth, aerial pt, fresh, early blm, (2)

Ref no 2-00-261

		As fed	Dry
Dry matter	%	21.6	100.0
Ash	%	2.1	9.8
Crude fiber	%	5.5	25.3
Ether extract	%	.8	3.6
N-free extract	%	9.0	41.7
Protein (N×6.25)	%	4.2	19.6
Horses	dig prot %	3.1	14.4
Energy			
Horses	DE kcal/kg	590.	2734.
Horses	ME kcal/kg	484.	2242.
Horses	TDN %	13.	62.
Calcium	%	.33	1.52
Magnesium	%	.08	.35
Phosphorus	%	.08	.37
Potassium	%	.84	3.87

ALFALFA-ORCHARDGRASS. Medicago sativa, Dactylis glomerata

Alfalfa-orchardgrass, aerial pt, ensiled, mn 50 dry matter, (3)

Ref no 3-08-143

		As fed	Dry
Dry matter	%	61.0	100.0
Ash	%	6.2	10.1
Crude fiber	%	18.6	30.5
Ether extract	%	2.6	4.3

(Continued)

(3) silages

(4) energy feeds

(5) protein supplements

Feed name or analyses		Mean	
		As fed	Dry
N-free extract	%	23.7	38.9
Protein (N×6.25)	%	9.9	16.2
Horses	dig prot %	5.7	9.4
Energy			
Horses	DE kcal/kg	1452.	2381.
Horses	ME kcal/kg	1190.	1952.
Horses	TDN %	33.	54.

ANIMAL. Scientific name not used

Animal, bone, cooked dehy grnd, mn 10 P, (6)
Feeding bone meal (CFA)

Ref no 6-00-397

		As fed	Dry
Dry matter	%	94.5	100.0
Ether extract	%	9.6	10.2
Protein (N×6.25)	%	17.8	18.8
Calcium	%	25.82	27.32
Phosphorus	%	12.35	13.07
Fluorine	mg/kg	2000.00	2116.40

Animal, bone, steamed dehy grnd, (6)
Bone meal, steamed (AAFCO)

Ref no 6-00-400

		As fed	Dry
Dry matter	%	95.0	100.0
Ash	%	71.8	75.6
Crude fiber	%	2.0	2.1
Ether extract	%	3.2	3.4
Protein (N×6.25)	%	12.1	12.7
Horses	dig prot %	8.2	8.6
Energy			
Horses	DE kcal/kg	670.	705.
Horses	ME kcal/kg	549.	578.
Horses	TDN %	15.	16.
Calcium	%	28.98	30.51
Iron	%	.084	.088
Magnesium	%	.64	.67
Phosphorus	%	13.59	14.31
Sodium	%	.46	.48
Cobalt	mg/kg	.100	.100
Copper	mg/kg	16.3	17.2
Manganese	mg/kg	30.4	32.0
Zinc	mg/kg	424.6	447.1
Niacin	mg/kg	4.2	4.4
Pantothenic acid	mg/kg	2.4	2.5
Riboflavin	mg/kg	.9	.9
Thiamin	mg/kg	.4	.4

Animal, bone charcoal, retort-charred grnd, (6)
Bone black (CFA)
Bone char (CFA)
Spent bone black

Ref no 6-00-403

		As fed	Dry
Dry matter	%	90.0	100.0
Protein (N×6.25)	%	8.5	9.4
Calcium	%	27.10	30.11
Magnesium	%	.53	.59
Phosphorus	%	12.73	14.14
Potassium	%	.14	.16
Arginine	%	1.80	2.00
Histidine	%	.20	.22
Isoleucine	%	.60	.67
Leucine	%	.80	.89
Lysine	%	1.00	1.11
Methionine	%	.20	.22
Phenylalanine	%	.50	.56
Threonine	%	.50	.56
Valine	%	.70	.78

(6) minerals

(7) vitamins

(8) additives

APPENDIX

TABLE I-1 (Continued)

Animal, bone phosphate, precip dehy, mn 17 P, (6)
Bone phosphate (AAFCO)

Ref no 6-00-406

Feed name or analyses		Mean	
		As fed	Dry
Dry matter	%	99.0	100.0
Ash	%	86.4	87.3
Ether extract	%	.3	.3
Protein (N×6.25)	%	.4	.4
Calcium	%	28.00	28.28
Phosphorus	%	11.20	11.31

BARLEY. Hordeum vulgare

Barley, grain, (4)

Ref no 4-00-530

Feed name or analyses		As fed	Dry
Dry matter	%	89.0	100.0
Ash	%	2.4	2.7
Crude fiber	%	5.0	5.6
Ether extract	%	1.9	2.1
N-free extract	%	68.2	76.6
Protein (N×6.25)	%	11.6	13.0
Horses	dig prot %	8.7	9.8
Energy	GE kcal/kg	4084.	4589.
Horses	DE kcal/kg	3257.	3660.
Horses	ME kcal/kg	2671.	3001.
Horses	TDN %	74.	83.
Calcium	%	.08	.09
Iron	%	.005	.006
Magnesium	%	.12	.14
Phosphorus	%	42	.47
Potassium	%	.56	.63
Sodium	%	.02	.02
Cobalt	mg/kg	.100	.100
Copper	mg/kg	7.6	8.6
Manganese	mg/kg	16.3	18.3
Zinc	mg/kg	15.3	17.2
Biotin	mg/kg	.20	.20
Choline	mg/kg	1030.	1157.
Folic acid	mg/kg	.50	.60
Niacin	mg/kg	57.4	64.5
Pantothenic acid	mg/kg	6.5	7.3
Riboflavin	mg/kg	2.0	2.2
Thiamin	mg/kg	5.1	5.7
a-tocopherol	mg/kg	6.1	6.8
Vitamin B₆	mg/kg	2.90	3.30
Arginine	%	.53	.60
Cystine	%	.18	.20
Glycine	%	.36	.40
Histidine	%	.27	.30
Isoleucine	%	.53	.60
Leucine	%	.80	.90
Lysine	%	.53	.60
Methionine	%	.18	.20
Phenylalanine	%	.62	.70
Threonine	%	.36	.40
Tryptophan	%	.18	.20
Tyrosine	%	.36	.40
Valine	%	.62	.70

Barley, grain, Pacific coast, (4)

Ref no 4-07-939

		As fed	Dry
Dry matter	%	89.0	100.0
Ash	%	2.3	2.6
Crude fiber	%	6.2	7.0
Ether extract	%	2.2	2.5
N-free extract	%	68.5	77.0
Protein (N×6.25)	%	9.7	10.9
Horses	dig prot %	7.3	8.2

(Continued)

Feed name or analyses		Mean	
		As fed	Dry
Energy			
Horses	DE kcal/kg	3218.	3616.
Horses	ME kcal/kg	2639.	2965.
Horses	TDN %	73.	82.
Calcium	%	.06	.07
Phosphorus	%	.40	.45
Choline	mg/kg	937.	1054.
Niacin	mg/kg	44.1	49.6
Pantothenic acid	mg/kg	7.3	8.2
Riboflavin	mg/kg	1.3	1.5
Thiamin	mg/kg	4.0	4.5

BEET, SUGAR. Beta saccharifera

Beet, sugar, molasses, mn 48 invert sugar mn 79.5 degrees brix, (4)
Beet molasses (AAFCO)
Molasses(CFA)

Ref no 4-00-668

		As fed	Dry
Dry matter	%	77.0	100.0
Ash	%	8.2	10.6
Ether extract	%	.2	.3
N-free extract	%	61.9	80.4
Protein (N×6.25)	%	6.7	8.7
Horses	dig prot %	3.8	5.0
Energy			
Horses	DE kcal/kg	3021.	3924.
Horses	ME kcal/kg	2478.	3218.
Horses	TDN %	68.	89.
Calcium	%	.16	.21
Iron	%	.010	.010
Magnesium	%	.23	.30
Phosphorus	%	.03	.04
Potassium	%	4.77	6.20
Sodium	%	1.17	1.52
Cobalt	mg/kg	.400	.500
Copper	mg/kg	17.6	22.9
Manganese	mg/kg	4.6	6.0
Niacin	mg/kg	42.2	54.8
Pantothenic acid	mg/kg	4.6	6.0
Riboflavin	mg/kg	2.4	3.1

Beet, sugar, pulp, dehy, (4)
Dried beet pulp (AAFCO)
Dried beet pulp (CFA)

Ref no 4-00-669

		As fed	Dry
Dry matter	%	91.0	100.0
Ash	%	3.6	3.9
Crude fiber	%	19.0	20.9
Ether extract	%	.6	.7
N-free extract	%	58.7	64.5
Protein (N×6.25)	%	9.1	10.0
Lignin	%	8.0	8.8
Horses	dig prot %	6.3	6.9
Energy	GE kcal/kg	3837.	4217.
Horses	DE kcal/kg	2889.	3175.
Horses	ME kcal/kg	2370.	2604.
Horses	TDN %	76.	83.
Calcium	%	.68	.75
Iron	%	.030	.033
Magnesium	%	.27	.30
Phosphorus	%	.10	.11
Potassium	%	.21	.23
Cobalt	mg/kg	.100	.100
Copper	mg/kg	12.5	13.7
Manganese	mg/kg	35.0	38.5
Zinc	mg/kg	.7	.8
Choline	mg/kg	829.	912.
Niacin	mg/kg	16.3	17.9
Pantothenic acid	mg/kg	1.5	1.6
Riboflavin	mg/kg	.7	.8

(Continued)

Feed name or analyses		Mean	
		As fed	Dry
Thiamin	mg/kg	.4	.4
Vitamin D₃	ICU/g	1.0	1.0
Arginine	%	.30	.33
Histidine	%	.20	.22
Isoleucine	%	.30	.33
Leucine	%	.60	.66
Lysine	%	.60	.66
Phenylalanine	%	.30	.33
Threonine	%	.40	.44
Tryptophan	%	.10	.11
Tyrosine	%	.40	.44
Valine	%	.40	.44

Beet, sugar, pulp w molasses, dehy, (4)

Ref no 4-00-672

		As fed	Dry
Dry matter	%	92.0	100.0
Ash	%	5.7	6.2
Crude fiber	%	16.0	17.4
Ether extract	%	.5	.5
N-free extract	%	60.7	66.0
Protein (N×6.25)	%	9.1	9.9
Horses	dig prot %	6.0	6.5
Energy			
Horses	DE kcal/kg	3002.	3263.
Horses	ME kcal/kg	2462.	2676.
Horses	TDN %	68.	74.
Calcium	%	.56	.61
Magnesium	%	.13	.14
Phosphorus	%	.08	.11
Potassium	%	1.64	1.78

BERMUDAGRASS. Cynodon dactylon

Bermudagrass, hay, s-c, (1)

Ref no 1-00-703

		As fed	Dry
Dry matter	%	91.1	100.0
Ash	%	6.1	6.7
Crude fiber	%	27.0	29.6
Ether extract	%	1.8	2.0
N-free extract	%	48.1	52.8
Protein (N×6.25)	%	8.1	8.9
Horses	dig prot %	4.4	4.8
Energy			
Horses	DE kcal/kg	1727.	1896.
Horses	ME kcal/kg	1417.	1555.
Horses	TDN %	39.	43.
Calcium	%	.42	.46
Iron	%	.026	.029
Magnesium	%	.15	.17
Phosphorus	%	.18	.20
Potassium	%	1.34	1.47
Iodine	mg/kg	.105	.115
Carotene	mg/kg	117.2	128.7

BERMUDAGRASS, COASTAL. Cynondon dactylon

Bermudagrass, coastal, hay, s-c, (1)

Ref no 1-00-716

		As fed	Dry
Ash	%	4.7	5.1
Dry matter	%	91.5	100.0
Crude fiber	%	27.9	30.5
Ether extract	%	2.0	2.2
N-free extract	%	48.2	52.7
Protein (N×6.25)	%	8.7	9.5
Horses	dig prot %	4.7	5.1

(Continued)

(1) dry forages and roughages
(2) pasture, range plants, and forages fed green
(3) silages
(4) energy feeds
(5) protein supplements
(6) minerals
(7) vitamins
(8) additives

TABLE I-1 (Continued)

Feed name or analyses		Mean	
		As fed	Dry
Energy			
Horses	DE kcal/kg	1775.	1940.
Horses	ME kcal/kg	1456.	1591.
Horses	TDN %	40.	44.
Calcium	%	.42	.46
Magnesium	%	.16	.17
Phosphorus	%	.16	.18

Birdsfoot trefoil - see Trefoil, birdsfoot

BLUEGRASS. Poa spp

Bluegrass, hay, s-c, (1)

Ref no 1-00-744

Dry matter	%	90.6	100.0
Ash	%	7.3	8.1
Crude fiber	%	27.4	30.3
Ether extract	%	2.7	3.0
N-free extract	%	42.6	47.0
Protein (N×6.25)	%	10.5	11.6
Horses	dig prot %	6.3	7.0
Energy			
Horses	DE kcal/kg	2517.	2778.
Horses	ME kcal/kg	2064.	2278.
Horses	TDN %	57.	63.
Calcium	%	.35	.39
Iron	%	.020	.030
Magnesium	%	.19	.21
Phosphorus	%	.24	.27
Potassium	%	1.56	1.72
Copper	mg/kg	9.0	9.9
Manganese	mg/kg	83.9	92.6
Carotene	mg/kg	224.8	248.1
Vitamin A equiv	IU/g	374.7	413.6

Bone - see Animal

Bone black - see Animal, bone charcoal

Bone char - see Animal, bone charcoal

Bone charcoal - see Animal

Bone phosphate - see Animal, bone phosphate

Bran - see Wheat

Brewers dried grains - see Grains

Brewers dried yeast - see Yeast, brewers

Feed name or analyses		Mean	
		As fed	Dry

BROME. Bromus spp

Brome, hay, s-c, (1)

Ref no 1-00-890

Dry matter	%	89.7	100.0
Ash	%	7.7	8.6
Crude fiber	%	28.7	32.0
Ether extract	%	2.3	2.6
N-free extract	%	40.4	45.0
Protein (N×6.25)	%	10.6	11.8
Horses	dig prot %	4.5	5.0
Energy			
Horses	DE kcal/kg	1740.	1940.
Horses	ME kcal/kg	1427.	1591.
Horses	TDN %	39.	44.

Brome, aerial pt, fresh, early blm, (2)

Ref no 2-00-893

Dry matter	%	30.0	100.0
Ash	%	2.4	8.1
Crude fiber	%	8.5	28.3
Ether extract	%	1.1	3.7
N-free extract	%	13.8	46.0
Protein (N×6.25)	%	4.2	13.9
Horses	dig prot %	2.9	9.7
Energy			
Horses	DE kcal/kg	899.	2998.
Horses	ME kcal/kg	737.	2458.
Horses	TDN %	20.	68.
Calcium	%	.12	.41
Magnesium	%	.03	.11
Phosphorus	%	.12	.39
Potassium	%	.80	2.67
Carotene	mg/kg	55.2	183.9
Vitamin A equiv	IU/g	92.0	306.6

CALCIUM PHOSPHATE, DIBASIC

Calcium phosphate, dibasic, comm, (6)
Dicalcium phosphate (AAFCO)

Ref no 6-01-080

Dry matter	%	96.0	100.0
Calcium	%	22.20	23.13
Phosphorus	%	17.90	18.65
Fluorine	mg/kg	768.00	800.00

CARROT. Daucus spp

Carrot, roots, fresh, (4)

Ref no 4-01-145

Dry matter	%	11.9	100.0
Ash	%	1.2	10.1
Crude fiber	%	1.1	9.2
Ether extract	%	.2	1.6
N-free extract	%	8.2	69.0
Protein (N×6.25)	%	1.2	10.1
Horses	dig prot %	.6	5.0
Energy			
Horses	DE kcal/kg	430.	3616.

(Continued)

Feed name or analyses		Mean	
		As fed	Dry
Horses	ME kcal/kg	353.	2965.
Horses	TDN %	10.	82.
Calcium	%	.05	.42
Chlorine	%	.06	.50
Iron	%	.002	.017
Magnesium	%	.02	.17
Phosphorus	%	.04	.34
Potassium	%	.25	2.10
Sodium	%	.19	1.60
Sulfur	%	.02	.17
Copper	mg/kg	1.3	10.9
Manganese	mg/kg	3.7	31.1
Carotene	mg/kg	106.0	890.8
Niacin	mg/kg	14.8	124.4
Pantothenic acid	mg/kg	2.0	16.8
Riboflavin	mg/kg	.7	5.9
Thiamin	mg/kg	.7	5.9

CATTLE. Bos spp

Cattle, milk, dehy, feed gr mx 8 moisture mn 26 fat, (5)
Dried whole milk (AAFCO)
Milk, whole, dried

Ref no 5-01-167

Dry matter	%	93.7	100.0
Ash	%	5.4	5.8
Crude fiber	%	.2	.2
Ether extract	%	26.4	28.2
N-free extract	%	36.4	38.9
Protein (N×6.25)	%	25.2	26.9
Horses	dig prot %	24.4	26.0
Energy			
Horses	DE kcal/kg	5795.0	6184.
Horses	ME kcal/kg	4752.	5071.
Horses	TDN %	108.	115.
Calcium	%	.89	.95
Chlorine	%	1.45	1.55
Iron	%	.017	.018
Phosphorus	%	.68	.72
Potassium	%	1.01	1.08
Sodium	%	.36	.38
Manganese	mg/kg	.4	.4
Biotin	mg/kg	.37	.39
Carotene	mg/kg	7.0	7.5
Niacin	mg/kg	8.4	9.0
Pantothenic acid	mg/kg	22.7	24.2
Riboflavin	mg/kg	19.6	20.9
Thiamin	mg/kg	3.7	3.9
Vitamin B₆	mg/kg	4.63	4.94
Vitamin A equiv	IU/g	11.7	12.5
Vitamin D₂	IU/g	.3	.3
Arginine	%	.90	.96
Histidine	%	.70	.75
Isoleucine	%	1.30	1.39
Leucine	%	2.50	2.67
Lysine	%	2.20	2.35
Methionine	%	.60	.64
Phenylalanine	%	1.30	1.39
Threonine	%	1.00	1.07
Tryptophan	%	.40	.43
Tyrosine	%	1.30	1.39
Valine	%	1.70	1.81

Cattle, milk, fresh, (5)
Milk, cattle, fresh

Ref no 5-01-168

Dry matter	%	12.0	100.0
Ash	%	.8	6.7
Ether extract	%	3.7	30.8
N-free extract	%	4.4	36.7

(Continued)

---

(1) dry forages and roughages
(2) pasture, range plants, and forages fed green

(3) silages
(4) energy feeds
(5) protein supplements

(6) minerals
(7) vitamins
(8) additives

TABLE I-1 (Continued)

Feed name or analyses		As fed	Dry
Protein (N×6.25)	%	3.1	25.8
Horses	dig prot %	3.0	24.8
Energy			
Horses	DE kcal/kg	688.	5732.
Horses	ME kcal/kg	564.	4700.
Horses	TDN %	16.	130.
Choline	mg/kg	876.	7296.
Niacin	mg/kg	1.8	15.0
Pantothenic acid	mg/kg	8.1	67.5
Riboflavin	mg/kg	1.8	15.0
Thiamin	mg/kg	0.4	3.3
Arginine	%	.10	.83
Histidine	%	.10	.83
Isoleucine	%	.20	1.67
Leucine	%	.30	2.50
Lysine	%	.30	2.50
Methionine	%	.10	.83
Phenylalanine	%	.10	.83
Threonine	%	.10	.83
Tyrosine	%	.20	1.67
Valine	%	.20	1.67

Cattle, milk, skim centrifugal, (5)

Ref no 5-01-170

		As fed	Dry
Dry matter	%	9.6	100.0
Ash	%	.6	6.1
Crude fiber	%	.0	.0
Ether extract	%	.1	1.5
N-free extract	%	6.1	63.9
Protein (N×6.25)	%	2.7	28.5
Horses	dig prot %	2.6	27.4
Energy			
Horses	DE kcal/kg	394.	4100.
Horses	ME kcal/kg	323.	3362.
Horses	TDN %	9.	93.
	%	.12	1.26
Calcium	%	.002	.017
Iron	%	.10	1.03
Phosphorus	%	.10	1.01
Potassium	%	.03	.32
Sulfur	mg/kg	.010	.110
Cobalt	mg/kg	.1	.9
Copper	mg/kg		.4
Manganese	mg/kg	1.1	11.5
Niacin	mg/kg	3.5	36.8
Pantothenic acid	mg/kg	2.0	20.7
Riboflavin	mg/kg	.4	4.6
Thiamin	%	1.20	12.50
Arginine	%	.90	9.38
Histidine	%	2.30	23.96
Isoleucine	%	3.30	34.38
Leucine	%	2.80	29.17
Lysine	%	1.50	15.62
Phenylalanine	%	1.60	16.67
Serine	%	1.40	14.58
Threonine			

Cattle, milk, skim dehy, mx 8 moisture, (5)
Dried skimmed milk, feed grade (AAFCO)
Milk, skimmed, dried

Ref no 5-01-175

		As fed	Dry
Dry matter	%	94.0	100.0
Ash	%	7.6	8.1
Crude fiber	%	.2	.2
Ether extract	%	.9	1.0
N-free extract	%	51.8	55.1
Protein (N×6.25)	%	33.5	35.6
Horses	dig prot %	30.1	22.0
Energy	GE kcal/kg	3456.	3677.
Horses	DE kcal/kg	3563.	3791.

(Continued)

(1) dry forages and roughages
(2) pasture, range plants, and forages fed green

Feed name or analyses		As fed	Dry
Horses	ME kcal/kg	2922.	3109.
Horses	TDN %	81.	86.
	%	1.26	1.34
Calcium	%	.005	.005
Iron	%	.11	.12
Magnesium	%	1.03	1.10
Phosphorus	%	1.67	1.78
Potassium	mg/kg	.110	.117
Cobalt	mg/kg	11.5	12.2
Copper	mg/kg	2.2	2.3
Manganese	mg/kg	.33	.35
Biotin	mg/kg	1426.	1517.
Choline	mg/kg	.62*	.66
Folic acid	mg/kg	11.5	12.2
Niacin	mg/kg	33.7	35.8
Pantothenic acid	mg/kg	20.1	21.4
Riboflavin	mg/kg	3.5	3.7
Thiamin	mg/kg	9.2	9.8
a-tocopherol	mg/kg	3.97	4.22
Vitamin B₆	mcg/kg	41.9	44.6
Vitamin B₁₂	IU/g	.4	.4
Vitamin D₂	%	1.20	1.28
Arginine	%	.50	.53
Cystine	%	6.80	7.24
Glutamic acid	%	.20	.21
Glycine	%	.90	.96
Histidine	%	2.30	2.45
Isoleucine	%	3.30	3.51
Leucine	%	2.80	2.98
Lysine	%	.80	.85
Methionine	%	1.50	1.60
Phenylalanine	%	1.40	1.49
Threonine	%	.40	.42
Tryptophan	%	1.30	1.38
Tyrosine	%	2.20	2.34
Valine			

Vitamin B₆ / B₁₂ / D₂ rows as transcribed

Cattle, whey, dehy, mn 65 lactose, (4)
Dried whey (AAFCO)
Whey, dried

Ref no 4-01-182

		As fed	Dry
Dry matter	%	94.0	100.0
Ash	%	9.7	10.3
	%	.8	.9
Ether extract	%	69.6	74.1
N-free extract	%	13.8	14.7
Protein (N×6.25)			
Horses	dig prot %	11.8	12.6
Energy			
Horses	DE kcal/kg	3695.	3930.
Horses	ME kcal/kg	3030.	3223.
Horses	TDN %	69.	73.
	%	.87	.93
Calcium	%	.016	.017
Iron	%	.13	.14
Magnesium	%	.79	.84
Phosphorus	mg/kg	.094	.100
Cobalt	mg/kg	43.1	45.9
Copper	mg/kg	4.6	4.9
Manganese	mg/kg	.40	.40
Biotin	mg/kg	20.	21.
Choline	mg/kg	.90	1.00
Folic acid	mg/kg	11.2	11.9
Niacin	mg/kg	47.7	50.8
Pantothenic acid	mg/kg	29.9	31.8
Riboflavin	mg/kg	3.7	3.9
Thiamin	%	.40	.43
Arginine	%	.30	.32
Cystine	%	.20	.21
Histidine	%	.90	.96
Isoleucine	%	1.40	1.49
Leucine	%	1.10	1.17
Lysine	%	.20	.21
Methionine	%	.40	.43
Phenylalanine	%	.80	.85
Threonine	%	.20	.21
Tryptophan	%	.30	.32
Tyrosine	%	.70	.74
Valine			

(3) silages
(4) energy feeds
(5) protein supplements

CLOVER, ALSIKE. Trifolium hybridum

Clover, alsike, hay, s-c, (1)

Ref no 1-01-313

		As fed	Dry
Dry matter	%	87.9	100.0
Ash	%	7.6	8.7
Crude fiber	%	25.8	29.4
Ether extract	%	2.5	2.9
N-free extract	%	38.9	44.3
Protein (N×6.25)	%	12.9	14.7
Horses	dig prot %	8.2	9.3
Energy	GE kcal/kg	3890.	4425.
Horses	DE kcal/kg	2326.	2646.
Horses	ME kcal/kg	1907.	2170.
Horses	TDN %	53.	60.
Calcium	%	1.15	1.31
Chlorine	%	.69	.78
Iron	%	.020	.030
Magnesium	%	.40	.45
Phosphorus	%	.22	.25
Potassium	%	1.50	1.70
Sodium	%	.40	.46
Sulfur	%	.18	.21
Copper	mg/kg	5.3	6.0
Manganese	mg/kg	60.7	69.0
Carotene	mg/kg	164.4	187.0
Vitamin A equiv	IU/g	274.0	311.7

CLOVER, CRIMSON. Trifolium incarnatum

Clover, crimson, hay, s-c, (1)

Ref no 1-01-328

		As fed	Dry
Dry matter	%	87.4	100.0
Ash	%	8.3	9.4
Crude fiber	%	28.1	32.2
Ether extract	%	2.0	2.3
N-free extract	%	34.2	39.2
Protein (N×6.25)	%	14.8	16.9
Horses	dig prot %	10.3	11.8
Energy			
Horses	DE kcal/kg	2313.	2646.
Horses	ME kcal/kg	1896.	2170.
Horses	TDN %	52.	60.
Calcium	%	1.24	1.42
Chlorine	%	.55	.63
Iron	%	.060	.070
Magnesium	%	.24	.27
Phosphorus	%	.16	.18
Potassium	%	1.35	1.54
Sodium	%	.34	.39
Sulfur	%	.24	.28
Manganese	mg/kg	149.7	171.3

CLOVER, LADINO. Trifolium repens

Clover, ladino, hay, s-c, (1)

Ref no 1-01-378

		As fed	Dry
Dry matter	%	91.2	100.0
Ash	%	8.7	9.5
Crude fiber	%	17.5	19.2
Ether extract	%	3.1	3.4
N-free extract	%	40.9	44.9
Protein (N×6.25)	%	21.0	23.0
Horses	dig prot %	13.2	14.5

(Continued)

(6) minerals
(7) vitamins
(8) additives

TABLE I-1 (Continued)

Feed name or analyses		Mean	
		As fed	Dry
Lignin	%	10.6	11.7
Energy			
Horses	DE kcal/kg	2453.	2690.
Horses	ME kcal/kg	2012.	2206.
Horses	TDN %	56.	61.
Calcium	%	1.26	1.38
Chlorine	%	.26	.28
Iron	%	.060	.060
Magnesium	%	.46	.50
Phosphorus	%	.36	.40
Potassium	%	1.97	2.17
Sodium	%	.12	.13
Sulfur	%	.20	.22
Cobalt	mg/kg	.140	.150
Copper	mg/kg	8.0	8.8
Manganese	mg/kg	120.8	132.5
Zinc	mg/kg	15.5	17.0
Carotene	mg/kg	147.0	161.2
Vitamin A equiv	IU/g	245.0	268.7

CLOVER, RED. Trifolium pratense

Clover, red, hay, s-c, (1)

Ref no 1-01-415

Dry matter	%	87.7	100.0
Ash	%	6.9	7.9
Crude fiber	%	26.4	30.1
Ether extract	%	2.5	2.9
N-free extract	%	38.8	44.2
Protein (N×6.25)	%	13.1	14.9
Horses	dig prot %	7.0	8.0
Cellulose	%	22.9	26.1
Lignin	%	12.8	14.6
Energy	GE kcal/kg	3900.	4447.
Horses	DE kcal/kg	1817.	2072.
Horses	ME kcal/kg	1490.	1699.
Horses	TDN %	41.	47.
Calcium	%	1.41	1.61
Chlorine	%	.23	.26
Iron	%	.010	.010
Magnesium	%	.39	.45
Phosphorus	%	.19	.22
Potassium	%	1.54	1.76
Sodium	%	.13	.15
Sulfur	%	.11	.17
Cobalt	mg/kg	.130	.150
Copper	mg/kg	9.8	11.2
Manganese	mg/kg	57.6	65.7
Zinc	mg/kg	15.1	17.2
Carotene	mg/kg	32.3	36.8
Vitamin A equiv	IU/g	53.8	61.3

COCONUT. Cocos nucifera

Coconut, meats, solv-extd grnd, (5)
Solvent extracted coconut meal (AAFCO)
Solvent extracted copra meal (AAFCO)

Ref no 5-01-573

Dry matter	%	92.0	100.0
Ash	%	5.6	6.1
Crude fiber	%	15.0	16.3
Ether extract	%	1.8	2.0
N-free extract	%	48.3	52.5
Protein (N×6.25)	%	21.3	23.1
Horses	dig prot %	17.2	18.7
Lignin	%	1.0	1.1
Energy			
Horses	DE kcal/kg	3002.	3263.
Horses	ME kcal/kg	2462.	2676.
Horses	TDN %	68.	74.

(Continued)

Feed name or analyses		Mean	
		As fed	Dry
Calcium	%	.17	.18
Chlorine	%	.03	.03
Phosphorus	%	.61	.66
Riboflavin	mg/kg	13.2	14.3
Thiamin	mg/kg	.9	1.0

CORN. Zea mays

Corn, aerial pt, ensiled, mature, well-eared mn 50 dry matter, (3)

Ref no 3-08-152

Dry matter	%	55.0	100.0
Ash	%	3.0	5.4
Crude fiber	%	12.6	23.0
Ether extract	%	1.6	2.9
N-free extract	%	33.5	60.9
Protein (N×6.25)	%	4.3	7.8
Horses	dig prot %	2.5	4.5
Energy			
Horses	DE kcal/kg	1722.	3130.
Horses	ME kcal/kg	1412.	2567.
Horses	TDN %	39.	71.
Calcium	%	.15	.27
Phosphorus	%	.10	.19

Corn, ears, grnd, (4)
Corn and cob meal (AAFCO)
Ear corn chop (AAFCO)
Ground ear corn (AAFCO)

Ref no 4-02-849

Dry matter	%	87.0	100.0
Ash	%	1.6	1.8
Crude fiber	%	8.0	9.2
Ether extract	%	3.2	3.7
N-free extract	%	66.1	76.0
Protein (N×6.25)	%	8.1	9.3
Horses	dig prot %	4.0	4.6
Energy			
Horses	DE kcal/kg	3452.	3968.
Horses	ME kcal/kg	2831.	3254.
Horses	TDN %	78.	90.
Calcium	%	.04	.05
Iron	%	.007	.008
Magnesium	%	.15	.17
Phosphorus	%	.27	.31
Potassium	%	.53	.61
Cobalt	mg/kg	.300	.300
Copper	mg/kg	7.7	8.8
Manganese	mg/kg	13.0	15.0

Corn, grits by-prod, mn 5 fat, (4)
Hominy feed (AAFCO)
Hominy feed (CFA)

Ref no 4-02-887

Dry matter	%	90.6	100.0
Ash	%	2.5	2.8
Crude fiber	%	5.0	5.5
Ether extract	%	6.5	7.2
N-free extract	%	65.9	72.7
Protein (N×6.25)	%	10.7	11.8
Horses	dig prot %	7.2	7.9
Energy	GE kcal/kg	4275.	4702.
Horses	DE kcal/kg	3795.	4189.
Horses	ME kcal/kg	3112.	3435.
Horses	TDN %	86.	95.
Calcium	%	.05	.06
Iron	%	.006	.007

(Continued)

Feed name or analyses		Mean	
		As fed	Dry
Magnesium	%	.24	.26
Phosphorus	%	.53	.58
Potassium	%	.67	.74
Sulfur	%	.03	.03
Cobalt	mg/kg	.060	.066
Copper	mg/kg	14.6	16.1
Manganese	mg/kg	14.6	16.1
Carotene	mg/kg	9.2	10.1
Niacin	mg/kg	51.1	56.2
Pantothenic acid	mg/kg	7.5	8.2
Riboflavin	mg/kg	2.0	2.2
Thiamin	mg/kg	7.9	8.7
Vitamin A equiv	IU/g	15.3	16.8

Corn, gluten, wet-mil dehy, (5)
Corn gluten meal (AAFCO)
Corn gluten meal (CFA)

Ref no 5-02-900

Dry matter	%	91.0	100.0
Ash	%	2.4	2.6
Crude fiber	%	4.0	4.4
Ether extract	%	2.3	2.5
N-free extract	%	39.5	43.4
Protein (N×6.25)	%	42.9	47.1
Horses	dig prot %	35.7	39.2
Energy			
Horses	DE kcal/kg	3371.	3704.
Horses	ME kcal/kg	2764.	3037.
Horses	TDN %	76.	84.
Calcium	%	.16	.18
Iron	%	.040	.040
Magnesium	%	.05	.05
Phosphorus	%	.40	.44
Potassium	%	.03	.03
Sodium	%	.10	.10
Cobalt	mg/kg	.100	.100
Copper	mg/kg	28.2	31.0
Manganese	mg/kg	7.3	8.0
Choline	mg/kg	330.	363.
Folic acid	mg/kg	.20	.20
Niacin	mg/kg	49.9	54.8
Pantothenic acid	mg/kg	10.3	11.3
Riboflavin	mg/kg	1.5	1.6
Thiamin	mg/kg	.2	.2
Arginine	%	1.40	1.54
Cystine	%	.60	.66
Glycine	%	1.50	1.65
Histidine	%	1.00	1.10
Isoleucine	%	2.30	2.53
Leucine	%	7.60	8.35
Lysine	%	.80	.88
Methionine	%	1.00	1.10
Phenylalanine	%	2.90	3.19
Threonine	%	1.40	1.54
Tryptophan	%	.20	.22
Tyrosine	%	1.00	1.10
Valine	%	2.20	2.42

Corn, gluten w bran, wet-mil dehy, (5)
Corn gluten feed (AAFCO)
Corn gluten feed (CFA)

Ref no 5-02-903

Dry matter	%	90.0	100.0
Ash	%	6.3	7.0
Crude fiber	%	8.0	8.9
Ether extract	%	2.4	2.7
N-free extract	%	48.1	53.4
Protein (N×6.25)	%	25.3	28.1
Horses	dig prot %	21.8	24.2
Energy	GE kcal/kg	4041.	4490.
Horses	DE kcal/kg	3254.	3616.
Horses	ME kcal/kg	2668.	2965.
Horses	TDN %	74.	82.
Calcium	%	.46	.51

(Continued)

(1) dry forages and roughages
(2) pasture, range plants, and
    forages fed green

(3) silages
(4) energy feeds
(5) protein supplements

(6) minerals
(7) vitamins
(8) additives

APPENDIX

TABLE I-1 (Continued)

Feed name or analyses		Mean As fed	Dry
Iron	%	.050	.060
Magnesium	%	.29	.32
Phosphorus	%	.77	.86
Potassium	%	.60	.67
Sodium	%	.95	1.06
Cobalt	mg/kg	.090	.100
Copper	mg/kg	47.7	53.0
Manganese	mg/kg	23.8	26.4
Biotin	mg/kg	.30	.30
Choline	mg/kg	1516.	1684.
Folic acid	mg/kg	.20	.20
Niacin	mg/kg	71.9	79.9
Pantothenic acid	mg/kg	17.2	19.1
Riboflavin	mg/kg	2.4	2.7
Thiamin	mg/kg	2.0	2.2
Arginine	%	.80	.89
Histidine	%	.60	.67
Isoleucine	%	1.20	1.33
Leucine	%	2.60	2.89
Lysine	%	.80	.89
Methionine	%	.30	.33
Phenylalanine	%	.90	1.00
Threonine	%	.80	.89
Tryptophan	%	.20	.22
Tyrosine	%	.90	1.00
Valine	%	1.30	1.44

CORN, DENT YELLOW. Zea mays indentata

Corn, dent yellow, grain, gr 2 US mn 54 wt, (4)

Ref no 4-02-931

		As fed	Dry
Dry matter	%	89.0	100.0
Ash	%	1.1	1.2
Crude fiber	%	2.0	2.2
Ether extract	%	3.9	4.4
N-free extract	%	73.1	82.2
Protein (N×6.25)	%	8.9	10.0
Horses	dig prot %	6.7	7.5
Energy	GE kcal/kg	3918.	4402.
Horses	DE kcal/kg	3571.	4012.
Horses	ME kcal/kg	2928.	3290.
Horses	TDN %	81.	91.
Calcium	%	.02	.02
Phosphorus	%	.31	.35
Carotene	mg/kg	1.8	2.0
Niacin	mg/kg	26.3	29.5
Pantothenic acid	mg/kg	3.9	4.4
Riboflavin	mg/kg	1.3	1.5
Thiamin	mg/kg	3.6	4.0
Vitamin A equiv	IU/g	3.0	3.3
Arginine	%	.45	.51
Cystine	%	.09	.10
Histidine	%	.18	.20
Isoleucine	%	.45	.51
Leucine	%	.99	1.11
Lysine	%	.18	.20
Methionine	%	.09	.10
Phenylalanine	%	.45	.51
Threonine	%	.36	.40
Tryptophan	%	.09	.10
Valine	%	.36	.40

COTTON. Gossypium spp

Cotton, seed w some hulls, mech-extd grnd, mn 41 prot mx 14 fbr mn 2 fat, (5)
Cottonseed meal, 41% protein

Ref no 5-01-617

		As fed	Dry
Dry matter	%	94.0	100.0
Ash	%	6.2	6.6

(Continued)

		As fed	Dry
Crude fiber	%	12.0	12.8
Ether extract	%	4.3	4.6
N-free extract	%	30.4	32.4
Protein (N×6.25)	%	41.0	43.6
Horses	dig prot %	33.2	35.3
Energy	GE kcal/kg	4600.	4893.
Horses	DE kcal/kg	3233.	3439.
Horses	ME kcal/kg	2651.	2820.
Horses	TDN %	73.	78.
Calcium	%	.16	.17
Iron	%	.030	.032
Magnesium	%	.56	.60
Phosphorus	%	1.20	1.28
Potassium	%	1.40	1.49
Sodium	%	.04	.04
Cobalt	mg/kg	.150	.160
Copper	mg/kg	19.5	20.7
Manganese	mg/kg	21.5	22.9
Choline	mg/kg	2780.	2957.
Folic acid	mg/kg	2.30	2.45
Niacin	mg/kg	39.5	42.0
Pantothenic acid	mg/kg	14.0	14.9
Riboflavin	mg/kg	5.0	5.3
Thiamin	mg/kg	6.5	6.9
Arginine	%	4.25	4.52
Cystine	%	.85	.90
Glycine	%	2.05	2.18
Histidine	%	1.10	1.17
Isoleucine	%	1.60	1.70
Leucine	%	2.50	2.66
Lysine	%	1.70	1.81
Methionine	%	.65	.69
Phenylalanine	%	2.35	2.50
Threonine	%	1.45	1.54
Tryptophan	%	.65	.69
Valine	%	2.05	2.18

Cotton, seed w some hulls, pre-press solv-extd grnd, 41 prot, (5)
Cottonseed meal, pre-press solvent extracted, 41% protein

Ref no 5-07-872

		As fed	Dry
Dry matter	%	92.5	100.0
Ash	%	6.2	6.7
Crude fiber	%	12.0	13.0
Ether extract	%	1.4	1.5
N-free extract	%	31.9	34.5
Protein (N×6.25)	%	41.0	44.3
Horses	dig prot %	34.8	35.9
Energy	GE kcal/kg	4200.	4540.
Horses	DE kcal/kg	3018.	3263.
Horses	ME kcal/kg	2475.	2676.
Horses	TDN %	68.	74.
Calcium	%	.16	.17
Iron	%	.030	.032
Magnesium	%	.56	.60
Phosphorus	%	1.20	1.30
Potassium	%	1.40	1.51
Sodium	%	.04	.04
Cobalt	mg/kg	.150	.162
Copper	mg/kg	19.5	21.1
Manganese	mg/kg	21.5	23.2
Choline	mg/kg	2860.	3092.
Folic acid	mg/kg	2.30	2.49
Niacin	mg/kg	39.5	42.7
Pantothenic acid	mg/kg	14.0	15.1
Riboflavin	mg/kg	5.0	5.4
Thiamin	mg/kg	6.5	7.0
Arginine	%	4.25	4.59
Cystine	%	.85	.92
Glycine	%	2.05	2.22
Histidine	%	1.10	1.19
Isoleucine	%	1.60	1.73
Leucine	%	2.50	2.70
Lysine	%	1.70	1.84
Methionine	%	.65	.70
Phenylalanine	%	2.35	2.54
Threonine	%	1.45	1.57
Tryptophan	%	.65	.70
Valine	%	2.05	2.22

Cotton, seed w some hulls, solv-extd grnd, mn 41 prot mx 14 fbr mn 0.5 fat, (5)
Cottonseed meal, solvent extracted, 41% protein

Ref no 5-01-621

		As fed	Dry
Dry matter	%	91.5	100.0
Ash	%	6.2	6.8
Crude fiber	%	12.0	13.1
Ether extract	%	2.0	2.2
N-free extract	%	30.3	33.1
Protein (N×6.25)	%	41.0	44.8
Horses	dig prot %	33.2	36.3
Energy	GE kcal/kg	4300.	4700.
Horses	DE kcal/kg	3026.	3307.
Horses	ME kcal/kg	2481.	2712.
Horses	TDN %	69.	75.
Calcium	%	.16	.17
Iron	%	.030	.033
Magnesium	%	.56	.61
Phosphorus	%	1.20	1.31
Potassium	%	1.40	1.53
Sodium	%	.04	.04
Cobalt	mg/kg	.150	.164
Copper	mg/kg	19.5	21.3
Manganese	mg/kg	21.5	23.5
Choline	mg/kg	2860.	3126.
Folic acid	mg/kg	2.30	2.51
Niacin	mg/kg	39.5	43.2
Pantothenic acid	mg/kg	14.0	15.3
Riboflavin	mg/kg	5.0	5.5
Thiamin	mg/kg	6.5	7.1
Arginine	%	4.25	4.64
Cystine	%	.85	.93
Glycine	%	2.05	2.24
Histidine	%	1.10	1.20
Isoleucine	%	1.60	1.75
Leucine	%	2.50	2.73
Lysine	%	1.70	1.86
Methionine	%	.65	.71
Phenylalanine	%	2.35	2.57
Threonine	%	1.45	1.58
Tryptophan	%	.65	.71
Valine	%	2.05	2.24

Cotton, seed wo hulls, pre-press solv-extd grnd, mn 50 prot, (5)
Cottonseed meal, pre-press solvent extracted, 50% protein

Ref no 5-07-874

		As fed	Dry
Dry matter	%	92.5	100.0
Ash	%	6.2	6.7
Crude fiber	%	8.5	9.2
Ether extract	%	1.2	1.3
N-free extract	%	26.6	28.8
Protein (N×6.25)	%	50.0	54.0
Horses	dig prot %	40.4	43.7
Energy	DE kcal/kg	3059.	3307.
Horses	ME kcal/kg	2509.	2712.
Horses	TDN %	69.	75.
Calcium	%	.16	.17
Iron	%	.011	.012
Magnesium	%	.46	.50
Phosphorus	%	1.01	1.09
Potassium	%	1.26	1.36
Sodium	%	.05	.05
Cobalt	mg/kg	2.000	2.162
Copper	mg/kg	18.0	19.4
Manganese	mg/kg	22.8	24.6
Zinc	mg/kg	73.3	79.2
Arginine	%	4.75	5.13
Cystine	%	1.00	1.08
Glycine	%	2.35	2.54

(Continued)

(1) dry forages and roughages
(2) pasture, range plants, and forages fed green
(3) silages
(4) energy feeds
(5) protein supplements
(6) minerals
(7) vitamins
(8) additives

TABLE I-1 (Continued)

Feed name or analyses		Mean As fed	Mean Dry
Histidine	%	1.25	1.35
Isoleucine	%	1.85	2.00
Leucine	%	2.80	3.03
Lysine	%	2.10	2.27
Methionine	%	.80	.86
Phenylalanine	%	2.75	2.97
Threonine	%	1.70	1.84
Tryptophan	%	.70	.76
Valine	%	2.05	2.22

FLAX. Linum usitatissimum

Flax, seed, mech-extd grnd, mx 0.5 acid insol ash, (5)
Linseed meal (AAFCO)
Linseed meal (CFA)
Linseed oil meal, expeller extracted
Linseed oil meal, hydraulic extracted
Linseed meal, old process

Ref no 5-02-045

		As fed	Dry
Dry matter	%	91.0	100.0
Ash	%	5.6	6.2
Crude fiber	%	9.0	9.9
Ether extract	%	5.2	5.7
N-free extract	%	35.8	39.4
Protein (N×6.25)	%	35.3	38.8
Horses	dig prot %	31.0	34.1
Energy			
Horses	DE kcal/kg	3250.	3571.
Horses	ME kcal/kg	2664.	2928.
Horses	TDN %	74.	81.
Calcium	%	.44	.48
Iron	%	.017	.019
Magnesium	%	.58	.64
Phosphorus	%	.89	.98
Potassium	%	1.24	1.36
Sodium	%	.11	.12
Cobalt	mg/kg	.400	.500
Copper	mg/kg	26.4	29.0
Manganese	mg/kg	39.4	43.3
Carotene	mg/kg	.2	.2
Choline	mg/kg	1863.	2048.
Folic acid	mg/kg	2.90	3.20
Niacin	mg/kg	35.6	39.1
Pantothenic acid	mg/kg	17.8	19.6
Riboflavin	mg/kg	3.5	3.8
Thiamin	mg/kg	5.1	5.6
Vitamin A equiv	IU/g	.3	.3
Methionine	%	.70	.77

Flax, seed, solv-extd grnd, mx 0.5 acid insol ash, (5)
Solvent extracted linseed meal (AAFCO)
Solvent extracted linseed meal (CFA)
Linseed oil meal, solvent extracted

Ref no 5-02-048

		As fed	Dry
Dry matter	%	91.0	100.0
Ash	%	5.8	6.4
Crude fiber	%	9.0	9.9
Ether extract	%	1.7	1.9
N-free extract	%	39.3	43.2
Protein (N×6.25)	%	35.1	38.6
Horses	dig prot %	30.9	34.0
Energy			
Horses	DE kcal/kg	3049.	3351.
Horses	ME kcal/kg	2501.	2748.
Horses	TDN %	69.	76.
Calcium	%	.40	.44
Iron	%	.033	.036
Magnesium	%	.60	.66

(Continued)

		As fed	Dry
Phosphorus	%	.83	.91
Potassium	%	1.38	1.52
Sodium	%	.14	.15
Cobalt	mg/kg	.20	.20
Copper	mg/kg	25.7	28.2
Manganese	mg/kg	37.6	41.3
Choline	mg/kg	1225.	1347.
Niacin	mg/kg	30.1	33.1
Riboflavin	mg/kg	2.9	3.2
Thiamin	mg/kg	9.5	10.4

GRAINS. Scientific name not used

Grains, brewers' grains, dehy, mx 3 dried spent hops, (5)
Brewers dried grains (AAFCO)
Brewers dried grains (CFA)

Ref no 5-02-141

		As fed	Dry
Dry matter	%	92.0	100.0
Ash	%	3.6	3.9
Crude fiber	%	15.0	16.3
Ether extract	%	6.2	6.7
N-free extract	%	41.4	45.0
Protein (N×6.25)	%	25.9	28.1
Horses	dig prot %	19.9	21.6
Energy			
Horses	DE kcal/kg	2069.	2249.
Horses	ME kcal/kg	1696.	1844.
Horses	TDN %	47.	51.
Calcium	%	.27	.29
Iron	%	.025	.027
Magnesium	%	.14	.15
Phosphorus	%	.50	.54
Potassium	%	.08	.09
Sodium	%	.26	.28
Cobalt	mg/kg	.100	.100
Copper	mg/kg	21.3	22.2
Manganese	mg/kg	37.6	40.9
Choline	mg/kg	1587.	1725.
Folic acid	mg/kg	.22	.24
Niacin	mg/kg	43.4	47.2
Pantothenic acid	mg/kg	8.6	9.3
Riboflavin	mg/kg	1.5	1.6
Thiamin	mg/kg	.7	.8
Vitamin B6	mg/kg	.66	.72
Arginine	%	1.30	1.41
Histidine	%	.50	.54
Isoleucine	%	1.50	1.63
Leucine	%	2.30	2.50
Lysine	%	.90	.98
Methionine	%	.40	.43
Phenylalanine	%	1.30	1.41
Threonine	%	.90	.98
Tryptophan	%	.40	.43
Tyrosine	%	1.20	1.30
Valine	%	1.60	1.74

Hominy feed - see Corn, grits by-prod

LESPEDEZA. Lespedeza spp

Lespedeza, hay, s-c, pre-blm, (1)

Ref no 1-07-954

		As fed	Dry
Dry matter	%	92.1	100.0
Ash	%	6.5	7.1
Crude fiber	%	21.8	23.7

(Continued)

		As fed	Dry
Ether extract	%	3.1	3.4
N-free extract	%	44.2	48.0
Protein (N×6.25)	%	16.4	17.8
Horses	dig prot %	11.4	12.4
Energy			
Horses	DE kcal/kg	2558.	2778.
Horses	ME kcal/kg	2098.	2278.
Horses	TDN %	58.	63.
Calcium	%	1.05	1.14
Phosphorus	%	.24	.26

Lespedeza, hay, s-c, mid-blm, (1)

Ref no 1-02-511

		As fed	Dry
Dry matter	%	93.0	100.0
Ash	%	5.5	5.9
Crude fiber	%	28.6	30.7
Ether extract	%	3.7	4.0
N-free extract	%	40.6	43.7
Protein (N×6.25)	%	14.6	15.7
Horses	dig prot %	9.8	10.5
Energy			
Horses	DE kcal/kg	2337.	2513.
Horses	ME kcal/kg	1917.	2061.
Horses	TDN %	53.	57.
Calcium	%	1.11	1.19
Iron	%	.030	.032
Magnesium	%	.25	.27
Phosphorus	%	.24	.26
Potassium	%	.98	1.05

LIMESTONE. Scientific name not applicable

Limestone, grnd, mn 33 Ca, (6)
Limestone, ground (AAFCO)

Ref no 6-02-632

		As fed	Dry
Dry matter	%	100.0	100.0
Ash	%	95.8	95.8
Calcium	%	33.84	33.84
Iron	%	.330	.330
Phosphorus	%	.02	.02
Sodium	%	.06	.06
Manganese	mg/kg	279.6	279.6

NATIVE PLANTS, INTERMOUNTAIN. Scientific name not used

Native plants, Intermountain, hay, s-c, (1)
Meadow hay

Ref no 1-03-181

		As fed	Dry
Dry matter	%	92.9	100.0
Ash	%	7.5	8.1
Crude fiber	%	28.0	30.1
Ether extract	%	2.8	3.0
N-free extract	%	46.2	49.7
Protein (N×6.25)	%	8.4	9.1
Horses	dig prot %	2.7	2.9
Energy			
Horses	DE kcal/kg	1884.	2028.
Horses	ME kcal/kg	1545.	1663.
Horses	TDN %	43.	46.
Calcium	%	.53	.57
Phosphorus	%	.16	.17

---

(1) dry forages and roughages
(2) pasture, range plants, and forages fed green

(3) silages
(4) energy feeds
(5) protein supplements

(6) minerals
(7) vitamins
(8) additives

TABLE I-1 (Continued)

Feed name or analyses		Mean	
		As fed	Dry

NATIVE PLANTS, MIDWEST. Scientific name not used

Native plants, Midwest, hay, s-c, immature, (1)
Prairie hay, immature

Ref no 1-03-183

Dry matter	%	89.5	100.0
Ash	%	8.3	9.3
Crude fiber	%	28.4	31.7
Ether extract	%	2.3	2.6
N-free extract	%	42.7	47.7
Protein (N×6.25)	%	7.8	8.7
Horses	dig prot %	2.1	2.4
Energy			
Horses	DE kcal/kg	2013.	2249.
Horses	ME kcal/kg	1650.	1844.
Horses	TDN %	46.	51.
Calcium	%	.51	.57
Iron	%	.01	.01
Magnesium	%	.22	.24
Phosphorus	%	.17	.19
Potassium	%	.97	1.08

Native plants, Midwest, hay, s-c, mid-blm, (1)
Prairie hay, mid-bloom

Ref no 1-07-956

Dry matter	%	91.0	100.0
Ash	%	8.7	9.6
Crude fiber	%	29.2	32.1
Ether extract	%	2.6	2.8
N-free extract	%	43.1	47.4
Protein (N×6.25)	%	7.4	8.1
Horses	dig prot %	3.7	4.1
Energy			
Horses	DE kcal/kg	2006.	2205.
Horses	ME kcal/kg	1645.	1808.
Horses	TDN %	46.	50.
Calcium	%	.31	.34
Phosphorus	%	.19	.21

Native plants, Midwest, hay, s-c, full blm, (1)
Prairie hay, full bloom

Ref no 1-03-184

Dry matter	%	83.3	100.0
Ash	%	8.5	10.2
Crude fiber	%	27.5	33.0
Ether extract	%	2.7	3.2
N-free extract	%	38.3	46.0
Protein (N×6.25)	%	6.3	7.6
Horses	dig prot %	1.7	2.1
Energy			
Horses	DE kcal/kg	1873.	2249.
Horses	ME kcal/kg	1536.	1844.
Horses	TDN %	42.	51.

Native plants, Midwest, hay, s-c, late blm, (1)
Prairie hay, late bloom

Ref no 1-07-957

Dry matter	%	91.3	100.0
Ash	%	8.6	9.4

(Continued)

Feed name or analyses		Mean	
		As fed	Dry

Crude fiber	%	29.7	32.5
Ether extract	%	3.0	3.3
N-free extract	%	44.0	48.2
Protein (N×6.25)	%	6.0	6.6
Horses	dig prot %	2.0	2.2
Energy			
Horses	DE kcal/kg	1972.	2160.
Horses	ME kcal/kg	1617.	1771.
Horses	TDN %	45.	49.
Calcium	%	.33	.36
Phosphorus	%	.12	.13

OATS. Avena sativa

Oats, hay, s-c, (1)

Ref no 1-03-280

Dry matter	%	88.2	100.0
Ash	%	6.6	7.5
Crude fiber	%	27.3	31.0
Ether extract	%	2.7	3.1
N-free extract	%	43.4	49.2
Protein (N×6.25)	%	8.1	9.2
Horses	dig prot %	3.9	4.4
Energy			
Horses	DE kcal/kg	2372.	2690.
Horses	ME kcal/kg	1946.	2206.
Horses	TDN %	54.	61.
Calcium	%	.23	.26
Chlorine	%	.46	.52
Iron	%	.04	.05
Magnesium	%	.26	.29
Phosphorus	%	.21	.24
Potassium	%	.85	.97
Sodium	%	.15	.17
Cobalt	mg/kg	.06	.07
Copper	mg/kg	3.9	4.4
Manganese	mg/kg	65.7	74.7
Carotene	mg/kg	88.9	101.0
Vitamin A equiv	IU/g	148.2	168.4

Oats, cereal by-prod, mx 4 fbr, (4)
Feeding oat meal (AAFCO)
Oat middlings (CFA)

Ref no 4-03-303

Dry matter	%	91.0	100.0
Ash	%	2.3	2.5
Crude fiber	%	4.0	4.4
Ether extract	%	5.8	6.4
N-free extract	%	63.1	69.3
Protein (N×6.25)	%	15.8	17.4
Horses	dig prot %	10.8	11.9
Energy			
Horses	DE kcal/kg	3691.	4056.
Horses	ME kcal/kg	3027.	3326.
Horses	TDN %	84.	92.
Calcium	%	.08	.09
Iron	%	.038	.042
Phosphorus	%	.49	.54
Manganese	mg/kg	44.0	48.4
Niacin	mg/kg	28.1	30.9
Pantothenic acid	mg/kg	23.1	25.4
Riboflavin	mg/kg	1.8	2.0
Thiamin	mg/kg	7.0	7.7
Arginine	%	.70	.77
Histidine	%	.30	.33
Lysine	%	.10	.11
Tyrosine	%	.91	1.00

Feed name or analyses		Mean	
		As fed	Dry

Oats, grain, (4)

Ref no 4-03-309

Dry matter	%	89.0	100.0
Ash	%	3.2	3.6
Crude fiber	%	11.0	12.4
Ether extract	%	4.5	5.1
N-free extract	%	58.5	65.7
Protein (N×6.25)	%	11.8	13.2
Horses	dig prot %	8.8	9.9
Cellulose	%	16.0	18.0
Lignin	%	8.9	10.0
Energy	GE kcal/kg	4187.	4704.
Horses	DE kcal/kg	2982.	3351.
Horses	ME kcal/kg	2446.	2748.
Horses	TDN %	68.	76.
Calcium	%	.10	.11
Iron	%	.007	.008
Magnesium	%	.17	.19
Phosphorus	%	.35	.39
Potassium	%	.37	.42
Sodium	%	.06	.07
Cobalt	mg/kg	.060	.070
Copper	mg/kg	5.9	6.6
Manganese	mg/kg	38.2	42.9
Biotin	mg/kg	.30	.30
Choline	mg/kg	1073.	1206.
Folic acid	mg/kg	.40	.40
Niacin	mg/kg	15.8	17.8
Pantothenic acid	mg/kg	12.9	14.5
Riboflavin	mg/kg	1.6	1.8
Thiamin	mg/kg	6.2	7.0
a-tocopherol	mg/kg	5.9	6.6
Vitamin B6	mg/kg	1.2	1.3
Arginine	%	.71	.80
Cystine	%	.18	.20
Histidine	%	.18	.20
Isoleucine	%	.53	.60
Leucine	%	.89	1.00
Lysine	%	.36	.40
Methionine	%	.18	.20
Phenylalanine	%	.62	.70
Threonine	%	.36	.40
Tryptophan	%	.18	.20
Tyrosine	%	.53	.60
Valine	%	.62	.70

Oats, grain, Pacific coast, (4)

Ref no 4-07-999

Dry matter	%	91.2	100.0
Ash	%	3.7	4.0
Crude fiber	%	11.0	12.1
Ether extract	%	5.4	5.9
N-free extract	%	62.1	68.1
Protein (N×6.25)	%	9.0	9.9
Horses	dig prot %	6.7	7.4
Energy			
Horses	DE kcal/kg	3096.	3395.
Horses	ME kcal/kg	2539.	2784.
Horses	TDN %	70.	77.
Calcium	%	.09	.10
Phosphorus	%	.33	.36

Oats, groats, (4)
Oat groats (AAFCO)
Oat groats (CFA)
Hulled oats (CFA)

Ref no 4-03-331

Dry matter	%	91.0	100.0
Ash	%	2.2	2.4

(Continued)

Footnotes

(1) dry forages and roughages
(2) pasture, range plants, and forages fed green
(3) silages
(4) energy feeds
(5) protein supplements
(6) minerals
(7) vitamins
(8) additives

TABLE I-1 (Continued)

Feed name or analyses		Mean As fed	Mean Dry
Crude fiber	%	3.0	3.3
Ether extract	%	5.8	6.4
N-free extract	%	63.2	69.5
Protein (N×6.25)	%	16.7	18.4
Horses	dig prot %	11.7	12.9
Energy			
Horses	DE kcal/kg	3731.	4100.
Horses	ME kcal/kg	3059.	3362.
Horses	TDN %	85.	93.
Calcium	%	.07	.08
Magnesium	%	.09	.10
Phosphorus	%	.43	.47
Potassium	%	.34	.37
Copper	mg/kg	6.4	7.0
Manganese	mg/kg	28.6	31.4
Niacin	mg/kg	8.1	8.9
Pantothenic acid	mg/kg	14.7	16.2
Riboflavin	mg/kg	1.3	1.4
Thiamin	mg/kg	6.8	7.5
Vitamin B_6	mg/kg	1.1	1.2

ORCHARDGRASS. Dactylis glomerata

Orchardgrass, hay, s-c, (1)

Ref no 1-03-438

		As fed	Dry
Dry matter	%	88.3	100.0
Ash	%	6.7	7.6
Crude fiber	%	30.0	34.0
Ether extract	%	3.0	3.4
N-free extract	%	40.0	45.3
Protein (N×6.25)	%	8.6	9.7
Horses	dig prot %	5.1	5.8
Cellulose	%	22.1	25.0
Lignin	%	6.7	7.6
Energy	GE kcal/kg	4059.	4597.
Horses	DE kcal/kg	2219.	2513.
Horses	ME kcal/kg	1820.	2061.
Horses	TDN %	50.	57.
Calcium	%	.40	.45
Chlorine	%	.36	.41
Iron	%	.01	.01
Magnesium	%	.28	.32
Phosphorus	%	.33	.37
Potassium	%	1.85	2.10
Sulfur	%	.23	.26
Cobalt	mg/kg	.02	.02
Copper	mg/kg	12.1	13.7
Manganese	mg/kg	220.4	249.6
Zinc	mg/kg	16.0	18.1
Carotene	mg/kg	29.6	33.5
Vitamin A equiv	IU/g	49.3	55.8

OYSTERS. Crassostrea spp, Ostrea spp

Oysters, shells, f-grnd, mn 33 Ca, (6)
Oyster shell flour (AAFCO)

Ref no 6-03-481

		As fed	Dry
Dry matter	%	100.0	100.0
Ash	%	80.8	80.8
Protein (N×6.25)	%	1.0	1.0
Calcium	%	38.05	38.05
Iron	%	.290	.290
Magnesium	%	.30	.30
Phosphorus	%	.07	.07
Potassium	%	.10	.10
Sodium	%	.21	.21
Manganese	mg/kg	133.3	133.3

PEANUT. Arachis hypogaea

Peanut, kernels, mech-extd grnd, mx 7 fbr, (5)
Peanut meal (AAFCO)
Peanut meal (CFA)
Peanut oil meal, expeller extracted

Ref no 5-03-649

		As fed	Dry
Dry matter	%	92.0	100.0
Ash	%	5.7	6.2
Crude fiber	%	11.0	12.0
Ether extract	%	5.9	6.4
N-free extract	%	23.6	25.6
Protein (N×6.25)	%	45.8	49.8
Horses	dig prot %	41.2	44.8
Energy			
Horses	DE kcal/kg	3367.	3660.
Horses	ME kcal/kg	2761.	3001.
Horses	TDN %	76.	83.
Calcium	%	.17	.18
Magnesium	%	.33	.36
Phosphorus	%	.57	.62
Potassium	%	1.15	1.25
Manganese	mg/kg	25.5	27.7
Choline	mg/kg	1683.	1829.
Niacin	mg/kg	169.0	183.7
Pantothenic acid	mg/kg	48.2	52.3
Riboflavin	mg/kg	5.3	5.8
Thiamin	mg/kg	7.3	7.9
Arginine	%	4.69	5.10
Histidine	%	1.00	1.09
Isoleucine	%	2.00	2.17
Leucine	%	3.10	3.37
Lysine	%	1.30	1.41
Methionine	%	.60	.65
Phenylalanine	%	2.30	2.50
Threonine	%	1.40	1.52
Tryptophan	%	.50	.54
Valine	%	2.20	2.39

Peanut, kernels, solv-extd grnd, mx 7 fbr, (5)
Solvent extracted peanut meal (AAFCO)
Groundnut oil meal, solvent extracted
Peanut oil meal, solvent extracted

Ref no 5-03-650

		As fed	Dry
Dry matter	%	92.0	100.0
Ash	%	4.5	4.9
Crude fiber	%	13.0	14.1
Ether extract	%	1.2	1.3
N-free extract	%	25.9	28.2
Protein (N×6.25)	%	47.4	51.5
Horses	dig prot %	42.7	46.4
Energy			
Horses	DE kcal/kg	3123.	3395.
Horses	ME kcal/kg	2561.	2784.
Horses	TDN %	71.	77.
Calcium	%	.20	.22
Magnesium	%	.04	.04
Phosphorus	%	.65	.71
Manganese	mg/kg	29.0	31.5
Choline	mg/kg	2000.	2174.
Niacin	mg/kg	170.1	184.9
Pantothenic acid	mg/kg	53.0	57.6
Riboflavin	mg/kg	11.0	12.0
Thiamin	mg/kg	7.3	7.9
Arginine	%	5.90	6.41
Histidine	%	1.20	1.30
Isoleucine	%	2.00	2.17
Leucine	%	3.70	4.02

(Continued)

Feed name or analyses		Mean As fed	Mean Dry
Lysine	%	2.30	2.50
Methionine	%	.40	.43
Phenylalanine	%	2.70	2.93
Threonine	%	1.50	1.63
Tryptophan	%	.50	.54
Tyrosine	%	1.80	1.96
Valine	%	2.80	3.04

PHOSPHATE, DEFLUORINATED

Phosphate, defluorinated grnd, mn 1 pt F per 100 pt P, (6)
Phosphate, defluorinated (AAFCO)
Defluorinated phosphate (CFA)

Ref no 6-01-780

		As fed	Dry
Dry matter	%	99.8	100.0
Calcium	%	33.00	33.07
Iron	%	.920	.922
Phosphorus	%	18.00	18.04
Potassium	%	.09	.09
Sodium	%	3.95	3.96
Fluorine	mg/kg	1800.00	1803.61

RICE. Oryza sativa

Rice, bran w germ, dry-mil, mx 13 fbr $CaCO_3$ declared above 3 mn, (4)
Rice bran (AAFCO)

Ref no 4-03-928

		As fed	Dry
Dry matter	%	91.0	100.0
Ash	%	10.9	12.0
Crude fiber	%	11.0	12.1
Ether extract	%	15.1	16.6
N-free extract	%	40.5	44.5
Protein (N×6.25)	%	13.5	14.8
Horses	dig prot %	8.7	9.6
Energy			
Horses	DE kcal/kg	2648.	2910.
Horses	ME kcal/kg	2171.	2386.
Horses	TDN %	60.	66.
Calcium	%	.06	.07
Iron	%	.019	.021
Magnesium	%	.95	1.04
Phosphorus	%	1.82	2.00
Potassium	%	1.74	1.91
Copper	mg/kg	13.0	14.3
Manganese	mg/kg	417.8	459.2
Zinc	mg/kg	29.9	32.9
Biotin	mg/kg	4.20	4.60
Choline	mg/kg	1254.	1378.
Niacin	mg/kg	303.2	333.2
Pantothenic acid	mg/kg	23.5	25.8
Riboflavin	mg/kg	2.6	2.9
Thiamin	mg/kg	22.4	24.6
Arginine	%	.50	.55
Cystine	%	.10	.11
Histidine	%	.20	.22
Isoleucine	%	.40	.44
Leucine	%	.60	.66
Lysine	%	.50	.55
Phenylalanine	%	.40	.44
Threonine	%	.40	.44
Tryptophan	%	.10	.11
Valine	%	.60	.66

(1) dry forages and roughages
(2) pasture, range plants, and forages fed green
(3) silages
(4) energy feeds
(5) protein supplements
(6) minerals
(7) vitamins
(8) additives

TABLE I-1 (Continued)

Feed name or analyses		As fed	Dry
RYE. Secale cereale			
Rye, grain, (4)			
Ref no 4-04-047			
Dry matter	%	89.0	100.0
Ash	%	1.7	1.9
Crude fiber	%	2.0	2.2
Ether extract	%	1.6	1.8
N-free extract	%	71.8	80.7
Protein (N×6.25)	%	11.9	13.4
Horses	dig prot %	9.4	10.6
Energy			
Horses	DE kcal/kg	3336.	3748.
Horses	ME kcal/kg	2735.	3073.
Horses	TDN %	76.	85.
Calcium	%	.06	.07
Iron	%	.008	.009
Magnesium	%	.12	.13
Phosphorus	%	.34	.38
Potassium	%	.46	.52
Sodium	%	.02	.02
Copper	mg/kg	7.8	8.8
Manganese	mg/kg	66.9	75.2
Zinc	mg/kg	30.5	34.3
Biotin	mg/kg	.06	.07
Folic acid	mg/kg	.60	.70
Niacin	mg/kg	1.2	1.3
Pantothenic acid	mg/kg	6.9	7.7
Riboflavin	mg/kg	1.6	1.8
Thiamin	mg/kg	3.9	4.4
a-tocopherol	mg/kg	15.0	17.4
Arginine	%	.53	.60
Cystine	%	.18	.20
Histidine	%	.27	.30
Isoleucine	%	.53	.60
Leucine	%	.71	.80
Lysine	%	.45	.51
Methionine	%	.18	.20
Phenylalanine	%	.62	.70
Threonine	%	.36	.40
Tryptophan	%	.09	.10
Tyrosine	%	.27	.30
Valine	%	.62	.70

SAFFLOWER. Carthamus tinctorius

Safflower, seed, (4)

Ref no 4-07-958

		As fed	Dry
Dry matter	%	93.1	100.0
Ash	%	2.9	3.1
Crude fiber	%	26.6	28.6
Ether extract	%	29.8	32.0
N-free extract	%	17.5	18.8
Protein (N×6.25)	%	16.3	17.5
Horses	dig prot %	13.0	14.0
Energy			
Horses	DE kcal/kg	3653.	3924.
Horses	ME kcal/kg	2996.	3218.
Horses	TDN %	83.	89.

Safflower, seed, mech-extd grnd, (5)
Whole pressed safflower seed (AAFCO)
Safflower oil meal, expeller extracted
Safflower oil meal, hydraulic extracted

Ref no 5-04-109

		As fed	Dry
Dry matter	%	91.0	100.0
Ash	%	3.7	4.1

(Continued)

(1) dry forages and roughages
(2) pasture, range plants, and
   forages fed green

Feed name or analyses		As fed	Dry
Crude fiber	%	31.0	34.1
Ether extract	%	6.0	6.6
N-free extract	%	30.5	33.5
Protein (N×6.25)	%	19.7	21.7
Horses	dig prot %	14.5	15.9
Energy			
Horses	DE kcal/kg	2287.	2513.
Horses	ME kcal/kg	1876.	2061.
Horses	TDN %	52.	57.
Calcium	%	.23	.25
Iron	%	.05	.05
Magnesium	%	.33	.36
Phosphorus	%	.71	.78
Potassium	%	.72	.79
Sodium	%	.05	.05
Copper	mg/kg	9.7	10.7
Manganese	mg/kg	17.8	19.6
Zinc	mg/kg	39.8	43.7
Biotin	mg/kg	1.4	1.5
Folic acid	mg/kg	.44	.48
Niacin	mg/kg	85.8	94.3
Pantothenic acid	mg/kg	4.0	4.4
Riboflavin	mg/kg	18.0	19.8
Arginine	%	1.20	1.32
Cystine	%	.80	.88
Lysine	%	.70	.77
Methionine	%	.40	.44
Tryptophan	%	.30	.33

Safflower, seed, solv-extd grnd, (5)
Solvent extracted whole pressed safflower seed
(AAFCO)

Ref no 5-04-110

		As fed	Dry
Dry matter	%	91.8	100.0
Ash	%	4.7	5.1
Crude fiber	%	32.3	35.2
Ether extract	%	3.9	4.2
N-free extract	%	29.6	32.2
Protein (N×6.25)	%	21.4	23.3
Horses	dig prot %	17.2	18.7
Energy			
Horses	DE kcal/kg	2226.	2425.
Horses	ME kcal/kg	1825.	1988.
Horses	TDN %	50.	55.
Calcium	%	.34	.37
Phosphorus	%	.84	.92

SODIUM PHOSPHATE, MONOBASIC

Sodium, phosphate, monobasic, NaH2PO4·H2O, tech, (6)
Monosodium phosphate (AAFCO)

Ref no 6-04-288

		As fed	Dry
Dry matter	%	96.7	100.0
Ash	%	96.7	100.0
Phosphorus	%	21.80	22.46
Sodium	%	32.3	33.4
		120.00	124.10

SODIUM TRIPOLYPHOSPHATE

Sodium, tripolyphosphate, comm, (6)
Sodium tripolyphosphate (AAFCO)

Ref no 6-08-076

		As fed	Dry
Dry matter	%	96.0	100.0
Phosphorus	%	24.94	25.98

(3) silages
(4) energy feeds
(5) protein supplements

Feed name or analyses		As fed	Dry
SORGHUM, GRAIN VARIETY. Sorghum vulgare			
Sorghum, grain variety, aerial pt, s-c, (1)			
Grain sorghum fodder, sun-cured			
Ref no 1-04-372			
Dry matter	%	90.3	100.0
Ash	%	8.5	9.4
Crude fiber	%	24.8	27.5
Ether extract	%	1.7	1.9
N-free extract	%	49.0	54.3
Protein (N×6.25)	%	6.2	6.9
Horses	dig prot %	2.3	2.6
Energy			
Horses	DE kcal/kg	2309.	2557.
Horses	ME kcal/kg	1894.	2097.
Horses	TDN %	52.	58.
Calcium	%	.56	.62
Phosphorus	%	.17	.19

Sorghum, grain variety, aerial pt wo heads, s-c, (1)
Grain sorghum stover, sun-cured

Ref no 1-07-961

		As fed	Dry
Dry matter	%	85.1	100.0
Ash	%	8.2	9.6
Crude fiber	%	27.7	32.6
Ether extract	%	1.8	2.1
N-free extract	%	42.9	50.4
Protein (N×6.25)	%	4.5	5.3
Horses	dig prot %	1.5	1.8
Energy			
Horses	DE kcal/kg	2138.	2513.
Horses	ME kcal/kg	1754.	2061.
Horses	TDN %	49.	57.
Calcium	%	.34	.40
Phosphorus	%	.09	.11

Sorghum, grain variety, grain, mn 6 mx 9 prot, (4)

Ref no 4-08-138

		As fed	Dry
Dry matter	%	88.0	100.0
Ash	%	2.0	2.3
Crude fiber	%	1.9	2.2
Ether extract	%	2.6	3.0
N-free extract	%	74.4	84.6
Protein (N×6.25)	%	7.0	7.9
Horses	dig prot %	4.0	4.5
Energy			
Horses	DE kcal/kg	3142.	3571.
Horses	ME kcal/kg	2577.	2928.
Horses	TDN %	71.	81.
Alanine	%	.61	.69
Arginine	%	.26	.29
Aspartic acid	%	.48	.54
Cysteine	%	.10	.11
Glutamic acid	%	1.36	1.54
Glycine	%	.26	.29
Histidine	%	.16	.18
Isoleucine	%	.26	.30
Leucine	%	.68	.77
Lysine	%	.18	.20
Methionine	%	.09	.10
Phenylalanine	%	.34	.39
Proline	%	.52	.59
Serine	%	.30	.34
Threonine	%	.23	.26
Tyrosine	%	.14	.16
Valine	%	.35	.40

(6) minerals
(7) vitamins
(8) additives

TABLE I-1 (Continued)

Feed name or analyses		As fed	Dry
		Mean	

Sorghum, grain variety, grain, mn 9 mx 12 prot, (4)

Ref no 4-08-139

		As fed	Dry
Dry matter	%	88.0	100.0
Ash	%	1.9	2.2
Crude fiber	%	2.1	2.4
Ether extract	%	2.6	2.9
N-free extract	%	71.1	80.8
Protein (N×6.25)	%	10.3	11.7
Horses	dig prot %	5.9	6.7
Lignin	%	1.1	1.3
Energy			
Horses	DE kcal/kg	3104.	3527.
Horses	ME kcal/kg	2545.	2892.
Horses	TDN %	70.	80.
Alanine	%	.97	1.10
Arginine	%	.33	.38
Aspartic acid	%	.70	.79
Cysteine	%	.14	.16
Glutamic acid	%	2.24	2.54
Glycine	%	.32	.37
Histidine	%	.23	.26
Isoleucine	%	.43	.49
Leucine	%	1.41	1.60
Lysine	%	.22	.25
Methionine	%	.13	.15
Phenylalanine	%	.53	.60
Proline	%	.84	.96
Serine	%	.44	.50
Threonine	%	.32	.37
Tyrosine	%	.22	.25
Valine	%	.53	.60

Sorghum, grain variety, grain, mn 12 mx 15 prot, (4)

Ref no 4-08-140

		As fed	Dry
Dry matter	%	88.0	100.0
Ash	%	2.3	2.6
Crude fiber	%	1.8	2.0
Ether extract	%	1.5	1.7
N-free extract	%	71.0	80.7
Protein (N×6.25)	%	11.4	13.0
Horses	dig prot %	6.5	7.4
Energy			
Horses	DE kcal/kg	3026.	3439.
Horses	ME kcal/kg	2482.	2820.
Horses	TDN %	69.	78.
Alanine	%	1.17	1.33
Arginine	%	.39	.43
Aspartic acid	%	.81	.92
Cysteine	%	.18	.20
Glutamic acid	%	2.59	2.94
Glycine	%	.35	.40
Histidine	%	.26	.29
Isoleucine	%	.49	.56
Leucine	%	1.77	2.01
Lysine	%	.23	.26
Methionine	%	.14	.16
Phenylalanine	%	.62	.70
Proline	%	.97	1.10
Serine	%	.51	.58
Threonine	%	.37	.42
Tyrosine	%	.26	.29
Valine	%	.61	.69

Feed name or analyses		As fed	Dry
		Mean	

SORGHUM, KAFIR. Sorghum vulgare

Sorghum, kafir, grain, (4)

Ref no 4-04-428

		As fed	Dry
Dry matter	%	90.0	100.0
Ash	%	1.5	1.7
Crude fiber	%	2.0	2.2
Ether extract	%	2.9	3.2
N-free extract	%	71.8	79.8
Protein (N×6.25)	%	11.8	13.1
Horses	dig prot %	6.8	7.6
Energy			
Horses	DE kcal/kg	2858.	3175.
Horses	ME kcal/kg	2344.	2604.
Horses	TDN %	65.	72.
Calcium	%	.04	.04
Iron	%	.010	.010
Phosphorus	%	.33	.37
Copper	mg/kg	6.3	7.0
Manganese	mg/kg	15.8	17.6
Niacin	mg/kg	36.6	40.7
Pantothenic acid	mg/kg	12.2	13.6
Riboflavin	mg/kg	1.4	1.5
Thiamin	mg/kg	3.8	4.2
Vitamin B6	mg/kg	6.80	7.50
Arginine	%	.36	.40
Histidine	%	.27	.30
Isoleucine	%	.54	.60
Leucine	%	1.62	1.80
Lysine	%	.27	.30
Methionine	%	.18	.20
Phenylalanine	%	.63	.70
Threonine	%	.45	.50
Tryptophan	%	.18	.20
Valine	%	.63	.70

SORGHUM, MILO. Sorghum vulgare

Sorghum, milo, grain, (4)

Ref no 4-04-444

		As fed	Dry
Dry matter	%	89.0	100.0
Ash	%	1.7	1.9
Crude fiber	%	2.0	2.2
Ether extract	%	2.8	3.1
N-free extract	%	71.6	80.4
Protein (N×6.25)	%	11.0	12.4
Horses	dig prot %	6.3	7.1
Energy			
Horses	GE kcal/kg	3906.	4389.
Horses	DE kcal/kg	3139.	3527.
Horses	ME kcal/kg	2574.	2892.
Horses	TDN %	71.0	80.
Calcium	%	.04	.04
Magnesium	%	.20	.22
Phosphorus	%	.29	.33
Potassium	%	.35	.39
Sodium	%	.01	.01
Cobalt	mg/kg	.100	.100
Copper	mg/kg	14.1	15.8
Manganese	mg/kg	12.9	14.5
Choline	mg/kg	678.	761.
Niacin	mg/kg	42.7	48.0
Pantothenic acid	mg/kg	11.4	12.8
Riboflavin	mg/kg	1.2	1.3
Thiamin	mg/kg	3.9	4.4
Vitamin B6	mg/kg	4.10	4.60
Arginine	%	.36	.40
Cystine	%	.18	.20
Histidine	%	.27	.30
Isoleucine	%	.53	.60
Leucine	%	1.42	1.60
Lysine	%	.27	.30

(Continued)

Feed name or analyses		As fed	Dry
		Mean	

		As fed	Dry
Methionine	%	.09	.10
Phenylalanine	%	.45	.51
Threonine	%	.27	.30
Tryptophan	%	.09	.10
Tyrosine	%	.36	.40
Valine	%	.53	.60

SOYBEAN. Glycine max

Soybean, seed, mech-extd grnd, mx 7 fbr, (5)
Soybean meal (AAFCO)
Soybean meal, expeller extracted
Soybean meal, hydraulic extracted
Soybean oil meal, expeller extracted
Soybean oil meal, hydraulic extracted

Ref no 5-04-600

		As fed	Dry
Dry matter	%	90.0	100.0
Ash	%	5.7	6.3
Crude fiber	%	6.0	6.7
Ether extract	%	4.7	5.2
N-free extract	%	29.8	33.1
Protein (N×6.25)	%	43.8	48.7
Horses	dig prot %	37.3	41.4
Energy			
	GE kcal/kg	4332.	4813.
Horses	DE kcal/kg	3373.	3748.
Horses	ME kcal/kg	2766.	3073.
Horses	TDN %	76.	85.
Calcium	%	.27	.30
Iron	%	.016	.018
Magnesium	%	.25	.28
Phosphorus	%	.63	.70
Potassium	%	1.71	1.90
Sodium	%	.24	.27
Cobalt	mg/kg	.200	.200
Copper	mg/kg	18.0	20.0
Manganese	mg/kg	32.3	35.9
Biotin	mg/kg	.30	.30
Choline	mg/kg	2673.	2970.
Folic acid	mg/kg	6.60	7.30
Niacin	mg/kg	30.4	33.8
Thiamin	mg/kg	4.0	4.4
Arginine	%	2.60	2.89
Cystine	%	.60	.67
Glycine	%	2.50	2.78
Histidine	%	1.10	1.22
Isoleucine	%	2.80	3.11
Leucine	%	3.60	4.00
Lysine	%	2.70	3.00
Methionine	%	.80	.89
Phenylalanine	%	2.10	2.33
Threonine	%	1.70	1.89
Tryptophan	%	.60	.67
Tyrosine	%	1.40	1.56
Valine	%	2.20	2.44

Soybean, seed, solv-extd grnd, mx 7 fbr, (5)
Solvent extracted soybean meal (AAFCO)
Soybean meal, solvent extracted
Soybean oil meal, solvent extracted

Ref no 5-04-604

		As fed	Dry
Dry matter	%	89.0	100.0
Ash	%	5.8	6.5
Crude fiber	%	6.0	6.7
Ether extract	%	.9	1.0
N-free extract	%	30.5	34.3
Protein (N×6.25)	%	45.8	51.5
Horses	dig prot %	39.0	43.8
Energy			
	GE kcal/kg	4198.	4719.
Horses	DE kcal/kg	3178.	3571.
Horses	ME kcal/kg	2606.	2928.
Horses	TDN %	72.	81.
Calcium	%	.32	.36

(Continued)

Footnotes

(1) dry forages and roughages
(2) pasture, range plants, and forages fed green

(3) silages
(4) energy feeds
(5) protein supplements

(6) minerals
(7) vitamins
(8) additives

TABLE I-1 (Continued)

Column 1 (continued feed)

Feed name or analyses		As fed	Dry
Iron	%	.012	.013
Magnesium	%	.27	.30
Phosphorus	%	.67	.75
Potassium	%	1.97	2.21
Sodium	%	.34	.38
Cobalt	mg/kg	.100	.100
Copper	mg/kg	36.3	40.8
Manganese	mg/kg	27.5	30.9
Choline	mg/kg	2743.	3083.
Folic acid	mg/kg	.70	.80
Niacin	mg/kg	26.8	30.1
Pantothenic acid	mg/kg	14.5	16.3
Riboflavin	mg/kg	3.3	3.7
Thiamin	mg/kg	6.6	7.4
Arginine	%	3.20	3.60
Histidine	%	1.10	1.24
Isoleucine	%	2.50	2.81
Leucine	%	3.40	3.82
Lysine	%	2.90	3.26
Methionine	%	.60	.67
Phenylalanine	%	2.20	2.47
Threonine	%	1.70	1.91
Tryptophan	%	.60	.67
Tyrosine	%	1.40	1.57
Valine	%	2.40	2.70

SUGARCANE. Saccharum officinarum

Sugarcane, molasses, dehy, (4)
Cane molasses, dried
Molasses, cane, dried

Ref no 4-04-695

		As fed	Dry
Dry matter	%	96.0	100.0
Ash	%	8.0	8.3
Crude fiber	%	5.0	5.2
Ether extract	%	1.0	1.0
N-free extract	%	71.7	74.8
Protein (N×6.25)	%	10.3	10.7
Horses	dig prot %	7.3	7.6
Energy	GE kcal/kg	3087.	3212.
Horses	DE kcal/kg	3293.	3429.
Horses	ME kcal/kg	2700.	2812.
Horses	TDN %	65.	68.

Sugarcane, molasses, mn 48 invert sugar mn 79.5 degrees brix, (4)
Cane molasses (AAFCO)
Molasses, cane

Ref no 4-04-696

		As fed	Dry
Dry matter	%	75.0	100.0
Ash	%	8.1	10.8
Ether extract	%	.1	.1
N-free extract	%	63.6	84.8
Protein (N×6.25)	%	3.2	4.3
Horses	dig prot %	1.8	2.4
Energy	GE kcal/kg	3086.	4114.
Horses	DE kcal/kg	3009.	4012.
Horses	ME kcal/kg	2468.	3290.
Horses	TDN %	68.	91.
Calcium	%	.89	1.19
Iron	%	.019	.025
Magnesium	%	.35	.47
Phosphorus	%	.08	.11
Potassium	%	2.38	3.17
Copper	mg/kg	59.6	79.4
Manganese	mg/kg	42.2	56.3
Choline	mg/kg	876.	1167.
Niacin	mg/kg	34.3	45.7
Pantothenic acid	mg/kg	38.3	51.1
Riboflavin	mg/kg	3.3	4.4
Thiamin	mg/kg	.9	1.2

TIMOTHY. Phleum pratense

Timothy, hay, s-c, pre-blm, (1)

Ref no 1-04-881

		As fed	Dry
Dry matter	%	88.6	100.0
Ash	%	6.6	7.5
Crude fiber	%	29.1	32.9
Ether extract	%	2.6	3.0
N-free extract	%	39.2	44.3
Protein (N×6.25)	%	10.9	12.3
Horses	dig prot %	5.8	6.6
Energy			
Horses	DE kcal/kg	2422.	2734.
Horses	ME kcal/kg	1986.	2242.
Horses	TDN %	55.	62.
Calcium	%	.58	.66
Phosphorus	%	.30	.34

Timothy, hay, s-c, early blm, (1)

Ref no 1-04-882

		As fed	Dry
Dry matter	%	87.7	100.0
Ash	%	5.4	6.2
Crude fiber	%	29.1	33.2
Ether extract	%	2.3	2.6
N-free extract	%	43.2	49.3
Protein (N×6.25)	%	7.6	8.7
Horses	dig prot %	4.4	5.0
Energy	GE kcal/kg	3893.	4439.
Horses	DE kcal/kg	2281.	2601.
Horses	ME kcal/kg	1871.	2133.
Horses	TDN %	52.	59.
Calcium	%	.53	.60
Phosphorus	%	.23	.26
Potassium	%	.81	.92

Timothy, hay, s-c, mid-blm, (1)

Ref no 1-04-883

		As fed	Dry
Dry matter	%	88.4	100.0
Ash	%	5.1	5.8
Crude fiber	%	29.6	33.5
Ether extract	%	2.4	2.7
N-free extract	%	43.8	49.5
Protein (N×6.25)	%	7.5	8.5
Horses	dig prot %	4.1	4.6
Energy	GE kcal/kg	3860.	4366.
Horses	DE kcal/kg	2378.	2690.
Horses	ME kcal/kg	1950.	2206.
Horses	TDN %	54.	61.
Calcium	%	.36	.41
Magnesium	%	.14	.16
Phosphorus	%	.17	.19
Carotene	mg/kg	47.2	53.4
Vitamin A equiv	IU/g	78.7	89.0

Timothy, hay, s-c, full blm, (1)

Ref no 1-04-884

		As fed	Dry
Dry matter	%	86.5	100.0
Ash	%	4.7	5.4
Crude fiber	%	29.3	33.9
Ether extract	%	2.3	2.7
N-free extract	%	43.3	50.1
Protein (N×6.25)	%	6.8	7.9
Horses	dig prot %	1.4	1.6

(Continued)

Column 3 (Timothy continued)

Feed name or analyses		As fed	Dry
Energy			
Horses	DE kcal/kg	1602.	1852.
Horses	ME kcal/kg	1314.	1519.
Horses	TDN %	36.	42.
Calcium	%	.30	.35
Chlorine	%	.54	.62
Iron	%	.010	.020
Magnesium	%	.12	.14
Phosphorus	%	.18	.21
Potassium	%	1.45	1.68
Sodium	%	.16	.18
Sulfur	%	.11	.13
Copper	mg/kg	4.2	4.8
Manganese	mg/kg	70.0	80.9

Timothy, hay, s-c, late blm, (1)

Ref no 1-04-885

		As fed	Dry
Dry matter	%	88.0	100.0
Ash	%	5.3	6.0
Crude fiber	%	28.5	32.4
Ether extract	%	2.2	2.5
N-free extract	%	44.7	50.8
Protein (N×6.25)	%	7.3	8.3
Horses	dig prot %	3.6	4.1
Energy			
Horses	DE kcal/kg	2250.	2557.
Horses	ME kcal/kg	1845.	2097.
Horses	TDN %	51.	58.
Calcium	%	.33	.38
Phosphorus	%	.16	.18

TREFOIL, BIRDSFOOT. Lotus corniculatus

Trefoil, birdsfoot, hay, s-c, (1)

Ref no 1-05-044

		As fed	Dry
Dry matter	%	91.2	100.0
Ash	%	6.0	6.6
Crude fiber	%	27.0	29.6
Ether extract	%	2.1	2.3
N-free extract	%	41.9	45.9
Protein (N×6.25)	%	14.2	15.6
Horses	dig prot %	9.8	10.7
Energy			
Horses	DE kcal/kg	2453.	2690.
Horses	ME kcal/kg	2012.	2206.
Horses	TDN %	56.	61.
Calcium	%	1.60	1.75
Phosphorus	%	.20	.22

WHEAT. Triticum spp

Wheat, hay, s-c, (1)

Ref no 1-05-172

		As fed	Dry
Dry matter	%	85.9	100.0
Ash	%	5.9	6.9
Crude fiber	%	23.9	27.8
Ether extract	%	1.7	2.0
N-free extract	%	47.9	55.8
Protein (N×6.25)	%	6.4	7.5
Horses	dig prot %	2.9	3.4
Energy			
Horses	DE kcal/kg	2500.	2910.
Horses	ME kcal/kg	2050.	2386.
Horses	TDN %	57.	66.
Carotene	mg/kg	95.9	111.6
Vitamin A equiv	IU/g	159.9	186.0

---

(1) dry forages and roughages
(2) pasture, range plants, and forages fed green
(3) silages
(4) energy feeds
(5) protein supplements
(6) minerals
(7) vitamins
(8) additives

TABLE I-1 (Continued)

Feed name or analyses		Mean As fed	Dry

Wheat, straw, (1)

Ref no 1-05-175

		As fed	Dry
Dry matter	%	90.1	100.0
Ash	%	7.3	8.1
Crude fiber	%	37.4	41.5
Ether extract	%	1.5	1.7
N-free extract	%	40.6	45.1
Protein (N×6.25)	%	3.2	3.6
Horses	dig prot %	.4	.4
Cellulose	%	45.1	50.1
Lignin	%	12.3	13.7
Energy			
Horses	DE kcal/kg	1906.	2116.
Horses	ME kcal/kg	1563.	1735.
Horses	TDN %	43.	48.
Calcium	%	.15	.17
Chlorine	%	.27	.30
Iron	%	.010	.020
Magnesium	%	.11	.12
Phosphorus	%	.07	.08
Potassium	%	1.00	1.11
Sodium	%	.13	.14
Sulfur	%	.17	.19
Cobalt	mg/kg	.040	.040
Copper	mg/kg	3.0	3.3
Manganese	mg/kg	36.4	40.4
Carotene	mg/kg	2.0	2.2
Vitamin A equiv	IU/g	3.3	3.7

Wheat, bran, dry-mil, (4)
Wheat bran (AAFCO)
Bran (CFA)

Ref no 4-05-190

		As fed	Dry
Dry matter	%	89.0	100.0
Ash	%	6.1	6.9
Crude fiber	%	10.0	11.2
Ether extract	%	4.1	4.6
N-free extract	%	52.8	59.3
Protein (N×6.25)	%	16.0	18.0
Horses	dig prot %	15.4	17.3
Energy	GE kcal/kg	4052.	4554.
Horses	DE kcal/kg	3571.	4012.
Horses	ME kcal/kg	2928.	3290.
Horses	TDN %	81.	91.
Calcium	%	.14	.16
Iron	%	.017	.019
Magnesium	%	.55	.62
Phosphorus	%	1.17	1.32
Potassium	%	1.24	1.39
Sodium	%	.06	.07
Cobalt	mg/kg	1.000	1.100
Copper	mg/kg	12.3	13.8
Manganese	mg/kg	115.7	130.0
Choline	mg/kg	988.	1110.
Folic acid	mg/kg	1.80	2.00
Niacin	mg/kg	209.2	235.1
Pantothenic acid	mg/kg	29.0	32.6
Riboflavin	mg/kg	3.1	3.5
Thiamin	mg/kg	7.9	8.9
a-tocopherol	mg/kg	10.8	12.1
Arginine	%	1.00	1.12
Cystine	%	.30	.34
Glycine	%	.90	1.01
Histidine	%	.30	.34
Isoleucine	%	.60	.67
Leucine	%	.90	1.01
Lysine	%	.60	.67
Methionine	%	.10	.11
Phenylalanine	%	.50	.56
Threonine	%	.40	.45
Tryptophan	%	.30	.34
Tyrosine	%	.40	.45
Valine	%	.70	.79

Wheat, flour by-prod, c-sift, mx 7 fbr, (4)
Wheat shorts, mx 7 fbr (AAFCO)
Shorts, mx 8 fbr (CFA)

Ref no 4-05-201

		As fed	Dry
Dry matter	%	90.0	100.0
Ash	%	3.9	4.3
Crude fiber	%	5.0	5.6
Ether extract	%	4.2	4.7
N-free extract	%	58.5	65.0
Protein (N×6.25)	%	18.4	20.4
Horses	dig prot %	13.2	14.7
Energy			
Horses	DE kcal/kg	3413.	3792.
Horses	ME kcal/kg	2798.	3109.
Horses	TDN %	77.	86.
Calcium	%	.11	.12
Iron	%	.010	.011
Magnesium	%	.26	.29
Phosphorus	%	.76	.84
Potassium	%	.85	.94
Sodium	%	.07	.08
Cobalt	mg/kg	.100	.100
Copper	mg/kg	9.2	10.3
Manganese	mg/kg	104.5	116.1
Choline	mg/kg	928.	1093.
Niacin	mg/kg	94.6	105.1
Pantothenic acid	mg/kg	17.6	19.6
Riboflavin	mg/kg	2.0	2.2
Thiamin	mg/kg	15.8	17.6
a-tocopherol	mg/kg	29.9	33.2

Wheat, flour by-prod, mx 9.5 fbr, (4)
Wheat middlings (AAFCO)
Wheat standard middlings

Ref no 4-05-205

		As fed	Dry
Dry matter	%	90.0	100.0
Ash	%	4.4	4.9
Crude fiber	%	8.0	8.9
Ether extract	%	4.6	5.1
N-free extract	%	55.8	62.0
Protein (N×6.25)	%	17.2	19.1
Horses	dig prot %	12.2	13.6
Energy			
Horses	DE kcal/kg	3294.	3660.
Horses	ME kcal/kg	2701.	3001.
Horses	TDN %	75.	83.
Calcium	%	.15	.16
Iron	%	.010	.010
Magnesium	%	.37	.41
Phosphorus	%	.91	1.01
Potassium	%	.98	1.08
Sodium	%	.22	.24
Cobalt	mg/kg	.100	.100
Copper	mg/kg	22.0	24.4
Manganese	mg/kg	118.4	131.5
Choline	mg/kg	1074.	1193.
Folic acid	mg/kg	.90	1.00
Niacin	mg/kg	98.6	109.5
Pantothenic acid	mg/kg	19.8	22.0
Riboflavin	mg/kg	2.0	2.2
Thiamin	mg/kg	12.8	14.2
Arginine	%	.90	1.00
Cystine	%	.20	.22
Glycine	%	.40	.44
Histidine	%	.40	.44
Isoleucine	%	.80	.88
Leucine	%	1.20	1.33
Lysine	%	.70	.77
Methionine	%	.20	.22
Phenylalanine	%	.70	.77
Threonine	%	.60	.66
Tryptophan	%	.20	.22
Tyrosine	%	.40	.44
Valine	%	.80	.88

Wheat, grain, thresher-run, mn 60 wt mx 5 fm, (4)

Ref no 4-08-164 Canada

		As fed	Dry
Dry matter	%	88.0	100.0
Ash	%	1.8	2.0
Crude fiber	%	2.2	2.5
Ether extract	%	1.4	1.6
N-free extract	%	69.1	78.5
Protein (N×6.25)	%	13.6	15.4
Horses	dig prot %	10.6	12.0
Energy	GE kcal/kg	4174.	4743.
Horses	DE kcal/kg	3414.	3880.
Horses	ME kcal/kg	2800.	3182.
Horses	TDN %	77.	88.

Wheat, grain, Pacific coast, (4)

Ref no 4-08-142

		As fed	Dry
Dry matter	%	89.2	100.0
Ash	%	1.9	2.1
Crude fiber	%	2.7	3.0
Ether extract	%	2.0	2.2
N-free extract	%	72.8	81.6
Protein (N×6.25)	%	9.9	11.1
Horses	dig prot %	7.7	8.6
Energy			
Horses	DE kcal/kg	3461.	3880.
Horses	ME kcal/kg	2838.	3182.
Horses	TDN %	78.	88.
Calcium	%	.12	.14
Phosphorus	%	.30	.34
Niacin	mg/kg	59.1	66.3
Pantothenic acid	mg/kg	11.5	12.9
Riboflavin	mg/kg	1.1	1.2
Thiamin	mg/kg	4.9	5.5

Wheat, grain, (4)

Ref no 4-05-211

		As fed	Dry
Dry matter	%	89.0	100.0
Ash	%	1.6	1.8
Crude fiber	%	3.0	3.4
Ether extract	%	1.7	1.9
N-free extract	%	70.0	78.6
Protein (N×6.25)	%	12.7	14.3
Horses	dig prot %	10.0	11.2
Energy	GE kcal/kg	4001.	4495.
Horses	DE kcal/kg	3453.	3880.
Horses	ME kcal/kg	2832.	3182.
Horses	TDN %	78.	88.
Calcium	%	.05	.06
Iron	%	.005	.006
Magnesium	%	.16	.18
Phosphorus	%	.36	.41
Potassium	%	.52	.58
Sodium	%	.09	.10
Cobalt	mg/kg	.080	.090
Copper	mg/kg	7.2	8.1
Manganese	mg/kg	48.8	54.8
Zinc	mg/kg	13.7	15.4
Biotin	mg/kg	.10	.10
Choline	mg/kg	830.	933.
Folic acid	mg/kg	.40	.40
Niacin	mg/kg	56.6	63.6
Pantothenic acid	mg/kg	12.1	13.6
Riboflavin	mg/kg	1.2	1.3
Thiamin	mg/kg	4.9	5.5
a-tocopherol	mg/kg	15.5	17.4
Arginine	%	.71	.80
Cystine	%	.18	.20
Glycine	%	.89	1.00

(Continued)

(1) dry forages and roughages
(2) pasture, range plants, and forages fed green
(3) silages
(4) energy feeds
(5) protein supplements
(6) minerals
(7) vitamins
(8) additives

TABLE I-1 (Continued)

Feed name or analyses		Mean	
		As fed	Dry
Histidine	%	.27	.30
Isoleucine	%	.53	.60
Leucine	%	.89	1.00
Lysine	%	.45	.51
Methionine	%	.18	.20
Phenylalanine	%	.62	.70
Threonine	%	.36	.40
Tryptophan	%	.18	.20
Tyrosine	%	.45	.51
Valine	%	.53	.60

Wheat, germ, grnd, mn 25 prot 7 fat, (5)
Wheat germ meal (AAFCO)

Ref no 5-05-218

		As fed	Dry
Dry matter	%	90.0	100.0
Ash	%	4.3	4.8
Crude fiber	%	3.0	3.3
Ether extract	%	10.9	12.1
N-free extract	%	45.6	50.7
Protein (N×6.25)	%	26.2	29.1
Horses	dig prot %	24.7	27.4
Energy	GE kcal/kg	4206.	4673.
Horses	DE kcal/kg	3770.	4189.
Horses	ME kcal/kg	3092.	3435.
Horses	TDN %	86.	95.
Calcium	%	.07	.08
Iron	%	.011	.012
Phosphorus	%	1.04	1.16
Copper	mg/kg	8.8	9.8
Manganese	mg/kg	134.9	149.9
Choline	mg/kg	3010.	3344.
Folic acid	mg/kg	2.00	2.20
Niacin	mg/kg	47.3	52.6
Pantothenic acid	mg/kg	11.2	12.4
Riboflavin	mg/kg	5.1	5.7
Thiamin	mg/kg	27.9	31.0
a-tocopherol	mg/kg	132.7	147.4
Arginine	%	1.60	1.78
Cystine	%	.50	.56
Histidine	%	.50	.56
Isoleucine	%	1.20	1.33
Leucine	%	1.10	1.22
Lysine	%	1.60	1.78
Methionine	%	.30	.33
Phenylalanine	%	.80	.89
Threonine	%	.80	.89
Tryptophan	%	.30	.33
Valine	%	1.10	1.22

WHEATGRASS, CRESTED. Agropyron cristatum

Wheatgrass, crested, hay, s-c, (1)

Ref no 1-05-418

		As fed	Dry
Dry matter	%	92.0	100.0
Ash	%	6.7	7.3
Crude fiber	%	30.0	32.6
Ether extract	%	1.8	2.0
N-free extract	%	43.5	47.3
Protein (N×6.25)	%	9.9	10.8
Horses	dig prot %	5.8	6.3

(Continued)

Feed name or analyses		Mean	
		As fed	Dry
Energy			
Horses	DE kcal/kg	2352.	2557.
Horses	ME kcal/kg	1929.	2097.
Horses	TDN %	53.	58.
Calcium	%	.30	.33
Phosphorus	%	.19	.21
Cobalt	mg/kg	.220	.240

Wheatgrass, crested, aerial pt, fresh, immature, (2)

Ref no 2-05-420

		As fed	Dry
Dry matter	%	30.8	100.0
Ash	%	3.3	10.6
Crude fiber	%	6.8	22.2
Ether extract	%	1.1	3.6
N-free extract	%	12.3	40.0
Protein (N×6.25)	%	7.3	23.6
Horses	dig prot %	5.5	18.0
Cellulose	%	10.5	34.1
Lignin	%	1.8	5.9
Energy	GE kcal/kg	1331.	4322.
Horses	DE kcal/kg	1005.	3263.
Horses	ME kcal/kg	824.	2676.
Horses	TDN %	23.	74.
Calcium	%	.14	.46
Magnesium	%	.09	.28
Phosphorus	%	.11	.35
Carotene	mg/kg	133.6	433.7
Vitamin A equiv	IU/g	222.7	723.0

YEAST. Saccharomyces cerevisiae

Yeast, brewers saccharomyces, dehy grnd, mn 40 prot, (7)
Brewers dried yeast (AAFCO)

Ref no 7-05-527

		As fed	Dry
Dry matter	%	93.0	100.0
Ash	%	6.4	6.9
Crude fiber	%	3.0	3.2
Ether extract	%	1.1	1.2
N-free extract	%	37.9	40.8
Protein (N×6.25)	%	44.6	47.9
Horses	dig prot %	41.0	44.1
Energy	GE kcal/kg	3958.	4255.
Horses	DE kcal/kg	3198.	3439.
Horses	ME kcal/kg	2623.	2820.
Horses	TDN %	72.	78.
Calcium	%	.13	.14
Iron	%	.010	.010
Magnesium	%	.23	.25
Phosphorus	%	1.43	1.54
Potassium	%	1.72	1.85
Sodium	%	.07	.08
Cobalt	mg/kg	.200	.200
Copper	mg/kg	33.0	35.5
Manganese	mg/kg	5.7	6.1
Zinc	mg/kg	38.7	41.6
Choline	mg/kg	3885.	4177.
Folic acid	mg/kg	9.70	10.40

(Continued)

Feed name or analyses		Mean	
		As fed	Dry
Niacin	mg/kg	447.5	481.1
Pantothenic acid	mg/kg	109.8	118.0
Riboflavin	mg/kg	35.0	37.6
Thiamin	mg/kg	91.7	98.6
Vitamin B6	mg/kg	43.30	46.60
Arginine	%	2.20	2.36
Cystine	%	.50	.54
Glycine	%	1.70	1.83
Histidine	%	1.10	1.18
Isoleucine	%	2.10	2.26
Leucine	%	3.20	3.44
Lysine	%	3.00	3.22
Methionine	%	.70	.75
Phenylalanine	%	1.80	1.93
Threonine	%	2.10	2.26
Tryptophan	%	.50	.54
Tyrosine	%	1.50	1.61
Valine	%	2.30	2.47

YEAST, TORULOPSIS. Torulopsis utilis

Yeast, torulopsis, dehy, mn 40 prot, (7)
Torula dried yeast (AAFCO)

Ref no 7-05-534

		As fed	Dry
Dry matter	%	93.0	100.0
Ash	%	7.8	8.4
Crude fiber	%	2.0	2.2
Ether extract	%	2.5	2.7
N-free extract	%	32.4	34.8
Protein (N×6.25)	%	48.3	51.9
Horses	dig prot %	43.9	47.2
Energy	GE kcal/kg	4433.	4763.
Horses	DE kcal/kg	3280.	3527.
Horses	ME kcal/kg	2690.	2892.
Horses	TDN %	74.	80.
Calcium	%	.57	.61
Iron	%	.010	.010
Magnesium	%	.13	.14
Phosphorus	%	1.68	1.81
Potassium	%	1.88	2.02
Sodium	%	.01	.01
Copper	mg/kg	13.4	14.4
Manganese	mg/kg	12.8	13.7
Zinc	mg/kg	99.2	106.7
Biotin	mg/kg	1.10	1.20
Choline	mg/kg	2911.	3129.
Folic acid	mg/kg	23.30	25.00
Niacin	mg/kg	500.3	537.8
Pantothenic acid	mg/kg	82.9	89.1
Riboflavin	mg/kg	44.4	47.7
Thiamin	mg/kg	6.2	6.7
Vitamin B6	mg/kg	29.50	31.70
Arginine	%	2.60	2.79
Cystine	%	.60	.65
Glycine	%	2.70	2.90
Histidine	%	1.40	1.51
Isoleucine	%	2.90	3.12
Leucine	%	3.50	3.76
Lysine	%	3.80	4.09
Methionine	%	.80	.86
Phenylalanine	%	3.00	3.23
Threonine	%	2.60	2.80
Tryptophan	%	.50	.54
Tyrosine	%	2.10	2.26
Valine	%	2.90	3.12

---

(1) dry forages and roughages
(2) pasture, range plants, and forages fed green
(3) silages
(4) energy feeds
(5) protein supplements
(6) minerals
(7) vitamins
(8) additives

SECTION II—ANIMAL UNITS

An animal unit is a common animal denominator, based on feed consumption. It is assumed that one mature cow represents an animal unit. Then, the comparative (to a mature cow) feed consumption of other age groups or species of animals determines the proportion of an animal unit which they represent. For example, it is generally estimated that it will require the ration of 1.3 mature cows to feed 1 mature horse; hence, 1 mature horse equals 1.3 animal units.

The original concept of an animal unit included a weight stipulation—an animal unit referred to a 1,000-lb cow, with or without a calf at side. Unfortunately, in recent years, the 1,000-lb qualification has been dropped. Cer-

tainly, there is a wide difference in the daily feed requirements of a 900-lb cow and a 1,100-lb horse. Both will consume dry matter on a daily basis at a level equivalent to about 2.5 percent of their body weight.

Also, the period of time to be grazed has an effect on the total carrying capacity. For example, if an animal is carried for one month only, it will take one-twelfth of the total feed required to carry the same animal one year. For this reason, the term "animal unit months" is becoming increasingly important. So, in addition to the weight factor, the time factor has a distinct bearing on the ultimate carrying capacity of a tract of land.

Table II-1 gives the animal units of different classes and ages of livestock.

TABLE II-1
ANIMAL UNITS

Type of Livestock	Animal Units
Horses:	
Horse, mature	1.3
Horse, yearling	1.0
Weanling colt or filly	0.75
Cattle:	
Cow, with or without unweaned calf at side, or heifer 2 yrs. old or older	1.0
Bull, 2 yrs. old or older	1.3
Young cattle, 1 to 2 years	0.8
Weaned calves to yearlings	0.6
Sheep:	
5 mature ewes, with or without unweaned lambs at side	1.0
5 rams, 2 yrs. old or over	1.3
5 yearlings	0.8
5 weaned lambs to yearlings	0.6
Swine:	
Sow	0.4
Boar	0.5
Pigs to 200 pounds	0.2
Chickens:	
75 layers or breeders	1.0
325 replacement pullets to 6 mo. of age	1.0
650 8-week-old broilers	1.0
Turkeys:	
35 breeders	1.0
40 turkeys raised to maturity	1.0
75 turkeys to 6 mo. of age	1.0

SECTION III—WEIGHTS AND MEASURES

METRIC VS U.S. CUSTOMARY SYSTEM[1]

FROM TIME TO TIME, stockmen and those who counsel with them have need to refer to metric vs U.S. weights and measures. These follow:

Length

Unit	Is Equal To	
Metric System		
		(U.S.)
1 millimicron (mμ)	.000000001 m	.000000039 in.
1 micron (μ)	.000001 m	.000039 in.
1 millimeter (mm)	.001 m	.0394 in.
1 centimeter (cm)	.01 m	.3937 in.
1 decimeter (dm)	.1 m	3.937 in.
1 meter (m)	1 m	39.37 in.; 3.281 ft; 1.094 yd
1 hectometer (hm)	100 m	328 ft; 1 in.; 19.8838 rd
1 kilometer (km)	1,000 m	3,280 ft; 10 in.; 0.621 mi
U.S. Customary System		
		(metric)
1 inch (in.)		2.54 cm
1 hand*	4 in.	
1 foot (ft)	12 in.	30.48 cm; .305 m
1 yard (yd)	3 ft	.914 m
1 fathom** (fath)	6.08 ft	1.829 m
1 rod (rd), pole, or perch	16½ ft; 5½ yd	5.029 m
1 furlong (fur.)	220 yd; 40 rd	201.168 m
1 mile (mi)	5,280 ft; 1,760 yd; 320 rd; 8 fur.	1,609.35 m 1.609 km
1 knot or nautical mile	6,080 ft; 1.15 land miles	
1 league (land)	3 mi (land)	
1 league (nautical)	3 mi (nautical)	

*Used in measuring height of horses.
**Used in measuring depth at sea.

CONVERSIONS

To Change	To	Multiply By
inches	centimeters	2.54
feet	meters	.305
meters	inches	39.37
miles	kilometers	1.609
kilometers	miles	.621

[1]For additional conversion factors, or for greater accuracy, see Misc. Pub. 233, the National Bureau of Standards.

Surface or Area

Unit	Is Equal To	
Metric System		(U.S.)
1 square millimeter (mm²)	.000001 m²	.00155 in.²
1 square centimeter (cm²)	.001 m²	.155 in.²
1 square decimeter (dm²)	.01 m²	15.50 in.²
1 square meter (m²)	1 centare (ca)	1,550 in.²; 10.76 ft²; 1.196 yd²
1 are (a)	100 m²	119.6 yd²
1 hectare (ha)	10,000 m²	2.47 acres
1 square kilometer (km²)	1,000,000 m²	247.1 acres; .386 mi²
U.S. Customary System		(metric)
1 square inch (in.²)	1 in. × 1 in.	6.452 cm²
1 square foot (ft²)	144 in.²	.093 m²
1 square yard (yd²)	1,296 in.²; 9 ft²	.836 m²
1 square rod (rd²)	272.25 ft²; 30.25 yd²	25.29 m²
1 rood	40 rd²	10.117 a
1 acre	43,560 ft²; 4,840 yd²; 160 rd²; 4 roods	4,046.87 m² 0.405 ha
1 square mile (mi²)	640 acres	2.59 km² or 259.0 ha
1 township	36 sections; 6 miles square	

CONVERSIONS

To Change	To	Multiply By
square inches	square centimeters	6.452
square centimeters	square inches	.155
square yards	square meters	.836
square meters	square yards	1.196

Volume

Unit	Is Equal To		
Liquid and Dry: Metric System		(U.S. Customary) (liquid)	(dry)
1 milliliter (ml)	.001 l	2.71 dram (fl)	.061 in.³
1 centiliter (cl)	.01 l	.338 oz (fl)	.610 in.³
1 deciliter (dl)	.1 l	3.38 oz (fl)	
1 liter (l)	1,000 cc	1.057 qt or 0.2642 gal (fl)	.908 qt
1 hectoliter (hl)	100 l	26.418 gal	2.838 bu
1 kiloliter (kl)	1,000 l	264.18 gal	1,308 yd³

U.S. Customary System Liquid:		(ounces)	(cubic inches)	(metric)
1 teaspoon (t)	60 drops	1/6		
1 dessert spoon	2 t			
1 tablespoon (T)	3 t	½		
1 fl oz		1	1.805	29.57 ml
1 gill (gi)	½ c	4	7.22	118.29 ml
1 cup (c)	16 T	8	14.44	236.58 ml
1 pint (pt)	2 c	16	28.88	.47 l
1 quart (qt)	2 pt	32	57.75	.95 l
1 gallon (gal)	4 qt	8.34 lb	231	3.79 l
1 barrel (bbl)	31½ gal			
1 hogshead (hhd)	2 bbl			
Dry:				
1 pint (pt)	½ qt		33.6	.55 l
1 quart (qt)	2 pt		67.20	1.10 l
1 peck (pk)	8 qt		537.61	8.81 l
1 bushel (bu)	4 pk		2,150.42	35.24 l

(Continued)

Unit	Is Equal To		
Solid: Metric System	Metric System		
1 cubic millimeter (mm³)	.001 cc		
1 cubic centimeter (cc)	1,000 mm³	.061	
1 cubic decimeter (dm³)	1,000 cc	61.023	
1 cubic meter (m³)	1,000 dm³	35.315 ft³ 1.308 yd³	
U.S. Customary System			(metric)
1 cubic inch (in.³)			16.387 cc
1 board foot (fbm)	144 in.³		2,359.8 cc
1 cubic foot (ft³)	1,728 in.³		.028 m³
1 cubic yard (yd³)	27 ft³		.765 m³
1 cord	128 ft³		3.625 m³

CONVERSIONS

To Change	To	Multiply By
ounces (fluid)	cubic centimeters	29.57
cubic centimeters	ounces (fluid)	.034
quarts	liters	.946
liters	quarts	1.057
cubic inches	cubic centimeters	16.387
cubic centimeters	cubic inches	.061
cubic yards	cubic meters	.765
cubic meters	cubic yards	1.308

Weight

Unit	Is Equal To	
Metric System		(U.S. Customary)
1 microgram (mcg)	.001 mg	
1 milligram (mg)	.001 g	.015432356 grain
1 centigram (cg)	.01 g	.15432356 grain
1 decigram (dg)	.1 g	1.5432 grains
1 gram (g)	1,000 mg	.03527396 oz
1 dekagram (dkg)	10 g	5.643833 dr
1 hectogram (hg)	100 g	3.527396 oz
1 kilogram (kg)	1,000 g	35.274 oz 2.2046223 lb
1 ton	1,000 kg	2,204.6 lb 1.102 tons (short) or 0.984 ton (long)
U.S. Customary System		(metric)
1 grain (gr)	.037 dr	64.798918 mg; .064798918 g
1 dram (dr)	.063 oz	1.771845 g
1 ounce (oz)	16 dr	28.349527 g
1 pound (lb)	16 oz	453.5924 g or 0.4536 kg
1 hundredweight (cwt)	100 lb	
1 ton (short)	2,000 lb	907.18486 kg or 0.907 (metric) ton
1 ton (long)	2,200 lb	1,016.05 kg or 1.016 (metric) ton
1 part per million (ppm)	1 microgram/gram 1 mg/l 1 mg/kg	.4535924 mg/lb .907 g/ton .0001 % .013 oz/gal
1 percent (%) (1 part in 100 parts)	10,000 ppm 10 g/l	1.28 oz/gal 8 lb/100 gal

(Continued)

CONVERSIONS

To Change	To	Multiply By
grains	milligrams	64.799
ounces (dry)	grams	28.35
pounds (dry)	kilograms	.4535924
kilograms	pounds	2.2046223
milligrams/pound	parts/million	2.2046223
parts/million	grams/ton	.90718486
grams/ton	parts/million	1.1
milligrams/pound	grams/ton	2
grams/ton	milligrams/pound	.5
grams/pound	grams/ton	2,000
grams/ton	grams/pound	.0005
grams/ton	pounds/ton	.0022
pounds/ton	grams/ton	453.5924
grams/ton	percent	.00011
percent	grams/ton	9,072

Weights and Measures per Unit

Unit	Is Equal To
Volume per unit area:	
1 liter/hectare	0.107 gal/acre
1 gallon/acre	9.354 l/ha
Weight per unit area:	
1 kilogram/cm^2	14.22 lb/in.^{2}
1 kilogram/hectare	0.892 lb/acre
1 pound/square inch	0.0703 kg/cm^2
1 pound/acre	1.121 kg/ha
Area per unit weight:	
1 square centimeter/kilogram	0.0703 in.^{2}/lb
1 square inch/pound	14.22 cm^2/kg

Temperature

One Centigrade (C) degree is 1/100 the difference between the temperature of melting ice and that of water boiling at standard atmospheric pressure. One Centigrade degree equals 1.8° F.

One Fahrenheit (F) degree is 1/180 of the difference between the temperature of melting ice and that of water boiling at standard atmospheric pressure. One Fahrenheit degree equals 0.556° C.

To Change	To	Multiply By
Degrees Centigrade	Degrees Fahrenheit	$9/5$ and add 32
Degrees Fahrenheit	Degrees Centigrade	Subtract 32, then multiply by $5/9$

WEIGHTS AND MEASURES OF COMMON FEEDS

In calculating rations and mixing concentrates, it is usually necessary to use weights rather than measures. However, in practical feeding operations it is often more convenient for the horseman to measure the concentrates. Table III-1 will serve as a guide in feeding by measure.

TABLE III-1

WEIGHTS AND MEASURES OF COMMON FEEDS

Feed	Approximate Weight	
	(lb per quart)	(lb per bushel)
Alfalfa meal	0.6	19
Barley	1.5	48
Beet pulp (dried)	0.6	19
Brewers' grain (dried)	0.6	19
Buckwheat	1.6	50
Buckwheat bran	1.0	29
Corn, cracked	1.6	50
Corn, husked ear	—	70
Corn, shelled	1.8	56
Corn meal	1.6	50
Corn-and-cob meal	1.4	45
Cottonseed meal	1.5	48
Cowpeas	1.9	60
Distillers' grain (dried)	0.6	19
Fish meal	1.0	35
Gluten feed	1.3	42
Linseed meal (new process)	0.9	29
Linseed meal (old process)	1.1	35
Meat scrap	1.3	42
Molasses feed	0.8	26
Oat middlings	1.5	48
Oats	1.0	32
Oats, ground	0.7	22
Peanut meal	1.0	32
Rice bran	0.8	26
Rye	1.7	56
Soybeans	1.8	60
Tankage	1.6	51
Velvet beans, shelled	1.8	60
Wheat	1.9	60
Wheat bran	0.5	16
Wheat middlings, standard	0.8	26
Wheat screenings	1.0	32

ESTIMATING HORSE WEIGHTS FROM BODY MEASUREMENTS

It is easy to estimate the weight of a horse from body measurements. Studies have revealed that the results obtained by the method herewith outlined are within three percent of the actual weight made on scales. The procedure is as follows:

1. Measure the heart girth in inches (C in Fig. III-1).
2. Measure the length of body from point of shoulder to point of buttocks (A to B in Fig. III-1).
3. Use the above two measurements to calculate the weight of the horse according to the following formula:

Heart girth × heart girth × length ÷ 300 + 50 lb = weight of horse

Example: A horse has a heart girth of 70 inches and a length of 65 inches. What's his estimated weight?

Answer: 70″ × 70″ × 65″ ÷ 300 + 50 lb = weight
4,900 × 65 = 318,500
318,500 ÷ 300 = 1,062 lb
1,062 + 50 = 1,112 lb body weight

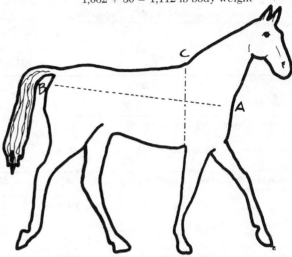

Fig. III-1. How and where to measure horses.

SECTION IV—GESTATION TABLE

The horseman who has information relative to breeding dates can easily estimate parturition dates from Table IV-1.

TABLE IV-1

GESTATION TABLE—MARE

Date Bred	Date Due, 336 Days	Date Bred	Date Due, 336 Days
Jan. 1	Dec. 3	July 5	June 6
Jan. 6	Dec. 8	July 10	June 11
Jan. 11	Dec. 13	July 15	June 16
Jan. 16	Dec. 18	July 20	June 21
Jan. 21	Dec. 23	July 25	June 26
Jan. 26	Dec. 28	July 30	July 1
Jan. 31	Jan. 2	Aug. 4	July 6
Feb. 5	Jan. 7	Aug. 9	July 11
Feb. 10	Jan. 12	Aug. 14	July 16
Feb. 15	Jan. 17	Aug. 19	July 21
Feb. 20	Jan. 22	Aug. 24	July 26
Feb. 25	Jan. 27	Aug. 29	July 31
Mar. 2	Feb. 1	Sept. 3	Aug. 5
Mar. 7	Feb. 6	Sept. 8	Aug. 10
Mar. 12	Feb. 11	Sept. 13	Aug. 15
Mar. 17	Feb. 16	Sept. 18	Aug. 20
Mar. 22	Feb. 21	Sept. 23	Aug. 25
Mar. 27	Feb. 26	Sept. 28	Aug. 30
April 1	Mar. 3	Oct. 3	Sept. 4
April 6	Mar. 8	Oct. 8	Sept. 9
April 11	Mar. 13	Oct. 13	Sept. 14
April 16	Mar. 18	Oct. 18	Sept. 19
April 21	Mar. 23	Oct. 23	Sept. 24
April 26	Mar. 28	Oct. 28	Sept. 29
May 1	April 2	Nov. 2	Oct. 4
May 6	April 7	Nov. 7	Oct. 9
May 11	April 12	Nov. 12	Oct. 14
May 16	April 17	Nov. 17	Oct. 19
May 21	April 22	Nov. 22	Oct. 24
May 26	April 27	Nov. 27	Oct. 29
May 31	May 2	Dec. 2	Nov. 3
June 5	May 7	Dec. 7	Nov. 8
June 10	May 12	Dec. 12	Nov. 13
June 15	May 17	Dec. 17	Nov. 18
June 20	May 22	Dec. 22	Nov. 23
June 25	May 27	Dec. 27	Nov. 28
June 30	June 1		

SECTION V—ALL-TIME TOP SALES

Horsemen and students frequently like to refer to the great sales in history of the many breeds. A summary of some of the record horse sales, both for individual animals and consignments, is presented in Table V-1. No claim is made that this all-time top sales list is either complete or accurate. However, it appears to be the only summary of its type available; hence, it should have considerable value and interest to many.

TABLE V-1

ALL-TIME TOP SALES

Breed	Year of Sale	Identity of Animal	Sex	Price	How Sold	Seller	Purchaser
American Creme Horse	1973	Coconut Nick	Stallion	$ 250	Private Treaty	Nola F. Cairns, Angelica, N.Y.	Connie Bradley, Bolivar, N.Y.
	1974	Cricket	Mare	1,100	Private Treaty	Lloyd R. Starks, Ft. Worth, Tex.	F. M. Stevenson, Boyd, Tex.
American Saddle Horse	1947	Beau Fortune	Stallion	50,000	Private Treaty	Teater and Reesler, Skokie, Chicago, Ill.	Crebilly Farm, West Chester, Penn.
	1947	The Invasion	Gelding	23,000	Auction	T. A. Walsh, Jr., Omaha, Neb.	Mrs. Jane Gordon, Malvern, Penn.
	1958	Delightful Society	Mare	30,000	Auction	Louis Greaspoon, St. Louis, Mo.	Donald Decker, Omaha, Neb.
	1960	Stonewall Imperial	Gelding	26,500	Auction	Candy Shaffer Stable	Julianna Schmuts, Louisville, Ky.
	1960	Skyrocket	Stallion	17,000	Auction	Candy Shaffer Stable	F. R. Sullivan, Orange, N.J.
	1962	Legal Tender	Gelding	30,000	Auction	T. N. Wood, Harvey's Lake, Penn.	Crabtree Stables, Simpsonville, Ky.
	1964	The Lancer	Gelding	10,000	Auction	Dodge Stables, Lexington, Ky.	Warren Atkinson, West Baden, Ind.
	1965	Radication	Mare	40,000	Private Treaty	Knolland Farm, Chicago, Ill.	Unknown
	1965	Rebel Air	Gelding	10,000	Private Treaty	Knolland Farm, Chicago, Ill.	Unknown
	1966	Nite Flight	Gelding	19,000	Private Treaty	Bill Gill, Oklahoma City, Okla.	Unknown
	1967	Red Squirl	Gelding	10,000	Private Treaty	Tanglewood Farm, Stann, Ill.	Unknown
	1968	Drummer Boy	Gelding	10,000	Private Treaty	Swamp Fox Farm, Chambersling, Penn.	Unknown
	1968	Knolland Fanfare	Mare	6,000	Private Treaty	Mrs. John Lehman, Beaver, Penn.	Unknown
	1969	So Exciting	Mare	29,500	Auction	Greystone Manor Stables, Lancaster, Penn.	A. E. Knowelton, Columbus, Ohio
	1969	Show Time	Gelding	25,000	Private Treaty	Knolland Farm, Richmond, Ill.	Unknown
	1970	Supreme Spirit	Stallion	100,000	Private Treaty	Tom Moore	Grape Tree Farms, Lexington, Ky.
	1970	Bellissima	Mare	50,000	Auction	Knolland Farms	Meadowbrook Farm, Ft. Wayne, Ind.
	1970	Barlites Tamborlane	Gelding	10,500	Auction	Jay P. Altmeyer, Mobile, Ala.	Art Simmons, Mexico, Mo.
	1971	Last Revenge	Gelding	10,750	Private Treaty	Simmons Stable, Mexico, Mo.	Unknown
	1971	Gay Gift	Mare	10,000	Auction	Holtsinger, Inc., Ft. Lauderdale, Fla.	Thomas Galbreath, Wayzata, Minn.
	1972	Supreme Melissa	Filly	21,000	Auction	Tattersalls for Julianne Schmutz, Glenview, Ky.	B. P. R. Newman, Ontario, Canada
	1972	Rimfire	Gelding	13,500	Private Treaty	Ouial Hills Stable, Romney, W.V.	Unknown

(Continued)

TABLE V-1 (Continued)

Breed	Year of Sale	Identity of Animal	Sex	Price	How Sold	Seller	Purchaser
	1973	Gay Hills Gay Aristocrat	Gelding	23,000	Auction	Mr. and Mrs. Paul Wyatt, Dallas, Tex.	Brandywine Farms, Hamel, Minn.
	1973	Petite Princess	Mare	13,500	Auction	B. S. Bridges, Goldsboro, N.C.	Art Simmons, Mexico, Mo.
	1974	Bellissima	Mare	37,500	Private Treaty	Crick Stables, Paducah, Ky.	Unknown
	1974	The Placemaker	Gelding	18,000	Auction	Wendell Jones, Lancaster, Penn.	Sabur Stables, Tulsa, Okla.
	1975	Supreme Spirit	Stallion	110,000	Auction	Grape Tree Farms, Lexington, Ky.	Laurie Anderson, Bloomington, Ill.
	1975	Erye Lad	Gelding	25,000	Private Treaty	Silar Brook Stable, Louisville, Ky.	Unknown
	1975	High Fashioned Sue	Mare	29,000	Auction	Dodge Stables, Lexington, Ky.	Robin Arbury, Midland, Mich.
American Walking Pony	1962	BT Sunday Summer	Mare	3,000	Private Treaty	Browntree Stables, Macon, Ga.	Mr. Floyd F. Scott, Willingboro, N.J.
American White Horse	1968	Thompson's Billy Boy	Stallion	400	Private Treaty	Ruth Thompson, Scio, Ore.	Dick Welb, Northridge, Calif.
	1969	Blanco Coliente	Gelding	500	Private Treaty	Kristen Graham, Boise, Ida.	Dick Welb, Northridge, Calif.
	1972	Marr's April	Mare	750	Private Treaty	George Marrs, Lebanon, Ore.	Dawn Higgins, East Leroy, Mich.
	1973	A. M. Milky Way	Mare	1,500	Private Treaty	Mrs. E. B. Adams, Blue Grass, Iowa	Karen Wales, Taylor Ridge, Ill.
	1973	Na-Ra Ha	Stallion	800	Private Treaty	Karen Wales, Taylor Ridge, Ill.	Dick Wallen, Sioux City, Iowa
	1974	Blue Beauty	Mare	400	Private Treaty	Leo W. Bernard, East Haddam, Conn.	J. Alan Brzys, Sturbridge, Mass.
Appaloosa	1960	Hanogie	Mare	6,300	Auction	Carey Appaloosa Ranch, Denver, Colo.	Paul Johnson, Cascade, Colo.
	1961	Top Hat	Stallion	9,000	Auction	Ace Hopper, Plainview Tex.	W. F. Hicks, Ft. Worth, Tex.
	1961	Tinker Bell Day	Mare	10,000	Private Treaty	Ed Hulseman, Red Bluff, Calif.	W. F. Sandercock, Dixon, Calif.
	1964	Quinta's Flying String	Colt	17,500	Auction	Quinta Dispersal, Napa, Calif.	Myrtle Brown, Arbuckle, Calif.
	1966	Chic Appeal	Stallion	15,500	Auction	Leo Marsters, Payette, Ida.	Dale Rumsey, Phoenix, Ariz.
	1967	Sutter's Show Boy	Stallion	44,000	Auction	Robert Heilmann, Grass Valley, Calif.	Partnership, Fiddlestix Farm, Grass Valley, Calif.
	1973	Star Diver	Stallion	100,000	Private Treaty	Charles Tanner, Jr., Ocala, Fla.	Bruce and Joyce Haak, and Dave and Bobbi Best, Mich.
Arabian	1961	Indriffnant	Mare	7,900	Auction	Al-Marah Arabian Horse Farm, Washington, D.C.	A. M. Work, Portland, Ore.
	1969	Naborr 25472	Stallion	150,000	Auction	Anne McCormick, Scottsdale, Ariz.	Tom Cauncey, Phoenix, Ariz.; and Wayne Newton, Prescott, Ariz.
	1969	Pallada	Mare	25,000	Auction	McCormick Arabians, Scottsdale, Ariz.	Marianne Hannah, Mountain Center, Calif.
	1971	Silhoulette	Mare	56,000	Auction	Lasma Arabians, Scottsdale, Ariz.	Howard Kale, Belleview, Wash.
	1971	The Judge	Stallion	30,000	Auction	Lasma Arabians, Scottsdale, Ariz.	James Cary, Houston, Tex.
Belgian	1917	Farceur	Stallion	47,500	Auction	Wm. Crownover, Hudson, Iowa	C. G. Good, Ogden, Iowa

(Continued)

TABLE V-1 (Continued)

Breed	Year of Sale	Identity of Animal	Sex	Price	How Sold	Seller	Purchaser
	1974		Mare	3,250	Auction	David D. Miller, Jr., Middlefield, Ohio	Unknown
Clydesdale	1911	Baron of Buchlyvie 11263	Stallion	47,500	Auction	J. Kilpatrick, Craigie Mains, Ayr., Scotland	William Dunlop, Dunure Mains, Ayr., Scotland
Paint Horse	1964	Q Ton Eagle	Stallion	7,200	Auction	Quention Foster, Broken Arrow, Okla.	J. D. Hooter, Alexandria, La.
	1966	Yellow Mount	Stallion	10,000	Private Treaty	Jack Bruns, Muleshoe, Tex.	Mr. and Mrs. S. H. Williamson, Iowa Park, Tex.
	1967	Dual Image	Stallion	15,000	Private Treaty	J. R. Archer, Corpus Christi, Tex.	Larry Swain, San Antonio, Tex.
	1968	Baldy Raider	Stallion	15,000	Private Treaty	Jim Smoot	Richard Harris, Atlanta, Ga.
	1969	Diablo Cochise	Stallion	6,500	Private Treaty	Lester Bloomenstiel, Baton Rouge, La.	Ed Pike, Lakeland, Fla.
	1970	Music Maker	Stallion	15,000	Private Treaty	Forrest Williamson, Arkansas City, Kan.	Kay Neal, Logan, Okla.
	1971	Ceasar Bar's Dinero	Stallion	10,000	Private Treaty	Joe Denman, Fort Worth, Tex.	Harley Webb, Arlington, Tex.
	1973	Powder Charge	Stallion	20,000	Private Treaty	Bud and Betty Cromp, Wynnewood, Okla.	C & H Horse Farm, Fergus Falls, Minn.
Palomino	1966	Shoshoni Bar	Stallion	2,100	Auction	Bent Arrow Ranch, Bent Arrow, Okla.	Richard G. William, La-Cross, Wisc.
	1967	Mr. Kickapoo Bars		3,350	Auction	Bent Arrow Ranch, Bent Arrow, Okla.	Paul Dick, Mt. Hope, Kan.
	1968	Golden Shoofly	Mare	2,850	Auction	Bent Arrow Ranch, Bent Arrow, Okla.	Hancock Ranch, Tupelo, Miss.
	1969	Instant Blonde	Mare	5,100	Auction	Bent Arrow Ranch, Bent Arrow, Okla.	Senator Peltier, La.
	1970	Bo-Beep Bos'n	Mare	2,500	Auction	Bent Arrow Ranch, Bent Arrow, Okla.	C. D. Fitzwilliam, Texas
		Bar Towell	Mare	2,500	Auction	Bent Arrow Ranch, Bent Arrow, Okla.	
	1971	Palomino Dream	Stallion	12,250	Auction	King Ranch Quarter Horse sale	Unknown
Percheron	1974	Commander's Duke	Stallion	4,000	Auction	Monroe J. Miller, Dundee, Ohio	Unknown
Pony of the Americas	1960	Hand's Ta-Ma-Naus T-828	Weanling Colt	2,500	Auction	Boomhower & Barrett	Robert Gatner
	1967	GR's Big Creek's Dandy T-5524	Yearling Filly	2,100	Auction	Ed Merfeld	Milford and Mary Lammers
	1967	Tomahawk's Big Creek 2547	Stallion	2,755	Auction	Ed Merfeld	John Ludtke
	1970	S. D.'s Flashy Maiden T-7452	Mare	2,500	Auction	Golden Rod Pony Farm	Seven Brook Pony Farm
	1970	Apache Scout	Gelding	2,000	Auction	Scott Stoltzfus	Andrea Lockner
	1971	Hi Vue's Sister	Weanling Filly	2,075	Auction	Howard Victor	Ray and Phyllis Franken
Quarter Horse	1949	Geronimo	Stallion	20,000	Auction	J. R. Bell, Canoga Park, Calif.	A. R. Levis, Henderson, Colo.
	1952	N. R. Paul A P-19	Stallion	30,000	Private Treaty	R. Q. Sutherland, Kansas City, Mo.	Gordon Wheeler, Riverside, Calif.
	1954	Miss Panama	Mare	8,000	Auction	Grace Ranch	Art Pollard
	1957	Paulyanna	Mare	10,400	Auction	R. Q. Sutherland, Overland Park, Kan.	J. P. Davidson, Albuquerque, N.M.
	1957	Poco Tom	Stallion	10,200	Auction	Volney Hildreth, Fort Worth, Tex.	Waldo Haythorne, Ogallala, Neb.

(Continued)

TABLE V-1 (Continued)

Breed	Year of Sale	Identity of Animal	Sex	Price	How Sold	Seller	Purchaser
	1957	Kip Mac	Gelding	5,500	Auction	Volney Hildreth, Fort Worth, Tex.	George Glascock, Cresson, Tex.
	1958	Skipity Scoot	Stallion	12,100	Auction	T. E. Connolly, San Francisco; F. Azevedo, Colsa, Calif.	J. P. Davidson, Albuquerque, N.M.
	1958	Pailalika	Mare	10,200	Auction	Pinehurst Stables, Houston, Tex.	Charles Coates, Chappel Hill, Tex.
	1959	King Glo	Stallion	50,000	Auction	J. O. Hankins, Rocksprings, Tex.	C. E. Boyd, Sweetwater, Tex.
	1960	Go Man Go	Stallion	125,000	Private Treaty	J. B. Ferguson, Wharton, Tex.	F. Vessels, Los Alamitos, Calif. and W. H. Peckham, Richmond, Tex.
	1960	Josie's Bar	Mare	37,200	Auction	E. L. Gosselin, Edmond, Okla.	Frank Vessels, Los Alamitos, Calif.
	1960	Cee Bars Jr.	Colt	12,000	Auction	John Askow, Fayette, Ark.	Ross Inman, Lamar, Colo.
	1961	Vandy II	Stallion	40,000	Auction	Paul Lomax, Skiatook, Okla.	Haden Livestock Co., Camarillo, Calif.
	1961	Three Deep	Mare	20,000	Auction	Sam Steiger, Prescott, Ariz.	Jay Scott, Littleton, Colo.
	1962	Robin Reed	Stallion	120,000	Private Treaty	Roy D. Barnes, Denver, Colo.	Chapparal Racing Stables, Wildorado, Tex.
	1963	Bar Depth	Stallion	100,000	Private Treaty	Lester Goodson, Houston, Tex.	Truman Johnson, Riverside, Calif.
	1963	Moolah Bar	Mare	45,000	Auction	Mawson Estate, Lompoc, Calif.	Red Bee Ranch, Wichita, Kan.
	1964	Leo Bar	Stallion	60,000	Auction	Lou Kosloff's Flying K Ranch	Don Brokaw, Apple Valley, Calif.
	1964	Scoop Bam	Mare	50,000	Auction	Gill Cattle Co., Tucson, Ariz.	Red Bee Ranch, Wichita, Kan.
	1965	May Moon	Mare	46,000	Auction	Belsby Ranch, Fresno, Calif.	Edd Richards, Dinuba, Calif.
	1966	Rocket Bar	Stallion	400,000	Private Treaty	George Kaufman, Modesto, Calif.	W. H. Peckham, Richmond; and S. F. Henderson, Odessa, Tex.
	1967	Go Josie Go	Mare	66,000	Auction	A. O. Phillips, Plano, Tex.	Burnett Estates, Fort Worth; and Clarence Scharbauer Jr., Midland, Tex.
	1968	Miss Gold Angel	Mare	87,000	Auction		Ray Marler, Ontario, Ore.
	1969	Nother Brother	Stallion	142,500	Private Treaty	Spencer Childers, Fresno, Calif.	Professional Group, Ogden, Utah
	1971	Speed Scene	Colt	100,000	Auction	Tom Neff, Ruidoso, N.M.	Lorna Call, Salt Lake City, Utah
	1972		Filly	7,000	Auction	King Ranch, Kingsville, Tex.	Unknown
	1975	Piqueno	Stallion	25,000	Auction	King Ranch, Kingsville, Tex.	Burrell Ranch, Whitesboro, Tex.
	1976	Easy Jet	Stallion	3,500,000	Private Treaty	Walter Merrick, Sayre, Okla.; and Joe McDermott, Houston, Tex.	Buena Suerte Ranch, Inc., Roswell, N.M.
Shetland Pony	1950	Hillswicks Oracle	Stallion	4,300	Auction	Mrs. Volney Diltz, Des Moines, Iowa	W. P. Atkinson, Oklahoma City, Okla.
	1950	Dunrovin Larigo Flame	Mare	1,750	Auction	Gene Lowrey, Nebraska City, Neb.	C. R. Donley, Anadarko, Okla.
	1953	Little Masterpiece	Stallion	7,500	Auction	V. Diltz, Des Moines, Iowa; and P. Carlile, Parny, Okla.	Sam Tayloe, Germantown, Tenn.
	1953	C—Jo's Toppy	Mare	6,000	Auction	Cliff and Jo Teague, Sherman, Tex.	I. B. Greene, Ridgway, Ill.

(Continued)

TABLE V-1 (Continued)

Breed	Year of Sale	Identity of Animal	Sex	Price	How Sold	Seller	Purchaser
	1954	Little Masterpiece	Stallion	25,000			Don Vestal, Parker, Colo.
	1954	Dora's Candy Lue	Mare	10,000	Auction	Vern Brewer, Gainsville, Tex.; and R. D. Peterson, Templeton, Tex.	L. W. Smith, Tulia, Tex.
	1957	C—Jo's Topper	Stallion	56,000	Auction	C—Jo Pony Farm, Sherman, Tex.	Syndicate of five: Boseman, Loewus, Frey, Casemore, and Blair, from Louisiana
	1957	Dainty Doll	Mare	12,500	Auction	Mrs. E. A. Barnes, Lafayette, Ind.	Clark McKelvex, Euless, Tex.
	1958	Supreme's Bit of Gold	Stallion	85,000	Auction	T. P. Parker, Valley View, Tex.	Happy Valley Pony Farm, Bloomfield, Iowa.
	1958	Valley Springs Golden Fleece	Mare	33,000	Auction	Ike Bozeman, Zachary, La.	Paul Loewer, Branch, La.
	1960	Captain Topper	Stallion	56,500	Auction	Vern Brewer, Gainesville, Tex.	Miss Patricia Burton, Dryden, Mich.
	1961	Atkinson's Hillswicke Bonny Cindy	Mare	14,500	Auction	Vern Brewer	C. C. Bales
	1962	Happy Valley's Red Christopher	Stallion	6,500	Auction	Happy Valley Pony	J. W. McClelland
	1963	Pierre Cody's Black Crystal	Mare	3,000	Auction	H. P. Kilkelly	Joe Finn
	1964	Ponyland's Globetrotter	Stallion	2,300	Auction	William Seekamp	L. B. Andersen
	1965	Larigo's Dark Magic	Stallion	5,000	Auction	Heyl Pony Farm	Paul Kitck
	1966	Holiday Edition	Mare	2,000	Auction	Burnidge Bros.	C. Elwood Thompson
	1967	Defender's Rambler	Stallion	4,000	Auction	John Hughes	Pat Butts
	1968	Tamerlane's Golden Rose	Mare	5,000	Auction	Burnidge Bros.	Tom Wells
	1969	Sunny Acres Billy Jack	Stallion	5,000	Auction	Elmer Williams	Roy Strawhacker
	1970	Wait & See's Delight	Mare	725	Auction	Ben Edwards	George Hart
	1971	Paladin's Lamplighter	Gelding	685	Auction	Jim Spurrier	W. W. Wetenkamp
	1973	Little Man	Stallion	4,750	Auction	J. R. Matthews, Great Mills, Md.	Mr. and Mrs. Delmer Moody, Belton, Mo.
Spanish-Barb	1973	Sung-Waw-Iyayuh, T-15	Mare	1,500	Private Treaty	Susan Banner, Colorado Springs, Colo.	Larry Belitz, Hot Springs, S.D.
	1974	Rawhide P-2	Stallion	1,500	Private Treaty	Bill Gaskins, Cody, Neb.	Peg Freitag, Farwell, Minn.
Standardbred	1889	Axtell	Stallion	105,000	Private Treaty	C. W. Williams, Independence, Iowa	W. P. Ijame, Terre Haute, Ind.; J. W. Conley Chicago, Ill.; and Fred Morgan, Detroit, Mich.
	1890	Director	Stallion	75,000	Private Treaty	Monroe Salisbury, Pleasanton, Calif.	A. H. Moore, Philadlephia, Penn.
	1891	Arion	Stallion	125,000	Private Treaty	Leland Stanford, Palo Alto, Calif.	J. M. Forbes, Milton Mass.
	1896	Anteeo	Stallion	60,000	Private Treaty	S. A. Brown, Kalamazoo, Mich.	H. S. Henry, Morrisville, Penn.
	1903	Dan Patch	Stallion	60,000	Private Treaty	M. E. Sturgis, New York, N.Y.	M. W. Savage, Minneapolis, Minn.
	1947	Algiers	Stallion	70,000	Auction	E. J. Baker, St. Charles, Ill.	C. F. Gaines, and Mrs. H. W. Nichols, Lexington, Ky.

(Continued)

TABLE V-1 (Continued)

Breed	Year of Sale	Identity of Animal	Sex	Price	How Sold	Seller	Purchaser
	1949	Nibble Hanover	Stallion	100,000	Private Treaty	D. W. Bostwick, Shelburne, Vt.	Hanover Shoe Farms, Hanover, Penn.
	1951	Tar Heel	Stallion	125,000	Auction	W. N. Reynolds, Est., Winston Salem, N.C.	Hanover Shoe Farms, Hanover, Penn.
	1951	Tar Heel	Stallion	125,000	Private Treaty		Hanover Shoe Farms, Hanover, Penn.
	1955	Adios	Stallion	500,000	Private Treaty		Hanover Shoe Farms, Hanover, Penn.
	1956	Good Time	Stallion	116,000	Private Treaty		Castleton Farm, Lexington, Ky.
	1957	Demon Hanover	Stallion	500,000	Private Treaty	R. Critchfield, Wooster, Ohio	(Syndicate) to be located at Walnut Hall Farm, Conerail, Ky.
	1957	Queen of Diamonds	Mare	30,000	Auction	Wallace McKenzie, Diamond, Ohio	H. Beever, St. Joseph, Mo.
	1958	Adios	Stallion	500,000	Private Treaty	Hanover Shoe Farms, Hanover, Penn.	Syndicate
	1959	Dancer Hanover	Colt	200,000	Private Treaty	Syndicate	Hanover Shoe Farms, Hanover, Penn.
	1960	Adios Butler	Stallion	600,000	Private Treaty	Paige West, Snow Hill Md.; A. Pellio, Scarsdale, N.Y.	Syndicated owners retained 20 shares
	1961	Jamin	Stallion	800,000	Private Treaty	Mme. Leon Lory-Roederer, France	Syndicate headed by Stanley Tananbaum, Yonkers Raceway
	1962	Painter	Stallion	130,000	Auction	Hunter Hill Farm, Cambridge City, Ind.	Two Gaits Farm, Castleton Farm, Marson, Indianapolis, Ind.
	1963	Safe Mission	Stallion	52,000	Auction	Almahurst Farm, Lexington, Ky.	Gilberto Melzi, Milan, Italy
	1964	Sprite Rodney	Mare	92,000	Auction	Eaton Ridge Farm, Lexington, Ky.	Hanover Shoe Farm, Hanover, Penn.
	1964	Effrat Hanover	Colt	65,000	Auction	Hanover Shoe Farms, Hanover, Penn.	Commanche Stables, Hanover, Penn.
	1965	Speedy Streak	Yearling Colt	113,000	Auction	Castleton Farm, Lexington, Ky.	Gainesway Farm, Lexington, Ky.
	1965	Starglow Hanover	Filly	40,000	Auction	Hanover Shoe Farms, Hanover, Penn.	Donner Packing Co., Milwaukee, Wisc.
	1966	Bret Hanover	Stallion	2,000,000	Private Treaty	Richard Downing, Shaker Heights, Ohio	Castleton Farm, Lexington, Ky.
	1966	Beautiful Hanover	Filly	52,000	Auction	Hanover Shoe Farms, Hanover, Penn.	Armstrong Bros., Brampton, Ontario, Canada
	1967	Bart Hanover	Yearling Colt	105,000	Auction	Hanover Shoe Farms, Hanover, Penn.	Rose Hild Farm, New Hope, Penn.; and Egyptian Acres Stable, New Egypt, N.J.
	1967	Spritely Way	Filly	70,000	Auction	Hanover Shoe Farms, Hanover, Penn.	K. D. Owen, Houston, Tex.; and Gainesway Farm, Lexington, Ky.
	1968	Nevele Bigshot	Yearling Colt	115,000	Auction	Hanover Shoe Farms, Hanover, Penn.	Nevele Acres, Ellenville, N.Y.
	1968	Betty Hanover	Filly	85,000	Auction	Hanover Shoe Farms, Hanover, Penn.	Oscar Kimelman, Purchase, N.Y.; Mike Kimelman, Pt. Chester, N.Y.; and Sheila Baird, New York, N.Y.
	1969	Dexter Hanover	Yearling Colt	125,000	Auction	Hanover Shoe Farms, Hanover, Penn.	Thomas and Mildred Dexter, Upper Saddle River, N.J.; Arthur Dexter, Jr., and Alice Schmidt, Nanuet, N.Y.; and Apache Stable, Orlando, Fla.

(Continued)

TABLE V-1 (Continued)

Breed	Year of Sale	Identity of Animal	Sex	Price	How Sold	Seller	Purchaser
	1969	Penola Hanover	Filly	47,000	Auction	Hanover Shoe Farms, Hanover, Penn.	Beejay Stables, Oshawa, Ontario, Canada
	1970	Rare Scotch	Filly	43,000	Auction	Castleton Farm, Lexington, Ky.	George Alexander, Sugar Grove, Ill.
	1970	Miracle Tip	Yearling Colt	117,000		Castleton Farm, Lexington, Ky.	Messenger Stables and Cliff Baker Ranch
	1971	Good Humor Man	Yearling Colt	210,000	Auction	Stoner Creek Stud	Vernon Goshneaur
Tennessee Walking Horse	1964	Perfection's Carbon Copy	Stallion	125,000	Private Treaty	Rodgers, Binns Raney & Welb	George L. Lenox
	1966	Triple Threat	Stallion	130,000	Private Treaty	Kreskie & Wright	Gotlob Koenig
	1968	Ace's Sensation	Stallion	100,000	Private Treaty	Beech & Hale	R. Randall Rollins
	1970	Ebony's Black Market	Stallion	100,001	Private Treaty	Beech & Hale	Dr. Harold McIver
	1975	Delight's Constructor	Stallion	36,500	Auction	Forest and Ashley King Continental Farms	B. O. Grandquest, Mobile, Ala.
Thoroughbred	1912	Rock Sand	Stallion	150,000	Private Treaty	August Belmont II	Syndicate
	1915	Tracery	Stallion	265,000	Private Treaty	August Belmont II	Senor Ungue, Argentina
	1922	Whiskaway	Stallion	125,000	Private Treaty	H. P. Whitney	Charles W. Clarke
	1925	Friar Rock	Stallion	130,000	Private Treaty	J. E. Madden	W. R. Coe
	1927	Hustle On	Colt	70,000	Auction	Himyar Stud	W. R. Coe
	1928	New Broom	Colt	75,000	Auction	Mr. T. J. Regan	Eastland Farm Syndicate
	1943	Pericles	Colt	66,000	Auction	A. B. Hancock	William Helis
	1945	Stardust	Stallion	448,000	Private Treaty	H. R. H. Aga Kahn	Syndicate of English Breeders
	1946	Bois Roussel	Stallion	320,000	Private Treaty	Peter Beatty	Prince Aly Kahn & Syndicate
	1947	Stepfather	3-yr. Colt	200,000	Auction	Louis B. Mayer	Harry M. Warner
	1947	Honeymoon	Mare in training	135,000	Auction	Louis B. Mayer	Harry M. Warner
	1947	Busher	Mare in training	135,000	Auction	Louis B. Mayer	Harry M. Warner
	1948	The Phoenix	Stallion	640,000	Private Treaty	Frederick Meyer (Ireland)	Syndicate of English Breeders
	1948	Algasir	Gelding in training	106,000	Auction	Est. A. C. Ernst	Mrs. F. Ambrose Clark
	1948	Busher	Mare	150,000	Private Treaty	Louis B. Mayer	Mrs. E. N. Graham
	1949	Nasrullah	Stallion	372,000	Private Treaty	Joseph McGrath	Syndicate
	1951	Say Blue	Mare	72,000	Auction	Coldstream Stud	Henry H. Knight
	1953	Tulyar	Stallion	700,000	Private Treaty	H. R. H. Aga Kahn	Irish National Stud
	1953	Lithe	Mare	85,000	Auction	Hal Price Headley	J. S. Phipps
	1954	Polynesian	Stallion	560,000	Private Treaty	Mrs. P. A. B. Widener, II	Ira Drymon & Syndicate
	1954	Festoon	Mare	105,840	Auction (Newmarket)	Est. Lord Dewar	A. B. Askew
	1955	Nashua	Stallion	1,251,200	Sealed Bid	Est. Wm. Woodward, Jr.	Leslie B. Combs II & Syndicate
	1955	No Strings	Mare	60,500	Auction	Henry H. Knight	Mrs. Parker B. Poe
	1956	Swaps	Stallion	2,000,000	Private Treaty	Rex Ellsworth	Mr. & Mrs. John W. Galbreath
	1956	Segula	Mare	126,000	Auction	Woolwine Syndicate	Stavros Niarchos
	1957	Round Table	Stallion	175,000	Private Treaty	A. B. Hancock, Jr.	Travis Kerr
	1958	Turn-To	Stallion	1,500,000	Private Treaty	Harry F. Guggenheim	Syndicate

(Continued)

TABLE V-1 (Continued)

Breed	Year of Sale	Identity of Animal	Sex	Price	How Sold	Seller	Purchaser
	1959	Ribot	Stallion Colt	1,350,000	Private Treaty (5-yr. lease)	Razza Dormello-Olgiata	John W. Galbreath
	1959	Highland Fling	Mare	80,000	Auction	Philip Godfrey	Keswick Stable
	1960	Tom Fool	Stallion	1,750,000	Private Treaty	Greentree Stud	Syndicate
	1960	Royal Native	Filly in training	250,000	Private Treaty	P. L. Grissom	William B. McDonald
	1961	Honey's Gem	Mare	137,000	Auction	E. Janss Jr. & Dr. J. K. Robbins	Frank C. Bishop Syndicate
	1962	Shirley Jones	Mare in training	105,000	Auction	Brae Burn Farm	Mrs. J. O. Burgwin
	1963	(Swaps Blue Star II)	Colt	85,000	Auction	Stonereath Farm	Penowa Farm
	1963	Flanders Field	Mare	66,000	Auction	Robert Courtney, Agent	Desi Arnaz
	1964	Gun Bow	Stallion	1,000,000	Private Treaty	Gedney Farms	Syndicate
	1964	La Dauphine	Mare	177,000	Auction	Leslie Combs II & John W. Hanes	Charles H. Wacker III
	1965	Tom Rolfe	Stallion	1,600,000	Private Treaty	Raymond Guest	A. B. Hancock, Jr. Syndicate
	1966	Graustark	Stallion	2,400,000	Private Treaty	John W. Galbreath	Syndicate
	1966	Berlo	Mare	235,000	Auction	Est. William duPont	John E. duPont
	1967	Buck Passer	Stallion	4,800,000	Private Treaty	Ogden Phipps	Syndicate
	1967	Quill	Mare	365,000	Auction	John A. Bell	A. B. Hancock Jr., Agent
	1968	Reine Enchanteur	Filly	405,000	Auction	Mrs. Julian G. Rogers	W. P. Rosso
	1968	Successor	Stallion	1,050,000	Private Treaty	Wheatley Stable	Flag Is Up Farm
	1969	Too Bald	Mare	225,000	Auction	Dispersal Sale of Cain Hoy Stable	Charles Engelhard Cragwood Estates
	1969	Rough Frolic	Colt	225,000	Auction	Ocala Stud Farm	Daniel Schwartz
	1970	Crowned Prince	Colt	510,000	Auction	Spendthrift Farm, Leslie Combs II	Frank McMahon, Vancouver, B.C.
	1970	Priceless Gem	Mare	395,000	Auction	Bieber/Jacobs Dispersal	A. B. Hancock, Agent
	1971	Nijinsky	Stallion	5,440,000	Private Treaty	Windfield Farm	Syndicate
	1971	Pass	Colt	235,000	Auction	Nydrie Stud	Marion duPont Scott
	1971	Julia B.	Filly	200,000	Auction	Mrs. George Proskauer	Henry Forrest, Agent
	1972	What a Treat	Mare	450,000	Auction	George D. Widener	Mr. F. Eugene Dixon, for office duPur Sang (France)
	1972	Casque Grise	Colt	235,000	Auction	Fasig-Tipton, Co.	Mrs. Marion duPont Scott
	1972	Cellini	Colt	240,000	Auction	Estate of A. B. Hancock, Jr.	BBA Ireland
	1973	Secretariat	Stallion	6,080,000	Private Treaty	Meadow Stable	Syndicated
	1973	Typecast	Mare	725,000	Auction	Estate of Fletcher Jones	Heron Bloodstock Agency
	1975	Wajima	Colt	7,200,000	Private Treaty	Spendthrift Farms	Syndicated
	1975	Trevisana	Mare	295,000	Auction	Peter Valenti, Farrell Jones, and the Murty Brothers	Jerry Frankel, Dallas, Tex.

TABLE V-2
ALL-TIME TOP CONSIGNMENT SALES

Breed	Year of Sale	Number of Animals	Average Price	Seller
Appaloosa	1967	19	$ 2,071	G. Newman and W. Pruitt
	1968	54	1,211	Texas Appaloosa Horse Club
	1969	45	906	North-Eastern Appaloosa Sale
	1970	58	1,150	North-Eastern Appaloosa Assn.
	1971	43	2,678	Jedd Van Kampen (Top O'the World Sale)
Arabian	1969	47	8,468	McCormick's Arabians, Scottsdale, Ariz.
	1970	39	5,250	International Arabian Horse Assn., Burbank, Calif.
	1971	27	19,822	Lasma Arabians, Scottsdale, Ariz.
	1972	45	10,916	International Arabian Horse Assn., Burbank, Calif.
	1973	49	14,427	Lancer Arabians, Brighton, Mich.
	1974	26	30,512	Lasma Arabians, Scottsdale, Ariz.
Paint Horse	1966	50	650	Broken Arrow Horse Farm
	1967	16	687	California Paint Horse Club
	1968	42	670	Broken Arrow Horse Farm
	1969	20	914	California Autumn Horse Sale
	1970	37	650	Michigan Paint Horse Club
	1971	19	1,066	Kansas Paint Horse Club
Palomino	1966	9 (colts)	1,450	Bent Arrow Ranch, Broken Arrow, Okla.
	1967	40	1,100	Bent Arrow Ranch, Broken Arrow, Okla.
	1968	40	1,015	Bent Arrow Ranch, Broken Arrow, Okla.
	1969	72	1,031	Bent Arrow Ranch, Broken Arrow, Okla.
	1970	77	873	Bent Arrow Ranch, Broken Arrow, Okla.
	1971	68	1,064	Bent Arrow Ranch, Broken Arrow, Okla.
Paso Fino and Peruvian Paso Horses	1971	30	1,780	Hacienda de Cupido's Peruvian Paso and Paso Fino Horses
Pony of the Americas	1971	150	468	Breed Promotion Sale
Quarter Horse	1948	34	1,208	Circle JR-Bellwood Ranch, Corona, Calif.
	1951	10	1,477	Grace Ranch, Tucson, Ariz.
	1952	36	1,255	Jinkens Bros., Fort Worth, Tex.
	1954	53	1,635	Three D Stock Farm, Arlington, Tex.
	1955	25	1,358	King Ranch, Kingsville, Tex.
	1956	26	1,598	R. L. Underwood, Wichita Falls, Tex.
	1957	44	3,401	R. Q. Sutherland, Overland Park, Kan.
	1958	29	3,403	Pinehurst Stables, Houston, Tex.
	1959	51	5,806	J. L. Taylor, Chino, Calif.
	1960	66	7,042	E. L. Gosselin (and guests), Edmond, Okla.
	1961	25	4,104	King Ranch, Kingsville, Tex.
	1968	130	4,167	All American Futurity Sale, Ruidoso Downs, N.M.
	1971	51	10,722	Ruidosa Downs, N.M.
	1972	22	3,179	King Ranch, Kingsville, Tex.

(Continued)

TABLE V-2 (Continued)

Breed	Year of Sale	Number of Animals	Average Price	Seller
Shetland Pony	1953	139	889	Southwestern Shetland Breed, Promotion Sale
	1956	133	1,611	National Breed Promotion Sale
	1957	22	7,935	C. C. Teague Consignment to Perry Carlile Sale, Perry, Okla.
	1958	120	4,935	Lowery Dispersal Sale at Perry Carlile Sale, Perry, Okla.
	1960	59	4,345	Vern Brewer Production Sale, Gainesville, Tex.
	1961	141	536.73	National Breed Promotion Sale
	1962	80	300.00	National Breed Promotion Sale
	1963	117	200.00	National Breed Promotion Sale
	1964	51	274.60	National Breed Promotion Sale
	1965	81	226.66	National Breed Promotion Sale
	1966	98	250.92	National Breed Promotion Sale
	1967	71	165.00	National Breed Promotion Sale
	1968	57	186.00	National Breed Promotion Sale
	1969	58	167.75	National Breed Promotion Sale
	1970	41	186.81	National Breed Promotion Sale
	1971	29	180.37	National Breed Promotion Sale
Standardbred	1952	36 (all ages)	14,850	W. N. Reynolds, Disposal, Harrisburg, Penn.
	1952	15 (yearlings)	6,533	Harrisburg, Penn.
	1956	847	2,376	Harrisburg, Penn.
	1958	867 (yearlings)	2,901	Harrisburg, Penn.
	1959	922	3,498	Standardbred Horse Sales Company
	1960	874	3,851	Harrisburg, Penn.
	1961	794 (all ages)	3,468	Harrisburg, Penn.
		305 (yearlings)	4,888	Tattersalls, Inc., Lexington, Ky.
	1962	722 (all ages)	3,869	Harrisburg, Penn.
		355 (yearling)	5,439	Tattersalls, Inc., Lexington, Ky.
	1963	707 (all ages)	4,827	Harrisburg, Penn.
		322 (yearlings)	5,988	Tattersalls, Inc., Lexington, Ky.
	1964	124	9,762	Hanover Shoe Farm, Hanover, Penn.
	1965	159	10,672	Hanover Shoe Farm, Hanover, Penn.
	1966	176	10,058	Hanover Shoe Farm, Hanover, Penn.
	1967	188	12,137	Hanover Shoe Farm, Hanover, Penn.
	1968	177	18,205	Hanover Shoe Farm, Hanover, Penn.
	1969	165	15,228	Hanover Shoe Farm, Hanover, Penn.
	1970	89	15,067	Castleton Farm, Lexington, Ky.
	1971	32	17,922	Stoner Creek Stud Farm
	1972	165	15,414	Hanover Shoe Farm, Hanover, Penn.
	1973	163	16,667	Hanover Shoe Farm, Hanover, Penn.
	1974	164	17,748	Hanover Shoe Farm, Hanover, Penn.
Thoroughbred	1946	415 (yearlings)	9,912	Keeneland Summer Sales
	1947	60 (race horses)	25,830	Louis B. Mayer (Dispersal)
		436 (yearlings)	6,827	Keeneland Summer Sales
	1949	9 (broodmares)	44,222	Est. Crispin Oglebay
	1950	42 (2-yr.-olds)	14,410	Louis B. Mayer
	1951	48 (broodmares)	20,635	Coldstream Stud

(Continued)

TABLE V-2 (Continued)

Breed	Year of Sale	Number of Animals	Average Price	Seller
	1952	47 (yearlings)	14,526	Almahurst Farm (Henry H. Knight)
	1953	302 (yearlings)	9,746	Keeneland Summer Sales
	1954	344 (yearlings)	9,940	Keeneland Summer Sales
		20 (broodmares)	26,955	Keeneland Summer Sales
	1955	68 (broodmares)	15,232	Henry H. Knight
		346 (yearlings)	11,174	Keeneland Summer Sales
		55 (weanlings)	6,609	Henry H. Knight
	1956	219 (yearlings)	10,133	Saratoga Yearling Sales
	1957	235 (yearlings)	11,789	Keeneland Summer Sales
	1958	357 (yearlings)	9,615	Keeneland Summer Sales
	1959	303 (yearlings)	11,664	Keeneland Summer Sales
	1960	303 (yearlings)	11,844	Keeneland Summer Sales
	1961	298 (yearlings)	14,177	Keeneland Summer Sales
	1962	273 (yearlings)	12,993	Keeneland Summer Sales
	1963	275 (yearlings)	14,191	Keeneland Summer Sales
	1964	212 (yearlings)	17,763	Saratoga Yearling Sales
	1965	25 (broodmares)	40,615	J. W. Hanes & Leslie Combs II
		282 (yearlings)	17,973	Keeneland Summer Sales
	1966	257 (yearlings)	19,535	Saratoga Yearling Sales
		72 (mixed)	39,842	Foxcatcher Gaines
	1967	255 (yearlings)	22,145	Saratoga Yearling Sales
	1968	248 (yearlings)	30,671	Keeneland Summer Sales, Lexington, Ky.
	1969	299 (yearlings)	25,699	Keeneland Summer Sales, Lexington, Ky.
	1970	262 (yearlings)	30,153	Keeneland Summer Sales, Lexington, Ky.
	1971	333 (yearlings)	31,775	Keeneland Summer Sales, Lexington, Ky.
	1972	40 (mixed)	83,930	George D. Widener
	1974	320 (yearlings)	53,489	Keeneland Summer Sales, Lexington, Ky.
	1974	224 (yearlings)	37,219	Saratoga Yearling Sales
	1975	1,103 (mixed)	14,654	Keeneland November Breeding Stock Sales, Lexington, Ky.
	1975	67 (mixed)	53,478	Fasig-Tipton Company

SECTION VI—UNITED STATES AND WORLD RECORDS FOR THOROUGHBREDS, STANDARDBREDS, AND QUARTER HORSES

The U.S. and world records for Thoroughbreds, Standardbreds, and Quarter Horses at some of the popular American distances are given in Tables VI-1, VI-2, and VI-3, respectively.

TABLE VI-1

UNITED STATES AND WORLD RECORDS FOR THOROUGHBREDS[1]

Distance	Name of Horse	Age of Horse	Weight Carried	Track	Date Record Established	Time	United States and/or World Record
		(yrs.)	(lbs.)				
1/4 mile	BOB WADE	4	122	Butte, Montana	1890	:21$^{1}/_4$	U.S.
1/4 mile	BIG RACKET	4	111	Hippedrome de Las Americas, Mexico City	1945	:20$^{4}/_5$	World
3/8 mile	KING RHYMER	2	118	Santa Anita, Arcadia, Calif.	1947	:32	U.S.&W.
1/2 mile	TAMRAN'S JET	2	118	Sunland Park, Sunland, N.M.	1968	44$^{4}/_5$	U.S.&W.
4$^{1}/_2$ furlongs[2]	THE PIMPERNAL	2	118	Belmont Park, N.Y.	1951	:49$^{4}/_5$	World
5/8 mile	ZIP POCKET	3	122	Turf Paradise, Phoenix, Ariz.	1967	:55$^{2}/_5$	U.S.&W.
5$^{1}/_2$ furlongs (straight course)	DELEGATE	7	113	Belmont Park, N.Y.	1951	1:01$^{3}/_5$	World
5$^{1}/_2$ furlongs (around 1 turn)	ZIP POCKET	3	129	Turf Paradise, Phoenix, Ariz.	1967	1:01$^{3}/_5$	U.S.&W.
3/4 mile (6 furlongs)	GREY PAPA	6	116	Longacres, Seattle, Wash.	1972	1:07$^{1}/_5$	U.S.&W.
6$^{1}/_2$ furlongs (straight course)	NATIVE DANCER	2	122	Belmont Park, N.Y.	1952	1:14$^{2}/_5$	U.S.&W.
6$^{1}/_2$ furlongs (around 1 turn)	BEST HITTER	4	114	Longacres, Seattle, Wash.	1973	1:13$^{4}/_5$	U.S.&W.
7/8 mile	TRIPLE BEND	4	123	Hollywood Park, Inglewood, Calif.	1972	1:19$^{4}/_5$	U.S.&W.
1 mile	DR. FAGER	4	134	Arlington Park, Chicago, Ill.	1968	1:32$^{1}/_5$	U.S.&W.
1 mile-70 yds.	DRILL SITE	5	115	Garden State Park, Cherry Hill, N.J.	1964	1:38$^{4}/_5$	U.S.&W.
1$^{1}/_{16}$ miles	SWAPS	4	130	Hollywood Park, Inglewood, Calif.	1956	1:39	U.S.&W.
1$^{1}/_8$ miles	SECRETARIAT	3	124	Belmont Park, Elmont, N.Y.	1973	1:45$^{2}/_5$	U.S.&W.
1$^{3}/_{16}$ miles	RIVA RIDGE	4	127	Aqueduct, Aqueduct, N.Y.	1973	1:52$^{2}/_5$	U.S.&W.
1$^{1}/_4$ miles	NOOR	5	127	Golden Gate, Calif.	1950	1:58$^{1}/_5$	U.S.&W.
1$^{3}/_8$ miles	MAN O'WAR	3	126	Belmont Park, N.Y.	1920	2:14$^{1}/_5$	U.S.&W.
1$^{1}/_2$ miles	SECRETARIAT	3	126	Belmont Park, Elmont, N.Y.	1973	2:24	U.S.
1$^{5}/_8$ miles	SWAPS	4	130	Hollywood Park, Calif.	1956	2:38$^{1}/_5$	U.S.&W.
2 miles	POLAZEL	3		Salisbury, England	1924	3:15	World
2$^{1}/_2$ miles	MISS GRILLO	6	118	Pimlico, Baltimore, Md.	1948	4:14$^{1}/_5$	U.S.&W.

[1]Data provided by The Jockey Club, Columbus, Ohio; and *The Blood Horse*, Lexington, Ky.
[2]A furlong is a measure of length equal to an eighth of a mile (or 40 rods, 220 yards, or 201.17 meters).

TABLE VI-2

UNITED STATES AND WORLD RECORDS FOR STANDARDBREDS[1]

Distance	Name of Horse	Track	Date Record Established	Time	United States and/or World Record
Pacing:					
1/2 mile	ALBATROSS	Delaware, Ohio	1972	1:55$^{1}/_5$	World
1/2 mile	SEATRAIN	Delaware, Ohio	1975	1:57	World
1/2 mile	SILK STOCKINGS	Delaware, Ohio	1975	1:57$^{2}/_5$	World
1 mile	ALBATROSS	Lexington, Ky.	1971	1:54$^{4}/_5$	World
1 mile	HANDLE WITH CARE	Inglewood, Calif.	1974	1:54$^{4}/_5$	World
1 mile	ARMBRO ONTARIO	Lexington, Ky.	1974	1:56$^{1}/_5$	World
1 mile	SLY ATTORNEY	Syracuse, N.Y.	1975	1:54$^{4}/_5$	World
Trotting:					
1/2 mile	DARN SAFE	Saratoga Springs, N.Y.	1957	1:59$^{4}/_5$	World
1/2 mile	ARMBRO FLIGHT	Delaware, Ohio	1965	1:59$^{1}/_5$	World
1/2 mile	NEVELE PRIDE	Saratoga Springs, N.Y.	1969	1:56$^{4}/_5$	World
1/2 mile	SAVOIR	Delaware, Ohio	1971	1:59$^{4}/_5$	World
1 mile	NOBLE VICTORY	Du Quoin, Ill.	1966	1:55$^{1}/_5$	World
1 mile	FLIRTH	Du Quoin, Ill.	1973	1:57$^{1}/_5$	World
1 mile	COLONIAL CHARM	Lexington, Ky.	1974	1:56$^{1}/_5$	World

[1]Data provided by the United States Trotting Assn., Columbus, Ohio.

TABLE VI-3

UNITED STATES AND WORLD RECORDS FOR QUARTER HORSES[1]

Distance	Name of Horse	Age of Horse	Weight Carried	Track	Date Record Established	Time	United States and/or World Record
		(yrs.)	(lb)				
220 yds.	JUNIOR MEYERS	4	120	La Mesa Park, N.M.	1973	:11.62	U.S.
250 yds.	JUNIOR MEYERS	6	121	La Mesa Park, N.M.	1973	:13.00	U.S.
300 yds.	JOLLY JET DECK	5	125	La Mesa Park, N.M.	1973	:15.24	U.S.
330 yds.	GOOD N TENSION	2	120	Sunland Park, N.M.	1974	:16.47	U.S.
350 yds.	VAN TOO TOO	5	118	Ruidoso Downs, N.M.	1970	:17.24	U.S.
400 yds.	TRUCKLE FEATURE	3	120	Sunland Park, N.M.	1971	:19.38	U.S.
440 yds.	TRUCKLE FEATURE	3	120	Ruidoso Downs, N.M.	1969	:21.02	U.S.

[1]Data provided by the American Quarter Horse Assn., Amarillo, Tex.

SECTION VII—LEADING MONEY-WINNING THOROUGHBREDS, STANDARDBREDS, AND QUARTER HORSES

The leading money-winning Thoroughbreds in the United States are listed, by rank, in Table VII-1. Similar information for Standardbreds is given in Table VII-2; and for Quarter Horses, in Table VII-3.

TABLE VII-1

LEADING MONEY-WINNING THOROUGHBREDS[1]

Horse	Total Money Won	Racing Years	Owner
Kelso	$1,977,896	1961-66	Mrs. Richard C. duPont
Round Table	1,749,869	1956-59	Travis Kerr
Buckpasser	1,462,014	1965-67	Ogden Phipps
Allez France	1,380,565	1972-75	Daniel Wildenstein
Dahlia	1,360,443	1972-	Nelson Bunker Hunt
Secretariat	1,316,808	1972-73	Secretariat syndicate
Nashua	1,288,565	1956-59	Belair Stud and Leslie Combs II
Susan's Girl	1,251,668	1971-75	Fred W. Hooper
Carry Back	1,241,165	1960-63	Jack A. Price
Damascus	1,176,781	1966-68	Mrs. Edith W. Bancroft
Forego	1,163,520	1972-	Lazy F Ranch
Cougar II	1,162,725	1968-73	Mrs. Mary F. Jones
Riva Ridge	1,111,497	1971-73	Riva Ridge syndicate
Citation	1,085,760	1947-51	Calumet Farm
Fort Marcy	1,109,791	1966-70	Rokeby Stable
Foolish Pleasure	1,045,353	1974-	John L. Greer
Native Diver	1,026,500	1961-67	L. K. Shapiro
Dr. Fager	1,002,642	1966-68	Dr. Fager syndicate
Swoon's Son	970,605	1955-58	E. G. Drake
Roman Brother	943,743	1962-65	Harbor View Farm
Stymie	918,485	1943-49	Mrs. Ethel D. Jacobs
T. V. Lark	902,194	1959-62	T. V. Lark syndicate

[1]Date provided by The Jockey Club, Columbus, Ohio; and The Blood Horse, Lexington, Ky.

TABLE VII-2

LEADING MONEY-WINNING STANDARDBREDS[1]

Horse	Total Money Won	Years Raced
Trotters		
Une de Mai	$1,660,627[2]	1967-73
Fresh Yankee	1,294,252	1965-72
Bellino II	1,088,255	1969-75
Savior	1,064,566	1970-75
Roquepine	956,161	1963-69
Timothy T	894,237	1969-75
Su Mac Lad	885,095	1956-65
Nevele Pride	873,238	1967-69
Delmonica Hanover	832,925	1971-75
Tidalium Pelo	758,603	1966-72
Dayan	668,974	1968-72
Speedy Scot	650,909	1962-65
Duke Rodney	639,408	1960-66
Elaine Rodney	610,685	1959-68
Super Bowl	601,006	1971-72
Spartan Hanover	565,697	1972-74
Tornese	546,404	1955-61
Speedy Crown	545,495	1970-72
Carlisle	544,136	1965-69
Agaunar	532,618	1965-73
Fine Shot	525,854	1967-73
Noble Victory	522,391	1964-66
Pacers		
Alabatross	1,201,470	1970-72
Rum Customer	1,001,548	1967-71
Cardigan Bay	1,000,837	1959-68
Bret Hanover	922,616	1964-66
Laverne Hanover	868,557	1968-71
Overcall	783,948	1965-69
Henry T. Adios	706,833	1960-64
Sir Dalrae	661,579	1972-75
Romeo Hanover	658,505	1965-67
Armbro Nesbit	625,964	1972-74
Handle With Care	616,606	1973-75
Song Cycle	597,390	1965-73
Fulla Napoleon	582,279	1967-70
Otaro Hanover	562,172	1972-75
Bye Bye Byrd	554,257	1957-61
Best of All	548,899	1966-68
Irvin Paul	548,518	1959-67
Adios Butler	509,844	1958-61
Nardins Byrd	507,844	1966-69
Keystone Smartie	504,375	1972-75

[1]Data provided by the United States Trotting Assn., Columbus, Ohio.
[2]Compiled by French authorities.

TABLE VII-3

LEADING MONEY-WINNING QUARTER HORSES[1]

Horse	Total Money Won	Racing Years	Owner
Easy Date	$848,809	1974-75	Walter Merrick
Timeto Thinkrich	612,858	1973-75	Vessels' Stallion Farm
Bugs Alive in '75	538,218	1975	Ralph W. Shebester
Pass Over	521,172	1973-75	Jack R. Delmar
Charger Bar	495,437	1970-75	Edward Allred and Kenneth Wright
Easy Jet	445,721	1969-70	Joe McDermott and Walter Merrick
Tiny's Gay	444,720	1974	John R. Colville
Laico Bird	435,654	1967-68	Floyd H., Jr., and Jimmy R. B. Jones
Possumjet	406,808	1972-73	Jack Byers
Kaweah Bar	373,577	1968-75	Bob R. Tanner

[1]Data provided by the American Quarter Horse Assn., Amarillo, Tex.

SECTION VIII—BREED REGISTRY ASSOCIATIONS

A breed registry association consists of a group of breeders banded together for the purposes of (1) recording the lineage of their animals, (2) protecting the purity of the breed, (3) encouraging further improvement of the breed, and (4) promoting interest in the breed. A list of the horse breed registry associations is given in Table VIII-1.

TABLE VIII-1

HORSE BREED REGISTRY ASSOCIATIONS

Class of Animal	Breed	Association and Address
Light Horses:	American Bashkir Curly	American Bashkir Curly Registry P. O. Box 453 Ely, Nev. 89301
	American Creme Horse	American Albino Assn. Box 79 Crabtree, Ore. 97335
	American Mustang	American Mustang Assn., Inc. P. O. Box 338 Yucaipa, Calif. 92399
	American Saddle Horse	American Saddle Horse Breeders Assn., Inc. 929 S. Fourth Street Louisville, Ky. 40203
	American White Horse	American Albino Assn. Box 79 Crabtree, Ore. 97335
	Andalusian	American Andalusian Assn. P. O. Box 1290 Silver City, N.M. 88061
	Appaloosa	Appaloosa Horse Club, Inc. P. O. Box 8403 Moscow, Ida. 83843
	Arabian	Arabian Horse Registry of America, Inc. 3435 South Yosemite Denver, Colo. 80231
	Buckskin	American Buckskin Registry Assn., Inc. P. O. Box 1125 Anderson, Calif. 96007
		International Buckskin Horse Assn., Inc. P. O. Box 357 St. John, Ind. 46373
	Chickasaw	Chickasaw Horse Assn., Inc., The P. O. Box 8 Love Valley, N.C. 28677
		National Chickasaw Horse Assn. Route 2 Clarinda, Iowa 51232
	Cleveland Bay	Cleveland Bay Assn. of America Middleburg, Va. 22117
	Galiceno	Galiceno Horse Breeders Assn., Inc. 111 E. Elm Street Tyler, Tex. 75701
	Hackney	American Hackney Horse Society P. O. Box 174 Pittsfield, Ill. 62363
	Hanoverian	American Hanoverian Society, The 809 W. 106th Street Carmel, Ind. 46032
	Hungarian Horse	Hungarian Horse Assn. Bitterroot Stock Farm Hamilton, Mont. 59840
	Lipizzan	American Lipizzan Horse Registry P. O. Box 415 Platteville, Wisc. 53818
	Missouri Fox Trotting Horse	Missouri Fox Trotting Horse Breed Assn., Inc. P. O. Box 637 Ava, Mo. 65608

(Continued)

TABLE VIII-1 (Continued)

Class of Animal	Breed	Association and Address
	Morab	Morab Horse Registry of America P. O. Box 143 Clovis, Calif. 93612
	Morgan	American Morgan Horse Assn., Inc. Box 1 Westmoreland, N.Y. 13490
	Morocco Spotted Horse	Morocco Spotted Horse Co-operative Assn. of America Route 1 Ridott, Ill. 61067
	Paint Horse	American Paint Horse Assn. P. O. Box 13486 Ft. Worth, Tex. 76118
	Palomino	Palomino Horse Assn., Inc., The P. O. Box 324 Jefferson City, Mo. 65101
		Palomino Horse Breeders of America P. O. Box 249 Mineral Wells, Tex. 76067
	Paso Fino	American Paso Fino Horse Assn., Inc. Mellan Bank Bldg., Room 3018 525 William Penn Place Pittsburgh, Penn. 15219
		Paso Fino Owners & Breeders Assn., Inc. P.O. Box 764 Columbus, N.C. 28722
	Peruvian Paso	American Assn. of Owners & Breeders of Peruvian Paso Horses P. O. Box 2035 California City, Calif. 93505
		Peruvian Paso Horse Registry of North America P. O. Box 816 Guerneville, Calif. 95446
	Pinto Horse	Pinto Horse Assn. of America, Inc. P. O. Box 3984 San Diego, Calif. 92103
	Quarter Horse	American Quarter Horse Assn. P. O. Box 200 Amarillo, Tex. 79105
		Standard Quarter Horse Assn. 4390 Fenton Denver, Colo. 80212
	Rangerbred	Colorado Ranger Horse Assn., Inc. 7023 Eden Mill Road Woodbine, Md. 21797
	Spanish-Barb	Spanish-Barb Breeders Assn. P. O. Box 7479 Colorado Springs, Colo. 80907
	Spanish Mustang	Spanish Mustang Registry Inc., The Route 2, Box 74 Marshall, Tex. 75670
	Standardbred	United States Trotting Assn. 750 Michigan Avenue Columbus, Ohio 43215
		National Trotting & Pacing Assn., Inc. 575 Broadway Hanover, Penn. 17331
	Tennessee Walking Horse	Tennessee Walking Horse Breeders Assn. of America P. O. Box 286 Lewisburg, Tenn. 37091
	Thoroughbred	Jockey Club, The 300 Park Avenue New York, N.Y. 10022

(Continued)

TABLE VIII-1 (Continued)

Class of Animal	Breed	Association and Address
	Trakehner	American Trakehner Assn., Inc. P. O. Box 268 Norman, Okla. 73069
	Welsh Cob	Welsh Cob Society of America Grazing Field Farm Head of the Bay Road Buzzard Bay, Mass. 02532
	Ysabella	Ysabella Saddle Horse Assn., Inc. c/o Prairie Edge Farm Route 3 Williamsport, Ind. 47993
Ponies:	American Gotland Horse	American Gotland Horse Assn. R. R. 2, Box 181 Elkland, Mo. 65644
	American Walking Pony	American Walking Pony Assn. Route 5, Box 88 Upper River Road Macon, Ga. 31201
	Connemara Pony	American Connemara Pony Society R. D. 1 Hoshiekon Farm Goshen, Conn. 06756
	National Appaloosa Pony	National Appaloosa Pony, Inc. Box 296 Gaston, Ind. 47342
	Pony of the Americas	Pony of the Americas Club P. O. Box 1447 Mason City, Iowa 50401
	Shetland Pony	American Shetland Pony Club P. O. Box 435 Fowler, Ind. 47944
	Welsh Pony	Welsh Pony Society of America P. O. Drawer A White Post, Va. 22663
Draft Horses:	Belgian	Belgian Draft Horse Corporation of America P. O. Box 335 Wabash, Ind. 46992
	Clydesdale	Clydesdale Breeders Assn. of the United States Route 3 Waverly, Iowa 50677
	Percheron	Percheron Horse Assn. of America R. R. 1 Belmont, Ohio 43718
	Shire	American Shire Horse Assn. 6960 Northwest Drive Ferndale, Wash. 98248
	Suffolk	American Suffolk Horse Assn., Inc. 672 Polk Blvd. Des Moines, Iowa 50312
Jacks, Donkeys, and Mules:	Jack and Jennet	Standard Jack and Jennet Registry of America 300 Todds Road Lexington, Ky. 40502
	Miniature Donkey	Miniature Donkey Registry of the United States, Inc. 1108 Jackson Street Omaha, Neb. 68102
	Donkey and Mule	American Donkey and Mule Society, Inc. 2410 Executive Drive Indianapolis, Ind. 46241
All Horses and Half-Breeds:	Any and all colors and types of horses (including animals not eligible for registry, eligible but not registered, or registered in existing	National Recording Office Box 79 Crabtree, Ore. 97335

(Continued)

TABLE VIII-1 (Continued)

Class of Animal	Breed	Association and Address
	associations) including both light and draft horses.	
	Half-bred Thoroughbreds:	American Remount Assn., Inc. (Half-Thoroughbred Registry)[1] P.O. Box 1066 Perris, Calif. 92370

Section 1: *The American Remount Half-Thoroughbred*—Must have one Thoroughbred parent registered in the American (Jockey Club) Stud Book.

Section 2: *The American Remount Anglo*—Must have one Thoroughbred parent registered in the American (Jockey Club) Stud Book and the other parent registered in the Stud Book of a recognized breed.

Section 3: *The American Remount Thoroughbred Kind*—Must have one Thoroughbred parent of a recognized Foreign Registry or must have both parents registered in the American (Jockey Club) Stud Book but be ineligible for registry in the American (Jockey Club) Stud Book.

Section 4: *The American Remount Hunter-Jumper*—Must be a minimum of 36 months of age; be performance certified by an approved Equine Practitioner, a Master of Fox Hounds, an Official of the American Horse Show Association, or a Steward of the American Remount Association; and be ineligible for registry in the American (Jockey Club) Stud Book.

Section 5: *The American Remount Polo Pony*—Must be performance certified by an approved Equine Practitioner, a five-goal rated player, an Officer of the U.S. Polo Association, or a Steward of the American Remount Association; and be ineligible for registry in the American (Jockey Club) Stud Book.

Section 6: *The American Remount Endurance Horse*—Must be performance certified by an approved Equine Practitioner, an Official of the American Horse Show Association, or a Steward of the American Remount Association; and be ineligible for registry in the American (Jockey Club) Stud Book.

Section 7: *The American Remount Record*—This is an Identification Certificate issued to a horse that has apparent Thoroughbred ancestry but is not otherwise eligible for registry in the American (Jockey Club) Stud Book or any other recognized Stud Book.

Class of Animal	Breed	Association and Address
	Half-bred Arabian:	International Arabian Horse Assn. 224 E. Olive Avenue Burbank, Calif. 91503

1. *Anglo-Arabs* must carry not more than ¾ and not less than ¼ Arabian blood. May be either —

  (a) By Thoroughbred stallions and out of registered Arabian mares;
  (b) By registered Arabian stallions and out of registered Thoroughbred mares;
  (c) By registered Thoroughbred or Arabian stallions and out of registered Anglo-Arab mares; or
  (d) By Anglo-Arab stallions and out of either registered Anglo-Arab mares, registered Thoroughbred mares, or registered Arabian mares.

2. *Half-Arabians* are by registered Arabian stallions and out of mares that are not registered Thoroughbreds or Arabians.

Class of Animal	Breed	Association and Address
	Half-bred, grade, and crossbred horses involving—American Saddle Horse, Appaloosa, Hackney, Morgan, Quarter Horse, Standardbred, Tennessee Walking Horse, Welsh Pony, and certain other breeds.	American Part-Blooded Horse Registry 4120 S. E. River Drive Portland, Ore. 97222

[1]Formerly the Half-Bred Stud Book operated by the American Remount Association, but now a privately owned registry. It records only foals sired by registered Thoroughbred stallions and out of mares not registered in the American (Jockey Club) Stud Book, or in The Arabian Stud Book.

SECTION IX—BREED MAGAZINES

The horse breed magazines publish news items and informative articles of special interest to horsemen. Also, many of them employ field representatives whose chief duty is to assist in the buying and selling of animals.

In the compilation of the list herewith presented (see Table IX-1), no attempt was made to list the general livestock magazines of which there are numerous outstanding ones. Only those magazines which are chiefly devoted to horses are included.

TABLE IX-1
BREED MAGAZINES

Breed	Publication	Address
General	American Horseman	257 Park Avenue South, New York, N.Y. 10010
	Arizona Horseman, The	5001 E. Washington, Suite 128, Phoenix, Ariz. 85034
	California Horseman's News	8808 National Avenue, South Gate, Calif. 90280
	Capital Horseman	14405 W. 52nd Ave., Arvada, Colo. 80002
	Carriage Journal	157 N. Saint Austin's Place, Staten Island, N.Y. 10310
	Chronicle of the Horse, The	Middleburg, Va. 22117
	Classic	551 Fifth Avenue, New York, N.Y. 10017
	Corinthian, The	1315 Finch Ave. W, Suite 309 Downsview, Ontario, Canada M3J 2G6
	Corral, The	Box 151, Medina, Ohio 44256
	Cuttin' Hoss Chatter, The	P. O. Box 12155, Ft. Worth, Tex. 76116
	Dressage	P. O. Box 2460, Cleveland, Ohio 44112
	Equestrian Trails	Box 2086, Toluca Station, North Hollywood, Calif. 91602
	Highpoint Bulletin	P. O. Box 1179, Santa Rosa, Calif. 95402
	Hoof and Horn	P. O. Box "C," Englewood, Colo. 80110
	Horse of Course!	RFD, Temple, N.H. 03084
	Horse and Horseman	34249 Camino Capistrano, Capistrano Beach, Calif. 92624
	Horse Lover's National Magazine	651 Brannan Street, San Francisco, Calif. 94107
	Horse & Rider	P. O. Box 555, Temecula, Calif. 92390
	Horse Show	527 Madison Avenue, New York, N.Y. 10022
	Horse World	P. O. Box 588, Lexington, Ky. 40501
	Horseman	5314 Bingle Road, Houston, Tex. 77018
	Horseman's Review	Rt. 1, Box 12, Monroe Center, Ill. 61062
	Horsemen's Gazette, The	Rural Route One, Badger, Minn. 56714
	Horsemen's Journal	Suite 317, 6000 Executive Blvd., Rockville, Md. 20852
	Horsemen's Yankee Pedlar	2805 Boston Road, Wilbraham, Mass. 01095

(Continued)

TABLE IX-1 (Continued)

Breed	Publication	Address
	Lariat, The	12675 S.W. First Street, Beaverton, Ore. 97005
	National Horse Journal, The	P. O. Box 927, Toronto-5, Ontario, Canada
	National Horseman, The	Box 4067, Baxter Station, Louisville, Ky. 40204
	Northeast Horseman	P. O. Box 131, Hampden, Me. 04444
	Practical Horseman	19 Wilmont Mews, West Chester, Penn. 19380
	Southern Horseman, The	P. O. Box 5735, Meridian, Miss. 39301
	Tack 'N Togs Merchandising	P. O. Box 67, Minneapolis, Minn. 55440
	Trail Rider, The	P. O. Box 397, Chatsworth, Ga. 30705
	Turf and Sport Digest	704 Norwood Drive, Pasadena, Calif. 91105
	USCTA News	One Winthrop Square, Boston, Mass. 02110
	Washington State Horseman Canter, The	P. O. Box "X", Kirkland, Wash. 98033
	Western Horseman, The	P. O. Box 7980, Colorado Springs, Colo. 80933
American Creme	Separator, The	Box 583, Marysville, Calif. 95901
American White	Separator, The	Box 583, Marysville, Calif. 95901
Appaloosa	Appaloosa News	Box 8403, Moscow, Ida. 83843
	Appy, The	15039 Rock Creek Road, Chardon, Ohio 44024
Arabian	Arabian Horse, The	1777 Wynkoop Street, Suite 1, Denver, Colo. 80202
	Arabian Horse News, The	P. O. Box 2692, Denver, Colo. 80201
	Arabian Horse Times, The	819 E. Elm Avenue, Waseca, Minn. 56093
	Arabian Horse World	2650 E. Bayshore Rd., Palo Alto, Calif. 94303
Belgian	Belgian Review (annual)	P. O. Box 335, Wabash, Ind. 46992
Buckskin	International Buckskin Horse Journal	P. O. Box 228, Pearl City, Ill. 61062
Connemara	Connemara, The (annual)	R.D. 1, Hoshiekon Farm, Goshen, Conn. 06756
Gotland	Gotland Glimpses	R. R. 2, Box 181, Elkland, Mo. 65644
Hackney	Hackney Journal, The	P. O. Box 630, Peekskill, N.Y. 10566
Morgan	Morgan Horse, The	Box 1, Westmoreland, N.Y. 13490
Paint Horse	Paint Horse Journal, The	P. O. Box 13486, Ft. Worth, Tex. 76118

(Continued)

TABLE IX-1 (Continued)

Breed	Publication	Address
Palomino	Palomino Horses	P. O. Box 249, Mineral Wells, Tex. 76066
	Palomino Parade	P. O. Box 324, Jefferson City, Mo. 65101
Percheron	Percheron Notes	R. R. 1, Belmont, Ohio 43718
Peruvian Paso	Peruvian Horse Review	P. O. Box 816, Guerneville, Calif. 95446
	Peruvian Horse World	P. O. Box 2035, California City, Calif. 93505
Pinto	Pinto Horse	910 W. Washington, San Diego, Calif. 92103
Pony of the Americas	Pony of the Americas	P. O. Box 1447, Mason City, Iowa 50401
Quarter Horse	Canadian Quarter Horse Journal	P. O. Box 65, Ancaster, Ontario, Canada L9G 3L3
	Intermountain Quarter Horse	P. O. Box "O", Sandy, Utah 84070
	Quarter Horse Digest	Gann Valley, S.D. 57341
	Quarter Horse Journal, The	Box 9105, Amarillo, Tex. 79105
Rangerbred	Rangerbred News	7023 Eden Mill Road, Woodbine, Md. 21797
Saddle Horse	Bluegrass Horseman, The	P. O. Box 389, Lexington, Ky. 40501
	Saddle & Bridle	2333 Brentwood Blvd., St. Louis, Mo. 63144
	Saddle Horse West	Route 1, Box 16-A, West Linn, Ore. 96068
Shetland Pony	American Shetland Pony Journal	P. O. Box 435, Fowler, Ind. 47944
Spanish-Barb	Spanish-Barb Quarterly, The	P. O. Box 7479, Colorado Springs, Colo. 80907
Spanish Mustang	Spanish Mustang Registry Inc., Newsletter, The	Rt. 2, Box 74, Marshall, Tex. 75670
Standardbred	Harness Horse	P. O. Box 1831, Harrisburg, Penn. 17105
	Hoof Beats	750 Michigan Avenue, Columbus, Ohio 43215
Tennessee Walking Horse	Nashville Tennessean	1100 Broad, Nashville, Tenn. 37201
	Voice of the Tennessee Walking Horse	Voice Pub. Co., P. O. Box 6009, Chattanooga, Tenn. 37401
	Walker, The	P. O. Box 286, Lewisburg, Tenn. 37091
	Walking Horse Report	P. O. Box 619, Shelbyville, Tenn. 37160
Thoroughbred	Arizona Thoroughbred, The	3723 Pueblo Way, Scottsdale, Ariz. 85251
	Backstretch, The	19363 James Couzens Hwy., Detroit, Mich. 48235
	Blood Horse	Box 4038, Lexington, Ky. 40504

(Continued)

APPENDIX

TABLE IX-1 (Continued)

Breed	Publication	Address
	B. C. Horseman, The	#212—20216 Fraser Hwy., Langley, B.C., Canada V3A 4E6
	British Columbia Thoroughbred	4023 E. Hasting Street, North Burnaby, British Columbia, Canada
	Florida Horse	Box 699, Ocala, Fla. 32670
	Maryland Horse, The	P. O. Box 4, Timonium, Md. 21093
	Oregon Thoroughbred Review	1001 N. Schmeer Road, Portland, Ore. 97217
	Thoroughbred of California, The	201 Colorado Place, Arcadia, Calif. 91006
	Thoroughbred Record, The	P. O. Box 11788, Lexington, Ky. 40511
	Washington Horse, The	13470 Empire Way So., Seattle, Wash. 98178
Welsh Pony	Welsh Pony World	4531 Dexter Street N.W., Washington, D.C. 20007
Donkey	Mr. Longears	100 Church Street, Amsterdam, N.Y. 12010

SECTION X—U.S. STATE COLLEGES OF AGRICULTURE (Land-Grant Institutions) AND CANADIAN PROVINCIAL UNIVERSITIES

Horsemen can obtain a list of available bulletins and circulars, and other information regarding livestock, by writing to (1) their State Agricultural College (Land-Grant Institution), or (2) the Superintendent of Documents, Washington, D.C.; or by going to the local County Extension Office (Farm Advisor) of the county in which they reside. Canadian stockmen may write to the Department of Agriculture of their province or to their provincial university. A list of U.S. Land-Grant Institutions and Canadian Provincial Universities follows:

State	Address
Alabama	School of Agriculture, Auburn University, Auburn, Ala. 36830
Alaska	Department of Agriculture, University of Alaska, Fairbanks, Alaska 99701
Arizona	College of Agriculture, University of Arizona, Tucson, Ariz. 85721
Arkansas	Division of Agriculture, University of Arkansas, Fayetteville, Ark. 72701
California	College of Agricultural and Environmental Sciences, University of California, Davis, Calif. 95616
Colorado	College of Agricultural Sciences, Colorado State University, Fort Collins, Colo. 80521
Connecticut	College of Agriculture and Natural Resources, University of Connecticut, Storrs, Conn. 06268
Delaware	College of Agricultural Sciences, University of Delaware, Newark, Del. 19711
Florida	College of Agriculture, University of Florida, Gainesville, Fla. 32611
Georgia	College of Agriculture, University of Georgia, Athens, Ga. 30601
Hawaii	College of Tropical Agriculture, University of Hawaii, Honolulu, Hawaii 96822
Idaho	College of Agriculture, University of Idaho, Moscow, Ida. 83843
Illinois	College of Agriculture, University of Illinois, Urbana, Ill. 61801
Indiana	School of Agriculture, Purdue University, Lafayette, Ind. 47907
Iowa	College of Agriculture, Iowa State University, Ames, Iowa 50010
Kansas	College of Agriculture, Kansas State University, Manhattan, Kan. 66506
Kentucky	College of Agriculture, University of Kentucky, Lexington, Ky. 40506
Louisiana	College of Agriculture, Louisiana State University and A&M College, University Station, Baton Rouge, La. 70803
Maine	College of Life Sciences and Agriculture, University of Maine, Orono, Me. 04473
Maryland	College of Agriculture, University of Maryland, College Park, Md. 20742
Massachusetts	College of Food and Natural Resources, University of Massachusetts, Amherst, Mass. 01002
Michigan	College of Agriculture and Natural Resources, Michigan State University, East Lansing, Mich. 48823
Minnesota	College of Agriculture, University of Minnesota, St. Paul, Minn. 55101
Mississippi	College of Agriculture, Mississippi State University, State College, Miss. 39762

State	Address
Missouri	College of Agriculture, University of Missouri, Columbia, Mo. 65201
Montana	College of Agriculture, Montana State University, Bozeman, Mont. 59715
Nebraska	College of Agriculture, University of Nebraska, Lincoln, Neb. 68503
Nevada	The Max C. Fleischmann College of Agriculture, University of Nevada, Reno, Nev. 89507
New Hampshire	College of Life Sciences and Agriculture, University of New Hampshire, Durham, N.H. 03824
New Jersey	College of Agriculture and Environmental Science, Rutgers University, New Brunswick, N.J. 08903
New Mexico	College of Agriculture and Home Economics, New Mexico State University, Las Cruces. N.M. 88003
New York	New York State College of Agriculture, Cornell University, Ithaca, N.Y. 14850
North Carolina	School of Agriculture, North Carolina State University, Raleigh, N.C. 27607
North Dakota	College of Agriculture, North Dakota State University, State University Station, Fargo, N.D. 58102
Ohio	College of Agriculture and Home Economics, Ohio State University, Columbus, Ohio 43210
Oklahoma	College of Agriculture and Applied Science, Oklahoma State University, Stillwater, Okla. 74074
Oregon	School of Agriculture, Oregon State University, Corvallis, Ore. 97331
Pennsylvania	College of Agriculture, Pennsylvania State University, University Park, Penn. 16802
Puerto Rico	College of Agricultural Sciences, University of Puerto Rico, Mayaguez, Puerto Rico 00708
Rhode Island	College of Resource Development, University of Rhode Island, Kingston, R.I. 02881
South Carolina	College of Agricultural Sciences, Clemson University, Clemson, S.C. 29631
South Dakota	College of Agriculture and Biological Sciences, South Dakota State University, Brookings, S.D. 57006
Tennessee	College of Agriculture, University of Tennessee, P. O. Box 1071, Knoxville, Tenn. 37901
Texas	College of Agriculture, Texas A&M University, College Station, Tex. 77843
Utah	College of Agriculture, Utah State University, Logan, Utah 84321
Vermont	College of Agriculture, University of Vermont, Burlington, Vt. 05401
Virginia	College of Agriculture, Virginia Polytechnic Institute, Blacksburg, Va. 24061
Washington	College of Agriculture, Washington State University, Pullman, Wash. 99163
West Virginia	College of Agriculture and Forestry, West Virginia University, Morgantown, W.Va. 26506
Wisconsin	College of Agricultural and Life Sciences, University of Wisconsin, Madison, Wisc. 53706
Wyoming	College of Agriculture, University of Wyoming, University Station, P. O. Box 3354, Laramie, Wyo. 82070

In Canada

Alberta	University of Alberta, Edmonton, Alberta
British Columbia	University of British Columbia, Vancouver, British Columbia
Manitoba	University of Manitoba, Winnipeg, Manitoba
New Brunswick	University of New Brunswick, Fredericton, New Brunswick
Ontario	University of Guelph, Guelph, Ontario
Quebec	Faculty d'Agriculture, University of Laval, Quebec City MacDonald College, Montreal, Quebec
Saskatchewan	University of Saskatchewan, Saskatoon, Saskatchewan

APPENDIX

SECTION XI—PRACTICES AND PROBLEMS OF HORSEMEN

The author surveyed,[1] from coast to coast, selected breeders of each of the three breeds that are used for racing; namely, (1) Thoroughbreds, (2) Standardbreds, and (3) Quarter Horses. A total of 74 Thoroughbred questionnaires, 16 Standardbred questionnaires, and 32 Quarter Horse questionnaires were executed and returned (the largest number of questionnaires were forwarded to Thoroughbred breeders).

No claim is made to having sampled, extensively and scientifically,[2] the breeds to which reference is made; also,

for this reason, breed comparisons are not valid. Yet, the facts and figures herewith presented are sufficiently reliable and authoritative (1) to reflect trends, and (2) to serve as guideposts. Also, this was the first serious independent study attempting to diagnose the practices and problems of more than one breed, and to propose economies for the light horse industry.

The important thing is that breeders and breed registry associations face up to the facts, whether good or bad, as applied to their favorite breeds, rather than ignore their weaknesses and problems. By facing the facts, they can best correct deficiencies and move ahead.

The questionnaire was designed to establish the knowns. Here is what was found.

I. *National Picture; for Registered Thoroughbreds, Standardbreds, and Quarter Horses* [3]

	Thoroughbred	Standardbred	Quarter Horses	All Three Breeds
Mares, average—				
No. covered (or bred) annually	22,250	8,500	52,800	83,550
No. live foals born, annually	12,223	6,000	37,000	55,223
Percent of foal crop	55	70	70	66
Percent of foals registered	89	90	90	90
No. foals produced in lifetime of mare	5	8	7	7
Stallions, average—				
No. mares bred to each stallion each year	10	11	12	11
No. years in service	10	15	10	11
No. living stallions	3,000	2,154	5,628	9,792
No. stallions used in service annually	2,000	1,000	4,400	7,400
Average age of horses at death:				
Males	15	20	15	16
Females	14	20	15	15

II. *Farm or Ranch Inventory*

	Thoroughbred	Standardbred	Quarter Horses	All Three Breeds
Average per establishment:—				
No. of acres	1,375	2,330	5,243	2,267
No. of horses:				
Stallions	1.6	3.0	2.7	2.1
Mares in production	9.8	23.9	21.6	14.7
Barren mares	4.2	6.7	3.3	4.3
Yearlings (as of Jan. 1, 1961)	7.6	19.4	11.2	10.0
Two-year-olds (as of Jan. 1, 1961)	4.8	4.1	3.8	4.4
Horses in training or racing	7.0	8.0	4.7	6.5
Other (than those listed above)	6.1	2.3	4.7	5.3
Total number of horses	44.4	67.4	50.9	47.3
Estimated current total of gross value of all horses	$243,100	$232,300	$149,000	$216,100
Estimated current total of gross value of farm or ranch	$246,700	$352,640	$216,430	$252,000
Estimated profit or loss in operations: In 1960—(+ or −)	+ $926	− $3,083	+ $17,789	+ $4,700
Average per year for past 3 years—(+ or −)	+ $2,449	− $5,272	+ $19,550	+ $5,700
Average % return on investment past 3 years	+0.5	−0.9	+5.3	+1.2

---

[1] *The Thoroughbred of California*, March 1961, p. 258.

[2] Actually, this limited survey points up the urgent need for a much more extensive and complete study of this type. A larger sample would (1) alleviate many of the wide fluctuations reported herein, and (2) eliminate the obvious errors in certain averages.

[3] Estimates in this section arrived at through various channels and deductions; not obtained from questionnaire to individual breeders.

The Farm or Ranch Inventory survey revealed the following pertinent facts:

1. It takes a great deal of capital to be in the horse business.

2. The physical plants are too expensive, perhaps due to location and/or too many elaborate buildings.

3. Most Thoroughbred and Standardbred breeders need a lucrative outside business to support their horses. By contrast, only one Quarter Horse breeder was losing money.

Generally speaking, those engaged in the light horse business might well be admonished to heed the advice of J. Pierpont Morgan, who told an inquiring friend, "If you have to ask what it costs to maintain a yacht, you can't afford it."

III. *Production Record (Breeding Animals)*

Mares, Average:	Thoroughbreds	Standardbreds	Quarter Horses	All Three Breeds
1. No. covered (or bred) annually	27.2	96.5	53.9	42.6
2. No. different heats each mare is covered each year	2.1	2.2	2.2	2.1
3. Where mares are taken away for breeding, no. weeks boarded at location of stallion	11.5	14.9	8.1	11.1
4. No. live foals born	13.0	45.7	22.5	19.7
5. Percent foal crop[4]	79.4	76.8	83.7	80.1
6. Percent of foals registered	92.9	97.6	96.0	94.3
7. No. foals produced in lifetime of mare	6.8	9.3	10.0	8.2
Stallions, average:				
1. No. services per conception	3.6	2.7	3.0	3.3
2. No. mares bred to each stallion each year	17.7	35.0	33.5	25.0
3. No. years in service	7.8	11.9	9.9	10.9
Average age of horses at death:				
Males	18.1	22.0	17.0	18.4
Females	18.2	21.2	17.8	18.4

IV. *Management Record (Breeding Animals)*

	Thoroughbreds	Standardbreds	Quarter Horses	All Three Breeds
1. Average cost per year of maintaining an *in-foal* mare (including interest on investment; facilities; feed costs; service cost of stallion; transportation and board if taken away for service; veterinary costs; labor; etc.)	$1,612	$1,386	$ 829	$1,391
2. Average *cost* per year for maintaining a mature *barren* mare, not in production (including interest on investment; facilities; feed cost; service cost of stallion, if any, even if not in-foal; transportation and board if taken away for service; veterinary cost; labor; etc.)	$1,157	$ 945	$ 731	$1,019
3. Average cost of raising a foal from birth to two years of age	$1,657	$1,104	$ 829	$1,365
4. Average cost per year for maintaining a mature stallion (including interest on investment; facilities; feed cost; veterinary cost; labor; etc.)	$1,829	$2,002	$1,271	$1,670
5. Average stallion cost per foal, either (1) in service fees or (2) in prorated cost of own stallion	$ 964	$ 605	$ 383	$ 736
6. Average annual expenditure per breeding animal (old and young) for drugs, vitamins, minerals, and tonics. (These to be over and above regular veterinary services.)	$ 80.50	$ 61.00	$ 61.00	$ 72.70
7. Average annual cost per head for veterinary service (including drugs and supplies prescribed by the DVM) of breeding animals.	$ 69.40	$ 112.50	$ 39.40	$ 66.40

---

[4]Obviously, the better producers were responding, because, for the U.S. as a whole, a foal crop of less than 60% is secured.

APPENDIX

The *Management Record (Breeding Animals)* revealed the high cost of raising an animal to two years of age. Since many mares are barren, their keep must also be charged against the foals that are produced. For the nation as a whole, it costs an average of $5,099, $3,648, and $2,309, respectively, to raise each a Thoroughbred, a Standardbred, and a Quarter Horse to two years of age. In this connection, it is noteworthy that, in 1960, a total of 1,910 U.S. Thoroughbred yearlings sold for an average of $5,258; and of course, these were the absolute tops. Among experienced horsemen, the feeling persists that only five percent of the matings result in profitable yearlings.

V. Racing Record (Racing Animals)

	Thoroughbreds	Standardbreds	Quarter Horses	All Three Breeds
1. Average cost per foal of futurity and stakes nominations and eligibilities ..	$ 153	$ 1,572	$1,105	$ 608
2. No. young animals placed in training each year	4.5	8.5	4.1	4.9
3. No. young animals placed in training each year that actually race	4.2	2.6	2.8	3.7
Percent trained that race	93.03	30.5	68.3	74.6
4. Of animals raced, average—				
(1) no. years of racing	4.0	3.1	2.7	3.5
(2) no. races	50.7	58.4	21.6	42.2
(3) lifetime earnings	$20,260	$24,250	$8,410	$17,320
5. Average annual cost of keeping a horse in training (trainer, feed and feed additives, veterinary service, etc.)	$ 3,410	$ 4,146	$2,370	$ 3,210
6. Average annual cost per head for veterinary services (including drugs and supplies prescribed by the DVM) of each animal in training or on the track	$ 122	$ 243	$ 317	$ 191

7. Most common causes for retiring a horse from the track (ranked from top to bottom with most common reason at top[5]):

Thoroughbreds	Standardbreds	Quarter Horses	All Three Breeds
a. Unsoundness, injury, or disease	Unsoundness, injury, or disease	Unsoundness, injury, or disease	Unsoundness, injury, or disease
b. Racing or training practices	Racing or training Practices	Racing or training practices	Racing or training practices
c. Old age	For breeding purposes	For breeding purposes	For breeding purposes
d. For breeding purposes	Old age	Old age	Old age
e. Bad manners or nervous	Bad manners or nervous	Bad manners or nervous	Bad manners or nervous

The section headed Racing Record (Racing Animals) shows that the average owner races for glory, or at least reasons other than profit. For an investment of $17,621 ($3,590 to raise an animal to two years of age—and it is reasonable to surmise that it would cost this much or more to purchase a comparable two-year-old, *plus* $14,031 expenses for three and one-half years on the track), lifetime earnings of $17,320[6] are secured, leaving a deficit of $301 for each horse raced. Hirsch Jacobs, one of the most astute observers on the racing scene, and the man who saddled more winners than anybody else in the history of the sport, estimated that only five percent of Thoroughbred racing stables make money.[7]

---

[5]It is recognized that many of these conditions are temporary in nature, requiring only a short rest and/or treatment; that horses are not "sent home" or permanently retired therefrom. Also, a horse with not enough speed on one track may be a winner on another track where (1) the competition is less keen, or (2) the conditions are more to the liking of the horse.

[6]Or earnings of $4,950 per year. In 1959, 28,623 starters competed for a gross of $92,848,541 in the United States, Canada and Northern Mexico, or an average of $3,244 per starter (from: *The Thoroughbred of California*, Feb. 1961, p. 143).

[7]From: *The Thoroughbred of California*, Feb. 1961, p. 143.

VI. *Horsemen's Experiences in Economy*

Without lowering the quality or size of their operations, the respondents reported that the following practices or programs, by rank, were most important (in breeding and racing) as ways of lowering costs:

Operation	Rank	Thoroughbreds	Standardbreds	Quarter Horses	All Three Breeds
Breeding	1	Breeding—24%	Feeding—23%	Breeding—44%	Breeding—30%
	2	Feeding—23%	Health and care—21%	Feeding—17%	Feeding—21%
	3	Health and care—20%	Breeding—20%	Management—13%	Management—18%
	4	Management—19%	Management—16%	Pastures—10%	Health and care—16%
	5	Pastures—8%	Buildings and equipment—12%	Health and care—9%	Pastures—8%
	6	Buildings and equipment—6%	Pastures—8%	Buildings and equipment—7%	Buildings and equipment—7%

Operation	Rank	Thoroughbreds	Standardbreds	Quarter Horses	All Three Breeds
Racing	1	Optimum racing stable—20%	Evaluate stock—21%	Train at home—54%	Optimum racing stable—21%
	2	Optimum training time—13%	Optimum training time—19% / Minimum futurity costs—19%	Optimum racing stable—34%	Train at home—15%
	3	Good care—11%	Train at home—17%	Buildings and equipment—12%	Optimum training time—12%
	4	Evaluate stock—10% / Claim sound horses—10%	Optimum racing stable—11%		Evaluate stock—10%
	5	Buildings and equipment—8%	Keep horse in its class—9%		Good care—8% / Claim sound horses—8% / All others—26%

The percentage figures of the "All Three Breeds" column under "Horsemen's Experiences in Economy" are particularly revealing. In the horse production operations, fifty percent of the horsemen stated that they have effected their greatest economies in breeding and feeding. By categories and rank, the following comments were most frequent:

1. *Breeding:* (a) Use proven stock, and (b) eliminate inferior animals.

2. *Feeding:* Keep feed costs to a minimum by (a) raising your own feed or purchasing feeds at the right time, and (b) using quality feeds.

3. *Management:* (a) Analyze expenditures, (b) plan well, (c) use a minimum and reliable labor force efficiently, and (d) maintain optimum size operation.

4. *Health and Care:* (a) Maintain constant vigilance, (b) prevent injuries, and (c) have an adequate parasite control program.

5. *Pastures:* (a) Make maximum use of pastures, and (b) have good pastures—not merely gymnasiums for horses.

6. *Buildings and Equipment:* (a) Design for efficiency and saving in labor, (b) use good feeding and watering equipment, and (c) own your own trailers and vans.

Those who race horses effected their greatest economies in the following areas, by rank:

1. *Optimum Racing Stable:* Only a minimum number of top horses in the racing stable should be maintained.

2. *Training at Home:* The general feeling prevailed that this minimized breakdowns and lessened costs.

3. *Optimum Training Time:* Particular emphasis was placed on avoiding unnecessary time in training, but training until fit and ready.

4. *Evaluate Stock:* There was general agreement that too many horsemen waste money by training a horse that simply doesn't have what it takes; you cannot make a winner out of a plow horse.

5. *Good Care:* Of course, the age-old argument continues; owners feel that trainers let them down, while trainers feel that heredity (genetics) is most important.

6. *Claim Sound Horses:* Several stated that they effect economies in racing simply by claiming sound horses only.

Among the respondents' sage advice and pungent statements appearing under "Horsemen's Experiences in Economy" were these:

1. "Feed them like wild animals, rather than like pampered domesticated creatures," and

2. "Don't try to keep up with the monied Joneses."

Index